JOB HUNTER'S SOURCEBOOK

ISSN 1053-1874

A   GALE   CAREER   INFORMATION   GUIDE

JOB HUNTER'S SOURCEBOOK

Where to find employment leads and other job search resources

FOURTEENTH EDITION
Volume 1

Sources of Job Hunting Information by Occupations

Occupations A-K
Entries 1-6671

Joseph Palmisano, Project Editor

GALE
CENGAGE Learning

Farmington Hills, Mich • San Francisco • New York • Waterville, Maine
Meriden, Conn • Mason, Ohio • Chicago

GALE
CENGAGE Learning®

Job Hunter's Sourcebook, 14th Edition

Product Management: Michele P. LeMeau

Project Editor: Joseph Palmisano

Editorial Support Services: Scott Flaugher

Composition and Electronic Prepress: Gary Leach

Manufacturing: Rita Wimberley

Gale, Cengage Learning
27500 Drake Rd.
Farmington Hills, MI 48331-3535

ISBN-13: 978-1-4144-9034-2 (set)
ISBN-13: 978-1-4144-9035-9 (vol. 1)
ISBN-13: 978-1-4144-9036-6 (vol. 2)
ISBN-13: 978-1-4144-9037-3 (vol. 3)

ISSN 1053-1874

Printed in the United States of America
1 2 3 4 5   18 17 16 15 14

Contents

"The person who gets hired is not necessarily the one who can do that job best; but, the one who knows the most about how to get hired."

Richard Bolles

What Color Is Your Parachute?

Job hunting is often described as a campaign, a system, a strategic process. According to Joan Moore, principal of The Arbor Consulting Group, Inc. in Plymouth, Michigan, "Launching a thorough job search can be a full-time job in itself. It requires as much energy as you would put into any other major project—and it requires a creative mix of approaches to ensure its success."

Job Hunting Is Increasingly Complex

Today's competitive job market has become increasingly complex, requiring new and resourceful approaches to landing a position. The help-wanted ads are no longer the surest route to employment. In fact, most estimates indicate that only a small percentage of all jobs are found through the classified sections of local newspapers.

Although approaches vary among individual job seekers and the levels of jobs sought, a thorough job search today should involve the use of a wide variety of resources. Professional associations, library research, executive search firms, college placement offices, direct application to employers, professional journals, and networking with colleagues and friends are all approaches commonly in use. Job hotlines and resume referral services may be elements of the search as well. High-tech components might include the use of resume databases, and electronic bulletin boards that list job openings.

Job Hunters Are Changing

Just as the methods of job seeking have changed, so have the job hunters themselves. As Joyce Slayton Mitchell notes in College to Career, "Today, the average young person can look forward to six or seven different jobs, six or seven mini-careers, that will make up his or her lifetime of work." Lifelong commitment to one employer is no longer the norm; profes-sionals seeking to change companies, workers re-entering the job market after a period of absence, and people exploring new career options are also represented in significant numbers in the job seeking pool. And in a time of significant corporate change, restructuring, divestiture, and downsizing, many job seekers are in the market unexpectedly. These include a growing number of white-collar workers who find themselves competing against other professionals in a shrinking market.

Help for Job Hunters

As the job market has become more competitive and complex, job seekers have increasingly looked for job search assistance. The rapid growth in the number of outplacement firms and employment agencies during the last 30 years reflects the perceived need for comprehensive help. Similarly, the library has become an increasingly important and valuable resource in the job hunt. In fact, some librarians report that their most frequently asked reference questions pertain to job seeking. In response to this need, many libraries have developed extensive collections of career and job-hunting publications, periodicals that list job openings, and directories of employers. Some libraries have developed centralized collections of career information, complemented by such offerings as resume preparation software, career planning databases, and interviewing skills videotapes.

Valuable Guide for Job Seekers

Job Hunter's Sourcebook (JHS) was designed to assist those planning job search strategies. Any job hunter—the student looking for an internship, the recent graduate, the executive hoping to relocate—will find *JHS* an important first step in the job search process because it identifies and organizes employment leads quickly and comprehensively. Best of all, *JHS* provides all the information a job hunter needs to turn a local public library into a customized employment agency, available free-of-charge. *Library Journal* and the New York Public Library concurred, and gave the first edition of this work their annual outstanding reference awards.

Job Hunter's Sourcebook (JHS) is a comprehensive guide to sources of information on employment leads and other job search resources. It streamlines the job-seeking process by identifying and organizing the wide array of publications, organizations, audio-visual and electronic resources, and other job hunting tools.

JHS completes much of the research needed to begin a job search, with in-depth coverage of information sources for more than 200 specific professional and vocational occupations. Listings of resources on more than 30 essential topics of interest to job hunters complement the profiles on specific occupations, providing the job seeker with leads to all the information needed to design a complete job search strategy.

Job Hunter's Sourcebook can be used to:

Find a job. JHS is designed for use by job seekers at all levels—from those seeking a first job, to executives on the move, to those in transition. Each individual may select from the wide range of resources presented to develop a customized job campaign.

Use career resources more effectively. As library research becomes an increasingly important component in the job hunting process, librarians are providing more information and support to job seekers. *JHS* helps users go directly to the most appropriate library material by providing comprehensive lists of job hunting resources on high-interest professional and vocational occupations.

Build a better career resources collection. Librarians, career counselors, outplacement firms, spouse relocation services, job referral agencies, and others who advise job seekers can use *JHS* to start or expand their collections of career and job hunting materials.

Comprehensive Coverage and Convenient Arrangement

The job search resources in *JHS* are conveniently arranged into three volumes, which are followed by a master index:

Volumes One and Two: Sources of Job-Hunting Information by Professions and Occupations—identifies information sources on employment opportunities for 258 specific types of jobs. A "List of Profiled Professions and Oc-

cupations" lists hundreds of alternate, popular, synonymous, and related job titles and links them to the jobs profiled in *JHS*, providing quick access to information sources on specific occupations or fields of interest by all their variant names—from accountant to aircraft mechanic and sports official to stockbroker. Each profile contains complete contact information and lists a variety of sources of job-opportunity information organized into eight easy-to-use categories:

1. Sources of Help-Wanted Ads
2. Placement and Job Referral Services
3. Employer Directories and Networking Lists
4. Handbooks and Manuals
5. Employment Agencies and Search Firms
6. Online Job Sources and Services
7. Tradeshows
8. Other Sources, including internships and resources such as job hotlines

Volume Three: Sources of Essential Job-Hunting Information—features such employment topics as:

- Interviewing Skills
- Employment Issues for Disabled Workers
- Electronic Job Search Information
- Working at Home
- Opportunities for Freelance Workers and Independent Contractors
- Opportunities for Temporary Workers

Each category includes:

- Reference Works
- Newspapers, Magazines, and Journals
- Audio/Visual Resources
- Online and Database Services
- Software
- Other Sources, such as special associations, job hunting kits, and organizers

The information sources listed under each topic are arranged by type of resource and include complete contact information.

Index to Information Sources—comprehensively lists all of the publications, organizations, electronic resources, and other sources of job hunting information contained in *JHS*.

Please consult the User's Guide for more information about the arrangement, content, and indexing of the information sources cited in *JHS*.

JHS Profiles High-Interest Professions and Occupations

JHS catalogs job hunting resources for more than 200 professional, technical, and trade occupations, carefully selected to provide a broad cross-section of occupations of interest to today's job seekers. The majority are profiled in the Department of Labor's *Occupational Outlook Handbook (OOH)*, a leading career resource containing detailed descriptions of professional and vocational occupations. Most of the professions cited in *OOH* are also included in *JHS*, as are representative vocational occupations selected from those listed in *OOH*. To round out this list, additional occupations were included on the basis of Bureau of Labor Statistics data projecting them as high-growth positions.

Coverage of Employment Alternatives and Trends

In addition to focusing on such "how-to" topics as resume writing and interviewing, the "Sources of Essential Job-Hunting Information" offers resources for non-traditional work options and diverse segments of the work force. Working part-time, at home, and in your own business are featured chapters, as are opportunities for minorities, older workers, women, disabled workers, and gay and lesbian job seekers. A chapter covering sources of electronic job search information is included, as well as a category titled, "Online Job Sources and Services." This category lists Internet websites related to specific job profiles.

New to this Edition

The fourteenth edition is a complete revision of the previous *JHS*, incorporating thousands of updates to organization and publication data. This edition also features 4 new career profiles, including rehabilitation counselors, school and career counselors, and substance abuse and behavioral disorder counselors.

Method of Compilation

JHS contains citations compiled from direct contact with a wide range of associations and organizations, from dozens of publisher catalogs and other secondary sources, and from selected information from other Gale databases. While many resources cited in *JHS* contain career planning information, their usefulness in the job hunting process was the primary factor in their selection. Their annotations are tailored to support that function.

Comments and Suggestions Are Welcome

Libraries, associations, employment agencies, executive search firms, referral services, publishers, database producers, and other organizations involved in helping job seekers find opportunities or companies find candidates are encouraged to submit information about their activities and products for use in future editions of *JHS*. Comments and suggestions for improving this guide are also welcome. Please contact:

Project Editor
Job Hunter's Sourcebook
Gale, Cengage Learning
27500 Drake Rd.
Farmington Hills, MI 48331-3535
Phone: (248) 699-4253
Fax: (248) 699-8075
URL: gale.cengage.com

Job Hunter's Sourcebook (JHS) is divided into three volumes:

- Volumes One and Two: Sources of Job-Hunting Information by Professions and Occupations
- Volume Three: Sources of Essential Job-Hunting Information

Access to entries is facilitated by a "List of Profiled Professions and Occupations" and an "Index to Information Sources." Users should consult each section to benefit fully from the information in JHS.

Master List of Profiled Professions and Occupations

A "List of Profiled Professions and Occupations" alphabetically lists the job titles used to identify the professions and occupations appearing in Volumes One and Two of JHS, as well as alternate, popular, synonymous, and related job titles and names, and occupational specialties contained within job titles. Citations include "See" references to the appropriate occupational profiles and their beginning page numbers.

JHS is designed to meet the needs of job seekers at all levels of experience in a wide range of fields. Managers as well as entry-level job hunters will find information sources that will facilitate their career-specific searches. In addition, information on professions and occupations related to those profiled will be found.

All Career Levels. The title assigned to each profile identifies its occupational field or subject area; these titles are not meant to indicate the level of positions for which information is provided. Information systems managers, for example, will find highly useful information in the "Computer Programmers" and "Computer Systems Analysts" profiles, while financial analysts will benefit from information in the "Financial Managers" profile. The "General Managers and Top Executives" profile, on the other hand, is broad in nature and useful to any management-level search; it does not focus upon a specific profession or occupation.

Other Occupations. Job seekers not finding their specific career fields listed in this guide will discover that related profiles yield valuable sources of information. For example, legal secretaries will find relevant information about employment agencies serving the legal profession and about prospective employers in the "Legal Assistants" and "Law-yers" profiles. An individual interested in finding a position in radio advertising sales might look to the entries in the broadcasting- and sales-related profiles to find appropriate resources. Career changers, too, can use JHS profiles to identify new professions to which their previously acquired skills would be transferable.

Volumes One and Two: Sources of Job-Hunting Information by Professions and Occupations

These volumes feature profiles of job-hunting information for 258 specific careers. Profiles are listed alphabetically by profession or occupation. Each profile contains up to eight categories of information sources, as described below. Within each category, entries are arranged in alphabetical order by name or title. Entries are numbered sequentially, beginning with the first entry in the first profile. All resources listed are included in each relevant profile (and in Volume Three chapters, as appropriate) providing a complete selection of information sources in each occupational profile.

Sources of Help-Wanted Ads. Includes professional journals, industry periodicals, association newsletters, placement bulletins, and online services. In most cases, periodicals that focus on a specific field are cited here; general periodical sources such as the National Business Employment Weekly are listed in Volume 3 under "Help-Wanted Ads." Publications specific to an industry will be found in all profiles related to that industry. Candidates in some occupational areas, such as word processing, are usually recruited from the local marketplace and therefore are not as likely to find openings through a professional publication. Profiles for these occupations may contain fewer ad sources as job hunters are better served by local newspapers and periodicals. Entries include: the source's title and the name, address, and phone number of its publisher or producer; publication frequency; subscription rate; description of contents; toll-free or additional phone numbers; and fax numbers, when applicable. Source titles appear in italics.

Placement and Job Referral Services. Various ser- vices designed to match job seekers with opportunities are included in this category. Primarily offered by professional associations, these services range from job banks to placement services to employment clearinghouses, operating on the national and local levels. Entries include: the association's or organization's name, address, and phone number; its membership, activities, and services; toll-free or additionall phone numbers; and fax numbers. E-mail and website addresses are provided, when available.

Employer Directories and Networking Lists. Covers directories and rankings of companies, membership rosters from professional associations, and other lists of organizations or groups that can be used to target prospective employers and identify potential contacts for networking purposes. In some cases, Who's Who titles are included where these can provide a source of contact information in a specialized field. General directories of companies such as Standard and Poor's Register of Corporations, Directors, and Executives are cited in Volume Three in the "Identifying Prospective Employers" profile. Entries include: the title and name, address, and phone number of the publisher or distributor; publication date or frequency; price; description of contents; arrangement; indexes; toll-free or additional phone numbers; and fax numbers, when available. Directory titles appear in italics.

Handbooks and Manuals. This category notes books, pamphlets, brochures, and other published materials that provide guidance and insight to the job-hunting process in a particular occupational field. Entries include: the title and name, address, and phone number of its publisher or distributor; editor's or author's name; publication date or frequency; price; number of pages; description of contents; toll-free or additional phone numbers; and fax numbers, when known. Publication titles appear in italics.

Employment Agencies and Search Firms. Features firms used by companies to recruit candidates for positions and, at times, by individuals to pursue openings. The follow- ing firms are covered:

1. Employment agencies, which are generally geared toward filling openings at entry- to mid-levels in the local job market. Candidates sometimes pay a fee for using their services. When possible, JHS lists agencies where the employer pays the fee.

2. Executive search firms, which are paid by the hiring organization to recruit professional and managerial candidates, usually for higher-level openings and from a regional or national market. Executive search firms are of two types: contingency, where the firm is paid only if it fills the position, and retainer, where the firm is compensated to undertake a recruiting assignment, regardless of whether or not that firm actually fills the opening. The majority of the search firms cited in JHS are contingency firms. Although executive search firms work for the hiring organization and contact candidates only when recruiting for a specific position, most will accept unsolicited resumes, and some may accept phone calls.

3. Temporary employment agencies, which also are included in some profiles because they can be a way to identify and obtain regular employment.

For the most part, each profile lists firms that typically service that career. Firms specializing in a particular industry are included in all profiles relevant to that industry. JHS cov-

ers a mix of large and small firms. Major national search firms, which are quite broad in scope, are listed only under the "General Managers and Top Executives" profile. Some occupations are not served by employment agencies or search firms (fire fighter, for example); therefore, there are no entries for this category in such profiles. Entries include: the firm's name, address, and phone number; whether it's an employment agency, executive search firm, or temporary agency; descriptive information, as appropriate; toll-free and additional phone numbers; and fax numbers, when applicable.

Online Job Sources and Services. Publicly available electronic databases, including websites that facilitate matching job hunters with openings are cited. Many are tailored to specific occupations. Entries include: the name of the product or service; the name, address, and phone number of the distributor or producer; price; special formats or arrangements; descriptive information; toll-free or additional phone numbers; and fax numbers, when applicable. For websites, URL is included along with descriptive information.

Tradeshows. Covers exhibitions and tradeshows held in the United States. Entries include: the name of the tradeshow; the name of the sponsoring organization; contact information for the sponsoring organization, including address, phone number, toll-free or additional phone numbers, fax number, email address, and URL; types of exhibits; and dates and location, when available.

Other Sources. This category comprises a variety of resources available to the job seeker in a specific field: job hotlines providing 24-hour recordings of openings; lists of internships, fellowships, and apprenticeships; bibliographies of job-hunting materials; video and audio cassettes; and salary surveys to be used as a guide when discussing compensation. Professional associations of significance or those that provide job hunting assistance (but not full placement services) are also included here. Because of the trend toward entrepreneurship, this section offers information sources on being one's own boss in a given field as well. Resources on job and career alternatives are provided for certain professions (such as educators), as is information on working abroad.

Entries for associations and organizations include: name, address, and phone number; the membership, activities, and services of associations; toll-free or additional phone numbers; and fax numbers. E-mail and website addresses are provided, when available. Entries for other resources include: title of the publication or name of the product or service; the name, address, and phone number of its publisher, distributor, or producer; editor's or author's name; pubication date or frequency; price, special formats or arrangements; descriptive information; hotline, toll-free, or additional phone phone numbers; and fax numbers, when available. Publication, videocassette, and audiocassette titles appear in italics.

Volume Three: Sources of Essential Job-Hunting Information

This volume presents 33 profiles on topics of interest to any job hunter, such as resume writing or interviewing, as well as those of specialized interest, such as working at home (see "List of Profiled Professions and Occupations" for the complete list). Profiles are arranged alphabetically by topic and contain up to six categories of information, as listed below. Within each category, citations are organized alphabetically by name or title. Entries are also numbered sequentially, continuing the number sequence from Volumes One and Two. The publications, periodicals, and other sources listed are fully cited in all relevant chapters (and in occupational profiles, as appropriate), providing the reader with a complete selection of resources in single, convenient location.

Reference Works. Includes handbooks and manuals, directories, pamphlets, and other published sources of information. Entries include: the title and name, address, and phone number of its publisher or distributor; editor's or author's name; publication date or frequency; price; number of pages; description of contents; toll free or additional phone numbers; and fax numbers, when known. Publication titles appear in italics.

Newspapers, Magazines, and Journals. Lists items published on a serial basis. Entries include: the title and name, address, and phone number of its publisher or distributor; frequency; price; description of contents; toll-free or additional phone numbers; and fax numbers, when known. Publication titles appear in italics.

Audio/Visual Resources. Features audiocassettes, videocassettes, and filmstrips. Entries include: the title and name, address, and phone number of its distributor or producer; date; price; special formats; descriptive information; toll-free or additional phone numbers; and fax numbers, when applicable. Videocassette and audiocassette titles appear in italics.

Online and Database Services. Publicly available electronic databases, including websites that facilitate matching job hunters with openings are cited. Entries include: the name of the product or service; the name, address, and phone number of the distributor or producer; price; special formats or arrangements; descriptive information; toll-free or additional phone numbers; and fax numbers, when applicable. For websites: the online address (URL) is included along with descriptive information.

Software. This category notes software programs designed to help with various aspects of job hunting, such as resume preparation. Entries include: the name of the product or service; the name, address, and phone number of the distributor or producer; price; special formats or arrangements; hardware compatibility, if relevant; descriptive information; toll-free or additional phone numbers; and fax numbers, when applicable.

Other Sources. Varied resources such as special associations and organizations and job-hunting bibliographies, kits, and organizers are covered in this section. Citations for journal and newspaper articles are provided if a topic is relatively new. Entries include: the title of the publication or name of the organization, product, or service; the name, address, and phone number of the organization, publisher, distributor, or producer; editor's or author's name; publication date or frequency; price; special formats or arrangements; descriptive information; toll-free or additional phone numbers; and fax numbers, when applicable. Publication titles appear in italics. For article citations: the article title, publication date, and journal or newspaper title, as well as a description of the article.

Index to Information Sources

JHS provides a comprehensive Index to Information Sources that lists all publications, periodicals, associations, organizations, firms, online and database services, and other resources cited in Volumes One, Two, and Three. Entries are arranged alphabetically and are referenced by their entry numbers. Titles of publications, audiocassettes, and videocassettes appear in italics.

List of Profiled Professions and Occupations

This list outlines references to occupations and professions by job titles, alternate names contained within job titles, popular names, and synonymous and related names. Beginning page numbers for each occupation's profile are provided. Titles of profiles appear in boldface.

LIST OF PROFILED PROFESSIONS AND OCCUPATIONS

SOURCES OF HELP-WANTED ADS

1 ■ *Accounting and Finance*
Blackwell Publishing Inc.
350 Main St.
Malden, MA 02148
Ph: (781)388-8200
Free: 800-216-2522
Fax: (781)388-8210
E-mail: journaladsusa@bos.blackwellpublishing.com
URL: http://as.wiley.com/WileyCDA/WileyTitle/productCd-ACFI.html

Frequency: Quarterly. **Price:** $469 Institutions print + online, Australia/New Zealand; $408 Institutions print or online, Australia/New Zealand; $633 Institutions print + online; $551 Institutions print or online; £441 Institutions print + online; £383 Institutions print or online. **Description:** Journal focusing on accounting and finance.

2 ■ *The Accounting Review*
American Accounting Association
5717 Bessie Dr.
Sarasota, FL 34233-2399
Ph: (941)921-7747
Fax: (941)923-4093
E-mail: tar@mccombs.utexas.edu
URL: http://aaahq.org/pubs/acctrev.htm

Frequency: Quarterly. **Price:** $410 Institutions print; $400 Institutions online from volume 74 through current issue; $465 Institutions online and print. **Description:** Includes job postings of organizations seeking to hire accounting professionals.

3 ■ *CFMA Building Profits*
Construction Financial Management Association
100 Village Blvd., Ste. 200
Princeton, NJ 08540
Ph: (609)452-8000
Free: 888-421-9996
Fax: (609)452-0474
E-mail: sbinstock@cfma.org
URL: http://www.cfma.org

Frequency: Bimonthly. **Price:** Included in membership dues. **Description:** Features tax and accounting alerts, risk management updates, employment and career opportunities and technical articles.

4 ■ *CFO Magazine*
CFO Publishing
111 W 57th St., 12th Fl.
New York, NY 10019
Ph: (212)698-9787
Fax: (212)459-3007
URL: http://www3.cfo.com

Description: Monthly. Free for U.S. residents; $120.00/year for subscribers outside U.S. Includes a job board for finance executives and employers.

5 ■ *The CPA Journal*
New York State Society of Certified Public Accountants
14 Wall St., 19th Fl.
New York, NY 10005
Ph: (212)719-8300
Free: 800-633-6320
Fax: (212)719-3364
E-mail: jbarry@nysscpa.org
URLs: http://www.cpajournal.com/; http://www.nysscpa.org/page/society-publications

Frequency: Monthly. **Price:** $59 Individuals U.S.; $30 Students 1 year; $71 Other countries 1 year; $89 Individuals 2 years, U.S.; $48 Two years student; $113 Other countries 2 years; $115 U.S. 3 years, individual; $149 Other countries 3 years. **Description:** Refereed accounting journal.

6 ■ *The Edge*
Accounting and Financial Women's Alliance
1760 Old Meadow Rd., Ste. 500
McLean, VA 22102
Ph: (703)506-3265
Free: 800-326-2163
Fax: (703)506-3266
E-mail: aswa@aswa.org
URL: http://www.aswachicago.org/membership

Description: Monthly. Included in membership. Magazine featuring member spotlights, career opportunities, committee activities, scheduled conferences, chapter news, and technical articles.

7 ■ *Internal Auditor*
Institute of Internal Auditors
247 Maitland Ave.
Altamonte Springs, FL 32701-4201
Ph: (407)937-1111
Fax: (407)937-1101
E-mail: iaonline@theiia.org
URL: http://www.theiia.org/intAuditor/index.cfm

Frequency: Bimonthly. **Price:** $75 Individuals electronic; $99 Other countries. **Description:** Internal auditing.

8 ■ *Journal of Accountancy*
American Institute of Certified Public Accountants
1211 Avenue of the Americas
New York, NY 10036-8775
Ph: (212)596-6200
Free: 888-777-7077
Fax: (212)596-6213
E-mail: service@aicpa.org
URL: http://www.journalofaccountancy.com/

Frequency: Monthly. **Price:** $75 Individuals; $60 Members. **Description:** Provides listings of accounting employment opportunities with public accounting firms, corporations, government agencies and non-profit organizations. Includes articles and features on career development.

9 ■ *Journal of Business Finance and Accounting*
Blackwell Publishing Inc.
350 Main St.
Malden, MA 02148
Ph: (781)388-8200
Free: 800-216-2522
Fax: (781)388-8210
E-mail: journaladsusa@bos.blackwellpublishing.com
URL: http://as.wiley.com/WileyCDA/WileyTitle/productCd-JBFA.html

Frequency: 10/yr. **Price:** $255 Individuals U.S. print + online; $2,372 Institutions U.S. print + online; $2,062 Institutions U.S. print or online. **Description:** Journal focusing on finance and economic aspects of accounting.

10 ■ *The Journal of Taxation*
RIA Group
395 Hudson St.
New York, NY 10014
Ph: (212)367-6300
Fax: (212)367-6314
URL: http://ria.thomson.com/estore/detail.aspx?ID=JTAX

Frequency: Monthly. **Price:** $410 Individuals print; $595 Individuals online/print bundle; $465 Individuals online. **Description:** Journal for sophisticated tax practitioners.

11 ■ *National Association of Black Accountants--News Plus*
National Association of Black Accountants
7474 Greenway Center Dr., Ste. 1120
Greenbelt, MD 20770
Ph: (301)474-6222
Free: 888-571-2939
Fax: (301)474-3114
E-mail: membership@nabainc.org
URL: http://www.nabainc.org

Frequency: Quarterly. **Price:** Included in membership. **Description:** Addresses concerns of black business professionals, especially in the accounting profession. Reports on accounting education issues, developments affecting the profession, and the Association's activities on the behalf of minorities in the accounting profession. Recurring features include member profiles, job listings, reports of meetings, news of research, and a calendar of events.

12 ■ *NewsAccount*
Colorado Society of Certified Public Accountants
7887 E Belleview Ave., Ste. 200
Englewood, CO 80111
Ph: (303)773-2877
Free: 800-523-9082
Fax: (303)773-6344
E-mail: mmedley@cocpa.org
URLs: http://www.cocpa.org; http://www.cocpa.org/members/news_account_advert.asp

Frequency: Bimonthly; 6/year. **Price:** Included in

membership. **Description:** Monthly. Recurring feature includes accounting job listings.

13 ■ *Research in Accounting Regulation*
Reed Elsevier Inc.
125 Park Ave., 23rd Fl.
New York, NY 10017-5529
Ph: (212)309-8100
Fax: (212)309-8187
E-mail: newyork@reedelsevier.com
URL: http://www.journals.elsevier.com/research-in
   -accounting-regulation/

Frequency: Semiannual. **Price:** $147 Single issue online only; $353 Institutions print only; single article. **Description:** Journal covering the field of accounting.

14 ■ *Strategic Finance: Leadership Strategies in Accounting, Finance, and Information Management*
Institute of Management Accountants
10 Paragon Dr., Ste. 1
Montvale, NJ 07645-1774
Ph: (201)573-9000
Free: 800-638-4427
Fax: (201)474-1600
E-mail: ima@imanet.org
URL: http://www.imanet.org/publications.asp

Frequency: Monthly. **Price:** $210 Nonmembers; $48 Members; $25 Students; $18 Single issue back issue. **Description:** Magazine reporting on corporate finance, accounting, cash management, and budgeting.

PLACEMENT AND JOB REFERRAL SERVICES

15 ■ **American Association of Attorney-CPAs**
8647 Richmond Hwy., Ste. 639
Alexandria, VA 22309
Ph: (703)352-8064
Free: 888-ATTY-CPA
Fax: (703)352-8073
E-mail: info@attorney-cpa.com
URL: http://www.attorney-cpa.com

Description: Represents persons who are licensed both as attorneys and as certified public accountants (CPAs). Maintains placement service. Offers referral service of potential clients.

16 ■ **Construction Financial Management Association**
100 Village Blvd., Ste. 200
Princeton, NJ 08540
Ph: (609)452-8000
Free: 888-421-9996
Fax: (609)452-0474
E-mail: sbinstock@cfma.org
URL: http://www.cfma.org

Description: Contractors, subcontractors, architects, real estate developers and engineers; associate members are equipment and material suppliers, accountants, lawyers, bankers and others involved with the financial management of the construction industry. Maintains placement service.

17 ■ **Registered Financial Planners Institute**
2001 Cooper Foster Park Rd.
Amherst, OH 44001
Ph: (440)282-7176
Fax: (440)282-8027
E-mail: info@rfpi.com
URL: http://rfpi.com

Description: Registered financial planners, including insurance and real estate agents, attorneys, accountants, certified public accountants, bankers, securities analysts, and stockbrokers. Sponsors referral service. **Members:** 300.

18 ■ **Utah Association of Certified Public Accountants**
1240 E 2100 S, Ste. 500
Salt Lake City, UT 84106
Ph: (801)466-8022
Fax: (801)485-6206
E-mail: mm@uacpa.org
URL: http://www.uacpa.org/content/home.aspx

Description: Certified public accountants. Offers free CPA referral service. **Members:** 3,200.

EMPLOYER DIRECTORIES AND NETWORKING LISTS

19 ■ *Accountancy: A Professional Reference Guide*
Frequency: Published fall 1991; new edition expected January 1995. **Price:** $99.95. **Pages:** 450. **Covers:** Accounting associations and major accounting firms. **Includes:** Accounting laws governing the reqmnts. for licensing of professional accountants in all 50 states, the Dist. of Columbia, Guam, Puerto Rico, and the U.S. Virgin Islands; list of ethical stds. & reqmnts.; bibliography. **Entries include:** For associations--Name, chapter locations, membership, international affiliates, student chapters. For firms--Name, address. **Arrangement:** Separate sections for associations and firms. **Indexes:** For school section--Subject, geographical. For publisher section--Title.

20 ■ *Accounting Executives Database*
Manufacturers' News Inc.
1633 Central St.
Evanston, IL 60201-1569
Ph: (847)864-7000
Free: 888-752-5200
Fax: (847)332-1100
E-mail: info@manufacturersnews.com
URL: http://www.manufacturersnews.com

Price: $1,031 Individuals EZ Select Full. **Covers:** 15,854 accounting executives. **Entries include:** Mailing and physical address, telephone, fax, toll-free, e-mail, website, year established, area of distribution, ownership, number of employees, annual sales, square footage, primary and secondary SIC, primary NAICS, product description, parent company information and contact person.

21 ■ *American Society of Women Accountants--Membership Directory*
Accounting and Financial Women's Alliance
1760 Old Meadow Rd., Ste. 500
McLean, VA 22102
Ph: (703)506-3265
Free: 800-326-2163
Fax: (703)506-3266
E-mail: aswa@aswa.org
URL: http://www.aswa.org

Frequency: Annual. **Covers:** Approximately 5,000 members in accounting and accounting-related fields. **Entries include:** Name, address, phone, fax, e-mail. **Arrangement:** Classified by chapter, then alphabetical.

22 ■ *American Woman's Society of Certified Public Accountants--Roster*
American Woman's Society of Certified Public Accountants
136 S Keowee St.
Dayton, OH 45402
Ph: (937)222-1872
Free: 800-297-2721
Fax: (937)222-5794
E-mail: info@awscpa.org
URL: http://www.awscpa.org

Frequency: Annual; October. **Pages:** 14. **No. of Listings:** 1,400. **Entries include:** Name, title; company name, address, phone; home address and phone; membership classification. **Arrangement:** Classified by type of membership, then geographical. **Indexes:** Alphabetical.

23 ■ *Crain's List--Chicago's Largest Accounting Firms*
Crain Communications Inc.
150 N Michigan Ave.
Chicago, IL 60601-7553
Ph: (312)649-5200
Free: 800-678-9595
Fax: (312)280-3150
E-mail: info@crain.com
URL: http://www.chicagobusiness.com/section/lists

Frequency: Published October 2010. **Price:** $25 Individuals PDF format; $45 Individuals Excel format. **Covers:** 25 accounting firms in Chicago ranked by number of local professional staff. **Entries include:** Firm name, address, web address, e-mail, managing partner in Chicago, professional staff in the Six-County area (as of June 30, 2009 and June 30, 2010), CPA's in Six-County area (as of June 30, 2010), CPAs firmwide (as of June 30, 2010), auditing, accounting, management advisory services, tax, specialties, firmwide professionals (as of June 30, 2010), Fiscal 2009 firmwide revenue, revenue firmwide percentage change, and local managing partner.

24 ■ *OSCPA White Pages*
Oregon Society of Certified Public Accountants
10206 SW Laurel St.
Beaverton, OR 97005-3209
Ph: (503)641-7200
Free: 800-255-1470
Fax: (503)626-2942
E-mail: oscpa@orcpa.org
URL: http://www.orcpa.org/store/000347LK-oscpa
   _white_pages_membership_directory

Frequency: Annual. **Price:** Free; $75 Individuals for additional copy. **Covers:** 5,000 accounting professionals in Oregon. **Entries include:** Business name, location, and services.

25 ■ *Vault Guide to the Top 50 Accounting Firms*
Vault.com Inc.
132 W 31st St., 17th Fl.
New York, NY 10001-3406
Ph: (212)366-4212
Free: 800-535-2074
Fax: (212)366-6117
E-mail: customerservice@vault.com
URL: http://www.vault.com

Frequency: Latest edition 2013. **Price:** $29.95 Individuals. **Pages:** 166. **Covers:** Accounting firms in United States and 750 accounting professionals. **Entries include:** Company name, address, phone and fax numbers, zip code, statistics and website address.

HANDBOOKS AND MANUALS

26 ■ *Accountants' Handbook*
John Wiley & Sons Inc.
111 River St.
Hoboken, NJ 07030-5774
Ph: (201)748-6000
Free: 800-225-5945
Fax: (201)748-6088
E-mail: info@wiley.com
URL: http://www.wiley.com

Description: D.R. Carmichael and Lynford Graham. 2012. $119.95. 1056 pages. Series covering accounting and financial reporting of interest to accountants, auditors, financial analysts, and users of accounting information.

27 ■ *Accounting Trends & Techniques*
American Institute of Certified Public Accountants
Harborside Financial Ctr.
201 Plaza Three
Jersey City, NJ 07311-3881
Ph: (201)938-3000
Free: 888-777-7077

Fax: (201)938-3329
URL: http://www.aicpa.org
Description: Rick Rikert. 2009. $168.75 (paper).

28 ■ *Great Jobs for Accounting Majors*
The McGraw-Hill Companies
7500 Chavenelle Rd.
Dubuque, IA 52002
Free: 877-833-5524
Fax: (614)759-3749
E-mail: pbg.ecommerce_custserv@mcgraw-hill.com
URL: http://www.mhprofessional.com/product.php
   ?isbn=0071438548
Description: Jan Goldberg. 2005. $15.95 (paper).
192 pages. Guide covering both the basics of a job
search as well as profiles of possible careers in the
accounting field. Helps in exploring a variety of job
options for accounting majors to determine what will
fit for personal, professional, and practical needs.

29 ■ *New Accountant*
Real Estate News Corp.
3550 W Peterson Ave.
Chicago, IL 60659
Ph: (773)866-9900
Fax: (773)866-9881
E-mail: editor@newaccountantusa.com
URL: http://www.newaccountantusa.com/
Frequency: 8/yr. **Price:** $38 Individuals graduates;
$35 Students faculty, new accounting grads, seniors;
$50 Libraries; $85 Individuals professional. **Description:** Magazine for business-oriented accountants of
all ages. Includes practical articles, features, and
columns on careers.

30 ■ *Opportunities in Financial Careers*
The McGraw-Hill Companies Inc.
PO Box 182604
Columbus, OH 43272
Ph: (212)512-2000
Free: 877-833-5524
Fax: (614)759-3749
E-mail: customer.service@mcgraw-hill.com
URL: http://www.mcgraw-hill.com
Description: Michael Sumichrast and Martin A.
Sumichrast. 2004. $13.95 (paper). 160 pages. A
guide to planning for and seeking opportunities in
this challenging field.

31 ■ *Opportunities in Insurance Careers*
The McGraw-Hill Companies Inc.
PO Box 182604
Columbus, OH 43272
Ph: (212)512-2000
Free: 877-833-5524
Fax: (614)759-3749
E-mail: customer.service@mcgraw-hill.com
URL: http://www.mcgraw-hill.com
Description: Robert M. Schrayer. Revised, 2007.
$14.95 (paper). 160 pages. A guide to planning for
and seeking opportunities in the field. Contains
bibliography and illustrations.

32 ■ *Vault Career Guide to Accounting*
Vault.com Inc.
132 W 31st St., 17th Fl.
New York, NY 10001-3406
Ph: (212)366-4212
Free: 800-535-2074
Fax: (212)366-6117
E-mail: customerservice@vault.com
URL: http://www.vault.com
Description: Jason Alba et al. 2008. $29.95 (paper).
160 pages. Features the ins and outs of a career in
accounting from the types of accounting, including
tax and audit, to the hiring process and workplace
culture of major accounting employers.

EMPLOYMENT AGENCIES AND SEARCH FIRMS

33 ■ A-lign Careers
2202 N Westshore Blvd., Ste. 200
Tampa, FL 33607

Ph: (940)648-5045
Free: 888-702-5446
URL: http://www.aligncareers.com
Description: Specializes in the recruitment of auditing, accounting, and finance personnel.

34 ■ AC Lordi Search
235 Montgomery St., Ste. 630
San Francisco, CA 94104
Ph: (415)781-8644
E-mail: info@aclordi.com
URL: http://www.aclordi.com
Description: Executive search firm for finance and
accounting. Uses referral-based outsourcing, affinity
networking, and cold-calling to identify talented accounting professionals.

35 ■ Access Staffing
360 Lexington Ave., 8th Fl.
New York, NY 10017
Ph: (212)687-5440
Fax: (212)557-2544
URL: http://www.accessstaffingco.com
Description: Serves as a staffing firm covering accounting/financial, advertising, bilingual Japanese,
creative, event planning, fashion/retail, healthcare/
human services, human resources, information
technology, insurance, legal, light industrial, and office support.

36 ■ Accountemps
1404 I St. NW, Ste. 400
Washington, DC 20005
Ph: (202)626-0120
Free: 800-803-8367
E-mail: washington.dc@accountemps.com
URL: http://www.accountemps.com
Description: Specializes in staffing for accounting,
finance and bookkeeping professionals. Provides
staffing support to all fields of an accounting department. Maintains offices all over the United States.

37 ■ Accounting Connections
5320 SW Macadam Ave., Ste. 260
Portland, OR 97296
Ph: (503)228-2335
Free: 866-956-2748
Fax: (503)228-2175
E-mail: info@staff4u.com
URL: http://www.staff4u.com
Description: Serves as a staffing agency specializing in accounting and finance professionals.

38 ■ Accounting and Finance Personnel Inc.
1702 E Highland Ave., Ste. 200
Phoenix, AZ 85016-4665
Ph: (602)277-3700
Fax: (602)926-2629
E-mail: contact@afpersonnel.com
URL: http://www.afpersonnel.com
Description: Specializes in placing accounting and
financial personnel.

39 ■ Accounting Partners
2025 Gateway Pl., Ste. 405
San Jose, CA 95110
Ph: (408)986-1990
Fax: (408)986-1411
URL: http://www.accountingpartners.com
Description: Provides contract, contact-to-hire, and
direct-hire solutions in a wide variety of accounting
and finance positions.

40 ■ Accounting Principals
Bldg. 200, Ste. 400
10151 Deerwood Park Blvd.
Jacksonville, FL 32256
Free: 800-981-3849
E-mail: info@accountingprincipals.com
URL: http://www.accountingprincipals.com
Description: Provides workforce solutions in the accounting and financial services industries. Offers a

range of services including temporary staffing, temp-
to-hire, direct placement, payroll services and
contract services.

41 ■ AccountSource
130 Milestone Way
Greenville, SC 29615
Ph: (864)213-8004
Fax: (864)213-9867
E-mail: recruiters@asijobs.com
URL: http://www.asijobs.com
Description: Acts as a premier placement service
for accounting and finance professionals. Offers a
wide variety of services including permanent placement, contract, and contract-to-hire staffing solutions.

42 ■ Action Employment Services
121 SW Morrison St., Ste. 425
Portland, OR 97204
Ph: (503)275-9011
Free: 866-208-1643
Fax: (503)241-8772
E-mail: inquiry@actionemployment.net
URL: http://www.actionemployment.net
Description: Provides administrative, office, accounting, and human resource positions.

43 ■ Advantage Group
350 N Old Woodward Ave., Ste. 218
Birmingham, MI 48009
Ph: (248)540-0400
Fax: (248)540-0401
E-mail: info@advantage-grp.com
URL: http://advantage-grp.com
Description: Specializes in the placement of accounting and financial executives.

44 ■ Ajilon Professional Staffing
521 5th Ave., 4th Fl.
New York, NY 10175
Ph: (212)953-7400
Free: 866-GOA-JILON
Fax: (212)867-8394
E-mail: staffing@ajilonfinance.com
URL: http://www.ajilonfinance.com
Description: Provides staffing service specializing in
the temporary and permanent placement of premier
accounting, finance and bookkeeping professionals.

45 ■ Albion Accounting Staffing Solutions
2520 NW 97th Ave., Ste. 110
Miami, FL 33172
Ph: (305)406-1000
Fax: (305)406-1010
E-mail: resumes@albionstaffing.com
URL: http://www.albionaccounting.com
Description: Specializes in the placement of
financial, accounting, bookkeeping, mortgage, and
banking positions on a temporary, temp-to-hire, or
direct hire basis. Offers full service recruiting and
consulting services.

46 ■ ATR Finance
1230 Oakmead Pkwy., Ste. 110
Sunnyvale, CA 94085
Ph: (408)328-8000
E-mail: corporate@atr1.com
URL: http://www.atr-finance.com
Description: Serves as an executive placement firm
for accounting and finance professionals. Offers
career opportunities for finance and accounting
professionals interested in either consulting or full-
time positions.

47 ■ Aureus Group
C&A Plz., 13609 California St., Ste. 100
Omaha, NE 68154-3503
Ph: (402)891-6900
Free: 888-239-5993
Fax: (402)891-1290
E-mail: omaha@aureusgroup.com
URL: http://www.aureusgroup.com
Description: Executive search and recruiting

consultants specializing in accounting and finance, information systems and technology, health care administration, and wealth management.

48 ■ BG & Associates
10112 Langhorne Ct., Ste. B
Bethesda, MD 20817-1250
Ph: (301)365-4046
Fax: (301)365-0435
E-mail: bgajob@erols.com

Description: Firm specializes in the recruitment and placement of consultants on a national basis primarily in the areas of information technology, finance/accounting, and human resources.

49 ■ Bolton Group
3500 Piedmont Rd., Ste. 340
Atlanta, GA 30305
Ph: (404)228-4280
Fax: (404)228-2060
URL: http://www.boltongroup.com

Description: Serves as a specialty niche search firm focusing solely in the areas of accounting and finance. Partners with progressive organizations throughout the country, providing accounting and finance specialists in a variety of areas including accounting, finance, tax, treasury, audit/SOX, and financial systems.

50 ■ Boyce Cunnane Inc.
PO Box 19064
Baltimore, MD 21284-9064
Ph: (410)583-5511
Fax: (410)583-5518
E-mail: bc@cunnane.com
URL: http://www.cunnane.com

Description: Executive search firm that recruits tax professionals, including CPAs, lawyers, and consultants, for commercial and corporate businesses.

51 ■ Buxbaum Rink Consulting L.L.C.
1 Bradley Rd., Ste. 901
Woodbridge, CT 06525-2296
Ph: (203)389-5949
Fax: (203)397-0615

Description: Personnel consulting firms offer contingency search, recruitment, and placement of accounting and finance, as well as other business management positions. In addition to serving these two major career areas, also provides similar services to operations, marketing and human resources executives. Industries served: manufacturing, financial services, and service.

52 ■ Capitol Staffing Inc.
460 Briarwood Dr., Briarwood 1 Bldg., Ste. 110
Jackson, MS 39206
Ph: (601)957-1755
Fax: (601)957-3880
E-mail: info@capitolstaffing.com
URL: http://www.capitolstaffing.com

Description: Personnel consultancy that focuses on office administration, management, sales, accounting, medical, information technology, accounting, and engineering/technical fields. Industries served: insurance, finance, medical, communications, investment, industry, and small businesses.

53 ■ Career Advocates International
1539 Ave. A
Katy, TX 77493
Ph: (281)371-0917
E-mail: hank@careeradvocates.org
URL: http://www.careeradvocates.org

Description: Provides permanent placement and temporary staffing for executive and staff level positions. Specializes in multiple niches including: sales and marketing, accounting and financial services, banking, communications, human resources, chemicals, oil and gas, medical and dental, legal, information technology, energy, technology, engineering, manufacturing, construction, and light industrial.

54 ■ Casey Accounting and Finance Resources
4902 Tollview Dr.
Rolling Meadows, IL 60008
Ph: (224)232-5925
E-mail: info@caseyresources.com
URL: http://www.caseyresources.com

Description: Specializes in the placement of accounting and finance professionals for direct hire, temp-to-hire, project staffing and temporary services.

55 ■ Catalyst Resource Group, LLC
2050 Marconi Dr., Ste. 300
Alpharetta, GA 30005
Ph: (678)366-3500
Free: 877-746-3400
Fax: (678)366-9710
E-mail: info@catalystresourcegroup.com
URL: http://www.catalystresourcegroup.com

Description: Serves as an executive search firm specializing in the placement of accounting and finance professionals.

56 ■ Centennial, Inc.
8044 Montgomery Rd., Ste. 260
Cincinnati, OH 45236
Ph: (513)366-3760
Fax: (513)366-3761
URL: http://www.centennialinc.com

Description: Serves as an executive search firm specializing in the areas of executive and general management, accounting and finance, human resources, information technology, manufacturing, engineering, marketing and advertising, not-for-profit, sales and business development, and supply chain and logistics.

57 ■ Chanko-Ward Ltd.
2 W 45th St., Ste. 1201
New York, NY 10036
Ph: (212)869-4040
Fax: (212)869-0281
E-mail: info@chankoward.com
URL: http://www.chankoward.com

Description: Primarily engaged in executive recruiting for individuals and corporations; where disciplines of accounting; planning, mergers and acquisitions; finance; or management information systems required.

58 ■ Clovis, LLC
10411 Motor City Dr., Ste. 450
Bethesda, MD 20817
Ph: (301)365-8480
Free: 888-925-6847
Fax: (301)576-3579
E-mail: solutions@clovisgroup.com
URL: http://www.clovisgroup.com

Description: Serves as recruitment outsourcing staffing firm for information technology, accounting, and finance professionals.

59 ■ Conselium
14850 Montfort Dr., Ste. 106
Dallas, TX 75254
Ph: (972)934-8444
URL: http://www.conselium.com

Description: Executive search firm with a core expertise in corporate compliance, audit, and information technology security.

60 ■ Consultants to Executive Management Company Ltd.
20 S Clark St., Ste. 610
Chicago, IL 60600
Ph: (312)855-1500
Free: 800-800-2362
Fax: (312)855-1510

Description: National personnel consultancy specializes in executive search with focus on accounting and finance, management information systems, professional medical and real estate fields. Industries served: All.

61 ■ Cornell Global
PO Box 7113
Wilton, CT 06897
Ph: (203)762-0730
E-mail: info@cornellglobal.com
URL: http://www.cornellglobal.com

Description: Executive search firm with areas of expertise in the following areas: advertising, public relations, marketing, sales, finance and accounting, risk management, private equity and venture capital, construction, industrial, manufacturing, life sciences, publishing, information technology, engineering, human resources, legal, and logisitics.

62 ■ Crowe Horwath L.L.P.
330 E Jefferson Blvd.
South Bend, IN 46624-0007
Ph: (574)232-3992
Fax: (574)236-8692
URL: http://www.crowehorwath.com

Description: Offers accounting and consulting services for the automotive, agricultural, commercial, construction, financial institutions, government, health care, manufacturing, and transportation industries.

63 ■ CSI Executive Search LLC
9600 Great Hills Trail, Ste. 150W
Austin, TX 78759
Ph: (512)301-1119
Fax: (512)301-5559
E-mail: info@csi-executivesearch.com
URL: http://www.csi-executivesearch.com

Description: Executive search firm that specializes in the following arenas: accounting, engineering, healthcare, information technology, and legal.

64 ■ CyberCoders, Inc.
6591 Irvine Center Dr., Ste. 200
Irvine, CA 92618
Ph: (949)885-5151
Fax: (949)885-5150
E-mail: info@cybercoders.com
URL: http://www.cybercoders.com

Description: Recruitment and job search firm specializing in engineering, executive, financial, accounting, and sales.

65 ■ DGL Consultants
3492 Hill Cir.
Colorado Springs, CO 80904
Ph: (719)634-7041
E-mail: info@dglconsultants.com
URL: http://www.dglconsultants.com

Description: Executive search firm with primary expertise in the financial services industry.

66 ■ Elinvar
1804 Hillsborough St.
Raleigh, NC 27605
URL: http://www.elinvar.com

Description: Accounting, finance, and human resources executive search firm.

67 ■ Financial Search Group, Ltd.
307 Fourth Ave., Ste. 810
Pittsburgh, PA 15222
Ph: (412)288-0505
Fax: (412)288-0699
E-mail: fsgltd@fsgltd.com
URL: http://www.fsgltd.com

Description: Provides accounting and financial staffing services on a wide variety of companies from contingency or retainer basis.

68 ■ Foster McKay Group
30 Vreeland Rd.
Florham Park, NJ 07932
Ph: (973)966-0909
Fax: (973)966-6925
E-mail: careers@fostermckaynj.com
URL: http://www.fostermckay.com

Description: Executive search firm that specializes in placing financial, accounting, and tax professionals.

69 ■ General Ledger Resources
13280 Evening Creek Dr. S, Ste. 225
San Diego, CA 92128
Ph: (858)391-1017
E-mail: atheodore@gl-resources.com
URL: http://www.gl-resources.com

Description: Serves as a finance and accounting professional services firm with practice areas in consulting services and search and placement.

70 ■ GK Finance
7242 Metro Blvd., Ste. 100
Edina, MN 55439
Ph: (952)835-5550
Fax: (952)835-7294
E-mail: info@georgekonik.com
URL: http://www.gkastaffing.com/index_financial.php

Description: Specializes in placing qualified candidates in finance and accounting positions. Offers three staffing options: contract (temporary) staffing, contract-to-direct, and direct hire opportunities from entry to senior or management level candidates.

71 ■ Harder Consulting Inc.
3429 Executive Center Dr., Ste. 101
Austin, TX 78731
Ph: (512)470-0000
Fax: (512)372-9900
E-mail: projects@harderconsulting.com
URL: http://www.harderconsulting.com

Description: A professional employment solutions firm specializing in the areas of accounting, finance, banking and human resources.

72 ■ International Search
9717 E 42nd St.
Tulsa, OK 74147-0898
Ph: (918)627-9070
Fax: (918)524-8604

Description: Personnel consulting group provides placement expertise in engineering, accounting, and data processing. Industries served: Energy, manufacturing, oil and gas, and services.

73 ■ Wendell L. Johnson Associates Inc.
12 Grandview Dr., Ste. 1117
Danbury, CT 06811-4321
Ph: (203)743-4112
Fax: (203)778-5377

Description: Executive search firm specializing in areas of workforce diversity, accounting/finance, human resources, marketing/sales, strategic planning and management information systems.

74 ■ Kforce Inc.
1001 E Palm Ave.
Tampa, FL 33605-3551
Ph: (813)552-5000
Free: 877-453-6723
Fax: (813)552-2493
URL: http://www.kforce.com

Description: Executive search firm specializing in the financial services, insurance, health care, and pharmaceuticals industries.

75 ■ KLR Executive Search Group L.L.C.
951 N Main St.
Providence, RI 02904
Ph: (401)274-2001
Fax: (401)831-4018
E-mail: info@klrsearchgroup.com
URL: http://www.klrsearchgroup.com

Description: Career recruitment firm specializes in the placement of accounting and financial and information technology professionals.

76 ■ Kramer Executive Resources, Inc.
17 W 67th St., No. 8A
New York, NY 10023

Ph: (917)923-0160
E-mail: info@kramerexec.com
URL: http://www.kramerexec.com

Description: Specializes in the recruitment of accounting, tax, and financial professionals in the New York metropolitan tri-state region.

77 ■ Houser Martin Morris
110th Ave. NE, 110 Atrium Pl., Ste. 580
Bellevue, WA 98004
Ph: (425)453-2700
Fax: (425)453-8726
E-mail: info@houser.com
URL: http://www.houser.com

Description: Focus is in the areas of retained executive search, professional, and technical recruiting. Areas of specialization include software engineering, sales and marketing, information technology, legal, human resources, accounting and finance, manufacturing, factory automation and engineering.

78 ■ Nesco Inc.
6140 Parkland Blvd., Ste. 110
Mayfield Heights, OH 44124-6106
Ph: (440)461-6000
Fax: (440)449-3111
E-mail: corporate@nescoresource.com
URL: http://www.nescoresource.com

Description: Offers staffing and consulting solutions in the fields of engineering, information technology, accounting and finance, manufacturing and distribution, and administrative and customer services.

79 ■ L.J. Parrish & Associates Inc.
PO Box 874
Charles Town, WV 25414
Ph: (304)725-3834
Fax: (301)733-5155

Description: Executive search and human resource consulting firm specializing in financial, general management, and operations management positions. Industries served: All private industry, public accounting firms, and government.

80 ■ Pate Resources Group Inc.
505 Orleans St., Ste. 300
Beaumont, TX 77701-3224
Ph: (409)833-4514
Fax: (409)833-4646

Description: Offers executive search and recruiting services to professionals who include physicians, health care administrators, accountants, financial managers; chemical, mechanical, industrial, and electrical engineers; sales and marketing managers, human resources administrators, and general managers and top executives in numerous disciplines. Industries served: health care, petrochemicals, accounting, utility, legal and municipalities.

81 ■ Penn Search Inc.
1045 1st Ave., Ste. 110
King of Prussia, PA 19406
Ph: (610)964-8820
Fax: (610)964-8916
E-mail: charlied@pennsearch.com
URL: http://www.pennsearch.com

Description: Assists in recruiting and hiring accounting and financial professionals from staff accountant to chief financial officer. Industries served: All.

82 ■ Phillip's Personnel/Phillip's Temps
1675 Broadway, Ste. 2410
Denver, CO 80204
Ph: (303)893-1850
Fax: (303)893-0639
E-mail: info@phillipspersonnel.com
URL: http://www.phillipspersonnel.com

Description: Personnel recruiting and staffing consultants in: accounting and finance, management information systems, sales and marketing, engineering, administration, and general and executive

management. Industries served: telecommunications, distribution, financial services, and general business.

83 ■ Pro Advantage Executive Search
295 Madison Ave., 12th Fl.
New York, NY 10017
Ph: (212)944-0222
Fax: (212)944-2666
E-mail: info@proadvantagejobs.com
URL: http://www.proadvantagejobs.com

Description: Executive recruiting and research firm specializes in financial services industries. Offers career opportunities in the field of accounting, internal auditing, finance, compliance, tax, operations, and marketing.

84 ■ Q&A Recruiting
J.P. Morgan International Plz., Bldg. III
14241 Dallas Pkwy., Ste. 550
Dallas, TX 75254
Ph: (972)720-1020
Fax: (972)720-1023
E-mail: jobs@qarecruiting.com
URL: http://www.qarecruiting.com

Description: Provides staffing services for accounting, finance, tax, information technology, payroll or accounting support, and human resources.

85 ■ Randstad Finance & Accounting
111 Anza Blvd., Ste. 202
Burlingame, CA 94010
Ph: (650)343-5111
Fax: (650)343-5485
URL: http://finance.randstadusa.com

Description: Provides permanent and temporary contract staffing for accounting, finance, financial services and data processing.

86 ■ Raymond Alexander Associates
97 Lackawanna Ave., Ste. 102
Totowa, NJ 07512-2332
Ph: (973)256-1000
Fax: (973)256-5871
E-mail: raa@raymondalexander.com
URL: http://www.raymondalexander.com

Description: Personnel consulting firm conducts executive search services in the specific areas of accounting, tax and finance. Industries served: manufacturing, financial services, and public accounting.

87 ■ Roberson & Co.
10751 Parfet St.
Broomfield, CO 80021
Ph: (303)410-6510
E-mail: roberson@recruiterpro.com
URL: http://www.recruiterpro.com

Description: Professional and executive recruiting firm working the national and international marketplace. Specializes in accounting, finance, data processing and information services, health care, environmental and mining engineering, manufacturing, human resources, and sales and marketing.

88 ■ Robert Half Finance & Accounting
2884 Sand Hill Rd.
Menlo Park, CA 94025
Free: 800-474-4253
URL: http://www.roberthalffinance.com

Description: Provides recruitment services in the areas of accounting and finance.

89 ■ Robert Half Management Resources
2884 Sand Hill Rd.
Menlo Park, CA 94025
Free: 888-400-7474
URL: http://www.roberthalfmr.com

Description: Serves as a provider of senior-level accounting and finance professionals on a project and interim basis.

90 ■ Rocky Mountain Recruiters, Inc.
1776 S Jackson St., Ste. 320
Denver, CO 80210
Ph: (303)296-2000
E-mail: resumes@rmrecruiters.com
URL: http://www.rmrecruiters.com

Description: Accounting and financial executive search firm.

91 ■ Sherpa LLC
1001 Morehead Square Dr., Ste. 600
Charlotte, NC 28203
Ph: (704)374-0001
URL: http://www.sherpallc.com

Description: Specializes in recruiting, staffing, and consulting services for accounting/finance, information technology, and project management in direct hire, temporary and project-based consulting positions.

92 ■ SHS of Cherry Hill
207 Barclay Pavilion W
Cherry Hill, NJ 08034
Ph: (856)216-9030
Fax: (856)219-2011
E-mail: shs@shsofcherryhill.com
URL: http://www.shsofcherryhill.com

Description: Personnel recruiters operating in the disciplines of accounting, sales, insurance, engineering and administration. Industries served: insurance, distribution, manufacturing and service.

93 ■ Spectrum Group, LLC
1919 Gallows Rd., Ste. 600
Vienna, VA 22182
Ph: (703)738-1200
Fax: (703)761-9477
E-mail: web@spectrumcareers.com
URL: http://www.spectrumcareers.com

Description: Serves as executive search firm for accounting and finance, information technology, and sales and marketing industries.

94 ■ S.R. Clarke
105 Huntercombe
Williamsburg, VA 23188
Ph: (703)344-0256
Fax: (949)608-5052
URL: http://www.srclarke.com/index.html

Description: Serves as an executive search and recruitment firm specializing in commercial construction, commercial real estate development, residential asset management, residential construction and development, subcontractor trades, finance, accounting, administration, heavy construction, architectural design and engineering design.

95 ■ Whitney & Associates Inc.
920 2nd Ave. S, Ste. 625
Minneapolis, MN 55402-4103
Ph: (612)338-5600
Fax: (612)349-6129

Description: Accounting and financial personnel recruiting consultants providing full time placement and temporary staffing service with specialized expertise and emphasis in the accounting discipline.

ONLINE JOB SOURCES AND SERVICES

96 ■ Accountantjobs.com
URL: http://www.accountantjobs.com

Description: Serves as a job site network and online portal for accounting careers worldwide. Features job postings, advertisements, resume access and other resources intended to provide both employers and job seekers their online recruitment needs.

97 ■ AccountExecutiveManager.com
URL: http://www.accountexecutivemanager.com

Description: Provides career and employment opportunities for aspiring account executive managers. Offers links, job and resume postings and more.

98 ■ Accounting Technician Jobs
URL: http://www.accountingtechnicianjobs.com

Description: Specializes in accounting technician careers and employment. Offers resume posting and job opening listings.

99 ■ AccountingBoard.com
URL: http://www.accountingboard.com

Description: Features job opportunities in the accounting field.

100 ■ AccountingClassifieds.com
URL: http://www.accountingclassifieds.com

Description: Serves as a specialized career site providing employment opportunities focused on the accounting industry.

101 ■ AccountingCoach.com
URL: http://www.accountingcoach.com

Description: Provides accounting information for business persons or students who are considering a career in accounting. Contains an accounting blog, forums, newsletters, links, advertisements, career resources, and other related information.

102 ■ Accounting.com
URL: http://www.accounting.com

Description: Job board for those seeking accounting jobs. Employers may also post positions available. Contains directory of CPA firms, discussion forum for job seekers, CPE resources, news bulletins and accounting links.

103 ■ AccountingCrossing.com
URL: http://www.accountingcrossing.com

Description: Offers collection of accounting jobs, including CPA, finance manager, corporate accountant, and forensic accounting positions. Features industry-specific articles relating to job searches and developments in the accounting industry.

104 ■ AccountingJobsite.com
URL: http://www.accountingjobsite.com

Description: Provides listings of accounting jobs, accounting clerk jobs, accounting auditing jobs, and other accounting employment opportunities.

105 ■ AccountingJobsToday.com
URL: http://www.accountingjobstoday.com

Description: Functions as a job resource for accounting and finance professionals worldwide. Offers several career resources including accounting job descriptions, sample accounting resumes, salary tools and education.

106 ■ AccountingProfessional.com
URL: http://www.accountingprofessional.com

Description: Acts as a job search and recruiting site for accountants, CPAs and related financial jobs. Provides resources for both job seekers and employers.

107 ■ AllAccountantJobs.com
URL: http://allaccountantjobs.com

Description: Provides job seekers access to resources and job opening opportunities in the area of accounting.

108 ■ American Association of Finance and Accounting
URL: http://www.aafa.com

Description: Alliance of executive search firms specializing in the recruitment and placement of finance and accounting professionals. Contains career opportunities site with job board for both job seekers and hiring employers. One does not have to be a member to search for jobs.

109 ■ AuditorCrossing.com
URL: http://www.auditorcrossing.com

Description: Offers a wide collection of top auditor job openings. Includes listings from Fortune 500 and Fortune 1000 companies.

110 ■ BankingCareers.com
URL: http://www.bankingcareers.com

Description: Provides lists of jobs and products to the banking and finance community.

111 ■ BookkeeperJobs.com
URL: http://www.bookkeeperjobs.com

Description: Serves as a niche board for bookkeeping jobs and resumes. Allows postings and searching of resumes for first-time and returning job seekers and employers.

112 ■ Business Job Finder
Ohio State University - Department of Finance
Max M. Fisher College of Business
700 Fisher Hall
2100 Neil Ave.
Columbus, OH 43210
Ph: (614)292-5026
Fax: (614)292-2418
E-mail: scholl_2@cob.osu.edu
URL: http://www.cob.ohio-state.edu/fin

Description: Internet site containing information on jobs in the business sector, primarily in accounting, finance, and consulting. Links to many corporations who hire extensively in this area are included for those wishing to make contacts and/or mail out resumes. Detailed information on job search aids and employer profiles are provided with job areas broken down into subject.

113 ■ California Society of Certified Public Accountants Classifieds
URL: http://www.calcpa.org/classifieds/public/search.aspx

Description: An accounting job search tool for CPAs in California. Details steps to become a CPA, provides job search posting opportunities for seekers and candidates' pages for employers looking to fill positions.

114 ■ CareerBank
URL: http://www.careerbank.com/home/index.cfm?site_id=8162

Description: Provides jobs in finance, banking, mortgage, insurance, and accounting. Specializes in online job posting and job search, resume upload and resume database search, and career advice services.

115 ■ Careers-In-Business
Careers-In-Business, LLC
4101 N.W. Urbandale Dr.
Urbandale, IA 50322
E-mail: bizjobs09l@gmail.com
URL: http://www.careers-in-business.com

Description: Careers-In-Business contains information on employment in the business sector, primarily in accounting, finance and consulting. Links to many corporations who hire extensively in this area are included for those wishing to make contacts and/or mail out resumes. Detailed information on job search aids and employer profiles provided. Links to many other career sites also available, as well as links to career-related books for sale through Amazon.

116 ■ CareersInAudit.com
URL: http://www.careersinaudit.com

Description: Serves as a career job board for audit, risk, and compliance professionals. Advertises job openings for heads of department, spanning internal audit, external audit, IT audit, risk, and compliance. Conducts research to monitor the latest industry trends.

117 ■ ControllerAccountingManager.com
URL: http://www.controlleraccountingmanager.com
Description: Lists job and career opportunities for aspiring controller accounting managers. Offers links, job listings, resume resources and more.

118 ■ Cost Accountant Jobs
URL: http://www.costaccountantjobs.org
Description: Serves as a job board for candidates seeking employment opportunities in the field of cost accounting.

119 ■ CPA-Resource.com
URL: http://www.cpa-resource.com
Description: Provides access to CPA education, training, forms, tools, CPA articles, white papers, CPA news, jobs, blogs, and more.

120 ■ CPAdirectory.com
CPAdirect Marketing Inc.
2001 Grove St.
Wantagh, NY 11793
Ph: (516)409-8357
Fax: (516)977-0643
E-mail: info@cpadirectoryinc.com
URL: http://www.cpadirectory.com
Price: Free. **Description:** Nationwide database of certified public accountants and CPA firms searchable by criteria including name, location and industry focus. Includes job postings and career information within the accounting profession.

121 ■ CPAjobs.com
URL: http://www.cpajobs.com
Description: Serves as a job site network that lists several accounting and finance jobs for Certified Public Accountants. Features employment listings for CPAs at all levels of their careers.

122 ■ Financial Accountant Jobs
URL: http://www.financialaccountantjobs.org
Description: Connects job seekers and employers in the accounting field. Features a searchable database of employment opportunities for financial accountants.

123 ■ FinancialJobBank.com
URL: http://www.financialjobbank.com
Description: Works as a job engine that helps individual to find job openings in the areas of accounting, finance, taxation, banking, and mortgage.

124 ■ FinancialJobs.com
URL: http://www.financialjobs.com
Description: Lists accounting and finance jobs for professionals at all levels of their careers. Features resume writing tips, relocation assistance, networking techniques, salary calculator, and other related links.

125 ■ iHireAccounting
URL: http://www.ihireaccounting.com
Description: Serves as a job site network that lists thousands of accounting jobs and includes exclusive job postings, internet job boards, newspapers and classified ads.

126 ■ Illinois Certified Public Accountant Society Career Center
URL: http://www.icpas.org/hc-career-center.aspx?id=2178
Description: Offers job hunting aid to members of the Illinois CPA Society only. Opportunity for non-members to join online. Main files include: Overview of Services, Resume Match, Career Seminars, Career Resources, Free Job Listings, Per Diem Pool, and Career Bibliographies.

127 ■ InternalAuditor.net
URL: http://www.internalauditor.net
Description: Provides access to books, magazines, articles, and education programs. Offers job search options, continuing education resources, lists of industry magazines, as well as links to other similar career job sites.

128 ■ Junior Accountant Jobs
URL: http://www.junioraccountantjobs.org
Description: Provides job seekers access to resources and job opening opportunities in the area of accounting.

129 ■ Locate Accounting Jobs
URL: http://www.locateaccountingjobs.com
Description: Serves as a niche job board that connects accounting job seekers and employers. Allows users to customize their search results by using keywords, job title, skills and location.

130 ■ Nationwide Accountant/CPA Database
The Data Supplier
9107 Wilshire Blvd., Ste. 450
Beverly Hills, CA 90210
Free: 888-930-3282
E-mail: contactus@thedatasupplier.com
URL: http://www.thedatasupplier.com

131 ■ Night Auditor Jobs
URL: http://www.nightauditorjobs.com
Description: Serves as clearinghouse for professionals seeking a position as a night auditor.

132 ■ SeniorAuditor.net
URL: http://www.seniorauditor.net
Description: Provides access to books, magazines, articles, and continuing education to senior finance professionals. Helps individuals find new jobs, post and search resumes, and access career resources for senior auditors.

133 ■ Spherion
URL: http://www.spherion.com
Description: Recruitment firm specializing in accounting and finance, sales and marketing, interim executives, technology, engineering, retail and human resources.

134 ■ StaffAccountantJobs.com
URL: http://www.staffaccountantjobs.com
Description: Serves professionals in the accounting industry. Provides resume writing services as well as job posting and job searching.

135 ■ TaxSites.com
URL: http://www.taxsites.com
Description: Provides listings of associations, companies, job opportunities, news, publications, career search and other resources in the fields of tax, accounting and payroll/HR.

TRADESHOWS

136 ■ Accounting & Financial Women's Alliance Conference
Accounting and Financial Women's Alliance
1760 Old Meadow Rd., Ste. 500
McLean, VA 22102
Ph: (703)506-3265
Free: 800-326-2163
Fax: (703)506-3266
E-mail: aswa@aswa.org
URL: http://www.aswa.org
Frequency: Annual. **Primary Exhibits:** Exhibits relating to accounting, auditing, tax, finance, management, industry, e-commerce, and software.

137 ■ American Accounting Association Annual Meeting
American Accounting Association
5717 Bessie Dr.
Sarasota, FL 34233-2399
Ph: (941)921-7747
Fax: (941)923-4093
E-mail: info@aaahq.org
URL: http://aaahq.org
Frequency: Annual. **Primary Exhibits:** Accounting equipment, supplies, and services.

138 ■ American Association of Attorney-Certified Public Accountants Annual Meeting and Educational Conference
American Association of Attorney-CPAs
8647 Richmond Hwy., Ste. 639
Alexandria, VA 22309
Ph: (703)352-8064
Free: 888-ATTY-CPA
Fax: (703)352-8073
E-mail: info@attorney-cpa.com
URL: http://www.attorney-cpa.com
Frequency: Annual. **Primary Exhibits:** Exhibits for persons licensed both as attorneys and CPAs.

139 ■ Annual Accounting Show
Florida Institute of Certified Public Accountants
PO Box 5437
Tallahassee, FL 32314
Ph: (850)224-2727
Free: 800-342-3197
Fax: (850)222-8190
E-mail: msc@ficpa.org
URL: http://www.ficpa.org
Primary Exhibits: Accounting information and services.

140 ■ Association of College and University Auditors Annual Conference
Association of College and University Auditors
PO Box 14306
Lenexa, KS 66285-4306
Ph: (913)895-4620
Fax: (913)895-4652
E-mail: acua-info@goamp.com
URL: http://www.acua.org/ACUA/College_University_Auditors.asp
Frequency: Annual. **Primary Exhibits:** Continuing research, professional training, and establishment of internal auditing courses in colleges and universities.

141 ■ Association of Healthcare Internal Auditors Annual Conference
Association of Healthcare Internal Auditors
10200 W 44th Ave., Ste. 304
Wheat Ridge, CO 80033
Ph: (303)327-7546
Free: 888-ASK-AHIA
Fax: (303)422-8894
E-mail: ahia@ahia.org
URL: http://www.ahia.org
Frequency: Annual. **Primary Exhibits:** Exhibits facilitating cost containment and increased productivity in health care institutions through internal auditing.

142 ■ California Accounting & Business Show and Conference
Flagg Management Inc.
353 Lexington Ave.
New York, NY 10016
Ph: (212)286-0333
Fax: (212)286-0086
E-mail: flaggmgmt@msn.com
URL: http://www.flaggmgmt.com
Primary Exhibits: Accounting and business systems and services, computer accounting systems, tax software, integrated accounting systems, Internet and e-accounting solutions, brokerage and investment advisory services, financial and business services, hardware, computer and business systems, and tax preparation, accounting, audit, and practice management software.

Accountants and Auditors

143 ■ Colorado Society of Certified Public Accountants Conference
Colorado Society of Certified Public Accountants
7887 E Belleview Ave., Ste. 200
Englewood, CO 80111
Ph: (303)773-2877
Free: 800-523-9082
Fax: (303)773-6344
E-mail: mmedley@cocpa.org
URL: http://www.cocpa.org

Frequency: Annual.

144 ■ CPA Associates International Annual Meeting
CPA Associates International
Meadows Office Complex
301 Rte., 17 N
Rutherford, NJ 07070
Ph: (201)804-8686
Fax: (201)804-9222
E-mail: homeoffice@cpaai.com
URL: http://www.cpaai.com

Frequency: Annual. **Primary Exhibits:** Exhibits relating to accounting.

145 ■ Educational Tax Conference
American Society of Tax Professionals
PO Box 1213
Lynnwood, WA 98046-1213
Ph: (425)774-1996
Free: 877-674-1996
Fax: (425)672-0461
E-mail: kraemerc@juno.com

Frequency: Annual. **Primary Exhibits:** Tax preparers, accountants, attorneys, bookkeepers, accounting services, and public accounting firms seeking to uphold high service standards in professional tax preparation.

146 ■ Institute of Internal Auditors - USA International Conference
Institute of Internal Auditors
247 Maitland Ave.
Altamonte Springs, FL 32701-4201
Ph: (407)937-1111
Fax: (407)937-1101
E-mail: customerrelations@theiia.org
URL: http://na.theiia.org/Pages/IIAHome.aspx

Frequency: Annual. **Primary Exhibits:** Internal auditing equipment, supplies, and services, software, computer related equipment.

147 ■ Institute of Management Accountants Conference
Institute of Management Accountants
10 Paragon Dr., Ste. 1
Montvale, NJ 07645-1774
Ph: (201)573-9000
Free: 800-638-4427
Fax: (201)474-1600
E-mail: ima@imanet.org
URL: http://www.imanet.org

Frequency: Annual. **Primary Exhibits:** Management accounting equipment, supplies, and services. Review courses, shipping companies, software companies, and risk management consultants.

148 ■ Insurance Accounting and Systems Association Conference
Insurance Accounting and Systems Association
PO Box 51340
Durham, NC 27717-1340
Ph: (919)489-0991
Fax: (919)489-1554
E-mail: tstillman@iasa.org
URL: http://www.iasa.org

Frequency: Annual. **Primary Exhibits:** Insurance equipment, supplies, and services.

149 ■ Media Financial Management Association Conference
Media Financial Management Association
550 W Frontage Rd., Ste. 3600
Northfield, IL 60093
Ph: (847)716-7000
Fax: (847)716-7004
E-mail: info@mediafinance.org
URL: http://www.mediafinance.org

Frequency: Annual. **Primary Exhibits:** Exhibits relating to the financial management of radio, television, and cable television operations, including issues such as industry - specific software, collection agencies, insurance, investments, banking, accounting firms and music licensing.

150 ■ National Association of Tax Professionals Conference
National Association of Tax Professionals
PO Box 8002
Appleton, WI 54914-8002
Free: 800-558-3402
Fax: (800)747-0001
E-mail: natp@natptax.com
URL: http://www.natptax.com/Pages/default.aspx

Frequency: Annual. **Primary Exhibits:** Computer hardware, tax accounting and planning software, tax research information, tax forms, one-write accounting, financial planning information, office products, business equipment, and tax business solutions.

151 ■ National Society of Accountants for Cooperatives Tax & Accounting Conference for Cooperatives
National Society of Accountants for Cooperatives
136 S Keowee St.
Dayton, OH 45402
Ph: (937)222-6707
Fax: (937)222-5794
E-mail: info@nsacoop.org
URL: http://www.nsacoop.org

Frequency: Annual. **Primary Exhibits:** Exhibits relating to tax and accounting.

152 ■ New Jersey Accounting, Business & Technology Show & Conference
Flagg Management Inc.
353 Lexington Ave.
New York, NY 10016
Ph: (212)286-0333
Fax: (212)286-0086
E-mail: flaggmgmt@msn.com
URL: http://www.flaggmgmt.com

Frequency: Annual. **Primary Exhibits:** Information and technology, financial and business services, computer accounting systems, software, tax preparation, accounting, audit, practice management software - windows, and computer and business systems. Banking, insurance, financial and business software. Internet, online systems and middle market software and investment services.

153 ■ Public Accountants Society of Colorado Convention
Public Accountants Society of Colorado
PO Box 1078
Eastlake, CO 80614-1078
Ph: (303)452-8227
Free: 800-578-4451
Fax: (303)457-0770
E-mail: executivedirector@coloradoaccountant.org
URL: http://www.coloradoaccountant.org

Frequency: Annual. **Primary Exhibits:** Professional society of accountants, membership.

ONLINE AND DATABASE SERVICES

154 ■ *Rutgers Accounting Web*
Ph: (973)353-5172
Fax: (973)353-1283
URL: http://raw.rutgers.edu

Description: RAW Web site provides extensive links to sources of national and international accounting information, such as the Big Six accounting firms, the Financial Accounting Standards Board (FASB), SEC filings (EDGAR), journals, publishers, software, the International Accounting Network, and "Internet's largest list of accounting firms in USA". Searching is offered. Fees: Free.

OTHER SOURCES

155 ■ Accountants Global Network
2851 S Parker Rd., Ste. 850
Aurora, CO 80014
Ph: (303)743-7880
Free: 800-782-2272
Fax: (303)743-7660
E-mail: rhood@agn.org
URL: http://www.agn-na.org

Description: Represents and promotes the fields of separate and independent accounting and consulting firms serving business organizations.

156 ■ Accountants Motivational Marketing Organization
1 Country Club Exec. Park
Glen Carbon, IL 62034
Ph: (618)288-8795
E-mail: charles@tzinberg.com
URL: http://accountantsadvmarketing.com

Description: Represents professionals and practitioners in marketing and accounting. Fosters excellence in accounting practice and services. Promotes the marketing and sales programs of members.

157 ■ Accounting and Financial Women's Alliance
1760 Old Meadow Rd., Ste. 500
McLean, VA 22102
Ph: (703)506-3265
Free: 800-326-2163
Fax: (703)506-3266
E-mail: aswa@aswa.org
URL: http://www.aswa.org

Description: Professional society of women accountants, educators and others in the field of accounting dedicated to the achievement of personal, professional and economic potential. Assists women accountants in their careers and promotes development in the profession. Conducts educational and research programs.

158 ■ Accreditation Council for Accountancy and Taxation
1010 N Fairfax St.
Alexandria, VA 22314-1574
Free: 888-289-7763
Fax: (703)549-2984
E-mail: info@acatcredentials.org
URL: http://www.connect.nsacct.org/ACAT/home/

Description: Strives to raise professional standards and improve the practices of accountancy and taxation. Identifies persons with demonstrated knowledge of the principles and practices of accountancy and taxation. Ensures the continued professional growth of accredited individuals by setting stringent continuing education requirements. Fosters increased recognition for the profession in the public, private, and educational sectors.

159 ■ American Accounts Payable Association
660 N Main Ave., Ste. 200
San Antonio, TX 78205-1217
Ph: (210)630-4373
Fax: (210)630-4410
E-mail: membership@americanap.org
URL: http://www.americanap.org

Description: Seeks to uphold the standards of practice in the accounts payable profession. Fosters the professional development of members. Offers

Job Hunter's Sourcebook, 14th Edition

comprehensive educational programs for accounts payable professionals.

160 ■ American Institute of Certified Public Accountants
1211 Avenue of the Americas
New York, NY 10036-8775
Ph: (212)596-6200
Free: 888-777-7077
Fax: (212)596-6213
E-mail: service@aicpa.org
URL: http://www.aicpa.org

Description: Professional society of accountants certified by the states and territories.

161 ■ American Society of Tax Professionals
PO Box 1213
Lynnwood, WA 98046-1213
Ph: (425)774-1996
Free: 877-674-1996
Fax: (425)672-0461
E-mail: kraemerc@juno.com

162 ■ American Woman's Society of Certified Public Accountants
136 S Keowee St.
Dayton, OH 45402
Ph: (937)222-1872
Free: 800-297-2721
Fax: (937)222-5794
E-mail: info@awscpa.org
URL: http://www.awscpa.org

Description: Citizens who hold Certified Public Accountant certificates as well as those who have passed the CPA examination but do not have certificates. Works to improve the status of professional women and to make the business community aware of the professional capabilities of the woman CPA. Conducts semiannual statistical survey of members; offers specialized education and research programs.

163 ■ Ascend
120 Wall St., 3rd Fl.
New York, NY 10005
Ph: (212)248-4888
Fax: (212)344-5636
E-mail: info@ascendleadership.org
URL: http://www.ascendleadership.org

Description: Enhances the influence and presence of Pan Asian leaders in the finance, accounting and business related professions. Cultivates the growth of finance, accounting and business knowledge. Advances business development opportunities.

164 ■ Association for Accounting Administration
136 S Keowee St.
Dayton, OH 45402
Ph: (937)222-0030
Fax: (937)222-5794
E-mail: aaainfo@cpaadmin.org
URL: http://www.cpaadmin.org

Description: Promotes the profession of accounting administration and office management in accounting firms and corporate accounting departments. Sponsors activities, including consulting and placement services, seminars, salary and trends surveys, and speakers' bureau. Provides a forum for representation and exchange. Offers group purchasing opportunities.

165 ■ Association of Certified Fraud Examiners
716 West Ave.
Austin, TX 78701-2727
Ph: (512)478-9000
Free: 800-245-3321
Fax: (512)478-9297
E-mail: memberservices@acfe.com
URL: http://www.acfe.com

Description: Association web site contains Career Center with job databank, giving the user the ability to post jobs and career resources and links. Must be a member of organization in order to access databank.

166 ■ Association of Chartered Accountants in the United States
3887 Punahele Rd.
Princeville, HI 96722
Ph: (508)395-0224
E-mail: admin@acaus.org
URL: http://www.acaus.org

Description: Chartered accountants from England, Wales, Scotland, Ireland, Canada, Australia, New Zealand and South Africa in commerce and public practice. Represents the interests of chartered accountants; promotes career development and international mobility of professionals. Offers educational and research programs. Maintains speakers' bureau and placement service. **Members:** 6,700.

167 ■ Association of College and University Auditors
PO Box 14306
Lenexa, KS 66285-4306
Ph: (913)895-4620
Fax: (913)895-4652
E-mail: acua-info@goamp.com
URL: http://www.acua.org/ACUA/College_University _Auditors.asp

Description: Represents universities, colleges, and affiliated organizations with an interest in internal auditing. Promotes productive performance of internal auditors by means of continuing research, professional training, and establishment of internal auditing courses in colleges and universities.

168 ■ Association of Credit Union Internal Auditors
PO Box 150908
Alexandria, VA 22315
Ph: (703)688-2284
Fax: (703)348-7602
E-mail: acuia@acuia.org
URL: http://www.acuia.org

Description: Professional credit union internal auditors. Dedicated to the practice of internal auditing in credit unions.

169 ■ Association of Government Accountants
2208 Mt. Vernon Ave.
Alexandria, VA 22301-1314
Ph: (703)684-6931
Free: 800-AGA-7211
Fax: (703)548-9367
E-mail: agamembers@agacgfm.org
URL: http://www.agacgfm.org

Description: Professional society of financial managers employed by federal, state, county, and city governments in financial management and administrative positions. Conducts research; offers education and professional development programs.

170 ■ Association of Healthcare Internal Auditors
10200 W 44th Ave., Ste. 304
Wheat Ridge, CO 80033
Ph: (303)327-7546
Free: 888-ASK-AHIA
Fax: (303)422-8894
E-mail: ahia@ahia.org
URL: http://www.ahia.org

Description: Health care internal auditors and other interested individuals. Promotes cost containment and increased productivity in health care institutions through internal auditing. Serves as a forum for the exchange of experience, ideas, and information among members; provides continuing professional education courses and informs members of developments in health care internal auditing. Offers employment clearinghouse services.

171 ■ Association of Insolvency and Restructuring Advisors
221 Stewart Ave., Ste. 207
Medford, OR 97501
Ph: (541)858-1665
Fax: (541)858-9187
E-mail: aira@aira.org
URL: http://www.aira.org

Description: Certified and licensed public accountants, attorneys, examiners, trustees and receivers. Seeks to define and develop the accountant's role provided by the Bankruptcy Reform Act of 1978 and to improve accounting skills used in insolvency cases. Promotes the primary role of creditors in insolvency situations and the enforcement of ethical standards of practice. Seeks to develop judicial reporting standards for insolvency and provide technical, analytical and accounting skills necessary in insolvent situations. Works to educate others in the field of the role of the accountant in order to foster better working relationships. Provides information about legislative issues that affect members and testifies before legislative bodies. Offers technical referral service. Administers the Certified Insolvency and Restructuring Advisor (CIRA) program.

172 ■ Association of Latino Professionals in Finance and Accounting
801 S Grand Ave., Ste. 650
Los Angeles, CA 90017
Ph: (213)243-0004
Fax: (213)243-0006
E-mail: ceo@national.alpfa.org
URL: http://www.alpfa.org

Description: Represents Hispanic certified public accountants from the private and public sectors, accounting firms, universities, and banks. Maintains and promotes professional and moral standards of Hispanics in the accounting field. Assists members in practice development and develops business opportunities for members. Sponsors continuing professional education seminars; provides employment services.

173 ■ BKR International
19 Fulton St., Ste. 401
New York, NY 10038
Ph: (212)964-2115
Free: 800-BKR-INTL
Fax: (212)964-2133
E-mail: bkr@bkr.com
URL: http://www.bkr.com

Description: Accounting firms in the U.S. and abroad. Seeks to create an international group of competent professional firms, which will provide full services in major markets of the world and enable member firms to send and receive referrals. Helps reduce operating costs of member firms by: developing consolidated purchasing arrangements for services and supplies at the lowest possible cost; developing recruiting programs, marketing materials, and advertising to reduce the collective recruiting effort of group members; expanding the group to reduce the burden on individual member firms and increase their potential scope of services. Compiles statistics to provide member firms with data helpful to sound management decisions. Organizes clinical and administrative peer reviews to insure quality and provide management with professional counsel. Develops forms, procedures, and manuals to provide guidance and accommodate the needs of partners. Conducts 12 continuing education programs per year in all areas of expertise. **Members:** 143.

174 ■ Colorado Society of Certified Public Accountants
7887 E Belleview Ave., Ste. 200
Englewood, CO 80111
Ph: (303)773-2877
Free: 800-523-9082
Fax: (303)773-6344
E-mail: mmedley@cocpa.org
URL: http://www.cocpa.org

Description: CPAs. Represents members' interests;

conducts lobbying activities. Holds seminars and workshops.

175 ■ CPA Associates International
Meadows Office Complex
301 Rte., 17 N
Rutherford, NJ 07070
Ph: (201)804-8686
Fax: (201)804-9222
E-mail: homeoffice@cpaai.com
URL: http://www.cpaai.com

Description: Independent firms of Certified Public Accountants (CPAs) offering professional accounting, auditing, tax, and management advisory services. Fosters exchange of ideas and information among members; works to improve the profitability and practice of the accounting profession.

176 ■ Financial Managers Society
1 N La Salle St., Ste. 3100
Chicago, IL 60602-4003
Ph: (312)578-1300
Free: 800-275-4367
Fax: (312)578-1308
E-mail: info@fmsinc.org
URL: http://www.fmsinc.org

Description: Works for the needs of finance and accounting professionals from banks, thrifts and credit unions. Offers career-enhancing education, specialized publications, national leadership opportunities and worldwide connections with other industry professionals.

177 ■ Foundation for Accounting Education
PO Box 10490
Uniondale, NY 11555-0490
Ph: (212)719-8383
Free: 866-495-1354
E-mail: jbarry@nysscpa.org
URL: http://www.nysscpa.org/page/continuing
    -education

Description: Conducts educational and technical programs, seminars, workshops, and conferences for CPAs in private practice and industry.

178 ■ Hawaii Society of Certified Public Accountants
900 Fort Street Mall, Ste. 850
Honolulu, HI 96813
Ph: (808)537-9475
Fax: (808)537-3520
E-mail: info@hscpa.org
URL: http://www.hscpa.org

179 ■ Hospitality Financial and Technology Professionals
11709 Boulder Ln., Ste. 110
Austin, TX 78726
Ph: (512)249-5333
Free: 800-646-4387
Fax: (512)249-1533
E-mail: membership@hftp.org
URL: http://www.hftp.org

Description: Accountants, financial officers and MIS managers in 50 countries working in hotels, resorts, casinos, restaurants, and clubs. Develops uniform system of accounts. Conducts education, training, and certification programs; offers placement service; maintains hall of fame.

180 ■ Information Systems Audit and Control Association and Foundation
3701 Algonquin Rd., Ste. 1010
Rolling Meadows, IL 60008
Ph: (847)253-1545
Fax: (847)253-1443
URL: http://www.isaca.org/Pages/default.aspx

Description: Acts as a harmonizing source for IT control practices and standards all over the world. Serves its members and other constituencies by providing education, research (through its affiliated Foundation), a professional certification, conferences and publications.

181 ■ Institute of Internal Auditors
247 Maitland Ave.
Altamonte Springs, FL 32701-4201
Ph: (407)937-1111
Fax: (407)937-1101
E-mail: customerrelations@theiia.org
URL: http://na.theiia.org/Pages/IIAHome.aspx

Description: Members in internal auditing, governance, internal control, IT audit, education and security. Provides comprehensive professional, educational and development opportunities; standards and other professional practice guidance; and certification programs.

182 ■ *Institute of Internal Auditors--Membership Directory*
Institute of Internal Auditors
247 Maitland Ave.
Altamonte Springs, FL 32701-4201
Ph: (407)937-1111
Fax: (407)937-1101
E-mail: customerrelations@theiia.org
URL: http://na.theiia.org/Pages/IIAHome.aspx

Covers: Approximately 50,000 member internal auditors; comptrollers, accountants, educators, computer specialists in the auditing field.

183 ■ Institute of Management Accountants
10 Paragon Dr., Ste. 1
Montvale, NJ 07645-1774
Ph: (201)573-9000
Free: 800-638-4427
Fax: (201)474-1600
E-mail: ima@imanet.org
URL: http://www.imanet.org

Description: Management accountants in industry, public accounting, government, and academia; other persons interested in internal and management uses of accounting. Conducts research on accounting methods and procedures and the management purposes served. Established Institute of Certified Management Accountants to implement and administer examinations for the Certified Management Accountant (CMA) program and the Certified in Financial Management (CFM) program. Annually presents chapter medals for competition, manuscripts and for the highest scores on the CMA Examination. Offers continuing education programs comprising courses, conferences, and a self-study program in management accounting areas. Offers ethics counseling services for members by telephone. Sponsors the Foundation for Applied Research.

184 ■ Interamerican Accounting Association
275 Fountainebleau Blvd., Ste. 245
Miami, FL 33172
Ph: (305)225-1991
Fax: (305)225-2011
E-mail: oficina@contadoresaic.org
URL: http://www.contadores-aic.org

Description: National associations representing 1,100,000 accountants in the Americas. Objectives are to maintain high technical and ethical standards for the accounting profession; further accounting as a scientific discipline by fostering contacts between members and institutions of higher learning; provide members with information on current accounting practices and concepts; encourage members to establish ties with accounting groups worldwide; assure that professional services rendered by members contribute to the social and economic development of their community. Operates speakers' bureau.

185 ■ International Federation of Accountants
529 5th Ave., 6th Fl.
New York, NY 10017
Ph: (212)286-9344
Fax: (212)286-9570
E-mail: communications@ifac.org
URL: http://www.ifac.org

Description: Accounting bodies recognized by law or general consensus representing over 1,000,000

individuals in 78 countries. Seeks to achieve international technical, ethical and educational guidelines and standards for the accountancy profession. Fosters cooperation among members and encourages development of regional groups with similar goals.

186 ■ International Society of Filipinos in Finance and Accounting
801 S Grand Ave., Ste. 400
Los Angeles, CA 90017
Free: 800-375-2689
E-mail: losangeles@isffa.org
URL: http://www.isffa.org

Description: Aims to assist, educate, train and mentor emerging professionals, both domestically as well as globally. Promotes a socially friendly and responsive environment among Filipinos, minority groups and Americans in their respective communities. Assists in providing professional continuing education and mentoring when needed, not only to the professional, but also to the community at large.

187 ■ Leading Edge Alliance
621 Cedar St.
Saint Charles, IL 60174
Ph: (630)513-9814
Fax: (630)524-9014
URL: http://www.leadingedgealliance.com

Description: Represents independently owned accounting and consulting firms. Provides business development, professional training and education, and peer-to-peer networking opportunities. Offers business advisory expertise and experience and conducts accounting, tax and consulting services.

188 ■ Media Financial Management Association
550 W Frontage Rd., Ste. 3600
Northfield, IL 60093
Ph: (847)716-7000
Fax: (847)716-7004
E-mail: info@mediafinance.org
URL: http://www.mediafinance.org

Description: Controllers, chief accountants, auditors, business managers, treasurers, secretaries and related newspaper executives, educators, and public accountants. Conducts research projects on accounting methods and procedures for newspapers. Offers placement service; maintains speakers' bureau. Produces conferences and seminars.

189 ■ Moore Stephens North America
250 Pehle Ave.
Park 80 W
Plaza II, Ste. 200
Saddle Brook, NJ 07663
Ph: (201)291-2660
Fax: (201)368-1944
E-mail: theteam@msnainc.com
URL: http://www.msnainc.com

Description: North American public accounting and consulting firms. Aids certified public accounting firms in increasing, expanding, and diversifying their practices. Capitalizes on diversity of resources resident throughout the network to build a stronger revenue base for all members. Sponsors training programs in areas such as industry niche development, service niche development tax, staff, and computer auditing; conducts tax and management seminars. Compiles statistics. Offers networking forums, marketing assistance, and technology consulting to member firms. **Members:** 51.

190 ■ National Association of Black Accountants
7474 Greenway Center Dr., Ste. 1120
Greenbelt, MD 20770
Ph: (301)474-6222
Free: 888-571-2939
Fax: (301)474-3114
E-mail: membership@nabainc.org
URL: http://www.nabainc.org

Description: Represents minority students and

professionals currently working, or interested in the fields of accounting, finance, technology, consulting or general business. Seeks, promotes, develops, and represents the interests of current and future minority business professionals.

191 ■ National Association of Certified Public Bookkeepers
140 N Union Ave., Ste. 240
Farmington, UT 84025
Free: 866-444-9989
Fax: (801)451-4688
E-mail: info@nacpb.org
URL: http://www.nacpb.org

Description: Aims to protect the public interest by ensuring that only qualified individuals provide public bookkeeping services. Fosters the professional development of public bookkeepers. Offers certification programs in bookkeeping.

192 ■ National Association of Tax Professionals
PO Box 8002
Appleton, WI 54914-8002
Free: 800-558-3402
Fax: (800)747-0001
E-mail: natp@natptax.com
URL: http://www.natptax.com/Pages/default.aspx

Description: Serves professionals who work in all areas of tax practice, including individual practitioners, enrolled agents, certified public accountants, accountants, attorneys and certified financial planners.

193 ■ National Society of Accountants
1010 N Fairfax St.
Alexandria, VA 22314
Ph: (703)549-6400
Free: 800-966-6679
Fax: (703)549-2984
E-mail: members@nsacct.org
URL: http://www.nsacct.org

Description: Professional organization and its affiliates represent 30,000 members who provide auditing, accounting, tax preparation, financial and estate planning, and management services to approximately 19 million individuals and business clients. Most members are sole practitioners or partners in small to mid-size accounting firms.

194 ■ National Society of Accountants for Cooperatives
136 S Keowee St.
Dayton, OH 45402
Ph: (937)222-6707

Fax: (937)222-5794
E-mail: info@nsacoop.org
URL: http://www.nsacoop.org

Description: Employees of cooperatives, certified public accountants, auditors, chief financial officers, attorneys and bankers. Unites persons performing accounting, auditing, financial and legal services for cooperative and non-profit associations. Holds technical sessions annually. Compiles statistics.

195 ■ National Society of Accountants for Cooperatives - Texas Chapter
c/o Gail Faries, Dir.
D. Williams and Company, PC
Lubbock, TX 79490
Ph: (806)785-5982
Fax: (806)785-9381
E-mail: gailf@dwilliams.net

Description: Represents employees of cooperatives, certified public accountants, auditors, chief financial officers, attorneys, and bankers. Unites persons performing accounting, auditing, financial, and legal services for cooperative and nonprofit associations.

196 ■ Northern New Jersey Chapter of the National Association of Black Accountants
PO Box 1091
Newark, NJ 07101
E-mail: nabannj@nabannj.com
URL: http://www.nabannj.org

Description: Works to develop, encourage and serve as a resource for greater participation by African Americans and other minorities in the accounting, finance, auditing, business, consulting, information technology, and other related professions. Seeks to address the professional needs which enable members and minorities to maximize career potential and build leaders.

197 ■ Ohio Society of CPAs
535 Metro Pl. S
Dublin, OH 43017-1810
Ph: (614)764-2727
Free: 800-686-2727
Fax: (614)764-5880
E-mail: oscpa@ohio-cpa.com
URL: http://www.ohioscpa.com

198 ■ Oregon Society of Certified Public Accountants
10206 SW Laurel St.
Beaverton, OR 97005-3209
Ph: (503)641-7200
Free: 800-255-1470

Fax: (503)626-2942
E-mail: oscpa@orcpa.org
URL: http://www.orcpa.org

199 ■ PKF North America
1745 N Brown Rd., Ste. 350
Lawrenceville, GA 30043
Ph: (770)279-4560
Fax: (770)279-4566
E-mail: tsnyder@pkfna.org
URL: http://www.pkfna.org

Description: Independent certified public accounting firms practicing on a regional or local basis. Objectives are to: strengthen accounting practices; increase competency and quality of service; provide a practice management program; maintain technical competence in accounting principles and auditing standards; make available a reservoir of specialists who are immediately accessible to members; provide for the sharing of skills, knowledge and experience. Offers technical, marketing, and public relations support; promotes continuing professional education; facilitates networking. Conducts 4 staff development, 2 tax training, and 3 manager/partner training courses per year; operates committees and task forces. **Members:** 85.

200 ■ Professional Accounting Society of America
986 Colina Vista
Ventura, CA 93003
E-mail: info@thepasa.org
URL: http://www.thepasa.org

Description: Represents entry-level and mid-level associates working at accounting firms across America. Addresses the issues that affect entry-level and mid-level accounting professionals. Serves as a voice for everyone in the public accounting industry.

201 ■ Professional Association of Small Business Accountants
6405 Metcalf Ave., Ste. 503
Shawnee Mission, KS 66202
Free: 866-296-0001
Fax: (913)432-1812
E-mail: sklein@dci-kansascity.com
URL: http://www.smallbizaccountants.com

Description: Represents certified public accountants, public accountants, and enrolled agents who provide accounting services to small businesses throughout the United States. Aims to improve the business management and marketing skills of its members. Strives to uphold and maintain high standards of good accounting practices.

Actors, Directors, and Producers

SOURCES OF HELP-WANTED ADS

202 ■ *ArtSEARCH*
Theatre Communications Group
520 8th Ave., 24th Fl.
New York, NY 10018-4156
Ph: (212)609-5900
Fax: (212)609-5901
E-mail: tcg@tcg.org
URL: http://www.tcg.org

Description: Biweekly. Publishes classified listings for job opportunities in the arts, especially theatre, dance, music, and educational institutions. Listings include opportunities in administration, artistic, education, production, and career development.

203 ■ *AV Video & Multimedia Producer*
Access Intelligence L.L.C.
4 Choke Cherry Rd., 2nd Fl.
Rockville, MD 20850
Ph: (301)354-2000
Free: 800-777-5006
Fax: (301)309-3847
E-mail: info@accessintel.com
URL: http://www.accessintel.com/

Frequency: Monthly. **Description:** Magazine covering audio-visual, video and multimedia production, presentation, people, technology and techniques.

204 ■ *Back Stage West*
Nielsen Business Media Inc.
770 Broadway
New York, NY 10003-9522
Ph: (646)654-4500
Free: 866-890-8541
Fax: (646)654-5584
E-mail: bmcomm@nielsen.com
URL: http://www.backstage.com/bso/index.jsp

Frequency: Weekly; 51/yr (plus 2 free issues). **Price:** $195 Individuals; $99 Individuals 6 months; $12.95 Individuals monthly. **Description:** Trade publication covering the entertainment industry.

205 ■ *Broadcasting & Cable*
Reed Elsevier Group plc - Reed Business Information
360 Park Ave. S
New York, NY 11010
Ph: (212)791-4209
E-mail: corporatecommunications@reedbusiness.com
URLs: http://www.reedbusiness.com; http://www.broadcastingcable.com

Frequency. 51/yr. **Price:** $199 Individuals; $249.99 Canada; $360.99 Other countries; $109 Individuals 6 months; $59 Individuals 3 months. **Description:** News magazine covering The Fifth Estate (radio, TV, cable, and satellite), and the regulatory commissions involved.

206 ■ *Contemporary Theatre Review*
Routledge Journals - Taylor & Francis Group
270 Madison Ave.
New York, NY 10016-0601
Ph: (212)216-7800
Fax: (212)563-2269
URL: http://www.tandfonline.com/toc/gctr20/current

Frequency: Quarterly. **Price:** $120 Individuals print only; $784 Institutions online only; $896 Institutions print and online. **Description:** Journal focusing on wide variety of playwrights to theatres.

207 ■ *Daily Variety*
Variety Media Publications
6 Bell Yard
London WC2A 2JR, United Kingdom
Ph: 44 20 75205200
Fax: 44 20 75205237
E-mail: richard.woolley@variety.co.uk
URLs: http://www.reedbusiness.com/index.asp?layout=theListProfile&theListID=535&groupid=28&industryid=28; http://www.variety.com

Frequency: Daily. **Price:** $329.99 Individuals. **Description:** Global entertainment newspaper (tabloid).

208 ■ *Filmmaker: The Magazine of Independent Film*
IFP
68 Jay St., Rm. 425
Brooklyn, NY 11201
Ph: (212)465-8200
Fax: (212)465-8525
URL: http://www.filmmakermagazine.com/

Frequency: Quarterly. **Price:** $18 Individuals; $30 Two years. **Description:** Magazine covering the craft and business of filmmaking.

209 ■ *FMedia!*
FM Atlas Publishing
241 Anderson Rd.
Esko, MN 55733-9413
Ph: (218)879-7676
Free: 800-605-2219
Fax: (218)879-8333
E-mail: fmatlas@aol.com
URL: http://members.aol.com/fmatlas/home.html

Frequency: Monthly. **Price:** $75 for broadcasters; $26 for individuals. **Description:** Lists information on the facilities and formats of FM radio, including new station grants and applications. Also provides official and unofficial news and comments, as well as FM Dxing and FM reception concerns. Recurring features include letters to the editor, news of research, job listings, and notices of publications available.

210 ■ *Job Contact Bulletin*
Southeastern Theatre Conference
1175 Revolution Mill Dr., Ste. 14
Greensboro, NC 27405
Ph: (336)272-3645

Fax: (336)272-8810
E-mail: dslusser@camden.k12.ga.us
URL: http://www.setc.org

Frequency: Monthly. **Price:** included in membership dues. **Description:** Lists jobs available in theatres.

211 ■ *Live Design: The Art & Technology of Show Business*
Penton
249 W 17th St.
New York, NY 10011
Ph: (913)341-1300
Free: 866-748-4926
Fax: (913)967-1905
E-mail: corporatecustomerservice@penton.com
URL: http://livedesignonline.com

Frequency: 9/yr. **Description:** The business of entertainment technology and design.

212 ■ *Millimeter*
NewBay Media, LLC
28 E 28th St., 12th Fl.
New York, NY 10016
Ph: (212)378-0400
Fax: (917)281-4704
URL: http://digitalcontentproducer.com/mil/

Frequency: Monthly. **Description:** Magazine focusing on the process of motion picture and television production.

213 ■ *Post: The International Magazine for Post Production Professionals*
Post Pro Publishing Inc.
One Park Ave.
New York, NY 10016
Ph: (212)951-6600
Fax: (212)951-6793
E-mail: info@advanstar.com
URL: http://www.postmagazine.com/

Frequency: Monthly. **Description:** Magazine serving the field of television, film, video production and post-production.

214 ■ *Producers Masterguide: The International Film Directory & Guide*
Producers Masterguide
60 E 8th St., 34th Fl.
New York, NY 10003-6514
Ph: (212)777-4002
Fax: (212)777-4101
E-mail: nypc@earthlink.net
URL: http://www.producers.masterguide.com/cover.html

Frequency: Annual. **Price:** $185 U.S.; $175 Canada; $205 Other countries. **Description:** An international film and TV production directory and guide for the professional motion picture, broadcast television, feature film, TV commercial, cable/satellite, digital and videotape industries in the U.S., Canada, the UK, the Caribbean Islands, Mexico, Australia, New Zealand, Europe, Israel, Morocco, the Far East, and South America.

215 ■ *Ross Reports Television and Film: Agents & Casting Directors-Television Production-Films in Development*
Nielsen Business Media Inc.
770 Broadway
New York, NY 10003-9522
Ph: (646)654-4500
Free: 866-890-8541
Fax: (646)654-5584
E-mail: bmcomm@nielsen.com
URLs: http://www.backstage.com; http://www.penrose-press.com/idd/MAG29876.card
Frequency: Bimonthly. **Price:** $65 Individuals; $10 Individuals. **Description:** Trade publication covering talent agents and casting directors in New York and Los Angeles, as well as television and film production. Special national issue of agents and casting directors is published annually. Sister publication to Back Stage, Back Stage West.

216 ■ *TelevisionWeek*
Crain Communications Inc.
6500 Wilshire Blvd., Ste. 2300
Los Angeles, CA 90048
Ph: (323)370-2417
E-mail: info@crain.com
URL: http://www.tvweek.com/
Frequency: Weekly. **Price:** $119 Individuals; $171 Canada incl. GST; $309 Other countries airmail. **Description:** Newspaper covering management, programming, cable and trends in the television and the media industry.

217 ■ *Variety: The International Entertainment Weekly*
Reed Elsevier Group plc - Reed Business Information
360 Park Ave. S
New York, NY 11010
Ph: (212)791-4208
E-mail: corporatecommunications@reedbusiness.com
URL: http://www.reedbusiness.com/us.html
Frequency: Weekly; 50/yr. **Price:** $259 Individuals; $25 Individuals monthly. **Description:** Newspaper (tabloid) reporting on theatre, television, radio, music, and movies.

EMPLOYER DIRECTORIES AND NETWORKING LISTS

218 ■ *501 Movie Directors: A Comprehensive Guide to the Nearest Filmmakers*
Barron's Educational Series Inc.
250 Wireless Blvd.
Hauppauge, NY 11788
Ph: (631)434-3311
Free: 800-645-3476
Fax: (631)434-3723
E-mail: barrons@barronseduc.com
URL: http://barronseduc.com/0764160222.html
Frequency: Latest edition 2008. **Price:** $29.99 Individuals list price; $26.99 Individuals web price. **Pages:** 640. **Covers:** 501 film directors.

219 ■ *Academy Players Directory*
Academy of Motion Picture Arts and Sciences
8949 Wilshire Blvd.
Beverly Hills, CA 90211
Ph: (310)247-3000
Fax: (310)859-9619
E-mail: publicity@oscars.org
URL: http://www.playersdirectory.com
Frequency: Semiannual; January and July. **Price:** $95.33 Individuals per issue. **Pages:** 1,500 4 volumes. **Covers:** Over 18,000 members of Screen Actors Guild (SAG), American Federation of Television and Radio Artists (AFTRA), and Actors Equity Association (AEA). All listings are paid. **Entries include:** Name of actor, name of agency and/or

personal manager with phone; photograph, contact number. **Arrangement:** Classified by role type in 4 sections: Part I, Academy Award Nominee and Winners, Leading women/Ingenues; Part II, Academy Award Nominees and Winners, Leading men/Younger male leads; Part III, Characters/Comedy actors and actresses; Part IV, Children/Master index. **Indexes:** General, ethnic/disabled.

220 ■ *Actors' Yearbook*
Bloomsbury Publishing PLC
50 Bedford Sq.
London WC1B 3DP, United Kingdom
Ph: 44 020 7631 5600
Fax: 020 7631 5800
E-mail: uk@bloomsbury.com
URL: http://www.bloomsbury.com/uk/actors-yearbook-2014-9781408185537/
Frequency: Latest Edition 2014. **Price:** $14.99 Individuals E-book; $13.49 Individuals Paperback. **Pages:** 496. **Covers:** Agents and production companies involved in television, film and theatre. **Entries include:** Name, address, phone, fax.

221 ■ *Agents, Managers & Casting Directors 411*
411 Publishing
5900 Wilshire Blvd., Ste. 3100
Los Angeles, CA 90036
Ph: (323)617-9400
Free: 800-357-4745
E-mail: suggestions@411publishing.com
URL: http://www.la411.com
Frequency: Semiannual; May and November. **Price:** $49 No charge for online access. **Covers:** Agents, managers, and casting directors for the film and television industry in Los Angeles, New York, Chicago, and other key cities. **Entries include:** Name and title of contact, name, address, phone, fax, submission policies, and whether the company attends showcases and workshops. Also includes articles and profiles.

222 ■ *Baseball America--Radio, TV, & Cable Directory*
Baseball America Inc.
4319 S Alston Ave.
Durham, NC 27713-2488
Ph: (919)682-9635
Fax: (919)682-2880
E-mail: customerservice@baseballamerica.com
URL: http://www.baseballamerica.com
Frequency: Annual. **Covers:** Local broadcasters (radio, TV, and cable stations) of major league baseball games; radio stations which cover minor league baseball; and suppliers of baseball videos. **Entries include:** For broadcasters--Call letters, station numbers, and contact information. For suppliers--Contact information.

223 ■ *Broadcasting & Cable Yearbook: A Broadcasting and R.R. Bowker Publication*
R.R. Bowker
630 Central Ave
New Providence, NJ 07974
Ph: (888)269-5372
Free: 888-269-5372
Fax: (908)464-3553
E-mail: info@bowker.com
URL: http://www.bowker.com
Frequency: Annual; latest edition 2010. **Price:** $395 Individuals softbound. **Covers:** Over 17,000 television and radio stations in the United States, its territories, and Canada; cable MSOs and their individual systems; television and radio networks, broadcast and cable group owners, station representatives, satellite networks and services, film companies, advertising agencies, government agencies, trade associations, schools, and suppliers of professional and technical services, including books, serials, and videos; communications lawyers. **Entries include:** Company name, address, phone, fax, names of executives. Station listings include broadcast power, other operating details. **Arrangement:** Stations and

systems are geographical, others are alphabetical. **Indexes:** Alphabetical.

224 ■ *Burrelle's Black/Hispanic Media Directory*
BurrellesLuce
75 E Northfield Rd.
Livingston, NJ 07039
Ph: (973)992-6600
Free: 800-631-1160
Fax: (973)992-7675
E-mail: sross@burrelleluce.com
URL: http://www.burrellesluce.com
Frequency: Irregular; previous edition 1989; latest edition 1992. **Price:** $145 plus $4.00 shipping. **Pages:** 295. **Covers:** Newspapers, magazines, newsletters, radio and television programs, and other media serving the interests of the Black and Hispanic population. **Entries include:** Publication or station name, address, phone, names and titles of key personnel, description of publication or program. **Arrangement:** Geographical. **Indexes:** Geographical.

225 ■ *Christian Media Directory*
James Lloyd Group
PO Box 448
Jacksonville, OR 97530
Ph: (541)899-8888
E-mail: james@christianmedianetwork.com
URL: http://www.christianmedianetwork.com
Frequency: Irregular. **Price:** $37.70 Individuals. **Covers:** Over 8,000 newspapers, periodicals, radio and television stations, video and film producers, and music record labels targeting a Christian audience. Provides market profiles and overview of television and music video networks. **Entries include:** Company or individual name, address, phone, fax, name of contact, description of service, programming, or product. **Arrangement:** Classified by line of business. **Indexes:** Product/service.

226 ■ The Complete Television, Radio & Cable Industry Directory
Grey House Publishing
4919 Rte. 22
Amenia, NY 12501
Ph: (518)789-8700
Free: 800-562-2139
Fax: (518)789-0556
E-mail: books@greyhouse.com
URL: http://gold.greyhouse.com/page/datatype96

227 ■ *Contemporary Theatre, Film, and Television*
Cengage Learning Inc.
200 1st Stamford Pl., Ste. 400
Stamford, CT 06902-6753
Ph: (203)965-8600
Free: 800-354-9706
Fax: (800)487-8488
E-mail: investors@cengage.com
URL: http://www.gale.cengage.com
Frequency: Bimonthly; Latest edition Volume 119. **Price:** $308 Individuals volume 116. **Covers:** 116 volumes, more than 20,000 leading and up-and-coming performers, directors, writers, producers, designers, managers, choreographers, technicians, composers, executives, and dancers in the United States, Canada, Great Britain and the world. Each volume includes updated biographies for people listed in previous volumes and in "Who's Who in the Theatre," which this series has superseded. **Entries include:** Name, agent and/or office addresses, personal and career data; stage, film, and television credits; writings, awards, other information. **Arrangement:** Alphabetical. **Indexes:** Cumulative name index also covers entries in "Who's Who in the Theatre" editions 1-17 and in "Who Was Who in the Theatre.".

228 ■ *Directors Guild of America--Directory of Members*
Directors Guild of America Inc.
7920 Sunset Blvd.
Los Angeles, CA 90046

Ph: (310)289-2000
Free: 800-421-4173
E-mail: dgawebsupport@dga.org
URL: http://www.dga.org
Frequency: Annual; February; Latest edition 2009.
Price: $25 plus $6 shipping. **Pages:** 600. **Covers:**
Over 15,000 motion picture and television directors
and their assistants providing films and tapes for
entertainment, commercial, industrial, and other non-
entertainment fields; international coverage. **Entries
include:** DGA member name; contact or representative address, phone; specialty; brief description of
experience and credits. **Arrangement:** Alphabetical.
Indexes: Geographical, women and minority
members, agents.

**229 ■ The Dramatists Guild Resource
Directory**
Dramatists Guild of America
1501 Broadway, Ste. 701
New York, NY 10036
Ph: (212)398-9366
Fax: (212)944-0420
E-mail: rsevush@dramatistsguild.com
URL: http://www.dramatistsguild.com
Frequency: Annual; Latest edition 2009. **Description:** Contains up-to-date information on agents, attorneys, grants, producers, conferences, and
workshops. **Publication includes:** Lists of Broadway
and off-Broadway producers; theater and producing
organizations; agents; regional theaters; sources of
grants, fellowships, residencies; conferences and
festivals; playwriting contests; and sources of
financial assistance. **Entries include:** For
producers--Name, address, credits, types of plays
accepted for consideration. For groups--Name, address, contact name, type of material accepted for
consideration, future commitment, hiring criteria,
response time. For agents--Name, address. For
theaters--Theater name, address, contact name,
submission procedure, types of plays accepted for
consideration, maximum cast, limitations, equity
contract, opportunities, response time. For grants,
fellowships, residencies, financial assistance, conferences, and festivals--Name, address, contact name,
description, eligibility and application requirements,
deadline. For play contests--Name, address, prize,
deadline, description. **Arrangement:** Contests are by
deadline; others are classified.

230 ■ Film Directors
Hollywood Creative Directory
5055 Wilshire Blvd.
Los Angeles, CA 90036-4396
Ph: (323)525-2369
Free: 800-815-0503
Fax: (323)525-2398
E-mail: hcdsales@hcdonline.com
URL: http://www.hcdonline.com
Frequency: Annual; latest edition 16. **Pages:** 800.
Covers: Over 5,000 living and primarily active
theatrical and television film directors who have
made films with running times of one hour or more;
over 350 deceased directors; directors of videotaped
television dramas are not included. **Includes:** Lists
over 42,000 film titles. **Entries include:** Name, date
and place of birth, address and phone (or that of
agent), and chronological list of films that meet
stated criteria. Over 42,000 film credits. **Arrangement:** Alphabetical. **Indexes:** Director, agent/
manager, film title, foreign director name, academy
awards and nominations by year, guilds.

**231 ■ Film Producers, Studios, Agents, and
Casting Directors Guide**
Hollywood Creative Directory
5055 Wilshire Blvd.
Los Angeles, CA 90036-4396
Ph: (323)525-2369
Free: 800-815-0503
Fax: (323)525-2398
E-mail: hcdsales@hcdonline.com
URL: http://www.loneeagle.com
Frequency: Annual. **Price:** $75 plus $7.50 shipping.

Pages: 600. **Covers:** Approximately 5,000 television
and motion picture producers, 1,700 studios executives and production companies, 1,800 agents and
casting directors, and over 14,000 film credits.
Entries include: For producers--Name, address,
phone, films worked on; name, address, phone of
contact. For studios--Name, address, phone, names
and titles of key personnel. For agents--Agency
name, address, phone, individual agents' names, job
titles. For casting directors--Credits. **Arrangement:**
Classified by line of business. **Indexes:** Film title,
producer, studio executive, agent, casting director,
academy awards and nominations by year.

**232 ■ Film & Television Directory: The
Production Maker Source**
Peter Glenn Publications
306 NE 2nd St., 2nd Fl.
Delray Beach, FL 33483
Ph: (561)404-4290
Free: 888-332-6700
Fax: (561)892-5786
URL: http://www.pgdirect.com/ftintro.asp
Frequency: Biennial. **Price:** $30 Individuals. **Pages:**
450. **Covers:** More than 11,000 producers/production
companies, crews, support services, and film commissions in the film, music, and video industries in
the United States and parts of Canada. **Entries
include:** Company name, address, phone, fax,
E-mail and URL addresses, name and title of
contact. **Arrangement:** Classified by line of business. **Indexes:** Product/service; advertisers by
name.

233 ■ The Film & TV Music Guide
The Music Business Registry Inc.
7510 Sunset Blvd., No. 1041
Los Angeles, CA 90046-3400
Ph: (818)781-1974
Free: 800-377-7411
Fax: (818)495-4875
E-mail: info@musicregistry.com
URL: http://musicregistry.com/frame.html
Frequency: Latest edition 14th. **Price:** $100 Single
issue PDF version; $135 Individuals print. **Descrip-
tion:** List of all movie studios, TV networks and
independent production company music departments, record and publishing film/TV departments,
music supervisors in film/TV, film composers, managers and agents, music clearance companies, and
music editors.

**234 ■ FINDERBINDER--Arizona: Arizona's
Updated Media Directory**
Rita Sanders Advertising Public Relations
432 E Southern Ave.
Tempe, AZ 85282
Ph: (480)967-8714
Fax: (480)894-6216
E-mail: rita@ritasanders.com
URL: http://www.finderbinderaz.com
Frequency: Annual. **Price:** $314.07 Individuals on-
line only; $399.88 Individuals print only; $464.86
Individuals print and online. **Pages:** 600. **Description:** "FINDERBINDER" directories are loose-leaf
directories of broadcast and print media covering
states or smaller areas published by companies, usually advertising and public relations firms, licensed to
use the name and format by Finderbinder. Types of
media covered include cable television systems;
daily and weekly newspapers; religious, ethnic, and
labor papers; business, trade, sports, recreation, and
general interest publications; college papers; and
radio and television stations in Arizona. **Entries
include:** Publication or station name, names of
management, editorial, and advertising personnel,
deadlines, frequency or circulation as appropriate,
and other data; cable TV listings. **Arrangement:**
Classified by type of medium. **Indexes:** Publication
or station name.

235 ■ FINDERBINDER--Cleveland
Morgan & Co. Public Relations
Box 395
Richfield, OH 44286

Frequency: Annual. **Description:** "FINDERBINDER"
directories are loose-leaf directories of broadcast and
print media covering states or smaller areas published
by companies, usually advertising and
public relations firms, licensed to use the name and
format by Finderbinder. Types of media covered
include daily and weekly local and outstate
newspapers; religious, ethnic, and labor papers;
business, trade, sports, recreation, and general interest publications; college papers; and radio and television stations in Cleveland and northeastern Ohio.
Entries include: Publication or station name, names
of management, editorial, and advertising personnel,
deadlines, frequency or circulation as appropriate,
and other data; cable TV listings show homes
served. **Arrangement:** Classified by type of medium.
Indexes: Publication or station name.

236 ■ FINDERBINDER--Greater Detroit
C & E Communications Inc.
PO Box 4952
East Lansing, MI 48826
Ph: (517)339-9160
Free: 877-515-9755
Fax: (517)339-7494
E-mail: info@michiganfinderbinder.com
URL: http://www.michiganfinderbinder.com
Frequency: Annual; September; bimonthly updates.
Price: $250 Individuals set including outside
Michigan. **Pages:** 300. **Description:** "FIND-
ERBINDER" directories are loose-leaf directories of
broadcast and print media covering states or smaller
areas published by companies, usually advertising
and public relations firms, licensed to use the name
and format by Finderbinder. Types of media covered
include cable television systems; daily and weekly
newspapers; religious, ethnic, and labor papers;
business, trade, sports, recreation, and general interest publications; college papers; and radio and television stations in the seven-county Detroit metro area.
Entries include: Publication or station name, names
of management, editorial, and advertising personnel,
deadlines, frequency or circulation as appropriate,
and other data; radio, TV, and cable TV listings give
name of public service announcement (PSA) director,
interview format programs. **Arrangement:** Classified
by type of medium. **Indexes:** Publication or station
name, geographical, cable by community.

**237 ■ FINDERBINDER--Kansas City: Greater
Kansas Cities News Media Directory**
E-mail: krisf@twowest.com
URL: http://www.twowest.com
Frequency: Annual; February. **Price:** $130 payment
must accompany order. **Pages:** 330. **Description:**
"FINDERBINDER" directories are loose-leaf
directories of broadcast and print media covering
states or smaller areas published by companies, usually advertising and public relations firms, licensed to
use the name and format by Finderbinder. Types of
media covered include cable television systems;
daily and weekly newspapers; religious, ethnic, and
labor papers; business, trade, sports, recreation, and
general interest publications; college papers; and
radio and television stations in the 14 county, Kansas
City metropolitan area. **Entries include:** Publication
or station name; names of management, editorial,
and advertising personnel; deadlines, frequency or
circulation as appropriate; advertising rates; public
relations contacts, including fax numbers, and email
addresses; cable TV listings show homes served.
Arrangement: Classified by type of medium.
Indexes: Publication or station name, geographic by
county, by interests covered.

238 ■ FINDERBINDER--New Mexico
Gary Beals Advertising and Public Relations
4679 Vista St.
San Diego, CA 92116
Ph: (619)284-1145
Description: "FINDERBINDER" directories are
loose-leaf directories of broadcast and print media
covering states or smaller areas published by
companies, usually advertising and public relations
firms, licensed to use the name and format by Find-

erbinder. Types of media covered include cable television systems; daily and weekly newspapers; religious, ethnic, and labor papers; business, trade, sports, recreation, and general interest publications; college papers; and radio and television stations in New Mexico. **Entries include:** Publication or station name, names of management, editorial, and advertising personnel, deadlines, frequency or circulation as appropriate, advertising rates, and other data; cable TV listings show homes served. **Arrangement:** Classified by type of medium. **Indexes:** Publication or station name.

239 ■ FINDERBINDER--Northeast Wisconsin
Bishea, Meili & Associates Inc.
9141 N Briarwood Ct., Ste. 201
Milwaukee, WI 53217
Ph: (414)540-1407
Fax: (414)540-1417
Description: "FINDERBINDER" directories are loose-leaf directories of broadcast and print media covering states or smaller areas published by companies, usually advertising and public relations firms, licensed to use the name and format by Finderbinder. Types of media covered include cable television systems; daily and weekly newspapers; religious, ethnic, and labor papers; business, trade, sports, recreation, and general interest publications; college papers; and radio and television stations in Northeast Wisconsin. **Entries include:** Publication or station name, names of management, editorial, and advertising personnel, deadlines, frequency or circulation as appropriate, advertising rates, and other data; cable TV listings show homes served. **Arrangement:** Classified by type of medium. **Indexes:** Publication or station name.

240 ■ FINDERBINDER--Oklahoma
FINDERBINDER of Oklahoma
PO Box 3093
Edmond, OK 73083
Ph: (405)570-3569
E-mail: support@finderbinderok.com
URL: http://www.finderbinderok.com
Frequency: Annual. **Price:** $175 online. **Description:** "FINDERBINDER" directories are loose-leaf directories of broadcast and print media covering states or smaller areas published by companies, usually advertising and public relations firms, licensed to use the name and format by Finderbinder. Types of media covered include cable television systems; daily and weekly newspapers; religious, ethnic, and labor papers; business, trade, sports, recreation, and general interest publications; college papers; and radio and television stations in Oklahoma. **Entries include:** Publication or station name, names of management, editorial, and advertising personnel, deadlines, frequency or circulation as appropriate, and other data; cable TV listings show homes served. **Arrangement:** Classified by type of medium. **Indexes:** Publication or station name.

241 ■ FINDERBINDER--Outstate Michigan
C & E Communications Inc.
PO Box 4952
East Lansing, MI 48826
Ph: (517)339-9160
Free: 877-515-9755
Fax: (517)339-7494
E-mail: info@michiganfinderbinder.com
URL: http://www.michiganfinderbinder.com
Frequency: Annual; Latest edition 16th. **Price:** $225 Individuals package; $180 Individuals binder only. **Pages:** 271. **Description:** "FINDERBINDER" directories are loose-leaf directories of broadcast and print media covering states or smaller areas published by companies, usually advertising and public relations firms, licensed to use the name and format by Finderbinder. Types of media covered include cable television systems; daily and weekly newspapers; religious, ethnic, and labor papers; business, trade, sports, recreation, and general interest publications; college papers; and radio and television stations outside the 7-county metropolitan Detroit area. **Entries include:** Publication title or sta-

tion name, address, phone, names and titles of key personnel, deadlines, frequency, circulation; radio and TV stations also list name of public service announcement director and interview programs. **Arrangement:** Classified by market, then by medium. **Indexes:** Dailies, community papers, other print, radio, TV, and print by topics.

242 ■ FINDERBINDER--Pittsburgh
Gary Beals Advertising and Public Relations
4679 Vista St.
San Diego, CA 92116
Ph: (619)284-1145
Description: "FINDERBINDER" directories are loose-leaf directories of broadcast and print media covering states or smaller areas published by companies, usually advertising and public relations firms, licensed to use the name and format by Finderbinder. Types of media covered include cable television systems; daily and weekly newspapers; religious, ethnic, and labor papers; business, trade, sports, recreation, and general interest publications; college papers; and radio and television stations in Pittsburgh. **Entries include:** Publication or station name, names of management, editorial, and advertising personnel, deadlines, frequency or circulation as appropriate, advertising rates, and other data; cable TV listings show homes served. **Arrangement:** Classified by type of medium. **Indexes:** Publication or station name.

243 ■ FINDERBINDER--Syracuse
Gary Beals Advertising and Public Relations
4679 Vista St.
San Diego, CA 92116
Ph: (619)284-1145
Description: "FINDERBINDER" directories are loose-leaf directories of broadcast and print media covering states or smaller areas published by companies, usually advertising and public relations firms, licensed to use the name and format by Finderbinder. Types of media covered include cable, advertising companies, cable television systems, billboard companies; daily and weekly newspapers; religious, ethnic, and labor papers; business, trade, sports, recreation, and general interest publications; college papers; and radio and television stations in Syracuse. **Entries include:** Publication or station name, names of management, editorial, and advertising personnel, deadlines, frequency or circulation as appropriate, advertising rates, and other data; cable TV listings show homes served. **Arrangement:** Classified by type of medium. **Indexes:** Publication or station name.

244 ■ Gale Directory of Publications and Broadcast Media
Cengage Learning Inc.
200 1st Stamford Pl., Ste. 400
Stamford, CT 06902-6753
Ph: (203)965-8600
Free: 800-354-9706
Fax: (800)487-8488
E-mail: investors@cengage.com
URL: http://www.gale.cengage.com
Frequency: Annual; Latest edition April 2011. **Price:** $1,297 Individuals. **Covers:** Approximately 57,000 publications and broadcasting stations, including newspapers, magazines, journals, radio stations, television stations, radio/television/cable networks, syndicates and cable systems in the U.S. and Canada. Newsletters and directories are excluded. **Includes:** Appendices with maps and statistical tables, city descriptions, state descriptions with statistics, broadcast and cable networks, news and features syndicates. **Entries include:** For publications--Title, publishing and editorial addresses, phone, fax, description, names of editor, publisher, and advertising manager, base advertising rate, page specifications, subscription rate, circulation, frequency, ISSN, former names, additional contacts. For broadcast media--Call letters or cable system name, address, phone, fax, format, networks, owner, date founded, former call letters, operating hours, names and titles of key personnel, local

programming, wattage, ad rates, additional contacts. **Arrangement:** Geographical. **Indexes:** Title; radio station format; publisher; geographic market; lists of agricultural, college, foreign language, Jewish, fraternal, black, women's, Hispanic, religious, general circulation, and trade and technical publications (by subject and/or geographical as needed); daily newspaper; daily periodical; free circulation newspaper; and shopping guides (each geographical); list of feature editors at daily newspapers with 50,000 or more circulation.

245 ■ Hispanic Talent Directory of South Florida
Teatro Avante
235 Alcazar Ave.
Coral Gables, FL 33134
Ph: (305)445-8877
Fax: (305)445-1301
E-mail: teavante@aol.com
URL: http://www.teatroavante.com
Frequency: Biennial; May of odd years. **Pages:** 20. **Covers:** Hispanic actors, directors, designers, writers, and producers in the south Florida area. **Entries include:** Name, address, phone, specialty, languages spoken. **Arrangement:** Alphabetical.

246 ■ HOLA Pages
Hispanic Organization of Latin Actors
107 Suffolk St., Ste. 302
New York, NY 10002
Ph: (212)253-1015
Fax: (212)256-9651
E-mail: holagram@hellohola.org
URLs: http://www.hellohola.org; http://www.hellohola.org/holapages.php
Frequency: Biennial; Annual; January of odd years. **Pages:** 115. **Covers:** About 500 Hispanic performing artists from New York, New Jersey, and California; all listings are paid. **Entries include:** Name, photograph, profession(s), phone number(s). Persons listed are contacted through the publisher. **Arrangement:** Alphabetical.

247 ■ Hudson's Washington News Media Contacts Directory
Grey House Publishing
4919 Rte. 22
Amenia, NY 12501
Ph: (518)789-8700
Free: 800-562-2139
Fax: (518)789-0556
E-mail: books@greyhouse.com
URL: http://www.greyhouse.com/hudsons.htm
Frequency: Annual; Latest edition 2013. **Price:** $329 Individuals online and print. **Covers:** Nearly 5,000 editors, free-lance writers, and news correspondents, plus 4,624 United States, Canadian, and foreign newspapers, radio-TV networks and stations, magazines, and periodicals based or represented in Washington, D.C. **Entries include:** For publications and companies--Name, address, phone, and name of editor or key personnel. For individuals--Name, assignment. **Arrangement:** Classified by activity (e.g., correspondents), media type, etc; newspapers and radio-TV stations sections are arranged geographically; specialized periodicals section is arranged by subject. **Indexes:** Subject.

248 ■ International Dictionary of Films and Filmmakers
St. James Press
PO Box 9187
Farmington Hills, MI 48333-9187
Ph: (248)699-4253
Free: 800-877-4253
Fax: (248)699-8035
E-mail: gale.galeord@cengage.com
URL: http://www.gale.cengage.com
Frequency: 64; Latest edition 2004. **Price:** $238 Individuals per set of 4 volumes. **Pages:** 5,000 in four volumes. **Covers:** In an illustrated multi-volume set, approximately 500 directors and filmmakers, 650 actors and actresses, and 520 writers and production

artists (in volumes 2, 3, and 4 respectively). Both historical and contemporary artists are listed, chosen on the basis of international importance in film history. **Entries include:** Name; personal, education and career data; address, when available; filmography; bibliography of monographs and articles on and by the subject, critical essay, illustrations. Volume 1 contains entries describing approximately 680 significant films. **Arrangement:** Alphabetical in each volume. **Indexes:** Film title and nationality indexes in volumes 2, 3, and 4; geographic and personal name indexes in volume 1.

249 ■ *International Motion Picture Almanac*
Quigley Publishing Co.
64 Wintergreen Ln.
Groton, MA 01450
Ph: (978)448-0272
Free: 800-231-8239
Fax: (860)228-0157
E-mail: quigleypub@quigleypublishing.com
URL: http://quigleypublishing.com/

Frequency: Annual; Latest edition 2011. **Price:** $235 Individuals; $400 set. **Pages:** 1,128. **Covers:** Motion picture producing companies, firms serving the industry, equipment manufacturers, casting agencies, literary agencies, advertising and publicity representatives, motion picture theater circuits, buying and booking organizations, independent theaters, international film festivals, associations, theatre equipment supply companies. **Includes:** "Who's Who in Motion Pictures & Television" sect. giving brief biographical dtls. & lists of motion picture, television & other performances, & positions & achievements for abt. 5,000 actors, actresses, producers, directors, etc. **Entries include:** Generally, company name, address, phone. For manufacturers--Products or service provided, name of contact. For producing companies--Additional details. For theaters--Name of owner, screen size. Companion volume is the "International Television and Video Almanac" (see separate entry). **Arrangement:** Classified by service or activity.

250 ■ *International Television and Video Almanac*
Quigley Publishing Co.
64 Wintergreen Ln.
Groton, MA 01450
Ph: (978)448-0272
Free: 800-231-8239
Fax: (860)228-0157
E-mail: quigleypub@quigleypublishing.com
URL: http://quigleypublishing.com/

Frequency: Annual; January; latest edition 2013. **Price:** $235 Individuals. **Covers:** "Who's Who in Motion Pictures and Television and Home Video," television networks, major program producers, major group station owners, cable television companies, distributors, firms serving the television and home video industry, equipment manufacturers, casting agencies, literary agencies, advertising and publicity representatives, television stations, associations, list of feature films produced for television; statistics, industry's year in review, award winners, satellite and wireless cable provider, primetime programming, video producers, distributors, wholesalers. **Entries include:** Generally, company name, address, phone; manufacturer and service listings may include description of products and services and name of contact; producing, distributing, and station listings include additional detail, and contacts for cable and broadcast networks. **Arrangement:** Classified by service or activity. **Indexes:** Full.

251 ■ *Media Directory San Diego County*
San Diego Chamber of Commerce
402 W Broadway, Ste. 1000
San Diego, CA 92101
Ph: (010)511 1200
E-mail: webinfo@sdchamber.org
URL: http://www.sdchamber.org

Frequency: Annual. **Price:** $5. **Pages:** 6. **Covers:** San Diego county newspapers, magazines, news bureaus, radio and television stations. **Entries**

include: For publications--Name of publication, address, phone. For radio and television stations--Call letters, frequency, address, mailing address, phone. **Arrangement:** Classified by type of media.

252 ■ *Minority Employment Report*
Federal Communications Commission - Wireless Telecommunications Bureau
445 12th St. SW
Washington, DC 20554
Free: 877-480-3201
E-mail: fccinfo@fcc.gov
URL: http://wireless.fcc.gov

Frequency: Annual; December. **Pages:** 1,480. **Covers:** Television and radio stations with ten or more full-time employees. **Entries include:** Station name (call letters or channel), city and state, class of station; total, female, and minority full-time employment in higher and lower pay occupations, and part-time employment for previous five years. **Arrangement:** By state and community.

253 ■ *New England Theatre Conference--Resource Directory*
New England Theatre Conference
215 Knob Hill Dr.
Hamden, CT 06518
Ph: (617)851-8535
E-mail: mail@netconline.org
URLs: http://www.netconline.org; http://www.netconline.org/netc-membership.php

Frequency: Annual; January. **Pages:** 84. **Covers:** 800 individuals and 100 groups. **Entries include:** For individuals--Name, address, telephone, e-mail and fax indicating type or level of theater activity, theater and school affiliation. For groups--Name, address; telephone, box office, fax, e-mail, names and addresses of delegates. **Arrangement:** Alphabetical. **Indexes:** Members by Division.

254 ■ *Newsclip's Illinois Media*
Newsclip Inc.
363 W Erie St., Ste. 7E
Chicago, IL 60610
Ph: (312)751-7300
E-mail: customerservice@newsclip.com
URL: http://www.newsclip.com/press.htm

Frequency: Annual; Latest edition 2009. **Pages:** 360. **Covers:** About 1,200 newspapers, magazines, and radio, television, and cable television stations located in or serving Illinois. **Entries include:** For print media--Name of publication, address, phone; names of publisher, editors, and advertising managers; deadlines; photo requirements; publication dates; circulation areas and figures; advertising rates. For stations--Address, phone; names of general manager, news director, and advertising manager; station format; wire services used; newscast times; interview shows offered; names of producers and other contacts; prime time advertising rates; broadcast areas and hours. **Arrangement:** Classified by type of medium, then geographical. **Indexes:** Geographical.

255 ■ *Radio-Television News Directors Association--Membership Directory and Resource Guide*
Radio-Television Digital News Association
529 14th St. NW, Ste. 1240
Washington, DC 20045
Fax: (202)223-4007
URL: http://rtdna.org

Frequency: Semiannual. **Price:** available to members only.

256 ■ *Southern California Media Directory*
Public Communicators of Los Angeles
1910 W Sunset Blvd., Ste. 860
Los Angeles, CA 90026-3247
Fax: (213)410 4000
URL: http://www.pcla.org

Frequency: Annual. **Pages:** 500 loose-leaf. **Covers:** 1,500 newspapers, magazines, radio and TV stations, and other media in eight-county southern

California area; also covers suppliers of public relations products and services. **Entries include:** Media entries include publication name, address, phone, fax, e-mail and internet address, personnel (up to 30-40 editors, columnists, producers, etc.), circulation, and dates of publication. Supplier entries include company name, address, phone, fax, contact name, list of products or services. **Arrangement:** Geographical.

257 ■ *Special Effects and Stunts Guide*
Hollywood Creative Directory
5055 Wilshire Blvd.
Los Angeles, CA 90036-4396
Ph: (323)525-2369
Free: 800-815-0503
Fax: (323)525-2398
E-mail: hcdsales@hcdonline.com

Frequency: Irregular; new edition expected January 1999. **Price:** $50. **Pages:** 350. **Covers:** Producers and coordinators of special effects and stunts for motion pictures. **Entries include:** Name, contact address, phone, chronological list of person's films. **Arrangement:** Classified by type of special effect, with separate section for stunt coordinators. **Indexes:** Film and job title.

258 ■ *Talk Show Yearbook*
Broadcast Interview Source Inc.
2233 Wisconsin Ave. NW, Ste. 301
Washington, DC 20007-4132
Ph: (202)333-5000
Free: 866-639-7735
Fax: (202)342-5411
E-mail: editor@yearbook.com
URL: http://www.expertclick.com

Frequency: Annual; winter. **Price:** $185 Individuals. **Pages:** 324. **Covers:** more than 700 contacts at radio and television talk shows. **Includes:** Reports on the top 100 markets in the country. **Entries include:** Name of contact, format, market, address, phone, fax, name of talk show, station call letters, ADI information. **Arrangement:** Geographical. **Indexes:** Station call letters or network name.

259 ■ *Television Directors Guide*
Hollywood Creative Directory
5055 Wilshire Blvd.
Los Angeles, CA 90036-4396
Ph: (323)525-2369
Free: 800-815-0503
Fax: (323)525-2398
E-mail: hcdsales@hcdonline.com

Frequency: Annual. **Covers:** Directors in the television industry. **Entries include:** Director name, address, phone, credits. **Arrangement:** Alphabetical.

260 ■ *Vault Guide to the Top Media & Entertainment Employers*
Vault.com Inc.
132 W 31st St., 17th Fl.
New York, NY 10001-3406
Ph: (212)366-4212
Free: 800-535-2074
Fax: (212)366-6117
E-mail: customerservice@vault.com
URL: http://www.vault.com

Frequency: Latest edition May, 2008. **Price:** $19.95 Individuals Online; $19.95 Members Gold. **Pages:** 336. **Covers:** Top media and entertainment employers in U.S. **Entries include:** Company name, contact person, address, location, statistics and email.

261 ■ *Who's Where in American Theatre: A Directory of Affiliated Theatre Artists in the U.S.A.*
Feedback Theatrebooks & Prospero Press
PO Box 174
Brooklin, ME 04616
Ph: (207)359-2781
URL: http://www.feedbacktheatrebooks.com

Frequency: Irregular; latest edition 1992; new edition expected, date not set. **Price:** $7.50. **Pages:** 208. **Covers:** over 3,300 producers, directors, performers, designers, writers, theater artists and scholars in the U.S. **Entries include:** Name, title or position, name of organization with which affiliated, address, phone. **Arrangement.** Alphabetical. **Indexes:** Field of specialty.

262 ■ *Writers Guide to Hollywood Producers*
Fade in Magazine
PO Box 2699
Beverly Hills, CA 90213
Ph: (310)275-0287
Free: 800-646-3896
URL: http://fadeinonline.com

Price: $59.95 Individuals. **Covers:** Hollywood producers. **Entries include:** Name, contact information, and web site.

HANDBOOKS AND MANUALS

263 ■ *Acting A to Z: The Young Person's Guide to a Stage or Screen Career*
Watson-Guptill Publications
1745 Broadway
New York, NY 10019
Ph: (212)782-9000
Free: 800-733-3000
Fax: (212)572-6066
E-mail: info@watsonguptill.com
URL: http://www.randomhouse.com

Description: Katherine Mayfield. 2nd Revised edition, 2007. $16.95 (paper). Author explains exactly what it's like to be an actor, including what kind of training the young person will need, comparisons of the different types of acting, how to find work, how to prepare for an audition, and what to expect during rehearsal. 192 pages.

264 ■ *The Actor's Other Career Book: Using Your Chops to Survive and Thrive*
Allworth Press
307 W 36th St., 11th Fl.
New York, NY 10018
Ph: (212)643-6816
Free: 800-491-2808
Fax: (212)643-6819
E-mail: pub@allworth.com
URL: http://www.allworth.com

Description: Lisa Mulcahy. 2006. $19.95. Fifty various positions for actors that are available in cruise ships, trade shows, retail stores, advertising agencies, corporate settings, education, social outreach, tourist attractions, physical fitness, and other areas are outlined.

265 ■ *A Career Handbook for TV, Radio, Film, Video and Interactive Media*
Bloomsbury Publishing PLC
50 Bedford Sq.
London WC1B 3DP, United Kingdom
Ph: 44 020 7631 5600
Fax: 020 7631 5800
E-mail: uk@bloomsbury.com
URL: http://www.bloomsbury.com/uk/a-career
   -handbook-for-tv-radio-film-video-and-interactive
   -media-9780713663204/

Frequency: Monthly. **Price:** £13.49 Individuals. **Covers:** TV, radio, film, video and interactive media specialists.

266 ■ *Creative Careers: Paths for Aspiring Actors, Artists, Dancers, Musicians and Writers*
SuperCollege
3286 Oak Ct.
Belmont, CA 94002
Ph: (650)618-2221
Fax: (650)618-2221
E-mail: supercollege@supercollege.com
URL: http://www.supercollege.com

Description: Elaina Loveland. 2009. $17.95. 352 pages. Provides tips and advice for job seekers aim-

ing for a career in the field of arts. Includes details on salaries, job descriptions, job outlook, training and education requirements for each artistic career.

267 ■ *Directing: A Handbook for Emerging Theatre Directors*
Bloomsbury Publishing PLC
50 Bedford Sq.
London WC1B 3DP, United Kingdom
Ph: 44 020 7631 5600
Fax: 020 7631 5800
E-mail: uk@bloomsbury.com
URL: http://www.bloomsbury.com/uk/directing-a
   -handbook-for-emerging-theatre-directors
   -9781408156629

Frequency: Latest edition 1st; Published September 29, 2011. **Price:** £13.49 Individuals paperback; £14.99 Individuals ebook. **Covers:** Key questions for emerging theater directors.

268 ■ *The Director's Craft: A Handbook for the Theatre*
Routledge
711 3rd Ave., 8th Fl.
New York, NY 10017
Ph: (212)216-7800
Free: 800-634-7064
Fax: (212)564-7854
E-mail: book.orders@tandf.co.uk
URL: http://www.routledge.com

Description: Katie Mitchell. 2008. $19.99 (paperback). $70 (hardback). 246 pages. Step-by-step guide to directing for the stage. Provides assistance with each aspect of the varied challenges facing all theatre directors.

269 ■ *Enter the Playmakers: Directors and Choreographers on the New York Stage*
The Scarecrow Press Inc.
4501 Forbes Blvd., Ste. 200
Lanham, MD 20706-4346
Ph: (301)459-3366
Free: 800-462-6420
Fax: (301)429-5748
E-mail: custserv@rowman.com
URL: http://www.scarecrowpress.com

Description: Thomas S. Hischak. 2006. $45.00. 154 pages. Features famous artists such as Elia Kazan and Jerome Robbins as well as lesser known artists of the American theatre. A biography of each director or choreographer is included.

270 ■ *FabJob Guide to Become a Television Producer*
FabJob Inc.
4616-25th Ave. NE, No. 224
Seattle, WA 98105
Ph: (403)873-1018
Free: 888-322-5621
URL: http://www.fabjob.com

Description: Gary Reynolds. $14.97(e-books). 157 pages. Contains information on how to start a career in television production. Offers useful resources and career advice.

271 ■ *Footlight Dreams: Following Your Passion for a Career in Musical Theatre: A Guide for Performers, Parents and Teachers*
Hal Leonard Corp.
7777 W Bluemound Rd.
Milwaukee, WI 53213-3439
Ph: (414)774-3630
Fax: (414)774-3259
E-mail: customerservice@amadeuspress.com
URL: http://www.halleonard.com

Description: David Ladd. 2011. $12.99. 104 pages. Serves as practical guide for performers, teachers and parents to help with the decision-making process of aspiring performers seeking a career in musical theatre. Includes a discussion on career options, opportunities and resources in the field.

272 ■ *Great Jobs for Theater Majors*
The McGraw-Hill Companies Inc.
PO Box 182604
Columbus, OH 43272
Ph: (212)512-2000
Free: 877-833-5524
Fax: (614)759-3749
E-mail: customer.service@mcgraw-hill.com
URL: http://www.mcgraw-hill.com

Description: Jan Goldberg and Julie DeGalan. 2005. $15.95 (paper). 192 pages.

273 ■ *A Killer Life: How an Independent Film Producer Survives Deals and Disasters in Hollywood and Beyond*
Hal Leonard Corp.
7777 W Bluemound Rd.
Milwaukee, WI 53213-3439
Ph: (414)774-3630
Fax: (414)774-3259
E-mail: customerservice@amadeuspress.com
URL: http://www.halleonard.com

Description: Christine Vachon, as told to Austin Bunn. $16.95. 320 pages. Christine Vachon chronicles twenty years of working in the film industry.

274 ■ *The New Business of Acting: How to Build a Career in a Changing Landscape*
Ingenuity Press USA
2275 Huntington Dr., Ste. 552
San Marino, CA 91108
Ph: (626)285-4040
E-mail: inquiries@ingenuitypressusa.com
URL: http://www.ingenuitypressusa.com

Description: Brad Lemack. 2010. $22.95. 225 pages. Offers new and working actors a vital perspective on the changing landscape of the business of acting. Covers chapters on the changing roles of agents and managers; the importance of creating, protecting and honoring an actor's 'brand'; and managing job expectations. Includes tips on creating and launching an action plan for career success.

275 ■ *Opportunities in Acting Careers*
The McGraw-Hill Companies Inc.
PO Box 182604
Columbus, OH 43272
Ph: (212)512-2000
Free: 877-833-5524
Fax: (614)759-3749
E-mail: customer.service@mcgraw-hill.com
URL: http://www.mcgraw-hill.com

Description: Dick Moore. 2005. $13.95 (paper). 160 pages. A guide to planning for and seeking opportunities in acting.

276 ■ *Opportunities in Film Careers*
The McGraw-Hill Companies Inc.
PO Box 182604
Columbus, OH 43272
Ph: (212)512-2000
Free: 877-833-5524
Fax: (614)759-3749
E-mail: customer.service@mcgraw-hill.com
URL: http://www.mcgraw-hill.com

Description: Jan Bone and Ana Fernandez. 2004. $19.95 (paper). 160 pages. Provides advice on obtaining a job in film and in corporate non-broadcast film/video production. Illustrated.

277 ■ *Promoting Your Acting Career: Step-by-Step Guide to Opening the Right Doors*
Allworth Press
307 W 36th St., 11th Fl.
New York, NY 10018
Ph: (212)643-6816
Free: 800-491-2808
Fax: (212)643-6819
E-mail: pub@allworth.com
URL: http://www.allworth.com

Description: Glenn Alterman. 2004. $22.95 (paper). 240 pages.

278 ■ *Resumes for Performing Arts Careers*

The McGraw-Hill Companies Inc.
PO Box 182604
Columbus, OH 43272
Ph: (212)512-2000
Free: 877-833-5524
Fax: (614)759-3749
E-mail: customer.service@mcgraw-hill.com
URL: http://www.mcgraw-hill.com

Description: 2004. $10.95 (paper). 160 pages.

279 ■ *The Seven Steps to Stardom: How to Become a Working Actor in Movies, TV, and Commercials*

Applause Theatre & Cinema Books
19 W 21st St., Ste. 201
New York, NY 10010
Ph: (212)575-9265
Free: 800-637-2852
Fax: (212)575-9270
E-mail: info@applausepub.com
URL: http://www.applausepub.com

Description: Christina Ferra-Gilmor and Wink Martindale. $19.95. 104 pages. The founder of a leading acting school offers seven steps for becoming an actor.

280 ■ *So You Want to be an Actor?*

Nick Hern Books
1045 Westgate Dr., Ste. 90
Saint Paul, MN 55114-1065
Ph: (651)221-9035
Free: 800-283-3572
Fax: (651)917-6406
URL: http://www.nickhernbooks.co.uk/index.cfm?nid
=home&isbn=1854598791&sr

Description: Timothy West and Prunella Scales. 2006. $20.95. Advice is given to any individual interested in the field of acting.

281 ■ *Stage Directors Handbook: Complete Opportunities for Directors and Choreographers*

Theatre Communications Group
520 8th Ave., 24th Fl.
New York, NY 10018-4156
Ph: (212)609-5900
Fax: (212)609-5901
E-mail: tcg@tcg.org
URL: http://www.tcg.org/ecommerce/showbookdetails
.cfm?ID=TCG5568

Frequency: Latest edition 2nd. **Price:** $19.95 Individuals paperback. **Pages:** 240. **Covers:** Resources for professional directors and choreographers. **Includes:** Essays by specialists treating selected topics. **Entries include:** Contact information, description.

EMPLOYMENT AGENCIES AND SEARCH FIRMS

282 ■ Filcro Media Staffing

521 5th Ave., 18th Fl.
New York, NY 10175
Ph: (212)599-0909
Fax: (212)599-1023
E-mail: mail@executivesearch.tv
URL: http://www.executivesearch.tv

Description: Executive search firm for the entertainment industry.

283 ■ Howard Fischer Associates International Inc.

1800 Kennedy Blvd., Ste. 700
Philadelphia, PA 19103
Ph: (215)568-8363

Fax: (215)568-4815
E-mail: search@hfischer.com
URL: http://www.hfischer.com

Description: Executive search firm. Branches in Campbell, CA and Boston, MA.

ONLINE JOB SOURCES AND SERVICES

284 ■ Acting-Jobs.com

URL: http://acting-jobs.com

Description: Provides information on all available acting jobs in the United States.

285 ■ Acting-Jobs.net

URL: http://www.acting-jobs.net

Description: Provides a searchable database of acting jobs in the United States.

286 ■ CasinoGigs.net

URL: http://www.casinogigs.net

Description: Serves as a career community for the gambling industry. Features job openings for casino workers, research into the arts, entertainment & gaming employment market, and a career articles section written and frequented by industry professionals.

287 ■ GetGigs.com

URL: http://www.getgigs.com

Description: Seeks to provide an on-line experience for creative types, performing artists, and musicians around the world by integrating internet technologies into a one-stop information resource. Also functions as a creative directory and talent network.

288 ■ Mandy's International Film and TV Production Directory

URL: http://www.mandy.com/1/filmtvjobs.cfm

Description: Employment site intended for film and TV professionals. Employers may post free Jobs Offered listings. Job seekers may post free Jobs Wanted ads.

289 ■ Media-Match.com

URL: http://www.media-match.com/usa

Description: Serves as an online database of TV and film professionals' resumes and availabilities. Provides an up-to-date television production jobs board and film production jobs board for new openings in the film and TV production business across the United States.

290 ■ OffStageJobs.com

URL: http://www.offstagejobs.com

Description: Lists behind-the-scenes jobs in the live entertainment industry. Also features backstage related news and information.

291 ■ *Producer's Directory*

IFILM Corp. - Hollywood Creative Directory Inc.
5055 Wilshire Blvd.
Hollywood, CA 90036-4396
Ph: (323)525-2369
Free: 800-815-0503
Fax: (323)525-2398
E-mail: hcdcustomerservice@hcdonline.com
URL: http://www.hcdonline.com

Price: 1 Year subscription: $199.95; Print version: $59.95. **Description:** Producer's Directory is an online source with information on film and television industry. Thoroughly researched and meticulously compiled, the PD lists up-to-date information on producers, studio and network executives. This Product covers: Over 7,800 names; Producers, Studio and Network Executives; Over 1,700 production companies, studios and networks; addresses, phone and fax numbers, staff and titles; selected credits and companies with studio deals. available as an online source, but also in print version, database is updated three times a year: March - July - November.

292 ■ ProductionHub.com

URL: http://www.productionhub.com

Description: Serves as an online resource and industry directory for film, television, video, live event and digital media production. Features job opportunities, events, directory and other resources for the production industry.

TRADESHOWS

293 ■ Southeastern Theatre Conference Convention

Southeastern Theatre Conference
1175 Revolution Mill Dr., Ste. 14
Greensboro, NC 27405
Ph: (336)272-3645
Fax: (336)272-8810
E-mail: dslusser@camden.k12.ga.us
URL: http://www.setc.org

Frequency: Annual; always the first full Wednesday-Sunday of March. auditions, workshops, commercial and non-commercial exhibits, theatre festivals.

294 ■ WonderCon

San Diego Comic-Con International
PO Box 128458
San Diego, CA 92112-8458
Ph: (619)491-2475
Fax: (619)414-1022
URL: http://www.comic-con.org/

Frequency: Annual. Comics and popular arts, including movie and television panels, anime, autographs, games, and portfolio review. Also premieres major motion pictures. San Francisco, CA.

OTHER SOURCES

295 ■ *100 Careers in the Music Business*

Barron's Educational Series Inc.
250 Wireless Blvd.
Hauppauge, NY 11788
Ph: (631)434-3311
Free: 800-645-3476
Fax: (631)434-3723
E-mail: barrons@barronseduc.com
URL: http://www.barronseduc.com

Description: Tanja L. Crouch. 2008. $15.29 (paper). 320 pages. Provides information on how and where to find employment opportunities in the music industry. **Includes:** Includes lists of names, addresses, and websites of music unions, organizations, directories, and periodicals, as well as schools offering degrees in music business management. Includes lists of names, addresses, and websites of music unions, organizations, directories, and periodicals, as well as schools offering degrees in music business management.

296 ■ Academy of Motion Picture Arts and Sciences

8949 Wilshire Blvd.
Beverly Hills, CA 90211
Ph: (310)247-3000
Fax: (310)859-9619
E-mail: publicity@oscars.org
URL: http://www.oscars.org

Description: Represents motion picture producers, directors, writers, cinematographer, editors, actors and craftsmen.

297 ■ Academy of Television Arts and Sciences

5220 Lankershim Blvd.
North Hollywood, CA 91601
Ph: (818)754-2800
E-mail: lewis.kay@pmkbnc.com
URL: http://www.emmys.com/

Description: Professionals in the television and film industry. Aims to advance the arts and sciences of television through services to the industry in education, preservation of television programs, and information and community relations; to foster creative leadership in the television industry. Sponsors Television Academy Hall of Fame. Maintains library on television credits and historical material, the Television Academy Archives, and archives at UCLA of over 35,000 television programs. Offers internships to students. Holds luncheon and speakers series and meetings on problems of the various crafts. **Members:** 18,000.

298 ■ Actors' Fund
729 7th Ave., 10th Fl.
New York, NY 10019
Ph: (212)221-7300
Free: 800-221-7303
E-mail: info@actorsfund.org
URL: http://www.actorsfund.org

Description: Helps all professionals - both performers and those behind the scenes - in performing arts and entertainment. Serves those in film, theatre, television, music, opera, and dance with a broad spectrum of programs including comprehensive social services, health services, supportive and affordable housing, emergency financial assistance, employment and training services, and skilled nursing and assisted living care. Administered from offices in New York, Los Angeles, and Chicago, it serves as a safety net, providing programs and services for those who are in need, crisis, or transition. **Members:** 6,000.

299 ■ Alliance for Inclusion in the Arts
1560 Broadway, Ste. 709
New York, NY 10036
Ph: (212)730-4750
E-mail: info@inclusioninthearts.org
URL: http://inclusioninthearts.org

Description: Advocates the elimination of discrimination in theatre, film, and television. Works to increase the employment of artists of color and artists with disabilities by encouraging cultural diversity throughout the artistic process and all levels of production and administration, and offering consultative services. Maintains the Artist Files containing pictures and resumes of 3,000 actors, directors, writers, designers, and stage managers of color as well as those with disabilities. Sponsors forums.

300 ■ Alliance of Resident Theatres/New York
520 8th Ave., Ste. 319
New York, NY 10018
Ph: (212)244-6667
Fax: (212)714-1918
E-mail: info@art-newyork.org
URL: http://www.art-newyork.org

Description: Nonprofit professional theatres in New York City and interested theatre-related associations. Promotes recognition of the nonprofit theatre community. Provides members with administrative services and resources pertinent to their field. Facilitates discussion among the theatres; helps to solve real estate problems; serves as a public information source. Acts as advocate on behalf of members with government, corporate, and foundation funders to encourage greater support for New York's not-for-profit theatres. Sponsors seminars, roundtables, and individual consultations for members in areas such as financial management, board development and marketing. Organizes Passports to Off Broadway, an industry-wide marketing campaign.

301 ■ American Association of Community Theatre
1300 Gendy St.
Fort Worth, TX 76107
Ph: (817)732-3177
Free: 866-687-2228
Fax: (817)732-3178
E-mail: info@aact.org
URL: http://www.aact.org

Description: Community theatre organizations and individuals involved in community theatre. Promotes excellence in community theatre through networking, workshops, publications, and festivals of community theatre productions. **Members:** 1,800,

302 ■ American Conservatory Theater Foundation
30 Grant Ave., 7th Fl.
San Francisco, CA 94108-5834
Ph: (415)834-3200
Fax: (415)749-2291
E-mail: tickets@act-sf.org
URL: http://www.act-sf.org

Description: Provides resources for the American Conservatory Theater which functions as a repertory theatre and accredited acting school, offering a Master of Fine Arts degree. Holds national auditions for the MFA program in Chicago, IL, New York City, and Los Angeles, CA, usually in February. Holds student matinees, school outreach programs, and in-theatre discussions between artist and audiences. Conducts professional actor-training programs, a summer training congress, and a young conservatory evening academy program for children aged 8-18. Offers children's services. Operates speakers' bureau and placement service.

303 ■ Association for Theatre in Higher Education
PO Box 1290
Boulder, CO 80306-1290
Ph: (303)530-2167
Free: 888-284-3737
Fax: (303)530-2168
E-mail: executivedirector@athe.org
URL: http://www.athe.org

Description: Universities, colleges, and professional education programs; artists, scholars, teachers, and other individuals; students. Promotes the exchange of information among individuals engaged in theatre study and research, performance, and crafts. Provides advocacy and support services. Encourages excellence in postsecondary theatre training, production, and scholarship. **Members:** 1,700.

304 ■ Career Opportunities in the Film Industry
InfoBase Holdings Inc.
132 W 31st., 17 Fl.
New York, NY 10001-3406
Ph: (212)967-8800
Fax: (800)678-3633
E-mail: info@infobasepublishing.com
URL: http://factsonfile.infobasepublishing.com

Frequency: Latest edition 2nd, 2009. **Price:** $49.50 Individuals hardcover. **Pages:** 296. **Description:** Fred Yager and Jan Yager. Second edition, 2009. 268 pages. **Covers:** More than 80 jobs in the field, from the high-profile positions of director, producer, screenwriter, and actor to the all-important behind-the-scenes positions such as casting director, gaffer, and production designer. **Includes:** Appendices of educational institutions, periodicals, directories, and associations.

305 ■ Career Opportunities in the Music Industry
InfoBase Holdings Inc.
132 W 31st., 17 Fl.
New York, NY 10001-3406
Ph: (212)967-8800
Fax: (800)678-3633
E-mail: info@infobasepublishing.com
URL: http://www.ferguson.infobasepublishing.com

Description: Shelly Field. Sixth edition, 2009. $49.50. **Includes:** Appendices of major agencies, unions, associations, periodicals, and directories. Appendices of major agencies, unions, associations, periodicals, and directories.

306 ■ Career Opportunities in Radio
InfoBase Holdings Inc.
132 W 31st., 17 Fl.
New York, NY 10001-3406
Ph: (212)967-8800
Fax: (800)678-3633
E-mail: info@infobasepublishing.com
URL: http://www.infobasepublishing.com

Frequency: Published April, 2004. **Price:** $49.50 Individuals hardcover. **Pages:** 336. **Description:** Shelly Field. 2004. 326 pages. **Covers:** More than 70 jobs, such as on-air personality/disc jockey, business reporter, sportscaster, advertising account representative, billing specialist, publicist, studio engineer, program director, website content producer, and more. **Includes:** Appendices of educational institutions, periodicals, directories, unions, and associations.

307 ■ Career Opportunities in Television and Cable
InfoBase Holdings Inc.
132 W 31st., 17 Fl.
New York, NY 10001-3406
Ph: (212)967-8800
Fax: (800)678-3633
E-mail: info@infobasepublishing.com
URL: http://www.ferguson.infobasepublishing.com

Description: 2006. $49.50. Covers job profiles in television and cable industry, followed by the descriptions of the nature of the job, earnings, prospects for employment, what kind of training and skills it requires, and sources of other relevant information.

308 ■ Career Opportunities in Theater and the Performing Arts
InfoBase Holdings Inc.
132 W 31st., 17 Fl.
New York, NY 10001-3406
Ph: (212)967-8800
Fax: (800)678-3633
E-mail: info@infobasepublishing.com
URL: http://www.infobasepublishing.com

Frequency: Latest edition 3rd; Published April, 2006. **Description:** Shelly Field. Third edition, 2006. 304 pages. **Covers:** 80 careers, from acting to designing to dance therapy. **Includes:** Appendices of major agencies, unions, associations, periodicals, and directories.

309 ■ Careers for the Stagestruck and Other Dramatic Types
The McGraw-Hill Companies Inc.
PO Box 182604
Columbus, OH 43272
Ph: (212)512-2000
Free: 877-833-5524
Fax: (614)759-3749
E-mail: customer.service@mcgraw-hill.com
URL: http://www.mcgraw-hill.com

Description: Lucia Mauro. Second edition, 2004. $13.95 (paper). 160 pages. **Includes:** Appendices of arts organizations, colleges and universities, and other job-hunting and arts education resources, as well as bibliographical references. Appendices of arts organizations, colleges and universities, and other job-hunting and arts education resources, as well as bibliographical references. **Entries include:** Name, address.

310 ■ Coalition of Asian Pacifics in Entertainment
10600 W Pico Blvd., Ste. 202
Los Angeles, CA 90064
Ph: (323)379-4509
E-mail: info@capeusa.org
URL: http://capeusa.org

Description: Supports Asian Pacifics in the arts and entertainment. Increases the social, educational and professional opportunities for Asian Pacifics in the entertainment industry. Serves as a forum for Asian Pacifics in feature film, television, video, publishing, music and other entertainment fields to share common interests and concerns through such programs as screenings, panels, workshops, and hosted conversations with notable executives and artists.

311 ■ Film Independent
9911 W Pico Blvd., 11th Fl.
Los Angeles, CA 90035
Ph: (310)432-1200
Fax: (310)432-1203
E-mail: spiritawards@filmindependent.org
URL: http://www.filmindependent.org

Description: Represents directors, writers, and producers. Strives to help independent filmmakers get their films made, build the audience for independent film, and increase diversity in the film industry. Provides cameras and casting rooms to rent, a resource library with computers, sample budget and business plans, and film periodicals. Offers free screenings and educational events every year.

312 ■ Health Science Communications Association
PO Box 31323
Omaha, NE 68131-0323
Ph: (402)915-5373
E-mail: hesca@hesca.org
URL: http://www.hesca.org

Description: Represents media managers, graphic artists, biomedical librarians, producers, faculty members of health science and veterinary medicine schools, health professional organizations, and industry representatives. Acts as a clearinghouse for information used by professionals engaged in health science communications. Coordinates Media Festivals Program that recognizes outstanding media productions in the health sciences. Offers placement service. **Members:** 400.

313 ■ *How to Break into Acting*
Tapeworm Video Distributors
25876 The Old Road #141
Stevenson Ranch, CA 91381
Ph: (661)257-4904
Fax: (661)257-4820
E-mail: sales@tapeworm.com
URL: http://www.tapeworm.com

Price: $19.95. **Description:** Contains interviews with actors, casting directors, agents, producers, and directors on how to get started in the acting profession in Hollywood. They discuss how to keep from getting ripped off, finding a respectable agent, and step-by-step instructions that cover from getting your head shots to landing your first job.

314 ■ Independent Film and Television Alliance
10850 Wilshire Blvd., 9th Fl.
Los Angeles, CA 90024-4321
Ph: (310)446-1000
Fax: (310)446-1600
E-mail: info@ifta-online.org
URL: http://www.ifta-online.org

Description: Trade association for the worldwide independent film and television industry. Contributes to negotiations with foreign producer associations; develops standardized theatrical, TV and video contracts for international distribution. Established and maintains the IFTA International Arbitration Tribunal, a system through which prominent entertainment attorneys throughout the world assist members and consenting clients in reaching equitable and binding agreements. Facilitates the formulation of policies, standardized private practices and language contracts and the exchange of information and experience among members. Produces the American Film Market (AFM), the largest international motion picture trade event in the world.

315 ■ International Documentary Association
3470 Wilshire Blvd., Ste. 980
Los Angeles, CA 90010
Ph: (213)232-1660

Fax: (213)232-1669
E-mail: michael@documentary.org
URL: http://www.documentary.org

Description: Represents nonfiction film and video makers. Supports the efforts of nonfiction film and video makers throughout the United States and the world. Promotes the documentary form and expands opportunities for the production, distribution, and exhibition of documentaries. Seeks to increase public appreciation and demand for documentary films, videos, and television programs across all ethnic, political, and socioeconomic boundaries.

316 ■ *Job Bulletin*
Radio-Television Digital News Association
529 14th St. NW, Ste. 1240
Washington, DC 20045
Fax: (202)223-4007
URL: http://rtdna.org

Frequency: Biweekly. **Price:** included in membership dues.

317 ■ Media Communications Association - International
2810 Crossroads Dr., Ste. 3800
Madison, WI 53705-0135
Free: 888-899-6224
Fax: (888)862-8150
E-mail: j.salci@yahoo.com
URL: http://www.mca-i.org

Description: Individuals engaged in multimedia communications needs analysis, scriptwriting, producing, directing, consulting, and operations management in the video, multimedia, and film fields. Seeks to advance the benefits and image of media communications professionals.

318 ■ National Association of Broadcasters
1771 N St. NW
Washington, DC 20036
Ph: (202)429-5300
Free: 800-342-2460
E-mail: nab@nab.org
URL: http://www.nab.org

Description: Serves as the voice for the nation's radio and television broadcasters. Advances the interests of members in federal government, industry and public affairs; improves the quality and profitability of broadcasting; encourages content and technology innovation; and spotlights the important and unique ways stations serve their communities. Delivers value to its members through advocacy, education and innovation. Relies on the grassroots strength of its television and radio members and state broadcast associations. Helps broadcasters seize opportunities in the digital age. Offers broadcasters a variety of programs to help them grow in their careers, promote diversity in the workplace and strengthen their businesses.

319 ■ National Association of Television Program Executives
5757 Wilshire Blvd., Penthouse 10
Los Angeles, CA 90036-3681
Ph: (310)453-4440
Fax: (310)453-5258
E-mail: info@natpe.org
URL: http://www.natpe.org

Description: Comprised of television program professionals, exhibitors, buyers and faculty. Focuses on the creation, development and distribution of televised programming in all forms across all mature and emerging media platforms. Provides members with education, networking, professional enhancement and technological guidance through year-round activities and events, and directories.

320 ■ *National Directory of Arts Internships*
National Network for Artist Placement
935 West Ave. 37
Los Angeles, CA 90065
Ph: (323)222-4035
E-mail: info@artistplacement.com
URL: http://www.artistplacement.com

Frequency: Biennial; odd years; latest edition 11th. **Price:** $95 Individuals softcover, plus $12 shipping and handling. **Covers:** Over 5,000 internship opportunities in dance, music, theater, art, design, film, and video & over 1,250 host organizations. **Entries include:** Name of sponsoring organization, address, name of contact; description of positions available, eligibility requirements, stipend or salary (if any), application procedures. **Arrangement:** Classified by discipline, then geographical.

321 ■ New England Theatre Conference
215 Knob Hill Dr.
Hamden, CT 06518
Ph: (617)851-8535
E-mail: mail@netconline.org
URL: http://netconline.org

Description: Individuals and theatre-producing groups in New England who are actively engaged in or have a particular interest in theatre activity either professionally or as an avocation. Aims to develop, expand, and assist theatre activity on community, educational, and professional levels in New England. Activities include: auditions for jobs in New England summer theatres; workshops on performance, administrative, and technical aspects of production.

322 ■ Radio-Television Digital News Association
529 14th St. NW, Ste. 1240
Washington, DC 20045
Fax: (202)223-4007
URL: http://rtdna.org

Description: Comprises of heads of news departments for broadcast and cable stations and networks; associate members are journalists engaged in the preparation and presentation of broadcast news and teachers of electronic journalism; other members represent industry services, public relations departments of business firms, public relations firms, and networks. Operates placement service and speakers' bureau.

323 ■ Screen Actors Guild - American Federation of Television and Radio Artists
5757 Wilshire Blvd., 7th Fl.
Los Angeles, CA 90036-3600
Ph: (323)954-1600
Free: 855-724-2387
E-mail: sagaftrainfo@sagaftra.org
URL: http://www.sagaftra.org

Description: Represents working actors in film, television, industrials, commercials, video games, music videos, and other new media. Aims to enhance actors' working conditions, compensation, and benefits. Serves and protects artists' rights.

324 ■ *Showbiz Labor Guide*
Media Services - Showbiz Software
500 S Sepulveda Blvd., 1st Fl.
Los Angeles, CA 90049
Ph: (310)471-9330
Free: 800-333-7518
E-mail: showbizsoftware@media-services.com
URL: http://www.showbizsoftware.com

325 ■ Southeastern Theatre Conference
1175 Revolution Mill Dr., Ste. 14
Greensboro, NC 27405
Ph: (336)272-3645
Fax: (336)272-8810
E-mail: dslusser@camden.k12.ga.us
URL: http://www.setc.org

Description: Serves the needs of individuals and theatre organizations involved in professional, university/college, community, children/youth, and secondary school theatres. Brings together people interested in theatre and theatre artists and craftsmen from 10 southeastern states of the U.S. across the nation and internationally in order to promote high standards and to stimulate creativity in all phases of theatrical endeavor. Services include: job contact service for technical hiring and job listings, resume service, etc.; playwriting projects for new plays; scholarships for a variety of theatre interests; and annual auditions (spring and fall) for professional, dinner, repertory, summer indoor and outdoor theatres, cruise lines and entertainment venues.

326 ■ **University Film and Video Association**
0000 Darnam Blvd., Ste. 103
Los Angeles, CA 90068
Free: 866-647-8382
E-mail: ufvahome@aol.com
URL: http://www.ufva.org
Description: Professors and video/filmmakers

concerned with the production and study of film and video in colleges and universities. Conducts research programs; operates placement service; presents annual grants. **Members:** 800.

327 ■ **Women in Film**
6100 Wilshire Blvd., Ste. 710
Los Angeles, CA 90048
Ph: (323)935-2211
Fax: (323)935-2212
E-mail: info@wif.org

URL: http://www.wif.org

Description: Supports women in the film and television industry and serves as a network for information on qualified women in the entertainment field. Sponsors screenings and discussions of pertinent issues. Provides speakers' bureau. Maintains Women in Film Foundation, which offers financial assistance to women for education, research, and/or completion of film projects. **Members:** 2,400.

328 ■ *Actuarial Digest*
URL: http://www.theactuarialdigest.com

Description: Quarterly. Covers issues of concern to working actuaries. Recurring features include letters to the editor, news of research, news of educational opportunities, job listings, book reviews, notices of publications available, and a column titled What's New.

329 ■ *ASCnet Quarterly*
Applied Systems Client Network
801 Douglas Ave., Ste. 205
Altamonte Springs, FL 32714
Ph: (407)869-0404
Free: 800-605-1045
Fax: (407)869-0418
E-mail: info@ascnet.org
URL: http://www.ascnet.org/AM/Template.cfm?Section=About

Frequency: Quarterly. **Price:** $24 Individuals. **Description:** Professional magazine covering technical information, association news, and industry information for insurance professionals.

330 ■ *Best's Review*
A.M. Best Company Inc.
Ambest Rd.
Oldwick, NJ 08858-7000
Ph: (908)439-2200
Fax: (908)439-3385
E-mail: customer_service@ambest.com
URLs: http://www.ambest.com/sales/newsoverview.asp#br; http://www.ambest.com/review/default.asp

Frequency: Monthly. **Price:** $50 Individuals. **Description:** Magazine covering issues and trends for the management personnel of life/health insurers, the agents, and brokers who market their products.

331 ■ *Business Insurance*
Crain Communications Inc.
1155 Gratiot Ave.
Detroit, MI 48207-2732
Ph: (313)446-6000
E-mail: info@crain.com
URL: http://www.businessinsurance.com

Frequency: Weekly. **Price:** $399 Individuals print; $149 Individuals print & digital; $69 Individuals digital edition. **Description:** International newsweekly reporting on corporate risk and employee benefit management news.

332 ■ *Contingencies: The Magazine of the Actuarial Profession*
American Academy of Actuaries
1850 M St. NW, Ste. 300
Washington, DC 20036
Ph: (202)223-8196
Fax: (202)872-1948
E-mail: downs@actuary.org
URL: http://www.contingencies.org

Frequency: Bimonthly. **Price:** $33 Other countries. **Description:** Magazine on actuarial science and its relevance to current business problems and social issues.

333 ■ *The Future Actuary*
Society of Actuaries
475 N Martingale Rd., Ste. 600
Schaumburg, IL 60173
Ph: (847)706-3500
Free: 888-697-3900
Fax: (847)706-3599
E-mail: feedback@soa.org
URL: http://www.soa.org

Description: Four issues/year. Provides actuarial students with the latest information on jobs, internships, study techniques, career development, professional conduct, and ethics. Recurring features include a calendar of events, news of educational opportunities, and job listings.

334 ■ *Best's Insurance Reports*
A.M. Best Company Inc.
Ambest Rd.
Oldwick, NJ 08858-7000
Ph: (908)439-2200
Fax: (908)439-3385
E-mail: customer_service@ambest.com
URL: http://www.ambest.com

Frequency: Annual; Latest edition 2014. **Pages:** 3,345 Life-health; 5,166 property-casualty. **Description:** Published in three editions: Life-health insurance, covering about 1,750 companies, property-casualty insurance, covering over 3,200 companies; and international, covering more than 1,200 insurers. Each edition lists state insurance commissioners and related companies and agencies (mutual funds, worker compensation funds, underwriting agencies, etc.). **Includes:** Review of financial performance, 5 years of exclusive Best's Ratings. **Entries include:** For each company--Company name, address, phone; history; states in which licensed; names of officers and directors; financial data; financial analysis and Best's rating. **Arrangement:** Alphabetical.

335 ■ *Directory of Actuarial Memberships*
Society of Actuaries
475 N Martingale Rd., Ste. 600
Schaumburg, IL 60173
Ph: (847)706-3500
Free: 888-697-3900
Fax: (847)706-3599
E-mail: feedback@soa.org
URL: http://www.soa.org

Frequency: Annual. **Description:** Contains information on members of the American Academy of Actuaries, American Society of Pension Professionals and Actuaries, Canadian Institute of Actuaries, Casualty Actuarial Society, Conference of Consulting Actuaries and the Society of Actuaries. **Covers:** Individuals trained in the application of mathematical probabilities to the design of insurance, pension, and employee benefit programs.

336 ■ *Insurance Phone Book*
Communication Publications & Resources
2807 N Parham Rd., Ste. 200
Richmond, VA 23294
Free: 800-780-4066
E-mail: customerservice@briefings.com
URLs: http://www.douglaspublications.com; http://www.thesalesmansguide.com

Frequency: Annual; latest edition 2009-2010. **Price:** $195 directory price; $389 directory/CD combo price. **Covers:** About 3,700 life, accident and health, worker's compensation, auto, fire and casualty, marine, surety, and other insurance companies; 2,300 executive contacts from presidents and CEOs to claims and customer service managers. **Entries include:** Company name, address, phone, fax, toll-free number, type of insurance provided. **Arrangement:** Alphabetical.

337 ■ *Variance: Advancing the Science of Risk*
Casualty Actuarial Society
4350 N Fairfax Dr., Ste. 250
Arlington, VA 22203
Ph: (703)276-3100
Fax: (703)276-3108
E-mail: office@casact.org
URL: http://www.variancejournal.org

Frequency: Semiannual; 2011 Volume 5; Issue 2. **Price:** $50 Individuals online. **Pages:** 376. **Covers:** Approximately 2,500 actuaries working in insurance other than life insurance. **Entries include:** Name, office address, date admitted to society, society's by-laws, codes of conduct, dues and discipline laws. **Arrangement:** Alphabetical by name.

338 ■ *Actuaries' Survival Guide: How to Succeed in One of the Most Desirable Professions*
Mosby Journal Div.
11830 Westline Industrial Dr.
Saint Louis, MO 63146-3318
Ph: (314)872-8370
Free: 800-325-4177
Fax: (314)432-1380
E-mail: info@elsevier.com
URL: http://www.us.elsevierhealth.com

Description: Fred E. Szabo. 2004. $48.95. 268 pages. Explores the function of actuaries.

339 ■ *Making the Grade: The Aspiring Actuary's Guidebook to Consistent Exam Success and Advancement in the Workplace*
ACTEX Publications
PO Box 974
Winsted, CT 06098
Ph: (860)379-5470
Free: 800-282-2839
Fax: (860)738-3152
E-mail: retail@actexmadriver.com
URL: http://www.actexmadriver.com

Description: Nicholas Mocciolo. 2010. $21.95. Serves as a reference on career development for aspiring actuaries. Focuses on suggested techniques to maximize success on actuarial exams. Includes information on actuarial organizations in the U.S. and introduction to non-technical skills for long-term success in the actuarial profession.

340 ■ *Opportunities in Insurance Careers*
The McGraw-Hill Companies Inc.
PO Box 182604
Columbus, OH 43272
Ph: (212)512-2000
Free: 877-833-5524
Fax: (614)759-3749
E-mail: customer.service@mcgraw-hill.com
URL: http://www.mcgraw-hill.com

Description: Robert M. Schrayer. Revised, 2007. $14.95 (paper). 160 pages. A guide to planning for and seeking opportunities in the field. Contains bibliography and illustrations.

341 ■ *Probability: An Introductory Guide for Actuaries and Other Business Professionals*
BPP Professional Education
4025 S Riverpoint Pkwy.
Phoenix, AZ 85040
E-mail: bppusainfo@bpp.com
URL: http://www.bpptraining.com/Html/Psolutions.htm

Description: David J. Carr and Michael A. Gauger. 2004.

EMPLOYMENT AGENCIES AND SEARCH FIRMS

342 ■ **Access Staffing**
360 Lexington Ave., 8th Fl.
New York, NY 10017
Ph: (212)687-5440
Fax: (212)557-2544
URL: http://www.accessstaffingco.com

Description: Serves as a staffing firm covering accounting/financial, advertising, bilingual Japanese, creative, event planning, fashion/retail, healthcare/human services, human resources, information technology, insurance, legal, light industrial, and office support.

343 ■ **Actuarial Careers, Inc.**
11 Martine Ave., 9th Fl.
White Plains, NY 10606
Ph: (914)285-5100
Free: 800-766-0070
Fax: (914)285-9375
E-mail: jobs@actuarialcareers.com
URL: http://www.actuarialcareers.com

Description: Specializes in the placement of actuaries on a worldwide basis and provides responsive and professional service in the industry. Provides actuarial candidates with opportunities to broaden and enhance their personal careers. Maintains a continually updated database containing new actuarial jobs.

344 ■ **Actuarial Jobs, Inc.**
2222 N Beech Daly Rd., Ste. 20
Dearborn Heights, MI 48127

Ph: (702)845-8631
Free: 800-395-6458
URL: http://www.actuarialjobsinc.com

Description: Specializes in the recruitment and placement of property and casualty actuaries, product managers and modelers. Provides a comprehensive recruitment service for qualified and studying actuarial professionals on both a permanent and contract/interim basis.

345 ■ **Actuary Resources**
115 N Castle Heights Ave., Ste. 202
Lebanon, TN 37087-2768
Ph: (615)360-5171
Fax: (615)360-5173
E-mail: info@actuaryresources.org
URL: http://www.actuaryresources.org

Description: Provides staffing services to several different types of industries. Offers a free screening service to clients.

346 ■ **The Alexander Group**
2700 Post Oak Blvd., Ste. 2400
Houston, TX 77056
Ph: (713)993-7900
URL: http://www.thealexandergroup.com

Description: Executive search firm. Second location in San Francisco.

347 ■ **Andover Research, Ltd.**
60 E 42nd St.
New York, NY 10165
Ph: (212)986-8484
Free: 800-AND-OVER
Fax: (212)983-0952
E-mail: actuaries@andoverresearch.com
URL: http://www.andoverresearch.com

Description: Specializes in the recruitment and placement of actuaries and benefit consultants worldwide.

348 ■ **Ashton Lane Group**
51 John F. Kennedy Pkwy., 1st Fl. W
Short Hills, NJ 07078
Ph: (212)372-9795
E-mail: info@ashtonlanegroup.com
URL: http://www.ashtonlanegroup.com

Description: Specializes in the recruitment of professionals in banking, insurance, and alternative investment industries.

349 ■ **Capstone Insurance Search Group**
2480 Berkshire Pkwy., Ste. A
Clive, IA 50325
Ph: (515)987-0242
Fax: (515)987-0004
E-mail: sdickerson@insurance-csg.com
URL: http://www.csgrecruiting.com

Description: Serves as an executive search firm dedicated to the insurance industry. Provides assistance with a variety of product lines including property and casualty, life, health, disability, annuity and pension.

350 ■ **Cornell Global**
PO Box 7113
Wilton, CT 06897
Ph: (203)762-0730
E-mail: info@cornellglobal.com
URL: http://www.cornellglobal.com

Description: Executive search firm with areas of expertise in the following areas: advertising, public relations, marketing, sales, finance and accounting, risk management, private equity and venture capital, construction, industrial, manufacturing, life sciences, publishing, information technology, engineering, human resources, legal, and logisitics.

351 ■ **Darwin Rhodes**
48 Wall St., 11th Fl.
New York, NY 10005
Ph: (212)918-4770

Fax: (212)918-4801
E-mail: newyork@darwinrhodes.com
URL: http://www.darwinrhodes.com

Description: Specializes in the placement of actuarial, employee benefits, insurance and financial planning professionals. Provides clients with a local recruitment and executive search service that are tailored to their particular goals and focus.

352 ■ **D.W. Simpson & Company**
4121 N Ravenswood Ave.
Chicago, IL 60613
Ph: (312)867-2300
Free: 800-837-8338
Fax: (312)951-8386
E-mail: actuaries@dwsimpson.com
URL: http://www.dwsimpson.com

Description: Serves the actuarial profession worldwide in all disciplines, recruiting at all levels from entry-level through fellowship, and works with clients on both retained and contingent searches.

353 ■ **Ezra Penland Actuarial Recruitment**
4256 N Ravenswood Ave., Ste. 200
Chicago, IL 60613
Free: 800-580-3972
Fax: (773)340-4209
E-mail: actuaries@ezrapenland.com
URL: http://www.ezrapenland.com

Description: Specializes on actuarial recruitment. Works with all levels of actuarial positions, from the actuarial analyst and actuarial assistant levels, up through associateship, fellowship, chief actuaries, consulting partners and executive management.

354 ■ **Health Actuary Search**
PO Box 102
Coeur D Alene, ID 83816
Free: 866-529-2159
Fax: (208)664-5350
E-mail: leslie@healthactuarysearch.com
URL: http://www.healthactuarysearch.com

Description: Provides targeted and personalized health actuarial recruiting services. Combines in-depth knowledge of the health marketplace with a commitment to individualized service, creating a dynamic nexus between candidate and employer.

355 ■ **International Insurance Personnel, Inc.**
300 W Wieuca Rd., Bldg. 2, Ste. 101
Atlanta, GA 30342
Ph: (404)255-9710
Fax: (404)255-9864
E-mail: iipjulie@bellsouth.net
URL: http://realpages.com/sites/intlinspersonnel/index.html

Description: Employment agency specializing in the area of insurance.

356 ■ **J Birch Corporation**
1505 S State Hwy. 8
New Boston, TX 75570
Free: 800-899-3064
E-mail: jbirch@thebirchcorp.com
URL: http://jbirchcorporation.com

Description: Specializes in actuarial placements in all areas of the insurance industry: life, health, pension, property and casualty and reinsurance. Works with all levels of actuaries from entry level to fellowship.

357 ■ **J. R. Peterman Associates, Inc.**
PO Box 3083
Stowe, VT 05672
Ph: (802)253-6304
Fax: (802)253-6314
E-mail: peterman@jrpeterman.com
URL: http://www.jrpeterman.com

Description: Recruit professionals in permanent and contract positions for the life and health insurance industry and employee benefits consulting.

358 ■ Kforce Inc.
1001 E Palm Ave.
Tampa, FL 33605-3551
Ph: (813)552-5000
Free: 877-453-6723
Fax: (813)552-2493
URL: http://www.kforce.com

Description: Executive search firm specializing in the financial services, insurance, health care, and pharmaceuticals industries.

359 ■ Lear & Associates, Inc.
43 E Pine St.
Orlando, FL 32801
Ph: (407)645-4611
Fax: (407)645-5735
E-mail: info@learsearch.com
URL: http://www.learsearch.com

Description: Serves as recruitment firm specializing in the insurance industry.

360 ■ Lighthouse Search Group
16610 W 159th St., Ste. 101
Lockport, IL 60441
Free: 888-317-1000
Fax: (815)588-3418
E-mail: info@lhsearch.com
URL: http://www.lhsearch.com

Description: Exists as an executive search firm specializing in the actuarial marketplace. Posts jobs from the largest actuarial consulting and insurance firms.

361 ■ Mitchell Actuarial Recruiting
4 Woodhaven Dr.
New City, NY 10956
Ph: (845)638-2700
Free: 800-648-2435
E-mail: info@mitchellactuarialrecruiting.com
URL: http://www.mitchellactuarialrecruiting.com

Description: Offers executive recruiting for the actuarial and benefits fields.

362 ■ Nationwide Actuarial Search
4680 S Polaris Ave., Ste. 240
Las Vegas, NV 89103
Ph: (702)454-9024
Free: 800-733-3536
Fax: (702)369-2881
E-mail: nas@actuary-recruiter.com
URL: http://www.actuary-recruiter.com/web/nas/home
    .asp

Description: Specializes in search and recruitment for property and casualty actuarial professionals at all levels.

363 ■ Pinnacle Group, Inc.
6 Greenleaf Woods, Ste. 201
Portsmouth, NH 03801
Ph: (603)427-1700
Free: 800-308-7205
Fax: (603)427-0526
E-mail: info@pinnaclejobs.com
URL: http://www.pinnaclejobs.com

Description: Provides recruiting services to insurance, consulting and investment firms. Offers career opportunities from entry-level to senior management.

364 ■ Questor Consultants, Inc.
2515 N Broad St.
Colmar, PA 18915
Ph: (215)997-9262
Fax: (215)997-9226
E-mail: sbevivino@questorconsultants.com
URL: http://www.questorconsultants.com

Description: Executive search firm specializing in the insurance and legal fields.

365 ■ Rollins Search Group, Inc.
849 Morningcreek Dr., Ste. 400
Kennesaw, GA 30152

Ph: (770)425-8230
E-mail: rsgwp@rollinssearch.com
URL: http://www.rollinssearch.com

Description: Specializes in permanent placement within the insurance industry for candidates with experience in actuarial and insurance information systems.

366 ■ S.C. International, Ltd.
1315 Butterfield Rd., Ste. 224
Downers Grove, IL 60515
Ph: (630)963-3033
Free: 800-543-2553
Fax: (630)963-3170
E-mail: search@scinternational.com
URL: http://www.scinternational.com

Description: Works as an executive search firm for the actuarial industry serving job seekers from entry level to senior officer executive positions.

367 ■ SHS of Cherry Hill
207 Barclay Pavilion W
Cherry Hill, NJ 08034
Ph: (856)216-9030
Fax: (856)219-2011
E-mail: shs@shsofcherryhill.com
URL: http://www.shsofcherryhill.com

Description: Personnel recruiters operating in the disciplines of accounting, sales, insurance, engineering and administration. Industries served: insurance, distribution, manufacturing and service.

368 ■ DW Simpson Global Actuarial Recruitment
4121 N Ravenswood Ave.
Chicago, IL 60613
Ph: (312)867-2300
Free: 800-837-8338
Fax: (312)951-8386
E-mail: actuaries@dwsimpson.com
URL: http://www.dwsimpson.com

Description: Serves the actuarial profession worldwide in all disciplines, recruiting at all levels from entry-level through fellowship.

369 ■ S.K. Associates
5825 Glenridge Dr., Bldg. 3, Ste. 101
Atlanta, GA 30328
Ph: (770)698-8504
Free: 877-SKA-SSOC
E-mail: actuarial@skassociates.com
URL: http://www.skassociates.com

Description: Exists as a recruiting firm specializing in all actuarial disciplines. Provides opportunities from CFO/chief actuaries, and practice leaders, to actuarial associate jobs and actuarial analyst jobs.

370 ■ Stewart Search Advisors, LLC
875 Greenland Rd., Ste. B8
Portsmouth, NH 03801
Ph: (603)430-2122
Free: 888-JOB-OPEN
Fax: (603)430-7339
E-mail: online@stewartsearch.com
URL: http://www.stewartsearch.com

Description: Exists as an executive search firm for the actuarial industry.

371 ■ Todd Mitchell Associates
3333 New Hyde Park Rd.
New Hyde Park, NY 11042
Free: 800-886-1562
Fax: (516)365-2460
E-mail: todd.mitchell@toddmitchell.com
URL: http://www.toddmitchell.com

Description: Executive search firm for the insurance industry. Specializes in the recruitment and placement of executive and technical personnel whose expertise is within the disciplines of underwriting, marketing, claims, and loss control.

Online Job Sources and Services

372 ■ ActuarialCrossing.com
URL: http://www.actuarialcrossing.com

Description: Offers a collection of research actuarial jobs worldwide. Focuses on the hiring needs of actuarial professionals and actuarial company in the United States.

373 ■ Actuary Jobs
URL: http://www.actuaryjob.net

Description: Features employment opportunities for actuaries.

374 ■ Actuary.com
URL: http://www.actuary.com

Description: Actuarial professionals. Focuses on serving as a major resource center for the actuarial community at large. Provides information regarding exams, seminars, actuarial news, actuarial recruiters, actuary job postings, discussion forums, actuarial schools, links to many resources, leading actuarial companies information and more.

375 ■ Great Insurance Jobs
URL: http://www.greatinsurancejobs.com

Description: Contains varied insurance positions. Job seekers may browse employee profiles, post resumes, and read descriptions of hundreds of recently-posted insurance jobs.

376 ■ InsuranceIndustryCentral.com
URL: http://www.insuranceindustrycentral.com

Description: Features insurance jobs and products to the insurance community.

377 ■ Jobs4Actuary.com
URL: http://www.jobs4actuary.com

Description: Provides users with advanced job search tools and employment resources for career advancement. Offers actuarial recruiting service and actuarial job database.

378 ■ National Insurance Recruiters Association
URL: http://www.insurancerecruiters.com

Description: Contains lists of recruiters (listed by department and line of business) and available insurance positions.

379 ■ UltimateInsuranceJobs.com
URL: http://www.ultimateinsurancejobs.com/index
    .asp

Description: Provides insurance job listings, recruiter directory, and resources. Offers job seekers the opportunity to post and edit their resumes, and employers the opportunity to search through insurance resumes.

Tradeshows

380 ■ Canadian Institute of Actuaries Meeting
Canadian Institute of Actuaries
360 Albert St., Ste. 1740
Ottawa, ON, Canada K1R 7X7
Ph: (613)236-8196
Fax: (613)233-4552
E-mail: executive.director@cia-ica.ca
URL: http://www.actuaries.ca
Frequency: Annual.

381 ■ International Association of Black Actuaries Meeting
International Association of Black Actuaries
PO Box 369
Windsor, CT 06095
Ph: (860)906-1286

Fax: (860)906-1369
E-mail: iaba@blackactuaries.org
URL: http://www.blackactuaries.org

Annual. Offers professional development workshops, discussion forums, and guest speakers covering topics in life insurance, pensions, and property/casualty insurance.

OTHER SOURCES

382 ■ American Academy of Actuaries
1850 M St. NW, Ste. 300
Washington, DC 20036
Ph: (202)223-8196
Fax: (202)872-1948
E-mail: downs@actuary.org
URL: http://www.actuary.org

Description: Ensures that the American public recognizes and benefits from the independent expertise of the actuarial profession in the formulation of public policy and the adherence of actuaries to high professional standards in discharging their responsibilities. Seeks to serve the public by providing leadership, objective expertise, and actuarial advice on risk and financial security issues. Maintains speakers' bureau.

383 ■ American Council of Life Insurers
101 Constitution Ave. NW, Ste. 700
Washington, DC 20001-2133
Ph: (202)624-2000
Free: 877-674-4659
E-mail: webadmin@acli.com
URL: http://www.acli.com

Description: Represents the interests of legal reserve life insurance companies in legislative, regulatory and judicial matters at the federal, state and municipal levels of government and at the NAIC. Member companies hold majority of the life insurance in force in the United States.

384 ■ American Society of Pension Professionals and Actuaries
4245 N Fairfax Dr., Ste. 750
Arlington, VA 22203-1648
Ph: (703)516-9300
Fax: (703)516-9308
E-mail: asppa@asppa.org
URL: http://www.asppa.org

Description: Aims to educate pension actuaries, consultants, administrators, and other benefits professionals. Seeks to preserve and enhance the private pension system as part of the development of a cohesive and coherent national retirement income policy.

385 ■ American Society of Pension Professionals and Actuaries - Greater Cincinnati
c/o Clare Peirce, Vice President
2133 Luray Ave.
Cincinnati, OH 45206-2604
Ph: (513)719-4166
Fax: (513)281-1799
E-mail: gstebbins@pencorp.com
URL: http://www.asppacincinnati.com

Description: Aims to educate pension actuaries, consultants, administrators, and other benefits professionals. Preserves and enhances the private pension system as part of the development of a cohesive and coherent national retirement income policy.

386 ■ *Career Opportunities in Science*
InfoBase Holdings Inc.
132 W 31st., 17 Fl.
New York, NY 10001-3406
Ph: (212)967-8800
Fax: (800)678-3633
E-mail: info@infobasepublishing.com
URL: http://factsonfile.infobasepublishing.com

Frequency: Latest edition 2008. **Price:** $49.50 Individuals hardcover. **Pages:** 344. **Description:** Susan Echaore-McDavid. Second edition, 2008. 332 pages. **Covers:** More than 80 jobs, such as biochemist, molecular biologist, bioinformatic specialist, pharmacologist, computer engineer, geographic information systems specialist, science teacher, forensic scientist, patent agent, as well as physicist, astronomer, chemist, zoologist, oceanographer, and geologist. **Includes:** Appendices of educational institutions, periodicals, directories, and associations.

387 ■ Casualty Actuarial Society
4350 N Fairfax Dr., Ste. 250
Arlington, VA 22203
Ph: (703)276-3100
Fax: (703)276-3108
E-mail: office@casact.org
URL: http://www.casact.org

Description: Professional society of property/casualty actuaries. Seeks to advance the body of knowledge of actuarial science applied to property, casualty and similar risk exposures, to maintain qualification standards, promote high standards of conduct and competence, and increase awareness of actuarial science. Examinations required for membership.

388 ■ Casualty Actuaries of the Mid-Atlantic Region
c/o Todd H. Dashoff, Secretary
Huggins Actuarial Services, Inc.
111 Veterans Sq., 2nd Fl.
300 N 2nd St.
Media, PA 19063
Ph: (717)238-5020
E-mail: camar.secy@gmail.com
URL: http://www.casact.org

Description: Seeks to advance the body of knowledge of actuarial science applied to property, casualty and similar risk exposures. Promotes high standards of conduct and competence, and increases awareness of actuarial science.

389 ■ Casualty Actuaries of the Southeast
c/o Keith W. Palmer, President
Pricewaterhouse Coopers
10 Tenth St., Ste 1400
Atlanta, GA 30309
Ph: (678)419-1034
Fax: (813)990-3343
E-mail: keith.w.palmer@us.pwc.com
URL: http://www.casact.org/affiliates/case

Description: Seeks to advance the body of knowledge of actuarial science applied to property, casualty and similar risk exposures. Promotes high standards of conduct and competence, and increases awareness of actuarial science.

390 ■ Conference of Consulting Actuaries
3880 Salem Lake Dr., Ste. H
Long Grove, IL 60047-5292
Ph: (847)719-6500
E-mail: conference@ccactuaries.org
URL: http://www.ccactuaries.org

Description: Full-time consulting actuaries or governmental actuaries. Develops and maintains structure and programs to reinforce, enhance, or add to members' knowledge and skills; this includes continuing education, through diverse delivery methods, for all practice areas and for consulting and business skills.

391 ■ Insurance Information Institute
110 William St.
New York, NY 10038
Ph: (212)346-5500
E-mail: members@iii.org
URL: http://www.iii.org

Description: Property and casualty insurance companies. Provides information and educational services to mass media, educational institutions, trade associations, businesses, government agencies, and the public.

392 ■ International Association of Black Actuaries
PO Box 369
Windsor, CT 06095
Ph: (860)906-1286
Fax: (860)906-1369
E-mail: iaba@blackactuaries.org
URL: http://www.blackactuaries.org

Description: Works to contribute to an increase in the number of black actuaries. Provides support to black students and professionals pursuing an actuarial career. Promotes and enhances the career development, civic growth and achievement of black actuaries. Provides networking opportunities and continuing education and development to actuarial students and professionals.

393 ■ International Association of Insurance Professionals
8023 E 63rd Pl., Ste. 540
Tulsa, OK 74133
Ph: (918)294-3700
Free: 800-766-6249
Fax: (918)294-3711
URL: http://naiw.site-ym.com

Description: Insurance industry professionals. Promotes continuing education and networking for the professional advancement of its members. Offers education programs, meetings, services, and leadership opportunities. Provides a forum to learn about other disciplines in the insurance industry.

394 ■ LOMA
2300 Windy Ridge Pkwy., Ste. 600
Atlanta, GA 30339-8443
Ph: (770)951-1770
E-mail: askloma@loma.org
URL: http://www.loma.org

Description: Life and health insurance companies and financial services in the U.S. and Canada; and overseas in 45 countries; affiliate members are firms that provide professional support to member companies. Provides research, information, training, and educational activities in areas of operations and systems, human resources, financial planning and employee development. Administers FLMI Insurance Education Program, which awards FLMI (Fellow, Life Management Institute) designation to those who complete the ten-examination program.

395 ■ Society of Actuaries
475 N Martingale Rd., Ste. 600
Schaumburg, IL 60173
Ph: (847)706-3500
Free: 888-697-3900
Fax: (847)706-3599
E-mail: feedback@soa.org
URL: http://www.soa.org

Description: Serves as a professional organization of individuals trained in the application of mathematical probabilities to the design of insurance, pension, and employee benefit programs. Sponsors series of examinations leading to designation of fellow or associate in the society. Maintains speakers' bureau; conducts educational and research programs.

SOURCES OF HELP-WANTED ADS

396 ■ *Acupressure News*
Jin Shin Do Foundation
PO Box 416
Idyllwild, CA 92549
Ph: (951)767-3393
Fax: (951)767-2200
E-mail: jinshindo@earthlink.net
URL: http://www.jinshindo.org/products.htm#newssub

Description: Annual. Provides information on body-mind acupressure, news, and main contacts in the U.S., Canada, and Europe. Features a product catalog, a class catalog and articles.

397 ■ *Chinese Medicine*
Scientific Research Publishing
PO Box 54821
Irvine, CA 92619-4821
E-mail: cm@scirp.org
URL: http://www.scirp.org/journal/cm/

Frequency: Quarterly. **Price:** $156 Individuals.
Description: Peer-reviewed journal publishing articles on the latest advancements in Chinese medicine.

EMPLOYER DIRECTORIES AND NETWORKING LISTS

398 ■ **Health Professionals Directory**
Sussex Directories Inc.
10 Market St., Ste. 750
Camana Bay
Grand Cayman, Cayman Islands
URL: http://sussexdirectories.com

399 ■ *Health & Wellness Resource Center--Alternative Health Module*
Cengage Learning Inc.
200 1st Stamford Pl., Ste. 400
Stamford, CT 06902-6753
Ph: (203)965-8600
Free: 800-354-9706
Fax: (800)487-8488
E-mail: gale.galeord@cengage.com
URL: http://www.gale.cengage.com

Includes: Focused upon alternative medicine topics this information is located in the Health Organization Directory component listings of agencies, schools and organizations; journals, newsletters, and publishers websites; hospitals, health care facilities, programs and special care. Data is derived from the Medical and Health Information Directory ((see separate entry)). **Entries include:** Contact information. Principal content of database is a medical encyclopedia, drug and herb locator, health assessment tools, medical dictionary, links to other sites, and health news and includes references to homeopathic treatments, yoga, massage therapy, etc.

HANDBOOKS AND MANUALS

400 ■ *Opportunities in Health and Medical Careers*
The McGraw-Hill Companies Inc.
PO Box 182604
Columbus, OH 43272
Ph: (212)512-2000
Free: 877-833-5524
Fax: (614)759-3749
E-mail: customer.service@mcgraw-hill.com
URL: http://www.mcgraw-hill.com

Description: I. Donald Snook, Jr. and Leo D'Orazio. 2004. $14.95 (paper). 157 pages. Covers the full range of medical and health occupations. Illustrated.

401 ■ *Opportunities in Holistic Health Care Careers*
The McGraw-Hill Companies Inc.
PO Box 182604
Columbus, OH 43272
Ph: (212)512-2000
Free: 877-833-5524
Fax: (614)759-3749
E-mail: customer.service@mcgraw-hill.com
URL: http://www.mcgraw-hill.com

Description: Gillian Tierney. 2006. $13.95 (paper). 160 pages.

ONLINE JOB SOURCES AND SERVICES

402 ■ **Acupuncture Today**
URL: http://www.acupuncturetoday.com

Description: Provides the latest news, articles and featured items that are of interest to, and can be implemented by, the acupuncture and Oriental medicine profession.

403 ■ **Acupuncture.com**
URL: http://www.acupuncture.com

Description: Serves as a gateway to Chinese medicine, health and wellness by featuring articles and research about acupuncture, resources, vendor opportunities, employment opportunities, strategic partnerships, programs and others services.

404 ■ **acupuncturistjobs.net**
URL: http://findacupuncturistjobs.jobamatic.com/a/jbb/find-jobs

Description: Helps job seekers find acupuncturist career opportunities with various companies. Assists employers and recruiters in matching qualified candidates with available positions.

405 ■ **HEALTHeCAREERS Network**
URL: http://www.healthecareers.com

Description: Career search site for jobs in all health care specialties; educational resources; visa and licensing information for relocation; interesting articles; relocation tools; links to professional organizations and general resources.

406 ■ **Medzilla.com**
URL: http://www.medzilla.com

Description: General medical website which matches employers and job hunters to their ideal employees and jobs through search capabilities. Main files include: Post Jobs, Search Resumes, Post Resumes, Search Jobs, Head Hunters, Articles, Salary Survey.

407 ■ **ProHealthJobs.com**
URL: http://prohealthjobs.com/jobboard

Description: Career resources site for the medical and health care field. Lists professional opportunities, product information, continuing education and open positions.

TRADESHOWS

408 ■ **Acupuncture Association of Colorado Conference**
Acupuncture Association of Colorado
4380 Harlan, Ste. 203
Wheat Ridge, CO 80033
Ph: (303)572-8744
Fax: (303)422-1377
E-mail: president@acucol.com
URL: http://www.acucol.com

Frequency: Annual. **Primary Exhibits:** Professional organization for acupuncture and Oriental medicine Practitioners, students, and others interested in traditional and modern acupuncture.

OTHER SOURCES

409 ■ **Accreditation Commission for Acupuncture and Oriental Medicine**
8941 Aztec Dr.
Eden Prairie, MN 55347
Ph: (952)212-2434
Fax: (301)313-0912
E-mail: coordinator@acaom.org
URL: http://www.acaom.org

Description: Acts as an independent body to evaluate first professional master's degree and first professional master's level certificate and diploma programs in acupuncture and in Oriental medicine with concentrations in both acupuncture and herbal therapy for a level of performance, integrity and quality that entitles them to the confidence of the educational community and the public they serve.

Evaluates doctoral programs in oriental medicine. Establishes accreditation criteria, arranges site visits, evaluates those programs that desire accredited status and publicly designates those programs that meet the criteria. **Members:** 73.

410 ■ Acupuncture for Veterans
119-40 Metropolitan Ave.
Concourse 102
Kew Gardens, NY 11415-2642
Ph: (718)847-7278
E-mail: contactus@acupunctureforveterans.com

Description: Aims to serve United States veterans who have served the country. Offers low-cost group acupuncture treatments for veterans, their families and 9/11 workers. Provides aid in the treatment of post traumatic stress, anxiety, depression and pain.

411 ■ American Abdominal Acupuncture Medical Association
4756 Barranca Pkwy.
Irvine, CA 92604
Ph: (949)653-1187
Fax: (949)653-1266
E-mail: sanacupuncture@gmail.com
URL: http://www.aaama.us

Description: Aims to link together acupuncture professionals interested in or are currently practicing abdominal acupuncture in the United States. Promotes the science of abdominal acupuncture and its benefits across the United States. Seeks to exchange and share knowledge among all acupuncture professionals and academics around the globe.

412 ■ American Academy of Acupuncture and Oriental Medicine
1925 W County Rd. B2
Roseville, MN 55113
Ph: (651)631-0204
Fax: (651)631-0361
E-mail: info@aaaom.edu
URL: http://www.aaaom.edu

Description: Seeks to advance acupuncture and oriental medicine.

413 ■ American Academy of Medical Acupuncture
1970 E Grand Ave., Ste. 330
El Segundo, CA 90245
Ph: (310)364-0193
Fax: (310)364-0196
E-mail: qigongdoc@tpsmc.com
URL: http://www.medicalacupuncture.org

Description: Professional society of physicians and osteopaths who utilize acupuncture in their practices. Provides ongoing training and information related to the Chinese practice of puncturing the body at specific points to cure disease or relieve pain. Offers educational and research programs.

414 ■ American Association of Acupuncture and Oriental Medicine
9650 Rockville Pike
Bethesda, MD 20814
Free: 866-455-7999
Fax: (301)634-7099
E-mail: info@aaaomonline.org
URL: http://www.aaaomonline.org

Description: Professional acupuncturists and Oriental Medicine Practitioners. Seeks to: elevate the standards of education and practice of acupuncture and oriental medicine; establish laws governing acupuncture; provide a forum to share information on acupuncture techniques; increase public awareness of acupuncture; support research in the field. Conducts educational programs; compiles statistics. Operates speakers' bureau. **Members:** 2,600.

415 ■ American Board of Oriental Reproductive Medicine
910 Hampshire Rd., Ste. A
Westlake Village, CA 91361

Ph: (805)497-1335
E-mail: info@aborm.org
URL: http://www.aborm.org

Description: Promotes education and research in integrative reproductive medicine. Advances knowledge of integrated fertility treatment methods including acupuncture, herbal therapy and standardized biomedical research. Offers certification among practitioners in oriental medicine in the field of reproductive health.

416 ■ American Manual Medicine Association
2040 Raybrook SE, Ste. 103
Grand Rapids, MI 49546
Free: 888-375-7245
Fax: (616)575-9066
URL: http://www.americanmanualmedicine.com

Description: Promotes manual therapy as an allied health care profession. Seeks to advance the practice of manual therapy and manual acupuncture through professional standards, education and testing. Offers training to clinicians in order for them to provide quality medical care to patients. Provides National Board Certification Diplomate status to qualified members.

417 ■ California State Oriental Medical Association
PO Box 2410
San Anselmo, CA 94979
Free: 800-477-4564
Fax: (415)357-1920
E-mail: info@csomaonline.org
URL: http://www.csomaonline.org

Description: Offers free referrals to over 800 California based member health professionals who practice Acupuncture and Oriental Medicine.

418 ■ *Career Opportunities in Health Care*
InfoBase Holdings Inc.
132 W 31st., 17 Fl.
New York, NY 10001-3406
Ph: (212)967-8800
Fax: (800)678-3633
E-mail: info@infobasepublishing.com
URL: http://www.ferguson.infobasepublishing.com

Description: Shelly Field. 2007. Third edition. $49.50. 304 pages. **Includes:** Appendices provide lists of educational institutions, periodicals, directories, associations, and unions. Appendices provide lists of educational institutions, periodicals, directories, associations, and unions.

419 ■ Community Acupuncture Network
Working Class Acupuncture
3526 NE 57th Ave.
Portland, OR 97213
Ph: (503)335-9440
E-mail: info@workingclassacupuncture.org

Description: Supports the practice of acupuncture in community settings as a sustainable and practical approach in promoting the health of the public. Strives to make acupuncture more affordable and accessible. Provides support and information on community acupuncture practice.

420 ■ Council for Acupuncture Research and Education
3448 Horseshoe Bend Rd.
Charlottesville, VA 22901
E-mail: info@councilforacupuncture.org
URL: http://www.councilforacupuncture.com

Description: Promotes comprehensive integration of acupuncture treatment into the American healthcare system. Develops an evidence-based scientific model of the acupuncture system for a Western audience.

421 ■ Council of Chiropractic Acupuncture
291 Main Rd.
Holden, ME 04429

Ph: (207)989-0000
URL: http://councilofchiropracticacupuncture.org

Description: Aims to provide excellent educational opportunities to elevate the quality of care, life and practice of chiropractic acupuncture. Serves as a platform for professional communication regarding the practice of acupuncture in the chiropractic profession.

422 ■ Council of Colleges of Acupuncture and Oriental Medicine
600 Wyndhurst Ave., Ste. 112
Baltimore, MD 21210
Ph: (410)464-6040
Fax: (410)464-6042
E-mail: ccaomcnt@comcast.net
URL: http://www.ccaom.org

Description: Represents acupuncture and oriental medicine colleges. Aims to advance the status of acupuncture and oriental medicine through educational programs. Works to provide high-quality classroom and clinical instruction. Promotes the improvement of research and teaching methods. **Members:** 51.

423 ■ *Health-Care Careers for the 21st Century*
JIST Publishing
875 Montreal Way
Saint Paul, MN 55102-4245
Ph: (317)613-4200
Free: 800-648-5478
Fax: (800)328-4564
E-mail: info@jist.com
URL: http://www.jist.com

Price: $9.95 Individuals Softcover. **Pages:** 448. **Covers:** Jobs for health care professionals and career opportunities for those pursuing a health-related career, organized into 80 careers in five groups. **Publication includes:** Appendixes listing job source resources and Web sites for health organizations.

424 ■ International Veterinary Acupuncture Society
1730 S College Ave., Ste. 301
Fort Collins, CO 80525
Ph: (970)266-0666
Fax: (970)266-0777
E-mail: office@ivas.org
URL: http://www.ivas.org

Description: Veterinarians and veterinary students. Encourages knowledge and research of the philosophy, technique, and practice of veterinary acupuncture. Fosters high standards in the field; promotes scientific investigation. Accumulates resources for scientific research and education; collects data concerning clinical and research cases where animals have been treated with acupuncture; disseminates information to veterinary students, practitioners, other scientific groups, and the public. Offers 120-contact hour basic veterinary acupuncture course; administers certification examination; also offers advanced traditional Chinese herbal veterinary medicine.

425 ■ National Certification Commission for Acupuncture and Oriental Medicine
76 S Laura St., Ste. 1290
Jacksonville, FL 32202
Ph: (904)598-1005
Fax: (904)598-5001
E-mail: info@nccaom.org
URL: http://www.nccaom.org

Description: Serves as national certification agency for practitioners of acupuncture, Chinese herbology, and Asian bodywork therapy in the United States. Establishes and maintains standards of competence for the safe and effective practice of Oriental medicine; to evaluate an applicant's qualifications in relation to these established standards through the administration of national board examinations; to certify practitioners who meet these standards. Acts as a consultant to state agencies in regulation, certification, and licensing of the practice of acupuncture and Oriental medicine. **Members:** 13,000.

426 ■ Society for Acupuncture Research
130 Cloverhurst Ct.
Winston-Salem, NC 27103-9503

Ph: (336)306-6888
E-mail: info@acupunctureresearch.org
URL: http://www.acupunctureresearch.org

Description: Seeks to elevate the standards of education and practice of acupuncture and Oriental medicine. Promotes, advances and disseminates scientific inquiry into Oriental medicine systems, which include acupuncture, herbal therapy and other modalities. Stimulates scholarship in acupuncture and Oriental medicine.

SOURCES OF HELP-WANTED ADS

427 ■ OfficePRO
Stratton Publishing and Marketing Inc.
5285 Shawnee Rd., Ste. 510
Alexandria, VA 22312-2334
Ph: (703)914-9200
Fax: (703)914-6777
E-mail: pubpros@strattonpub.com
URL: http://www.iaap-hq.org/publications/officepro

Frequency: 7/yr. **Price:** $25 Individuals; $40 Individuals two years; $57 Individuals three years; $59 Individuals international; $109 Individuals international, two years. **Description:** Magazine for administrative assistants, office managers, and secretaries featuring information on trends in business, technology, career development, and management.

HANDBOOKS AND MANUALS

428 ■ Administrative Assistant's and Secretary's Handbook
AMACOM Publishing
c/o American Management Association
1601 Broadway
New York, NY 10019-7434
Ph: (212)586-8100
Free: 800-714-6395
Fax: (518)891-0368
E-mail: pubs_cust_serv@amanet.org
URL: http://www.amacombooks.org

Description: James Stroman, Kevin Wilson, and Jennifer Wauson. 2008. $34.95 (hardback). 592 pages. Provides insights and procedures on administrative duties and high-tech office activities from using the phone and making travel arrangements to keyboarding skills and deciphering legal documents.

429 ■ Administrative Assistant's Update
MPL Communications Inc.
133 Richmond St. W
Ste. 700
Toronto, ON, Canada M5H 3M8
Ph: (416)869-1177
Free: 800-804-8846
Fax: (416)869-0456
E-mail: investors@mplcomm.com
URL: http://www.adviceforinvestors.com

Frequency: Monthly. **Price:** $189 Individuals Annual. **Pages:** 8.

430 ■ Basic Administrative Law for Paralegals
Wolters Kluwer Law and Business
76 9th Ave., 7th Fl.
New York, NY 10011-4962
Ph: (212)771-0600

Free: 800-234-1660
Fax: (800)901-9075
URL: http://www.wolterskluwerlb.com

Description: Anne Adams. Fourth edition, 2009. $89.95. 384 pages. Explore the basics of Administrative Law.

431 ■ The Corporate Secretary
Society of Corporate Secretaries and Governance Professionals
65 Broadway, Ste. 605-606
New York, NY 10006
Ph: (212)430 6866
Fax: (212)425-7589
E-mail: research@governanceprofessionals.org
URLs: http://www.corporatesecretary.com; http://www.governanceprofessionals.org/society/Corporate_Secretary_magazine.asp?SnID=2

Frequency: Monthly. **Price:** $250 Individuals; $4.81 per week. **Description:** Provides an overview of the duties and responsibilities of the corporate secretarial function.

432 ■ Definitive Personal Assistant and Secretarial Handbook
Kogan Page Publishers
1518 Walnut St., Ste. 1100
Philadelphia, PA 19102
Ph: (215)928-9112
Fax: (215)928-9113
E-mail: info@koganpage.com
URL: http://www.koganpageusa.com

Description: Sue France. 2009. $24.95 (paper). 256 pages. Serves as a guide for management assistants, personal assistants, secretaries, and executive assistants. Discusses the administrative roles and the necessary skills for secretaries and personal assistants including: relationship management, communication, confidence, the secrets of body language, listening and questioning skills, coping with pressure and stress, dealing with difficult people, time management, and personal organization.

433 ■ Great Jobs for History Majors
The McGraw-Hill Companies Inc.
PO Box 182604
Columbus, OH 43272
Ph: (212)512-2000
Free: 877-833-5524
Fax: (614)759-3749
E-mail: customer.service@mcgraw-hill.com
URL: http://www.mcgraw-hill.com

Description: Julie DeGalan and Stephen Lambert. 2007. $16.95 (paper). 192 pages.

434 ■ OfficePro
Stratton Publishing and Marketing Inc.
5285 Shawnee Rd., Ste. 510
Alexandria, VA 22312-2334
Ph: (703)914-9200

Fax: (703)914-6777
E-mail: pubpros@strattonpub.com
URL: http://www.strattonpub.com

Description: Nine times a year. $25.00 per year. Provides statistics and other information about secretaries and office trends. Formerly *Secretary*.

435 ■ Opportunities in Administrative Assistant Careers
The McGraw-Hill Companies Inc.
PO Box 182604
Columbus, OH 43272
Ph: (212)512-2000
Free: 877-833-5524
Fax: (614)759-3749
E-mail: customer.service@mcgraw-hill.com
URL: http://www.mcgraw-hill.com

Description: Blanche Ettinger. 2007. $13.95. 160 pages. Provides a complete overview of the job possibilities, salary figures and experience required to become an administrative assistant.

EMPLOYMENT AGENCIES AND SEARCH FIRMS

436 ■ Access Staffing
360 Lexington Ave., 8th Fl.
New York, NY 10017
Ph: (212)687-5440
Fax: (212)557-2544
URL: http://www.accessstaffingco.com

Description: Serves as a staffing firm covering accounting/financial, advertising, bilingual Japanese, creative, event planning, fashion/retail, healthcare/human services, human resources, information technology, insurance, legal, light industrial, and office support.

437 ■ Action Employment Services
121 SW Morrison St., Ste. 425
Portland, OR 97204
Ph: (503)275-9011
Free: 866-208-1643
Fax: (503)241-8772
E-mail: inquiry@actionemployment.net
URL: http://www.actionemployment.net

Description: Provides administrative, office, accounting, and human resource positions.

438 ■ Actuary Resources
115 N Castle Heights Ave., Ste. 202
Lebanon, TN 37087-2768
Ph: (615)360-5171
Fax: (615)360-5173
E-mail: info@actuaryresources.org
URL: http://www.actuaryresources.org

Description: Provides staffing services to several different types of industries. Offers a free screening service to clients.

439 ■ Apple One Employment Services
18538 Hawthorne Blvd.
Torrance, CA 90504
Ph: (310)370-0708
Free: 800-564-5644
E-mail: torrance-ca@appleone.com
URL: http://www.appleone.com

Description: Employment agency. Additional offices in Anaheim, Oakland, Cerritos, San Francisco, Manhattan Beach, and Glendale.

440 ■ ATR Professional
1230 Oakmead Pkwy., Ste. 110
Sunnyvale, CA 94085
Ph: (408)328-8000
E-mail: corporate@atr1.com
URL: http://www.atr-professional.com

Description: Serves as an executive search firm specializing in the placement of administrative, clerical, and customer service, HR, and marketing personnel.

441 ■ Capitol Staffing Inc.
460 Briarwood Dr., Briarwood 1 Bldg., Ste. 110
Jackson, MS 39206
Ph: (601)957-1755
Fax: (601)957-3880
E-mail: info@capitolstaffing.com
URL: http://www.capitolstaffing.com

Description: Personnel consultancy that focuses on office administration, management, sales, accounting, medical, information technology, accounting, and engineering/technical fields. Industries served: insurance, finance, medical, communications, investment, industry, and small businesses.

442 ■ Career Advocates International
1539 Ave. A
Katy, TX 77493
Ph: (281)371-3917
E-mail: hank@careeradvocates.org
URL: http://www.careeradvocates.org

Description: Provides permanent placement and temporary staffing for executive and staff level positions. Specializes in multiple niches including: sales and marketing, accounting and financial services, banking, communications, human resources, chemicals, oil and gas, medical and dental, legal, information technology, energy, technology, engineering, manufacturing, construction, and light industrial.

443 ■ Career Center, Inc.
2184 Morris Ave.
Union, NJ 07083
Ph: (908)687-1812
Free: 800-227-3379
E-mail: career@careercenterinc.com
URL: http://www.careercenterinc.com

Description: Employment agency.

444 ■ Express Professional Staffing
8516 NW Expressway
Oklahoma City, OK 73162
Ph: (405)840-5000
Free: 800-222-4057
E-mail: onlineinfo@expresspros.com
URL: http://www.expresspros.com/us

Description: Temporary help service. Also provides some permanent placements. Several locations across the United States as well as international offices.

445 ■ The Linde Group, Inc.
301 Sovereign Ct.
Ballwin, MO 63021
Ph: (636)207-1118
Fax: (636)207-1371
E-mail: lincoln@thelindegroup.com
URL: http://www.thelindegroup.com

Description: Permanent placement and temporary help service.

446 ■ Nesco Inc.
6140 Parkland Blvd., Ste. 110
Mayfield Heights, OH 44124-6106
Ph: (440)461-6000
Fax: (440)449-3111
E-mail: corporate@nescoresource.com
URL: http://www.nescoresource.com

Description: Offers staffing and consulting solutions in the fields of engineering, information technology, accounting and finance, manufacturing and distribution, and administrative and customer services.

447 ■ OfficeTeam.com
2884 Sand Hill Rd.
Menlo Park, CA 94025
Free: 800-804-8367
URL: http://www.officeteam.com

Description: Serves as a specialized temporary staffing service for administrative professionals including executive assistant, administrative assistant, office manager, project coordinator, receptionist, human resource assistant, marketing assistant, customer service representative, and data entry specialist.

448 ■ Phillip's Personnel/Phillip's Temps
1675 Broadway, Ste. 2410
Denver, CO 80204
Ph: (303)893-1850
Fax: (303)893-0639
E-mail: info@phillipspersonnel.com
URL: http://www.phillipspersonnel.com

Description: Personnel recruiting and staffing consultants in: accounting and finance, management information systems, sales and marketing, engineering, administration, and general and executive management. Industries served: telecommunications, distribution, financial services, and general business.

449 ■ Pro Staff
7301 N State Hwy. 161, Ste. 110
Irving, TX 75039
Ph: (972)831-1200
Fax: (972)831-0013
E-mail: dfw@prostaff.com
URL: http://www.prostaff.com

Description: Administrative and light industrial staffing firm.

450 ■ Sullivan and Cogliano
230 2nd Ave.
Waltham, MA 02451
Ph: (781)890-7890
Fax: (781)906-7801
E-mail: jobs@sullivancogliano.com
URL: http://www.sullivancogliano.com

Description: Technical staffing firm.

ONLINE JOB SOURCES AND SERVICES

451 ■ AdminAssistantJobs.com
URL: http://www.adminassistantjobs.com

Description: Features job opportunities and resume searching and posting for administrative assistants.

452 ■ AdminCareers.com
URL: http://www.admincareers.com

Description: Serves as a niche job board for administrative related jobs, including administrative assistants, receptionists, secretaries, office managers, executive assistants and all office professionals.

453 ■ AdminCrossing.com
URL: http://www.admincrossing.com

Description: Offers a wide database of administrative job openings worldwide. Includes openings from Fortune 500 and Fortune 1000 companies.

454 ■ AdministrativeCareers.com
URL: http://www.administrativecareers.com

Description: Serves as a niche job board for administrative jobs and resumes. Allows postings and searching of resumes for first-time and returning job seekers and employers.

455 ■ Office Worker Jobs
URL: http://www.officeworkerjobs.com

Description: Features office jobs in various industries. Features full-time, temporary, and part-time vacancies.

TRADESHOWS

456 ■ Association of Executive and Administrative Professionals Annual Conference
Association of Executive and Administrative Professionals
900 S Washington St., Ste. G-13
Falls Church, VA 22046
Ph: (703)237-8616
Fax: (703)533-1153
E-mail: headquarters@theaeap.com
URL: http://www.theaeap.com

Frequency: Annual. Features guest speakers and provides networking opportunities among peers to encourage professional development.

457 ■ Society of Corporate Secretaries and Governance Professionals Annual Conference
Society of Corporate Secretaries and Governance Professionals
240 W 35th St., Ste. 400
New York, NY 10001-2506
Ph: (212)681-2000
Fax: (212)681-2005
E-mail: research@governanceprofessionals.org
URL: http://www.governanceprofessionals.org

Frequency: Annual. **Primary Exhibits:** Exhibits relating to corporate secretaries.

OTHER SOURCES

458 ■ Association of Executive and Administrative Professionals
900 S Washington St., Ste. G-13
Falls Church, VA 22046
Ph: (703)237-8616
Fax: (703)533-1153
E-mail: headquarters@theaeap.com
URL: http://www.theaeap.com

Description: Represents professionals dedicated to promoting the careers of those who, are associated with the leaders of the business world. Assists members in achieving their career goals by keeping them informed of advances and changes in professional practice and technology. Offers a variety of educational programs and promotes the free exchange of ideas among peers to enhance job satisfaction and encourage professional development.

459 ■ Society of Corporate Secretaries and Governance Professionals
240 W 35th St., Ste. 400
New York, NY 10001-2506
Ph: (212)681-2000
Fax: (212)681-2005
E-mail: research@governanceprofessionals.org
URL: http://www.governanceprofessionals.org

Description: Corporate secretaries, assistant secretaries, officers and executives of corporations and others interested in corporate practices and procedures. Conducts surveys and research. Sponsors educational programs for members. Maintains a central information and reference service.

Sources of Help-Wanted Ads

460 ■ Adoptalk
North American Council on Adoptable Children
970 Raymond Ave., Ste. 106
Saint Paul, MN 55114
Ph: (651)644-3036
Fax: (651)644-9848
E-mail: info@nacac.org
URL: http://www.nacac.org
Description: Quarterly. Provides legal and activity updates concerning adoption.

461 ■ Adoption
National Adoption Center
1500 Walnut St., Ste. 701
Philadelphia, PA 19102
Ph: (215)735-9988
Free: 800-TO-ADOPT
Fax: (215)735-9410
E-mail: kmullner@nacenter.adopt.org
URL: http://www.adopt.org
Description: Semiannual. Informs on activities of the center. Recurring features include interviews, news of research, and a calendar of events.

462 ■ Adoption Advocate
National Council for Adoption
225 N Washington St.
Alexandria, VA 22314-2561
Ph: (703)299-6633
Fax: (703)299-6004
E-mail: ncfa@adoptioncouncil.org
URL: http://www.adoptioncouncil.org
Description: Monthly. Reviews news and developments concerning adoption programs and services. Provides legislative updates, research reports, and Council news.

463 ■ National Adoption Reports
National Council for Adoption
225 N Washington St.
Alexandria, VA 22314-2561
Ph: (703)299-6633
Fax: (703)299-6004
E-mail: ncfa@adoptioncouncil.org
URL: http://www.adoptioncouncil.org
Description: Quarterly. Provides information on current issues, legislation, events, practices, and policies for adoption. Recurring features include news of research, a calendar of events, reports of meetings, book reviews, and notices of publications available.

Employer Directories and Networking Lists

464 ■ Standards For Supervised Visitation Practice
Supervised Visitation Network
3955 Riverside Ave.
Jacksonville, FL 32205

Ph: (904)419-7861
Fax: (904)239-5888
E-mail: info@svnetwork.net
URL: http://www.svnetwork.net
Covers: Forums for networking and sharing of information between supervised child access providers and other professionals involved in providing support to children and parents who are not living together.

Online Job Sources and Services

465 ■ Adoption Forums
URL: http://forums.adoption.com
Description: Includes job postings for adoption professionals.

Tradeshows

466 ■ American Adoption Congress Conference
American Adoption Congress
1025 Connecticut Ave.
Ste. 1012
Washington, DC 20036
Ph: (202)483-3399
E-mail: pdj27@aol.com
URL: http://www.americanadoptioncongress.org/
Frequency: Annual. **Primary Exhibits:** Adopted persons, birthparents, and adoptive parents; members of related organizations devoted to leadership in adoption reform.

467 ■ North American Council on Adoptable Children Conference
North American Council on Adoptable Children
970 Raymond Ave., Ste. 106
Saint Paul, MN 55114
Ph: (651)644-3036
Fax: (651)644-9848
E-mail: info@nacac.org
URL: http://www.nacac.org
Frequency: Annual. **Primary Exhibits:** Exhibits related to adoption and post-adoption.

Other Sources

468 ■ Adoptee-Birthparent Support Network
6439 Woodridge Rd.
Alexandria, VA 22312-1336
Ph: (301)442-9106
E-mail: absnmail@verizon.net
URL: http://adopteebirthparentsupportnetwork.org
Description: Adoptees, adoptive parents, birthparents (biological parents), and siblings; social workers, and adoption professionals. Seeks to provide support, information, and education to members and

help them come to terms with the effects of adoption. Provides search assistance to adoptees and birthparents who wish to locate their biological relatives. Administers public outreach and education programs; conducts legislative efforts. **Members:** 200.

469 ■ Adoption Information Services
1840 Old Nocross Rd., Ste. 400
Lawrenceville, GA 30044
Ph: (770)339-7236
Fax: (770)456-5961
E-mail: aisteam@adoptioninfosvcs.com
URL: http://www.adoptioninfosvcs.com
Description: Adoptive parents, adoptees, birth parents. Dedicated to providing information regarding adoption, long term foster care opportunities and search information. Sponsors adoption information events. **Members:** 25.

470 ■ American Adoption Congress
228 Monticello Ave.
Durham, NC 27707
Ph: (202)483-3399
E-mail: westbenn@cox.net
URL: http://www.americanadoptioncongress.org
Description: Adopted persons, birthparents, and adoptive parents; members of related organizations devoted to leadership in adoption reform. Furthers information on adoptions and related social-psychological issues in the U.S. by study, research, teaching, and conferences; collect, publish, and disseminate information; acts as a national clearinghouse and public information center. Develops alternative model plans for adoption; conducts regional educational conferences; provides research referrals to adoption-related services.

471 ■ Association of Administrators of the Interstate Compact on the Placement of Children
American Public Human Services Association
1133 19th St. NW, Ste. 400
Washington, DC 20036
Ph: (202)682-0100
Fax: (202)289-6555
E-mail: icpcinbox@aphsa.org
URL: http://icpc.aphsa.org
Description: State public social service agency personnel who have been appointed compact administrators and who are responsible for the operation of the Interstate Compact on the Placement of Children. (ICPC is a uniform law that has been enacted in 50 states, the District of Columbia, and the Virgin Islands. Governs the placement of children across state lines for foster care and pre-adoptive placement by legally establishing the extension of responsibility and jurisdiction of the sending party, and the concomitant responsibility of the receiving state.) Enhances arrangements for the delivery of protective and supportive services in situations having interjurisdictional considerations. Provides forum for cooperation, consultation, and exchange of information among the states in relation

to the placement of children from one state to another. Compiles statistics. **Members:** 52.

472 ■ Foster Care to Success
21351 Gentry Dr., Ste. 130
Sterling, VA 20166
Ph: (571)203-0270
Fax: (571)203-0273
E-mail: info@fc2success.org
URL: http://www.fc2success.org

Description: Orphaned and abandoned youth; volunteers and contributors. Assists orphaned, abandoned, and foster-care youth by providing guidance, support, friendship, and emergency help that is seldom available to children raised outside of the traditional family setting. Advocates orphaned and abandoned youth rights nationwide; administers project that develops public policy initiatives. Offers independent living support services and volunteer referral services. Sponsors Project Bridge Program, a community-based volunteer support network that assists youth in their transition from the child welfare system to independent young adulthood. Adult volunteers guide and assist orphans in goal planning, independent living and life skills, career development, job search, maintaining employment, and recreation. Provides research services. Maintains speakers' bureau, resource center, and orphan hall of fame.

473 ■ National Adoption Center
1500 Walnut St., Ste. 701
Philadelphia, PA 19102
Ph: (215)735-9988

Free: 800-TO-ADOPT
Fax: (215)735-9410
E-mail: kmullner@nacenter.adopt.org
URL: http://www.adopt.org

Description: Expands adoption opportunities for children throughout the United States, particularly the adoption of children with special needs and children from minority cultures, through public awareness and information and referral with families nationwide. Pictures and descriptions of waiting children are highlighted on Website.

474 ■ National Council for Adoption
225 N Washington St.
Alexandria, VA 22314-2561
Ph: (703)299-6633
Fax: (703)299-6004
E-mail: ncfa@adoptioncouncil.org
URL: http://www.adoptioncouncil.org

Description: Represents voluntary agencies, adoptive parents, adoptees, and birthparents. Works to protect the institution of adoption and ensure the confidentiality of all involved in the adoption process. Promotes appropriate adoption practice with legislators, policymakers, human service agencies and staff, and the public. Strives for the regulation of all adoptions to ensure the protection of birthparents, children, and adoptive parents. Serves as an information clearinghouse; provides technical assistance. Conducts research programs; monitors state and national legislation affecting adoption and maternity services. Maintains hall of fame. Compiles statistics. Operates speakers' bureau; compiles statistics.

475 ■ North American Council on Adoptable Children
970 Raymond Ave., Ste. 106
Saint Paul, MN 55114
Ph: (651)644-3036
Fax: (651)644-9848
E-mail: info@nacac.org
URL: http://www.nacac.org

Description: Members of citizen adoption groups (composed primarily of adoptive parents of "special needs" children) and other individuals from judicial, child welfare, and legislative areas. Advocates the right of every child to a permanent, loving home. Provides direct assistance to local and state advocacy efforts; acts as a clearinghouse for adoption information; liaises with other adoption organizations. Sponsors an annual national training conference. Also sponsors Adoption Awareness Month. Conducts extensive education and outreach through the media and pre- and post-adoptive support programs. Provides resources for local advocacy programs.

476 ■ Stars of David International
3175 Commercial Ave., Ste. 100
Northbrook, IL 60062-1915
Free: 800-STAR-349
E-mail: statsofdavid@aol.com
URL: http://www.starsofdavid.org

Description: Works as a Jewish adoption information and support network. Provides a network of support, adoption information and education to prospective parents, adoptive families, adult adoptees, birth families, and the Jewish community.

Sources of Help-Wanted Ads

477 ■ *Community Colleges Journal*
American Association of Community Colleges
1 Dupont Cir. NW, Ste. 410
Washington, DC 20036-1145
Ph: (202)728-0200
Fax: (202)833-2467
E-mail: aaccpub@pmds.com
URL: http://www.aacc.nche.edu/Publications/CCJ/
    Pages/default.aspx
Frequency: 6/yr. Price: $36 Nonmembers; $36
Members. Description: Educational magazine.

478 ■ *Tech Directions: Linking Education to Careers*
Prakken Publications Inc.
2851 Boardwalk Dr.
Ann Arbor, MI 48104
Ph: (734)975-2800
Free: 800-530-9673
Fax: (734)975-2787
E-mail: tdedit@techdirections.com
URL: http://www.techdirections.com

Frequency: Monthly; (Aug. through May). Price: $30
Individuals U.S.; $47 Institutions; $50 Other
countries; $100 Individuals domestic. Description:
Magazine covering issues, programs, and projects in
industrial education, technology education, trade and
industry, and vocational-technical career education.
Articles are geared for teacher and administrator use
and reference from elementary school through post-
secondary levels.

Employer Directories and Networking Lists

479 ■ *Career College & Technology School Databook*
Chronicle Guidance Publications Inc.
66 Aurora St.
Moravia, NY 13118-3569
Ph: (315)497-0330
Free: 800-899-0454
Fax: (315)497-0339
E-mail: CustomerService@ChronicleGuidance.com
URL: http://www.chronicleguidance.com

Frequency: Annual; latest edition 2009-2010. Price:
$26.73 Individuals Softbound. Pages: 148. Covers:
Over 940 programs of study offered by more than
1,580 vocational schools. Includes: An appendix
lists some additional details, including dates
programs begin for some schools. Entries include:
School name, city and ZIP code, phone, programs
offered, admissions requirements, costs, enrollment,
financial aid programs, year established, and student
services. Arrangement: Geographical. Indexes:
Vocation/course.

480 ■ *Chronicle Two-Year College Databook*
Chronicle Guidance Publications Inc.
66 Aurora St.
Moravia, NY 13118-3569
Ph: (315)497-0330
Free: 800-899-0454
Fax: (315)497-0339
E-mail: CustomerService@ChronicleGuidance.com
URL: http://www.chronicleguidance.com

Frequency: Annual; latest edition 2009-2010. Price:
$26.74 Individuals softbound. Pages: 478. Covers:
Over 954 associate, certificate, occupational, and
transfer programs offered by more than 2,509 technical institutes, two-year colleges, and universities in
the United States. Includes: College admissions
information. Entries include: College charts section
gives college name, address, phone; accreditation,
enrollment, admissions, costs, financial aid; accrediting associations' names, addresses, and phone
numbers. Arrangement: Part I is classified by college major; part II is geographical. Indexes: College
name.

481 ■ *National Faculty Directory*
Cengage Learning Inc.
200 1st Stamford Pl., Ste. 400
Stamford, CT 06902-6753
Ph: (203)965-8600
Free: 800-354-9706
Fax: (800)487-8488
E-mail: investors@cengage.com
URL: http://www.gale.cengage.com

Frequency: Annual; Latest edition 43rd; October,
2011. Price: $1,391 Individuals. Covers: More than
900,000 (60,000 more in supplement) teaching
faculty members at over 4,600 junior colleges, colleges, and universities in the United States and those
in Canada that give instruction in English. Includes:
Geographical list of schools covered. Entries
include: Name, department name, institution, address, and phone and fax numbers. Directory
combines main edition and supplement. Arrangement: Alphabetical.

482 ■ *School Guide*
School Guide Publications
210 North Ave.
New Rochelle, NY 10801
Ph: (914)632-7771
Free: 800-433-7771
E-mail: mridder@schoolguides.com
URL: http://distance.schoolguides.com

Frequency: Annual; Latest edition 2008. Pages:
290. Covers: Over 3,000 colleges, vocational
schools, and nursing schools in the United States.
Entries include: Institution name, address, phone,
courses offered, degrees awarded. Arrangement:
Classified by type of institution, then geographical.
Indexes: Subject.

Handbooks and Manuals

483 ■ *Building Professional Pride in Literacy: A Dialogical Guide to Professional Development for Practitioners of Adult Literacy and Basic Education*
Description: B. Allan Quigley. 2006. $38. 244 pages.
Professional development for adult literacy
practitioners.

484 ■ *Employment Opportunities in Education*
Delmar Cengage Learning
5 Maxwell Dr.
Clifton Park, NY 12065
Free: 800-648-7450
E-mail: esales@cengage.com
URL: http://www.delmarlearning.com/about/contact
    .aspx
Description: Jeanne Machado. 2006. $40.95.
Provides current information on education-related
jobs and opportunities. Includes information on job
locations, qualifications, cover letters, resumes,
interview tips, checklists and forms that aid in seek-
ing, holding or advancing a career in education.

485 ■ *Ferguson Career Coach: Managing Your Career in Education*
InfoBase Holdings Inc.
132 W 31st., 17 Fl.
New York, NY 10001-3406
Ph: (212)967-8800
Fax: (800)678-3633
E-mail: info@infobasepublishing.com
URL: http://www.ferguson.infobasepublishing.com
Description: Shelly Field. 2008. $39.95 (hardcover).
272 pages. Contains tips on achieving career suc-
cess in the field of education. Provides students with
advice on making contacts, interviewing, and career
strategies.

486 ■ *Opportunities in Adult Education Careers*
McGraw-Hill Professional
PO Box 182604
Columbus, OH 43272
Ph: (877)833-5524
Free: 800-262-4729
Fax: (614)759-3749
E-mail: pbg.ecommerce_custserv@mcgraw-hill.com
URL: http://www.mhprofessional.com/product.php
    ?isbn=0071493069
Description: Blythe Camenson. 2008. $14.95
(paperback). 160 pages. Provides a complete
overview of the job possibilities, salary figures, and
experience required to enter the field of adult educa-
tion.

Tradeshows

487 ■ *Missouri Association for Career and Technical Education Meeting*
Missouri Association for Career and Technical
Education
213 E Capitol Ave.
Jefferson City, MO 65102

Ph: (573)634-7366
Fax: (573)635-6258
E-mail: info@mo-acte.org
URL: http://www.mo-acte.org
Frequency: Annual. **Primary Exhibits:** Promotes the development of vocational-technical education within the state of Missouri; exhibits of interest to vocational teachers, administrators, and counselors.

REFERENCE WORKS

488 ■ Expert Resumes for Teachers and Educators
JIST Publishing
875 Montreal Way
Saint Paul, MN 55102-4245
Ph: (317)613-4200
Free: 800-648-5478
Fax: (800)328-4564
E-mail: info@jist.com
URL: http://www.jist.com
Description: Louise M. Kursmark and Wendy Enelow. 2011. $17.95 (softcover). 336 pages. Gives job seekers strategies and ideas needed to craft outstanding resumes and cover letters. Includes samples of cover letters and resumes, an appendix of online career and job search resources, and tips on winning interviews.

OTHER SOURCES

489 ■ American Association for Adult and Continuing Education
10111 Martin Luther King, Jr. Hwy., Ste. 200C
Bowie, MD 20720
Ph: (301)459-6261
Fax: (301)459-6241
E-mail: office@aaace.org
URL: http://www.aaace.org
Description: Provides leadership in advancing adult education as a lifelong learning process. Serves as a central forum for a wide variety of adult and continuing education special interest groups. Works to stimulate local, state, and regional adult continuing education efforts; encourages mutual cooperation and support; monitors proposed legislation and offers testimony to congress.

490 ■ American Association of Blind Teachers
c/o John Buckley
1025 Ree Way
Knoxville, TN 37909
Ph: (865)692-4888
E-mail: johnbuckley25@comcast.net
URL: http://www.blindteachers.net
Description: Public school teachers, teachers of the visually impaired, college and university professors, and teachers in residential schools for the blind. Promotes employment and professional goals of blind persons entering the teaching profession or those established in their respective teaching fields. Serves as a vehicle for the dissemination of information and the exchange of ideas addressing special problems of members.

491 ■ American Association of Community Colleges
1 Dupont Cir. NW, Ste. 410
Washington, DC 20036-1145
Ph: (202)728-0200
Fax: (202)833-2467
E-mail: aaccpub@pmds.com
URL: http://www.aacc.nche.edu
Description: Community colleges; individual associates interested in community college development; corporate, educational, foundation, and international associate members. Office of Federal Relations monitors federal educational programming and legislation. Compiles statistics through data collection

and policy analysis. Conducts seminars and professional training programs.

492 ■ American Association for Women in Community Colleges
PO Box 3098
Gaithersburg, MD 20885
Ph: (301)442-3374
E-mail: info@aawccnatl.org
URL: http://www.aawccnatl.org
Description: Women faculty members, administrators, staff members, students, and trustees of community colleges. Objectives are to: develop communication and disseminate information among women in community, junior, and technical colleges; encourage educational program development; obtain grants for educational projects for community college women. Disseminates information on women's issues and programs. Conducts regional and state professional development workshops and forums. Recognizes model programs that assist women in community colleges. An affiliate council of the American Association of Community Colleges.

493 ■ American Federation of Teachers
555 New Jersey Ave. NW
Washington, DC 20001
Ph: (202)879-4400
URL: http://www.aft.org
Description: Affiliated with the AFL-CIO. Works with teachers and other educational employees at the state and local level in organizing, collective bargaining, research, educational issues, and public relations. Conducts research in areas such as educational reform, teacher certification, and national assessments and standards. Represents members' concerns through legislative action; offers technical assistance. Serves professionals with concerns similar to those of teachers, including state employees, healthcare workers, and paraprofessionals.

494 ■ Association for Career and Technical Education
1410 King St.
Alexandria, VA 22314
Ph: (703)683-3111
Free: 800-826-9972
Fax: (703)683-7424
E-mail: acte@acteonline.org
URL: http://www.acteonline.org
Description: Represents teachers, supervisors, administrators, and others interested in the development and improvement of vocational, Technical, and practical arts education. Areas of interest include: secondary, postsecondary, and adult vocational education; education for special population groups; cooperative education. Works with such government agencies as: Bureau of Apprenticeship in Department of Labor; Office of Vocational Rehabilitation in Department of Health and Human Services; Veterans Administration; Office of Vocational and Adult Education of the Department of Education. Maintains hall of fame.

495 ■ Career Opportunities in Education and Related Services
InfoBase Holdings Inc.
132 W 31st., 17 Fl.
New York, NY 10001-3406
Ph: (212)967-8800
Fax: (800)678-3633
E-mail: info@infobasepublishing.com
URL: http://www.infobasepublishing.com
Frequency: Latest edition 2nd; Published April, 2006. **Price:** $49.50 Individuals Hardcover. **Pages:** 320. **Description:** Susan Echaore-McDavid. Second edition, 2006. 320 pages. **Covers:** 103 job titles in education, including job profiles, duties, salaries, prospects, experience, skills, and more. **Includes:** Appendixes with addresses of colleges and universities offering programs for featured jobs as well as organizations and Internet resources. **Entries**

include: Web sites and addresses of professional organizations.

496 ■ College Reading and Learning Association
66 George St.
Charleston, SC 29424
E-mail: thomasmm1@cofc.edu
URL: http://www.crla.net
Description: Professionals involved in college/adult reading, learning assistance, developmental education, and tutorial services. Promotes communication for the purpose of professional growth. **Members:** 1,200.

497 ■ The International Educator
PO Box 513
Cummaquid, MA 02637
Ph: (508)790-1990
Free: 877-375-6668
Fax: (508)790-1922
E-mail: tie@tieonline.com
URL: http://www.tieonline.com
Description: Facilitates the placement of teachers and administrators in American, British, and international schools. Seeks to create a network that provides for professional development opportunities and improved financial security of members. Offers advice and information on international school news, recent educational developments, job placement, and investment, consumer, and professional development opportunities. Makes available insurance and travel benefits. Operates International Schools Internship Program. **Members:** 3,500.

498 ■ International Reading Association
800 Barksdale Rd.
Newark, DE 19714-8139
Ph: (302)731-1600
Free: 800-336-7323
Fax: (302)731-1057
E-mail: customerservice@reading.org
URL: http://www.reading.org
Description: Represents teachers, reading specialists, consultants, administrators, supervisors, researchers, psychologists, librarians, and parents interested in promoting literacy. Seeks to improve the quality of reading instruction and promote literacy worldwide. Disseminates information pertaining to research on reading, including information on adult literacy, early childhood and literacy development, international education, literature for children and adolescents, and teacher education and professional development. Maintains over 40 special interest groups and over 70 committees.

499 ■ International Technology and Engineering Educators Association - Council for Supervision and Leadership
Maryland Dept. of Education
200 W Baltimore St.
Baltimore, MD 21201
Ph: (410)767-0177
Fax: (410)333-2099
E-mail: lrhine@msde.state.md.us
URL: http://iteea-csl.org
Description: Technology education supervisors from the U.S. Office of Education; local school department chairpersons; state departments of education, local school districts, territories, provinces, and foreign countries. Improves instruction and supervision of programs in technology education. Conducts research; compiles statistics. Sponsors competitions. Maintains speakers' bureau. **Members:** 300.

500 ■ Missouri Association for Career and Technical Education
213 E Capitol Ave.
Jefferson City, MO 65102
Ph: (573)634-7366
Fax: (573)635-6258
E-mail: info@mo-acte.org
URL: http://www.mo-acte.org
Description: Promotes the development of

vocational-technical education within the state of Missouri. Gives emphasis on continued support of vocational-technical education at the secondary, post-secondary, and adult levels, while fostering partnerships with business and industry in the training and retraining of the Missouri workforce. Provides an open forum for the study and discussion of all questions involved in career, practical arts, technical and vocational education. Works with other states and agencies for the advancement of career, practical arts, technical and vocational education, in the state, and in the United States, and as an ally of the Association of Career and Technical Education. Supports local, state and national legislation for career, practical arts, technical and vocational education. Members join one of twelve divisions.

501 ■ National Community Education Association
3929 Old Lee Hwy., No. 91-A
Fairfax, VA 22030-2401
Ph: (703)359-8973
Fax: (703)359-0972
E-mail: ncea@ncea.com
URL: http://www.ncea.com

Description: Community school directors, principals, superintendents, professors, teachers, students, and laypeople. Promotes and establishes community schools as an integral part of the educational plan of every community. Emphasizes community and parent involvement in the schools, lifelong learning, and enrichment of K-12 and adult education. Serves as a clearinghouse for the exchange of ideas and information, and the sharing of efforts. Offers leadership training.

502 ■ National Council of Teachers of Mathematics
1906 Association Dr.
Reston, VA 20191-1502
Ph: (703)620-9840
Free: 800-235-7566
Fax: (703)476-2970
E-mail: nctm@nctm.org
URL: http://www.nctm.org

Description: Aims to improve teaching and learning of mathematics.

503 ■ North American Council of Automotive Teachers
PO Box 80010
Charleston, SC 29416
Ph: (843)556-7068
Fax: (843)556-7068
E-mail: office@nacat.com
URL: http://www.nacat.com

Description: Provides support for automotive educators, secondary, post-secondary, and industry. Enhances technical training opportunities, peer interaction and resources sharing. Represents automotive teachers on councils and committees where automotive teachers' interests are involved. **Members:** 725.

504 ■ *Overseas Employment Opportunities for Educators: Department of Defense Dependents Schools*
DIANE Publishing Co.
PO Box 617
Darby, PA 19023-0617
Ph: (610)461-6200
Free: 800-782-3833
Fax: (610)461-6130
E-mail: dianepublishing@gmail.com
URL: http://www.dianepublishing.net

Description: Barry Leonard, editor. $20.00. 52 pages. An introduction to teachings positions in the Dept. of Defense Dependents Schools (DoDDS), a worldwide school system, operated by the DoD in 14 countries.

505 ■ *Recruiter's Guide: Job Fairs for Educators*
American Association for Employment in Education
947 E Johnstown Rd., No. 170
Gahanna, OH 43230
Ph: (614)485-1111
Fax: (360)244-7802
E-mail: office@aaee.org
URL: http://www.aaee.org

Frequency: Latest edition 2008. **Pages:** 30. **Covers:** Lists of job and career fairs and the institutions which sponsor the programs or participate in programs sponsored by consortia. **Entries include:** Contact information, date and title of event, location, number of expected employers and candidates, percentage of minority candidates expected, employers fees, registration deadlines, e-mail and website addresses.

SOURCES OF HELP-WANTED ADS

506 ■ *Aerospace America Magazine*
American Institute of Aeronautics and Astronautics
1801 Alexander Bell Dr., Ste. 500
Reston, VA 20191-4344
Ph: (703)264-7500
Free: 800-639-2422
Fax: (703)264-7551
E-mail: custserv@aiaa.org
URL: http://www.aerospaceamerica.org/Pages/Table-OfContents.aspx

Frequency: Monthly. **Price:** $200 Institutions non member, domestic; $163 for nonmembers in U.S. **Description:** Monthly. Free to members; non-members, $140.00 per year. Covers aeronautics and space technology with special attention to aerospace defense, design, and electronics.

507 ■ *Aerospace Engineering & Manufacturing*
Society of Automotive Engineers International
400 Commonwealth Dr.
Warrendale, PA 15096-0001
Ph: (724)776-4841
Free: 877-606-7323
Fax: (724)776-0790
E-mail: aero@sae.org
URL: http://www.sae.org/magazines/

Frequency: 10/yr. **Price:** $65 U.S., Canada, and Mexico; $100 Other countries; $100 U.S., Canada, and Mexico 2 years; $155 Two years other countries; Free. **Description:** Magazine for aerospace manufacturing engineers providing technical and design information.

508 ■ *Aerospace Manufacturing and Design*
URL: http://www.onlineamd.com/

Price: $45 Canada and Mexico; $85 Individuals UK & Europe; $175 Other countries. **Description:** Magazine covering aerospace manufacturing and design.

509 ■ *AeroSpaceNews.com*
AeroSpaceNews.com
PO Box 1748
Ojai, CA 93024-1748
Ph: (805)985-2320
URL: http://aerospacenews.com/

Frequency: Monthly. **Price:** $19.95 Individuals private. **Description:** Journal reporting on the insights, impressions and images of tomorrow's technological wonders in the field of aerospace.

510 ■ *AIE Perspectives Newsmagazine*
American Institute of Engineers
4630 Appian Way, Ste. 206
El Sobrante, CA 94803-1875
Ph: (510)758-6240

Fax: (510)758-6240
E-mail: aie@aieonline.org
URL: http://www.members-aie.org

Frequency: Monthly. **Price:** included in membership dues. **Description:** Professional magazine covering engineering.

511 ■ *Air Jobs Digest*
World Air Data
PO Box 42724
Washington, DC 20015
Ph: (301)990-6800
Free: 800-247-5627
E-mail: staff@airjobsdaily.com
URL: http://www.airjobsdigest.com/

Frequency: Monthly. **Price:** $96 Individuals. **Description:** Newspaper covering job listings in aviation and aerospace worldwide.

512 ■ *Aviation Maintenance*
ASI Publications Ltd. - Aerospace & Security Media
5590 N Diversey Blvd., Ste. 209
Milwaukee, WI
Ph: (414)967-4997
URL: http://www.avm-mag.com

Frequency: 6/yr. **Price:** Free. **Description:** Magazine covering aviation maintenance.

513 ■ *Aviation Week & Space Technology*
The McGraw-Hill Companies Inc.
1200 G St. NW, Ste. 922
Washington, DC 20005
Ph: (202)383-2360
Fax: (202)383-2346
E-mail: customer.service@mcgraw-hill.com
URL: http://www.aviationweek.com/awst.aspx?channel=awst

Frequency: Weekly. **Price:** $79 Canada; $79 Individuals; $119 Other countries. **Description:** Magazine serving the aviation and aerospace market worldwide.

514 ■ *Engineering*
Scientific Research Publishing
PO Box 54821
Irvine, CA 92619-4821
E-mail: eng@scirp.org
URL: http://www.scirp.org/journal/eng/

Frequency: Monthly. **Price:** $468 Individuals. **Description:** Peer-reviewed journal publishing articles on the latest advancements in engineering.

515 ■ *Flying*
Bonnier Corp.
460 N Orlando Ave., Ste. 200
Winter Park, FL 32789
Ph: (407)628-4802
Fax: (407)628-7061
URL: http://www.flyingmag.com

Frequency: Monthly. **Price:** $14 Individuals print; $22 Two years print; $33 Canada print; $33 Other

countries print. **Description:** General aviation magazine.

516 ■ *Graduating Engineer & Computer Careers*
Career Recruitment Media
2 LAN Dr., Ste. 100
Westford, MA 01886
Ph: (978)692-5092
Fax: (978)692-4174
E-mail: hshulick@alloyeducation.com
URL: http://www.graduatingengineer.com

Frequency: Quarterly. **Price:** $16.95 Individuals. **Description:** Magazine focusing on employment, education, and career development for entry-level engineers and computer scientists.

517 ■ *NSBE Magazine: National Society of Black Engineers*
NSBE Publications
205 Daingerfield Rd.
Alexandria, VA 22314
Ph: (703)549-2207
Fax: (703)683-5312
E-mail: info@nsbe.org
URL: http://www.nsbe.org/News-Media/Magazines/About-NSBE-Magazine.aspx

Frequency: 3/yr. **Price:** $20 Individuals; $35 Other countries; $15 Students. **Description:** Journal providing information on engineering careers, self-development, and cultural issues for recent graduates with technical majors.

518 ■ *PE*
National Society of Professional Engineers
1420 King St.
Alexandria, VA 22314-2794
Ph: (703)684-2800
Fax: (703)836-4875
E-mail: memserv@nspe.org
URL: http://www.nspe.org/PEmagazine/index.html

Frequency: Semimonthly; 10/yr. **Price:** included in membership dues; $50 for nonmembers. **Description:** Covers matters of importance to engineering educators and students.

519 ■ *Rotor & Wing*
Access Intelligence L.L.C.
4 Choke Cherry Rd., 2nd Fl.
Rockville, MD 20850
Ph: (301)354-2000
Free: 800-777-5006
Fax: (301)309-3847
E-mail: info@accessintel.com
URL: http://www.aviationtoday.com/rw/

Frequency: Monthly. **Price:** Free. **Description:** Magazine covering helicopters.

520 ■ *SWE, Magazine of the Society of Women Engineers*
Society of Women Engineers
203 N La Salle St., Ste. 1675
Chicago, IL 60601

Ph: (312)596-5223
Free: 877-SWE-INFO
Fax: (312)596-5252
E-mail: hq@swe.org
URL: http://societyofwomenengineers.swe.org/index
.php

Frequency: Quarterly. **Price:** $30 Nonmembers. **Description:** Magazine for engineering students and for women and men working in the engineering and technology fields. Covers career guidance, continuing development and topical issues.

521 ■ *Woman Engineer*
Equal Opportunity Publications Inc.
445 Broad Hollow Rd., Ste. 425
Melville, NY 11747
Ph: (631)421-9421
Fax: (631)421-1352
E-mail: info@eop.com
URL: http://www.eop.com

Description: Annual. Magazine that is offered at no charge to qualified female engineering, computer-science, and information-technology students and professionals seeking to find employment and advancement in their careers.

Employer Directories and Networking Lists

522 ■ *Directory of Contract Staffing Firms*
C.E. Publications Inc.
PO Box 3006
Bothell, WA 98041-3006
Ph: (425)806-5200
Fax: (425)806-5585
E-mail: staff@cjhunter.com
URL: http://www.cjhunter.com/dcsf/overview.html

Frequency: Annual. **Covers:** Nearly 1,300 contract firms actively engaged in the employment of engineering, IT/IS, and technical personnel for 'temporary' contract assignments throughout the world. **Entries include:** Company name, address, phone, name of contact, email, web address. **Arrangement:** Alphabetical. **Indexes:** Geographical.

523 ■ *Indiana Society of Professional Engineers--Directory*
Indiana Society of Professional Engineers
c/o Lauraine M. Howe, Executive Director
PO Box 20806
Indianapolis, IN 46220
Ph: (317)255-2267
Fax: (317)255-2530
E-mail: indspe@gmail.com
URL: http://www.indspe.org

Frequency: Annual; fall. **Pages:** 150. **Covers:** Member registered engineers, land surveyors, engineering students, and engineers in training. **Entries include:** Member name, address, phone, type of membership, business information, specialty. **Arrangement:** Alpha by chapter area.

524 ■ *Journal of Air Traffic Control*
Air Traffic Control Association
1101 King St., Ste. 300
Alexandria, VA 22314
Ph: (703)299-2430
Fax: (703)299-2437
E-mail: info@atca.org
URL: http://atca.kma.net/index.asp?bid=33

Frequency: Quarterly. **Price:** $78 U.S.; $88 Other countries. **Description:** Magazine for air traffic controllers, aviation personnel, pilots and systems engineers. **Includes:** Directory of member organizations. **Entries include:** Organization name, city, state.

525 ■ *National Air Transportation Association--Aviation Resource and Membership Directory*
National Air Transportation Association
4226 King St.
Alexandria, VA 22302

Ph: (703)845-9000
Free: 800-808-6282
Fax: (703)845-8176
E-mail: rmulholland@nata.aero
URL: http://www.nata.aero

Frequency: Annual; Latest Edition 2012. **Price:** $50 Nonmembers; $25 Members. **Covers:** More than 1,000 regular, associate, and affiliate members; regular members include airport service organizations, air taxi operators, and commuter airlines. **Entries include:** Company name, address, phone, fax number, name and title of contact. **Arrangement:** Regular members are classified by service; associate and affiliate members are alphabetical in separate sections. **Indexes:** Geographical.

526 ■ *Plunkett's Engineering and Research Industry Almanac: The Only Complete Guide to the Business of Research, Development, and Engineering*
Plunkett Research Ltd.
4102 Bellaire Blvd.
Houston, TX 77025-1004
Ph: (713)932-0000
Fax: (713)932-7080
E-mail: customersupport@plunkettresearch.com
URL: http://www.plunkettresearch.com

Frequency: Annual; Latest edition 2013; New edition expected June 2014. **Price:** $349.99 Individuals eBook, print and CD-ROM. **Pages:** 690. **Covers:** 500 of the largest companies involved in research, engineering and development in the biotech, electronics, aerospace and infotech industries. **Entries include:** Name, address, phone, fax, names and titles of key personnel, subsidiary and branch names and locations, financial data, salaries and benefits, description of products/services, overview of company culture/activities. **Indexes:** Industry, location, sales rank, profit rank.

527 ■ *Who's Who in Engineering*
American Association of Engineering Societies
1801 Alexander Bell Dr.
Reston, VA 20191
Ph: (202)296-2237
Free: 888-400-2237
Fax: (202)296-1151
E-mail: dbateson@aaes.org
URL: http://www.aaes.org

Frequency: Triennial; Latest edition 9th. **Covers:** About 15,000 engineers who have received professional recognition for outstanding achievement. **Entries include:** Name, address; education and employment history; awards and achievements. **Arrangement:** Alphabetical. **Indexes:** Geographical, field of specialization.

Handbooks and Manuals

528 ■ *Expert Resumes for Engineers*
JIST Publishing
875 Montreal Way
Saint Paul, MN 55102-4245
Ph: (317)613-4200
Free: 800-648-5478
Fax: (800)328-4564
E-mail: info@jist.com
URL: http://www.jist.com

Description: Louise M. Kursmark and Wendy S. Enelow. 2009. $16.95 (softcover). 272 pages. Features a collection of written resume samples for all types of engineers including civil, mechanical, industrial, electrical, electronics, computer, and more. Contains tips and strategies for writing engineering resumes and finding the best jobs.

529 ■ *Great Jobs for Engineering Majors*
The McGraw-Hill Companies Inc.
PO Box 182604
Columbus, OH 43272
Ph: (212)512-2000
Free: 877-833-5524

Fax: (614)759-3749
E-mail: customer.service@mcgraw-hill.com
URL: http://www.mcgraw-hill.com

Description: Geraldine O. Garner. Second edition, 2008. $16.95. 192 pages. Covers all the career options open to students majoring in engineering.

Employment Agencies and Search Firms

530 ■ Aerospace Solutions
2323 E Magnolia St., Ste. 107
Phoenix, AZ 85034
Ph: (602)354-8180
Fax: (602)354-8589
E-mail: info@aero-us.com
URL: http://aero-us.com

Description: Provides professional staffing, direct placement and outsourcing for firms working exclusively in aerospace and defense-related disciplines.

531 ■ Amtec Human Capital
2749 Saturn St.
Brea, CA 92821
Ph: (714)993-1900
Fax: (714)993-2419
E-mail: info@amtechc.com
URL: http://www.amtechc.com

Description: Employment agency.

532 ■ The Aspire Group
711 Boylston St.
Boston, MA 02116-2616
Free: 800-487-2967
Fax: (617)500-7284
URL: http://www.bmanet.com/Aspire/index.html

Description: Employment agency.

533 ■ Career Advocates International
1539 Ave. A
Katy, TX 77493
Ph: (281)371-3917
E-mail: hank@careeradvocates.org
URL: http://www.careeradvocates.org

Description: Provides permanent placement and temporary staffing for executive and staff level positions. Specializes in multiple niches including: sales and marketing, accounting and financial services, banking, communications, human resources, chemicals, oil and gas, medical and dental, legal, information technology, energy, technology, engineering, manufacturing, construction, and light industrial.

534 ■ Centennial, Inc.
8044 Montgomery Rd., Ste. 260
Cincinnati, OH 45236
Ph: (513)366-3760
Fax: (513)366-3761
URL: http://www.centennialinc.com

Description: Serves as an executive search firm specializing in the areas of executive and general management, accounting and finance, human resources, information technology, manufacturing, engineering, marketing and advertising, not-for-profit, sales and business development, and supply chain and logistics.

535 ■ Cornell Global
PO Box 7113
Wilton, CT 06897
Ph: (203)762-0730
E-mail: info@cornellglobal.com
URL: http://www.cornellglobal.com

Description: Executive search firm with areas of expertise in the following areas: advertising, public relations, marketing, sales, finance and accounting, risk management, private equity and venture capital, construction, industrial, manufacturing, life sciences, publishing, information technology, engineering, human resources, legal, and logisitics.

536 ■ DMR Global Inc.
10230 W Sample Rd.
Coral Springs, FL 33065
Ph: (954)796-5043
Fax: (954)796-5044
URL: http://www.dmrglobal.com
Description: Executive search firm.

537 ■ Engineer One Inc.
2315 Laurel Lake Rd.
Knoxville, TN 37932
Ph: (865)692-0404
Fax: (865)691-0110
E-mail: engineerone@engineerone.com
URL: http://www.engineerone.com
Description: Engineering employment service specializing in engineering and management in the chemical process, power utilities, manufacturing, mechanical, electrical, and electronic industries. Maintains an Information Technology Division that works nationwide across all industries. Also provides systems analysis consulting services specializing in VAX based systems.

538 ■ Fisher Personnel Management Services
2351 N Filbert Rd.
Exeter, CA 93221
Ph: (559)594-5774
Fax: (559)594-5777
E-mail: hookme@fisheads.net
URL: http://www.fisheads.net
Description: Executive search firm.

539 ■ Focus Learning Corp.
1880 Santa Barbara St., Ste. 120
San Luis Obispo, CA 93401
Ph: (805)543-4895
Free: 800-458-5116
Fax: (805)543-4897
E-mail: info@focuslearning.com
URL: http://www.focuslearning.com
Description: Provider of professional services to corporations for the development and implementation of training programs. Assists clients with needs assessment related to training and professional development, goals definition, and development of training materials. Industries served include: government, utility, aerospace, business, and computer.

540 ■ Global Employment Solutions Inc.
10375 Park Meadows Dr., Ste. 475
Littleton, CO 80124-6724
Ph: (303)216-9500
Fax: (303)216-9533
URL: http://www.gesnetwork.com
Description: Employment agency.

541 ■ International Staffing Consultants Inc.
31655 2nd Ave.
Laguna Beach, CA 92651
Ph: (949)255-5857
Fax: (949)767-5959
E-mail: iscinc@iscworld.com
URL: http://www.iscworld.com
Description: Employment agency. Provides placement on regular or temporary basis. Affiliate office in London.

542 ■ Johnson Personnel Co.
1639 N Alpine Rd.
Rockford, IL 61107
Ph: (815)964-0840
Fax: (815)964-0855
E-mail: darrell@johnsonpersonnel.com
URL: http://www.johnsonpersonnel.com
Description: Provide technical and managerial placement in industry. Industries served: Aerospace, automotive, machine tool and consumer products.

543 ■ J.R. Bechtle & Company
67 S Bedford St., Ste. 400 W
Burlington, MA 01803-5177
Ph: (781)229-5804
Fax: (781)359-1829
URL: http://www.jrbechtle.com
Description: Executive search firm.

544 ■ Louis Rudzinsky Associates Inc.
7 Mystic St., Ste. 203
Arlington, MA 02474
Ph: (781)862-6727
Fax: (781)862-6868
E-mail: lra@lra.com
URL: http://www.lra.com
Description: Provider of recruitment, placement, and executive search to industry (software, electronics, optics) covering positions in general management, manufacturing, engineering, and marketing. Personnel consulting activities include counsel to small and startup companies. Industries served: electronics, aerospace, optical, laser, computer, software, imaging, electro-optics, biotechnology, advanced materials, and solid-state/semiconductor.

545 ■ Houser Martin Morris
110th Ave. NE, 110 Atrium Pl., Ste. 580
Bellevue, WA 98004
Ph: (425)453-2700
Fax: (425)453-8726
E-mail: info@houser.com
URL: http://www.houser.com
Description: Focus is in the areas of retained executive search, professional, and technical recruiting. Areas of specialization include software engineering, sales and marketing, information technology, legal, human resources, accounting and finance, manufacturing, factory automation and engineering.

546 ■ Nesco Inc.
6140 Parkland Blvd., Ste. 110
Mayfield Heights, OH 44124-6106
Ph: (440)461-6000
Fax: (440)449-3111
E-mail: corporate@nescoresource.com
URL: http://www.nescoresource.com
Description: Offers staffing and consulting solutions in the fields of engineering, information technology, accounting and finance, manufacturing and distribution, and administrative and customer services.

547 ■ Phillip's Personnel/Phillip's Temps
1675 Broadway, Ste. 2410
Denver, CO 80204
Ph: (303)893-1850
Fax: (303)893-0639
E-mail: info@phillipspersonnel.com
URL: http://www.phillipspersonnel.com
Description: Personnel recruiting and staffing consultants in: accounting and finance, management information systems, sales and marketing, engineering, administration, and general and executive management. Industries served: telecommunications, distribution, financial services, and general business.

548 ■ Robert Drexler Associates Inc.
PO Box 151
Saddle River, NJ 07458
Ph: (201)760-2300
Fax: (201)760-2301
E-mail: drexler@engineeringemployment.com
URL: http://www.engineeringemployment.com
Description: Executive search firm.

549 ■ S.R. Clarke
105 Huntercombe
Williamsburg, VA 23188
Ph: (703)344-0256
Fax: (949)608-5052
URL: http://www.srclarke.com/index.html
Description: Serves as an executive search and recruitment firm specializing in commercial construction, commercial real estate development, residential asset management, residential construction and development, subcontractor trades, finance, accounting, administration, heavy construction, architectural design and engineering design.

550 ■ Strom Aviation
109 S Elm St.
Waconia, MN 55387
Ph: (952)544-3611
Free: 800-743-8988
Fax: (952)544-3948
E-mail: jillp@stromaviation.com
URL: http://www.stromaviation.com
Description: Serves as a staffing firm specializing in hiring all types of aircraft technicians to provide manpower to service centers, repair stations, and OEMs.

551 ■ Techtronix Technical Search
5401 N 76th St.
Milwaukee, WI 53217-0173
Ph: (414)466-3100
Fax: (414)466-3598
Description: Firm specializes in recruiting executives for the engineering, information systems, manufacturing, marketing, finance and human resources industries. Industries include electronic, manufacturing and finance.

ONLINE JOB SOURCES AND SERVICES

552 ■ AeroIndustryJobs.com
URL: http://www.aeroindustryjobs.com/home/index .cfm?site_id=13641
Description: Lists careers in the aerospace, defense and advanced materials industries. Helps industry employers connect with qualified, career-focused job seekers.

553 ■ Aerospace Engineering Jobs
URL: http://www.aerospaceengineeringjobs.us
Description: Provides an online source for aerospace engineering jobs. Features updated job listings for candidates and job posting for employers.

554 ■ AerospaceCrossing.com
URL: http://www.aerospacecrossing.com
Description: Consolidates jobs from employer websites, job portals, and aerospace websites.

555 ■ AerospaceEngineer.com
URL: http://www.aerospaceengineer.com
Description: Provides job opportunities in the aerospace engineering field.

556 ■ AeroVents.com
URL: http://www.aerovents.com/body.shtml
Description: Seeks to spread the word about aviation events. Covers aviation events from conventions, space launches, seminars, model rocketry and aircraft, ballooning, sky diving, plane pulls, open houses, air shows and fly-ins.

557 ■ Air Transportation Jobs
URL: http://air.transportation.jobs.jobsearchsite.com
Description: Provides available air transportation jobs and career resources. Allows employers to post jobs and search resumes to find qualified candidates.

558 ■ AircraftEngineers.com
URL: http://www.aircraftengineers.com
Description: Lists aircraft maintenance engineering jobs and aerospace vacancies. Provides career information for individuals who wish to start a career as an aircraft engineer.

559 ■ AirJobsDaily.com
URL: http://www.airjobsdaily.com
Description: Serves as a source of current aviation and aerospace job openings.

560 ■ AirlineCareer.com
URL: http://www.airlinecareer.com

Description: Web-based training center. Provides flight attendant job placement services.

561 ■ AirlineCareer.info
URL: http://www.airlinecareer.info

Description: Provides jobs in the airline community covering airport careers, aircraft manufacturing, aerospace careers, and cabin crew careers.

562 ■ American Institute of Aeronautics and Astronautics Career Planning and Placement Services
URL: http://www.aiaa.org

Description: Site for AIAA members to place recruitment advertisements, browse career opportunities listings, post resumes, and seek additional employment assistance. Non-members may become members though this site.

563 ■ AvCrew.com
URL: http://www.avcrew.com

Description: Provides service designed exclusively for career employment in the business aviation sector. Features flight crew jobs, conducts applicant screening, and assists selected flight departments with candidate searches.

564 ■ The Aviation MD
URL: http://www.theaviationmd.com

Description: Serves as international aviation database for employers and jobseekers in the aviation industry.

565 ■ AviationCrossing.com
URL: http://www.aviationcrossing.com

Description: Provides aviation jobs for agents, managers, mechanics, operators, specialists, supervisors, technicians, engineers, maintenance, pilots and other related aviation professionals.

566 ■ AviationEmployment.com
URL: http://www.aviationemployment.com

Description: Serves as an online job search service provider specializing in aviation and aerospace jobs and employment opportunities.

567 ■ AvJobs.com
URL: http://www.avjobs.com

Description: Provides information on a number of different careers in the aviation and aerospace industry. Features aviation schools directory, affiliate programs, research and networking, employment resources, salaries and wages, aviation careers descriptions, aviation guide and other resources.

568 ■ BestAviation.net
URL: http://www.bestaviation.net

Description: Provides source for information on flight school training, helicopter schools, aviation college programs, flight attendant careers, aircraft maintenance and pilot jobs.

569 ■ Engineering Classifieds
URL: http://www.engineeringclassifieds.com

Description: Serves as a career site for engineering professionals. Provides services including job search agents, resume creation and posting.

570 ■ EngineerJobs.com
URL: http://www.engineerjobs.com

Description: Provides job opportunities for engineering professionals in the following disciplines: aerospace, agricultural, biomedical, chemical, civil, electrical, environmental, industrial, manufacturing, marine, materials, mechanical, mining, nuclear, petroleum, process, project, quality, sales, software, solar, systems, and structural.

571 ■ Engineer.net
URL: http://www.engineer.net

Description: Provides engineering employment tools such as job search, job posting, and engineering resumes.

572 ■ FlightLevelJobs.com
URL: http://www.flightleveljobs.com

Description: Serves as a source of aviation employment information. Features aviation and aerospace jobs and employment opportunities.

573 ■ JetEmployment.com
URL: http://jetemployment.com

Description: Features employment opportunities for pilots and other workers in the airline, airport, and business aviation industry.

574 ■ PlaneJobs.com
URL: http://planejobs.com

Description: Serves as an employment, resume, career, and job search database for the aviation industry.

575 ■ Spherion
URL: http://www.spherion.com

Description: Recruitment firm specializing in accounting and finance, sales and marketing, interim executives, technology, engineering, retail and human resources.

576 ■ ThinkEnergyGroup.com
URL: http://www.thinkenergygroup.com

Description: Serves as a job board for professionals looking for positions in engineering, power plant, energy, and technical fields. Contains advice and tips on interviews, job searching, resume writing, hiring, and management. Provides choices of work location, pay rates in the field of expertise and contract, temp-to-hire, and direct hiring options.

TRADESHOWS

577 ■ AeroMat Conference and Exposition
ASM International
9639 Kinsman Rd.
Materials Pk., OH 44073-0002
Free: 800-336-5152
E-mail: memberservicecenter@asminternational.org
URL: http://www.asminternational.org

Frequency: Annual. **Primary Exhibits:** Providing information covering materials, material applications and processes for designing the next generation of aviation and space vehicles and systems.

578 ■ Aerospace Manufacturing and Automated Fastening Conference & Exhibition
Society of Automotive Engineers International
400 Commonwealth Dr.
Warrendale, PA 15096-0001
Ph: (724)776-4841
Free: 877-606-7323
Fax: (724)776-0790
E-mail: customerservice@sae.org
URL: http://www.sae.org

Frequency: Biennial. **Primary Exhibits:** Aerospace parts, materials, components, systems, and techniques.

579 ■ Aerospace Medical Association Annual Scientific Meeting
Aerospace Medical Association
320 S Henry St.
Alexandria, VA 22314-3579
Ph: (703)739-2240
Fax: (703)739-9652
E-mail: jsventek@asma.org
URL: http://www.asma.org

Frequency: Annual. **Primary Exhibits:** Products

related to aerospace medicine; safety products; diagnostic and research instrumentation for the field of human factors.

580 ■ AIAA Aerospace Sciences Meeting and Exhibition
American Institute of Aeronautics and Astronautics
1801 Alexander Bell Dr., Ste. 500
Reston, VA 20191-4344
Ph: (703)264-7500
Free: 800-639-2422
Fax: (703)264-7551
E-mail: custserv@aiaa.org
URL: http://www.aiaa.org

Frequency: Annual. **Primary Exhibits:** Computer and software technologies for the aerospace industry.

581 ■ AIAA/ASME/SAE/ASEE Joint Propulsion Conference and Exhibit
American Institute of Aeronautics and Astronautics
1801 Alexander Bell Dr., Ste. 500
Reston, VA 20191-4344
Ph: (703)264-7500
Free: 800-639-2422
Fax: (703)264-7551
E-mail: custserv@aiaa.org
URL: http://www.aiaa.org

Frequency: Annual. **Primary Exhibits:** Aerospace propulsion related exhibits.

582 ■ Air & Space Conference and Technology Exposition
Air Force Association
1501 Lee Hwy.
Arlington, VA 22209-1198
Ph: (703)247-5800
Free: 800-727-3337
Fax: (703)247-5853
E-mail: membership@afa.org
URL: http://www.afa.org

Frequency: Annual. **Primary Exhibits:** Aerospace technology, airplanes, rockets, helicopters, radar, computers, software, and communications systems.

OTHER SOURCES

583 ■ Acoustical Society of America
2 Huntington Quadrangle, Ste. 1N01
Melville, NY 11747-4505
Ph: (516)576-2360
Fax: (516)576-2377
E-mail: asa@aip.org
URL: http://acousticalsociety.org

Description: Represents members from various fields related to sound including physics, electrical, mechanical and aeronautical engineering, oceanography, biology, physiology, psychology, architecture, speech, noise and noise control, and music. Aims to increase and diffuse the knowledge of acoustics and its practical applications. Organizes meetings, provides reprints of out-of-print classic texts in acoustics, and translation books.

584 ■ Aeronautical Repair Station Association
121 N Henry St.
Alexandria, VA 22314-2903
Ph: (703)739-9543
Fax: (703)739-9488
E-mail: arsa@arsa.org
URL: http://arsa.org

Description: Works with legislators to advance an agenda that benefits the membership and aviation safety in general. Helps develop guidance, policy and interpretations that are clear, concise, consistent and applied uniformly to all similarly situated companies and individuals.

585 ■ Aerospace Industries Association
1000 Wilson Blvd., Ste. 1700
Arlington, VA 22209-3928

Ph: (703)358-1000
E-mail: marion.blakey@aia-aerospace.org
URL: http://www.aia-aerospace.org

Description: Manufacturers and suppliers of civil, military, and business aircraft, helicopters, unmanned aerial vehicles, space systems, aircraft engines, missiles, and related components, equipment, services, and information technology. Aims to ensure the United States aerospace, defense, and homeland security industry remains preeminent and its members are successful and profitable in a changing global market. Establishes industry goals and strategies, achieving consensus among members and national and global stakeholders and implementing solutions to industry issues related to national and homeland security, civil aviation, and space.

586 ■ Air Traffic Control Association
1101 King St., Ste. 300
Alexandria, VA 22314
Ph: (703)299-2430
Fax: (703)299-2437
E-mail: info@atca.org
URL: http://www.atca.org

Description: Air traffic controllers; private, commercial, and military pilots; private and business aircraft owners and operators; aircraft and electronics engineers; airlines, aircraft manufacturers, and electronic and human engineering firms.

587 ■ American Association of Engineering Societies
1801 Alexander Bell Dr.
Reston, VA 20191
Ph: (202)296-2237
Free: 888-400-2237
Fax: (202)296-1151
E-mail: dbateson@aaes.org
URL: http://www.aaes.org

Description: Coordinates the efforts of the member societies in the provision of reliable and objective information to the general public concerning issues which affect the engineering profession and the field of engineering as a whole; collects, analyzes, documents, and disseminates data which will inform the general public of the relationship between engineering and the national welfare; provides a forum for the engineering societies to exchange and discuss their views on matters of common interest; and represents the U.S. engineering community abroad through representation in WFEO and UPADI.

588 ■ American Engineering Association
c/o Harold Ruchelman
533 Waterside Blvd.
Monroe Township, NJ 08831
Ph: (201)664-6954
E-mail: aea@aea.org
URL: http://www.aea.org

Description: Members consist of Engineers and engineering professionals. Purpose to advance the engineering profession and U.S. engineering capabilities. Issues of concern include age discrimination, immigration laws, displacement of U.S. Engineers by foreign workers, trade agreements, off shoring of U.S. Engineering and manufacturing jobs, loss of U.S. manufacturing and engineering capability, and recruitment of foreign students. Testifies before Congress. Holds local Chapter meetings.

589 ■ American Indian Science and Engineering Society
PO Box 9828
Albuquerque, NM 87119-9828
Ph: (505)765-1052
Fax: (505)765-5608
E-mail: pam@aises.org
URL: http://www.aises.org

Description: Represents American Indian and non-Indian students and professionals in science, technology, and engineering fields; corporations representing energy, mining, aerospace, electronic, and computer fields. Seeks to motivate and encour-

age students to pursue undergraduate and graduate studies in science, engineering, and technology. Sponsors science fairs in grade schools, teacher training workshops, summer math/science sessions for 8th-12th graders, professional chapters, and student chapters in colleges. Offers scholarships. Adult members serve as role models, advisers, and mentors for students. Operates placement service.

590 ■ American Institute of Aeronautics and Astronautics
1801 Alexander Bell Dr., Ste. 500
Reston, VA 20191-4344
Ph: (703)264-7500
Free: 800-639-2422
Fax: (703)264-7551
E-mail: custserv@aiaa.org
URL: http://www.aiaa.org

Description: Represents scientists and engineers in the field of aeronautics and astronautics. Facilitates interchange of technological information through publications and technical meetings in order to foster overall technical progress in the field and increase the professional competence of members. Operates Public Policy program to provide federal decision-makers with the technical information and policy guidance needed to make effective policy on aerospace issues. Public Policy program activities include congressional testimony, position papers, section public policy activities, and workshops. Offers placement assistance; compiles statistics; offers educational programs. Provides abstracting services through its AIAA Access.

591 ■ American Institute of Engineers
4630 Appian Way, Ste. 206
El Sobrante, CA 94803-1875
Ph: (510)758-6240
Fax: (510)758-6240
E-mail: aie@aieonline.org
URL: http://www.aieonline.org

Description: Professional association for engineers, scientists, and mathematicians. Multi-disciplined, non-technical association who aims to improve the stature and image of engineers, scientists, and mathematicians. Provides endorsements, awards and opportunities for small business start-ups within the AIE Councils. Sponsors "LA Engineer", a comedy-drama television series; produces annual "Academy Hall of FAME (TV)".

592 ■ *Career Opportunities in Aviation and the Aerospace Industry*
InfoBase Holdings Inc.
132 W 31st., 17 Fl.
New York, NY 10001-3406
Ph: (212)967-8800
Fax: (800)678-3633
E-mail: info@infobasepublishing.com
URLs: http://www.infobasepublishing.com; http://www.infobasepublishing.com/Bookdetail.aspx?ISBN=1438110642&eBooks=1

Frequency: Published January, 2005. **Description:** Susan Echaore-McDavid. 2004. 305 pages. **Covers:** Eighty up-to-date job profiles, providing detailed information about the duties, salaries, and prospects of aviation mechanics, designers, technicians, scientists, and administrators. **Includes:** Appendices of educational institutions, periodicals, directories, and associations.

593 ■ *Career Opportunities in Engineering*
InfoBase Holdings Inc.
132 W 31st., 17 Fl.
New York, NY 10001-3406
Ph: (212)967-8800
Fax: (800)678-3633
E-mail: info@infobasepublishing.com
URL: http://www.ferguson.infobasepublishing.com

Description: 2006. $49.50. 336 pages. Provides an overview of engineering, followed by a selection of jobs profiled in detail, including the nature of the job, earnings, prospects for employment, what kind of training and skills it requires and sources for further

information. **Includes:** Appendices of educational institutions, periodicals, directories, and associations. Appendices of educational institutions, periodicals, directories, and associations.

594 ■ Cultural Vistas
440 Park Ave. S, 2nd Fl.
New York, NY 10016
Ph: (212)497-3500
Fax: (212)497-3535
E-mail: info@culturalvistas.org
URL: http://culturalvistas.org

Description: Providers worldwide of on-the-job training programs for students and professionals seeking international career development and life-changing experiences. Arranges workplace exchanges in hundreds of professional fields, bringing employers and trainees together from around the world. Client list ranges from small farming communities to Fortune 500 companies.

595 ■ Engineering Society of Detroit
20700 Civic Center Dr., Ste. 450
Southfield, MI 48076
Ph: (248)353-0735
Fax: (248)353-0736
E-mail: esd@esd.org
URL: http://ww2.esd.org/home.htm

Description: Engineers from all disciplines; scientists and technologists. Conducts technical programs and engineering refresher courses; sponsors conferences and expositions. Maintains speakers' bureau; offers placement services; although based in Detroit, MI, society membership is international. **Members:** 6,000.

596 ■ High Frontier
500 N Washington St.
Alexandria, VA 22314
Ph: (703)535-8774
E-mail: info@highfrontier.org
URL: http://highfrontier.org

Description: Represents scientists, space engineers, strategists and economists. Maintains speakers' bureau; sponsors educational programs.

597 ■ International Black Aerospace Council
7120 Sugar Maple Dr.
Irving, TX 75063
Ph: (972)373-9551
Fax: (972)373-9551
URL: http://www.blackaerospace.com

Description: Coordinates and develops activities of the world aerospace community to enhance outreach efforts pertaining to minorities in aerospace career fields. Serves as a clearing house for the exchange of information, ideas and prospects for scholastic and employment opportunities for minorities in aerospace careers.

598 ■ International Experimental Aerospace Society
14870 Granada Ave., No. 316
Apple Valley, MN 55124
Ph: (952)583-2145
URL: http://www.ieas.org

Description: Represents education and research societies of rocketry and space technology experimenters from around the world. Promotes experimental aerospace. Provides opportunities for exchange of information and coordination of services that will enable private individuals to safely engage in experimental aerospace activities. Assists and encourages regulatory authorities to permit safe experimental activities.

599 ■ ISA -The International Society of Automation
67 Alexander Dr.
Research Triangle Park, NC 27709
Ph: (919)549-8411

Fax: (919)549-8288
E-mail: info@isa.org
URL: http://www.isa.org

Description: Sets the standard for automation by helping over 30,000 worldwide members and other professionals solve difficult technical problems, while enhancing their leadership and personal career capabilities. Develops standards; certifies industry professionals; provides education and training; publishes books and technical articles; and hosts the largest conference and exhibition for automation professionals in the Western Hemisphere. Is the founding sponsor of The Automation Federation.

600 ■ Korean-American Scientists and Engineers Association
1952 Gallows Rd., Ste. 300
Vienna, VA 22182
Ph: (703)748-1221
Fax: (703)748-1331
E-mail: sejong@ksea.org
URL: http://www.ksea.org

Description: Represents scientists and engineers holding single or advanced degrees. Promotes friendship and mutuality among Korean and American scientists and engineers; contributes to Korea's scientific, technological, industrial, and economic developments; strengthens the scientific, technological, and cultural bonds between Korea and the U.S. Sponsors symposium. Maintains speakers' bureau, placement service, and biographical archives. Compiles statistics. **Members:** 10,000.

601 ■ National Action Council for Minorities in Engineering
440 Hamilton Ave., Ste. 302
White Plains, NY 10601-1813
Ph: (914)539-4010
Free: 800-888-9929
Fax: (914)539-4032
E-mail: ajohnson@nacme.org
URL: http://www.nacme.org

Description: Leads the national effort to increase access to careers in engineering and other science-based disciplines. Conducts research and public policy analysis, develops and operates national demonstration programs at precollege and university levels, and disseminates information through publications, conferences and electronic media. Serves as a privately funded source of scholarships for minority students in engineering.

602 ■ National Society of Professional Engineers
1420 King St.
Alexandria, VA 22314-2794
Ph: (703)684-2800
Fax: (703)836-4875
E-mail: memserv@nspe.org
URL: http://www.nspe.org

Description: Represents professional engineers and engineers-in-training in all fields registered in accordance with the laws of states or territories of the U.S. or provinces of Canada; qualified graduate engineers, student members, and registered land surveyors. Is concerned with social, professional, ethical, and economic considerations of engineering as a profession; encompasses programs in public relations, employment practices, ethical considerations, education, and career guidance. Monitors legislative and regulatory actions of interest to the engineering profession.

603 ■ Society of Hispanic Professional Engineers
13181 Crossroads Pkwy. N, Ste. 450
City of Industry, CA 91746-3496
Ph: (323)725-3970
E-mail: shpenational@shpe.org
URL: http://national.shpe.org

Description: Represents engineers, student engineers, and scientists. Aims to increase the number of Hispanic engineers by providing motivation and support to students. Sponsors competitions and educational programs. Maintains placement service and speakers' bureau; compiles statistics. **Members:** 8,000.

604 ■ Society of Women Engineers
203 N La Salle St., Ste. 1675
Chicago, IL 60601
Ph: (312)596-5223
Free: 877-SWE-INFO
Fax: (312)596-5252
E-mail: hq@swe.org
URL: http://societyofwomenengineers.swe.org

Description: Educational and service organization representing both students and professional women in engineering and technical fields.

605 ■ Women in Aerospace
204 E St. NE
Washington, DC 20002

Ph: (202)547-0229
Fax: (202)547-6348
E-mail: info@womeninaerospace.org
URL: http://www.womeninaerospace.org

Description: Women and men working in aerospace and related fields, allied organizations and businesses. Aims to expand women's opportunities for leadership and to increase their visibility in the aerospace community. Facilitates discussion of issues facing women, as well as the aerospace industry. Organizes monthly programs geared towards a broad spectrum of aerospace issues, including human space flight, aviation, remote sensing, satellite communications, robotic space exploration, and the policy issues surrounding these fields.

606 ■ Women in Engineering ProActive Network
1901 E Asbury Ave., Ste. 220
Denver, CO 80208
Ph: (303)871-4643
Fax: (303)871-4628
URL: http://www.wepan.org

Description: Women in engineering professions. Includes key strategies such as education and training, research, collaboration, leadership, diversity, advocacy, networking, sustainability, accountability, and volunteerism in order to be a catalyst for change that enhances the success of women in the engineering professions.

607 ■ World Aerospace Database
Aviation Week Group
1200 G St.NW, Ste. 922
Washington, DC 20005-3814
Free: 800-525-5003
Fax: (712)755-7423
E-mail: wad@mcgraw-hill.com
URL: http://www.aviationweek.com

Frequency: Semiannual. **Price:** $269 U.S. print; $1,295 U.S. CD-ROM, incl. 1 year print sub., 2 editions; $595 U.S. online, incl. 1 year print sub., 2 editions; $495 U.S. special online; $149 U.S. special print. **Description:** Covers more than 25,000 companies and 120,000 key executives to the aviation and aerospace industries worldwide. **Arrangement:** Classified by major activity (manufacturers, airlines, etc.). **Indexes:** Company and organization, personnel, product, trade name.

SOURCES OF HELP-WANTED ADS

608 ■ **AIE Perspectives Newsmagazine**
American Institute of Engineers
4630 Appian Way, Ste. 206
El Sobrante, CA 94803-1875
Ph: (510)758-6240
Fax: (510)758-6240
E-mail: aie@aieonline.org
URL: http://www.members-aie.org

Frequency: Monthly. **Price:** included in membership dues. **Description:** Professional magazine covering engineering.

609 ■ *Engineering*
Scientific Research Publishing
PO Box 54821
Irvine, CA 92619-4821
E-mail: eng@scirp.org
URL: http://www.scirp.org/journal/eng/

Frequency: Monthly. **Price:** $468 Individuals. **Description:** Peer-reviewed journal publishing articles on the latest advancements in engineering.

610 ■ *Farmland News*
Farmland News
104 Depot St.
Archbold, OH 43502-0240
Ph: (419)445-9456
Fax: (419)445-4444
E-mail: news@farmlandnews.com
URL: http://www.farmlandnews.com

Frequency: Weekly (Tues.). **Price:** $42 Individuals; $78 Two years. **Description:** Rural human-interest newspaper (tabloid).

611 ■ *Feedstuffs*
Miller Publishing Co.
5810 W 78th St., Ste. 200
Bloomington, MN 55439
Ph: (952)930-4344
Fax: (952)938-1832
E-mail: tlundeen@feedstuffs.com
URL: http://www.feedstuffs.com

Frequency: Weekly. **Price:** $144 Individuals; $230 Two years; $150 Canada; $235 Individuals Europe and Mid East; airmail; $280 Other countries Japan, Far E./Aus. airmail; $210 Individuals Mexico/Central/South America; $196 Individuals print & internet version; $334 Two years print & internet version; $202 Canada print & internet version; $334 Canada print & internet version, 2 years. **Description:** Magazine serving the grain and feed industries and animal agriculture.

612 ■ *Graduating Engineer & Computer Careers*
Career Recruitment Media
2 LAN Dr., Ste. 100
Westford, MA 01886

Ph: (978)692-5092
Fax: (978)692-4174
E-mail: hshulick@alloyeducation.com
URL: http://www.graduatingengineer.com

Frequency: Quarterly. **Price:** $16.95 Individuals. **Description:** Magazine focusing on employment, education, and career development for entry-level engineers and computer scientists.

613 ■ *Journal of Agricultural Science*
Canadian Center of Science and Education
1120 Finch Ave. W, Ste. 701-309
Toronto, ON, Canada M3J 3H7
Ph: (416)642-2606
Fax: (416)642-2608
E-mail: info@ccsenet.org
URL: http://ccsenet.org/journal/index.php/jas/

Description: Peer-reviewed journal publishing original research, applied, and educational articles in all areas of agricultural science.

614 ■ *NSBE Magazine: National Society of Black Engineers*
NSBE Publications
205 Daingerfield Rd.
Alexandria, VA 22314
Ph: (703)549-2207
Fax: (703)683-5312
E-mail: info@nsbe.org
URL: http://www.nsbe.org/News-Media/Magazines/About-NSBE-Magazine.aspx

Frequency: 3/yr. **Price:** $20 Individuals; $35 Other countries; $15 Students. **Description:** Journal providing information on engineering careers, self-development, and cultural issues for recent graduates with technical majors.

615 ■ *PE*
National Society of Professional Engineers
1420 King St.
Alexandria, VA 22314-2794
Ph: (703)684-2800
Fax: (703)836-4875
E-mail: memserv@nspe.org
URL: http://www.nspe.org/PEmagazine/index.html

Frequency: Semimonthly; 10/yr. **Price:** included in membership dues; $50 for nonmembers. **Description:** Covers matters of importance to engineering educators and students.

616 ■ *Resource: Engineering and Technology for Sustainable World*
American Society of Agricultural and Biological Engineers
2950 Niles Rd.
Saint Joseph, MI 49085-8607
Ph: (269)429-0300
Free: 800-371-2723
Fax: (269)429-3852
E-mail: hq@asabe.org
URL: http://www.asabe.org

Description: $10.75/single issue for nonmembers;

$5.50/single issues for members. Facilitates the exchange of technical information and promoting the science and art of engineering in agricultural, food, and biological systems. Includes a reader opinion page, research on recent developments and trends, an employment section for both job seekers and employers, and agricultural or biological engineering consultant advertisements.

617 ■ *SWE, Magazine of the Society of Women Engineers*
Society of Women Engineers
203 N La Salle St., Ste. 1675
Chicago, IL 60601
Ph: (312)596-5223
Free: 877-SWE-INFO
Fax: (312)596-5252
E-mail: hq@swe.org
URL: http://societyofwomenengineers.swe.org/index.php

Frequency: Quarterly. **Price:** $30 Nonmembers. **Description:** Magazine for engineering students and for women and men working in the engineering and technology fields. Covers career guidance, continuing development and topical issues.

618 ■ *Woman Engineer*
Equal Opportunity Publications Inc.
445 Broad Hollow Rd., Ste. 425
Melville, NY 11747
Ph: (631)421-9421
Fax: (631)421-1352
E-mail: info@eop.com
URL: http://www.eop.com

Description: Annual. Magazine that is offered at no charge to qualified female engineering, computer-science, and information-technology students and professionals seeking to find employment and advancement in their careers.

PLACEMENT AND JOB REFERRAL SERVICES

619 ■ **ASA-CSSA-SSSA Career Placement Center**
5585 Guilford Rd.
Madison, WI 53711
Ph: (608)273-8080
Fax: (608)273-2021
URL: http://www.careerplacement.org

Description: Serves as a clearinghouse for resumes and personnel listings. Promotes and encourages career opportunities in the agronomic, crop, soil, and environmental sciences.

EMPLOYER DIRECTORIES AND NETWORKING LISTS

620 ■ *Directory of Contract Staffing Firms*
C.E. Publications Inc.
PO Box 3006
Bothell, WA 98041-3006

Ph: (425)806-5200
Fax: (425)806-5585
E-mail: staff@cjhunter.com
URL: http://www.cjhunter.com/dcsf/overview.html
Frequency: Annual. **Covers:** Nearly 1,300 contract firms actively engaged in the employment of engineering, IT/IS, and technical personnel for 'temporary' contract assignments throughout the world. **Entries include:** Company name, address, phone, name of contact, email, web address. **Arrangement:** Alphabetical. **Indexes:** Geographical.

621 ■ *Feedstuffs--Reference Issue and Buyers Guide*
Miller Publishing Co.
5810 W 78th St., Ste. 200
Bloomington, MN 55439
Ph: (952)930-4344
Fax: (952)938-1832
E-mail: tlundeen@feedstuffs.com
URL: http://www.feedstuffs.com
Frequency: Annual; Latest edition 2014. **Price:** $40 Individuals. **Includes:** Information on animal nutrition and health and feed production statistics. **Publication includes:** List of 2,000 suppliers of products and equipment for the feed, grain, and feeding industry; trade associations. **Entries include:** Company name, address, phone, fax, e-mail, website. **Arrangement:** Alphabetical. **Indexes:** Product, company.

622 ■ *Indiana Society of Professional Engineers--Directory*
Indiana Society of Professional Engineers
c/o Lauraine M. Howe, Executive Director
PO Box 20806
Indianapolis, IN 46220
Ph: (317)255-2267
Fax: (317)255-2530
E-mail: indspe@gmail.com
URL: http://www.indspe.org
Frequency: Annual; fall. **Pages:** 150. **Covers:** Member registered engineers, land surveyors, engineering students, and engineers in training. **Entries include:** Member name, address, phone, type of membership, business information, specialty. **Arrangement:** Alpha by chapter area.

623 ■ *Who Is Who: A Directory of Agricultural Engineers Available for Work in Developing Countries*
Frequency: Irregular; previous edition 1985; latest edition 1993. **Price:** $25 plus $2.50 shipping. **Pages:** 210. **Covers:** More than 600 individuals from 60 countries, primarily agricultural engineers available for work in developing regions in land and water management, farm structures, mechanization, electrification, and other aspects of the field. **Entries include:** Name, address, phone, qualification or area of expertise and other biographical data. **Arrangement:** Separate geographical and alphabetical sections. **Indexes:** Specialty.

624 ■ *Who's Who in Engineering*
American Association of Engineering Societies
1801 Alexander Bell Dr.
Reston, VA 20191
Ph: (202)296-2237
Free: 888-400-2237
Fax: (202)296-1151
E-mail: dbateson@aaes.org
URL: http://www.aaes.org
Frequency: Triennial; Latest edition 9th. **Covers:** About 15,000 engineers who have received professional recognition for outstanding achievement. **Entries include:** Name, address; education and employment history; awards and achievements. **Arrangement:** Alphabetical. **Indexes:** Geographical, field of specialization.

HANDBOOKS AND MANUALS

625 ■ *Expert Resumes for Engineers*
JIST Publishing
875 Montreal Way
Saint Paul, MN 55102-4245

Ph: (317)613-4200
Free: 800-648-5478
Fax: (800)328-4564
E-mail: info@jist.com
URL: http://www.jist.com
Description: Louise M. Kursmark and Wendy S. Enelow. 2009. $16.95 (softcover). 272 pages. Features a collection of written resume samples for all types of engineers including civil, mechanical, industrial, electrical, electronics, computer, and more. Contains tips and strategies for writing engineering resumes and finding the best jobs.

626 ■ *Great Jobs for Engineering Majors*
The McGraw-Hill Companies Inc.
PO Box 182604
Columbus, OH 43272
Ph: (212)512-2000
Free: 877-833-5524
Fax: (614)759-3749
E-mail: customer.service@mcgraw-hill.com
URL: http://www.mcgraw-hill.com
Description: Geraldine O. Garner. Second edition, 2008. $16.95. 192 pages. Covers all the career options open to students majoring in engineering.

EMPLOYMENT AGENCIES AND SEARCH FIRMS

627 ■ ACNI-Associates
116 W 47th St.
Kansas City, MO 64112
Ph: (816)531-7980
Free: 800-550-7980
Fax: (816)531-7982
E-mail: gip@agriassociates.com
URL: http://www.agriassociates.com
Description: Agribusiness executive search firm.

628 ■ Boyle & Associates Retained Search Group
PO Box 16658
Saint Paul, MN 55116
Ph: (651)223-5050
Fax: (651)699-5378
E-mail: paul@talenthunt.com
URL: http://www.talenthunt.com
Description: Executive search firm.

629 ■ The Employment Place
719 Van Lennen Ave.
Cheyenne, WY 82009
Ph: (307)632-0534
Fax: (307)638-2104
E-mail: agrecruit@juno.com
Description: A twofold placement firm operates as a general employment agency offering services to all areas of employment. Also serves as Ag Recruiters offering services to the agricultural professional. Industries served: All areas including government agencies in the U.S.; also serve fields of plant science, animal science, engineering, agri-business, management, sales and service.

630 ■ First Search America Inc.
PO Box 85
Ardmore, TN 38449
Free: 800-468-9214
E-mail: firstsearch@ardmore.net
URL: http://www.firstsearchamerica.com
Description: Executive search firm.

631 ■ Florasearch, Inc.
1740 Lake Markham Rd.
Sanford, FL 32771
Ph: (407)320-8177
Fax: (407)320-8083
E-mail: search@florasearch.com
URL: http://www.florasearch.com

Description: Employment agency for the horticulture industry.

632 ■ The Jack De Jong Group
3301 S Goldfield Rd.
Apache Junction, AZ 85119
Free: 800-266-0515
E-mail: jack@jackdejonggroup.com
URL: http://www.jackdejonggroup.com
Description: Agribusiness executive search firm.

633 ■ Miller & Associates Inc.
9036 NW 37th St.
Polk City, IA 50226-2073
Ph: (515)965-5727
Free: 888-965-2727
Fax: (515)965-5794
E-mail: millagsrch@aol.com
URL: http://www.ag-careers.com
Description: Agricultural personnel agency.

634 ■ The Montgomery Group Inc.
PO Box 30791
Knoxville, TN 37930-0791
Ph: (865)693-0325
Fax: (865)691-1900
E-mail: tmg@tmgincknox.com
URL: http://www.tmgincknox.com
Description: Executive search firm for the food and agribusiness industries.

635 ■ Robert Drexler Associates Inc.
PO Box 151
Saddle River, NJ 07458
Ph: (201)760-2300
Fax: (201)760-2301
E-mail: drexler@engineeringemployment.com
URL: http://www.engineeringemployment.com
Description: Executive search firm.

636 ■ Search North America Inc.
PO Box 3577
Sunriver, OR 97707
E-mail: mylinda@searchna.com
URL: http://www.searchna.com
Description: An executive search and recruiting firm whose focus is placing engineers, operations and maintenance managers, sales and marketing management, financial and general management executives (both domestic and international). Industries served: forest products, pulp and paper, waste to energy, environmental services, consulting and equipment suppliers for above related industries.

637 ■ Sherwood Lehman Massucco Inc.
3455 W Shaw Ave., Ste. 110
Fresno, CA 93711-3201
Ph: (559)276-8572
Free: 800-277-8572
Fax: (559)276-2351
E-mail: slinc@employmentexpert.com
URL: http://www.employmentexpert.com
Description: Executive search firm.

638 ■ Smith, Brown & Jones
5817 W 163rd Terr.
Stilwell, KS 66085
Ph: (913)814-8177
E-mail: staff@smithbrownjones.com
URL: http://www.smithbrownjones.com
Description: Executive search firm.

639 ■ Spencer Stuart Management Consultants N.V.
353 N Clark
Chicago, IL 60654-4704
Ph: (312)822-0088
Fax: (312)822-0116
E-mail: contact@spencerstuart.com
URL: http://www.spencerstuart.com
Description: Executive search firm.

640 ■ Trambley The Recruiter
5325 Wyoming Blvd. NE, Ste. 200
Albuquerque, NM 87109-3132
Ph: (505)821-5440
Fax: (505)821-8509

Description: Personnel consultancy firm recruits and places engineering professionals in specific areas of off-road equipment design and manufacturing. Industries served: Construction, agricultural, lawn and garden, oil exploration and mining equipment manufacturing.

ONLINE JOB SOURCES AND SERVICES

641 ■ Agricultural Engineering Jobs
URL: http://www.agriculturalengineeringjobs.org

Description: Provides an online source for agricultural engineering job. Features updated job listings for candidates and job posting for employers.

642 ■ AgriculturalCrossing.com
URL: http://www.agriculturalcrossing.com

Description: Provides a database of agricultural job openings worldwide. Includes openings in Fortune 500 and Fortune 1000 companies.

643 ■ AgricultureJobs.com
URL: http://www.agriculturejobs.com

Description: Provides new job openings for agriculturists in addition to research into the farming, fishing and forestry employment markets. Maintains a career articles section written and frequented by industry professionals.

644 ■ Engineering Classifieds
URL: http://www.engineeringclassifieds.com

Description: Serves as a career site for engineering professionals. Provides services including job search agents, resume creation and posting.

645 ■ EngineerJobs.com
URL: http://www.engineerjobs.com

Description: Provides job opportunities for engineering professionals in the following disciplines: aerospace, agricultural, biomedical, chemical, civil, electrical, environmental, industrial, manufacturing, marine, materials, mechanical, mining, nuclear, petroleum, process, project, quality, sales, software, solar, systems, and structural.

646 ■ Engineer.net
URL: http://www.engineer.net

Description: Provides engineering employment tools such as job search, job posting, and engineering resumes.

647 ■ Justmeans - CSR JOBS
URL: http://www.justmeans.com

Description: Serves as online resource that provides available career opportunities for the sustainable business industry.

648 ■ Spherion
URL: http://www.spherion.com

Description: Recruitment firm specializing in accounting and finance, sales and marketing, interim executives, technology, engineering, retail and human resources.

049 ■ ThinkEnergyGroup.com
URL: http://www.thinkenergygroup.com

Description: Serves as a job board for professionals looking for positions in engineering, power plant, energy, and technical fields. Contains advice and tips on interviews, job searching, resume writing, hiring, and management. Provides choices of work location, pay rates in the field of expertise and contract, temp-to-hire, and direct hiring options.

TRADESHOWS

650 ■ Agricultural Equipment Technology Conference
American Society of Agricultural and Biological Engineers
2950 Niles Rd.
Saint Joseph, MI 49085-8607
Ph: (269)429-0300
Free: 800-371-2723
Fax: (269)429-3852
E-mail: hq@asabe.org
URL: http://www.asabe.org

Frequency: Annual. Brings together engineers, managers, researchers and other professionals in the agricultural equipment industry to exchange information, discuss opportunities and address challenges for production agriculture in the 21st century.

OTHER SOURCES

651 ■ American Engineering Association
c/o Harold Ruchelman
533 Waterside Blvd.
Monroe Township, NJ 08831
Ph: (201)664-6954
E-mail: aea@aea.org
URL: http://www.aea.org

Description: Members consist of Engineers and engineering professionals. Purpose to advance the engineering profession and U.S. engineering capabilities. Issues of concern include age discrimination, immigration laws, displacement of U.S. Engineers by foreign workers, trade agreements, off shoring of U.S. Engineering and manufacturing jobs, loss of U.S. manufacturing and engineering capability, and recruitment of foreign students. Testifies before Congress. Holds local Chapter meetings.

652 ■ American Institute of Engineers
4630 Appian Way, Ste. 206
El Sobrante, CA 94803-1875
Ph: (510)758-6240
Fax: (510)758-6240
E-mail: aie@aieonline.org
URL: http://www.aieonline.org

Description: Professional association for engineers, scientists, and mathematicians. Multi-disciplined, non-technical association who aims to improve the stature and image of engineers, scientists, and mathematicians. Provides endorsements, awards and opportunities for small business start-ups within the AIE Councils. Sponsors "LA Engineer", a comedy-drama television series; produces annual "Academy Hall of FAME (TV)".

653 ■ American Society of Agricultural and Biological Engineers
2950 Niles Rd.
Saint Joseph, MI 49085-8607
Ph: (269)429-0300
Free: 800-371-2723
Fax: (269)429-3852
E-mail: hq@asabe.org
URL: http://www.asabe.org

Description: International professional and technical organization of individuals interested in engineering and technology for agriculture, food and biological systems. Publishes textbooks and journals. Develops engineering standards used in agriculture, food and biological systems. Sponsors technical meetings and continuing education programs. Maintains biographical archives and placement services. Sponsors competitions and special in-depth conferences. Maintains over 200 committees.

654 ■ American Society of Agricultural and Biological Engineers, District 5 - Pacific Northwest Section
c/o Quentin Nesbitt
Idaho Power Co.
Boise, ID 83707
Ph: (208)388-2519
E-mail: quentin.nebitt@idahopower.com
URL: http://www.asabe.org/membership/sections/dist5pnw.html

Description: Promotes the science and art of engineering in agricultural, food and biological systems. Encourages the professional improvement of members. Fosters education and develops engineering standards used in agriculture, food and biological systems.

655 ■ *Career Opportunities in Engineering*
InfoBase Holdings Inc.
132 W 31st., 17 Fl.
New York, NY 10001-3406
Ph: (212)967-8800
Fax: (800)678-3633
E-mail: info@infobasepublishing.com
URL: http://www.ferguson.infobasepublishing.com

Description: 2006. $49.50. 336 pages. Provides an overview of engineering, followed by a selection of jobs profiled in detail, including the nature of the job, earnings, prospects for employment, what kind of training and skills it requires and sources for further information. **Includes:** Appendices of educational institutions, periodicals, directories, and associations. Appendices of educational institutions, periodicals, directories, and associations.

656 ■ Council for Agricultural Science and Technology
4420 W Lincoln Way
Ames, IA 50014-3447
Ph: (515)292-2125
Fax: (515)292-4512
E-mail: cast@cast-science.org
URL: http://www.cast-science.org

Description: Scientific societies, associate societies, individuals, corporations, foundations, and trade associations. Promotes science-based information on food, fiber, agricultural, natural resource, and related societal and environmental issues.

657 ■ Farm and Ranch Freedom Alliance
PO Box 809
Cameron, TX 76520
Ph: (254)697-2661
E-mail: info@farmandranchfreedom.org
URL: http://farmandranchfreedom.org

Description: Strives to save family farms and individuals from expensive and unnecessary government regulation. Works to assure the independence of farmers, ranchers, livestock owners and homesteaders in the management, control, identification and marketing of their products. Supports and enhances sustainable agriculture, family farms and domestic agricultural products.

658 ■ National Coalition for Food and Agricultural Research
1800 S Oak St., Ste. 100
Champaign, IL 61820-6974
Ph: (217)356-3182
Fax: (217)398-4119
E-mail: ncfar@assochq.org
URL: http://www.ncfar.org

Description: Represents food, agriculture, nutrition, conservation and natural resource stakeholders. Aims to support the sustaining and increasing public investment at the national level in food and agricultural research, extension and education. Seeks to sustain and enhance federal funding for food and agricultural research, extension and education. Strives to help bring about research outcomes that provide a range of major public benefits.

659 ■ Women in Engineering ProActive Network
1901 E Asbury Ave., Ste. 220
Denver, CO 80208
Ph: (303)871-4643

Fax: (303)871-4628
URL: http://www.wepan.org
Description: Women in engineering professions. Includes key strategies such as education and training, research, collaboration, leadership, diversity, advocacy, networking, sustainability, accountability, and volunteerism in order to be a catalyst for change that enhances the success of women in the engineering professions.

SOURCES OF HELP-WANTED ADS

660 ■ Cell
Cell Press
600 Technology Sq.
Cambridge, MA 02139
Ph: (617)661-7057
Free: 866-314-2355
Fax: (617)661-7061
E-mail: celleditor@cell.com
URL: http://www.cell.com

Frequency: 26/yr. **Price:** $212 U.S. and Canada individual, print and online; $320 Other countries individual, print and online; $212 U.S. and Canada online only, individual; $212 Other countries online only, individual; $1,425 U.S. and Canada institution, print only; $1,605 Institutions, other countries print only. **Description:** Peer-reviewed journal on molecular and cell biology.

661 ■ CSANews
American Society of Agronomy
5585 Guilford Rd.
Madison, WI 53711-5801
Ph: (608)273-8080
Fax: (608)273-2021
E-mail: headquarters@sciencesocieties.org
URL: http://www.agronomy.org

Description: Monthly. $36/volume for non-members; $54 for international postage. Publishes information on agronomy, crop science, soil science, and related topics. Provides news of the societies and members; reports of annual meetings; listings of publications; announcements of awards, retirements, and deaths; job listings; and a calendar of events.

662 ■ Culture and Agriculture
American Anthropological Association - Association for Africanist Anthropology
2200 Wilson Blvd., Ste. 600
Arlington, VA 22201-3357
Ph: (703)528-1902
Free: 800-545-4703
Fax: (703)528-3546
E-mail: africananthro@gmail.com
URL: http://www.aaanet.org

Description: Quarterly. Provides information on agriculture and related policies and practices and the consequences they have on the environment and human life.

663 ■ Farmland News
Farmland News
104 Depot St.
Archbold, OH 43502-0240
Ph: (419)445-9456
Fax: (419)445-4444
E-mail: news@farmlandnews.com
URL: http://www.farmlandnews.com

Frequency: Weekly (Tues.). **Price:** $42 Individuals;

$78 Two years. **Description:** Rural human-interest newspaper (tabloid).

664 ■ Feedstuffs
Miller Publishing Co.
5810 W 78th St., Ste. 200
Bloomington, MN 55439
Ph: (952)930-4344
Fax: (952)938-1832
E-mail: tlundeen@feedstuffs.com
URL: http://www.feedstuffs.com

Frequency: Weekly. **Price:** $144 Individuals; $230 Two years; $150 Canada; $235 Individuals Europe and Mid East; airmail; $280 Other countries Japan, Far E./Aus. airmail; $210 Individuals Mexico/Central/South America; $196 Individuals print & internet version; $334 Two years print & internet version; $202 Canada print & internet version; $334 Canada print & internet version, 2 years. **Description:** Magazine serving the grain and feed industries and animal agriculture.

665 ■ Journal of Agricultural Science
Canadian Center of Science and Education
1120 Finch Ave. W, Ste. 701-309
Toronto, ON, Canada M3J 3H7
Ph: (416)642-2606
Fax: (416)642-2608
E-mail: info@ccsenet.org
URL: http://ccsenet.org/journal/index.php/jas/

Description: Peer-reviewed journal publishing original research, applied, and educational articles in all areas of agricultural science.

PLACEMENT AND JOB REFERRAL SERVICES

666 ■ ASA-CSSA-SSSA Career Placement Center
5585 Guilford Rd.
Madison, WI 53711
Ph: (608)273-8080
Fax: (608)273-2021
URL: http://www.careerplacement.org

Description: Serves as a clearinghouse for resumes and personnel listings. Promotes and encourages career opportunities in the agronomic, crop, soil, and environmental sciences.

EMPLOYER DIRECTORIES AND NETWORKING LISTS

667 ■ American Men and Women of Science: A Biographical Dictionary of Today's Leaders in Physical, Biological, and Related Sciences
R.R. Bowker
630 Central Ave
New Providence, NJ 07974

Ph: (888)269-5372
Free: 888-269-5372
Fax: (908)464-3553
E-mail: info@bowker.com
URL: http://www.gale.cengage.com

Frequency: Biennial; even years; New edition expected 29th, June 2011. **Price:** $1,368 Individuals. **Covers:** Over 135,000 U.S. and Canadian scientists active in the physical, biological, mathematical, computer science, and engineering fields; includes references to previous edition for deceased scientists and nonrespondents. **Entries include:** Name, address, education, personal and career data, memberships, honors and awards, research interest. **Arrangement:** Alphabetical. **Indexes:** Discipline (in separate volume).

668 ■ Directory of State Departments of Agriculture
U.S. Department of Agriculture - Agricultural Marketing Service - Compliance and Analysis
1400 Independence Ave. SW, Rm. 2503-S
Washington, DC 20250-0254
Ph: (202)690-4944
Fax: (202)720-0016
E-mail: chuck.martin@usda.gov
URL: http://www.ams.usda.gov

Frequency: Biennial; late summer of odd years. **Price:** Free. **Pages:** 87. **Covers:** State departments of agriculture and their officials. **Entries include:** Department name, address, phone, names and titles of key personnel, department branches. **Arrangement:** Geographical.

669 ■ Peterson's Graduate Programs in the Biological Sciences
Peterson's
461 From Rd.
Paramus, NJ 07652
Ph: (609)896-1800
Free: 800-338-3282
Fax: (402)458-3042
E-mail: custsvc@petersons.com
URL: http://www.petersons.com/

Frequency: Annual; latest edition 2013. **Price:** $54.95 Individuals. **Pages:** 1,152. **Covers:** Colleges and universities in the United States and Canada that offer more than 4,000 accredited graduate and professional programs in the biological and agricultural science fields. **Entries include:** School name, address, phone; name, title, and phone number of contact; admission requirements, description of school and programs. Publication is third in a series called 'Grad Guides.'. **Arrangement:** Classified by academic field. **Indexes:** School name, subject.

670 ■ Physical and Earth Sciences Graduate Program Directories
EducationDynamics LLC - Prospecting Services Div. - GradSchools.com
1350 Edgmont Ave., Ste. 1100
Chester, PA 19013

Ph: (484)766-2910
Free: 866-GRAD-COM
Fax: (610)499-9205
E-mail: info@edudirectories.com
URL: http://www.gradschools.com

EMPLOYMENT AGENCIES AND SEARCH FIRMS

671 ■ Agra Placements, Ltd.
8435 University Ave., Ste. 6
Des Moines, IA 50325
Ph: (515)225-6563
Free: 888-696-5624
Fax: (515)225-7733
E-mail: careers@agrapl.com
URL: http://www.agraplacements.com

Description: Executive search firm. Branch offices in Peru, IN, Lincoln, IL, and Andover, KS.

672 ■ The Employment Place
719 Van Lennen Ave.
Cheyenne, WY 82009
Ph: (307)632-0534
Fax: (307)638-2104
E-mail: agrecruit@juno.com

Description: A twofold placement firm operates as a general employment agency offering services to all areas of employment. Also serves as Ag Recruiters offering services to the agricultural professional. Industries served: All areas including government agencies in the U.S.; also serve fields of plant science, animal science, engineering, agri-business, management, sales and service.

673 ■ Wellington Executive Search
3162 Johnson Ferry Rd., Ste. 260
Marietta, GA 30062
Ph: (770)645-5799
Fax: (678)278-0928
E-mail: jobs@wellingtonsearch.com
URL: http://www.wellingtonsearch.com

Description: Serves as an executive search firm covering sales representative, research and development, food scientists, and purchasing managers.

ONLINE JOB SOURCES AND SERVICES

674 ■ AgCareers.com
URL: http://www.agcareers.com

Description: Serves as an agriculture employment search engine. Supplies human resource services to the agriculture, food, natural resources and biotechnology industry.

675 ■ AgricultureJobs.com
URL: http://www.agriculturejobs.com

Description: Provides new job openings for agriculturists in addition to research into the farming, fishing and forestry employment markets. Maintains a career articles section written and frequented by industry professionals.

TRADESHOWS

676 ■ Agri News Farm Show
Agri News Farm Show
18 1st Ave. SE
Rochester, MN 55903-6118
Ph: (507)285-7600
Free: 800-533-1727
URL: http://www.agrinews.com

Frequency: Annual. **Primary Exhibits:** Agricultural equipment, supplies, and services. **Dates and Locations:** Rochester, MN; Graham Arena.

677 ■ American Seed Trade Association Convention
American Seed Trade Association
1701 Duke St., Ste. 275
Alexandria, VA 22314-3415
Ph: (703)837-8140
Fax: (703)837-9365
E-mail: info@amseed.org
URL: http://www.amseed.com

Frequency: Annual. Brings together seed industry professionals across all divisions of the association. Prepares attendees for the trends and issues facing the seed industry. Features special events and networking opportunities with colleagues across all commodities, both seed companies and suppliers alike.

678 ■ Empire Farm Days
Empire State Potato Growers, Inc.
PO Box 566
Stanley, NY 14561
Ph: (585)526-5356
Free: 877-697-7837
Fax: (585)526-6576
E-mail: mwickham@nypotatoes.org
URL: http://www.empirepotatogrowers.com

Frequency: Annual. **Primary Exhibits:** Agricultural equipment, supplies, and services. **Dates and Locations:** New York, NY; Rodman Lott & Sons Farm.

679 ■ Farm Progress Show
Prairie Farmer
c/o Josh Flint
812 Kelley Dr.
O'Fallon, IL 62269
Ph: (618)726-7528
URL: http://www.prairiefarmer.com

Frequency: Annual. **Primary Exhibits:** Farm machinery and equipment, trucks, livestock equipment, buildings, seed, chemicals, computers, and other agricultural products and services.

680 ■ Mid-America Farm Exposition
Salina Area Chamber of Commerce
120 W Ash St.
Salina, KS 67401-2308
Ph: (785)827-9301
Fax: (785)827-9758
E-mail: dlauver@salinakansas.org
URL: http://www.salinakansas.org

Frequency: Annual. **Primary Exhibits:** Agricultural equipment, supplies, and services, including irrigation equipment, fertilizer, farm implements, hybrid seed, agricultural chemicals, tractors, feed, farrowing crates and equipment, silos and bins, storage equipment, and farm buildings. **Dates and Locations:** Salina, KS; Bicentennial Center.

681 ■ Mid-South Farm and Gin Supply Exhibit
Southern Cotton Ginners Association
874 Cotton Gin Pl.
Memphis, TN 38106
Ph: (901)947-3104
Fax: (901)947-3103
URL: http://www.southerncottonginners.org

Frequency: Annual. **Primary Exhibits:** Agricultural equipment, supplies and services. **Dates and Locations:** Memphis, TN; Memphis Cook Convention Center.

682 ■ Midwest Farm Show
North Country Enterprises LLC
5322 250th St.
Cadott, WI 54727
Ph: (715)289-4632
Fax: (715)289-4632
E-mail: nceinfo@yahoo.com
URL: http://www.northcountryenterprises.com

Frequency: Annual. **Primary Exhibits:** Farm materials handling equipment, supplies, and services.

683 ■ National Western Stock Show
The Western Stock Show Association
4655 Humboldt St.
Denver, CO 80216
Ph: (303)297-1166
Fax: (303)292-1708
URL: http://www.nationalwestern.com

Frequency: Annual. **Primary Exhibits:** Jewelry, apparel, household goods, agricultural products, and service groups. A blend of agriculture, western and urban products including agriculture equipment, supplies and services, horse items, household products, apparel, jewelry, buildings, children's items, art, food and tools. **Dates and Locations:** Denver, CO; National Western Complex.

684 ■ Northwest Agricultural Show
Oregon Association of Nurseries
29751 SW Town Center Loop W
Wilsonville, OR 97070
Ph: (503)682-5089
Free: 800-342-6401
Fax: (503)682-5099
E-mail: info@oan.org
URL: http://www.oan.org

Frequency: Annual. **Primary Exhibits:** Agricultural equipment and services.

685 ■ Triumph of Agriculture Exposition - Farm and Ranch Machinery Show
Mid-America Expositions, Inc.
7015 Spring St.
Omaha, NE 68106-3518
Ph: (402)346-8003
Free: 800-475-SHOW
Fax: (402)346-5412
E-mail: info@showofficeonline.com
URL: http://www.showofficeonline.com

Frequency: Annual. **Primary Exhibits:** Farm equipment and supplies. **Dates and Locations:** Omaha, NE; Civic Auditorium.

686 ■ Western Farm Show
SouthWestern Association
638 W 39th St.
Kansas City, MO 64141-2910
Ph: (816)561-5323
Free: 800-762-5616
Fax: (816)561-1249
E-mail: oholcombe@swassn.com
URL: http://www.southwesternassn.com

Frequency: Annual. **Primary Exhibits:** equipment, supplies, and services relating to the agricultural industry. **Dates and Locations:** Kansas City, MO; American Royal Complex.

OTHER SOURCES

687 ■ American Institute of Biological Sciences
1313 Dolley Madison Blvd.
McLean, VA 22101
Ph: (703)790-1745
Fax: (703)790-2672
E-mail: adm@aibs.org
URL: http://www.aibs.org

Description: Professional member organization and federation of biological associations, laboratories, and museums whose members have an interest in the life sciences. Promotes unity and effectiveness of effort among persons engaged in biological research, education, and application of biological sciences, including agriculture, environment, and medicine. Seeks to further the relationships of biological sciences to other sciences and industries. Conducts roundtable series; provides names of prominent biologists who are willing to serve as speakers and curriculum consultants; provides advisory committees and other services to the Department of Energy, Environmental Protection Agency, National Science Foundation, Department of Defense, and National

Aeronautics and Space Administration. Maintains educational consultant panel. **Members:** 6,000.

688 ■ American Seed Trade Association
1701 Duke St., Ste. 275
Alexandria, VA 22314-3415
Ph: (703)837-8140
Fax: (703)837-9365
E-mail: info@amseed.org
URL: http://www.amseed.com

Description: Represents companies involved in seed production and distribution, plant breeding and related industries in North America. Promotes the development of better seed to produce better crops for a better quality of life. Informs members about environmental and conservation issues and new developments in plant breeding such as the use of modern biotechnology.

689 ■ American Society of Agricultural and Biological Engineers, District 5 - Pacific Northwest Section
c/o Quentin Nesbitt
Idaho Power Co.
Boise, ID 83707
Ph: (208)388-2519
E-mail: quentin.nebitt@idahopower.com
URL: http://www.asabe.org/membership/sections/dist5pnw.html

Description: Promotes the science and art of engineering in agricultural, food and biological systems. Encourages the professional improvement of members. Fosters education and develops engineering standards used in agriculture, food and biological systems.

690 ■ American Society of Agronomy
5585 Guilford Rd.
Madison, WI 53711-5801
Ph: (608)273-8080
Fax: (608)273-2021
E-mail: headquarters@sciencesocieties.org
URL: http://www.agronomy.org

Description: Professional society of agronomists, plant breeders, physiologists, soil scientists, chemists, educators, technicians, and others concerned with crop production and soil management, and conditions affecting them. Sponsors fellowship program and student essay and speech contests. Provides placement service.

691 ■ American Society for Horticultural Science
1018 Duke St.
Alexandria, VA 22314-2851
Ph: (703)836-4606
Fax: (703)836-2024
E-mail: webmaster@ashs.org
URL: http://ashs.org

Description: Promotes and encourages scientific research and education in horticulture throughout the world. Members represent all areas of horticulture science.

692 ■ Association of Applied IPM Ecologists
PO Box 1119
Coarsegold, CA 93614
Ph: (559)761-1064
E-mail: director@aaie.net
URL: http://aaie.net

Description: Professional agricultural pest management consultants, entomologists, and field personnel. Promotes the implementation of integrated pest management in agricultural and urban environments. Provides a forum for the exchange of technical information on pest control. Offers placement service.

693 ■ *Career Opportunities in Science*
InfoBase Holdings Inc.
132 W 31st., 17 Fl.
New York, NY 10001-3406
Ph: (212)967-8800

Fax: (800)678-3633
E-mail: info@infobasepublishing.com
URL: http://factsonfile.infobasepublishing.com

Frequency: Latest edition 2008. **Price:** $49.50 Individuals hardcover. **Pages:** 344. **Description:** Susan Echaore-McDavid. Second edition, 2008. 332 pages. **Covers:** More than 80 jobs, such as biochemist, molecular biologist, bioinformatic specialist, pharmacologist, computer engineer, geographic information systems specialist, science teacher, forensic scientist, patent agent, as well as physicist, astronomer, chemist, zoologist, oceanographer, and geologist. **Includes:** Appendices of educational institutions, periodicals, directories, and associations.

694 ■ Council for Agricultural Science and Technology
4420 W Lincoln Way
Ames, IA 50014-3447
Ph: (515)292-2125
Fax: (515)292-4512
E-mail: cast@cast-science.org
URL: http://www.cast-science.org

Description: Scientific societies, associate societies, individuals, corporations, foundations, and trade associations. Promotes science-based information on food, fiber, agricultural, natural resource, and related societal and environmental issues.

695 ■ Crop Science Society of America
5585 Guilford Rd.
Madison, WI 53711-5801
Ph: (608)273-8080
Fax: (608)273-2021
E-mail: headquarters@sciencesocieties.org
URL: http://www.crops.org

Description: Commits to the conservation and wise use of natural resources to produce food, feed and fiber crops while maintaining and improving the environment. Supports its members through publications, recognition and awards, placement service, certification programs, meetings and student activities.

696 ■ Cultural Vistas
440 Park Ave. S, 2nd Fl.
New York, NY 10016
Ph: (212)497-3500
Fax: (212)497-3535
E-mail: info@culturalvistas.org
URL: http://culturalvistas.org

Description: Providers worldwide of on-the-job training programs for students and professionals seeking international career development and life-changing experiences. Arranges workplace exchanges in hundreds of professional fields, bringing employers and trainees together from around the world. Client list ranges from small farming communities to Fortune 500 companies.

697 ■ Farm and Ranch Freedom Alliance
PO Box 809
Cameron, TX 76520
Ph: (254)697-2661
E-mail: info@farmandranchfreedom.org
URL: http://farmandranchfreedom.org

Description: Strives to save family farms and individuals from expensive and unnecessary government regulation. Works to assure the independence of farmers, ranchers, livestock owners and homesteaders in the management, control, identification and marketing of their products. Supports and enhances sustainable agriculture, family farms and domestic agricultural products.

698 ■ Federation of American Societies for Experimental Biology
9650 Rockville Pike
Bethesda, MD 20814
Ph: (301)634-7000
Free: 800-433-2732
Fax: (301)634-7001
E-mail: info@faseb.org
URL: http://www.faseb.org

Description: Federation of scientific societies with a total of 40,000 members: the American Physiological Society; American Society for Biochemistry and Molecular Biology; American Society for Pharmacology and Experimental Therapeutics; American Society for Investigative Pathology; American Society for Nutritional Sciences; the American Association of Immunologists; the American Society for Bone and Mineral Research; the American Society for Clinical Investigation; the Indocrine Society; the American Society of Human Genetics; Society for Developmental Biology; Biophysical Society; American Association of Anatomists; and the Protein Society. Maintains placement service.

699 ■ *Feedstuffs--Reference Issue and Buyers Guide*
Miller Publishing Co.
5810 W 78th St., Ste. 200
Bloomington, MN 55439
Ph: (952)930-4344
Fax: (952)938-1832
E-mail: tlundeen@feedstuffs.com
URL: http://www.feedstuffs.com

Frequency: Annual; Latest edition 2014. **Price:** $40 Individuals. **Includes:** Information on animal nutrition and health and feed production statistics. **Publication includes:** List of 2,000 suppliers of products and equipment for the feed, grain, and feeding industry; trade associations. **Entries include:** Company name, address, phone, fax, e-mail, website. **Arrangement:** Alphabetical. **Indexes:** Product, company.

700 ■ Korean-American Scientists and Engineers Association
1952 Gallows Rd., Ste. 300
Vienna, VA 22182
Ph: (703)748-1221
Fax: (703)748-1331
E-mail: sejong@ksea.org
URL: http://www.ksea.org

Description: Represents scientists and engineers holding single or advanced degrees. Promotes friendship and mutuality among Korean and American scientists and engineers; contributes to Korea's scientific, technological, industrial, and economic developments; strengthens the scientific, technological, and cultural bonds between Korea and the U.S. Sponsors symposium. Maintains speakers' bureau, placement service, and biographical archives. Compiles statistics. **Members:** 10,000.

701 ■ Minorities in Agriculture, Natural Resources and Related Sciences
1720 Peachtree Rd. NW, Ste. 776 S
Atlanta, GA 30309
Ph: (404)347-2975
Fax: (404)892-9405
E-mail: exec.office@manrrs.org
URL: http://www.manrrs.org

Description: Promotes natural and agricultural sciences and other related fields among ethnic minorities in all phases of career preparation and participation. Provides a network to support the professional development of minorities.

702 ■ National Coalition for Food and Agricultural Research
1800 S Oak St., Ste. 100
Champaign, IL 61820-6974
Ph: (217)356-3182
Fax: (217)398-4119
E-mail: ncfar@assochq.org
URL: http://www.ncfar.org

Description: Represents food, agriculture, nutrition, conservation and natural resource stakeholders. Aims to support the sustaining and increasing public investment at the national level in food and agricultural research, extension and education. Seeks to sustain and enhance federal funding for food and agricultural research, extension and education. Strives to help bring about research outcomes that provide a range of major public benefits.

703 ■ **National Postsecondary Agricultural Student Organization**
1055 SW Praire Trail Pkwy.
Ankeny, IA 50023
Ph: (515)964-6866
E-mail: camcenany@dmacc.edu
URL: http://www.nationalpas.org

Description: Agriculturally-related student organization; provides opportunity for individual growth, leadership and career preparation. Promotes development of leadership abilities through employment programs, course work, and organization activities. **Members:** 1,115.

704 ■ **Soil Science Society of America**
5585 Guilfor Rd.
Madison, WI 53711
Ph: (608)273-8080
Fax: (608)273-2021
E-mail: headquarters@soils.org
URL: http://www.soils.org

Description: Professional soil scientists, including soil physicists, soil classifiers, land use and management specialists, chemists, microbiologists, soil fertility specialists, soil cartographers, conservationists, mineralogists, engineers, and others interested in fundamental and applied soil science.

705 ■ **Soil Science Society of America - Consulting Soil Scientists Division**
PO Box 2175
Spokane, WA 99210-2175
Ph: (509)838-9860
E-mail: philip.small@landprofile.com
URL: http://www.soils.org/membership/divisions/
consulting-soil-scientists

Description: Represents the consulting, service, and business interests of professional soil scientists. Advances the discipline and practice of soil science and promotes interaction between professional soil scientists and their communities. Facilitates the exchange of business and soil science experiences within the society.

SOURCES OF HELP-WANTED ADS

706 ■ AI Magazine
Association for the Advancement of Artificial Intelligence
2275 E Bayshore Blvd., Ste. 160
Palo Alto, CA 94303
Ph: (650)328-3123
Fax: (650)321-4457
URLs: http://www.aaai.org/Magazine/magazine.php;
http://www.aaai.org
Frequency: Quarterly. **Price:** included in membership dues; $95 Individuals; $190 Institutions; Membership in AAAI. **Description:** Informs members about new research and literature on the field of artificial intelligence.

707 ■ Robotics World: The End User's Magazine of Flexible Automation
Communication Publications & Resources
2807 N Parham Rd., Ste. 200
Richmond, VA 23294
Free: 800-780-4066
E-mail: customerservice@briefings.com
URL: http://www.roboticsworld.com
Frequency: 6/yr. **Price:** Free; $99 Canada and Mexico; $112 Other countries; $162 Canada and Mexico 2 years; $162 Other countries 2 years. **Description:** Professional magazine covering flexible automation and intelligent machines.

EMPLOYER DIRECTORIES AND NETWORKING LISTS

708 ■ Advanced Manufacturing Technology
John Wiley & Sons Inc. - Scientific, Technical, Medical, and Scholarly Div. (Wiley-Blackwell)
111 River St.
Hoboken, NJ 07030-5774
Ph: (201)748-6000
Fax: (201)748-6088
E-mail: amtinfo@insights.com
URL: http://www.apnf.org/frostbody.htm
Frequency: Monthly. **Publication includes:** List of companies involved in developing advanced manufacturing technologies such as robotics, artificial intelligence in computers, ultrasonics, lasers, and waterjet cutters; also lists sources of information and education on high-technology. **Entries include:** Company or organization name, address, phone, name of contact; description of process, product, or service. Principal content is articles and analysis of advanced manufacturing technology. **Arrangement:** Classified by subject.

709 ■ The AI Week Directory
R.R. Bowker
630 Central Ave
New Providence, NJ 07974

Ph: (888)269-5372
Free: 888-269-5372
Fax: (908)464-3553
E-mail: info@bowker.com
URL: http://www.ulrichsweb.com
Frequency: Irregular. **Price:** $99. **Pages:** 150. **Covers:** The US and international artificial intelligence community and related businesses. **Entries include:** Company name, size, and financial status; names of key personnel; products and services. **Indexes:** Alphabetical, Geographical.

710 ■ Critical Technologies Sourcebook
Frequency: Annual; February. **Price:** $5,000 payment must accompany order. **Pages:** 400. **Covers:** Over 300 companies involved in the development of artificial intelligence technology such as voice recognition systems, intelligent text systems, computer programming languages, virtual reality, and fuzzy logic. **Includes:** Discussion of trends and sectors of the artificial intelligence industry. **Entries include:** Company name, address, phone, contact person, year established, whether public or private, description of research and technology. **Arrangement:** Company name. **Indexes:** Alphabetical (with phone).

HANDBOOKS AND MANUALS

711 ■ Expert Resumes for Computer and Web Jobs
JIST Publishing
875 Montreal Way
Saint Paul, MN 55102-4245
Ph: (317)613-4200
Free: 800-648-5478
Fax: (800)328-4564
E-mail: info@jist.com
URL: http://www.jist.com
Description: Wendy Enelow and Louise Kursmark. Third edition, 2011. $17.95 (paper). 304 pages. Contains a collection of sample resumes and resume writing advice including how to create and use an electronic resume. Contains an appendix that includes internet resources for an online job search, writing cover letters, as well as a collection of sample letters.

ONLINE JOB SOURCES AND SERVICES

712 ■ AIJobs.net
URL: http://www.aijobs.net
Description: Features artificial intelligence jobs and careers, resumes search and postings.

713 ■ ComputerJobs.com
URL: http://www.computerjobs.com
Description: Provides listings of computer-related job opportunities.

714 ■ Guru.com
URL: http://www.guru.com
Description: Job board specializing in contract jobs for creative and information technology professionals. Also provides online incorporation and educational opportunities for independent contractors along with articles and advice.

715 ■ ZDNet Tech Jobs
URL: http://www.zdnet.com
Description: Site houses a listing of national employment opportunities for professionals in high tech fields. Also contains resume building tips and relocation resources.

TRADESHOWS

716 ■ International Joint Conference on Artificial Intelligence
International Joint Conferences on Artificial Intelligence
PO Box 5490
Somerset, NJ 08875
Ph: (313)667-4669
Fax: (313)667-4966
E-mail: info@ijcai.org
URL: http://www.ijcai.org
Frequency: Biennial. **Primary Exhibits:** Artificial intelligence systems, projects, and services.

OTHER SOURCES

717 ■ AAAI Press
2275 E Bayshore Rd., Ste. 160
Palo Alto, CA 94303
Ph: (650)328-3123
Fax: (650)321-4457
URL: http://www.aaai.org/Press/press.php
Description: Manufacturing: Publishes edited collections, monographs, proceedings, and technical reports in the field of Artificial Intelligence. Co-publishes with MIT Press. Accepts unsolicited manuscripts. Reaches market through direct mail, trade sales, wholesalers and MIT Press.

718 ■ Association for the Advancement of Artificial Intelligence
2275 E Bayshore Blvd., Ste. 160
Palo Alto, CA 94303
Ph: (650)328-3123
Fax: (650)321-4457
URL: http://www.aaai.org/home.html
Description: Artificial Intelligence researchers; students, libraries, corporations, and others interested in the subject. (Artificial Intelligence is a discipline in which an attempt is made to approximate the human thinking process through computers.) Seeks to unite researchers and develop-

ers of Artificial Intelligence in order to provide an element of cohesion in the field. Serves as focal point and organizer for conferences; areas of interest include interpretation of visual data, robotics, expert systems, natural language processing, knowledge representation, and Artificial Intelligence programming technologies. Holds tutorials. Also publishes AI Magazine and AI Review.

719 ■ Association for Computing Machinery
2 Penn Plz., Ste. 701
New York, NY 10121-0701
Ph: (212)626-0500
Free: 800-342-6626
Fax: (212)944-1318
E-mail: acmhelp@acm.org
URL: http://www.acm.org

Description: Biological, medical, behavioral, and computer scientists; hospital administrators; programmers and others interested in application of computer methods to biological, behavioral, and medical problems.

720 ■ Association for Computing Machinery - Special Interest Group on Artificial Intelligence
2 Penn Plz., Ste. 701
New York, NY 10121-0701
Ph: (212)626-0605
Free: 800-342-6626
Fax: (212)944-1318
E-mail: frawley@acm.org
URL: http://www.sigart.org

Description: A special interest group of the Association for Computing Machinery. Individuals interested in the application of computers to tasks normally requiring human intelligence. Enhances the capabilities of computers in this area. **Members:** 1,300.

721 ■ Association for Computing Machinery - Special Interest Group on Simulation and Modelling
2 Penn Plz., Ste. 701
New York, NY 10121-0701
Ph: (212)626-0605
URL: http://www.sigsim.org

Description: A special interest group of Association for Computing Machinery. Researchers and practitioners in computer simulation including professionals in business and industry. Holds technical meetings at annual conference of ACM. Promotes research and conducts surveys on topics such as the type of computer simulation courses being offered at colleges and universities. Researches the application of simulation principles and theory to sub disciplines of computer science. **Members:** 2,074.

722 ■ *Career Opportunities in Science*
InfoBase Holdings Inc.
132 W 31st., 17 Fl.
New York, NY 10001-3406
Ph: (212)967-8800
Fax: (800)678-3633
E-mail: info@infobasepublishing.com
URL: http://factsonfile.infobasepublishing.com

Frequency: Latest edition 2008. **Price:** $49.50 Individuals hardcover. **Pages:** 344. **Description:** Susan Echaore-McDavid. Second edition, 2008. 332 pages. **Covers:** More than 80 jobs, such as biochemist, molecular biologist, bioinformatic specialist, pharmacologist, computer engineer, geographic information systems specialist, science teacher,

forensic scientist, patent agent, as well as physicist, astronomer, chemist, zoologist, oceanographer, and geologist. **Includes:** Appendices of educational institutions, periodicals, directories, and associations.

723 ■ Cognitive Science Society
10200 W 44th Ave., Ste. 304
Wheat Ridge, CO 80033-2840
Ph: (303)327-7547
Fax: (720)881-6101
E-mail: css@resourcenter.com
URL: http://www.cognitivesciencesociety.org

Description: Represents published PhD's; students and PhD's not actively publishing in the fields of psychology, artificial intelligence, and cognitive science. Promotes the dissemination of research in cognitive science and allied sciences. (Cognitive science is a branch of artificial intelligence that seeks to simulate human reasoning and associative powers on a computer, using specialized software).

724 ■ Computing Research Association
1828 L St. NW, Ste. 800
Washington, DC 20036-4632
Ph: (202)234-2111
Fax: (202)667-1066
E-mail: info@cra.org
URL: http://www.cra.org

Description: An association of more than 200 North American academic departments of computer science, computer engineering, and related fields; laboratories and centers in industry government, and academia engaging in basic computing research; and affiliated professional societies.

725 ■ IEEE Computer Society
2001 L St. NW, Ste. 700
Washington, DC 20036
Ph: (202)371-0101
Free: 800-272-6657
Fax: (202)728-9614
E-mail: help@computer.org
URL: http://www.computer.org

Description: Computer professionals. Promotes the development of computer and information sciences and fosters communication within the information processing community. Sponsors conferences, symposia, workshops, tutorials, technical meetings, and seminars. Operates Computer Society Press. Presents scholarships; bestows technical achievement and service awards and certificates. **Members:** 90,000.

726 ■ IEEE - Systems, Man, and Cybernetics Society
3 Park Ave., 17th Fl.
New York, NY 10016-5997
Ph: (212)419-7900
Fax: (212)752-4929
E-mail: philip.chen@ieee.org
URL: http://www.ieeesmc.org

Description: A society of the Institute of Electrical and Electronics Engineers. Serves as a forum on the theoretical and practical considerations of systems engineering, human machine systems, and cybernetics--with a particular focus on synthetic and natural systems involving humans and machines. **Members:** 3,895.

727 ■ IMAGE Society
PO Box 6221
Chandler, AZ 85246-6221
E-mail: image@image-society.org
URL: http://image-society.org

Description: Individuals and organizations interested in the technological advancement and application of real-time visual simulation (medical, virtual reality, telepresence, aeronautical, and automotive) and other related virtual reality technologies.

728 ■ International Association for Artificial Intelligence and Law
c/o Jack G. Conrad, President
610 Opperman Dr.
Saint Paul, MN 55123-1340
E-mail: jack.g.conrad@thomsonreuters.com
URL: http://www.iaail.org

Description: Computer science and law academics and professionals. Promotes research and development in the field of artificial intelligence and law. **Members:** 760.

729 ■ International Society of Applied Intelligence
Texas State University, San Marcos
Department of Computer Science
601 University Dr.
San Marcos, TX 78666-4616
Ph: (512)245-8050
Fax: (512)245-8750
E-mail: ma04@txstate.edu
URL: http://isai.cs.txstate.edu

Description: Researchers, academicians, computer scientists, industry, and government. Promotes dissemination of Research in the area of intelligent systems' technology and improves scientific literacy. Sponsors an International conference on Industrial, Engineering, and other Applications of Applied Intelligent Systems.

730 ■ MIT Computer Science and Artificial Intelligence Laboratory
32 Vassar St.
Cambridge, MA 02139
Ph: (617)253-5851
Fax: (617)258-8682
URL: http://www.csail.mit.edu

Description: Active since 1959. Interdisciplinary laboratory of over 200 people that spans several academic departments and has active projects ongoing with members of every academic school at MIT. Offers research, current job listings, and educational outreach.

731 ■ Society for Modeling and Simulation International
2598 Fortune Way, Ste. I
Vista, CA 92081
Ph: (858)277-3888
Fax: (858)277-3930
E-mail: scs@scs.org
URL: http://www.scs.org

Description: Persons professionally engaged in simulation, particularly through the use of computers and similar devices that employ mathematical or physical analogies. Maintains speakers' bureau.

732 ■ SRI International Artificial Intelligence Center
333 Ravenswood Ave.
Menlo Park, CA 94025-3493
Ph: (650)859-2641
Fax: (650)859-3735
E-mail: action@ai.sri.com
URL: http://www.ai.sri.com

Description: Seeks to develop methods for building computer-based systems to solve problems.

SOURCES OF HELP-WANTED ADS

733 ■ *Air Jobs Digest*
World Air Data
PO Box 42724
Washington, DC 20015
Ph: (301)990-6800
Free: 800-247-5627
E-mail: staff@airjobsdaily.com
URL: http://www.airjobsdigest.com/

Frequency: Monthly. **Price:** $96 Individuals. **Description:** Newspaper covering job listings in aviation and aerospace worldwide.

734 ■ *Air Safety Week*
Access Intelligence L.L.C.
4 Choke Cherry Rd., 2nd Fl.
Rockville, MD 20850
Ph: (301)354-2000
Free: 800-777-5006
Fax: (301)309-3847
E-mail: info@accessintel.com
URL: http://www.accessintel.com/products/defense

Description: Weekly. $1,319/year. Covers air safety issues, crashes, regulations, legal cases, air traffic control technology, maintenance, engineering, and aviation and airport security. Also available online and via e-mail.

735 ■ *ATCA Bulletin*
Air Traffic Control Association
1101 King St., Ste. 300
Alexandria, VA 22314
Ph: (703)299-2430
Fax: (703)299-2437
E-mail: info@atca.org
URL: http://www.atca.org

Description: Monthly. Features news of the Association, which is interested in the establishment and maintenance of a safe and efficient air traffic control system.

736 ■ *Aviation Today*
Access Intelligence L.L.C.
4 Choke Cherry Rd., 2nd Fl.
Rockville, MD 20850
Ph: (301)354-2000
Free: 800-777-5006
Fax: (301)309-3847
E-mail: info@accessintel.com
URL: http://www.accessintel.com

Description: Covers the commuter/regional airline industry, including airline management, marketing, labor, personnel changes, aircraft acquisitions, new products, and the financial and operational environment. Recurring features include interviews, news of research, a calendar of events, reports of meetings, job listings, and notices of publications available.

737 ■ *Aviation Week & Space Technology*
The McGraw-Hill Companies Inc.
1200 G St. NW, Ste. 922
Washington, DC 20005
Ph: (202)383-2360
Fax: (202)383-2346
E-mail: customer.service@mcgraw-hill.com
URL: http://www.aviationweek.com/awst.aspx?channel=awst

Frequency: Weekly. **Price:** $79 Canada; $79 Individuals; $119 Other countries. **Description:** Magazine serving the aviation and aerospace market worldwide.

738 ■ *Flying*
Bonnier Corp.
460 N Orlando Ave., Ste. 200
Winter Park, FL 32789
Ph: (407)628-4802
Fax: (407)628-7061
URL: http://www.flyingmag.com

Frequency: Monthly. **Price:** $14 Individuals print; $22 Two years print; $33 Canada print; $33 Other countries print. **Description:** General aviation magazine.

739 ■ *In Flight USA*
In Flight USA
PO Box 5402
San Mateo, CA 94402
Ph: (650)358-9908
Fax: (650)358-9254
E-mail: staff@inflightusa.com
URL: http://inflight.squarespace.com

Frequency: Monthly. **Price:** $24.95 Individuals; $44.95 Two years. **Description:** Magazine on Aviation.

EMPLOYER DIRECTORIES AND NETWORKING LISTS

740 ■ *AOPA's Airport Directory: The Pilot and FBO Flight Planning Guide*
Aircraft Owners and Pilots Association
421 Aviation Way
Frederick, MD 21701
Ph: (301)695-2000
Free: 800-872-2672
Fax: (301)695-2375
E-mail: airportdirectory@aopa.org
URL: http://www.aopa.org/airports/

Frequency: Biennial; January; Latest edition 2009-2010. **Price:** $3,995 Individuals. **Pages:** 680. **Covers:** 5,300 U.S. public-use landing facilities, including airports, heliports, seaplane bases, and approximately 1,800 private-use landing facilities; 5,000 aviation service companies. **Includes:** ATC and FSS phone numbers and frequencies; U.S. Customs airports and airports and airports of entry for Canada, Mexico, and the Caribbean. **Entries include:** For

landing facilities--Airport type and name, city, phone, runway dimensions, types of instrument approaches, hours operated, communications frequencies, runway light system, local attractions, ground transportation, restaurants, hotels. For aviation service companies--Company name, phone, airport affiliation, operating hours, fuel type, Unicom frequency. **Arrangement:** Geographical. **Indexes:** Cross-reference index of U.S. landing facilities.

741 ■ *FAA Airmen Directory*
National Institute for Computer-Assisted Reporting
141 Neff Annex
Columbia, MO 65211
Ph: (573)882-2042
Fax: (573)884-5544
E-mail: info@ire.org
URL: http://ire.org/nicar

742 ■ *Journal of Air Traffic Control*
Air Traffic Control Association
1101 King St., Ste. 300
Alexandria, VA 22314
Ph: (703)299-2430
Fax: (703)299-2437
E-mail: info@atca.org
URL: http://atca.kma.net/index.asp?bid=33

Frequency: Quarterly. **Price:** $78 U.S.; $88 Other countries. **Description:** Magazine for air traffic controllers, aviation personnel, pilots and systems engineers. **Includes:** Directory of member organizations. **Entries include:** Organization name, city, state.

743 ■ *National Air Transportation Association--Aviation Resource and Membership Directory*
National Air Transportation Association
4226 King St.
Alexandria, VA 22302
Ph: (703)845-9000
Free: 800-808-6282
Fax: (703)845-8176
E-mail: rmulholland@nata.aero
URL: http://www.nata.aero

Frequency: Annual; Latest Edition 2012. **Price:** $50 Nonmembers; $25 Members. **Covers:** More than 1,000 regular, associate, and affiliate members; regular members include airport service organizations, air taxi operators, and commuter airlines. **Entries include:** Company name, address, phone, fax number, name and title of contact. **Arrangement:** Regular members are classified by service; associate and affiliate members are alphabetical in separate sections. **Indexes:** Geographical.

744 ■ *World Aerospace Database*
Aviation Week Group
1200 G St.NW, Ste. 922
Washington, DC 20005-3814
Free: 800-525-5003

Fax: (712)755-7423
E-mail: wad@mcgraw-hill.com
URL: http://www.aviationweek.com

Frequency: Semiannual. **Price:** $269 U.S. print; $1,295 U.S. CD-ROM, incl. 1 year print sub., 2 editions; $595 U.S. online, incl. 1 year print sub., 2 editions; $495 U.S. special online; $149 U.S. special print. **Description:** Covers more than 25,000 companies and 120,000 key executives to the aviation and aerospace industries worldwide. **Arrangement:** Classified by major activity (manufacturers, airlines, etc.). **Indexes:** Company and organization, personnel, product, trade name.

HANDBOOKS AND MANUALS

745 ■ Air Traffic Control Career Prep
Aviation Supplies & Academics, Inc.
7005 132nd Pl. SE
Newcastle, WA 98059
Ph: (425)235-1500
Free: 800-272-2359
Fax: (425)235-0128
URL: http://www.asa2fly.com/index.aspx

Description: Patrick Mattson. 2006. $49.95 (paper). 240 pages. Provides introduction on air traffic controller career and helps readers improve chances of earning a high score on the FAA's air traffic selection and training aptitude test. Features general information on opportunities, working conditions, training and qualification requirements, available roles and positions, pay and benefits, and contact phone numbers.

746 ■ Master the Air Traffic Controller Test
Peterson's
461 From Rd.
Paramus, NJ 07652
Ph: (609)896-1800
Free: 800-338-3282
Fax: (402)458-3042
E-mail: custsvc@petersons.com
URL: http://www.petersons.com

Description: Michael S. Nolan. 2007. 360 pages. Gives readers the information needed to score high on the FAA entrance exams and launch a career in air traffic control. Contains a thorough explanation of the U.S. air traffic control system, 700 sample knowledge questions and answers and navigation charts.

747 ■ Voices: A Glimpse Into the Careers of Air Traffic Controllers
National Air Traffic Controllers Association
1325 Massachusetts Ave. NW
Washington, DC 20005
Ph: (202)628-5451
Free: 800-266-0895
Fax: (202)628-5767
E-mail: prinaldi@natcadc.org
URL: http://www.natca.org

Description: Features the challenging and rewarding profession of being an air traffic controller.

ONLINE JOB SOURCES AND SERVICES

748 ■ Air Transportation Jobs
URL: http://air.transportation.jobs.jobsearchsite.com

Description: Provides available air transportation jobs and career resources. Allows employers to post jobs and search resumes to find qualified candidates.

749 ■ AirJobsDaily.com
URL: http://www.airjobsdaily.com

Description: Serves as a source of current aviation and aerospace job openings.

750 ■ AirlineCareer.info
URL: http://www.airlinecareer.info

Description: Provides jobs in the airline community covering airport careers, aircraft manufacturing, aerospace careers, and cabin crew careers.

751 ■ Airportjobs.Us
URL: http://www.airportjobs.us

Description: Helps job seekers find airport career opportunities with top companies. Allows employers and recruiters to match qualified candidates with open airport postions.

752 ■ The Aviation MD
URL: http://www.theaviationmd.com

Description: Serves as international aviation database for employers and jobseekers in the aviation industry.

753 ■ AviationCrossing.com
URL: http://www.aviationcrossing.com

Description: Provides aviation jobs for agents, managers, mechanics, operators, specialists, supervisors, technicians, engineers, maintenance, pilots and other related aviation professionals.

754 ■ AviationEmployment.com
URL: http://www.aviationemployment.com

Description: Serves as an online job search service provider specializing in aviation and aerospace jobs and employment opportunities.

755 ■ AvJobs.com
URL: http://www.avjobs.com

Description: Provides information on a number of different careers in the aviation and aerospace industry. Features aviation schools directory, affiliate programs, research and networking, employment resources, salaries and wages, aviation careers descriptions, aviation guide and other resources.

756 ■ TransportationCareers.net
URL: http://www.transportationcareers.net

Description: Offers updated job database, research, and articles related to the transportation industry.

TRADESHOWS

757 ■ Air Traffic Control Global
Air Traffic Control Association
1101 King St., Ste. 300
Alexandria, VA 22314
Ph: (703)299-2430
Fax: (703)299-2437
E-mail: info@atca.org
URL: http://www.atca.org

Frequency: Annual. **Primary Exhibits:** Air traffic control information.

758 ■ Airports Council International - North America Convention
Airports Council International
1775 K St. NW, Ste. 500
Washington, DC 20006
Ph: (202)293-8500
Free: 888-424-7767
Fax: (202)331-1362
E-mail: memberservices@aci-na.org
URL: http://www.aci-na.org

Frequency: Annual. **Primary Exhibits:** Air Aviation industry equipment, products and services.

OTHER SOURCES

759 ■ Air Traffic Control Association
1101 King St., Ste. 300
Alexandria, VA 22314
Ph: (703)299-2430
Fax: (703)299-2437
E-mail: info@atca.org
URL: http://www.atca.org

Description: Air traffic controllers; private, commercial, and military pilots; private and business aircraft owners and operators; aircraft and electronics engineers; airlines, aircraft manufacturers, and electronic and human engineering firms.

760 ■ National Black Coalition of Federal Aviation Employees
PO Box 845
Hampton, GA 30228
Free: 888-311-1622
E-mail: info@nbcfae.org
URL: http://nbcfae.org

Description: Federal Aviation Administration employees. Purposes are to: promote professionalism and equal opportunity in the workplace; locate and train qualified minorities for FAA positions; help the FAA meet its affirmative action goals; monitor black, female, and minority trainees; educate members and the public about their rights and FAA personnel and promotion qualifications; develop a voice for black, female, and minority FAA employees. Recruits minorities from community and schools who qualify for employment; sponsors seminars for members and for those who wish to be employed by the FAA. Maintains speaker's bureau; sponsors competitions.

Aircraft Mechanics and Engine Specialists

SOURCES OF HELP-WANTED ADS

761 ■ AeroSpaceNews.com
AeroSpaceNews.com
PO Box 1748
Ojai, CA 93024-1748
Ph: (805)985-2320
URL: http://aerospacenews.com/

Frequency: Monthly. **Price:** $19.95 Individuals private. **Description:** Journal reporting on the insights, impressions and images of tomorrow's technological wonders in the field of aerospace.

762 ■ Air Jobs Digest
World Air Data
PO Box 42724
Washington, DC 20015
Ph: (301)990-6800
Free: 800-247-5627
E-mail: staff@airjobsdaily.com
URL: http://www.airjobsdigest.com/

Frequency: Monthly. **Price:** $96 Individuals. **Description:** Newspaper covering job listings in aviation and aerospace worldwide.

763 ■ Aviation Maintenance
ASI Publications Ltd. - Aerospace & Security Media
5590 N Diversey Blvd., Ste. 209
Milwaukee, WI
Ph: (414)967-4997
URL: http://www.avm-mag.com

Frequency: 6/yr. **Price:** Free. **Description:** Magazine covering aviation maintenance.

764 ■ Aviation Week & Space Technology
The McGraw-Hill Companies Inc.
1200 G St. NW, Ste. 922
Washington, DC 20005
Ph: (202)383-2360
Fax: (202)383-2346
E-mail: customer.service@mcgraw-hill.com
URL: http://www.aviationweek.com/awst.aspx?channel=awst

Frequency: Weekly. **Price:** $79 Canada; $79 Individuals; $119 Other countries. **Description:** Magazine serving the aviation and aerospace market worldwide.

765 ■ Flying
Bonnier Corp.
460 N Orlando Ave., Ste. 200
Winter Park, FL 32789
Ph: (407)628-4802
Fax: (407)628-7061
URL: http://www.flyingmag.com

Frequency: Monthly. **Price:** $14 Individuals print; $22 Two years print; $33 Canada print; $33 Other countries print. **Description:** General aviation magazine.

766 ■ In Flight USA
In Flight USA
PO Box 5402
San Mateo, CA 94402
Ph: (650)358-9908
Fax: (650)358-9254
E-mail: staff@inflightusa.com
URL: http://inflight.squarespace.com

Frequency: Monthly. **Price:** $24.95 Individuals; $44.95 Two years. **Description:** Magazine on Aviation.

767 ■ Rotor & Wing
Access Intelligence L.L.C.
4 Choke Cherry Rd., 2nd Fl.
Rockville, MD 20850
Ph: (301)354-2000
Free: 800-777-5006
Fax: (301)309-3847
E-mail: info@accessintel.com
URL: http://www.aviationtoday.com/rw/

Frequency: Monthly. **Price:** Free. **Description:** Magazine covering helicopters.

EMPLOYER DIRECTORIES AND NETWORKING LISTS

768 ■ AOPA's Airport Directory: The Pilot and FBO Flight Planning Guide
Aircraft Owners and Pilots Association
421 Aviation Way
Frederick, MD 21701
Ph: (301)695-2000
Free: 800-872-2672
Fax: (301)695-2375
E-mail: airportdirectory@aopa.org
URL: http://www.aopa.org/airports/

Frequency: Biennial; January; Latest edition 2009-2010. **Price:** $3,995 Individuals. **Pages:** 680. **Covers:** 5,300 U.S. public-use landing facilities, including airports, heliports, seaplane bases, and approximately 1,800 private-use landing facilities; 5,000 aviation service companies. **Includes:** ATC and FSS phone numbers and frequencies; U.S. Customs airports and airports and airports of entry for Canada, Mexico, and the Caribbean. **Entries include:** For landing facilities--Airport type and name, city, phone, runway dimensions, types of instrument approaches, hours operated, communications frequencies, runway light system, local attractions, ground transportation, restaurants, hotels. For aviation service companies--Company name, phone, airport affiliation, operating hours, fuel type, Unicom frequency. **Arrangement:** Geographical. **Indexes:** Cross-reference index of U.S. landing facilities.

769 ■ FAA Airmen Directory
National Institute for Computer-Assisted Reporting
141 Neff Annex
Columbia, MO 65211

Ph: (573)882-2042
Fax: (573)884-5544
E-mail: info@ire.org
URL: http://ire.org/nicar

770 ■ Journal of Air Traffic Control
Air Traffic Control Association
1101 King St., Ste. 300
Alexandria, VA 22314
Ph: (703)299-2430
Fax: (703)299-2437
E-mail: info@atca.org
URL: http://atca.kma.net/index.asp?bid=33

Frequency: Quarterly. **Price:** $78 U.S.; $88 Other countries. **Description:** Magazine for air traffic controllers, aviation personnel, pilots and systems engineers. **Includes:** Directory of member organizations. **Entries include:** Organization name, city, state.

771 ■ National Air Transportation Association--Aviation Resource and Membership Directory
National Air Transportation Association
4226 King St.
Alexandria, VA 22302
Ph: (703)845-9000
Free: 800-808-6282
Fax: (703)845-8176
E-mail: rmulholland@nata.aero
URL: http://www.nata.aero

Frequency: Annual; Latest Edition 2012. **Price:** $50 Nonmembers; $25 Members. **Covers:** More than 1,000 regular, associate, and affiliate members; regular members include airport service organizations, air taxi operators, and commuter airlines. **Entries include:** Company name, address, phone, fax number, name and title of contact. **Arrangement:** Regular members are classified by service; associate and affiliate members are alphabetical in separate sections. **Indexes:** Geographical.

772 ■ World Aerospace Database
Aviation Week Group
1200 G St.NW, Ste. 922
Washington, DC 20005-3814
Free: 800-525-5003
Fax: (712)755-7423
E-mail: wad@mcgraw-hill.com
URL: http://www.aviationweek.com

Frequency: Semiannual. **Price:** $269 U.S. print; $1,295 U.S. CD-ROM, incl. 1 year print sub., 2 editions; $595 U.S. online, incl. 1 year print sub., 2 editions; $495 U.S. special online; $149 U.S. special print. **Description:** Covers more than 25,000 companies and 120,000 key executives to the aviation and aerospace industries worldwide. **Arrangement:** Classified by major activity (manufacturers, airlines, etc.). **Indexes:** Company and organization, personnel, product, trade name.

HANDBOOKS AND MANUALS

773 ■ *Engineering, Mechanics, and Architecture*
InfoBase Holdings Inc.
132 W 31st., 17 Fl.
New York, NY 10001-3406
Ph: (212)967-8800
Fax: (800)678-3633
E-mail: info@infobasepublishing.com
URL: http://www.ferguson.infobasepublishing.com

Description: Kelly Wiles. 2010. $39.95. 160 pages (hardcover). Serves as a guide for readers interested in switching jobs. Contains useful advice, career tips, interviews and self-asessment questions.

EMPLOYMENT AGENCIES AND SEARCH FIRMS

774 ■ **Amtec Human Capital**
2749 Saturn St.
Brea, CA 92821
Ph: (714)993-1900
Fax: (714)993-2419
E-mail: info@amtechc.com
URL: http://www.amtechc.com

Description: Employment agency.

775 ■ **Jet Professionals**
114 Charles A. Lindbergh Dr.
Teterboro, NJ 07608
Free: 800-441-6016
Fax: (201)462-4081
E-mail: jobs@jet-professionals.com
URL: http://www.jet-professionals.com

Description: Provides staffing services to the aviation industry. Offers jobs for corporate aviation executives, chief pilots, flight attendants, maintenance professionals, dispatchers, schedulers and more.

776 ■ **Strom Aviation**
109 S Elm St.
Waconia, MN 55387
Ph: (952)544-3611
Free: 800-743-8988
Fax: (952)544-3948
E-mail: jillp@stromaviation.com
URL: http://www.stromaviation.com

Description: Serves as a staffing firm specializing in hiring all types of aircraft technicians to provide manpower to service centers, repair stations, and OEMs.

ONLINE JOB SOURCES AND SERVICES

777 ■ **AeroIndustryJobs.com**
URL: http://www.aeroindustryjobs.com/home/index.cfm?site_id=13641

Description: Lists careers in the aerospace, defense and advanced materials industries. Helps industry employers connect with qualified, career-focused job seekers.

778 ■ **AeroVents.com**
URL: http://www.aerovents.com/body.shtml

Description: Seeks to spread the word about aviation events. Covers aviation events from conventions, space launches, seminars, model rocketry and aircraft, ballooning, sky diving, plane pulls, open houses, air shows and fly-ins.

779 ■ **Air Transportation Jobs**
URL: http://air.transportation.jobs.jobsearchsite.com

Description: Provides available air transportation jobs and career resources. Allows employers to post jobs and search resumes to find qualified candidates.

780 ■ **AircraftEngineers.com**
URL: http://www.aircraftengineers.com

Description: Lists aircraft maintenance engineering jobs and aerospace vacancies. Provides career information for individuals who wish to start a career as an aircraft engineer.

781 ■ **AircraftMechanicJobs.org**
URL: http://aircraftmechanicjobs.org

Description: Lists aircraft mechanic jobs from different companies throughout the country.

782 ■ **AirJobsDaily.com**
URL: http://www.airjobsdaily.com

Description: Serves as a source of current aviation and aerospace job openings.

783 ■ **AirlineCareer.com**
URL: http://www.airlinecareer.com

Description: Web-based training center. Provides flight attendant job placement services.

784 ■ **AirlineCareer.info**
URL: http://www.airlinecareer.info

Description: Provides jobs in the airline community covering airport careers, aircraft manufacturing, aerospace careers, and cabin crew careers.

785 ■ **AvCrew.com**
URL: http://www.avcrew.com

Description: Provides service designed exclusively for career employment in the business aviation sector. Features flight crew jobs, conducts applicant screening, and assists selected flight departments with candidate searches.

786 ■ **AviaNation**
URL: http://www.avianation.com

Description: Features aviation jobs, pilot jobs, flight attendant jobs, jobs for A&P mechanics, and other aviation job openings around the world.

787 ■ **AviationCrossing.com**
URL: http://www.aviationcrossing.com

Description: Provides aviation jobs for agents, managers, mechanics, operators, specialists, supervisors, technicians, engineers, maintenance, pilots and other related aviation professionals.

788 ■ **AviationEmployment.com**
URL: http://www.aviationemployment.com

Description: Serves as an online job search service provider specializing in aviation and aerospace jobs and employment opportunities.

789 ■ **AvJobs.com**
URL: http://www.avjobs.com

Description: Provides information on a number of different careers in the aviation and aerospace industry. Features aviation schools directory, affiliate programs, research and networking, employment resources, salaries and wages, aviation careers descriptions, aviation guide and other resources.

790 ■ **BestAviation.net**
URL: http://www.bestaviation.net

Description: Provides source for information on flight school training, helicopter schools, aviation college programs, flight attendant careers, aircraft maintenance and pilot jobs.

791 ■ **FlightLevelJobs.com**
URL: http://www.flightleveljobs.com

Description: Serves as a source of aviation employment information. Features aviation and aerospace jobs and employment opportunities.

792 ■ **JetEmployment.com**
URL: http://jetemployment.com

Description: Features employment opportunities for pilots and other workers in the airline, airport, and business aviation industry.

793 ■ **PlaneJobs.com**
URL: http://planejobs.com

Description: Serves as an employment, resume, career, and job search database for the aviation industry.

OTHER SOURCES

794 ■ **Air Traffic Control Association**
1101 King St., Ste. 300
Alexandria, VA 22314
Ph: (703)299-2430
Fax: (703)299-2437
E-mail: info@atca.org
URL: http://www.atca.org

Description: Air traffic controllers; private, commercial, and military pilots; private and business aircraft owners and operators; aircraft and electronics engineers; airlines, aircraft manufacturers, and electronic and human engineering firms.

795 ■ **Aircraft Electronics Association**
3570 NE Ralph Powell Rd.
Lee's Summit, MO 64064
Ph: (816)347-8400
Fax: (816)347-8405
E-mail: info@aea.net
URL: http://www.aea.net

Description: Companies engaged in the sales, engineering, installation, and service of electronic aviation equipment and systems. Seeks to: advance the science of aircraft electronics; promote uniform and stable regulations and uniform standards of performance; establish and maintain a code of ethics; gather and disseminate technical data; advance the education of members and the public in the science of aircraft electronics. Offers supplement type certificates, test equipment licensing, temporary FCC licensing for new installations, spare parts availability and pricing, audiovisual technician training, equipment and spare parts loan, profitable installation, and service facility operation. Provides employment information, equipment exchange information and service assistance on member installations anywhere in the world.

796 ■ *Career Opportunities in Aviation and the Aerospace Industry*
InfoBase Holdings Inc.
132 W 31st., 17 Fl.
New York, NY 10001-3406
Ph: (212)967-8800
Fax: (800)678-3633
E-mail: info@infobasepublishing.com
URLs: http://www.infobasepublishing.com; http://www.infobasepublishing.com/Bookdetail.aspx?ISBN=1438110642&eBooks=1

Frequency: Published January, 2005. **Description:** Susan Echaore-McDavid. 2004. 305 pages. **Covers:** Eighty up-to-date job profiles, providing detailed information about the duties, salaries, and prospects of aviation mechanics, designers, technicians, scientists, and administrators. **Includes:** Appendices of educational institutions, periodicals, directories, and associations.

797 ■ **Professional Aviation Maintenance Association**
972 E Tuttle Rd., Bldg. 204
Ionia, MI 48846
Free: 800-356-1671
E-mail: hq@pama.org
URL: http://pama.org

Description: Airframe and powerplant (A&P) technicians and aviation industry-related companies. Strives to increase the professionalism of the individual aviation technician through technical knowledge and better understanding of safety

requirements. Establishes communication among technicians throughout the country. Fosters and

improves methods, skills, learning and achievement in the aviation maintenance field.

Sources of Help-Wanted Ads

798 ■ *Aerospace America Magazine*
American Institute of Aeronautics and Astronautics
1801 Alexander Bell Dr., Ste. 500
Reston, VA 20191-4344
Ph: (703)264-7500
Free: 800-639-2422
Fax: (703)264-7551
E-mail: custserv@aiaa.org
URL: http://www.aerospaceamerica.org/Pages/Table-OfContents.aspx

Frequency: Monthly. **Price:** $200 Institutions non member, domestic; $163 for nonmembers in U.S. **Description:** Monthly. Free to members; nonmembers, $140.00 per year. Covers aeronautics and space technology with special attention to aerospace defense, design, and electronics.

799 ■ *Aerospace Engineering & Manufacturing*
Society of Automotive Engineers International
400 Commonwealth Dr.
Warrendale, PA 15096-0001
Ph: (724)776-4841
Free: 877-606-7323
Fax: (724)776-0790
E-mail: aero@sae.org
URL: http://www.sae.org/magazines/

Frequency: 10/yr. **Price:** $65 U.S., Canada, and Mexico; $100 Other countries; $100 U.S., Canada, and Mexico 2 years; $155 Two years other countries; Free. **Description:** Magazine for aerospace manufacturing engineers providing technical and design information.

800 ■ *Aerospace Manufacturing and Design*
URL: http://www.onlineamd.com/

Price: $45 Canada and Mexico; $85 Individuals UK & Europe; $175 Other countries. **Description:** Magazine covering aerospace manufacturing and design.

801 ■ *AeroSpaceNews.com*
AeroSpaceNews.com
PO Box 1748
Ojai, CA 93024-1748
Ph: (805)985-2320
URL: http://aerospacenews.com/

Frequency: Monthly. **Price:** $19.95 Individuals private. **Description:** Journal reporting on the insights, impressions and images of tomorrow's technological wonders in the field of aerospace.

802 ■ *AIE Perspectives Newsmagazine*
American Institute of Engineers
4630 Appian Way, Ste. 206
El Sobrante, CA 94803-1875
Ph: (510)758-2490

Fax: (510)758-6240
E-mail: aie@aieonline.org
URL: http://www.members-aie.org

Frequency: Monthly. **Price:** included in membership dues. **Description:** Professional magazine covering engineering.

803 ■ *Air Jobs Digest*
World Air Data
PO Box 42724
Washington, DC 20015
Ph: (301)990-6800
Free: 800-247-5627
E-mail: staff@airjobsdaily.com
URL: http://www.airjobsdigest.com/

Frequency: Monthly. **Price:** $96 Individuals. **Description:** Newspaper covering job listings in aviation and aerospace worldwide.

804 ■ *Air Safety Week*
Access Intelligence L.L.C.
4 Choke Cherry Rd., 2nd Fl.
Rockville, MD 20850
Ph: (301)354-2000
Free: 800-777-5006
Fax: (301)309-3847
E-mail: info@accessintel.com
URL: http://www.accessintel.com/products/defense

Description: Weekly. $1,319/year. Covers air safety issues, crashes, regulations, legal cases, air traffic control technology, maintenance, engineering, and aviation and airport security. Also available online and via e-mail.

805 ■ *AOPA Pilot*
Aircraft Owners and Pilots Association
421 Aviation Way
Frederick, MD 21701
Ph: (301)695-2000
Free: 800-872-2672
Fax: (301)695-2375
URL: http://www.aopa.org/pilot/

Frequency: Monthly. **Price:** $8 Members; $5 Nonmembers; available to members only. **Description:** Magazine for general aviation pilots and aircraft owners who are members of the Aircraft Owners and Pilots Assn. Articles are tailored to address the special informational requirements of both recreational and business pilots.

806 ■ *Aviation Maintenance*
ASI Publications Ltd. - Aerospace & Security Media
5590 N Diversey Blvd., Ste. 209
Milwaukee, WI
Ph: (414)967-4997
URL: http://www.avm-mag.com

Frequency: 6/yr. **Price:** Free. **Description:** Magazine covering aviation maintenance.

807 ■ *Aviation Today*
Access Intelligence L.L.C.
4 Choke Cherry Rd., 2nd Fl.
Rockville, MD 20850
Ph: (301)354-2000
Free: 800-777-5006
Fax: (301)309-3847
E-mail: info@accessintel.com
URL: http://www.accessintel.com

Description: Covers the commuter/regional airline industry, including airline management, marketing, labor, personnel changes, aircraft acquisitions, new products, and the financial and operational environment. Recurring features include interviews, news of research, a calendar of events, reports of meetings, job listings, and notices of publications available.

808 ■ *Aviation Week & Space Technology*
The McGraw-Hill Companies Inc.
1200 G St. NW, Ste. 922
Washington, DC 20005
Ph: (202)383-2360
Fax: (202)383-2346
E-mail: customer.service@mcgraw-hill.com
URL: http://www.aviationweek.com/awst.aspx?channel=awst

Frequency: Weekly. **Price:** $79 Canada; $79 Individuals; $119 Other countries. **Description:** Magazine serving the aviation and aerospace market worldwide.

809 ■ *Collegiate Aviation News Newsletter*
University Aviation Association
2415 Moore's Mill Rd., Ste. 265-216
Auburn, AL 36830-6444
Ph: (334)844-2434
Fax: (334)844-2432
E-mail: uaamail@uaa.aero
URL: http://www.uaa.aero/

Description: Quarterly. $42/yr. for non-members. Provides information on Association activities and projects, events of other aviation organizations that bear on higher education, and the future impact of collegiate aviation education. Recurring features include feature articles on outstanding individual and institutional members, statistics, a calendar of events, news of members, news of research, an editorial, letters to the editor, book reviews, employment information, and the president's report.

810 ■ *Flying*
Bonnier Corp.
460 N Orlando Ave., Ste. 200
Winter Park, FL 32789
Ph: (407)628-4802
Fax: (407)628-7061
URL: http://www.flyingmag.com

Frequency: Monthly. **Price:** $14 Individuals print; $22 Two years print; $33 Canada print; $33 Other countries print. **Description:** General aviation magazine.

811 ■ *Graduating Engineer & Computer Careers*
Career Recruitment Media
2 LAN Dr., Ste. 100
Westford, MA 01886
Ph: (978)692-5092
Fax: (978)692-4174
E-mail: hshulick@alloyeducation.com
URL: http://www.graduatingengineer.com

Frequency: Quarterly. **Price:** $16.95 Individuals. **Description:** Magazine focusing on employment, education, and career development for entry-level engineers and computer scientists.

812 ■ *In Flight USA*
In Flight USA
PO Box 5402
San Mateo, CA 94402
Ph: (650)358-9908
Fax: (650)358-9254
E-mail: staff@inflightusa.com
URL: http://inflight.squarespace.com

Frequency: Monthly. **Price:** $24.95 Individuals; $44.95 Two years. **Description:** Magazine on Aviation.

813 ■ *International Women Pilots*
The Ninety-Nines
4300 Amelia Earhart Rd.
Oklahoma City, OK 73159
Ph: (405)685-7969
Free: 800-994-1929
Fax: (405)685-7985
E-mail: 99s@ninety-nines.org
URL: http://www.ninety-nines.org/index.cfm/99_news_magazine.htm

Description: Bimonthly. $20 for non-members. Includes material of interest to the members of The Ninety-Nines, Inc., an international organization of women pilots. Recurring features include interviews, news of research, letters to the editor, news of educational opportunities, a calendar of events, and columns titled President's and Careers.

814 ■ *NAFI Mentor*
National Association of Flight Instructors
3101 E Milham Ave.
Portage, MI 49002
Free: 866-806-6156
E-mail: nafi@nafinet.org
URL: http://www.nafinet.org

Frequency: Quarterly. **Price:** included in membership dues. **Description:** Monthly. Supports NAFI in its efforts to serve as a central point for dissemination of knowledge, methodology, and new information relative to flight instruction. Recurring features include letters to the editor, news of research, reports of meetings, and notices of publications available. Also includes news of relevant legislative and regulatory activity.

815 ■ *NSBE Magazine: National Society of Black Engineers*
NSBE Publications
205 Daingerfield Rd.
Alexandria, VA 22314
Ph: (703)549-2207
Fax: (703)683-5312
E-mail: info@nsbe.org
URL: http://www.nsbe.org/News-Media/Magazines/About-NSBE-Magazine.aspx

Frequency: 3/yr. **Price:** $20 Individuals; $35 Other countries; $15 Students. **Description:** Journal providing information on engineering careers, self-development, and cultural issues for recent graduates with technical majors.

816 ■ *PE*
National Society of Professional Engineers
1420 King St.
Alexandria, VA 22314-2794
Ph: (703)684-2800

Fax: (703)836-4875
E-mail: memserv@nspe.org
URL: http://www.nspe.org/PEmagazine/index.html

Frequency: Semimonthly; 10/yr. **Price:** included in membership dues; $50 for nonmembers. **Description:** Covers matters of importance to engineering educators and students.

817 ■ *Rotor & Wing*
Access Intelligence L.L.C.
4 Choke Cherry Rd., 2nd Fl.
Rockville, MD 20850
Ph: (301)354-2000
Free: 800-777-5006
Fax: (301)309-3847
E-mail: info@accessintel.com
URL: http://www.aviationtoday.com/rw/

Frequency: Monthly. **Price:** Free. **Description:** Magazine covering helicopters.

818 ■ *SWE, Magazine of the Society of Women Engineers*
Society of Women Engineers
203 N La Salle St., Ste. 1675
Chicago, IL 60601
Ph: (312)596-5223
Free: 877-SWE-INFO
Fax: (312)596-5252
E-mail: hq@swe.org
URL: http://societyofwomenengineers.swe.org/index.php

Frequency: Quarterly. **Price:** $30 Nonmembers. **Description:** Magazine for engineering students and for women and men working in the engineering and technology fields. Covers career guidance, continuing development and topical issues.

819 ■ *Woman Engineer*
Equal Opportunity Publications Inc.
445 Broad Hollow Rd., Ste. 425
Melville, NY 11747
Ph: (631)421-9421
Fax: (631)421-1352
E-mail: info@eop.com
URL: http://www.eop.com

Description: Annual. Magazine that is offered at no charge to qualified female engineering, computer-science, and information-technology students and professionals seeking to find employment and advancement in their careers.

EMPLOYER DIRECTORIES AND NETWORKING LISTS

820 ■ *AOPA's Airport Directory: The Pilot and FBO Flight Planning Guide*
Aircraft Owners and Pilots Association
421 Aviation Way
Frederick, MD 21701
Ph: (301)695-2000
Free: 800-872-2672
Fax: (301)695-2375
E-mail: airportdirectory@aopa.org
URL: http://www.aopa.org/airports/

Frequency: Biennial; January; Latest edition 2009-2010. **Price:** $3,995 Individuals. **Pages:** 680. **Covers:** 5,300 U.S. public-use landing facilities, including airports, heliports, seaplane bases, and approximately 1,800 private-use landing facilities; 5,000 aviation service companies. **Includes:** ATC and FSS phone numbers and frequencies; U.S. Customs airports and airports and airports of entry for Canada, Mexico, and the Caribbean. **Entries include:** For landing facilities--Airport type and name, city, phone, runway dimensions, types of instrument approaches, hours operated, communications frequencies, runway light system, local attractions, ground transportation, restaurants, hotels. For aviation service companies--Company name, phone, airport affiliation, operating hours, fuel type, Unicom

frequency. **Arrangement:** Geographical. **Indexes:** Cross-reference index of U.S. landing facilities.

821 ■ *Directory of Contract Staffing Firms*
C.E. Publications Inc.
PO Box 3006
Bothell, WA 98041-3006
Ph: (425)806-5200
Fax: (425)806-5585
E-mail: staff@cjhunter.com
URL: http://www.cjhunter.com/dcsf/overview.html

Frequency: Annual. **Covers:** Nearly 1,300 contract firms actively engaged in the employment of engineering, IT/IS, and technical personnel for 'temporary' contract assignments throughout the world. **Entries include:** Company name, address, phone, name of contact, email, web address. **Arrangement:** Alphabetical. **Indexes:** Geographical.

822 ■ *FAA Airmen Directory*
National Institute for Computer-Assisted Reporting
141 Neff Annex
Columbia, MO 65211
Ph: (573)882-2042
Fax: (573)884-5544
E-mail: info@ire.org
URL: http://ire.org/nicar

823 ■ *Indiana Society of Professional Engineers--Directory*
Indiana Society of Professional Engineers
c/o Lauraine M. Howe, Executive Director
PO Box 20806
Indianapolis, IN 46220
Ph: (317)255-2267
Fax: (317)255-2530
E-mail: indspe@gmail.com
URL: http://www.indspe.org

Frequency: Annual; fall. **Pages:** 150. **Covers:** Member registered engineers, land surveyors, engineering students, and engineers in training. **Entries include:** Member name, address, phone, type of membership, business information, specialty. **Arrangement:** Alpha by chapter area.

824 ■ *Journal of Air Traffic Control*
Air Traffic Control Association
1101 King St., Ste. 300
Alexandria, VA 22314
Ph: (703)299-2430
Fax: (703)299-2437
E-mail: info@atca.org
URL: http://atca.kma.net/index.asp?bid=33

Frequency: Quarterly. **Price:** $78 U.S.; $88 Other countries. **Description:** Magazine for air traffic controllers, aviation personnel, pilots and systems engineers. **Includes:** Directory of member organizations. **Entries include:** Organization name, city, state.

825 ■ *National Air Transportation Association--Aviation Resource and Membership Directory*
National Air Transportation Association
4226 King St.
Alexandria, VA 22302
Ph: (703)845-9000
Free: 800-808-6282
Fax: (703)845-8176
E-mail: rmulholland@nata.aero
URL: http://www.nata.aero

Frequency: Annual; Latest Edition 2012. **Price:** $50 Nonmembers; $25 Members. **Covers:** More than 1,000 regular, associate, and affiliate members; regular members include airport service organizations, air taxi operators, and commuter airlines. **Entries include:** Company name, address, phone, fax number, name and title of contact. **Arrangement:** Regular members are classified by service; associate and affiliate members are alphabetical in separate sections. **Indexes:** Geographical.

826 ■ Plunkett's Engineering and Research Industry Almanac: The Only Complete Guide to the Business of Research, Development, and Engineering
Plunkett Research Ltd.
4102 Bellaire Blvd.
Houston, TX 77025-1004
Ph: (713)932-0000
Fax: (713)932-7080
E-mail: customersupport@plunkettresearch.com
URL: http://www.plunkettresearch.com

Frequency: Annual; Latest edition 2013; New edition expected June 2014. **Price:** $349.99 Individuals eBook, print and CD-ROM. **Pages:** 690. **Covers:** 500 of the largest companies involved in research, engineering and development in the biotech, electronics, aerospace and infotech industries. **Entries include:** Name, address, phone, fax, names and titles of key personnel, subsidiary and branch names and locations, financial data, salaries and benefits, description of products/services, overview of company culture/activities. **Indexes:** Industry, location, sales rank, profit rank.

827 ■ Who's Who in Engineering
American Association of Engineering Societies
1801 Alexander Bell Dr.
Reston, VA 20191
Ph: (202)296-2237
Free: 888-400-2237
Fax: (202)296-1151
E-mail: dbateson@aaes.org
URL: http://www.aaes.org

Frequency: Triennial; Latest edition 9th. **Covers:** About 15,000 engineers who have received professional recognition for outstanding achievement. **Entries include:** Name, address; education and employment history; awards and achievements. **Arrangement:** Alphabetical. **Indexes:** Geographical, field of specialization.

828 ■ World Aerospace Database
Aviation Week Group
1200 G St.NW, Ste. 922
Washington, DC 20005-3814
Free: 800-525-5003
Fax: (712)755-7423
E-mail: wad@mcgraw-hill.com
URL: http://www.aviationweek.com

Frequency: Semiannual. **Price:** $269 U.S. print; $1,295 U.S. CD-ROM, incl. 1 year print sub., 2 editions; $595 U.S. online, incl. 1 year print sub., 2 editions; $495 U.S. special online; $149 U.S. special print. **Description:** Covers more than 25,000 companies and 120,000 key executives to the aviation and aerospace industries worldwide. **Arrangement:** Classified by major activity (manufacturers, airlines, etc.). **Indexes:** Company and organization, personnel, product, trade name.

HANDBOOKS AND MANUALS

829 ■ Airline Pilot Technical Interviews
Aviation Supplies & Academics, Inc.
7005 132nd Pl. SE
Newcastle, WA 98059
Ph: (425)235-1500
Free: 800-272-2359
Fax: (425)235-0128
URL: http://www.asa2fly.com/index.aspx

Description: Ronald D. McElroy. 2005. $29.95 (paper). 144 pages. Provides guidelines for a successful airline checkride and technical interview.

830 ■ Expert Resumes for Engineers
JIST Publishing
875 Montreal Way
Saint Paul, MN 55102-4245
Ph: (317)613-4200
Free: 800-648-5478

Fax: (800)328-4564
E-mail: info@jist.com
URL: http://www.jist.com

Description: Louise M. Kursmark and Wendy S. Enelow. 2009. $16.95 (softcover). 272 pages. Features a collection of written resume samples for all types of engineers including civil, mechanical, industrial, electrical, electronics, computer, and more. Contains tips and strategies for writing engineering resumes and finding the best jobs.

831 ■ Great Jobs for Engineering Majors
The McGraw-Hill Companies Inc.
PO Box 182604
Columbus, OH 43272
Ph: (212)512-2000
Free: 877-833-5524
Fax: (614)759-3749
E-mail: customer.service@mcgraw-hill.com
URL: http://www.mcgraw-hill.com

Description: Geraldine O. Garner. Second edition, 2008. $16.95. 192 pages. Covers all the career options open to students majoring in engineering.

832 ■ Professional Pilot Career Guide
The McGraw-Hill Companies Inc.
PO Box 182604
Columbus, OH 43272
Ph: (212)512-2000
Free: 877-833-5524
Fax: (614)759-3749
E-mail: customer.service@mcgraw-hill.com
URL: http://www.mcgraw-hill.com

Description: Robert Mark. 2007. $14.99 (paper). 455 pages. Provides sources for professional flying opportunities. Contains detailed coverage of pilot ratings and practical test standards, plus goal-achieving tips on job hunting, networking, regional airlines, the majors, and more.

833 ■ Reporting Clear?: A Pilot's Interview Guide to Background Checks & Presentation of Personal History
Aviation Supplies & Academics, Inc.
7005 132nd Pl. SE
Newcastle, WA 98059
Ph: (425)235-1500
Free: 800-272-2359
Fax: (425)235-0128
URL: http://www.asa2fly.com/index.aspx

Description: Cheryl A. Cage. 2006. $19.95 (paper). 94 pages. Provides pilots with interview guides to background checks and the proper presentation of personal history.

EMPLOYMENT AGENCIES AND SEARCH FIRMS

834 ■ Aviation Recruiting
1845 Town Center Blvd., Ste. 210
Fleming Island, FL 32003
Ph: (904)264-0097
Fax: (904)264-0230
E-mail: staffing@aviationrecruiting.net
URL: http://www.aviationrecruiting.net

Description: Specializes in recruitment for the aviation industry. Offers aviation employment services to companies that specialize in commercial/cargo airlines, MRO facilities, military aircraft, manufacturing and completion centers, rotary wing aircraft and corporate aircraft.

835 ■ Jet Professionals
114 Charles A. Lindbergh Dr.
Teterboro, NJ 07608
Free: 800-441-6016
Fax: (201)462-4081
E-mail: jobs@jet-professionals.com
URL: http://www.jet-professionals.com

Description: Provides staffing services to the aviation industry. Offers jobs for corporate aviation execu-

tives, chief pilots, flight attendants, maintenance professionals, dispatchers, schedulers and more.

ONLINE JOB SOURCES AND SERVICES

836 ■ AeroIndustryJobs.com
URL: http://www.aeroindustryjobs.com/home/index.cfm?site_id=13641

Description: Lists careers in the aerospace, defense and advanced materials industries. Helps industry employers connect with qualified, career-focused job seekers.

837 ■ AeroVents.com
URL: http://www.aerovents.com/body.shtml

Description: Seeks to spread the word about aviation events. Covers aviation events from conventions, space launches, seminars, model rocketry and aircraft, ballooning, sky diving, plane pulls, open houses, air shows and fly-ins.

838 ■ Air Transportation Jobs
URL: http://air.transportation.jobs.jobsearchsite.com

Description: Provides available air transportation jobs and career resources. Allows employers to post jobs and search resumes to find qualified candidates.

839 ■ AircraftEngineers.com
URL: http://www.aircraftengineers.com

Description: Lists aircraft maintenance engineering jobs and aerospace vacancies. Provides career information for individuals who wish to start a career as an aircraft engineer.

840 ■ AirJobsDaily.com
URL: http://www.airjobsdaily.com

Description: Serves as a source of current aviation and aerospace job openings.

841 ■ AirlineCareer.com
URL: http://www.airlinecareer.com

Description: Web-based training center. Provides flight attendant job placement services.

842 ■ AirlineCareer.info
URL: http://www.airlinecareer.info

Description: Provides jobs in the airline community covering airport careers, aircraft manufacturing, aerospace careers, and cabin crew careers.

843 ■ Airportjobs.Us
URL: http://www.airportjobs.us

Description: Helps job seekers find airport career opportunities with top companies. Allows employers and recruiters to match qualified candidates with open airport postions.

844 ■ AvCrew.com
URL: http://www.avcrew.com

Description: Provides service designed exclusively for career employment in the business aviation sector. Features flight crew jobs, conducts applicant screening, and assists selected flight departments with candidate searches.

845 ■ AviaNation
URL: http://www.avianation.com

Description: Features aviation jobs, pilot jobs, flight attendant jobs, jobs for A&P mechanics, and other aviation job openings around the world.

846 ■ Aviation Jobs Online
URL: http://www.aviationjobsonline.com

Description: Provides list of various jobs within the aviation industry.

847 ■ The Aviation MD
URL: http://www.theaviationmd.com

Description: Serves as international aviation

database for employers and jobseekers in the aviation industry.

848 ■ AviationCrossing.com
URL: http://www.aviationcrossing.com

Description: Provides aviation jobs for agents, managers, mechanics, operators, specialists, supervisors, technicians, engineers, maintenance, pilots and other related aviation professionals.

849 ■ AviationEmployment.com
URL: http://www.aviationemployment.com

Description: Serves as an online job search service provider specializing in aviation and aerospace jobs and employment opportunities.

850 ■ AvJobs.com
URL: http://www.avjobs.com

Description: Provides information on a number of different careers in the aviation and aerospace industry. Features aviation schools directory, affiliate programs, research and networking, employment resources, salaries and wages, aviation careers descriptions, aviation guide and other resources.

851 ■ BestAviation.net
URL: http://www.bestaviation.net

Description: Provides source for information on flight school training, helicopter schools, aviation college programs, flight attendant careers, aircraft maintenance and pilot jobs.

852 ■ Engineering Classifieds
URL: http://www.engineeringclassifieds.com

Description: Serves as a career site for engineering professionals. Provides services including job search agents, resume creation and posting.

853 ■ EngineerJobs.com
URL: http://www.engineerjobs.com

Description: Provides job opportunities for engineering professionals in the following disciplines: aerospace, agricultural, biomedical, chemical, civil, electrical, environmental, industrial, manufacturing, marine, materials, mechanical, mining, nuclear, petroleum, process, project, quality, sales, software, solar, systems, and structural.

854 ■ Engineer.net
URL: http://www.engineer.net

Description: Provides engineering employment tools such as job search, job posting, and engineering resumes.

855 ■ FindaPilot.com
URL: http://www.findapilot.com

Description: Exists as a niche pilot jobs website. Provides a database of pilot jobs, allows posting of employments ads, and features a pilot directory.

856 ■ FlightLevelJobs.com
URL: http://www.flightleveljobs.com

Description: Serves as a source of aviation employment information. Features aviation and aerospace jobs and employment opportunities.

857 ■ FlyContract.com
URL: http://www.flycontract.com

Description: Provides a directory to help corporate pilots and corporate flight attendants obtain jobs.

858 ■ JetEmployment.com
URL: http://jetemployment.com

Description: Features employment opportunities for pilots and other workers in the airline, airport, and business aviation industry.

859 ■ PlaneJobs.com
URL: http://planejobs.com

Description: Serves as an employment, resume, career, and job search database for the aviation industry.

860 ■ Spherion
URL: http://www.spherion.com

Description: Recruitment firm specializing in accounting and finance, sales and marketing, interim executives, technology, engineering, retail and human resources.

861 ■ ThinkEnergyGroup.com
URL: http://www.thinkenergygroup.com

Description: Serves as a job board for professionals looking for positions in engineering, power plant, energy, and technical fields. Contains advice and tips on interviews, job searching, resume writing, hiring, and management. Provides choices of work location, pay rates in the field of expertise and contract, temp-to-hire, and direct hiring options.

862 ■ TransportationCareers.net
URL: http://www.transportationcareers.net

Description: Offers updated job database, research, and articles related to the transportation industry.

863 ■ USPilot.com
URL: http://www.uspilot.com

Description: Provides information on pilot job openings, interview gouge, forums, and evaluation of pilot resumes.

TRADESHOWS

864 ■ AOPA Aviation Summit - Aircraft Owners and Pilots Association
Aircraft Owners and Pilots Association
421 Aviation Way
Frederick, MD 21701
Ph: (301)695-2000
Free: 800-872-2672
Fax: (301)695-2375
URL: http://www.aopa.org

Frequency: Annual. **Primary Exhibits:** Single-engine and multi-engine aircraft, avionics, airframes, power plant and equipment, financing information, and related equipment, supplies, and services.

OTHER SOURCES

865 ■ Air Traffic Control Association
1101 King St., Ste. 300
Alexandria, VA 22314
Ph: (703)299-2430
Fax: (703)299-2437
E-mail: info@atca.org
URL: http://www.atca.org

Description: Air traffic controllers; private, commercial, and military pilots; private and business aircraft owners and operators; aircraft and electronics engineers; airlines, aircraft manufacturers, and electronic and human engineering firms.

866 ■ American Institute of Engineers
4630 Appian Way, Ste. 206
El Sobrante, CA 94803-1875
Ph: (510)758-6240
Fax: (510)758-6240
E-mail: aie@aieonline.org
URL: http://www.aieonline.org

Description: Professional association for engineers, scientists, and mathematicians. Multi-disciplined, non-technical association who aims to improve the stature and image of engineers, scientists, and mathematicians. Provides endorsements, awards and opportunities for small business start-ups within the AIE Councils. Sponsors "LA Engineer", a comedy-drama television series; produces annual "Academy Hall of FAME (TV)".

867 ■ Career Opportunities in Aviation and the Aerospace Industry
InfoBase Holdings Inc.
132 W 31st., 17 Fl.
New York, NY 10001-3406
Ph: (212)967-8800
Fax: (800)678-3633
E-mail: info@infobasepublishing.com
URLs: http://www.infobasepublishing.com; http://www
.infobasepublishing.com/Bookdetail.aspx?ISBN
=1438110642&eBooks=1

Frequency: Published January, 2005. **Description:** Susan Echaore-McDavid. 2004. 305 pages. **Covers:** Eighty up-to-date job profiles, providing detailed information about the duties, salaries, and prospects of aviation mechanics, designers, technicians, scientists, and administrators. **Includes:** Appendices of educational institutions, periodicals, directories, and associations.

868 ■ Career Opportunities in Engineering
InfoBase Holdings Inc.
132 W 31st., 17 Fl.
New York, NY 10001-3406
Ph: (212)967-8800
Fax: (800)678-3633
E-mail: info@infobasepublishing.com
URL: http://www.ferguson.infobasepublishing.com

Description: 2006. $49.50. 336 pages. Provides an overview of engineering, followed by a selection of jobs profiled in detail, including the nature of the job, earnings, prospects for employment, what kind of training and skills it requires and sources for further information. **Includes:** Appendices of educational institutions, periodicals, directories, and associations. Appendices of educational institutions, periodicals, directories, and associations.

869 ■ National Black Coalition of Federal Aviation Employees
PO Box 845
Hampton, GA 30228
Free: 888-311-1622
E-mail: info@nbcfae.org
URL: http://nbcfae.org

Description: Federal Aviation Administration employees. Purposes are to: promote professionalism and equal opportunity in the workplace; locate and train qualified minorities for FAA positions; help the FAA meet its affirmative action goals; monitor black, female, and minority trainees; educate members and the public about their rights and FAA personnel and promotion qualifications; develop a voice for black, female, and minority FAA employees. Recruits minorities from community and schools who qualify for employment; sponsors seminars for members and for those who wish to be employed by the FAA. Maintains speaker's bureau; sponsors competitions.

870 ■ Ninety-Nines, International Organization of Women Pilots
4300 Amelia Earhart Dr., Ste. A
Oklahoma City, OK 73159
Ph: (405)685-7969
Free: 800-994-1929
Fax: (405)685-7985
E-mail: 99s@ninety-nines.org
URL: http://www.ninety-nines.org

Description: Represents women pilots. Fosters a better understanding of aviation. Encourages cross-country flying; provides consulting service and gives indoctrination flights; flies missions for charitable assistance programs; endorses air races. Develops programs and courses for schools and youth organizations and teaches ground school subjects. Participates in flying competitions. Maintains resource center and women's aviation museum. Conducts lecture on personal aviation experience, and charitable event. Compiles statistics.

871 ■ Organization of Black Airline Pilots
1 Westbrook Corporate Ctr., Ste. 300
Westchester, IL 60154

Ph: (703)753-2047
Free: 800-JET-OBAP
Fax: (703)753-1251
E-mail: nationaloffice@obap.org
URL: http://www.obap.org

Description: Cockpit crew members of commercial air carriers, corporate pilots and other interested individuals. Seeks to enhance minority participation in the aerospace industry. Maintains liaison with airline presidents and minority and pilot associations.

Conducts lobbying efforts, including congressional examinations into airline recruitment practices. Provides scholarships; cosponsors Summer Flight Academy for Youth. Offers job placement service and charitable program; operates speakers' bureau; compiles statistics on airline hiring practices.

872 ■ Women in Engineering ProActive Network
1901 E Asbury Ave., Ste. 220
Denver, CO 80208

Ph: (303)871-4643
Fax: (303)871-4628
URL: http://www.wepan.org

Description: Women in engineering professions. Includes key strategies such as education and training, research, collaboration, leadership, diversity, advocacy, networking, sustainability, accountability, and volunteerism in order to be a catalyst for change that enhances the success of women in the engineering professions.

SOURCES OF HELP-WANTED ADS

873 ■ *Journal of Studies on Alcohol and Drugs*
Rutgers University - Center of Alcohol Studies
607 Allison Rd.
Piscataway, NJ 08854-8001

Ph: (732)445-3510
Fax: (732)445-3500
E-mail: alclib@rci.rutgers.edu
URL: http://www.jsad.com/

Frequency: Bimonthly. **Price:** $140 Individuals; $29 Single issue. **Description:** Peer-reviewed journal containing original research reports about alcohol and other drugs, their use and misuse, and their biomedical, behavioral, and sociocultural effects.

EMPLOYER DIRECTORIES AND NETWORKING LISTS

874 ■ Find an Allergist
American Academy of Allergy Asthma & Immunology
555 E Wells St., Ste. 1100
Milwaukee, WI 53202-3823
Ph: (414)272-6071
E-mail: info@aaaai.org
URL: http://www.aaaai.org
Description: Contains directory listings and contact information for allergists and related medical professionals in the United States. Includes directory listings for members of the American Academy of Allergy, Asthma, and Immunology. Provides physician name, address, company or hospital affiliation, telephone number, and driving directions to office. Includes information on doctor's specialties, education, board certifications, professional affiliations, type of practice, and areas of expertise. Offers listings for physicians specializing in areas such as occupational allergies, pediatric allergies, animal allergies, rhinitis, sinusitis, food allergies, drug allergies, anaphylaxis, ocular allergies, latex allergies, insect allergies, and more.

875 ■ The Official American Board of Medical Specialties (ABMS)--Directory of Board Certified Allergists and Immunologists
URL: http://www.reedref.com
Frequency: Biennial. **Price:** $99.95. **Pages:** 128.
Covers: 3,500 certified allergists and immunologists.
Entries include: Name, address, phone, certification and educational data, professional association membership. **Arrangement:** Geographical. **Indexes:** Alphabetical.

876 ■ Physicians Career Opportunities
Physicians Career Resource
American Medical Association
515 N State St.
Chicago, IL 60610
Ph: (800)955-3565
Fax: (312)464-4184
Frequency: Monthly. **Price:** $50 Free to AMA member physicians seeking positions. **Pages:** 14.
Covers: Employment or practice opportunities for physicians. Also has lists of practices for sale, state medical societies, executive and professional recruiting firms, hospital or clinic management companies, medical schools, national medical specialty societies, health maintenance organizations, etc. **Entries include:** Medical specialty, location and type of practice, beginning financial arrangements, income range, size of community, physician population, date available. For entries in other lists--Name, address, phone. A companion volume, "Physician Placement Register," lists key from registered physicians seeking positions. **Arrangement:** Opportunities listed geographically, then by medical specialty. **Indexes:** Medical specialty.

OTHER SOURCES

877 ■ American Medical Association
515 N State St.
Chicago, IL 60654
Ph: (312)464-4430
Free: 800-621-8335
Fax: (312)464-5226
E-mail: amalibrary@ama-assn.org
URL: http://www.ama-assn.org
Description: Represents county medical societies and physicians. Disseminates scientific information to members and the public. Informs members on significant medical and health legislation on state and national levels and represents the profession before Congress and governmental agencies. Cooperates in setting standards for medical schools, hospitals, residency programs, and continuing medical education courses. Offers physician placement service and counseling on practice management problems. Operates library that lends material and provides specific medical information to physicians. Maintains Ad-hoc committees for such topics as health care planning and principles of medical ethics.

878 ■ Career Opportunities in Health Care
InfoBase Holdings Inc.
132 W 31st., 17 Fl.
New York, NY 10001-3406
Ph: (212)967-8800
Fax: (800)678-3633
E-mail: info@infobasepublishing.com
URL: http://www.ferguson.infobasepublishing.com
Description: Shelly Field. 2007. Third edition. $49.50. 304 pages. **Includes:** Appendices provide lists of educational institutions, periodicals, directories, associations, and unions. Appendices provide lists of educational institutions, periodicals, directories, associations, and unions.

879 ■ Health-Care Careers for the 21st Century
JIST Publishing
875 Montreal Way
Saint Paul, MN 55102-4245
Ph: (317)613-4200
Free: 800-648-5478
Fax: (800)328-4564
E-mail: info@jist.com
URL: http://www.jist.com
Price: $9.95 Individuals Softcover. **Pages:** 448. **Covers:** Jobs for health care professionals and career opportunities for those pursuing a health-related career, organized into 80 careers in five groups. **Publication includes:** Appendixes listing job source resources and Web sites for health organizations.

Animal Caretakers, Technicians, and Trainers

SOURCES OF HELP-WANTED ADS

880 ■ *American Bee Journal*
Dadant and Sons Inc.
51 S 2nd St., Ste. 2
Hamilton, IL 62341-1397
Ph: (217)847-3324
Free: 888-922-1293
Fax: (217)847-3660
E-mail: info@americanbeejournal.com
URL: http://www.americanbeejournal.com

Frequency: Monthly. **Price:** $27 Individuals; $51 Two years; $41 Canada; $79 Canada 2 years; $50 Other countries; $96 Other countries 2 years; $61 Canada airmail; $80 Other countries airmail. **Description:** Magazine for hobbyist and professional beekeepers. Covers hive management, honey handling, disease control, honey markets, foreign beekeeping, beekeeping history, bee laws, honey plants, marketing, and government beekeeping research.

881 ■ *American Mustang and Burro Association Journal*
American Mustang and Burro Association
PO Box 608
Greenwood, DE 19950
E-mail: info@ambainc.net
URL: http://www.ambainc.net/

Frequency: Quarterly. **Description:** Journal covering horses and burros.

882 ■ *Animal Keepers' Forum*
American Association of Zoo Keepers
8476 E Speedway Blvd., Ste. 204
Tucson, AZ 85710
Ph: (785)273-9149
Fax: (785)273-1980
E-mail: aazkoffice@zk.kscoxmail.com
URL: http://aazk.org/category/akf/toc/

Frequency: Monthly. **Price:** $10 Members; $20 Canada members. **Description:** Professional journal of the American Association of Zoo Keepers, Inc.

883 ■ *ASA Bulletin*
Avicultural Society of America
PO Box 3161
San Dimas, CA 91773
Ph: (951)780-4102
Fax: (951)789-9366
E-mail: info@asabirds.org
URL: http://www.asabirds.org/publication.htm

Frequency: Bimonthly. **Price:** $12 Students; $25 Individuals; $33 Other countries. **Description:** Covers the care, feeding, and breeding of birds in captivity. Contains membership roster and listings of bird specialty organizations and new members.

884 ■ *DVM Newsmagazine: The Newsmagazine of Veterinary Medicine*
Advanstar Communications Inc.
24950 Country Club Blvd., Ste. 200
North Olmsted, OH 44070
Fax: (440)891-2740
E-mail: dvmnewsmagazine@advanstar.com
URLs: http://veterinarynews.dvm360.com/dvm/cath-ome/catHome6.jsp?categoryId=7568; http://www.dvmnews.com

Frequency: Monthly. **Description:** Magazine for veterinarians in private practices in the U.S.

885 ■ *Newsletter-Animal Behavior Society*
Animal Behavior Society
Indiana University
402 N Park Ave.
Bloomington, IN 47408
Ph: (812)856-5541
Fax: (812)856-5542
E-mail: aboffice@indiana.edu
URL: http://animalbehaviorsociety.org/central-office/abs-newsletters

Description: Quarterly. Informs members of the Society of activities, events, meetings, announcements and opportunities in the field of animal behavior. Recurring features include news of educational opportunities, job listings, and notices of publications available.

886 ■ *TRENDS Magazine*
American Animal Hospital Association
12575 W Bayaud Ave.
Lakewood, CO 80228
Ph: (303)986-2800
Free: 800-883-6301
Fax: (303)986-1700
E-mail: info@aahanet.org
URLs: http://www.aahanet.org/publications/trends-magazine.aspx; http://trends.aahanet.org/eweb/

Frequency: Bimonthly; 6-8/yr. **Price:** $60 U.S. and Canada; $70 Other countries; $20 Single issue; included in membership dues; $60/year for nonmembers in U.S. and Canada; $70/year for nonmembers outside U.S. and Canada; $20/copy for nonmembers. **Description:** Covers management trends, social issues, paraprofessional topics in veterinary medicine; includes association news, and CE calendar.

887 ■ *Veterinary Practice News*
Bowtie Inc.
PO Box 6050
Mission Viejo, CA 92690-6050
Ph: (949)855-8822
Fax: (949)855-3045
URL: http://www.veterinarypracticenews.com/

Frequency: Monthly. **Price:** $42 U.S. and Canada digital; $48 Individuals print. **Description:** Magazine covering veterinary practice in the United States featuring developments and trends affecting companion animals and livestock.

EMPLOYER DIRECTORIES AND NETWORKING LISTS

888 ■ *Breeders & Trainers Directory*
American Paint Horse Association
PO Box 961023
Fort Worth, TX 76161-0023
Ph: (817)834-2742
Fax: (817)834-3152
E-mail: askapha@apha.com
URL: http://www.apha.com/publications/index.shtml

Frequency: Latest edition 2006-2007. **Covers:** 400 ALPHA regional clubs in North America. **Entries include:** Company name, address, phone, fax, contact person and e-mail. **Arrangement:** Alphabetical by state.

889 ■ *International Marine Animal Trainers Association--Membership Directory*
International Marine Animal Trainers Association
1200 S Lake Shore Dr.
Chicago, IL 60605
Ph: (312)692-3193
Fax: (312)939-2216
E-mail: info@imata.org
URL: http://www.imata.org/

Covers: List of contact information of members including marine animal trainers and anyone who has actively participated in the training, husbandry and management of marine animals.

ONLINE JOB SOURCES AND SERVICES

890 ■ *Animal Career Guide.com*
URL: http://www.animalcareerguide.com

Description: Serves as an online tool that guides and helps people find animal jobs and careers.

891 ■ *AnimalJobs.com*
URL: http://www.animaljobs.com

Description: Functions as a niche job board for people who work with animals including veterinarians, pet stores, groomers, farmers, horse breeders, rescuers, and shelters.

892 ■ *AVMA Online Search Form*
1931 N Meacham Rd., Ste. 100
Schaumburg, IL 60173
Ph: (847)925-8070
Free: 800-248-2862
Fax: (847)925-1329
URL: http://www.avma.org/

893 ■ *FindAVet Job Board*
URL: http://jobs.findavet.us/a/jobs/find-jobs

Description: Lists available career opportunities in veterinary industry. Allows job seekers to search jobs by title, company, location, and type.

894 ■ Get Veterinary Jobs
URL: http://www.getveterinaryjobs.com
Description: Serves as a source of employment and career opportunities for veterinary professionals.

895 ■ Go Pets America
URL: http://www.gopetsamerica.com
Description: Provides information and resources for dog, cat, bird, small pet, and horse owners. Features available jobs in animal care.

896 ■ Veterinary Help Wanted
URL: http://www.veterinaryhelpwanted.com
Description: Provides job postings of all kinds of veterinary professions. Allows job seekers to search for jobs according to category, location, company, relevance, or date updated.

897 ■ Veterinary Jobs Database
URL: http://www.vetbroker.com/vet_jobs.htm
Description: Offers a free database of nationwide veterinary job postings.

898 ■ VeterinaryCareers.net
URL: http://www.veterinarycareers.net
Description: Provides up-to-date career opportunities listings, research, and articles related to the field of veterinary medicine.

899 ■ VeterinaryJobsite.com
URL: http://www.veterinaryjobsite.com
Description: Provides updated listings of job opportunities in veterinary medicine. Features research into the healthcare and medical employment market and an informative career articles section.

900 ■ Veterinaryjobs.Us
URL: http://www.veterinaryjobs.us
Description: Offers a searchable database of different veterinary jobs across the United States.

TRADESHOWS

901 ■ Association of Pet Dog Trainers Annual Conference
Association of Pet Dog Trainers
104 S Calhoun St.
Greenville, SC 29601
Free: 800-PET-DOGS
Fax: (864)331-0767
E-mail: information@apdt.com
URL: http://www.apdt.com
Frequency: Annual. **Primary Exhibits:** Exhibits relating to dog training.

902 ■ Global Pet Expo
American Pet Products Association
255 Glenville Rd.
Greenwich, CT 06831
Ph: (203)532-0000
Free: 800-452-1225
Fax: (203)532-0551
URL: http://www.americanpetproducts.org
Frequency: Annual. Exhibits relating to pets and pet care products.

903 ■ Super Zoo
World Pet Association
135 W Lemon Ave.
Monrovia, CA 91016-2809
Ph: (626)447-2222
Free: 800-999-7295
Fax: (626)447-8350
E-mail: info@wpamail.org
URL: http://www.worldpetassociation.org/files/homepage/index.html
Frequency: Annual. **Primary Exhibits:** Pet care foods, equipment, products and services. **Dates and Locations:** Long Beach, CA; Convention Center.

OTHER SOURCES

904 ■ American Animal Hospital Association
12575 W Bayaud Ave.
Lakewood, CO 80228
Ph: (303)986-2800
Free: 800-883-6301
Fax: (303)986-1700
E-mail: info@aahanet.org
URL: http://www.aahanet.org
Description: Represents veterinary care providers who treat companion animals. Accredits veterinary hospitals throughout the U.S. and Canada. Conducts stringent accreditation process that covers patient care, client service and medical protocols.

905 ■ American Association of Equine Veterinary Technicians and Assistants
539 Wild Horse Ln.
San Marcos, CA 92078
Fax: (760)301-0349
E-mail: dbreeder@gmail.com
URL: http://www.aaevt.org
Description: Represents veterinary technicians, assistants, and support staff interested in equine practice, and professionals employed in the veterinary health care industry. Offers continuing education courses, events, news, networking and job opportunities accessible to equine techncians and assistants.

906 ■ American Association for Laboratory Animal Science
9190 Crestwyn Hills Dr.
Memphis, TN 38125-8538
Ph: (901)754-8620
Fax: (901)753-0046
E-mail: info@aalas.org
URL: http://www.aalas.org
Description: Persons and institutions professionally concerned with the production, use, care, and study of laboratory animals. Serves as clearinghouse for collection and exchange of information on all phases of laboratory animal care and management and on the care, use, and procurement of laboratory animals used in biomedical research. Conducts examinations and certification through its Animal Technician Certification Program.

907 ■ American Association of Wildlife Veterinarians
c/o Dr. Megin Nichols, Treas.
5 Calle Festiva
Santa Fe, NM 87507
E-mail: colin.m.gillin@state.or.us
URL: http://www.aawv.net
Description: Consists of veterinary practitioners, pathologists, researchers and policy makers. Seeks to enhance the contribution of veterinary medicine to the welfare of wildlife resources. Promotes and encourages the utilization of veterinarians in the fields of wildlife management, conservation and research.

908 ■ American Border Leicester Association
N6639 Wisconsin Pkwy.
Delavan, WI 53115
Ph: (608)883-6916
E-mail: mkkorf@gmail.com
URL: http://www.ablasheep.org
Description: Owners and admirers of Border Leicester sheep. Promotes Border Leicesters as a source of wool and meat. Sets breed standards and confers certification; maintains breed registry. Sponsors competitions; conducts educational programs. **Members:** 175.

909 ■ American Water Spaniel Club
6 Golfview Ln.
Lake Barrington, IL 60010-1941

Ph: (847)754-0777
E-mail: kevinsmg@sbcglobal.net
URL: http://www.americanwaterspanielclub.org
Description: Owners, breeders, and admirers of water spaniels. Promotes quality breeding and acceptance of breed standards as approved by the American Kennel Club. Represents the interests of breeders; provides shelter and care to abandoned and abused water spaniels; conducts educational programs; sponsors competitions; compiles statistics. **Members:** 250.

910 ■ Association of Zoos and Aquariums
8403 Colesville Rd., Ste. 710
Silver Spring, MD 20910-3314
Ph: (301)562-0777
Fax: (301)562-0888
E-mail: generalinquiry@aza.org
URL: http://www.aza.org
Description: 218 accredited members. Promotes the welfare of animals and encourages the advancement of education, animal care, conservation and sciences.

911 ■ *Career Opportunities Working with Animals*
InfoBase Holdings Inc.
132 W 31st., 17 Fl.
New York, NY 10001-3406
Ph: (212)967-8800
Fax: (800)678-3633
E-mail: info@infobasepublishing.com
URL: http://www.ferguson.infobasepublishing.com
Description: Shelly Field. 2011. $49.50 (hardcover). 308 pages. Describes more than 80 occupations in animal-related fields. **Includes:** Appendices include colleges and universities; zoos, aquariums, and animal sanctuaries; animal advocacy organizations; thoroughbred race tracks; harness racing tracks; trade associations; and career and job web sites. Appendices include colleges and universities; zoos, aquariums, and animal sanctuaries; animal advocacy organizations; thoroughbred race tracks; harness racing tracks; trade associations; and career and job web sites.

912 ■ International Forensic Entomology Detection Canine Association
1913 Hooper Ave.
Toms River, NJ 08753
Ph: (732)255-1649
Fax: (732)255-1539
E-mail: info@actionpestcontrol.com
URL: http://www.ifedca.com
Description: Represents the interests of trained canines, teams and facilities within the forensic entomology detection canine industry. Promotes quality and fair business practices within the canine detection industry. Provides training, education and certification to members.

913 ■ International Marine Animal Trainers Association
1200 S Lake Shore Dr.
Chicago, IL 60605
Ph: (312)692-3193
Fax: (312)939-2216
E-mail: info@imata.org
URL: http://www.imata.org
Description: Advances the humane care and handling of marine animals by fostering communication among professionals that serve marine animal science. Provides opportunities for marine animal trainers to exchange and disseminate knowledge, research, and training information.

914 ■ International Police Work Dog Association
PO Box 7455
Greenwood, IN 46142
E-mail: ipwda1@yahoo.com
URL: http://www.ipwda.org
Description: Aims to unite and assist all law

enforcement agencies in the training and continued progress of all police work dogs. Seeks to establish a working standard for all police work dogs, handlers, and trainers through an accreditation program. Promotes the image of the police work dog.

915 ■ National Animal Control Association
101 N Church St.
Olathe, KS 66061
Ph: (913)768-1319
Fax: (913)768-1378
E-mail: NACA@INTERSERV.COM
URL: http://www.nacanet.org
Description: Animal control agencies, humane societies, public health and safety agencies, corporations, and individuals. Works to educate and train personnel in the animal care and control professions. Seeks to teach the public responsible pet ownership; operates the NACA Network to provide animal control information; evaluates animal control programs. Provides training guides for animal control officers; makes available audiovisual materials. Conducts research. Operates placement service and speakers' bureau.

916 ■ National Dog Groomers Association of America
PO Box 101
Clark, PA 16113-0101
Ph: (724)962-2711

Fax: (724)962-1919
E-mail: ndga@nationaldoggroomers.com
URL: http://www.nationaldoggroomers.com
Description: Dog groomers and supply distributors organized to upgrade the profession. Conducts state and local workshops; sponsors competitions and certification testing. Makes groomer referrals.

917 ■ National Entomology Scent Detection Canine Association
PO Box 121
Pleasant Mount, PA 18453
E-mail: contact@nesdca.com
URL: http://www.nesdca.com
Description: Unites and assists entomology scent detection canine teams in the training and continued improvement. Strives to improve the image of the entomology scent-detecting canine teams. Educates consumers about the benefits of using trained entomology scent detecting dog teams in the process of locating and eradicating pest problems.

918 ■ Pet Care Services Association
2670 Academy Blvd.
Colorado Springs, CO 80917
Ph: (719)667-1600
Free: 877-570-7788

Fax: (719)667-0116
E-mail: membership@petcareservices.org
URL: http://www.petcareservices.org

Description: Persons or firms that board pets; kennel suppliers; others interested in the facility boarding kennel industry. Seeks to upgrade the industry through accreditation educational programs, seminars and conventions. Provides insurance resources for members and supplies pet care information to the public. Promotes code of ethics and accreditation program for recognition and training of superior kennel operators. Compiles boarding facility statistics.

919 ■ Walking Horse Trainers Association
1101 N Main St.
Shelbyville, TN 37160
Ph: (931)684-5866
Fax: (931)684-5895
E-mail: whtrainers@gmail.com
URL: http://www.walkinghorsetrainers.com

Description: Trainers of Tennessee Walking horses. Works for unity in the horse industry. Sponsors continuing research. **Members:** 850.

SOURCES OF HELP-WANTED ADS

920 ■ Anthropology of Consciousness
American Anthropological Association - Association
for Africanist Anthropology
2200 Wilson Blvd., Ste. 600
Arlington, VA 22201-3357
Ph: (703)528-1902
Free: 800-545-4703
Fax: (703)528-3546
E-mail: africananthro@gmail.com
URL: http://www.aaanet.org

Description: 2/year. Serves as an information exchange for researchers investigating the effect of culture on man's psychological and supernatural behavior patterns. Examines the topics of dreaming, altered states of consciousness, spirit possession, healing, divination, extrasensory perception, mysticism, myth, shamanism, and psychic archeology. Recurring features include book reviews, queries, notices of publications and symposia, news of members, and obituaries.

921 ■ Anthropology News
American Anthropological Association - Association
for Africanist Anthropology
2200 Wilson Blvd., Ste. 600
Arlington, VA 22201-3357
Ph: (703)528-1902
Free: 800-545-4703
Fax: (703)528-3546
E-mail: africananthro@gmail.com
URL: http://www.aaanet.org/issues/anthronews

Frequency: 9/year; 9/yr. **Description:** Periodical covering anthropology, including archaeological, biological, ethnological, and linguistic research.

922 ■ Anthropology of Work Review
American Anthropological Association - Association
for Africanist Anthropology
2200 Wilson Blvd., Ste. 600
Arlington, VA 22201-3357
Ph: (703)528-1902
Free: 800-545-4703
Fax: (703)528-3546
E-mail: africananthro@gmail.com
URL: http://www.aaanet.org

Description: Quarterly. Promotes the development of ideas, data, and methods concerning all aspects of the study of anthropology of work.

923 ■ AnthroSource
Blackwell Publishing Inc.
350 Main St.
Malden, MA 02148
Ph: (781)388-8200
Free: 800-216-2522
Fax: (781)388-8210
E-mail: journaladsusa@bos.blackwellpublishing.com
URL: http://www.anthrosource.net

Frequency: Irregular. **Description:** Journal serving the research, teaching, and professional needs of anthropologists.

924 ■ The Asia Pacific Journal of Anthropology
Routledge Journals - Taylor & Francis Group
270 Madison Ave.
New York, NY 10016-0601
Ph: (212)216-7800
Fax: (212)563-2269
URL: http://www.tandfonline.com/toc/rtap20/current

Frequency: 5/yr. **Price:** $141 Individuals print only; $550 Institutions online only; $629 Institutions print and online. **Description:** Journal focusing on anthropological study.

925 ■ General Anthropology
John Wiley & Sons Inc.
111 River St.
Hoboken, NJ 07030-5774
Ph: (201)748-6000
Free: 800-225-5945
Fax: (201)748-6088
E-mail: info@wiley.com
URL: http://as.wiley.com/WileyCDA/WileyTitle/productCd-GENA.html

Frequency: 2/yr. **Price:** $16 Institutions Americas (print and online); £8 Institutions UK (print and online); €10 Institutions Europe (print and online); $14 Institutions, other countries print and online; $14 Institutions Americas (online only); £7 Institutions UK (online only); €8 Institutions Europe (online only); $12 Institutions, other countries online only. **Description:** Journal covering the fields of anthropology and applied anthropology.

926 ■ Histories of Anthropology Annual
University of Nebraska Press
1111 Lincoln Mall
Lincoln, NE 68588-0630
Ph: (402)472-3581
Free: 800-848-6224
Fax: (402)472-6214
E-mail: pressmail@unl.edu
URL: http://www.nebraskapress.unl.edu

Price: $38 Individuals; $66 Institutions; $54 Other countries; $82 Institutions, other countries. **Description:** Journal covering historical approaches in teaching, learning, and applying anthropology.

927 ■ International Journal of Paleopathology
Elsevier Science Inc.
c/o Jane Buikstra, Ed.-in-Ch.
900 S Cady Mall, Rm. 233
School of Human Evolution & Social Change
Arizona State University
Tempe, AZ 85287-2402
Ph: (212)633-3980
Free: 888-437-4636

Fax: (212)633-3975
URL: http://www.journals.elsevier.com/international-journal-of-paleopathology/

Frequency: 4/yr. **Price:** $79 Individuals; $309 Institutions. **Description:** Journal publishing research studies on paleopathology.

928 ■ ISEM Newsletter
Institute for the Study of Earth and Man
N.L. Heroy Hall
Southern Methodist University
Dallas, TX 75275-0274
Ph: (214)768-2425
Fax: (214)768-4289
E-mail: isem@mail.smu.edu
URL: http://www.smu.edu/isem

Description: Semiannual. Reports on research in the anthropological, geological, and statistical sciences. Includes notices of research funds, grants, and contracts awarded. Provides biographical sketches of new faculty members in the anthropological, geological, and statistical sciences departments at Southern Methodist University. Recurring features include news of research and news of members.

929 ■ Journal of the Society for the Anthropology of Europe
Blackwell Publishing Inc.
350 Main St.
Malden, MA 02148
Ph: (781)388-8200
Free: 800-216-2522
Fax: (781)388-8210
E-mail: journaladsusa@bos.blackwellpublishing.com
URL: http://www.wiley.com/bw/journal.asp?ref=1535-5632&site=1

Frequency: Semiannual. **Price:** $53 Institutions print & online; $48 Institutions online only. **Description:** Journal containing articles and book reviews related to European anthropology.

930 ■ Kansas Anthropological Association Newsletter
Kansas Anthropological Association
PO Box 750962
Topeka, KS 66675-0962
Ph: (785)272-8681
URL: http://www.kshs.org/p/kansas-anthropological-association-kaa/14619

Description: Four issues/year. Covers Association field projects, conferences, and fundraising activities. Contains reports from local chapters. Recurring features include news of research, a calendar of events, and news of educational opportunities.

931 ■ NAPA Bulletin
Blackwell Publishing Inc.
350 Main St.
Malden, MA 02148
Ph: (781)388-8200
Free: 800-216-2522

Fax: (781)388-8210
E-mail: journaladsusa@bos.blackwellpublishing.com
URL: http://onlinelibrary.wiley.com/journal/10.1111/
(ISSN)1556-4797
Frequency: Annual. **Price:** $58 Institutions print & online; $52 Institutions online. **Description:** Journal focusing on information relevant to the advancement of professionals in the field from the National Association for the Practice of Anthropology (NAPA).

932 ■ North American Dialogue
American Anthropological Association - Association for Africanist Anthropology
2200 Wilson Blvd., Ste. 600
Arlington, VA 22201-3357
Ph: (703)528-1902
Free: 800-545-4703
Fax: (703)528-3546
E-mail: africananthro@gmail.com
URL: http://www.blackwellpublishing.com/journal.asp
?ref=1539-2546&site=1
Frequency: Semiannual. **Price:** $13 Institutions online only; $11 Institutions, other countries online only. **Description:** Journal of the Society for the Anthropology of North America.

933 ■ SFAA Newsletter
Society for Applied Anthropology
PO Box 2436
Oklahoma City, OK 73101-2436
Ph: (405)843-5113
Fax: (405)843-8553
E-mail: info@sfaa.net
URL: http://www.sfaa.net
Description: Quarterly. $10.00 for U.S. residents; $15.00 for non-U.S. residents. Features issues of interest and latest information about the society and its members.

934 ■ Society for Historical Archaeology Newsletter
Society for Historical Archaeology
13017 Wisteria Dr., Ste. 395
Germantown, MD 20874
Ph: (301)972-9684
Fax: (866)285-3512
E-mail: hq@sha.org
URL: http://www.sha.org
Description: Quarterly. Supports the aims of the Society, which "promotes scholarly research and the dissemination of knowledge concerning historical archeology." Presents information on current research, legislative developments, and Society meetings and activities. Recurring features include editorials, letters to the editor, news of members, and a calendar of events.

935 ■ Voices
American Anthropological Association - Association for Africanist Anthropology
c/o Amy E. Harper, PhD, Ed.
Central Oregon Community College
2600 NW College Way
Bend, OR 97701
Ph: (541)383-7268
E-mail: africananthro@gmail.com
URL: http://www.aaanet.org/sections/afa/Voices/
voices.html
Frequency: Annual. **Description:** Periodical covering activities in feminist anthropology.

936 ■ WAS Newsletter
World Archaeological Society
120 Lakewood Dr.
Hollister, MO 65672
Ph: (417)334-2377
Fax: (417)334-5501
E-mail: ronwriterartist@aol.com
URL: http://www.worldarchaeologicalsociety.com
Description: Periodic. Promotes the scientific and constructive study of antiquity within the international fields of archaeology, anthropology, and art history. Recurring features include announcements of recom-

mended books; items on people, museums, and societies; news of research; letters to the editor; obituaries; verses; and columns titled Career Notes and Democracy Club.

EMPLOYER DIRECTORIES AND NETWORKING LISTS

937 ■ American Journal of Physical Anthropology--American Association of Physical Anthropologists Membership Directory Issue
American Association of Physical Anthropologists
c/o Karen Rosenberg, President
135 John Munroe Hall
University of Delaware
Newark, DE 19716
Ph: (302)831-1855
Fax: (302)831-4002
E-mail: krr@udel.edu
URL: http://www.physanth.org/publications
Frequency: Annual; December. **Publication includes:** 1,500 physical anthropologists and scientists in closely related fields interested in the advancement of the science of physical anthropology through research and teaching of human variation, primate paleoanthropology, and primate evolution. **Entries include:** Name, affiliation, address. **Arrangement:** Alphabetical.

938 ■ Newsletter--Society for Historical Archaeology Membership Directory Issue
Society for Historical Archaeology
13017 Wisteria Dr., Ste. 395
Germantown, MD 20874
Ph: (301)972-9684
Fax: (866)285-3512
E-mail: hq@sha.org
URL: http://www.sha.org
Frequency: Quarterly; Latest edition 2011. **Publication includes:** List of about 2,100 member archaeologists, historians, anthropologists, and ethnohistorians, and other individuals and institutions having an interest in historical archeology or allied fields. **Entries include:** Name, address. **Arrangement:** Alphabetical.

HANDBOOKS AND MANUALS

939 ■ The Anthropology Graduate's Guide: From Student to a Career
Left Coast Press
1630 N Main St., No. 400
Walnut Creek, CA 94596
Ph: (925)935-3380
Fax: (925)935-2916
E-mail: explore@lcoastpress.com
URL: http://www.lcoastpress.com/book.php?id=152
Description: Carol J. Ellick and Joe E. Watkins. 2011. $24.95 (paper). 160 pages. Contains a set of practical steps that will guide an individual through the transition from the life of being a student into a career within a wide range of professions involving an anthropology degree. Includes stories, scenarios, and activities pertinent to building a career in anthropology.

940 ■ Opportunities in Social Science Careers
The McGraw-Hill Companies Inc.
PO Box 182604
Columbus, OH 43272
Ph: (212)512-2000
Free: 877-833-5524
Fax: (614)759-3749
E-mail: customer.service@mcgraw-hill.com
URL: http://www.mcgraw-hill.com
Description: Rosanne J. Marek. 2004. $13.95. 160 Pages. VGM Opportunities Series.

941 ■ Visions of Culture: An Introduction to Anthropological Theories and Theorists
AltaMira Press
4501 Forbes Blvd., Ste. 200
Lanham, MD 20706
Ph: (301)459-3366
Free: 800-462-6420
Fax: (301)429-5748
E-mail: custserv@rowman.com
URL: http://www.rowman.com
Description: Jerry D. Moore. Third edition, 2008. $39.95 (paper). 416 pages. Focused on college students interested in Anthropology.

TRADESHOWS

942 ■ American Association of Physical Anthropologists Scientific/Professional Meeting
American Association of Physical Anthropologists
c/o Karen Rosenberg, President
135 John Munroe Hall
University of Delaware
Newark, DE 19716
Ph: (302)831-1855
Fax: (302)831-4002
E-mail: krr@udel.edu
URL: http://www.physanth.org
Frequency: Annual. **Primary Exhibits:** Exhibits for the advancement of the science of physical anthropology through research and teaching of human variation, primate paleoanthropology, and primate evolution.

943 ■ American Society for Ethnohistory Conference
American Society for Ethnohistory
c/o James Buss, Secretary
1101 Camden Ave.
Salisbury, MD 21801
E-mail: jjbuss@salisbury.edu
URL: http://ethnohistory.org
Frequency: Annual. **Primary Exhibits:** Exhibits relating to the cultural history of ethnic groups worldwide.

944 ■ Congress of the International Society for Human Ethology
International Society for Human Ethology
PO Box 418
Nyack, NY 10960
Ph: (207)581-2044
Fax: (207)581-6128
URL: http://www.ishe.org
Frequency: Biennial. **Primary Exhibits:** Books, journals, and equipment for observational research.

945 ■ Organization of American Historians Annual Meeting
Organization of American Historians
112 N Bryan Ave.
Bloomington, IN 47408-4141
Ph: (812)855-7311
Fax: (812)855-0696
E-mail: oah@oah.org
URL: http://www.oah.org
Frequency: Annual. **Primary Exhibits:** Equipment, supplies, and services of interest to historians, including textbooks and computer software.

OTHER SOURCES

946 ■ African Studies Association
Rutgers University
Livingston Campus
54 Joyce Kilmer Ave.
Piscataway, NJ 08854
Ph: (848)445-8173

Fax: (732)445-1366
E-mail: secretariat@africanstudies.org
URL: http://www.africanstudies.org
Description: Persons specializing in teaching, writing, or research on Africa including political scientists, historians, geographers, anthropologists, economists, librarians, linguists, and government officials; persons who are studying African subjects; institutional members are universities, libraries, government agencies, and others interested in receiving information about Africa. Seeks to foster communication and to stimulate research among scholars on Africa. Sponsors placement service; conducts panels and discussion groups; presents exhibits and films.

947 ■ American Academy of Forensic Sciences
2906 Lafayette Ave.
Newport Beach, CA 92663
Ph: (949)230-7321
E-mail: damartell@aol.com
URL: http://www.aafs.org
Description: Represents criminalists, scientists, members of the bench and bar, pathologists, biologists, psychiatrists, examiners of questioned documents, toxicologists, odontologists, anthropologists, and engineers. Works to: encourage the study, improve the practice, elevate the standards, and advance the cause of the forensic sciences; improve the quality of scientific techniques, tests, and criteria; plan, organize, and administer meetings, reports, and other projects for the stimulation and advancement of these and related purposes. Maintains Forensic Sciences Job Listing; conducts selected research for the government; offers forensic expert referral service.

948 ■ American Anthropological Association - Association for Africanist Anthropology
2200 Wilson Blvd., Ste. 600
Arlington, VA 22201-3357
Ph: (703)528-1902
Free: 800-545-4703
Fax: (703)528-3546
E-mail: africananthro@gmail.com
URL: http://www.aaanet.org/sections/afaa
Description: Aims to further the professional interests of anthropologists; to disseminate anthropological knowledge and its use to address human problems; to promote the entire field of anthropology in all its diversity; to represent the discipline nationally and internationally, in the public and private sectors; to bring together anthropologists from all subfields and specializations, providing networking opportunities across the broad range of the discipline.

949 ■ American Association of Physical Anthropologists
c/o Karen Rosenberg, President
135 John Munroe Hall
University of Delaware
Newark, DE 19716
Ph: (302)831-1855
Fax: (302)831-4002
E-mail: krr@udel.edu
URL: http://www.physanth.org
Description: Professional society of physical anthropologists and scientists in closely related fields interested in the advancement of the science of physical anthropology through research and teaching of human variation, paleoanthropology and primatology.

950 ■ American Society for Eighteenth-Century Studies
PO Box 7867
Winston-Salem, NC 27109-6253
Ph: (336)727-4694
Fax: (336)727-4697
E-mail: asecs@wfu.edu
URL: http://asecs.press.jhu.edu
Description: Scholars and others interested in the

cultural history of the 18th century. Encourages and advances study and research in this area; promotes the interchange of information and ideas among scholars from different disciplines (such as librarianship and bibliography) who are interested in the 18th century. Co-sponsors seven fellowship programs; sponsors Graduate Student Caucus.

951 ■ American Society of Primatologists
Trinity University
Dept. of Psychology
One Trinity Pl.
San Antonio, TX 78212
Ph: (210)999-7102
Fax: (210)999-8323
E-mail: kimberley.phillips@trinity.edu
URL: http://www.asp.org
Description: Promotes the discovery and exchange of information regarding nonhuman primates, including all aspects of their anatomy, behavior, development, ecology, evolution, genetics, nutrition, physiology, reproduction, systematics, conservation, husbandry and use in biomedical research. **Members:** 600.

952 ■ American Studies Association
1120 19th St. NW, Ste. 301
Washington, DC 20036
Ph: (202)467-4783
Fax: (202)467-4786
E-mail: asastaff@theasa.net
URL: http://www.theasa.net
Description: Serves as professional society of persons interested in American literature, American history, sociology, anthropology, political science, philosophy, fine arts, and other disciplines; librarians, museum directors, and government officials. Concerned with any field of study relating to American life and culture, past and present. Members are interested in research and teaching that crosses traditional departmental lines.

953 ■ Amerind Foundation
2100 N Amerind Rd.
Dragoon, AZ 85609
Ph: (520)586-3666
Fax: (520)586-4679
E-mail: amerind@amerind.org
URL: http://www.amerind.org
Description: Conducts research in anthropology and archaeology of the greater American southwest and northern Mexico and ethnology in the Western Hemisphere. Offers artist shows; volunteer opportunities, public programs, and visiting scholar program. Operates museum.

954 ■ Association of Black Anthropologists
AAA Member Services
2200 Wilson Blvd., Ste. 600
Arlington, VA 22201-3357
Ph: (703)528-1902
E-mail: abawebinfo@gmail.com
URL: http://www.aaanet.org/sections/aba
Description: A section of the American Anthropological Association. Anthropologists and others interested in the study of blacks and other people subjected to exploitation and oppression. Works to: formulate conceptual and methodological frameworks to advance understanding of all forms of human diversity and commonality; advance theoretical efforts to explain the conditions that produce social inequalities based on race, ethnicity, class, or gender; develop research methods that involve the people studied and local scholars in all stages of investigation and dissemination of findings.

955 ■ Biological Anthropology Section
University of Delaware
Dept. of Anthropology
John Munroe Hall
Newark, DE 19716
Ph: (302)831-1855
E-mail: krr@udel.edu
URL: http://www.aaanet.org/sections/bas

Description: A unit of American Anthropological Association. International group of anthropologists concerned with the biological aspects of anthropology. Aims to maintain communication among biological anthropologists. Promotes scientific and public understanding of human origins and the interaction between biological and cultural dimensions that underlie the evolution of humans. **Members:** 512.

956 ■ *Careers for History Buffs & Others Who Learn from the Past*
The McGraw-Hill Companies Inc.
PO Box 182604
Columbus, OH 43272
Ph: (212)512-2000
Free: 877-833-5524
Fax: (614)759-3749
E-mail: customer.service@mcgraw-hill.com
URL: http://www.mcgraw-hill.com
Description: Blythe Camenson. Third edition, 2008. $14.95 (paper). 176 pages. **Includes:** Appendices of living-history museums, U.S. National Park Service regional offices, and associations. Appendices of living-history museums, U.S. National Park Service regional offices, and associations. **Entries include:** Organization name, address.

957 ■ Institute for the Study of Man
1133 13th St. NW, Ste. C-2
Washington, DC 20005
E-mail: iejournal@aol.com
URL: http://www.jies.org
Description: Aims to publish books and journals in areas related to anthropology, historical linguistics, and the human sciences.

958 ■ International Studies Association
324 Social Sciences
Tucson, AZ 85721
Ph: (520)621-7754
Fax: (520)621-5780
E-mail: isa@isanet.org
URL: http://www.isanet.org
Description: Social scientists and other scholars from a wide variety of disciplines who are specialists in international affairs and cross-cultural studies; academicians; government officials; officials in international organizations; business executives; students. Promotes research, improved teaching, and the orderly growth of knowledge in the field of international studies; emphasizes a multidisciplinary approach to problems. Conducts conventions, workshops and discussion groups.

959 ■ International Women's Anthropology Conference
New York University
Anthropology Department
25 Waverly Pl.
New York, NY 10003
Ph: (212)998-8550
Fax: (212)995-4014
E-mail: constance.sutton@nyu.edu
URL: http://homepages.nyu.edu/~crs2/index.html
Description: Women anthropologists and sociologists who are researching and teaching topics such as women's role in development, feminism, and the international women's movement. Encourages the exchange of information on research, projects, and funding; addresses policies concerning women from an anthropological perspective. Conducts periodic educational meetings with panel discussions. **Members:** 600.

960 ■ Kroeber Anthropological Society
University of California, Berkeley
Dept. of Anthropology
232 Kroeber Hall
Berkeley, CA 94720-3710
E-mail: kas@berkeley.edu
URL: http://kas.berkeley.edu
Description: Represents anthropologists, students, interested laypersons and institutional members (300

major universities and anthropological institutions).
Members: 500.

961 ■ National Association for the Practice of Anthropology
American Anthropological Association
2200 Wilson Blvd., Ste. 600
Arlington, VA 22201
Ph: (703)528-1902
Fax: (703)528-3546
E-mail: tmwallace@mindspring.com
URL: http://www.practicinganthropology.org

Description: A section of the American Anthropological Association. Professional anthropologists serving social service organizations, government agencies, and business and industrial firms. Works to help anthropologists develop and market their expertise in areas such as social and political analysis, and program design, evaluation, and management. Compiles statistics. **Members:** 1,000.

962 ■ Society for Applied Anthropology
PO Box 2436
Oklahoma City, OK 73101-2436
Ph: (405)843-5113
Fax: (405)843-8553
E-mail: info@sfaa.net
URL: http://www.sfaa.net

Description: Professional society of anthropologists, sociologists, psychologists, health professionals, industrial researchers, and educators. Promotes scientific investigation of the principles controlling relations between human beings, and encourages wide application of these principles to practical problems.

963 ■ Society for Cultural Anthropology
c/o Jessica Cattelino, Treasurer
University of California, Los Angeles
Dept. of Anthropology
341 Haines Hall
Los Angeles, CA 90095
Ph: (831)459-5717
E-mail: culanth@culanth.org
URL: http://www.culanth.org

Description: A section of the American Anthropological Association, dedicated to the study of culture. Compiles statistics. **Members:** 1,531.

964 ■ Society for Historical Archaeology
13017 Wisteria Dr., Ste. 395
Germantown, MD 20874
Ph: (301)972-9684
Fax: (866)285-3512
E-mail: hq@sha.org
URL: http://www.sha.org

Description: Represents archaeologists, historians, anthropologists, and ethnohistorians; other individuals and institutions with an interest in historical archaeology or allied fields. Aims to bring together persons interested in studying specific historic sites, manuscripts, and published sources, and to develop generalizations concerning historical periods and cultural dynamics as these emerge through the techniques of archaeological excavation and analysis. Main focus is the era beginning with the exploration of the non-European world by Europeans, and geographical areas in the Western Hemisphere, but also considers Oceanian, African, and Asian archaeology during the relatively late periods.

965 ■ Society for Linguistic Anthropology
UCSD
Dept. of Anthropology, 0532
9500 Gilman Dr.
La Jolla, CA 92093-5004
Ph: (858)534-4639
Fax: (858)534-5946
E-mail: kwoolard@ucsd.edu
URL: http://www.linguisticanthropology.org

Description: Serves as section of the American Anthropological Association. Represents University faculty; students. Promotes the anthropological study of language. **Members:** 726.

966 ■ Society for Urban, National and Transnational/Global Anthropology
American Anthropological Association
2200 Wilson Blvd., Ste. 600
Arlington, VA 22201
Ph: (703)528-1902

Fax: (703)528-3546
E-mail: nabelman@illinois.edu
URL: http://www.sunta.org

Description: Seeks to advance the science and profession of urban, national and transnational/global anthropology. Promotes the advancement of research and the professional interests of urban national and transnational/global anthropologists. Encourages the distribution and application of knowledge acquired in the study of urban, national and transnational/global anthropology.

967 ■ Syracuse University - Program for the Advancement of Research on Conflict and Collaboration
400 Eggers Hall
Maxwell School of Citizenship & Public Affairs
Syracuse, NY 13244-1020
Ph: (315)443-2367
Fax: (315)443-3818
E-mail: roleary@maxwell.syr.edu
URL: http://www.maxwell.syr.edu/parcc.aspx

Description: Anthropologists. Fosters research on the social and cultural dynamics of peace and war. Provides curricular services; operates speakers' bureau and placement service; compiles statistics. Sponsors seminars and professional workshops. **Members:** 500.

968 ■ World Archaeological Society
120 Lakewood Dr.
Hollister, MO 65672
Ph: (417)334-2377
Fax: (417)334-5501
E-mail: ronwriterartist@aol.com
URL: http://www.worldarchaeologicalsociety.com

Description: Professional and amateur archaeologists, anthropologists, and art historians in 32 countries. Promotes the scientific and constructive study of antiquity within the fields of archaeology, anthropology, and art history. Conducts research on biblical archaeology, democracy, and the anthropology of drug addiction. Projects include the "Living" Museum of Democracy and the restoration of old Bibles. Conducts special research projects upon request. Supplies tape lectures for special programs. Provides ink and color illustrations for researchers.

SOURCES OF HELP-WANTED ADS

969 ■ American Archaeology
Archaeological Conservancy
1717 Girard Blvd. NE
Albuquerque, NM 87106
Ph: (505)266-1540
E-mail: tacinfo@nm.net
URL: http://www.americanarchaeology.com/aamaga-zine.html

Frequency: Quarterly. **Price:** $25 Individuals; included in membership dues. **Description:** Features news relating to archeology in the Americas.

970 ■ American Journal of Archaeology
Archaeological Institute of America
656 Beacon St., 6th Fl.
Boston, MA 02215-2006
Ph: (617)353-9361
Fax: (617)353-6550
E-mail: aia@aia.bu.edu
URLs: http://www.archaeological.org/webinfo.php
?page=10041; http://www.ajaonline.org/

Frequency: Quarterly. **Price:** included in membership dues; $75/year for individuals in U.S.; $95/year for individuals outside U.S.; $250/year for institutions in U.S.; $80 Individuals print; $50 Students print; $280 Institutions print; $50 Students print; $90 Individuals print & electronic; $60 Students print & electronic; $310 Institutions print & electronic; $120 Other countries print & electronic. **Description:** Covers archaeological subjects; illustrated with black-and-white photographs, drawings, and diagrams. Includes book reviews.

971 ■ ASOR Newsletter
American Schools of Oriental Research
656 Beacon St., 5th Fl.
Boston, MA 02215
Ph: (617)353-6570
Free: 888-847-8753
Fax: (617)353-6575
E-mail: asor@bu.edu
URL: http://www.asor.org

Frequency: Quarterly. **Description:** Quarterly. Carries news and reports from archaeological institutes in Amman, Jerusalem, and Cyprus. Recurring features include news of research, a calendar of events, reports of meetings, news of educational opportunities, job listings, and notices of publications available.

972 ■ Geoarchaeology: An International Journal
John Wiley & Sons Inc.
111 River St.
Hoboken, NJ 07030-5774
Ph: (201)748-6000
Free: 800-225-5945

Fax: (201)748-6088
E-mail: info@wiley.com
URL: http://onlinelibrary.wiley.com/journal/10.1002/
(ISSN)1520-6548

Frequency: Bimonthly. **Price:** $293 U.S., Canada, and Mexico individual (print only); $349 Other countries individual (print only); $2,466 Institutions print and online; $2,578 Institutions, Canada and Mexico print and online; $2,634 Institutions, other countries print and online; $2,144 Institutions print only; $2,256 Institutions, Canada and Mexico print only; $2,312 Institutions, other countries print only. **Description:** Journal covering the methodological and theoretical interface between archaeology and the geosciences.

973 ■ International Journal of Paleopathology
Elsevier Science Inc.
c/o Jane Buikstra, Ed.-in-Ch.
900 S Cady Mall, Rm. 233
School of Human Evolution & Social Change
Arizona State University
Tempe, AZ 85287-2402
Ph: (212)633-3980
Free: 888-437-4636
Fax: (212)633-3975
URL: http://www.journals.elsevier.com/international
-journal-of-paleopathology/

Frequency: 4/yr. **Price:** $79 Individuals; $309 Institutions. **Description:** Journal publishing research studies on paleopathology.

974 ■ SAA Bulletin
Society for American Archaeology
1111 14th St. NW, Ste. 800
Washington, DC 20005
Ph: (202)789-8200
Fax: (202)789-0284
E-mail: headquarters@saa.org
URL: http://www.saa.org

Description: 5/yr. Publishes informative articles about archaeology. Recurring features include letters to the editor, job listings, a calendar of events, notices of publications available, and columns titled Obituaries and News and Notes.

975 ■ Stanford Journal of Archaeology
Stanford University - Department of Sociology
Bldg. 120, Rm. 160
Stanford, CA 94305-2047
Ph: (650)723-3956
Fax: (650)725-6471
E-mail: sociology@stanford.edu
URL: http://www.stanford.edu/dept/archaeology/
journal/

Frequency: Irregular. **Price:** Free. **Description:** Online scholarly journal publishing research in archaeology.

EMPLOYER DIRECTORIES AND NETWORKING LISTS

976 ■ Andean Explorers Foundation & Ocean Sailing Club--Membership Roster
Andean Explorers Foundation & Ocean Sailing Club
PO Box 3279
Reno, NV 89505
Ph: (775)348-1818
Fax: (775)332-3086
E-mail: info@aefosc.org
URL: http://www.aefosc.org

Covers: Non-profit group of archeological enthusiasts and explorers conducting research on archeological remains and making documented works available to scientific institutions, museums, and specialists in Peru and other countries.

977 ■ Newsletter--Society for Historical Archaeology Membership Directory Issue
Society for Historical Archaeology
13017 Wisteria Dr., Ste. 395
Germantown, MD 20874
Ph: (301)972-9684
Fax: (866)285-3512
E-mail: hq@sha.org
URL: http://www.sha.org

Frequency: Quarterly; Latest edition 2011. **Publication includes:** List of about 2,100 member archaeologists, historians, anthropologists, and ethnohistorians, and other individuals and institutions having an interest in historical archeology or allied fields. **Entries include:** Name, address. **Arrangement:** Alphabetical.

HANDBOOKS AND MANUALS

978 ■ FabJob Guide to Become an Archaeologist
FabJob Inc.
4616-25th Ave. NE, No. 224
Seattle, WA 98105
Ph: (403)873-1018
Free: 888-322-5621
URL: http://www.fabjob.com

Description: Robert Larkin. $14.97(e-book). 112 pages. Offers valuable advice about where to look for jobs, how to approach employers, and what markets may be best for employment. Highlights the qualities employers are looking for, how to ace the interview, and how to advance through networking and professional development.

979 ■ Opportunities in Social Science Careers
The McGraw-Hill Companies Inc.
PO Box 182604
Columbus, OH 43272

Ph: (212)512-2000
Free: 877-833-5524
Fax: (614)759-3749
E-mail: customer.service@mcgraw-hill.com
URL: http://www.mcgraw-hill.com
Description: Rosanne J. Marek. 2004. $13.95. 160
Pages. VGM Opportunities Series.

ONLINE JOB SOURCES AND SERVICES

980 ■ ArchaeologyFieldwork.com
URL: http://www.archaeologyfieldwork.com/AFW
Description: Provides an archaeology resource
database that includes employment listings, resume
and CV postings, job hunt, archaeology announcements, and archaeology volunteer opportunities.
Features other resources such as a forum for discussions on wages and per diem in CRM, working
conditions, professional organizations and unions,
and other issues of interest for field archaeologists.

981 ■ Cultural Resource Network
URL: http://www.culturalresourcenetwork.com
Description: Provides sources of news, jobs, announcements, consultant listings, and resources for
the cultural resource industry.

982 ■ ScientistCrossing.com
URL: http://www.scientistcrossing.com
Description: Provides job listings and other
resources related to scientist employment opportunities.

TRADESHOWS

**983 ■ American Society for Ethnohistory
Conference**
American Society for Ethnohistory
c/o James Buss, Secretary
1101 Camden Ave.
Salisbury, MD 21801
E-mail: jjbuss@salisbury.edu
URL: http://ethnohistory.org
Frequency: Annual. **Primary Exhibits:** Exhibits
relating to the cultural history of ethnic groups
worldwide.

**984 ■ Conference on Historical and
Underwater Archaeology**
Society for Historical Archaeology
13017 Wisteria Dr., Ste. 395
Germantown, MD 20874
Ph: (301)972-9684
Fax: (866)285-3512
E-mail: hq@sha.org
URL: http://www.sha.org
Frequency: Annual. **Primary Exhibits:** Archaeolo-
gists, historians, anthropologists, and ethnohistori-
ans; other individuals and institutions with an interest
in historical archaeology or allied fields.

**985 ■ Society for American Archaeology
Conference**
Society for American Archaeology
1111 14th St. NW, Ste. 800
Washington, DC 20005
Ph: (202)789-8200
Fax: (202)789-0284
E-mail: headquarters@saa.org
URL: http://www.saa.org
Frequency: Annual. **Primary Exhibits:** Archaeologi-
cal equipment, supplies, and services academic
books, GPS, GIS, software.

OTHER SOURCES

986 ■ American Philological Association
University of Pennsylvania
220 S 40th St., Ste. 201E
Philadelphia, PA 19104-3512

Ph: (215)898-4975
Fax: (215)573-7874
E-mail: apaclassics@sas.upenn.edu
URL: http://www.apaclassics.org
Description: Teachers of Latin and Greek, classical
archaeologists with literary interests, and comparative linguists. Works for the advancement and diffu-
sion of philological information. Sponsors placement
service and campus advisory service to provide
advice on instructional programs in classical studies.

987 ■ Amerind Foundation
2100 N Amerind Rd.
Dragoon, AZ 85609
Ph: (520)586-3666
Fax: (520)586-4679
E-mail: amerind@amerind.org
URL: http://www.amerind.org
Description: Conducts research in anthropology and
archaeology of the greater American southwest and
northern Mexico and ethnology in the Western
Hemisphere. Offers artist shows; volunteer opportuni-
ties, public programs, and visiting scholar program.
Operates museum.

988 ■ Archaeological Conservancy
1717 Girard Blvd. NE
Albuquerque, NM 87106
Ph: (505)266-1540
E-mail: tacinfo@nm.net
URL: http://www.americanarchaeology.com
Description: People interested in preserving
prehistoric and historic sites for interpretive or
research purposes (most members are not professional archaeologists). Seeks to acquire for
permanent preservation, through donation or
purchase, the ruins of past American cultures,
primarily those of American Indians. Works
throughout the U.S. to preserve cultural resources
presently on private lands and protect them from the
destruction of looters, modern agricultural practices,
and urban sprawl. Operates with government agencies, universities, and museums to permanently
preserve acquired sites.

989 ■ Archaeological Institute of America
656 Beacon St., 6th Fl.
Boston, MA 02215-2006
Ph: (617)353-9361
Fax: (617)353-6550
E-mail: aia@aia.bu.edu
URL: http://www.archaeological.org
Description: Educational and scientific society of
archaeologists and others interested in archaeological study and research. Founded five schools of
archaeology: American School of Classical Studies
(Athens, 1881); School of Classical Studies of the
American Academy (Rome, 1895); American Schools
of Oriental Research (Jerusalem, 1900 and Bagh-
dad, 1921); School of American Research (1907,
with headquarters at Santa Fe, NM). Is allied with
three research institutes: American Research
Institute in Turkey; American Institute of Iranian Studies; American Research Center in Egypt. Maintains
annual lecture programs for all branch societies.
Operates placement service for archeology educators. Sponsors educational programs for middle
school children.

**990 ■ ASPRS, The Imaging and Geospatial
Information Society**
5410 Grosvenor Ln., Ste. 210
Bethesda, MD 20814-2160
Ph: (301)493-0290
Fax: (301)493-0208
E-mail: asprs@asprs.org
URL: http://www.asprs.org
Description: Firms, individuals, government
employees and academicians engaged in photogrammetry, photointerpretation, remote sensing, and
geographic information systems and their application
to such fields as archaeology, geographic information
systems, military reconnaissance, urban planning,
engineering, traffic surveys, meteorological observa-

tions, medicine, geology, forestry, agriculture,
construction and topographic mapping. Seeks to
advance knowledge and improve understanding of
these sciences and promote responsible applications. Offers voluntary certification program open to
persons associated with one or more functional area
of photogrammetry, remote sensing and GIS.
Surveys the profession of private firms in photogrammetry and remote sensing in the areas of products
and services.

**991 ■ Careers for History Buffs & Others
Who Learn from the Past**
The McGraw-Hill Companies Inc.
PO Box 182604
Columbus, OH 43272
Ph: (212)512-2000
Free: 877-833-5524
Fax: (614)759-3749
E-mail: customer.service@mcgraw-hill.com
URL: http://www.mcgraw-hill.com
Description: Blythe Camenson. Third edition, 2008.
$14.95 (paper). 176 pages. **Includes:** Appendices of
living-history museums, U.S. National Park Service
regional offices, and associations. Appendices of
living-history museums, U.S. National Park Service
regional offices, and associations. **Entries include:**
Organization name, address.

**992 ■ Careers for Mystery Buffs and Other
Snoops and Sleuths**
The McGraw-Hill Companies Inc.
PO Box 182604
Columbus, OH 43272
Ph: (212)512-2000
Free: 877-833-5524
Fax: (614)759-3749
E-mail: customer.service@mcgraw-hill.com
URL: http://www.mcgraw-hill.com
Description: Blythe Camenson. Second edition.
$14.95 (hardback). 160 pages. **Publication
includes:** Appendix of associations that provide
information about various careers, publish newslet-
ters listing job and internship opportunities, and offer
employment services to members. **Entries include:**
Name, address.

**993 ■ Center for American Archeology -
Kampsville Archeological Center**
PO Box 366
Kampsville, IL 62053
Ph: (618)653-4316
Fax: (618)653-4232
E-mail: caa@caa-archeology.org
URL: http://www.caa-archeology.org
Description: Philanthropic organizations, foundations, corporations, professional and amateur
archaeologists, students, and others interested in
archaeology in the U.S. Conducts archaeological
research and disseminates the results. Excavates,
analyzes, and conserves archaeological sites and
artifacts. Sponsors tours, lectures, and educational
and outreach programs, including university, middle
school and junior high, and high school field schools;
offers professional training at levels of detail ranging
from secondary to postgraduate. Maintains speakers'
bureau. Operates Visitors Center. **Members:** 500.

994 ■ Epigraphic Society
97 Village Post Rd.
Danvers, MA 01923
Ph: (978)774-1275
E-mail: donalbb@epigraphy.org
URL: http://www.epigraphy.org
Description: Launches expeditions to North America
and overseas. Reports discoveries and decipher-
ments and assesses their historical implications.
Participates in group lecture and teaching programs
with other archaeological societies and university
departments of archaeology and history.

995 ■ Exploring Solutions Past: The Maya Forest Alliance
PO Box 3962
Santa Barbara, CA 93130
Ph: (805)893-8191
Fax: (805)893-7995
E-mail: ford@marc.ucsb.edu
URL: http://www.espmaya.org

Description: Strives to come up with solutions to today's environmental crisis through archaeology. Supports exploration of the archaeological and contemporary Maya traditions. Works to preserve endangered resources through local and international education.

996 ■ Register of Professional Archaeologists
3601 E Joppa Rd.
Baltimore, MD 21234
Ph: (410)931-8100
Fax: (410)931-8111
E-mail: info@rpanet.org
URL: http://www.rpanet.org

Description: Represents archaeologists satisfying basic requirements in training and experience, including private consultants, individuals working with large firms, and academic personnel. Seeks to define professionalism in archaeology; provide a measure against which to evaluate archaeological actions and research; establish certification standards; provide for grievance procedures; demonstrate to other archaeologists and the public the nature of professional archaeology. Monitors related legislative activities; maintains register archives. Is developing educational programs and drafting standards and guidelines for field schools.

997 ■ Society for American Archaeology
1111 14th St. NW, Ste. 800
Washington, DC 20005
Ph: (202)789-8200
Fax: (202)789-0284
E-mail: headquarters@saa.org
URL: http://www.saa.org

Description: Professionals, vocationals, students, and others interested in American archaeology. Stimulates scientific research in the archaeology of the New World by: creating closer professional relations among archaeologists, and between them and others interested in American archaeology; advocating the conservation of archaeological data and furthering the control or elimination of commercialization of archaeological objects; promoting a more rational public appreciation of the aims and limitations of archaeological research. Maintains placement service and educational programs.

998 ■ Society for Historical Archaeology
13017 Wisteria Dr., Ste. 395
Germantown, MD 20874
Ph: (301)972-9684
Fax: (866)285-3512
E-mail: hq@sha.org
URL: http://www.sha.org

Description: Represents archaeologists, historians, anthropologists, and ethnohistorians; other individuals and institutions with an interest in historical archaeology or allied fields. Aims to bring together persons interested in studying specific historic sites, manuscripts, and published sources, and to develop generalizations concerning historical periods and cultural dynamics as these emerge through the techniques of archaeological excavation and analysis. Main focus is the era beginning with the exploration of the non-European world by Europeans, and geographical areas in the Western Hemisphere, but also considers Oceanian, African, and Asian archaeology during the relatively late periods.

999 ■ World Archaeological Society
120 Lakewood Dr.
Hollister, MO 65672
Ph: (417)334-2377
Fax: (417)334-5501
E-mail: ronwriterartist@aol.com
URL: http://www.worldarchaeologicalsociety.com

Description: Professional and amateur archaeologists, anthropologists, and art historians in 32 countries. Promotes the scientific and constructive study of antiquity within the fields of archaeology, anthropology, and art history. Conducts research on biblical archaeology, democracy, and the anthropology of drug addiction. Projects include the "Living" Museum of Democracy and the restoration of old Bibles. Conducts special research projects upon request. Supplies tape lectures for special programs. Provides ink and color illustrations for researchers.

Architects

SOURCES OF HELP-WANTED ADS

1000 ■ *American Institute of Architects-AIArchitect*
American Institute of Architects Press
1735 New York Ave., NW
Washington, DC 20006-5292
Ph: (202)626-7566
Fax: (202)626-7547
E-mail: infocentral@aia.org
URL: http://www.aia.org

Description: Monthly. Concerned with the architectural profession. Discusses business and legislative trends, practice and design information, and AIA activities. Recurring features include news of members and a calendar of events.

1001 ■ *Architect Magazine*
Russell S. Ellis
One Thomas Cir. NW, Ste. 600
Washington, DC 20005
Ph: (202)452-0800
Fax: (202)785-1974
E-mail: rellis@hanleywood.com
URL: http://www.architectmagazine.com

Description: Monthly. Free of charge to those who qualify. Online edition is also available. Provides the practicing architect with vital business tips, design inspiration, plus ideas for skill development and practice management.

1002 ■ *Architectural Products*
Construction Business Media L.L.C.
579 First Bank Dr., Ste. 220
Palatine, IL 60067
Ph: (847)359-6493
Fax: (847)359-6754
E-mail: tim@arch-products.com
URL: http://www.arch-products.com/

Frequency: 10/yr. **Price:** $55 Other countries. **Description:** Magazine provides product and product application information to architects, designers, and product specifiers.

1003 ■ *Architectural Record*
The McGraw-Hill Companies Inc.
Two Penn Plz., 9th Fl.
New York, NY 10121-2298
Ph: (212)904-2594
Fax: (212)904-4256
E-mail: customer.service@mcgraw-hill.com
URL: http://archrecord.construction.com

Frequency: Monthly. **Price:** $49 Individuals; $59 Canada; $129 Other countries. **Description:** Magazine focusing on architecture.

1004 ■ *Axis Journal*
American Institute of Architects, Golden Empire Chapter
1201 24th St., Ste. B110-164
Bakersfield, CA 93301

Ph: (661)836-4300
E-mail: info@aiage.org
URL: http://www.aiage.org

Description: Monthly. Covers activities of American Institute of Architects, Golden Empire Chapter. Provides information to clients and public leaders on architects' concerns and activities.

1005 ■ *Builder and Developer*
Peninsula Publishing Inc.
1602 Monrovia Ave.
Newport Beach, CA 92663-2808
Ph: (949)631-0308
Fax: (949)631-2475
E-mail: nslevin@penpubinc.com
URL: http://www.bdmag.com

Frequency: 11/yr. **Description:** Magazine for home-builders.

1006 ■ *Builder: The Magazine of the National Association of Home Builders*
DoveTale Publishers
1 Thomas Cir. NW
Washington, DC 20005
Ph: (202)339-0744
Free: 877-275-8647
Fax: (202)785-1974
E-mail: builder@omeda.com
URLs: http://www.hanleywood.com/default.aspx?page=magazines; http://www.builderonline.com

Frequency: 13/yr. **Price:** $29.95 U.S. and Canada; $54.95 U.S. and Canada 2 years; $192 Other countries. **Description:** Magazine covering housing and construction industry.

1007 ■ *Building Industry Technology*
U.S. Department of Commerce - Technology Administration - National Technical Information Service
5301 Shawnee Rd.
Alexandria, VA 22312
Ph: (703)605-6040
Free: 800-553-NTIS
Fax: (703)605-6900
E-mail: info@ntis.gov
URL: http://www.ntis.gov/products/alerts.aspx

Description: Biweekly. $255. Consists of abstracts of reports on architectural and environmental design, building standards, construction materials and equipment, and structural analyses. Recurring features include a form for ordering reports from NTIS. Also available via e-mail.

1008 ■ *Civil Engineering-ASCE*
American Society of Civil Engineers - Architectural Engineering Institute
1801 Alexander Bell Dr.
Reston, VA 20191-4400
Free: 800-548-2723
E-mail: aei@asce.org
URL: http://pubs.asce.org/magazines/CEMag/

Frequency: Monthly. **Price:** $230 Institutions; $275

Institutions, other countries; $230 Individuals; $275 Other countries; $30 Members domestic; $69 Other countries member; $30 Students member; domestic; $69 Students member; international. **Description:** Professional magazine.

1009 ■ *Daily Journal of Commerce*
New Orleans Publishing Group Inc.
111 Veterans Blvd., Ste. 1440
Metairie, LA 70005
Ph: (504)834-9292
Fax: (504)832-3550
E-mail: mail@nopg.com
URLs: http://www.djc-gp.com; http://www.djcgulfcoast.com

Frequency: Daily. **Price:** $525 Individuals online; $375 Individuals 6 months; $225 Individuals 3 months. **Description:** Trade newspaper covering construction news in Louisiana and Mississippi.

1010 ■ *Design Cost Data: Cost Estimating Magazine for Design and Construction*
DC & D Technologies Inc.
PO Box 948
Valrico, FL 33595-0948
Ph: (813)662-6830
Free: 800-533-5680
Fax: (813)662-6793
E-mail: webmaster@dcd.com
URL: http://www.dcd.com

Frequency: Bimonthly. **Price:** $94 Individuals silver; $157 Two years silver; $149 Individuals gold; $239 Two years gold. **Description:** Publication providing real cost data case studies of various types completed around the country for design and building professionals.

1011 ■ *Design Line*
American Institute of Building Design
529 14th St. NW, Ste. 750
Washington, DC 20045
Free: 800-366-2423
Fax: (866)204-0293
URL: http://www.aibd.org

Description: Quarterly. Focuses on all aspects of building design. Recurring features include letters to the editor, interviews, a collection, reports of meetings, news of educational opportunities, and notices of publications available.

1012 ■ *Design Lines Magazine*
American Institute of Building Design
529 14th St. NW, Ste. 750
Washington, DC 20045
Free: 800-366-2423
Fax: (866)204-0293
URL: http://www.aibd.org/publications/design_lines_magazine.php

Frequency: Quarterly. **Description:** Magazine focusing on issues, education, and events in the building design industry.

1013 ■ *Fabric Architecture: The International Membrane Structure and Design Magazine*
Industrial Fabrics Association International
1801 County Rd. B W
Roseville, MN 55113-4061
Ph: (651)222-2508
Free: 800-225-4324
Fax: (651)631-9334
E-mail: generalinfo@ifai.com
URLs: http://fabricarchitecturemag.com/; http://www.ifai.com/Home/magazinesplash.cfm

Frequency: Bimonthly. **Price:** $39 Two years; $49 Two years Canada and Mexico; $69 Two years international. **Description:** Magazine specializing in interior and exterior design ideas and technical information for architectural fabric applications in architecture and the landscape.

1014 ■ *Green Home Builder: America's Premier Green Homebuilding Resource*
Peninsula Publishing Inc.
1602 Monrovia Ave.
Newport Beach, CA 92663-2808
Ph: (949)631-0308
Fax: (949)631-2475
E-mail: nslevin@penpubinc.com
URL: http://www.greenhomebuildermag.com/

Frequency: Quarterly. **Description:** Magazine for home builders and home building industry.

1015 ■ *Grey Room*
The MIT Press
PO Box 250834
New York, NY 10025
Ph: (617)253-5646
Free: 800-356-0343
Fax: (617)258-6779
E-mail: editors@greyroom.org
URL: http://www.mitpressjournals.org/loi/grey

Frequency: Quarterly. **Price:** $66 Individuals online only; $73 Individuals print & online; $43 Students print and online, retired; $39 Students online only, retired; $254 Institutions online only; $291 Institutions print and online. **Description:** Scholarly journal devoted to the theorization of modern and contemporary architecture, art, media, and politics. Dedicated to the task of promoting and sustaining critical investigation into each of these fields separately and into their mutual interactions. Develops a rigorous, cross-disciplinary dialogue among the fields of architecture, art, and media to forge and promote a politically-informed, critical discourse uniquely relevant to the current historical situation.

1016 ■ *Kitchen and Bath Design News*
Cygnus Business Media Inc.
1233 Janesville Ave.
Fort Atkinson, WI 53538
Free: 800-547-7377
E-mail: info@cygnus.com
URL: http://www.cygnusb2b.com/PropertyPub.cfm?PropertyID=78

Frequency: Monthly. **Description:** Trade journal.

1017 ■ *Masonry Magazine*
Mason Contractors Association of America
1481 Merchant Dr.
Algonquin, IL 60102
Ph: (224)678-9709
Free: 800-536-2225
Fax: (224)678-9714
E-mail: bennett@lionhrtpub.com
URL: http://www.masoncontractors.org

Description: Monthly. $43.00/2 years; $29.00/year. Covers every aspect of the mason contractor profession, from equipment and techniques to building codes and standards, training the future masonry labor force, business planning, promoting business, job interviewing, negotiation and legal issues.

1018 ■ *Metal Architecture*
Modern Trade Communications Inc.
7450 Skokie Blvd.
Skokie, IL 60077
Ph: (847)674-2200
Fax: (847)674-3676
E-mail: boneill@moderntrade.com
URL: http://www.metalarchitecture.com

Frequency: Monthly. **Price:** $75 Canada and Mexico; $150 Other countries; $45 Individuals. **Description:** Trade journal serving architectural, engineering, and construction firms.

1019 ■ *The Military Engineer*
Society of American Military Engineers
607 Prince St.
Alexandria, VA 22314-3117
Ph: (703)549-3800
Fax: (703)684-0231
E-mail: rwolff@same.org
URL: http://www.same.org/i4a/pages/index.cfm?pageid=4273

Frequency: Bimonthly. **Price:** $88 U.S. and Canada individuals, second class mail; $168 U.S. and Canada two years; $222 U.S. and Canada three years; $188 Other countries air mail, individuals; $358 Other countries two years, air mail; $458 Other countries three years, air mail; $22 Students U.S., Canada, and foreign (regular mail). **Description:** Journal on military and civil engineering.

1020 ■ *Municipal Art Society Newsletter*
Municipal Art Society
111 W 57th St.
New York, NY 10019
Ph: (212)935-3960
URL: http://mas.org

Description: Six issues/year. Provides updates on advocacy efforts, exhibitions, and programming on urban issues. Recurring features include a calendar of events and tour schedule.

1021 ■ *Professional Builder: The Magazine of the Housing and Light Construction Industry*
SGC Horizon L.L.C.
3030 W Salt Creek Ln., Ste. 201
Arlington Heights, IL 60005
Ph: (847)391-1000
Fax: (847)390-0408
URL: http://www.housingzone.com/professionalbuilder

Frequency: Monthly. **Price:** Free. **Description:** The integrated engineering magazine of the building construction industry.

1022 ■ *Residential Architect*
DoveTale Publishers
1 Thomas Cir. NW
Washington, DC 20005
Ph: (202)339-0744
Free: 877-275-8647
Fax: (202)785-1974
E-mail: res@omeda.com
URL: http://www.residentialarchitectmediakit.com/r5/home.asp

Frequency: 9/yr. **Price:** $39.95 Individuals; $66 Canada; $132.50 Other countries. **Description:** Magazine for architects, designers, and building professionals.

1023 ■ *Residential Contractor: The U.S. Home Construction Industry Source*
Peninsula Publishing Inc.
1602 Monrovia Ave.
Newport Beach, CA 92663-2808
Ph: (949)631-0308
Fax: (949)631-2475
E-mail: nslevin@penpubinc.com
URL: http://www.residentialcontractormag.com/

Frequency: Quarterly. **Description:** Magazine for small volume residential builders, contractors, and specialty trades.

1024 ■ *SARAScope*
Society of American Registered Architects
305 E 46th St.
New York, NY 10017
Ph: (218)728-4293
Free: 888-985-7272
Fax: (218)728-5361
E-mail: bdpArch@cpinternet.com
URL: http://www.sara-national.org

Description: Bimonthly. Tracks Society activities at national and local levels.

1025 ■ *Texas Architect*
Texas Society of Architects
500 Chicon St.
Austin, TX 78702
Ph: (512)478-7386
Free: 800-242-3837
Fax: (512)478-0528
E-mail: coti@texasarchitect.org
URL: http://texasarchitect.org/publications.php?sess_id=66b886ac944dc4eab5254ee13780b45b

Frequency: Bimonthly. **Price:** $25 Students/year; $30 Nonmembers/year; $53 Two years; Included in membership. **Description:** Magazine for design professionals and their clients.

PLACEMENT AND JOB REFERRAL SERVICES

1026 ■ **Construction Financial Management Association**
100 Village Blvd., Ste. 200
Princeton, NJ 08540
Ph: (609)452-8000
Free: 888-421-9996
Fax: (609)452-0474
E-mail: sbinstock@cfma.org
URL: http://www.cfma.org

Description: Contractors, subcontractors, architects, real estate developers and engineers; associate members are equipment and material suppliers, accountants, lawyers, bankers and others involved with the financial management of the construction industry. Maintains placement service.

EMPLOYER DIRECTORIES AND NETWORKING LISTS

1027 ■ *Almanac of Architecture and Design*
The Greenway Group Inc.
25 Technology Pky. S, Ste. 101
Norcross, GA 30092
Ph: (678)879-0929
Free: 800-726-8603
Fax: (678)879-0930
URL: http://www.greenway.us

Frequency: Annual; Latest edition 13th, 2012. **Price:** $149 Individuals. **Publication includes:** Lists of professional organizations, degree programs, and leading firms in architecture and design. Principal content of publication is a collection of information regarding architecture and design.

1028 ■ *ArchitectureWeek*
Artifice Inc.
1342 High St.
Eugene, OR 97401
Ph: (541)345-7421
Free: 800-203-8324
Fax: (541)345-7438
E-mail: artifice@artifice.com
URL: http://www.architectureweek.com

Description: Weekly. Provides information and images for architects, builders, designers, planners and other AEC industry professionals. Also caters to home makers, students and teachers of design. Covers buildings as they open worldwide.

1029 ■ Athletic Business--Professional Directory Section
Athletic Business Publications Inc.
4130 Lien Rd.
Madison, WI 53704
Ph: (608)249-0186
Free: 800-722-8764
Fax: (608)249-1153
E-mail: editors@hardwoodfloorsmag.com
URL: http://www.athleticbusiness.com

Frequency: Monthly; Latest edition 2010. **Price:** $8 per issue. **Publication includes:** List of architects, engineers, contractors, and consultants in athletic facility planning and construction; all listings are paid. **Entries include:** Company name, address, phone, fax and short description of company. **Arrangement:** Alphabetical.

1030 ■ ENR--Top 500 Design Firms Issue
The McGraw-Hill Companies Inc.
PO Box 182604
Columbus, OH 43272
Ph: (212)512-2000
Free: 877-833-5524
Fax: (614)759-3749
E-mail: customer.service@mcgraw-hill.com
URL: http://enr.construction.com/toplists/
    sourcebooks/2010/designfirms/

Frequency: Annual; latest edition 2010. **Price:** $82 Individuals yearly subscription; $87 Individuals print and online. **Publication includes:** List of 500 leading architectural, engineering, and specialty design firms selected on basis of annual billings. **Entries include:** Company name, headquarters location, type of firm, current and prior year rank in billings, types of services, countries in which operated in preceding year. **Arrangement:** Ranked by billings.

1031 ■ The Military Engineer--Directory
Society of American Military Engineers
607 Prince St.
Alexandria, VA 22314-3117
Ph: (703)549-3800
Fax: (703)684-0231
E-mail: rwolff@same.org
URL: http://www.same.org

Frequency: updated daily. **Pages:** 2,800. **Includes:** Firm name, address, phone, E-mail, home page, names of principals, business class, type of ownership, number of employees, and the engineering specialties of the firm. **Arrangement:** Alphabetical. **Indexes:** Alphabetical by state and country; alphabetical by business class.

1032 ■ ProFile--The Architects Sourcebook
Reed Construction Data Inc.
30 Technology Pky. S, Ste. 100
Norcross, GA 30092
Ph: (770)417-4000
Free: 800-424-3996
Fax: (770)417-4002
E-mail: profile@reedbusiness.com
URL: http://www.reedfirstsource.com

Frequency: Annual. **Pages:** 2,400. **Covers:** more than 27,000 architectural firms. **Entries include:** For firms--Firm name, address, phone, fax, year established, key staff and their primary responsibilities (for design, specification, etc.), number of staff personnel by discipline, types of work, geographical area served, projects. "ProFile" is an expanded version of, and replaces, the "Firm Directory." **Arrangement:** Firms are geographical. **Indexes:** Firm name, key individuals, specialization by category, consultants. Firm name, key individuals, specialization by category, consultants.

HANDBOOKS AND MANUALS

1033 ■ Architecture Student's Handbook of Professional Practice
John Wiley & Sons, Inc.
1 Wiley Dr.
Somerset, NJ 08873

Free: 877-762-2974
Fax: (800)597-3299
E-mail: custserv@wiley.com
URL: http://www.wiley.com

Description: The American Institute of Architects. Fourteenth edition, 2008. $100.00. 720 pages.

1034 ■ Construction
InfoBase Holdings Inc.
132 W 31st., 17 Fl.
New York, NY 10001-3406
Ph: (212)967-8800
Fax: (800)678-3633
E-mail: info@infobasepublishing.com
URL: http://www.ferguson.infobasepublishing.com

Price: $30 Hardcover. **Description:** 2010. 128 pages. Contains profiles of 20 careers in the field of construction with emphasis on the nature of work, requirements, salary, and career outlook. Includes full-color photographs, index, glossary, resources, and side bars.

1035 ■ Information Technologies for Construction Managers, Architects, and Engineers
Cengage Learning Inc.
200 1st Stamford Pl., Ste. 400
Stamford, CT 06902-6753
Ph: (203)965-8600
Free: 800-354-9706
Fax: (800)487-8488
E-mail: investors@cengage.com
URL: http://www.cengage.com

Description: Trefor Williams. 2007. $102.95. 256 pages. Profiles information technology applications in construction trades, from traditional computer applications to emerging Web-based and mobile technologies.

1036 ■ Opportunities in Architecture Careers
The McGraw-Hill Companies Inc.
PO Box 182604
Columbus, OH 43272
Ph: (212)512-2000
Free: 877-833-5524
Fax: (614)759-3749
E-mail: customer.service@mcgraw-hill.com
URL: http://www.mcgraw-hill.com

Description: Robert J. Piper. 2006. $13.95 (paper). 160 pages. Guide to planning for and seeking opportunities in the field. Illustrated. Includes training and education requirements, salary statistics, and professional and Internet resources.

EMPLOYMENT AGENCIES AND SEARCH FIRMS

1037 ■ Agra Placements, Ltd.
8435 University Ave., Ste. 6
Des Moines, IA 50325
Ph: (515)225-6563
Free: 888-696-5624
Fax: (515)225-7733
E-mail: careers@agrapl.com
URL: http://www.agraplacements.com

Description: Executive search firm. Branch offices in Peru, IN, Lincoln, IL, and Andover, KS.

1038 ■ Capitol Staffing Inc.
460 Briarwood Dr., Briarwood 1 Bldg., Ste. 110
Jackson, MS 39206
Ph: (601)957-1755
Fax: (601)957-3880
E-mail: info@capitolstaffing.com
URL: http://www.capitolstaffing.com

Description: Personnel consultancy that focuses on office administration, management, sales, accounting, medical, information technology, accounting, and engineering/technical fields. Industries served: insur-

ance, finance, medical, communications, investment, industry, and small businesses.

1039 ■ Claremont-Branan, Inc.
1298 Rockbridge Rd., Ste. B
Stone Mountain, GA 30087
Free: 800-875-1292
URL: http://cbisearch.com

Description: Employment agency. Executive search firm.

1040 ■ The Coxe Group Inc.
1904 3rd Ave., Securities Bldg., Ste. 229
Seattle, WA 98101-1194
Ph: (206)467-4040
Fax: (206)467-4038
E-mail: info@coxegroup.com
URL: http://www.coxegroup.com

Description: Executive search firm.

1041 ■ ENTEGEE Inc.
70 Blanchard Rd., Ste. 102
Burlington, MA 01803-5100
Free: 800-368-3433
E-mail: corporate@entegee.com
URL: http://www.entegee.com

Description: Specializes in recruiting experienced professionals in the engineering and technical industries. Features a searchable database of employment opportunities in the engineering and technical fields.

1042 ■ Interior Talent
1430 Lake Baldwin Ln., Ste. A
Orlando, FL 32814
Free: 800-915-3012
Fax: (407)228-1935
E-mail: info@interiortalent.com
URL: http://www.interiortalent.com

Description: Recruiters for architecture and design professionals worldwide.

1043 ■ Metzner Group
10130 Harmony Rd.
Myersville, MD 21773
Ph: (301)293-4206
Fax: (301)293-4207
E-mail: carol@themetznergroup.com
URL: http://www.themetznergroup.com

Description: Specializes in the recruitment of architects, civil engineers, environmental engineers and planners for the A/E/P communities.

1044 ■ RitaSue Siegel Resources, Inc.
PO Box 845
New York, NY 10150
Ph: (917)725-1603
E-mail: contact@ritasue.com
URL: http://www.ritasue.com

Description: Executive search firm specializing in industrial and product design.

1045 ■ S.R. Clarke
105 Huntercombe
Williamsburg, VA 23188
Ph: (703)344-0256
Fax: (949)608-5052
URL: http://www.srclarke.com/index.html

Description: Serves as an executive search and recruitment firm specializing in commercial construction, commercial real estate development, residential asset management, residential construction and development, subcontractor trades, finance, accounting, administration, heavy construction, architectural design and engineering design.

ONLINE JOB SOURCES AND SERVICES

1046 ■ A/E/C JobBank
URL: http://www.aecjobbank.com

Description: Helps job seekers find employment opportunities in the construction industry. Allows employers and recruiters to post construction jobs and source top resumes.

1047 ■ AECWorkForce.com
URL: http://aecworkforce.com

Description: Serves as job board for professionals and employers in architecture, engineering and construction.

1048 ■ AEJob.com
URL: http://aejob.com

Description: Provides lists of architectural jobs, engineering jobs and environmental consulting jobs nationwide.

1049 ■ Archinect.com
URL: http://archinect.com

Description: Functions as an online destination for progressive-design oriented students, architects, educators and fans. Brings together designers from around the world to introduce new ideas from all disciplines.

1050 ■ Architect Jobs.com
URLs: http://www.architectjobs.com; http://www.jobsarchitect.org

Description: Features architect jobs, resumes, interview tips, degree programs, recruiters lists, salary information, and other career resources.

1051 ■ ArchitectureCrossing.com
URL: http://www.architecturecrossing.com

Description: Offers a comprehensive collection of architectural job openings worldwide. Includes job listings from top companies and from virtually every employer career webpage and job board in America.

1052 ■ Bright Green Talent - Green Jobs
URL: http://www.brightgreentalent.com/green-jobs

Description: Serves as online tool that offers green jobs listing and career advice to candidates interested and engaged in environmental career.

1053 ■ Builder Jobs
URL: http://builderjobs.pro.adicio.com

Description: Serves as an online career resource for home building professionals. Features career development articles, salary tools, home building and construction job listings, resume postings, and job alerts.

1054 ■ Construction Executive Online
URL: http://www.constructionexecutive.com

Description: Serves as a career management center for construction executives. Provides members access to a job board of executive construction jobs and to career counseling from top executive coaches.

1055 ■ Construction Jobs Network
URL: http://constructionjobs.net

Description: Provides job seekers access to construction employment opportunities for both construction management, construction professional and construction trade jobs. Features construction jobs, employer, and resume directories.

1056 ■ ConstructionJobs.com
URL: http://www.constructionjobs.com/index_eng.cfm

Description: Serves as an employment job board and resume database built exclusively for the construction, design, and building industries. Provides targeted candidate searches by geographic region, specific industries, job titles, education, and experience.

1057 ■ ENR Industry Jobs Site
URL: http://industry-jobs.enr.com/main/default.asp

Description: Provides job searching and recruitment services in the field of architecture, engineering and

construction (AEC) industry. Offers comprehensive database of career opportunities for job seekers and resume of top AEC professionals for employers.

1058 ■ iHireConstruction
URL: http://www.ihireconstruction.com

Description: Helps recruiters and hiring managers find qualified candidates in different fields and specialties of construction industry. Provides job listings, customizable online profiles, resume writing services, and job alerts to job seekers.

1059 ■ Interior Architect Jobs
URL: http://www.interiorarchitectjobs.com

Description: Serves as a niche job board for employment opportunities in the field of interior architecture.

1060 ■ Locate Architecture Jobs
URL: http://www.locatearchitecturejobs.com

Description: Serves as an employment and job posting resource for the architectural field.

1061 ■ New Architecture Jobs
URL: http://www.newarchitecturejobs.com

Description: Provides job seekers the opportunity to easily contact employers with available architecture jobs in all specialties.

1062 ■ Referwork Jobs
URL: http://www.referwork-jobs.com

Description: Provides a searchable database of major jobs in construction and related specialties.

1063 ■ USA Construction Jobs
URL: http://www.usaconstructionjobs.com

Description: Features job listings in construction and general labor.

TRADESHOWS

1064 ■ American Institute of Architects National Convention
American Institute of Architects
1735 New York Ave. NW
Washington, DC 20006-5209
Ph: (202)626-7300
Fax: (202)626-7547
E-mail: infocentral@aia.org
URL: http://www.aia.org

Frequency: Annual. **Primary Exhibits:** Architecture equipment, supplies, and services.

1065 ■ American Society of Golf Course Architects Annual Meeting
American Society of Golf Course Architects
125 N Executive Dr., Ste. 302
Brookfield, WI 53005-6035
Ph: (262)786-5960
Fax: (262)786-5919
E-mail: info@asgca.org
URL: http://www.asgca.org

Frequency: Annual. Serves as an event for interaction, innovation and education relating to golf course architecture in the United States.

1066 ■ Association of Licensed Architects Conference & Product Show
Association of Licensed Architects
1 E Northwest Hwy., Ste. 200
Palatine, IL 60067
Ph: (847)382-0630
Fax: (847)382-8380
E-mail: ala@alatoday.org
URL: http://www.alatoday.org

Frequency: Annual. Serves as a continuing education event for design professionals and an opportunity for showcasing what architects, contractors, owners and engineers need to know to improve knowledge and compete in their jobs.

1067 ■ National Organization of Minority Architects Conference
National Organization of Minority Architects
Howard University
College of Engineering, Architecture and Computer Sciences
School of Architecture and Design
2366 Sixth St. NW, Rm. 100
Washington, DC 20059
Ph: (202)686-2780
E-mail: president@noma.net
URL: http://www.noma.net

Frequency: Annual. Provides an opportunity to reach design professionals that include architecture, engineering, planning, landscape design, contracting and building, urban design, interior design, building operations and maintenance, green or sustainable design and downtown revitalization and economic development officials.

1068 ■ Society of Architectural Historians Annual Meeting
Society of Architectural Historians
1365 N Astor St.
Chicago, IL 60610-2144
Ph: (312)573-1365
Fax: (312)573-1141
E-mail: info@sah.org
URL: http://www.sah.org

Frequency: Annual. Features a preservation colloquium, workshops for historians, roundtable discussions, reunions, evening lectures and receptions, and an extensive array of local and regional tours.

1069 ■ Texas Society of Architects Design Products & Ideas Expo
Texas Society of Architects
500 Chicon St.
Austin, TX 78702
Ph: (512)478-7386
Free: 800-242-3837
Fax: (512)478-0528
E-mail: info@texasarchitect.org
URL: http://www.texasarchitect.org/

Frequency: Annual. **Primary Exhibits:** Designing and building materials and systems for both interior/exterior residential and commercial projects.

OTHER SOURCES

1070 ■ American Concrete Institute
38800 Country Club Dr.
Farmington Hills, MI 48331-3439
Ph: (248)848-3700
Fax: (248)848-3701
E-mail: ann.daugherty@acifoundation.org
URL: http://www.concrete.org

Description: Comprised of engineers, architects, contractors, educators, and others interested in improving techniques of design construction and maintenance of concrete products and structures. Advances engineering and technical education, scientific investigation and research, and development of standards for design and construction incorporating concrete and related materials. Gathers, correlates, and disseminates information for the improvement of the design, construction, manufacture, use and maintenance of concrete products and structures. **Members:** 20,000.

1071 ■ American Institute of Architects
1735 New York Ave. NW
Washington, DC 20006-5209
Ph: (202)626-7300
Fax: (202)626-7547
E-mail: infocentral@aia.org
URL: http://www.aia.org

Description: Represents architects, licensed architects, graduate architects, not yet licensed and retired architects. Fosters professionalism and accountability among members through continuing education and training. Promotes design excellence by influencing change in the industry. Sponsors educational programs with schools of architecture, graduate students, and elementary and secondary schools. Advises on professional competitions. Supplies construction documents. Established the American Architectural Foundation. Sponsors Octagon Museum; operates bookstore; stages exhibitions; compiles statistics. Provides monthly news service on design and construction. Conducts professional development programs, research programs, charitable activities, and children's services.

1072 ■ American Institute of Building Design
529 14th St. NW, Ste. 750
Washington, DC 20045
Free: 800-366-2423
Fax: (866)204-0293
URL: http://www.aibd.org

Description: Represents professional building designers engaged in the professional practice of designing residential and light commercial buildings. Other membership categories include draftspersons, educators, and students. Corporate members are residential and light commercial building manufacturers. Keeps members informed of techniques and principles of building design; seeks to stimulate public interest in the aesthetic and practical efficiency of building design; engages in legislative activities and lobbying; provides consumer referral service. Aids in the development of better and continuing education. Local groups meet monthly.

1073 ■ ArchVoices
1014 Curtis St.
Albany, CA 94706
Ph: (510)757-6213
E-mail: editors@archvoices.org
URL: http://www.archvoices.org

Description: Aims to advance the profession of architecture. Fosters a culture of communication through the collection and dissemination of architectural information and research. Compiles data and research on architecture and other licensed professions.

1074 ■ Asian American Architects and Engineers
1167 Mission St., 4th Fl.
San Francisco, CA 94103
E-mail: info@aaaenc.org
URL: http://www.aaaenc.org

Description: Minorities. Provides contracts and job opportunities for minorities in the architectural and engineering fields. Serves as a network for the promotion in professional fields. **Members:** 120.

1075 ■ Association of Architecture Organizations
224 S Michigan Ave., Ste. 116
Chicago, IL 60604
Ph: (312)922-3432
E-mail: aao@architecture.org
URL: http://aaonetwork.org

Description: Fosters the development of an alliance of like-minded organizations that inform and engage the public about architecture and the built environment. Supports the creation of new architecture centers. Facilitates knowledge sharing between members, partner organizations and other similar entities.

1076 ■ Association of Licensed Architects
1 E Northwest Hwy., Ste. 200
Palatine, IL 60067
Ph: (847)382-0630
Fax: (847)382-8380
E-mail: ala@alatoday.org
URL: http://www.alatoday.org

Description: Represents architects and related professionals who are united to advance the profession of architecture. Works to advance the architectural profession through education and by supporting and improving the profession's role in the built environment. Unites, educates, promotes and advances the architectural profession and addresses critical issues confronting it.

1077 ■ CoreNet Global
133 Peachtree St. NE, Ste. 3000
Atlanta, GA 30303-1815
Ph: (404)589-3200
Free: 800-726-8111
Fax: (404)589-3201
E-mail: acain@corenetglobal.org
URL: http://www.corenetglobal.org

Description: Executives, attorneys, real estate department heads, architects, engineers, analysts, researchers and anyone responsible for the management, administration and operation of national and regional real estate departments of national and international corporations. Encourages professionalism within corporate real estate through education and communication; protects the interests of corporate realty in dealing with adversaries, public or private; maintains contact with other real estate organizations; publicizes the availability of fully qualified members to the job market. Conducts seminars, including concentrated workshops on the corporate real estate field. Compiles statistics; sponsors competitions; maintains biographical archives and placement service. **Members:** 7,200.

1078 ■ Council of Educational Facility Planners International
11445 E Via Linda, Ste. 2-440
Scottsdale, AZ 85259
Ph: (480)391-0840
E-mail: dwaggone@heery.com
URL: http://www.cefpi.org

Description: Individuals and firms who are responsible for planning, designing, creating, maintaining, and equipping the physical environment of education. Sponsors an exchange of information, professional experiences, best practices research results, and other investigative techniques concerning educational facility planning. Activities include publication and review of current and emerging practices in educational facility planning; identification and execution of needed research; development of professional training programs; strengthening of planning services on various levels of government and in institutions of higher learning; leadership in the development of higher standards for facility design and the physical environment of education. Operates speakers' bureau; sponsors placement service; compiles statistics.

1079 ■ Cultural Vistas
440 Park Ave. S, 2nd Fl.
New York, NY 10016
Ph: (212)497-3500
Fax: (212)497-3535
E-mail: info@culturalvistas.org
URL: http://culturalvistas.org

Description: Providers worldwide of on-the-job training programs for students and professionals seeking international career development and life-changing experiences. Arranges workplace exchanges in hundreds of professional fields, bringing employers and trainees together from around the world. Client list ranges from small farming communities to Fortune 500 companies.

1080 ■ Fusion Architecture
PO Box 66853
Phoenix, AZ 85082-6853
E-mail: info@fusionarchitecture.org
URL: http://www.fusionarchitecture.org

Description: Represents the interests of architecture, urban design, graphic design, engineering and cultural practitioners. Encourages young designers to create design solutions to socio-cultural issues. Promotes the use of graphic and information design tools to reach out and produce projects that have influence on the economics, politics, cultural and social structure facing urban communities.

1081 ■ Institute of Destination Architects and Designers
3590 Round Bottom Rd.
PMB F273796
Cincinnati, OH 45244-3026
Ph: (434)334-1909
E-mail: office@idad.org
URL: http://www.idad.org/idadh.htm

Description: Represents the interests of architects from various disciplines, designers in various specialties, managers, scientists, and executives. Focuses on developing and disseminating techniques which can make resort and hydro-scape zones successful. Conducts projects, design developments, and research inquiries dealing with the development of tourism destinations including themed, entertainment, resort, and coastal architecture.

1082 ■ Ministry Architecture
1904 S Union Pl.
Lakewood, CO 80228
Ph: (720)937-9664
Fax: (303)989-0884
E-mail: ministryarchitecture@hotmail.com
URL: http://www.ministryarchitecture.com

Description: Represents design professionals and architecture students. Works primarily on giving architectural, engineering and planning services to evangelical ministries in developing countries.

1083 ■ National Center for Construction Education and Research
13614 Progress Blvd.
Alachua, FL 32615-9407
Ph: (386)518-6500
Free: 888-622-3720
Fax: (386)518-6303
E-mail: marketing@nccer.org
URL: http://www.nccer.org

Description: Education foundation committed to the development and publication of Contren(TM) Learning Series, the source of craft training, management education and safety resources for the construction industry.

1084 ■ National Council of Architectural Registration Boards
1801 K St. NW, Ste. 700-K
Washington, DC 20006-1301
Ph: (202)783-6500
Fax: (202)783-0290
E-mail: customerservice@ncarb.org
URL: http://www.ncarb.org

Description: Federation of state boards for the registration of architects in the United States, District of Columbia, Puerto Rico, Virgin Islands, Guam, and the Northern Mariana Islands.

1085 ■ National Organization of Minority Architects
Howard University
College of Engineering, Architecture and Computer Sciences
School of Architecture and Design
2366 Sixth St. NW, Rm. 100
Washington, DC 20059
Ph: (202)686-2780
E-mail: president@noma.net
URL: http://www.noma.net

Description: Seeks to increase the number and influence of minority architects by encouraging minority youth and taking an active role in the education of new architects. Works in cooperation with other associations, professionals, and architectural firms to promote the professional advancement of members. Sponsors competitions; offers children's services, educational programs, and charitable programs; maintains speakers' bureau; compiles statistics.

1086 ■ **Organization of Women Architects and Design Professionals**
PO Box 10078
Berkeley, CA 94709
E-mail: info@owa-usa.org
URL: http://owa-usa.org

Description: Comprised of architects, interior designers, landscape architects, planners, lighting designers, graphic designers, photographers, artists, writers, educators and students. Strives to improve the professional standing of women in architecture and design-related fields. Advocates young women and students entering design related fields through mentoring, education, and employment opportunities.

1087 ■ **Professional Women in Construction**
315 E 56th St.
New York, NY 10022-3730
Ph: (212)486-7745
Fax: (212)486-0228
URL: http://www.pwcusa.org

Description: Management-level women and men in construction and allied industries; owners, suppliers, architects, engineers, field personnel, office personnel and bonding/surety personnel. Provides a forum for exchange of ideas and promotion of political and legislative action, education and job opportunities for women in construction and related fields; forms liaisons with other trade and professional groups; develops research programs. Strives to reform abuses and to assure justice and equity within the construction industry. Sponsors mini-workshops. Maintains Action Line, which provides members with current information on pertinent legislation and on the association's activities and job referrals.

1088 ■ **Public Architecture**
1211 Folsom St., 4th Fl.
San Francisco, CA 94103
Ph: (415)861-8200
Fax: (415)431-9695
E-mail: info@publicarchitecture.org
URL: http://www.publicarchitecture.org

Description: Works to put the resources of architecture in the service of public interest. Encourages and inspires architecture and design firms to participate in pro bono work. Acts as a catalyst for public discourse through education, advocacy and the design of public spaces and amenities.

1089 ■ **Society of American Registered Architects**
PO Box 280
Newport, TN 37822
Ph: (423)721-0129
Free: 888-385-7272
E-mail: cmoscato@sara-national.org
URL: http://www.sara-national.org

Description: Architects registered or licensed under the laws of states and territories of the U.S. Sponsors seminars and professional and student design competitions. Offers placement service. **Members:** 800.

1090 ■ **Society of Architectural Historians**
1365 N Astor St.
Chicago, IL 60610-2144
Ph: (312)573-1365
Fax: (312)573-1141
E-mail: info@sah.org
URL: http://www.sah.org

Description: Architects and city planners, educators, scholars, libraries, historical societies, interior designers, museum personnel, students, and others interested in architecture. Promotes the preservation of buildings of historical and aesthetic significance. Encourages scholarly research in the field. Conducts tours in the U.S. and abroad.

1091 ■ **Society of Iranian Architects and Planners**
PO Box 643066
Los Angeles, CA 90064
E-mail: webmaster@siap.org
URL: http://www.siap.org

Description: Represents Iranian graduates in the field of architecture, planning, interior design and landscape architecture. Promotes cultural, scientific and professional aspects in the field architecture and encourages members to develop and advance their skills and abilities in the profession. Provides members with a means of communication for coordination of mutual professional and cultural relationships with similar Iranian organizations around the globe.

SOURCES OF HELP-WANTED ADS

1092 ■ *AMIA Newsletter*
Association of Moving Image Archivists
1313 N Vine St.
Hollywood, CA 90028
Ph: (323)463-1500
Fax: (323)463-1506
E-mail: amia@amianet.org
URL: http://www.amianet.org

Description: Quarterly. $50/year. Presents information on the preservation of film and video materials, and the moving image archival profession. REC news of research, a calendar of events, reports of meetings, job listings, book reviews, and notices of publications available.

1093 ■ *Annotation*
National Historical Publications and Records Commission
National Archives and Records Administration
700 Pennsylvania Ave. NW, Rm. 114
Washington, DC 20408-0001
Ph: (202)357-5263
Fax: (202)357-5914
E-mail: nhprc@nara.gov
URL: http://www.archives.gov/nhprc/annotation

Description: Quarterly. Contains information of interest to National Historical Publications and Records Commission members. Recurring features include columns titled From the Editor, and The Executive Director's Column.

1094 ■ *Archival Outlook*
Society of American Archivists
17 N State St., Ste. 1425
Chicago, IL 60602-4061
Ph: (312)606-0722
Free: 866-722-7858
Fax: (312)606-0728
E-mail: servicecenter@archivists.org
URL: http://www.archivists.org/periodicals/

Description: Bimonthly. Publishes news of relevance to the professional archival community. Recurring features include a calendar of events, news from constituent groups, news of educational opportunities, professional resources available, and job listings.

1095 ■ *Conference of Inter-Mountain Archivists Newsletter*
Conference of Inter-Mountain Archivists
PO Box 2048
Salt Lake City, UT 84110
Ph: (801)581-8863
Fax: (801)974-0336
E-mail: walter.jones@utah.edu
URL: http://cimarchivists.org

Description: Quarterly. $12/year for members; $25/year for institutions. Concerned with the preservation and use of archival and manuscript materials in the Inter-mountain West and adjacent areas. Disseminates information on research materials and archival methodology; provides a forum for the discussion of common concerns; and cooperates with similar cultural and educational organizations. Recurring features include news of research, preservation, members, and job openings.

1096 ■ *ConservatioNews*
Arizona State University Libraries
Box 871006
Tempe, AZ 85287
Ph: (480)965-6164
Fax: (480)965-9233
URL: http://library.lib.asu.edu/record=b3078319

Description: Quarterly. Concerned with the preservation of paper documents, magnetic media, published materials, photographs, and film. Carries articles on the theory and practice of conservation, questions and answers to specific problems, and product news. Recurring features include news of members, book reviews, and a calendar of events.

1097 ■ *Dirty Goat*
Host Publications, Inc.
277 Broadway, Ste. 210
New York, NY 10007
Ph: (212)905-2365
Fax: (212)905-2369
E-mail: tracey@hostpublications.com
URL: http://www.thedirtygoat.com/index.html

Frequency: Semiannual. **Price:** $10 Individuals. **Description:** Journal covering poetry, prose, drama, literature and visual art.

1098 ■ *Dispatch*
American Association for State and Local History
1717 Church St.
Nashville, TN 37203-2991
Ph: (615)320-3203
Fax: (615)327-9013
E-mail: membership@aaslh.org
URL: http://www.aaslh.org/pdispatch.htm

Frequency: Monthly. **Description:** Monthly. Offers general information about state and local historical societies and the study of state and local history in the U.S. and Canada. Informs members of new training programs, seminars, and exhibits in the field. Recurring features include information on grant opportunities, updates on legislation, Association activities, and historical society personnel, interviews, job listings, and notices of publications available.

1099 ■ *Film History: An International Journal*
Indiana University Press
c/o Richard Koszarski, Ed.-in-Ch.
Box 10
Teaneck, NJ 07666
Ph: (812)855-8817
Free: 800-842-6796
Fax: (812)855-7931
E-mail: filmhist@aol.com
URL: http://inscribe.iupress.org/loi/fil

Frequency: Quarterly. **Price:** $82.50 Individuals print and online; $75 Individuals print only; $67.50 Individuals online only; $273.50 Institutions print and online; $199.50 Institutions print only; $179.50 Institutions online only. **Description:** Journal tracing the history of the motion picture with reference to social, technological, and economic aspects, covering various aspects of motion pictures such as production, distribution, exhibition, and reception.

1100 ■ *History News*
American Association for State and Local History
1717 Church St.
Nashville, TN 37203-2991
Ph: (615)320-3203
Fax: (615)327-9013
E-mail: membership@aaslh.org
URL: http://www.aaslh.org/historynews.htm

Frequency: Quarterly. **Description:** Includes a handy technical leaflet in each issue.

1101 ■ *Infinity*
BWT Austria GmbH
Walter-Simmer-Strasse 4
5310 Mondsee, Austria
Ph: 43 06232 50 11-0
Fax: 43 06232 40 58
E-mail: office@bwt.at
URL: http://www2.archivists.org

Description: Quarterly. Informs members of the Society of archives news and events. Recurring features include news of research, a calendar of events, reports of meetings, news of educational opportunities, book reviews, notices of publications available, and a column titled From the Chair.

1102 ■ *Journal of Access Services*
Routledge Journals - Taylor & Francis Group
270 Madison Ave.
New York, NY 10016-0601
Ph: (212)216-7800
Fax: (212)563-2269
URL: http://www.tandfonline.com/toc/wjas20/current

Frequency: Quarterly. **Price:** $89 Individuals online only; $97 Individuals print + online; $236 Institutions online only; $270 Institutions print + online. **Description:** Journal focusing on the basic business of providing library users with access to information, and helping librarians stay up to date on continuing education and professional development in the field of access services.

1103 ■ *Journal of Interlibrary Loan, Document Delivery & Electronic Reserve*
Routledge Journals - Taylor & Francis Group
270 Madison Ave.
New York, NY 10016-0601
Ph: (212)216-7800

Fax: (212)563-2269
URL: http://www.tandfonline.com/toc/wild20/current

Frequency: 5/yr. **Price:** $104 Individuals online only; $112 Individuals print + online; $412 Institutions online only; $458 Institutions print + online. **Description:** Journal focusing on a broad spectrum of library and information center functions that rely heavily on interlibrary loan, document delivery, and electronic reserve.

1104 ■ MAC Newsletter
Midwest Archives Conference
4440 PGA Blvd., Ste. 600
Palm Beach Gardens, FL 33410
E-mail: amy.cary@marquette.edu
URL: http://www.midwestarchives.org

Description: Quarterly. Covers activities of Midwest Archives Conference. Includes employment opportunities, conference reports, financial statements, meeting minutes, news of members, and listing of publications available.

1105 ■ MAHD Bulletin
Special Libraries Association, Museums, Arts, and Humanities Division
331 S Patrick St.
Alexandria, VA 22314-3501
Ph: (703)647-4900
Fax: (703)647-4901
E-mail: membership@sla.org
URL: http://units.sla.org/division/dmah

Description: Four issues/year. Discusses pertinent events, issues, and publications concerning special libraries. Recurring features include interviews, news of research, a calendar of events, reports of meetings, news of educational opportunities, book reviews, notices of publications available, and a column titled On My Mind.

1106 ■ Mid-Atlantic Archivist
Mid-Atlantic Regional Archives Conference
Dickinson College
Carlisle, PA 17013-2896
Ph: (717)713-9973
Fax: (717)245-1439
E-mail: administrator@marac.info
URL: http://www.marac.info

Description: Quarterly. $35 per year. Contains news and information for and about members of the Conference. Seeks exchange of information between colleagues, improvement of competence among archivists, and encourages professional involvement of persons actively engaged in the preservation and use of historical research materials. Recurring features include letters to the editor, news of members, book reviews, a calendar of events, and columns titled Preservation News, Reference Shelf, Session Abstracts, Software News, and Employment Opportunities.

1107 ■ Museum Archivist
Society of American Archivists, Museum Archives Section
17 N State St., Ste. 1425
Chicago, IL 60602
Ph: (312)606-0722
Free: 866-722-7858
Fax: (312)606-0728
E-mail: info@archivists.org
URL: http://www2.archivists.org

Description: 2/year. Provides news of Society and Section activities, meetings, symposia, educational programs, project research, repository reports, notes, and announcements. Recurring features include letters to the editor, news of research, reports of meetings, and news of educational opportunities.

1108 ■ New England Archivists Newsletter
New England Archivists
c/o WPI Archives and Special Collections
Gordon Library
100 Institute Rd.
Worcester, MA 01609
E-mail: neamembership@gmail.com
URL: http://www.newenglandarchivists.org

Description: Quarterly. Contains regional archival news and announcements. Recurring features include a calendar of events, reports of meetings, job listings, book reviews, workshops, reports on repositories, and feature articles on archival subjects.

1109 ■ Preservation
National Trust for Historic Preservation
2600 Virginia Ave., Ste. 1000
Washington, DC 20037
Ph: (202)588-6000
Free: 800-944-6847
E-mail: info@savingplaces.org
URL: http://www.preservationnation.org/

Frequency: Bimonthly. **Price:** $20 Members individual; $30 Members family; $50 Members contributing; $100 Members sustaining; $250 Members preservation council steward; $1,000 Members preservation council heritage society. **Description:** Magazine featuring historic preservation.

1110 ■ The Primary Source
Society of Mississippi Archivists
PO Box 4024
Clinton, MS 39058
E-mail: info@msarchivists.org
URL: http://www.msarchivists.org

Description: Annually. Focuses on activities and trends in the archival and library community both regionally and nationally. Includes information on conservation and articles on state repositories and their holdings. Recurring features include news of research, book reviews, and a calendar of events.

1111 ■ The Rocky Mountain Archivist
Society of Rocky Mountain Archivists
c/o Beverly Allen, Pres.
University Library, 6th Fl.
2200 Bonforte Blvd.
Colorado State University
Pueblo, CO 81001-4901
Ph: (719)549-2475
E-mail: srmapres@srmarchivists.org
URL: http://www.srmarchivists.org/

Description: Quarterly. Covers activities of Society of Rocky Mountain Archivists. Includes local and national news on archives and special collections.

1112 ■ The Southwestern Archivist
Society of Southwest Archivists
PO Box 301311
Austin, TX 78703-0022
URL: http://southwestarchivists.org

Description: Quarterly. Supports the aims of the Society, which include: "to provide a means for effective cooperation among people concerned with the documentation of human experience," and "to promote the adoption of sound principles and standards for the preservation and administration of records." Recurring features include news of research, news of members, and a calendar of events.

1113 ■ Tennessee Archivist
Society of Tennessee Archivists
1301 E Main St.
Murfreesboro, TN 37132-0002
Ph: (615)898-5884
Fax: (615)898-5829
E-mail: info@tennesseearchivists.org
URL: http://www.tennesseearchivists.org/newsletter
.html

Description: Quarterly. Provides information on state and national archival activities. Announces professional meetings and workshops, archival job openings, and new collections. Features articles on archives and records repositories in Tennessee. Recurring features include a calendar of events, reports of meetings, news of educational opportunities, job listings, notices of publications available, and columns titled Editorial, Message from the President, and Committee Reports.

EMPLOYER DIRECTORIES AND NETWORKING LISTS

1114 ■ Directory of Special Libraries and Information Centers
Cengage Learning Inc.
200 1st Stamford Pl., Ste. 400
Stamford, CT 06902-6753
Ph: (203)965-8600
Free: 800-354-9706
Fax: (800)487-8488
E-mail: investors@cengage.com
URL: http://www.gale.cengage.com

Frequency: Annual; Latest edition 40th; March, 2011. **Price:** $1,610 Individuals volume 1; $966 Individuals volume 2. **Covers:** Over 34,800 special libraries, information centers, documentation centers, etc.; about 500 networks and consortia; major special libraries abroad also included. Volume 1 part 3 contains 6 other appendices (besides networks and consortia): Regional and Subregional Libraries for the Blind & Physically Handicapped, Patent & Trademark Depository Libraries, Regional Government Depository Libraries, United Nations Depository Libraries, World Bank Depository Libraries, and European Community Depository Libraries. **Entries include:** Library name, address, phone, fax, e-mail address; contact; year founded; sponsoring organization; special collections; subject interests; names and titles of staff; services (copying, online searches); size of collection; subscriptions; computerized services and automated operations; Internet home page address; publications; special catalogs; special indexes. For consortia and networks--Name, address, phone, contact. Other appendices have varying amounts of directory information. Contents of Volume 1 are available in "Subject Directory of Special Libraries and Information Centers" (see separate entry). **Arrangement:** Libraries are alphabetical by name of sponsoring organization or institution; consortia and networks are geographical. **Indexes:** Subject. Geographic and personnel indexes constitute volume 2.

1115 ■ Guide to Employment Sources in the Library & Information Professions
American Library Association - Social Responsibilities Round Table
50 E Huron St.
Chicago, IL 60611
Ph: (312)280-4294
Free: 800-545-2433
Fax: (312)280-3256
E-mail: customerservice@ala.org
URL: http://www.ala.org

Frequency: Annual; Latest edition 2009. **Covers:** Library job sources, such as specialized and state and regional library associations, state library agencies, federal library agencies, and overseas exchange programs. **Entries include:** Library, company, or organization name, address, phone; contact name, description of services, publications, etc. This is a reprint of a segment of the "Bowker Annual of Library and Book Trade Information," described separately. **Arrangement:** Classified by type of source.

1116 ■ Midwest Archives Conference--Membership Directory
Midwest Archives Conference
4440 PGA Blvd., Ste. 600
Palm Beach Gardens, FL 33410
E-mail: amy.cary@marquette.edu
URL: http://www.midwestarchives.org

Frequency: Annual. **Covers:** More than 1,150 individual and institutional members, largely librarians, archivists, records managers, manuscripts curators, historians, and museum and historical society personnel; about 25 archival associations in the Midwest. **Entries include:** For institutions--Name of archives, parent organization, address, phone. For individuals--Name, title, business address, phone.

Arrangement: Separate alphabetical sections for individuals and institutions.

HANDBOOKS AND MANUALS

1117 ■ Creative Careers in Museums
Allworth Press
307 W 36th St., 11th Fl.
New York, NY 10018
Ph: (212)643-6816
Free: 800-491-2808
Fax: (212)643-6819
E-mail: pub@allworth.com
URL: http://www.allworth.com

Description: Jan E. Burdick. 2008. $15.95 (paperback). 210 pages. Details how to land a museum job, where to look, how to put together a successful resume and cover letter, and what to expect at interviews. Contains information on professional associations, museum studies programs, and job search resources in the museum field.

1118 ■ Ferguson Career Coach: Managing Your Career in the Art Industry
InfoBase Holdings Inc.
132 W 31st., 17 Fl.
New York, NY 10001-3406
Ph: (212)967-8800
Fax: (800)678-3633
E-mail: info@infobasepublishing.com
URL: http://www.ferguson.infobasepublishing.com

Description: Shelly Field. 2008. $39.95 (hardcover). 304 pages. Contains tips for students who dream of a career as a graphic artist or an art gallery curator.

1119 ■ Great Jobs for History Majors
The McGraw-Hill Companies Inc.
PO Box 182604
Columbus, OH 43272
Ph: (212)512-2000
Free: 877-833-5524
Fax: (614)759-3749
E-mail: customer.service@mcgraw-hill.com
URL: http://www.mcgraw-hill.com

Description: Julie DeGalan and Stephen Lambert. 2007. $16.95 (paper). 192 pages.

1120 ■ Great Jobs for Liberal Arts Majors
The McGraw-Hill Companies Inc.
PO Box 182604
Columbus, OH 43272
Ph: (212)512-2000
Free: 877-833-5524
Fax: (614)759-3749
E-mail: customer.service@mcgraw-hill.com
URL: http://www.mcgraw-hill.com

Description: Blythe Camenson. Second edition, 2007. $16.95 (paper). 192 pages.

1121 ■ Museum Archives: An Introduction
Society of American Archivists
17 N State St., Ste. 1425
Chicago, IL 60602-4061
Ph: (312)606-0722
Free: 866-722-7858
Fax: (312)606-0728
E-mail: servicecenter@archivists.org
URL: http://www2.archivists.org

Description: Deborah Wythe. Second edition, 2004. $62.00. 256 pages.

1122 ■ Museum Careers: A Practical Guide for Students and Novices
Left Coast Press
1630 N Main St., No. 400
Walnut Creek, CA 94596
Ph: (925)935-3380
Fax: (925)935-2916
E-mail: explore@lcoastpress.com
URL: http://www.lcoastpress.com/book.php?id=152

Description: N. Elizabeth Schlatter. 2008. $24.95

(paperback). 184 pages. Outlines the nature of the profession as a whole, the rewards and challenges of museum work, types of museums, and jobs within museums, including salary ranges.

1123 ■ Opportunities in Museum Careers
The McGraw-Hill Companies Inc.
PO Box 182604
Columbus, OH 43272
Ph: (212)512-2000
Free: 877-833-5524
Fax: (614)759-3749
E-mail: customer.service@mcgraw-hill.com
URL: http://www.mcgraw-hill.com

Description: Blythe Camenson. 2006. $13.95 (paper). 160 pages.

ONLINE JOB SOURCES AND SERVICES

1124 ■ Archivist Jobs
URL: http://www.archivistjobs.us

Description: Serves as an online source for archivist recruiting and job listings.

1125 ■ Cultural Resource Network
URL: http://www.culturalresourcenetwork.com

Description: Provides sources of news, jobs, announcements, consultant listings, and resources for the cultural resource industry.

1126 ■ Get Curator Jobs
URL: http://www.getcuratorjobs.com

Description: Features a searchable database for curator job listings.

1127 ■ Museum Employment Resource Center
URL: http://www.museum-employment.com

Description: Provides job listings and other information related to the museum, heritage management, and cultural resource communities.

TRADESHOWS

1128 ■ Art Libraries Society of North America Conference
Art Libraries Society of North America
7044 S 13th St.
Oak Creek, WI 53154
Ph: (414)768-8000
Free: 800-817-0621
Fax: (414)768-8001
E-mail: g-most@nga.gov
URL: http://www.arlisna.org

Frequency: Annual. Provides networking opportunities for attendees.

1129 ■ Society of American Archivists Annual Meeting
Society of American Archivists
17 N State St., Ste. 1425
Chicago, IL 60602-4061
Ph: (312)606-0722
Free: 866-722-7858
Fax: (312)606-0728
E-mail: servicecenter@archivists.org
URL: http://www2.archivists.org

Frequency: Annual.

OTHER SOURCES

1130 ■ American Alliance of Museums
1575 Eye St. NW, Ste. 400
Washington, DC 20005
Ph: (202)289-1818

Fax: (202)289-6578
E-mail: fbell@aam-us.org
URL: http://www.aam-us.org

Description: Represents directors, curators, registrars, educators, exhibit designers, public relations officers, development officers, security managers, trustees, and volunteers in museums as well as all museums, including art, history, science, military and maritime, and youth, as well as aquariums, zoos, botanical gardens, arboretums, historic sites, and science and technology centers. Dedicated to promoting excellence within the museum community. Assists museum staff, boards, and volunteers through advocacy, professional education, information exchange, accreditation, and guidance.

1131 ■ American Association for State and Local History
1717 Church St.
Nashville, TN 37203-2991
Ph: (615)320-3203
Fax: (615)327-9013
E-mail: membership@aaslh.org
URL: http://www.aaslh.org

Description: Works to preserve and promote history. Ensures the highest-quality expressions of state and local history in publications, exhibitions, and public programs through its diverse services. Represents more than 6,200 individual and institutional members.

1132 ■ American Institute for Conservation of Historic & Artistic Works
1156 15th St. NW, Ste. 320
Washington, DC 20005
Ph: (202)452-9545
Fax: (202)452-9328
E-mail: info@conservation-us.org
URL: http://www.conservation-us.org

Description: Professionals, scientists, administrators, and educators in the field of art conservation; interested individuals. Advances the practice and promotes the importance of the preservation of cultural property. Coordinates the exchange of knowledge, research, and publications. Establishes and upholds professional standards. Publishes conservation literature. Compiles statistics. Represents membership to allied professional associations and advocates on conservation-related issues. Solicits and dispenses money exclusively for charitable, scientific, and educational objectives.

1133 ■ American Society for Information Science and Technology
8555 16th St., Ste. 850
Silver Spring, MD 20910
Ph: (301)495-0900
Fax: (301)495-0810
E-mail: asis@asis.org
URL: http://www.asis.org

Description: Information specialists, scientists, librarians, administrators, social scientists, and others interested in the use, organization, storage, retrieval, evaluation, and dissemination of recorded specialized information. Seeks to improve the information transfer process through research, development, application, and education. Provides a forum for the discussion, publication, and critical analysis of work dealing with the theory, practice, research, and development of elements involved in communication of information. Members are engaged in a variety of activities and specialties including classification and coding systems, automatic and associative indexing, machine translation of languages, special librarianship and library systems analysis, and copyright issues. Sponsors National Auxiliary Publications Service, which provides reproduction services and a central depository for all types of information. Maintains placement service. Sponsors numerous special interest groups. Conducts continuing education programs and professional development workshops.

1134 ■ Art Libraries Society of North America
7044 S 13th St.
Oak Creek, WI 53154
Ph: (414)768-8000
Free: 800-817-0621
Fax: (414)768-8001
E-mail: g-most@nga.gov
URL: http://www.arlisna.org

Description: Consists of architecture and art librarians, visual resources professionals, artists, curators, educators, publishers, students, and others interested in visual arts information. Promotes the advancement of art library and information professionals. Collaborates with other professional and educational organizations through participation in international forums. **Members:** 1,500.

1135 ■ *Career Opportunities in Library and Information Science*
InfoBase Holdings Inc.
132 W 31st., 17 Fl.
New York, NY 10001-3406
Ph: (212)967-8800
Fax: (800)678-3633
E-mail: info@infobasepublishing.com
URLs: http://www.infobasepublishing.com; http://www.infobasepublishing.com/Bookdetail.aspx?ISBN=0816075468

Frequency: Published July, 2009. **Price:** $49.50 Individuals hardcover. **Pages:** 392. **Description:** Linda P. Carvell. 2005. 225 pages. **Covers:** More than 85 different jobs typically held by librarians, including academic, government, K-12, outside the library, public, and special. **Includes:** Appendices of educational institutions, periodicals, directories, and associations.

1136 ■ *Careers for History Buffs & Others Who Learn from the Past*
The McGraw-Hill Companies Inc.
PO Box 182604
Columbus, OH 43272
Ph: (212)512-2000
Free: 877-833-5524
Fax: (614)759-3749
E-mail: customer.service@mcgraw-hill.com
URL: http://www.mcgraw-hill.com

Description: Blythe Camenson. Third edition, 2008. $14.95 (paper). 176 pages. **Includes:** Appendices of living-history museums, U.S. National Park Service regional offices, and associations. Appendices of living-history museums, U.S. National Park Service regional offices, and associations. **Entries include:** Organization name, address.

1137 ■ *Careers for Mystery Buffs and Other Snoops and Sleuths*
The McGraw-Hill Companies Inc.
PO Box 182604
Columbus, OH 43272
Ph: (212)512-2000
Free: 877-833-5524
Fax: (614)759-3749
E-mail: customer.service@mcgraw-hill.com
URL: http://www.mcgraw-hill.com

Description: Blythe Camenson. Second edition. $14.95 (hardback). 160 pages. **Publication includes:** Appendix of associations that provide information about various careers, publish newsletters listing job and internship opportunities, and offer employment services to members. **Entries include:** Name, address.

1138 ■ College Art Association
50 Broadway, 21st Fl.
New York, NY 10004
Ph: (212)691-1051
Fax: (212)627-2381
E-mail: nyoffice@collegeart.org
URL: http://www.collegeart.org

Description: Professional organization of artists, art historians and fine art educators, museum directors, and curators. Seeks to raise the standards of scholarship and of the teaching of art and art history throughout the country.

1139 ■ Print Council of America
The Art Institute of Chicago
Dept. of Drawings and Prints
111 S Michigan Ave.
Chicago, IL 60603
Ph: (312)857-7162
E-mail: mtedeschi@artic.edu
URL: http://www.printcouncil.org

Description: Museum professionals. Fosters the study and appreciation of new and old prints, drawings, and photographs; stimulates discussion. Sponsors educational programs and research publications; offers placement services. **Members:** 242.

1140 ■ Society of American Archivists
17 N State St., Ste. 1425
Chicago, IL 60602-4061

Ph: (312)606-0722
Free: 866-722-7858
Fax: (312)606-0728
E-mail: servicecenter@archivists.org
URL: http://www2.archivists.org

Description: Individuals and institutions concerned with the identification, preservation, and use of records of historical value.

1141 ■ Special Libraries Association
331 S Patrick St.
Alexandria, VA 22314-3501
Ph: (703)647-4900
Fax: (703)647-4901
E-mail: janice@sla.org
URL: http://www.sla.org

Description: International association of information professionals who work in specialized information environments such as business, research, government, universities, newspapers, museums, and institutions. Seeks to advance the leadership role of information professionals through learning, networking and advocacy. Offers consulting services to organizations that wish to establish or expand a library or information services. Conducts strategic learning and development courses, public relations, and government relations programs. Provides employment services. Operates knowledge exchange on topics pertaining to the development and management of special libraries. **Members:** 9,000.

1142 ■ Women's Caucus for Art
PO Box 1498
New York, NY 10013
Ph: (212)634-0007
E-mail: info@nationalwca.org
URL: http://www.nationalwca.org

Description: Professional women in visual art fields: artists, critics, art historians, museum and gallery professionals, arts administrators, educators and students, and collectors of art. Aims to increase recognition for contemporary and historical achievements of women in art. Ensures equal opportunity for employment, art commissions, and research grants. Encourages professionalism and shared information among women in art. Stimulates and publicizes research and publications on women in the visual arts. Conducts workshops, periodic affirmative action research, and statistical surveys.

SOURCES OF HELP-WANTED ADS

1143 ■ *American Art Therapy Association Newsletter*
American Art Therapy Association
4875 Eisenhower Ave., Ste. 240
Alexandria, VA 22304
Ph: (703)548-5860
Free: 888-290-0878
Fax: (703)783-8468
E-mail: info@arttherapy.org
URL: http://www.arttherapy.org

Description: Quarterly. Publishes news of developments and events in art therapy. Provides information on Association activities, related organizations, and available resources. Recurring features include legislative updates, letters to the editor, news of members, a calendar of events, board and committee reports, conference and symposia information.

1144 ■ *ArtSEARCH*
Theatre Communications Group
520 8th Ave., 24th Fl.
New York, NY 10018-4156
Ph: (212)609-5900
Fax: (212)609-5901
E-mail: tcg@tcg.org
URL: http://www.tcg.org

Description: Biweekly. Publishes classified listings for job opportunities in the arts, especially theatre, dance, music, and educational institutions. Listings include opportunities in administration, artistic, education, production, and career development.

1145 ■ *Dirty Goat*
Host Publications, Inc.
277 Broadway, Ste. 210
New York, NY 10007
Ph: (212)905-2365
Fax: (212)905-2369
E-mail: tracey@hostpublications.com
URL: http://www.thedirtygoat.com/index.html

Frequency: Semiannual. **Price:** $10 Individuals.
Description: Journal covering poetry, prose, drama, literature and visual art.

1146 ■ *Film History: An International Journal*
Indiana University Press
c/o Richard Koszarski, Ed.-in-Ch.
Box 10
Teaneck, NJ 07666
Ph: (812)855-8817
Free: 800-842-6796
Fax: (812)855-7931
E-mail: filmhist@aol.com
URL: http://inscribe.iupress.org/loi/fil

Frequency: Quarterly. **Price:** $82.50 Individuals print and online; $75 Individuals print only; $67.50 Individuals online only; $273.50 Institutions print and online; $199.50 Institutions print only; $179.50

Institutions online only. **Description:** Journal tracing the history of the motion picture with reference to social, technological, and economic aspects, covering various aspects of motion pictures such as production, distribution, exhibition, and reception.

HANDBOOKS AND MANUALS

1147 ■ *Art Therapy Activities: A Practical Guide for Teachers, Therapists and Parents*
Charles C. Thomas Publisher Ltd.
2600 S 1st St.
Springfield, IL 62704-4730
Ph: (217)789-8980
Free: 800-258-8980
Fax: (217)789-9130
E-mail: books@ccthomas.com
URL: http://www.ccthomas.com

Description: Pamela J. Stack. 2006. $31.95. 154 pages. Profiles activities used for art therapy.

1148 ■ *Counseling As an Art: The Creative Arts in Counseling*
American Counseling Association
5999 Stevenson Ave.
Alexandria, VA 22304
Free: 800-347-6647
Fax: (703)823-0252
E-mail: membership@counseling.org
URL: http://www.counseling.org

Description: Samuel T. Gladding. Third edition, 2004. $42.95 (paper). 237 pages.

1149 ■ *Introduction to Art Therapy*
Routledge
711 3rd Ave., 8th Fl.
New York, NY 10017
Ph: (212)216-7800
Free: 800-634-7064
Fax: (212)564-7854
E-mail: book.orders@tandf.co.uk
URL: http://www.routledge.com

Description: Judith A. Rubin. 2009. $52.95. 356 pages. Part of the Basic Principles Into Practice Series.

1150 ■ *A Therapist's Guide to Art Therapy Assessments: Tools of the Trade*
Charles C. Thomas Publisher Ltd.
2600 S 1st St.
Springfield, IL 62704-4730
Ph: (217)789-8980
Free: 800-258-8980
Fax: (217)789-9130
E-mail: books@ccthomas.com
URL: http://www.ccthomas.com

Description: Stephanie L. Brooke. Second edition, 2004. $53.95. 256 pages.

ONLINE JOB SOURCES AND SERVICES

1151 ■ *ActivityJobs.com*
URL: http://www.activityjobs.com

Description: Provides employment listing for recreation therapists, activity therapists, activity coordinators, creative arts therapists and leisure counselors.

TRADESHOWS

1152 ■ **American Art Therapy Association Conference**
American Art Therapy Association
225 N Fairfax St.
Reston, VA 22314
Ph: (703)548-5860
Free: 888-290-0878
Fax: (703)783-8468
E-mail: info@arttherapy.org
URL: http://www.arttherapy.org/

Frequency: Annual. **Primary Exhibits:** Art supplies, books, therapeutic materials, and schools.

OTHER SOURCES

1153 ■ **American Art Therapy Association**
4875 Eisenhower Ave., Ste. 240
Alexandria, VA 22304
Ph: (703)548-5860
Free: 888-290-0878
Fax: (703)783-8468
E-mail: info@arttherapy.org
URL: http://www.arttherapy.org

Description: Art therapists, students, and individuals in related fields. Supports the progressive development of therapeutic uses of art, the advancement of research, and improvements in the standards of practice. Has established specific professional criteria for training art therapists. Facilitates the exchange of information and experience. Compiles statistics.

1154 ■ **Art Therapy Connection**
1800 Ridge Ave., Unit 211
Evanston, IL 60201
E-mail: info@arttherapyconnection.net
URL: http://www.arttherapyconnection.net

Description: Promotes art therapy as a form of psychotherapy. Works with children and teenagers to develop self-awareness and self-management skills by integrating art and creativity with therapy. Increases the concentration levels, self-control and interpersonal skills of youth and children.

1155 ■ **International Expressive Arts Therapy Association**
PO Box 320399
San Francisco, CA 94132-0399
Ph: (415)522-8959
E-mail: info@ieata.org
URL: http://www.ieata.org

Description: Provides resources about the expressive arts and how they may relate to other disciplines, such as psychology, education and business.

1156 ■ **National Art Education Association**
1806 Robert Fulton Dr., Ste. 300
Reston, VA 20191
Ph: (703)860-8000
Free: 800-299-8321

Fax: (703)860-2960
E-mail: info@arteducators.org
URL: http://www.arteducators.org
Description: Teachers of art at elementary, middle, secondary, and college levels; colleges, libraries, museums, and other educational institutions. Studies problems of teaching art; encourages research and experimentation. Serves as a clearinghouse for information on art education programs, materials, and methods of instruction. Sponsors special institutes. Cooperates with other national organizations for the furtherance of creative art experiences for youth.

1157 ■ **National Coalition of Creative Arts Therapies Associations**
8455 Colesville Rd., Ste. 1000
Silver Spring, MD 20910
E-mail: 61diamonds@gmail.com
URL: http://www.nccata.org

Description: Creative arts therapists. Promotes therapeutic and rehabilitative uses of the arts in medicine, mental health, special education, and forensic and social services; coordinates member associations' activities and efforts in meeting common objectives while supporting and advancing each group's discipline. Works to: represent members' interests in legislative activities; define joint positions on public policy issues; facilitate communication among members; initiate educational and research programs. Compiles statistics. **Members:** 15,000.

Sources of Help-Wanted Ads

1158 ■ *Journal of Athletic Training*
National Athletic Trainers' Association
c/o Hughston Sports Medicine Foundation
6262 Veterans Pky.
Columbus, GA 31908
Ph: (706)494-3345
Fax: (706)494-3348
E-mail: jthornton@clarion.edu
URL: http://www.nata.org/business-opportunities/
  advertise/journal-athletic-training
Frequency: Bimonthly. **Price:** $32/year; $267 institutions in US, print & online; $303 institutions outside US, print & online; $128 individual; $75 Individuals; $100 Institutions; $125 Other countries. **Description:** Includes latest developments, research and clinical studies in athletic training.

Employer Directories and Networking Lists

1159 ■ *ALATA--Membership Directory*
Alabama Athletic Trainers Association
University of Alabama
1201 Coleman Coliseum
Tuscaloosa, AL 35401
Ph: (205)348-5347
Fax: (205)348-4419
E-mail: alatapres@gmail.com
URL: http://www.alata.org/membership.htm
Covers: Over 150 athletic trainers in Alabama.
Entries include: Name, address and business affiliations.

Handbooks and Manuals

1160 ■ *Athletic Training Student Primer: A Foundation for Success*
SLACK Inc.
6900 Grove Rd.
Thorofare, NJ 08086-9447
Ph: (856)848-1000
Free: 877-307-5225
Fax: (856)848-6091
E-mail: customerservice@slackinc.com
URL: http://www.slackinc.com
Description: Andrew P. Winterstein. 2009. $54.95 (softcover). 336 pages. Covers topics relevant to the study of athletic training. Prepares students for what they will learn, study, encounter and achieve during their educational and professional career.

1161 ■ *Become a Certified Personal Trainer*
McGraw-Hill Professional
PO Box 182604
Columbus, OH 43272
Ph: (877)833-5524
Free: 800-262-4729
Fax: (614)759-3749
E-mail: pbg.ecommerce_custserv@mcgraw-hill.com
URL: http://www.mhprofessional.com/product.php
  ?isbn=0071493069
Description: Robert Wolff. 2009. $21.95 (paperback). 288 pages. Serves as a guide through the entire certification process. Provides sample questions and offers advice about the business side of the job.

1162 ■ *Core Concepts in Athletic Training and Therapy with Web Resource*
Human Kinetics
PO Box 5076
Champaign, IL 61825-5076
Free: 800-747-4457
Fax: (217)351-1549
E-mail: info@hkusa.com
URL: http://www.humankinetics.com
Description: Susan Kay Hillman. 2012. $94.00 (hardback). 640 pages. Covers breadth and theory and application of athletic training, including evidence-based practice, prevention, and health promotion. Contains case studies and general information on the athletic trainer profession, such as training, education, licensure, certification and employment opportunities.

1163 ■ *Encyclopedia of Sports Medicine*
Pine Forge Press
2455 Teller Rd.
Thousand Oaks, CA 91320-2234
Ph: (805)499-4224
Free: 800-818-7243
Fax: (805)499-0871
E-mail: sales@pfp.sagepub.com
URL: http://www.sagepub.com/sociologybooks
Description: Lyle J. Micheli. 2011. $1,045.00. 1880 pages (hardcover). Provides relevant information in the field of sports medicine. Includes contributions from preeminent healthcare professionals, tables and images, illustrations of diagnostic and treatment techniques, and details on the various career opportunities in the profession.

1164 ■ *Introduction to Sports Medicine and Athletic Training*
Delmar Cengage Learning
PO Box 6904
Florence, KY 41022-6904
Free: 800-354-9706
Fax: (800)487-8488
E-mail: esales@cengage.com
URL: http://www.cengage.com
Description: Robert C. France. 2011. $143.95 (hardcover). 720 pages. 2nd edition. Covers sports medicine, athletic training, including anatomy and physiology. Offers discussion and insight on a wide range of careers related to sports medicine.

1165 ■ *Practical Guide to Athletic Training*
Jones & Bartlett Learning
5 Wall St.
Burlington, MA 01803
Free: 800-832-0034
E-mail: info@jblearning.com
URL: http://www.jblearning.com
Description: Ted Eaves. 2010. $86.95 (paper). 256 pages. Provides an essential guide for students interested in the fields of sports medicine and athletic training. Contains information on how to enter the workforce and succeed as an athletic professional.

1166 ■ *Praeger Handbook of Sports Medicine and Athlete Health*
ABC-Clio Inc.
130 Cremona Dr.
Santa Barbara, CA 93117-5516
Ph: (805)968-1911
Free: 800-368-6868
Fax: (805)685-9685
E-mail: crussell@abc-clio.com
URL: http://www.abc-clio.com
Description: Claude T. Moorman, Donald T. Kirkendall, and Ruben J. Echemendia. 2010. $154.95 (hardcover). 915 pages (3 volumes). Covers all aspects of sports medicine and the career paths available in the field. Includes topics on specific injury and anatomical locations, and treatment. Also includes glossary of sports medicine terms and abbreviations.

Online Job Sources and Services

1167 ■ *AT Placement*
URL: http://www.atplacement.com
Description: Serves as a platform for athletic trainers where they can post resumes, search job boards and contact potential employers. Maintains up-to-date information on placement notices pertinent to the athletic training profession.

1168 ■ *AT4HIRE.com*
URL: http://www.at4hire.com
Description: Aims to help certified athletic trainers find the most comprehensive database of sport camps, events, full-time and part-time jobs.

1169 ■ *Athletic Administration Jobs*
URL: http://www.athleticadministrationjobs.com
Description: Serves as a job board for athletic administration professionals. Offers updated job listings for candidates and job posting for employers.

1170 ■ *Athletic Jobs*
URL: http://www.athleticjobs.org
Description: Serves as niche job board that provides listings on athletic jobs.

1171 ■ Athletic Trainer Jobs
URL: http://www.athletictrainerjobs.org

Description: Features a searchable database of employment opportunities for athletic trainers.

1172 ■ Athletic Training Jobs
URL: http://www.athletictrainingjobs.org

Description: Serves as a niche job board that focuses on athletic training employment opportunities and candidate recruiting. Features athletic training positions posted by top employers in the industry.

1173 ■ Athletictrainer4hire.com
URL: http://www.athletictrainer4hire.com

Description: Serves as a resource for athletic trainers and event coordinators to communicate and match their respective needs.

1174 ■ athletictrainerjobs.us
URL: http://www.athletictrainerjobs.us

Description: Serves as a niche job board that focuses on athletic trainer employment opportunities and candidate recruiting. Assists employers and recruiters by matching qualified candidates with open athletic trainer positions.

1175 ■ Coachjobs.us
URL: http://www.coachjobs.us

Description: Serves as a job board that focuses on coach employment opportunities and candidate recruiting.

1176 ■ Get Athletic Trainer Jobs
URL: http://www.getathletictrainerjobs.com

Description: Serves as an informational resource for athletic trainer job seekers and employers. Offers free athletic trainer job postings and career opportunities.

1177 ■ iHireSportsandRecreation.com
URL: http://www.ihiresportsandrecreation.com

Description: Features sports and recreation jobs from job postings, internet job boards, newspapers and classified ads.

1178 ■ Sports Trainer Jobs
URL: http://www.sportstrainerjobs.com

Description: Serves as a niche job board that features job posting functionality for employers, recruiters and hiring managers as well as job search options for employment candidates in the field of athletic training.

1179 ■ SportsMedicineJobs.org
URL: http://sportsmedicinejobs.org

Description: Provides job search engine that finds job listings from company career pages, other job boards, newspapers and associations.

1180 ■ TrainerJobs.org
URL: http://trainerjobs.org

Description: Features search job boards, company career pages and associations for athletic trainer jobs.

1181 ■ trainerjobs.us
URL: http://www.trainerjobs.us

Description: Serves as a niche job board that focuses on trainer employment opportunities and candidate recruiting. Assists employers and recruiters by matching qualified candidates with open trainer positions.

OTHER SOURCES

1182 ■ American Medical Athletic Association
4405 E West Hwy., Ste. 405
Bethesda, MD 20814
Ph: (301)913-9517
Free: 800-776-2732
Fax: (301)913-9520
E-mail: amaa@americanrunning.org
URL: http://www.amaasportsmed.org

Description: Provides information on training, diet, injury prevention, and sports medicine to physicians and other healthcare professionals as leaders of active and healthy lifestyles. Hosts a sports medicine professional referral service made up of doctors, nutritionists, and other sports-oriented professionals.

1183 ■ American Medical Society for Sports Medicine
4000 W 114th St., Ste. 100
Leawood, KS 66211
Ph: (913)327-1415
Fax: (913)327-1491
E-mail: office@amssm.org
URL: http://www.amssm.org

Description: Aims to advance the discipline of sports medicine through education, research, advocacy and excellence in patient care. Promotes collegial relationship among sports medicine specialists. Includes an electronic recruitment resource for the sports medicine industry.

1184 ■ Athletic Trainer System
24 Village Park Dr.
Grove City, PA 16127-6358
Ph: (724)458-5289
Free: 888-328-2577
Fax: (724)458-0621
URL: http://www.athletictrainersystem.com

Description: Serves as a flexible and customizable software designed to assist athletic trainers in tracking and reporting information relating to athletes, students or employees.

1185 ■ *Career Opportunities in the Sports Industry*
InfoBase Holdings Inc.
132 W 31st., 17 Fl.
New York, NY 10001-3406
Ph: (212)967-8800
Fax: (800)678-3633
E-mail: info@infobasepublishing.com
URL: http://factsonfile.infobasepublishing.com

Frequency: Latest edition 4th, May 2010. **Price:** $49.50 Individuals hardcover. **Pages:** 400. **Description:** Shelly Field. Fourth edition, 2010. 380 pages. **Covers:** 73 jobs in a variety of areas in the sports industry, including professional athletes and teams, sports business and administration, coaching and education, sports officiating, journalism, recreation and fitness, boxing and wrestling, racing, wholesaling and retailing, and sports medicine. **Includes:** Nineteen appendixes, including listings of degree programs, minor and major baseball leagues, NBA teams, professional football leagues. **Entries include:** Description of job, duties, salary, employment prospects, best locations for work, prerequisites, and tips for entering the field.

1186 ■ College Athletic Trainer's Society
PO Box 250325
Atlanta, GA 30325
E-mail: jlee@collegeathletictrainer.org
URL: http://www.collegeathletictrainer.org

Description: Consists of athletic trainers, team physicians and allied health care professionals who are interested in supporting the college and university athletic trainer. Provides high quality care to student-athletes and promotes intercollegiate athletics. Addresses the needs and concerns of full-time head and assistant athletic trainers at colleges and universities.

1187 ■ *Health-Care Careers for the 21st Century*
JIST Publishing
875 Montreal Way
Saint Paul, MN 55102-4245
Ph: (317)613-4200
Free: 800-648-5478
Fax: (800)328-4564
E-mail: info@jist.com
URL: http://www.jist.com

Price: $9.95 Individuals Softcover. **Pages:** 448. **Covers:** Jobs for health care professionals and career opportunities for those pursuing a health-related career, organized into 80 careers in five groups. **Publication includes:** Appendixes listing job source resources and Web sites for health organizations.

1188 ■ Mental Health Challenges in the Athletic Training Room: A Team Physician's Perspective
401 W Michigan St.
Indianapolis, IN 46202-3233
Ph: (317)637-9200
Fax: (317)634-7817
URL: http://www.acsmstore.org

Description: DVD. Focuses on the role of physicians as primary care providers in the field of athletic training. Provides basic overview of the clinical features, diagnostic criteria, and screening tools appropriate for mental health conditions diagnosed in primary care sports medicine clinics.

1189 ■ National Collegiate Athletic Association
PO Box 6222
Indianapolis, IN 46206-6222
Ph: (317)917-6222
Fax: (317)917-6888
URL: http://www.ncaa.org

Description: Consists of universities, colleges, and allied educational athletics associations devoted to the administration of intercollegiate athletics. Aims to govern competition in a fair, safe, equitable and sportsmanlike manner and integrate intercollegiate athletics into higher education.

SOURCES OF HELP-WANTED ADS

1190 ■ The Auctioneer
National Auctioneers Association
8880 Ballentine St.
Overland Park, KS 66214
Ph: (913)541-8084
Fax: (913)894-5281
E-mail: support@auctioneers.org
URL: http://www.auctioneers.org/advertise

Frequency: 10/yr. **Description:** Trade magazine for auctioneers.

PLACEMENT AND JOB REFERRAL SERVICES

1191 ■ Florida Auctioneer Academy
201870 US 27, Bldg. 3, Unit 301
Clermont, FL 34712-1279
Ph: (407)886-4900
Free: 800-422-9155
E-mail: info@f-a-a.com
URL: http://www.f-a-a.com

Purpose: School for the training of auctioneers. **Activities:** Provides students information on career opportunities and licensing, as well as acting as a job placement service upon graduation.

EMPLOYER DIRECTORIES AND NETWORKING LISTS

1192 ■ Antique Week
Mayhill Publications - Midcountry Media
27 N Jefferson St.
Knightstown, IN 46148
Ph: (765)345-5133
Free: 800-876-5133
Fax: (765)345-3398
E-mail: mthoe@midcountrymedia.com
URL: http://www.antiqueweek.com

Frequency: Weekly. **Price:** $30 Individuals; $55 Two years. **Description:** Periodical covering antiques and collectibles as well as auctions and shows in Illinois, Indiana, Iowa, Kentucky, Michigan, Minnesota, Missouri, Ohio, western Pennsylvania, Tennessee, and Wisconsin. **Covers:** In each issue, 100-150 antiques auctions and antique shows, occurring during the week or two after publication. Each issue also contains separate calendar of about 200-300 antique shows, flea markets, and auctions occurring during the months after publication; separate Central edition (Illinois, Indiana, Iowa, Kentucky, Michigan, Minnesota, Missouri, Ohio, western Pennsylvania, Tennessee, and Wisconsin), and Eastern edition (Connecticut, Delaware, District of Columbia, Maryland, New Jersey, New York, North Carolina, Pennsylvania, Rhode Island, South Carolina, Virginia, and West Virginia). **Entries include:** Name of event, location, type of event, dates, name of show manager or auctioneer. **Arrangement:** Geographical.

1193 ■ Auctioneer--Directory Issue
National Auctioneers Association
8880 Ballentine St.
Overland Park, KS 66214
Ph: (913)541-8084
Fax: (913)894-5281
E-mail: support@auctioneers.org
URL: http://www.auctioneers.org

Frequency: Annual; February. **Publication includes:** List of about 6,000 auctioneers. **Entries include:** Name, address, phone, fax, e-mail, website, specialization. **Arrangement:** Geographical and alphabetical.

1194 ■ Directory of Licensed Auctioneers, Apprentice Auctioneers, and Auction Firms Engaged in the Auction Profession
South Carolina Department of LLR-Auctioneers Commission
Synergy Business Pk., Kingstree Bldg.
110 Centerview Dr.
Columbia, SC 29210
Ph: (803)896-4300
Fax: (803)896-4393
E-mail: contactllr@llr.sc.gov
URL: http://www.llr.state.sc.us

Frequency: Annual; December. **Price:** Free. **Pages:** 135. **Covers:** Approximately 1,500 auctioneers, apprentices, and firms licensed in South Carolina, including resident and non-resident licensees. **Includes:** List of auctioneering laws and regulations, background information, reciprocal states, accredited auction schools. **Entries include:** Company or personal name, address, phone, and license number. **Arrangement:** Geographical. **Indexes:** Alphabetical.

1195 ■ National Auto Auction Association--Membership Directory
National Auto Auction Association
5320 Spectrum Dr., Ste. D
Frederick, MD 21703
Ph: (301)696-0400
Fax: (301)631-1359
E-mail: naaa@naaa.com
URL: http://www.naaa.com

Frequency: Annual; Latest edition 2014. **Price:** $15; $15 Members; $35 Nonmembers. **Covers:** 25,446 automobile auction firms. **Entries include:** Company name, address, names and phone numbers of auction personnel; pick up, delivery, and reconditioning services available. **Arrangement:** Geographical.

HANDBOOKS AND MANUALS

1196 ■ Auctioneer Exam Secrets Study Guide
Mometrix Media, LLC
3827 Phelan Blvd., No. 179
Beaumont, TX 77707
Free: 800-673-8175
Fax: (866)235-0173
E-mail: css@mometrix.com
URL: http://www.mo-media.com

Description: 2011. $39.99. Helps test takers ace the Auctioneer exam. Includes specific content areas, study tips and essential skills needed for the exam.

ONLINE JOB SOURCES AND SERVICES

1197 ■ AuctioneerJobs.com
URL: http://auctioneerjobs.com/a/jobs/find-jobs

Description: Features a searchable database of job listings for auctioneers.

1198 ■ National Auction List
URL: http://www.nationalauctionlist.com

Description: Provides a list of professional auctioneers, a list of upcoming auctions, and current auction news.

OTHER SOURCES

1199 ■ AuctionServices.com
PO Box 20038
Roanoke, VA 24018
Ph: (540)206-3311
Fax: (877)644-4571
URL: http://auctionservices.com

Purpose: Develops and creates websites for professional auctioneers. Provides secure hosting for individual websites. **Activities:** Offers the auction industry websites to promote professionalism and connect with other auctioneers worldwide.

1200 ■ California State Auctioneers Association
1869 Old Baldy Way
Upland, CA 91784
E-mail: info@caauctioneers.org
URL: http://www.caauctioneers.org

Members: Professional auctioneers. **Purpose:** Promotes professionalism, growth, and competency in the auction profession. **Activities:** Develops ethical standards in the industry, provides members with learning opportunities, reviews and develops information on technology changes in the industry, and provides opportunities to network and exchange ideas with professionals in the industry.

1201 ■ Careers for Self-Starters and Other Entrepreneurial Types
The McGraw-Hill Companies Inc.
PO Box 182604
Columbus, OH 43272
Ph: (212)512-2000
Free: 877-833-5524

Fax: (614)759-3749
E-mail: customer.service@mcgraw-hill.com
URL: http://www.mcgraw-hill.com
Blythe Camenson. **Frequency:** September 2004.
Price: $9.95 (US).; $13.95 (US). **Description:** Blythe
Camenson. Second edition, 2004. $9.95 (paper). 129
pages. **Includes:** Appendix of associations that
provide information on education, training, and
certification opportunities, as well as advice on starting businesses; recommended reading list. Appendix
of associations that provide information on education,
training, and certification opportunities, as well as
advice on starting businesses; recommended reading
list. **Entries include:** Name, address, brief description of information resources.

1202 ■ Industrial Auctioneers Association
3213 Ayr Ln.
Dresher, PA 19025
Ph: (215)366-5450
Free: 800-805-8359
Fax: (215)657-1964
E-mail: info@industrialauctioneers.org
URL: http://www.industrialauctioneers.org
Description: Represents industrial machinery and
equipment auctioneers. Promotes the use of auction
sales in idle industrial equipment. Maintains ethical
and professional standards among member
auctioneers.

1203 ■ Kentucky Auctioneers Association
1306 Euclid Ave.
Bowling Green, KY 42103
Ph: (270)904-6902
E-mail: kyactioneerassoc@gmail.com
URL: http://kentuckyauctioneers.org
Description: Provides continuing education classes
for auctioneers. Promotes use of the auction method

of marketing in both the private and public sectors.
Members: Professional auctioneers. **Purpose:**
Promotes and advances the profession and fosters
and encourages cooperation and mutual aid among
those engaged in the auction profession. **Activities:**
Acts as a networking forum for its members, provides
information for writing contracts, and publishes a
membership directory and quarterly magazine.

**1204 ■ Michigan State Auctioneers
Association**
4529 Gibbs NW
Grand Rapids, MI 49544
Ph: (616)785-8288
Fax: (616)447-3761
E-mail: info@msaa.org
URL: http://msaa.org
Members: Professional auctioneers. **Purpose:**
Represents the interests of auctioneers and provides
a forum for networking and sharing ideas and experi-
ences. **Activities:** Sponsors educational courses and
seminars, publishes an annual directory, and
provides networking opportunities with other
auctioneers.

**1205 ■ National Association of Public Auto
Auctions**
PO Box 41368
Raleigh, NC 27629
Ph: (919)876-0687
E-mail: elaine@execman.net
URL: http://www.publicautoauctionassoc.org
Description: Aims to uphold the standards of
practices within the automotive auction industry.
Strives to protect the general public, dealers, and
fleet accounts from unscrupulous practices. Fosters
honesty and integrity in all dealings.

1206 ■ National Auctioneers Association
8880 Ballentine St.
Overland Park, KS 66214
Ph: (913)541-8084
Fax: (913)894-5281
E-mail: support@auctioneers.org
URL: http://www.auctioneers.org
Description: Professional auctioneers. Provides
continuing education classes for auctioneers,
promotes use of the auction method of marketing in
both the private and public sectors. Encourages the
highest ethical standards for the profession.

1207 ■ Virginia Auctioneers Association
PO Box 41368
Raleigh, NC 27629
Ph: (919)878-0601
Free: 888-878-0601
Fax: (919)878-7413
E-mail: vaauctioneers@vaa.org
URL: http://vaa.org
Members: Professional auctioneers. **Activities:**
Provides a membership directory and networking op-
portunities with other auctioneers.

1208 ■ World Wide College of Auctioneering
PO Box 949
Mason City, IA 50402
Ph: (641)423-5242
Free: 800-423-5242
Fax: (641)423-3067
E-mail: wwca@netconx.net
URL: http://www.worldwidecollegeofauctioneering
.com
Purpose: Provides instruction and training in profes-
sional auctioneering. **Activities:** Offers advice on
setting up an auctioneering business upon comple-
tion of the course.

Auto and Diesel Mechanics

SOURCES OF HELP-WANTED ADS

1209 ■ *Automotive Fleet*
Bobit Business Media
3520 Challenger St.
Torrance, CA 90503
Ph: (310)533-2400
Fax: (310)533-2500
E-mail: info@lctmag.com
URL: http://www.automotive-fleet.com/

Frequency: Monthly. **Price:** Free. **Description:** Automotive magazine covering the car and light truck fleet market.

1210 ■ *Automotive News*
Crain Communications Inc.
1155 Gratiot Ave.
Detroit, MI 48207-2732
Ph: (313)446-6000
E-mail: info@crain.com
URL: http://www.autonews.com

Frequency: Weekly. **Price:** $159 Individuals print and digital online; $99 Individuals digital/online; $199 Individuals data center only; $24.95 Individuals 1 month, website access only; $14.95 Individuals 1 week, website access only. **Description:** Tabloid reporting on all facets of the automotive and truck industry, as well as related businesses.

1211 ■ *Blue Seal Tech News*
National Institute for Automotive Service Excellence
101 Blue Seal Dr. SE, Ste. 101
Leesburg, VA 20175
Ph: (703)669-6600
Free: 877-346-9327
Fax: (703)669-6127
E-mail: asehelp@ase.com
URL: http://www.asecert.org

Description: Quarterly. Covers news of the Institute's efforts to certify auto, medium/heavy truck, engine machinists, collision repair technicians, and parts specialists. Discusses industry trends, vehicle repair tips, and training information, and highlights activities of ASE-certified technicians.

1212 ■ *BodyShop Business: The Magazine that Delivers the Collision Repair Industry*
Babcox
3550 Embassy Pky.
Akron, OH 44333
Ph: (330)670-1234
E-mail: bbabcox@babcox.com
URLs: http://www.bodyshopbusiness.com; http://www.babcox.com/site/our-brands/bodyshop-business

Frequency: Monthly. **Description:** Magazine providing management and technical information that can be applied to running an efficient and profitable collision repair shop.

1213 ■ *Bus Ride*
Power Trade Media L.L.C.
4742 N 24th St., Ste. 340
Phoenix, AZ 85016
Ph: (602)265-7600
Free: 800-541-2670
Fax: (602)227-7588
URL: http://busride.com

Frequency: Monthly. **Price:** $39 Individuals; $64 Individuals; $42 Canada; $69 Two years Canada; $98 Canada 3 years; $75 Other countries; $125 Two years other countries; $175 Two years 3 years. **Description:** Magazine for managers of bus, motorcoach and transit operations.

1214 ■ *Cooling Journal*
NARSA
300 Village Run Rd., Ste. 103, No. 221
Wexford, PA 15090-6315
Ph: (724)799-8415
Fax: (724)799-8416
E-mail: acj@narsa.org
URL: http://narsa.org/publication/cooling-journal/

Frequency: Monthly. **Price:** $65 Individuals; $130 Other countries; $97 Canada. **Description:** Automotive trade magazine.

1215 ■ *Engine Builder: Serving Engine Builders and Rebuilders since 1964*
Babcox
3550 Embassy Pky.
Akron, OH 44333
Ph: (330)670-1234
E-mail: bbabcox@babcox.com
URLs: http://www.enginebuildermag.com; http://www.babcox.com/site/our-brands/engine-builder

Frequency: Monthly. **Description:** Magazine covering management topics, technical information, and new product news for owners and managers of leading volume rebuilding businesses.

1216 ■ *GEARS Magazine*
Automatic Transmission Rebuilders Association
2400 Latigo Ave.
Oxnard, CA 93030
Ph: (805)604-2000
Free: 866-464-2872
Fax: (805)604-2003
E-mail: membership@atra.com
URL: http://www.atra.com

Description: Monthly. Contains news of the Association, its chapters, and Association programs. Lists service contract and insurance information, job listings, and personnel changes in the Association. Recurring features include news of research, notices of publications available, reports of meetings, news of educational opportunities, and a calendar of events.

1217 ■ *Import Automotive Parts & Accessories*
Meyers Publishing
799 Camarillo Springs Rd.
Camarillo, CA 93012-8111

Ph: (805)445-8881
Fax: (805)445-8882
E-mail: len@meyerspublishing.com
URL: http://www.meyerspublishing.com/IAPA%20Home%20Page_6.hlmcms

Frequency: Monthly. **Price:** $75 Canada and Mexico; $105 Other countries; $55 Individuals; $10 Single issue; $25 Individuals import industry sourcebook; $35 Individuals import industry sourcebook outside the U.S.; $20 Single issue outside the U.S. **Description:** Trade magazine for the automotive aftermarket.

1218 ■ *ImportCar: The Complete Import Service Magazine*
Babcox
3550 Embassy Pky.
Akron, OH 44333
Ph: (330)670-1234
E-mail: bbabcox@babcox.com
URLs: http://www.import-car.com; http://www.babcox.com/site/our-brands/importcar

Frequency: Monthly. **Price:** Free. **Description:** Magazine focusing on import specialist repair shops that derive more than 50% of revenue from servicing import nameplates.

1219 ■ *The Motion Systems Distributor*
Intertec Publishing
5 Penn Plz., 13th Fl.
New York, NY 10001-1810
Ph: (212)613-9700
Free: 800-795-5445
Fax: (212)613-9749
E-mail: bethany.weaver@penton.com
URL: http://www.penton.com/

Frequency: Bimonthly. **Description:** Completely separate from PT Design, this bi-monthly publication is tailored to the informational needs of the motion systems distributor. Published six times, this sales and management magazine goes to sales and branch management personnel, owners/operators of distributor companies in the U.S. and their technical personnel, and selected suppliers.

1220 ■ *Motor Age: The Journal for Professional Automotive Repair*
Adams Business Media/Green Media
833 W Jackson Blvd.
7th Fl.
Chicago, IL 60607
Ph: (312)846-4600
Fax: (312)846-4638
URL: http://www.motorage.com

Frequency: Monthly. **Price:** $49 Individuals; $75 Two years; $90 Other countries. **Description:** Magazine for auto repair shops.

1221 ■ *Popular Mechanics*
Hearst Magazines International
1271 Ave. of the Americas
New York, NY 10020

Ph: (212)649-4115
Free: 800-544-6748
Fax: (212)767-5612
E-mail: popularmechanics@hearst.com
URLs: http://www.popularmechanics.com/; http://www.hearst.com/magazines/popular-mechanics.php
Frequency: Monthly. **Price:** $12 Individuals; $20 Two years. **Description:** Magazine focusing on autos, the home, and leisure. Prints Latin American Edition.

1222 ■ *Transmission Digest: The Automotive Powertrain Industry Journal*
MD Publications Inc.
3057 E Cairo St.
Springfield, MO 65802
Ph: (417)866-3917
Free: 800-274-7890
Fax: (417)866-2781
E-mail: mdickemann@mdpublications.com
URL: http://www.transmissiondigest.com/
Frequency: Monthly. **Description:** Automotive transmission industry news.

1223 ■ *Undercar Digest*
MD Publications Inc.
3057 E Cairo St.
Springfield, MO 65802
Ph: (417)866-3917
Free: 800-274-7890
Fax: (417)866-2781
E-mail: mdickemann@mdpublications.com
URL: http://www.undercardigest.com/
Frequency: Monthly. **Price:** $49 Individuals. **Description:** Magazine for the undercar service and supply industry.

1224 ■ *Underhood Service*
Babcox
3550 Embassy Pky.
Akron, OH 44333
Ph: (330)670-1234
E-mail: bbabcox@babcox.com
URLs: http://www.underhoodservice.com; http://www.babcox.com/site/our-brands/underhood-service
Frequency: Monthly. **Description:** Magazine covering service and repair shops doing 50% or more of service underhood.

HANDBOOKS AND MANUALS

1225 ■ *Denman's Handbook for Auto Mechanics and Technicians*
Xlibris Corporation
1663 Liberty Dr.
Ste. 200
Bloomington, IN 47403
Ph: (610)915-5214
Free: 888-795-4274
Fax: (610)915-0294
E-mail: info@xlibris.com
URL: http://www2.xlibris.com/
Description: Ernest Denman. 2011. $24.99 (casebound hardcover). 63 pages. Serves as a quick-reference aid for technicians specializing in auto mechanics, heavy equipment, hydraulics or welding.

ONLINE JOB SOURCES AND SERVICES

1226 ■ AutoJobs.com
URL: http://www.autojobs.com
Description: Provides job lists and career opportunities for the automotive industry including dealerships, manufacturers, automotive aftermarket companies, and independent service and body shops.

1227 ■ AutomotiveCrossing.com
URL: http://www.automotivecrossing.com
Description: Offers a comprehensive collection of researched job openings in the automotive field. Includes free job postings, free job searching, free resuming posting, free resume searching, and job management tools.

1228 ■ AutoPersonnel.com
URL: http://www.autopersonnel.com
Description: Specializes in automotive staffing covering sales, office management, accounting, technicians and other positions.

1229 ■ Diesel Mechanic Jobs
URL: http://www.dieselmechanicjobs.com
Description: Features job opportunities for diesel mechanics.

1230 ■ FindAMechanic.com
URL: http://www.findamechanic.com
Description: Connects employers with mechanics and technicians. Focuses on auto, truck, diesel, equipment and/or marine mechanics and other positions in the industry.

1231 ■ iHireAutomotiveProfessionals
URL: http://www.ihireautomotiveprofessionals.com
Description: Provides job listings for automotive professionals.

1232 ■ NeedTechs.com
URL: http://www.needtechs.com
Description: Provides resources for automotive employment and technician jobs. Matches employers who need auto techs with employees who need auto tech jobs.

1233 ■ TransportationCareers.net
URL: http://www.transportationcareers.net
Description: Offers updated job database, research, and articles related to the transportation industry.

TRADESHOWS

1234 ■ AERA Expo
Engine Rebuilders Association
500 Coventry Ln.
Crystal Lake, IL 60014-7592
Ph: (815)526-7600
Free: 888-326-2372
Fax: (815)526-7601
E-mail: info@aera.org
URL: http://www.aera.org
Frequency: Annual. **Primary Exhibits:** Automotive services equipment, parts, tools, supplies, and services.

1235 ■ National Automotive Radiator Service Association Annual Trade Show and Convention
National Automotive Radiator Service Association
3000 Village Run Rd., Ste. 103, No. 221
Wexford, PA 15090-6315
Ph: (724)799-8415
Free: 800-551-3232
Fax: (724)799-8416
E-mail: info@narsa.org
URL: http://narsa.org
Frequency: Annual. **Primary Exhibits:** Manufacturers in the automotive cooling industry.

OTHER SOURCES

1236 ■ Association of Diesel Specialists
400 Admiral Blvd.
Kansas City, MO 64106
Ph: (816)285-0810

Free: 888-401-1616
Fax: (847)770-4952
E-mail: info@diesel.org
URL: http://diesel.org
Description: Represents the interests of independent repair shops specializing in diesel fuel injection, governor and turbocharger service, manufacturers and distributors of replacement parts and allied equipment, and post-secondary schools offering programs in diesel mechanic training.

1237 ■ Automotive Service Association
8190 Precinct Line Rd., Ste. 100
Colleyville, TX 76034-7675
Ph: (817)514-2900
Free: 800-272-7467
Fax: (817)514-0770
E-mail: asainfo@asashop.org
URL: http://www.asashop.org
Description: Automotive service businesses including body, paint, and trim shops, engine rebuilders, radiator shops, brake and wheel alignment services, transmission shops, tune-up services, and air conditioning services; associate members are manufacturers and wholesalers of automotive parts, and the trade press. Represents independent business owners and managers before private agencies and national and state legislative bodies. Promotes confidence between consumer and the automotive service industry, safety inspection of motor vehicles, and better highways.

1238 ■ *Career Opportunities in the Automotive Industry*
InfoBase Holdings Inc.
132 W 31st., 17 Fl.
New York, NY 10001-3406
Ph: (212)967-8800
Fax: (800)678-3633
E-mail: info@infobasepublishing.com
URL: http://factsonfile.infobasepublishing.com
Frequency: Published 2005. **Price:** $49.50 Individuals hardcover. **Pages:** 224. **Description:** G. Michael Kennedy. 2005. 224 pages. **Covers:** 70 jobs from pit crew mechanic to restoration expert, from mechanical engineer to parts distribution director, from RV specialist to exotic car museum director. **Includes:** Appendices of educational institutions, periodicals, directories, and associations.

1239 ■ Gasoline and Automotive Service Dealers Association
29 Thornhill Rd.
Riverside, CT 06878
Ph: (203)327-4773
Fax: (203)323-6935
E-mail: mike@gasda.org
URL: http://gasda.org
Description: Owners/operators or dealers of service stations or automotive repair facilities; interested individuals. Aims to educate, inform and help increase professionalism of members and of the industry. Offers periodic technical training clinics and other educational programs including advanced automotive technical training, prepaid group legal services plan and group health insurance and liaison with government agencies. Informs members of political and legislative action or changes affecting their industry. **Members:** 1,500.

1240 ■ International Society of Automation
67 TW Alexander Dr.
Research Triangle Park, NC 27709-0185
Ph: (919)549-8411
Fax: (919)549-8288
E-mail: info@isa.org
URL: http://www.isa.org
Description: Automation professionals. Helps members and other professionals solve difficult technical problems, while enhancing their leadership and personal career capabilities. Develops standards

and certifies industry professionals. Maintains a career library that provides information about educational institutions, certification programs and jobs in automation.

1241 ■ National Institute for Automotive Service Excellence
101 Blue Seal Dr. SE, Ste. 101
Leesburg, VA 20175
Ph: (703)669-6600
Free: 877-346-9327
Fax: (703)669-6127
E-mail: asehelp@ase.com
URL: http://www.ase.com

Description: Governed by a 40-member board of directors selected from all sectors of the automotive service industry and from education, government, and consumer groups. Encourages and promotes the highest standards of automotive service in the public interest. Conducts continuing research to determine the best methods for training automotive technicians; encourages the development of effective training programs. Tests and certifies the competence of automobile, medium/heavy truck, collision repair, school bus and engine machinist technicians as well as parts specialists.

1242 ■ Truck-Frame and Axle Repair Association
364 W 12th St.
Erie, PA 16501
Free: 877-735-1687
Fax: (877)735-1688
E-mail: leafspg@aol.com
URL: http://www.taraassociation.com

Description: Owners and operators of heavy-duty truck repair facilities and their mechanics; allied and associate members are manufacturers of heavy-duty trucks and repair equipment, engineers, trade press and insurance firms. Seeks to help members share skills and technical knowledge and keep abreast of new developments and technology to better serve customers in areas of minimum downtime, cost and maximum efficiency. Conducts studies and surveys regarding safety, fuel conservation and heavy-duty truck maintenance and repairs. Has formed TARA's Young Executives to help make young people at members' repair facilities more proficient in normal business functions and to ensure the future of the Association.

SOURCES OF HELP-WANTED ADS

1243 ■ AIE Perspectives Newsmagazine
American Institute of Engineers
4630 Appian Way, Ste. 206
El Sobrante, CA 94803-1875
Ph: (510)758-6240
Fax: (510)758-6240
E-mail: aie@aieonline.org
URL: http://www.members-aie.org
Frequency: Monthly. **Price:** included in membership dues. **Description:** Professional magazine covering engineering.

1244 ■ Engineering
Scientific Research Publishing
PO Box 54821
Irvine, CA 92619-4821
E-mail: eng@scirp.org
URL: http://www.scirp.org/journal/eng/
Frequency: Monthly. **Price:** $468 Individuals. **Description:** Peer-reviewed journal publishing articles on the latest advancements in engineering.

1245 ■ Graduating Engineer & Computer Careers
Career Recruitment Media
2 LAN Dr., Ste. 100
Westford, MA 01886
Ph: (978)692-5092
Fax: (978)692-4174
E-mail: hshulick@alloyeducation.com
URL: http://www.graduatingengineer.com
Frequency: Quarterly. **Price:** $16.95 Individuals. **Description:** Magazine focusing on employment, education, and career development for entry-level engineers and computer scientists.

1246 ■ PE
National Society of Professional Engineers
1420 King St.
Alexandria, VA 22314-2794
Ph: (703)684-2800
Fax: (703)836-4875
E-mail: memserv@nspe.org
URL: http://www.nspe.org/PEmagazine/index.html
Frequency: Semimonthly; 10/yr. **Price:** included in membership dues; $50 for nonmembers. **Description:** Covers matters of importance to engineering educators and students.

1247 ■ SWE, Magazine of the Society of Women Engineers
Society of Women Engineers
203 N La Salle St., Ste. 1675
Chicago, IL 60601
Ph: (312)596-5223
Free: 877-SWE-INFO
Fax: (312)596-5252
E-mail: hq@swe.org
URL: http://societyofwomenengineers.swe.org/index.php
Frequency: Quarterly. **Price:** $30 Nonmembers. **Description:** Magazine for engineering students and for women and men working in the engineering and technology fields. Covers career guidance, continuing development and topical issues.

1248 ■ Woman Engineer
Equal Opportunity Publications Inc.
445 Broad Hollow Rd., Ste. 425
Melville, NY 11747
Ph: (631)421-9421
Fax: (631)421-1352
E-mail: info@eop.com
URL: http://www.eop.com
Description: Annual. Magazine that is offered at no charge to qualified female engineering, computer-science, and information-technology students and professionals seeking to find employment and advancement in their careers.

EMPLOYER DIRECTORIES AND NETWORKING LISTS

1249 ■ Directory of Contract Staffing Firms
C.E. Publications Inc.
PO Box 3006
Bothell, WA 98041-3006
Ph: (425)806-5200
Fax: (425)806-5585
E-mail: staff@cjhunter.com
URL: http://www.cjhunter.com/dcsf/overview.html
Frequency: Annual. **Covers:** Nearly 1,300 contract firms actively engaged in the employment of engineering, IT/IS, and technical personnel for 'temporary' contract assignments throughout the world. **Entries include:** Company name, address, phone, name of contact, email, web address. **Arrangement:** Alphabetical. **Indexes:** Geographical.

1250 ■ Indiana Society of Professional Engineers--Directory
Indiana Society of Professional Engineers
c/o Lauraine M. Howe, Executive Director
PO Box 20806
Indianapolis, IN 46220
Ph: (317)255-2267
Fax: (317)255-2530
E-mail: indspe@gmail.com
URL: http://www.indspe.org
Frequency: Annual; fall. **Pages:** 150. **Covers:** Member registered engineers, land surveyors, engineering students, and engineers in training. **Entries include:** Member name, address, phone, type of membership, business information, specialty. **Arrangement:** Alpha by chapter area.

1251 ■ Who's Who in Engineering
American Association of Engineering Societies
1801 Alexander Bell Dr.
Reston, VA 20191
Ph: (202)296-2237
Free: 888-400-2237
Fax: (202)296-1151
E-mail: dbateson@aaes.org
URL: http://www.aaes.org
Frequency: Triennial; Latest edition 9th. **Covers:** About 15,000 engineers who have received professional recognition for outstanding achievement. **Entries include:** Name, address; education and employment history; awards and achievements. **Arrangement:** Alphabetical. **Indexes:** Geographical, field of specialization.

HANDBOOKS AND MANUALS

1252 ■ Expert Resumes for Engineers
JIST Publishing
875 Montreal Way
Saint Paul, MN 55102-4245
Ph: (317)613-4200
Free: 800-648-5478
Fax: (800)328-4564
E-mail: info@jist.com
URL: http://www.jist.com
Description: Louise M. Kursmark and Wendy S. Enelow. 2009. $16.95 (softcover). 272 pages. Features a collection of written resume samples for all types of engineers including civil, mechanical, industrial, electrical, electronics, computer, and more. Contains tips and strategies for writing engineering resumes and finding the best jobs.

1253 ■ Great Jobs for Engineering Majors
The McGraw-Hill Companies Inc.
PO Box 182604
Columbus, OH 43272
Ph: (212)512-2000
Free: 877-833-5524
Fax: (614)759-3749
E-mail: customer.service@mcgraw-hill.com
URL: http://www.mcgraw-hill.com
Description: Geraldine O. Garner. Second edition, 2008. $16.95. 192 pages. Covers all the career options open to students majoring in engineering.

EMPLOYMENT AGENCIES AND SEARCH FIRMS

1254 ■ Career Advocates International
1539 Ave. A
Katy, TX 77493
Ph: (281)371-3917
E-mail: hank@careeradvocates.org
URL: http://www.careeradvocates.org

Description: Provides permanent placement and temporary staffing for executive and staff level positions. Specializes in multiple niches including: sales and marketing, accounting and financial services, banking, communications, human resources, chemicals, oil and gas, medical and dental, legal, information technology, energy, technology, engineering, manufacturing, construction, and light industrial.

1255 ■ Centennial, Inc.
8044 Montgomery Rd., Ste. 260
Cincinnati, OH 45236
Ph: (513)366-3760
Fax: (513)366-3761
URL: http://www.centennialinc.com

Description: Serves as an executive search firm specializing in the areas of executive and general management, accounting and finance, human resources, information technology, manufacturing, engineering, marketing and advertising, not-for-profit, sales and business development, and supply chain and logistics.

1256 ■ International Search
9717 E 42nd St.
Tulsa, OK 74147-0898
Ph: (918)627-9070
Fax: (918)524-8604

Description: Personnel consulting group provides placement expertise in engineering, accounting, and data processing. Industries served: Energy, manufacturing, oil and gas, and services.

1257 ■ Houser Martin Morris
110th Ave. NE, 110 Atrium Pl., Ste. 580
Bellevue, WA 98004
Ph: (425)453-2700
Fax: (425)453-8726
E-mail: info@houser.com
URL: http://www.houser.com

Description: Focus is in the areas of retained executive search, professional, and technical recruiting. Areas of specialization include software engineering, sales and marketing, information technology, legal, human resources, accounting and finance, manufacturing, factory automation and engineering.

1258 ■ Nesco Inc.
6140 Parkland Blvd., Ste. 110
Mayfield Heights, OH 44124-6106
Ph: (440)461-6000
Fax: (440)449-3111
E-mail: corporate@nescoresource.com
URL: http://www.nescoresource.com

Description: Offers staffing and consulting solutions in the fields of engineering, information technology,

accounting and finance, manufacturing and distribution, and administrative and customer services.

1259 ■ Phillip's Personnel/Phillip's Temps
1675 Broadway, Ste. 2410
Denver, CO 80204
Ph: (303)893-1850
Fax: (303)893-0639
E-mail: info@phillipspersonnel.com
URL: http://www.phillipspersonnel.com

Description: Personnel recruiting and staffing consultants in: accounting and finance, management information systems, sales and marketing, engineering, administration, and general and executive management. Industries served: telecommunications, distribution, financial services, and general business.

1260 ■ SHS of Cherry Hill
207 Barclay Pavilion W
Cherry Hill, NJ 08034
Ph: (856)216-9030
Fax: (856)219-2011
E-mail: shs@shsofcherryhill.com
URL: http://www.shsofcherryhill.com

Description: Personnel recruiters operating in the disciplines of accounting, sales, insurance, engineering and administration. Industries served: insurance, distribution, manufacturing and service.

ONLINE JOB SOURCES AND SERVICES

1261 ■ Engineering Classifieds
URL: http://www.engineeringclassifieds.com

Description: Serves as a career site for engineering professionals. Provides services including job search agents, resume creation and posting.

1262 ■ Engineer.net
URL: http://www.engineer.net

Description: Provides engineering employment tools such as job search, job posting, and engineering resumes.

1263 ■ Spherion
URL: http://www.spherion.com

Description: Recruitment firm specializing in accounting and finance, sales and marketing, interim executives, technology, engineering, retail and human resources.

1264 ■ ThinkEnergyGroup.com
URL: http://www.thinkenergygroup.com

Description: Serves as a job board for professionals looking for positions in engineering, power plant, energy, and technical fields. Contains advice and tips

on interviews, job searching, resume writing, hiring, and management. Provides choices of work location, pay rates in the field of expertise and contract, temp-to-hire, and direct hiring options.

OTHER SOURCES

1265 ■ American Institute of Engineers
4630 Appian Way, Ste. 206
El Sobrante, CA 94803-1875
Ph: (510)758-6240
Fax: (510)758-6240
E-mail: aie@aieonline.org
URL: http://www.aieonline.org

Description: Professional association for engineers, scientists, and mathematicians. Multi-disciplined, non-technical association who aims to improve the stature and image of engineers, scientists, and mathematicians. Provides endorsements, awards and opportunities for small business start-ups within the AIE Councils. Sponsors "LA Engineer", a comedy-drama television series; produces annual "Academy Hall of FAME (TV)".

1266 ■ *Career Opportunities in the Automotive Industry*
InfoBase Holdings Inc.
132 W 31st., 17 Fl.
New York, NY 10001-3406
Ph: (212)967-8800
Fax: (800)678-3633
E-mail: info@infobasepublishing.com
URL: http://factsonfile.infobasepublishing.com

Frequency: Published 2005. **Price:** $49.50 Individuals hardcover. **Pages:** 224. **Description:** G. Michael Kennedy. 2005. 224 pages. **Covers:** 70 jobs from pit crew mechanic to restoration expert, from mechanical engineer to parts distribution director, from RV specialist to exotic car museum director. **Includes:** Appendices of educational institutions, periodicals, directories, and associations.

1267 ■ Women in Engineering ProActive Network
1901 E Asbury Ave., Ste. 220
Denver, CO 80208
Ph: (303)871-4643
Fax: (303)871-4628
URL: http://www.wepan.org

Description: Women in engineering professions. Includes key strategies such as education and training, research, collaboration, leadership, diversity, advocacy, networking, sustainability, accountability, and volunteerism in order to be a catalyst for change that enhances the success of women in the engineering professions.

1268 ■ *Milling & Baking News*
Sosland Publishing Co.
4800 Main St., Ste. 100
Kansas City, MO 64112
Ph: (816)756-1000
Fax: (816)756-0494
E-mail: mbncirc@sosland.com?subject=mbn
URL: http://www.bakingbusiness.com

Frequency: Weekly (Tues.). **Price:** $135 U.S. and Canada; $210 U.S. and Canada 2 years; $290 U.S. and Canada 3 years; $190 Out of country; $320 Out of country 2 years; $455 Out of country 3 years. **Description:** Trade magazine covering the grain-based food industries.

HANDBOOKS AND MANUALS

1269 ■ *How to Open a Financially Successful Bakery*
Atlantic Publishing Co.
1210 SW 23rd Pl.
Ocala, FL 34471-1825
Ph: (352)622-1825
Free: 800-814-1132
Fax: (352)622-1875
E-mail: sales@atlantic-pub.com
URL: http://www.atlantic-pub.com

Description: Sharon L. Fullen. 2004. $39.95 (CD-ROM, paper). Success in business for bakers. 288 pages.

1270 ■ *Opportunities in Restaurant Careers*
The McGraw-Hill Companies Inc.
PO Box 182604
Columbus, OH 43272
Ph: (212)512-2000
Free: 877-833-5524
Fax: (614)759-3749
E-mail: customer.service@mcgraw-hill.com
URL: http://www.mcgraw-hill.com

Description: Carol Caprione Chmelynski. 2004. $13.95 (paper). 160 pages. Covers opportunities in the food service industry and details salaries, benefits, training opportunities, and professional associations. Special emphasis is put on becoming a successful restaurant manager by working up through the ranks. Illustrated.

EMPLOYMENT AGENCIES AND SEARCH FIRMS

1271 ■ **Chefs' Professional Agency**
870 Market St., 863
San Francisco, CA 94102

Ph: (415)392-1563
E-mail: hospitality@chefsprofessional.com
URL: http://chefsprofessional.com

Description: Locates talent for restaurants, hotels, clubs and resorts. Provides resume kits, career tools, and other candidate resources while also providing resources for employers.

ONLINE JOB SOURCES AND SERVICES

1272 ■ **BakingJobs.org**
URL: http://bakingjobs.org

Description: Features job sites, company career pages and associations for baking jobs.

1273 ■ **BestfoodJobs.com**
URL: http://www.bestfoodjobs.com

Description: Provides information on employment opportunities for the restaurant and food service industry.

1274 ■ **Foodservice.com**
URL: http://www.foodservice.com

Description: Serves as an online community of foodservice professionals. Provides services such as a virtual foodshow, employment center, market reports, daily industry news and editorials, discussion forums, culinary school connections, and the weekly foodservice.com express e-Newsletter.

1275 ■ **New Restaurant and Food Jobs**
URL: http://www.newrestaurantandfoodjobs.com

Description: Provides an online listing of companies with available restaurant and food jobs in all specialties.

1276 ■ **PastryBakerChef.com**
URL: http://www.pastrybakerchef.com

Description: Features employment opportunities for bakers and pastry chefs.

TRADESHOWS

1277 ■ **Dairy-Deli-Bake Seminar and Expo**
International Dairy-Deli-Bakery Association
PO Box 5528
Madison, WI 53705-0528
Ph: (608)310-5000
Fax: (608)238-6330
E-mail: iddba@iddba.org
URL: http://www.iddba.org

Frequency: Annual. **Primary Exhibits:** Dairy, deli, and bakery products, packaging, and equipment.

1278 ■ **Institute of Food Technologists Annual Meeting and Food Expo**
Institute of Food Technologists
525 W Van Buren St., Ste. 1000
Chicago, IL 60607

Ph: (312)782-8424
Free: 800-438-3663
Fax: (312)782-8348
E-mail: info@ift.org
URL: http://www.ift.org

Frequency: Annual. **Primary Exhibits:** Food ingredients, equipment, laboratory equipment and supplies, and other services rendered to the food processing industry.

1279 ■ **International Baking Industry Exposition**
IBIE Exhibition Management
401 N. Michigan Ave.
Chicago, IL 60611
Ph: (312)644-6610
Fax: (312)644-0575
E-mail: pdwyer@smithbucklin.com
URL: http://ibie2013.org

Primary Exhibits: Baking equipment, supplies, and services.

1280 ■ **National Restaurant Association Restaurant and Hotel-Motel Show**
National Restaurant Association Convention Office
2055 L St., NW
Washington, DC 20036
Ph: (202)331-5900
URL: http://www.restaurant.org

Frequency: Annual. **Primary Exhibits:** Food service equipment, supplies, and services and food and beverage products for the hospitality industry. Includes international cuisine pavilion. **Dates and Locations:** Chicago, IL; McCormick Place.

OTHER SOURCES

1281 ■ **AIB International**
1213 Bakers Way
Manhattan, KS 66505-3999
Ph: (785)537-4750
Free: 800-242-2534
Fax: (785)537-1493
E-mail: sales@aibonline.org
URL: http://www.aibonline.org

Description: Baking research and educational center. Conducts basic and applied research, educational and hands-on training, and in-plant sanitation and worker safety audits. Maintains museum. Provides bibliographic and reference service. Serves as registrar for ISO-9000 quality certification.

1282 ■ **Allied Trades of the Baking Industry**
2001 Shawnee Mission Pkwy.
Mission Woods, KS 66205
URL: http://atbi.org

Description: Salespeople from the allied trades servicing the baking industry. Promotes the industry through cooperative service to national, state, and local bakery associations; encourages mutual understanding and goodwill between the baking industry and the allied trades. Carries out promotional and service activities. **Members:** 1,000.

1283 ■ American Bakers Association
1300 I St. NW, Ste. 700 W
Washington, DC 20005
Ph: (202)789-0300
Fax: (202)898-1164
E-mail: rmackie@americanbakers.org
URL: http://americanbakers.org

Description: Manufacturers and wholesale distributors of bread, rolls, and pastry products; suppliers of goods and services to bakers. Conducts seminars and expositions. **Members:** 300.

1284 ■ American Culinary Federation
180 Center Place Way
Saint Augustine, FL 32095
Free: 800-624-9458
Fax: (904)825-4758
E-mail: acf@acfchefs.net
URL: http://www.acfchefs.org

Description: Aims to promote the culinary profession and provide on-going educational training and networking for members. Provides opportunities for competition, professional recognition, and access to educational forums with other culinary experts at local, regional, national, and international events. Operates the National Apprenticeship Program for Cooks and pastry cooks. Offers programs that address certification of the individual chef's skills, accreditation of culinary programs, apprenticeship of cooks and pastry cooks, professional development, and the fight against childhood hunger.

1285 ■ American Society of Baking
PO Box 336
Swedesboro, NJ 08085
Ph: (847)920-9885
Free: 800-713-0462
Fax: (888)315-2612
E-mail: info@asbe.org
URL: http://www.asbe.org

Description: Professional organization of persons engaged in bakery production; chemists, production supervisors, engineers, technicians, and others from allied fields. Maintains information service and library references to baking and related subjects.

1286 ■ *Career Opportunities in the Food and Beverage Industry*
InfoBase Holdings Inc.
132 W 31st., 17 Fl.
New York, NY 10001-3406
Ph: (212)967-8800
Fax: (800)678-3633
E-mail: info@infobasepublishing.com
URL: http://www.ferguson.infobasepublishing.com

Description: Barbara Sims-Bell. 2010. $18.95 (paper). 223 pages. Provides information about locating and landing 80 skilled and unskilled jobs in the food and beverage industry. **Includes:** Appendices of trade associations, recruiting organizations, and major agencies. Appendices of trade associations, recruiting organizations, and major agencies.

1287 ■ Independent Bakers Association
PO Box 3731
Washington, DC 20007
Ph: (202)333-8190
Fax: (202)337-3809
E-mail: independentbaker@yahoo.com
URL: http://www.independentbaker.net/
   independentbakersassociation

Description: Trade association representing small-medium wholesale bakers and allied trade members. Represents independent wholesale bakers on federal legislative and regulatory issues. Offers annual Smith-Schaus-Smith internships. **Members:** 415.

1288 ■ International Association of Culinary Professionals
1221 Avenue of the Americas, 42nd Fl.
New York, NY 10020
Ph: (646)358-4957
Free: 866-358-4951
Fax: (866)358-2524
E-mail: info@iacp.com
URL: http://www.iacp.com

Description: Represents cooking school owners, food writers, chefs, caterers, culinary specialists, directors, teachers, cookbook authors, food stylists, food photographers, student/apprentices, and individuals in related industries in 20 countries. Promotes the interests of cooking schools, teachers, and culinary professionals. Encourages the exchange of information and education. Promotes professional standards and accreditation procedures. Maintains a Foundation to award culinary scholarships and grants.

1289 ■ International Council on Hotel, Restaurant, and Institutional Education
2810 N Parham Rd., Ste. 230
Richmond, VA 23294
Ph: (804)346-4800
Fax: (804)346-5009
E-mail: publications@chrie.org
URL: http://www.chrie.org

Description: Schools and colleges offering specialized education and training in hospitals, recreation, tourism and hotel, restaurant, and institutional administration; individuals, executives, and students. Provides networking opportunities and professional development.

1290 ■ Les Amis d'Escoffier Society of New York
787 Ridgewood Rd.
Millburn, NJ 07041-1541
Ph: (212)414-5820
Fax: (973)379-3117
URL: http://www.escoffier-society.com

Description: An educational organization of professionals in the food and wine industries. Maintains museum, speakers' bureau, hall of fame, and placement service. Sponsors charitable programs. **Members:** 1,650.

1291 ■ Quality Bakers of America Cooperative
1275 Glenlivet Dr., Ste. 100
Allentown, PA 18106-3107
E-mail: info@qba.com
URL: http://www.qba.com

Description: Independent national and international wholesale bakeries; composed of three major consulting divisions: marketing, manufacturing and technical research. Offers expertise in business strategy and management, product development, marketing and consumer research, process development, training and procurement.

1292 ■ Retail Bakers of America
15941 Harlem Ave., No. 347
Tinley Park, IL 60477
Free: 800-638-0924
E-mail: info@rbanet.com
URL: http://www.retailbakersofamerica.org

Description: Independent and in-store bakeries, food service, specialty bakeries, suppliers of ingredients, tools and equipment; other. Provides information, management, production, merchandising and small business services.

SOURCES OF HELP-WANTED ADS

1293 ■ *Accounting and Finance*
Blackwell Publishing Inc.
350 Main St.
Malden, MA 02148
Ph: (781)388-8200
Free: 800-216-2522
Fax: (781)388-8210
E-mail: journaladsusa@bos.blackwellpublishing.com
URL: http://as.wiley.com/WileyCDA/WileyTitle/productCd-ACFI.html

Frequency: Quarterly. **Price:** $469 Institutions print + online, Australia/New Zealand; $408 Institutions print or online, Australia/New Zealand; $633 Institutions print + online; $551 Institutions print or online; £441 Institutions print + online; £383 Institutions print or online. **Description:** Journal focusing on accounting and finance.

1294 ■ *Brookings Papers on Economic Activity*
Brookings Institution Press
1775 Massachusetts Ave. NW
Washington, DC 20036
Ph: (202)797-6000
Free: 800-275-1447
Fax: (202)797-6195
E-mail: brookingspapers@brookings.edu
URL: http://www.brookings.edu/about/projects/bpea

Frequency: Semiannual. **Price:** $60 Individuals; $100 Institutions; $74 Other countries; $114 Institutions, other countries. **Description:** Publication covering economics and business.

1295 ■ *Business Credit: The Publication for Credit and Finance Professionals*
National Association of Credit Management
8840 Columbia 100 Pkwy.
Columbia, MD 21045-2158
Ph: (410)740-5560
Fax: (410)740-5574
E-mail: nacm_national@nacm.org
URL: http://www.nacm.org/index.php?option=com_content&view=category&layout=blog&id=77&Itemid=188

Frequency: 10/yr. **Price:** C$60 Canada; $65 Other countries; $54 Individuals; $48 Libraries; $7 Single issue. **Description:** Magazine covering finance, business risk management, providing information for the extension of credit, maintenance of accounts receivable, and cash asset management.

1296 ■ *Commercial Lending Review*
Wolters Kluwer Law & Business - CCH
CCH Inc.
2700 Lake Cook Rd.
Riverwoods, IL 60015
Ph: (847)267-7000

Fax: (978)371-2961
E-mail: cust_serv@cch.com
URL: http://www.commerciallendingreview.com/

Frequency: Bimonthly. **Price:** $445 Individuals. **Description:** Journal covering all aspects of lending for commercial banks, community and regional banks and other financial institutions.

1297 ■ *Foundations and Trends in Finance*
Now Publishers
PO Box 1024
Hanover, MA 02339-1001
Ph: (781)871-0245
E-mail: zac.rolnik@nowpublishers.com
URL: http://www.nowpublishers.com/product.aspx?product=FIN

Frequency: Irregular. **Price:** $400 Individuals online only; $470 Individuals print and online; €400 Other countries online only; €470 Other countries print and online. **Description:** Academic journal that covers corporate finance, financial markets, asset pricing, and derivatives.

1298 ■ *Journal of Applied Finance*
Financial Management Association International
University of South Florida
College of Business Administration
4202 E Fowler Ave., BSN 3331
Tampa, FL 33620-5500
Ph: (813)974-2084
Fax: (813)974-3318
E-mail: fma@coba.usf.edu
URL: http://69.175.2.130/~finman/Publications/JAF.htm

Frequency: Semiannual; in spring and fall. **Price:** $75 Individuals; $150 Individuals/2 years; $150 Individuals/3 years, special offer. **Description:** Features scientific debate on the theory, practice, and education of finance.

1299 ■ *U.S. Banker: Charting the Future of Financial Services*
SourceMedia Inc.
1 State Street Plz., 27th Fl.
New York, NY 10004
Ph: (212)803-6066
Free: 800-221-1809
Fax: (212)843-9635
E-mail: custserv@sourcemedia.com
URL: http://www.americanbanker.com/usb.html

Frequency: Monthly. **Price:** $109 Individuals; $139 Individuals Canada; $139 Individuals outside North America; $179 Two years; $239 Two years Canada; $239 Two years outside North America. **Description:** Magazine serving the financial services industry.

1300 ■ *Wilmott Magazine*
John Wiley & Sons Inc.
111 River St.
Hoboken, NJ 07030-5774
Ph: (201)748-6000
Free: 800-225-5945

Fax: (201)748-6088
E-mail: info@wiley.com
URLs: http://www.wilmott.com; http://onlinelibrary.wiley.com/journal/10.1002/(ISSN)1541-8286

Frequency: Bimonthly. **Price:** €528 Institutions, other countries print only; £395 Institutions print only; $695 Institutions, other countries print only. **Description:** Journal focusing on the quantitative finance community and concentrating on practicalities.

EMPLOYMENT AGENCIES AND SEARCH FIRMS

1301 ■ *American Human Resources Associates Ltd.*
PO Box 18269
Cleveland, OH 44118-0269
Ph: (440)317-0981
E-mail: ahra@ahrasearch.com
URL: http://www.ahrasearch.com

Description: Executive search firm. Focused on real estate, banking and credit & collection.

1302 ■ *Robert Half Finance & Accounting*
2884 Sand Hill Rd.
Menlo Park, CA 94025
Free: 800-474-4253
URL: http://www.roberthalffinance.com

Description: Provides recruitment services in the areas of accounting and finance.

ONLINE JOB SOURCES AND SERVICES

1303 ■ *BillingJobs.com*
URL: http://www.billingjobs.com

Description: Features billing jobs, billing resumes, accounts payable jobs, and billing careers.

OTHER SOURCES

1304 ■ *Allied Finance Adjusters*
956 S Bartlett Rd., Ste. 321
Bartlett, IL 60103
Free: 800-843-1232
Fax: (888)949-8520
E-mail: alliedfinanceadjusters@gmail.com
URL: http://www.alliedfinanceadjusters.com

Description: Association of professional repossessors, investigators, and recovery agents.

1305 ■ *American Bankers Association*
1120 Connecticut Ave. NW
Washington, DC 20036
Ph: (202)663-5268
Free: 800-226-5377

Fax: (202)828-5053
E-mail: custserv@aba.com
URL: http://www.aba.com

Description: Members are principally commercial banks and trust companies; combined assets of members represent approximately 90% of the U.S. banking industry; approximately 94% of members are community banks with less than $500 million in assets. Seeks to enhance the role of commercial bankers as preeminent providers of financial services through communications, research, legal action, lobbying of federal legislative and regulatory bodies, and education and training programs. Serves as spokesperson for the banking industry; facilitates exchange of information among members. Maintains the American Institute of Banking, an industry-sponsored adult education program. Conducts educational and training programs for bank employees and officers through a wide range of banking schools and national conferences. Maintains liaison with federal bank regulators; lobbies Congress on issues affecting commercial banks; testifies before congressional committees; represents members in U.S. postal rate proceedings. Serves as secretariat of the International Monetary Conference and the Financial Institutions Committee for the American National Standards Institute. Files briefs and lawsuits in major court cases affecting the industry. Conducts teleconferences with state banking associations on such issues as regulatory compliance; works to build consensus and coordinate activities of leading bank and financial service trade groups. Provides services to members including: public advocacy; news media contact; insurance program providing directors and officers with liability coverage, financial institution bond, and trust errors and omissions coverage; research service operated through ABA Center for Banking Information; fingerprint set processing in conjunction with the Federal Bureau of Investigation; discounts on operational and income-producing projects through the Corporation for American Banking. Conducts conferences, forums, and workshops covering subjects such as small business, consumer credit, agricultural and community banking, trust management, bank operations, and automation. Sponsors ABA Educational Foundation and the Personal Economics Program, which educates schoolchildren and the community on banking, economics, and personal finance. **Members:** 1,000.

1306 ■ American Financial Services Association
919 18th St. NW, Ste. 300
Washington, DC 20006-5526
E-mail: cstinebert@afsamail.org
URL: http://www.afsaonline.org

Description: Represents companies whose business is primarily direct credit lending to consumers and/or the purchase of sales finance paper on consumer goods. Has members that have insurance and retail subsidiaries; some are themselves subsidiaries of highly diversified parent corporations. Encourages the business of financing individuals and families for necessary and useful purposes at reasonable charges, including interest; promotes consumer understanding of basic money manage-

ment principles as well as constructive uses of consumer credit. Includes educational services such as films, textbooks and study units for the classroom and budgeting guides for individuals and families. Compiles statistical reports; offers seminars.

1307 ■ Association of Credit and Collection Professionals
PO Box 390106
Minneapolis, MN 55439
Ph: (952)926-6547
Fax: (952)926-1624
E-mail: aca@acainternational.org
URL: http://www.acainternational.org

Description: Organization of credit and collection professionals that provides accounts receivable management services.

1308 ■ Association for Financial Professionals
4520 E West Hwy., Ste. 750
Bethesda, MD 20814
Ph: (301)907-2862
Fax: (301)907-2864
URL: http://www.afponline.org

Description: Seeks to establish a national forum for the exchange of concepts and techniques related to improving the management of treasury and the careers of professionals through research, education, publications and recognition of the treasury management profession through a certification program. Conducts educational programs. Operates career center.

1309 ■ *Career Opportunities in Banking, Finance, and Insurance*
InfoBase Holdings Inc.
132 W 31st., 17 Fl.
New York, NY 10001-3406
Ph: (212)967-8800
Fax: (800)678-3633
E-mail: info@infobasepublishing.com
URL: http://factsonfile.infobasepublishing.com

Frequency: Latest edition 2nd; Published February, 2007. **Price:** $49.50 Individuals hardcover. **Description:** Thomas P. Fitch. Second edition, 2007. 267 pages. Lists of colleges with programs supporting banking, finance, and industry; professional associations; professional certifications; regulatory agencies; and Internet resources for career planning. **Publication includes:** Lists of colleges with programs supporting banking, finance, and industry; professional associations; professional certifications; regulatory agencies; and Internet resources for career planning. Principal content of publication is job descriptions for professions in the banking, finance, and insurance industries. **Indexes:** Alphabetical.

1310 ■ Commercial Finance Association
370 7th Ave., Ste. 1801
New York, NY 10001-3979
Ph: (212)792-9390
Fax: (212)564-6053
URL: http://www.cfa.com

Description: Organizations engaged in asset-based financial services including commercial financing and

factoring and lending money on a secured basis to small- and medium-sized business firms. Acts as a forum for information and consideration about ideas, opportunities and legislation concerning asset-based financial services. Seeks to improve the industry's legal and operational procedures. Offers job placement and reference services for members. Sponsors School for Field Examiners and other educational programs. Compiles statistics; conducts seminars and surveys; maintains speakers' bureau and 21 committees.

1311 ■ Consumer Data Industry Association
1090 Vermont Ave. NW, Ste. 200
Washington, DC 20005-4964
Ph: (202)371-0910
Fax: (202)371-0134
E-mail: cdia@cdiaonline.org
URL: http://www.cdiaonline.org

Description: Serves as international association of credit reporting and collection service offices. Maintains hall of fame and biographical archives; conducts specialized educational programs. Offers computerized services and compiles statistics.

1312 ■ Credit Professionals International
10726 Manchester Rd., Ste. 210
Saint Louis, MO 63122
Ph: (314)821-9393
Fax: (314)821-7171
E-mail: creditpro@creditprofessionals.org
URL: http://www.creditprofessionals.org

Description: Represents individuals employed in credit or collection departments of business firms or professional offices. Conducts educational program in credit work. Sponsors Career Club composed of members who have been involved in credit work for at least 25 years. **Members:** 700.

1313 ■ National Association of Credit Management
8840 Columbia 100 Pkwy.
Columbia, MD 21045-2158
Ph: (410)740-5560
Fax: (410)740-5574
E-mail: nacm_national@nacm.org
URL: http://www.nacm.org

Description: Provides information, products and services for effective business credit and accounts receivable management.

1314 ■ National Association of Credit Union Services Organizations
3419 Via Lido
PMB 135
Newport Beach, CA 92663
Ph: (949)645-5296
Free: 888-462-2870
Fax: (949)645-5297
E-mail: info@nacuso.org
URL: http://www.nacuso.org

Description: Credit union service organizations and their employees. Promotes professional advancement of credit union service organization staff; seeks to insure adherence to high standards of ethics and practice among members. Conducts research and educational programs; formulates and enforces standards of conduct and practice; maintains speakers' bureau; compiles statistics. **Members:** 400.

SOURCES OF HELP-WANTED ADS

1315 ■ *ASBMB Today*
American Society for Biochemistry and Molecular Biology
11200 Rockville Pike, Ste. 302
Rockville, MD 20852-3110
Ph: (240)283-6600
Fax: (301)881-2080
E-mail: asbmb@asbmb.org
URL: http://www.asbmb.org/asbmbtoday

Frequency: Monthly. **Description:** Monthly. Features an extensive coverage of awards, meetings, research highlights, job placement advertising and human interest articles. Provides insight and updates on budgetary and legislative issues and their impacts on biological research to members of the biochemical science community. Offers career development resources such as continuing education and discussions on non-traditional careers in science.

1316 ■ *Bulletin of Mathematical Biology*
Society for Mathematical Biology
Murray State University
Dept. of Mathematics and Statistics
Faculty Hall, Rm. 6C
Murray, KY 42071
Ph: (270)809-2491
E-mail: kfister@murraystate.edu
URLs: http://www.springer.com/
new+%26+forthcoming+titles+%28default%29/
journal/11538; http://www.springer.com/
new+%26+forthcoming+titles+(default)/journal/
11538

Frequency: Monthly; Bimonthly. **Price:** Included in membership; $1,413 Institutions print or online; $1,696 Institutions print and online. **Description:** Features articles in computational, theoretical, and experimental biology. Articles offer a combination of theory and experiment, documenting theoretical advances with expositions on how they further biological understanding.

1317 ■ *Current Bioinformatics*
Bentham Science Publishers Ltd.
PO Box 446
Oak Park, IL 60303-0446
Ph: (708)308-4203
Fax: (312)275-7530
E-mail: morrissy@benthamscience.org
URL: http://www.benthamscience.com/cbio/index.htm

Description: $1,210/year for corporate; $690/year for academic; $190/year for individuals. Focuses on reviews of advances in computational molecular or structural biology, encompassing areas such as computing in biomedicine and genomics, computational proteomics and systems biology, and metabolic pathway engineering. Contains advertisements of products, events, and services.

1318 ■ *Evolutionary Computation*
The MIT Press
55 Hayward St.
Cambridge, MA 02142-1493
Ph: (617)253-5646
Free: 800-356-0343
Fax: (617)258-6779
E-mail: ewfaran@mit.edu
URL: http://www.mitpressjournals.org/loi/evco

Frequency: Quarterly. **Price:** $84 Individuals print & online; $79 Individuals online; $472 Institutions print & online; $419 Institutions online only; $45 Students print and online, retired; $39 Students online only, retired. **Pages:** 176 per issue. **Description:** Journal providing an international forum for facilitating and enhancing the exchange of information among researchers involved in both the theoretical and practical aspects of computational systems of an evolutionary nature. Publishes both theoretical and practical developments of computational systems drawing their inspiration from nature, with particular emphasis on evolutionary algorithms (EAs), including, but not limited to, genetic algorithms (GAs), evolution strategies (ESs), evolutionary programming (EP), genetic programming (GP), classifier systems (CSs), and other natural computation techniques.

1319 ■ *Molecular and Cellular Proteomics*
American Society for Biochemistry and Molecular Biology
11200 Rockville Pike, Ste. 302
Rockville, MD 20852-3110
Ph: (240)283-6600
Fax: (301)881-2080
E-mail: asbmb@asbmb.org
URL: http://www.asbmb.org

Frequency: Monthly. **Price:** $300 Members print and online; $545 Institutions print only; $1,380 Institutions print and online; $925 Institutions online only; $545 Nonmembers print only; $1,095 Nonmembers print and online; $60 Other countries single issue; $90/year for members; $137/year for members in Canada; $375/year for nonmembers; $442/year for nonmembers in Canada. **Description:** Monthly. $890.00/year online only. Online journal that features articles and reviews that advance the understanding of the structural and functional properties of proteins and their expression. Offers specifically targeted placement opportunities, with research focusing on protein effects on biological responses, and protein and cellular interactions. Contains banner advertising and career placement ads.

1320 ■ *Proteins: Structure, Function, and Bioinformatics*
John Wiley & Sons Inc.
111 River St.
Hoboken, NJ 07030-5774
Ph: (201)748-6000
Free: 800-225-5945
Fax: (201)748-6088
E-mail: info@wiley.com
URLs: http://onlinelibrary.wiley.com/journal/10.1002/
(ISSN)1097-0134; http://as.wiley.com/WileyCDA/
WileyTitle/productCd-PROT.html; http://mc
.manuscriptcentral.com/prot

Frequency: Bimonthly; 16/yr. **Price:** $374 U.S., Canada, and Mexico print only; $6,662 Institutions print & online; $486 Other countries print only; $5,792 Institutions print only; $6,016 Institutions, Canada and Mexico print only; $6,128 Institutions, other countries print only; $386 Individuals online only; $6,119 Institutions online only. **Description:** 16 issues. $363.00/year for individuals in USA, Canada & Mexico; $475.00/year for individuals in other countries; $5,464.00/year for institutions in USA; $5,688.00/year for institutions in Canada & Mexico; $5,800.00/year for institutions in other countries. Features original reports of significant experimental and analytic research in all areas of protein research: structure, function, computation, genetics, and design.

HANDBOOKS AND MANUALS

1321 ■ *Career Development in Bioengineering and Biotechnology*
Springer
233 Spring St.
New York, NY 10013
Ph: (212)460-1500
Fax: (212)460-1575
URL: http://www.springer.com

Description: Guruprasad Madhavan, Barbara Oakley, and Luis Kun (Editors.) 2009. $49.95. 485 pages. Provides a roadmap to the broad and varied career development opportunities in bioengineering, biotechnology, and related fields.

1322 ■ *Opportunities in Biotechnology Careers*
The McGraw-Hill Companies Inc.
PO Box 182604
Columbus, OH 43272
Ph: (212)512-2000
Free: 877-833-5524
Fax: (614)759-3749
E-mail: customer.service@mcgraw-hill.com
URL: http://www.mcgraw-hill.com

Description: Sheldon S. Brown. 2007. $13.95 (paper). 160 pages. Contains information on biotechnology careers, training and educational requirements for each career, salary statistics for different positions within each field, as well as professional and internet resources.

EMPLOYMENT AGENCIES AND SEARCH FIRMS

1323 ■ *Executec Search Agency, Inc*
3156 E Russell Rd.
Las Vegas, NV 89120

Ph: (702)892-8008
URL: http://www.executecsearch.com

Description: Serves as an executive recruiting firm in the scientific instrument and services marketplace. Provides searches for clients in the industries of biotechnology, molecular biology instruments and reagents, cell biology, genetic identity, genomics, proteomics, bioinformatics, high throughput screening instruments, analytical instrument, process, semiconductor, and health & safety.

1324 ■ Exigent Group
91 Central Ave., Ste. 5
Stirling, NJ 07980
Free: 800-929-5813
E-mail: jobs@exigrp.com
URL: http://www.exigrp.com

Description: Serves as a professional recruitment/search firm for the pharmaceutical, biotechnology, and medical device industries. Specializes in clinical biostatistics and clinical statistical SAS programming.

1325 ■ Greylock Recruiting
749 Main St.
Williamstown, MA 01267
Ph: (617)680-1952
Fax: (617)716-4444
E-mail: info@greylock-recruiting.com
URL: http://greylock-recruiting.com

Description: Executive search firm that focuses on providing employment services for scientific professionals within the pharmaceutical and biotechnology industries.

1326 ■ JD Strategies
444 Castro St., Ste. 318
Mountain View, CA 94041
Ph: (650)941-2900
Fax: (650)567-9720
E-mail: career@jdstrategies.com
URL: http://www.jdstrategies.net

Description: Specializes in providing workforce solutions for the technical and functional staffing needs of technology companies. Focuses on all areas of engineering product development, testing, and quality assurance.

1327 ■ Joseph Associates
229 Main St.
Huntington, NY 11743
Ph: (631)351-5805
Fax: (631)421-4123
E-mail: inquiries@jaexecutivesearch.com
URL: http://www.jaexecutivesearch.com

Description: Serves as a recruitment firm for pharmaceutical, biomedical, biotechnical, healthcare, and medical device industries. Specializes in the following job titles: biostatisticians, computational biologists, epidemiologists, HEOR specialists, medical directors, directors of pharmaco epidemiology and pharmaco vigilance, and statisticians.

1328 ■ Neil Michael Group Inc.
9 Park Pl.
Great Neck, NY 11021
Ph: (516)482-8810
Fax: (516)482-3343
E-mail: contactus@nmgsearch.com
URL: http://www.nmgsearch.com

Description: Executive search firm that is dedicated to the life sciences industry. Specializes in the following specific areas: biotechnology, biopharmaceuticals, genomics, proteomics, bioinformatics, big pharma, medical diagnostics, and medical devices.

1329 ■ Powell Search Associates
123 Harbor Dr., Ste. 202
Stamford, CT 06902
Ph: (203)327-7671
E-mail: info@powellsearch.com
URL: http://powellsearch.com

Description: Serves as a pharmaceutical and biotech executive search firm. Conducts retained

searches, exclusive contingency searches, and contingency searches.

ONLINE JOB SOURCES AND SERVICES

1330 ■ Biohealthmatics.com
URL: http://www.biohealthmatics.com

Description: Serves as a job search networking site for the biotechnology and healthcare IT fields. Allows users to interact with other professionals in the industry and show the knowledge they have picked up as part of their daily involvement in their particular field.

1331 ■ Bioinformatics, Databases and Software for Medicine
URL: http://www.bio-computing.org

Description: Serves as a bioinformatics portal that compiles information about the latest research in bio-computing, databases, and software for medicine. Features job opportunities in the bioinformatics field.

1332 ■ Bioinformatics Directory
URL: http://bioinformaticsdirectory.com

Description: Features white papers, books, general knowledge, magazines, classes, company listings, and job openings in the field of bioinformatics.

1333 ■ BioJobNet
URL: http://www.biojobnet.com

Description: Features job listings in biotechnology, pharmaceuticals, medical devices, and life sciences.

1334 ■ BioPlanet
URL: http://www.bioplanet.com

Description: Provides information about bioinformatics and the skills needed to start a career in the field. Features job postings and bioinformatics companies. Maintains a forum for professionals who wish to discuss their questions and news about the bioinformatics field.

1335 ■ BiosciRegister.com
URL: http://www.biosciregister.com

Description: Serves as an online directory or reference database of suppliers of products and services used in the biotechnology and life sciences industries. Contains job listings.

1336 ■ BiostatisticianCareers.com
URL: http://www.biostatisticiancareers.com

Description: Serves as a job board for biostatisticians. Offers jobs and resume postings.

1337 ■ BiostatisticianJobs.com
URL: http://www.biostatisticianjobs.com

Description: Provides biostatistician employment opportunities. Features jobs from all over the United States.

1338 ■ Biotech Career Center
URL: http://www.biotechcareercenter.com

Description: Serves as a portal for scientists seeking career advancement and/or job opportunities in biotech companies. Provides links to biology career and information sites.

1339 ■ BiotechEmployment.org
URL: http://biotechemployment.org

Description: Provides listings of biotech jobs and other employment opportunities in the United States.

1340 ■ BiotechGigs.com
URL: http://www.biotechgigs.com

Description: Lists new job openings for biotechnologists. Features research in the science and biotech employment market as well as a career articles section.

1341 ■ CCL.net
URL: http://www.ccl.net

Description: Serves as an independent electronic forum for chemistry researchers and educators to find approaches on solving current problems, share experiences, discuss the latest software, and learn about workshops and conferences. Offers job listings for positions in the field of computer applications in chemistry, materials research, and life sciences.

1342 ■ Discover8.com
URL: http://www.discover8.com

Description: Focuses on the dissemination and intelligent discussion of life science news, discoveries, hypotheses, and procedures. Features resume postings and career listings.

1343 ■ FierceBiotech
URL: http://www.fiercebiotech.com

Description: Provides information and news about the biotech industry. Offers job listings for life science professionals.

1344 ■ Genomeweb
URL: http://www.genomeweb.com

Description: Contains news focusing on advanced research tools in genomics, proteomics, and bioinformatics. Serves the global community of scientists, technology professionals, and executives who use and develop the latest advanced tools in molecular biology research. Contains job listings.

1345 ■ HireBio.com
URL: http://www.hirebio.com

Description: Features pharmaceutical and biotech jobs, employment resources, as well as education and career resources in bioinformatics.

1346 ■ Hum-Molgen.org
URL: http://hum-molgen.org

Description: Provides resources for the latest information in human molecular genetics. Features biotechnical sources, diagnostics, ethical, legal and social implications, meetings and conferences, and positions in bioscience and medicine. Provides the opportunity to communicate with scientists, physicians, and other genetics professionals worldwide.

1347 ■ Naturejobs.com
URL: http://www.nature.com/naturejobs/science/

Description: Lists jobs in the following disciplines of science: cell biology, biochemistry, bioinformatics, materials, and nanotechnology. Features scientific career information as well as news and advice.

TRADESHOWS

1348 ■ Experimental Biology Meeting
Federation of American Societies for Experimental Biology
9650 Rockville Pike
Bethesda, MD 20814
Ph: (301)634-7000
Free: 800-433-2732
Fax: (301)634-7001
E-mail: info@faseb.org
URL: http://www.faseb.org

Frequency: Annual. Features plenary and award lectures, pre-meeting workshops, oral and poster sessions, on-site career services, and exhibits of equipment, supplies and publications required for research labs and experimental study.

OTHER SOURCES

1349 ■ Federation of American Societies for Experimental Biology
9650 Rockville Pike
Bethesda, MD 20814

Ph: (301)634-7000
Free: 800-433-2732
Fax: (301)634-7001
E-mail: info@faseb.org
URL: http://www.faseb.org

Description: Federation of scientific societies with a total of 40,000 members: the American Physiological Society; American Society for Biochemistry and Molecular Biology; American Society for Pharmacology and Experimental Therapeutics; American Society for Investigative Pathology; American Society for Nutritional Sciences; the American Association of Immunologists; the American Society for Bone and Mineral Research; American Society for Clinical Investigation; the Indocrine Society; the American Society of Human Genetics; Society for Developmental Biology; Biophysical Society; American Association of Anatomists; and the Protein Society. Maintains placement service.

1350 ■ International Society for Computational Biology
9500 Gilman Dr., MC 0505
La Jolla, CA 92093-0505
Ph: (858)534-0852
Fax: (619)374-2890
E-mail: admin@iscb.org
URL: http://www.iscb.org

Description: Represents researchers in bioinformatics and computational biology. Promotes the application of computational methods to problems of biological significance. Facilitates basic and applied research, scientific communication, education, and international cooperation in computational biology.

1351 ■ Life Sciences Society
160 Redland Rd.
Woodside, CA 94062
Ph: (650)851-4588
Fax: (650)851-8643
E-mail: vicky@lifesciencessociety.org
URL: http://www.lifesciencessociety.org

1352 ■ National Human Genome Research Institute
Bldg. 31, Rm. 4B09
31 Center Dr., MSC 2152
9000 Rockville Pike
Bethesda, MD 20892-2152
Ph: (301)402-0911
Fax: (301)402-2218
URL: http://www.genome.gov

Description: Aims to apply genome technologies to the study of specific diseases. Provides training, educational programs, health professional education, and online careers and training resources.

1353 ■ RCSB Protein Data Bank
Rutgers, the State University of New Jersey
Center for Integrative Proteomics Research
174 Frelinghuysen Rd.
Piscataway, NJ 08854-8087
E-mail: info@rcsb.org
URL: http://www.rcsb.org/pdb/home/home.do

Description: Serves an international community of users including biologists and other scientists in fields such as bioinformatics, software developers for data analysis and visualization, students and educators, media writers, illustrators, textbook authors, and the general public. Functions as an information portal to biological macromolecular structures including proteins and nucleic acids. Features job listings for open positions in the molecular biology field.

1354 ■ Society for Mathematical Biology
Murray State University
Dept. of Mathematics and Statistics
Faculty Hall, Rm. 6C
Murray, KY 42071
Ph: (270)809-2491
E-mail: kfister@murraystate.edu
URL: http://www.smb.org

Description: Promotes and fosters interactions among mathematical and biological sciences communities through membership, journal publications, travel support, and conferences.

SOURCES OF HELP-WANTED ADS

1355 ■ AAPG Explorer
American Association of Petroleum Geologists
1444 S Boulder Ave.
Tulsa, OK 74119
Ph: (918)584-2555
Free: 800-364-2274
Fax: (918)560-2665
E-mail: lkrystinik@fossilcreekres.com
URL: http://www.aapg.org/explorer/

Frequency: Monthly. **Price:** $75 Nonmembers; $147 Individuals airmail service; $55 Members airmail. **Description:** Magazine containing articles about energy issues with an emphasis on exploration for hydrocarbons and energy minerals.

1356 ■ American Biotechnology Laboratory
International Scientific Communications Inc.
30 Controls Dr.
Shelton, CT 06484-0870
Ph: (650)243-5600
Fax: (203)926-9310
E-mail: iscpubs@iscpubs.com
URL: http://www.americanbiotechnologylaboratory.com

Frequency: 10/yr. **Description:** Biotechnology magazine.

1357 ■ American Journal of Respiratory Cell and Molecular Biology
American Thoracic Society
25 Broadway, 18th Fl.
New York, NY 10004
Ph: (212)315-8600
Fax: (212)315-6498
E-mail: atsinfo@thoracic.org
URLs: http://ajrcmb.atsjournals.org/; http://www.thoracic.org

Frequency: Monthly. **Price:** $150 Individuals online only; $285 Institutions online only; $100 Single issue; $110 Single issue international. **Description:** Monthly. Contains original and basic research in the area of pulmonary biology including cellular, biochemical, molecular, development, genetic, and immunologic studies of lung cells and molecules. Displays professional recruitment and announcement advertising.

1358 ■ American Laboratory News
International Scientific Communications Inc.
30 Controls Dr.
Shelton, CT 06484-0870
Ph: (650)243-5600
Fax: (203)926-9310
E-mail: iscpubs@iscpubs.com
URL: http://www.americanlaboratory.com

Frequency: Monthly. **Description:** Trade magazine for scientists.

1359 ■ Annual Review of Genetics
Annual Reviews
4139 El Camino Way
Palo Alto, CA 94306-4010
Ph: (650)493-4400
Free: 800-523-8635
Fax: (650)855-9815
E-mail: service@annualreviews.org
URL: http://www.annualreviews.org/journal/genet

Frequency: Annual. **Price:** $86 Individuals print & online; $263 Institutions print & online; $219 Institutions online; $219 Institutions print. **Description:** Periodical covering issues in genetics and the biological sciences.

1360 ■ Annual Review of Microbiology
Annual Reviews
4139 El Camino Way
Palo Alto, CA 94306-4010
Ph: (650)493-4400
Free: 800-523-8635
Fax: (650)855-9815
E-mail: service@annualreviews.org
URL: http://www.annualreviews.org/journal/micro

Frequency: Annual. **Price:** $86 Individuals print & online; $263 Institutions print & online; $219 Institutions online; $219 Institutions print. **Description:** Periodical covering microbiology and the biological sciences.

1361 ■ ASPB News
American Society of Plant Biologists
15501 Monona Dr.
Rockville, MD 20855-2768
Ph: (301)251-0560
Fax: (301)279-2996
E-mail: info@aspb.org
URL: http://www.aspb.org/newsletter

Description: Bimonthly. $30/year for nonmember. Offers news of interest to plant physiologists, biochemists, horticulturists, and plant molecular and cell biologists engaged in research and teaching. Alerts members to public policy issues, educational opportunities, meetings, seminars, and conventions pertinent to the field. Recurring features include letters to the editor, reports of meetings, job listings, a calendar of events, news from regional sections, and teaching ideas.

1362 ■ Basic and Applied Pathology
Blackwell Publishing Inc.
350 Main St.
Malden, MA 02148
Ph: (781)388-8200
Free: 800-216-2522
Fax: (781)388-8210
E-mail: journaladsusa@bos.blackwellpublishing.com
URL: http://onlinelibrary.wiley.com/journal/10.1111/(ISSN)1755-9294/

Frequency: Quarterly. **Description:** Journal covering the fields of experimental, anatomical, clinical,

molecular, forensic and legal, and toxicological pathology in humans and animals.

1363 ■ Biochemistry and Molecular Biology Education
John Wiley & Sons Inc.
111 River St.
Hoboken, NJ 07030-5774
Ph: (201)748-6000
Free: 800-225-5945
Fax: (201)748-6088
E-mail: info@wiley.com
URL: http://onlinelibrary.wiley.com/journal/10.1002/(ISSN)1539-3429

Frequency: Bimonthly. **Price:** $618 Institutions print only; $702 Institutions, Canada and Mexico print only; $744 Institutions, other countries print only. **Description:** Journal covering the field of biochemistry, molecular biology, and related sciences.

1364 ■ CBE--Life Sciences Education
American Society for Cell Biology
8120 Woodmont Ave., Ste. 750
Bethesda, MD 20814-2762
Ph: (301)347-9300
Fax: (301)347-9310
E-mail: ascbinfo@ascb.org
URL: http://www.lifescied.org/

Frequency: Quarterly. **Description:** Journal that focuses on life science education at the K-12, undergraduate, and graduate levels.

1365 ■ Cell
Cell Press
600 Technology Sq.
Cambridge, MA 02139
Ph: (617)661-7057
Free: 866-314-2355
Fax: (617)661-7061
E-mail: celleditor@cell.com
URL: http://www.cell.com

Frequency: 26/yr. **Price:** $212 U.S. and Canada individual, print and online; $320 Other countries individual, print and online; $212 U.S. and Canada online only, individual; $212 Other countries online only, individual; $1,425 U.S. and Canada institution, print only; $1,605 Institutions, other countries print only. **Description:** Peer-reviewed journal on molecular and cell biology.

1366 ■ Chemistry & Biology
Elsevier Science Inc.
Secondary Publishing Division
650 Ave. of the Americas
New York, NY 10011
Ph: (212)633-3980
Free: 888-437-4636
Fax: (212)633-3975
URL: http://www.elsevier.com/wps/find/journaldescription.cws_home/601281/description#description

Frequency: Monthly. **Price:** $2,137 Institutions print;

$442 U.S. and other countries online only; $457 Other countries print + online; $442 U.S. and Canada print; $843 Institutions online. **Description:** Journal focused on genetic, computational, or theoretical information of chemistry and biology, substantiating experimental data.

1367 ■ Current Advances in Cell & Developmental Biology
Reed Elsevier Inc.
125 Park Ave., 23rd Fl.
New York, NY 10017-5529
Ph: (212)309-8100
Fax: (212)309-8187
E-mail: newyork@reedelsevier.com
URL: http://www.elsevier.com/

Frequency: Monthly. **Price:** $4,426 Institutions print only; $532,000 Institutions, other countries print only; $4,041 Institutions, other countries print only. **Description:** Journal covering the field of biology.

1368 ■ Current Advances in Genetics & Molecular Biology
Elsevier Science Inc.
Secondary Publishing Division
650 Ave. of the Americas
New York, NY 10011
Ph: (212)633-3980
Free: 888-437-4636
Fax: (212)633-3975
URL: http://www.elsevier.com/journals/current
-advances-in-genetics-and-molecular-biology/0741
-1642

Frequency: Monthly. **Price:** ¥25,500 Individuals associate; $221 Individuals associate; €221 Individuals associate; $6,340 Institutions; ¥755,700 Institutions; €5,713 Institutions. **Description:** Journal covering current details of genetics and molecular biology.

1369 ■ The Electrochemical Society Interface
Electrochemical Society
c/o Krishan Rajeshwar, Ed.
University of Texas at Arlington
Department of Chemistry & Biochemistry
502 Yates St.
Arlington, TX 76019
Ph: (817)272-3810
Fax: (817)272-3808
E-mail: interface@electrochem.org
URL: http://www.electrochem.org/dl/interface/

Frequency: Quarterly. **Price:** $69 Individuals tier 1, print & online; $84 Canada tier 1, print & online; $92 Other countries tier 1, print & online. **Description:** Publication featuring news and articles of interest to members of the Electrochemical Society.

1370 ■ Engineering in Life Sciences
John Wiley & Sons Inc.
111 River St.
Hoboken, NJ 07030-5774
Ph: (201)748-6000
Free: 800-225-5945
Fax: (201)748-6088
E-mail: info@wiley.com
URL: http://onlinelibrary.wiley.com/journal/10.1002/
(ISSN)1618-2863

Frequency: Bimonthly. **Price:** €1,069 Institutions European, online only; $1,403 Institutions, Canada and Mexico online only; $1,403 Institutions, other countries online only; £717 Institutions European, online only; $1,403 Institutions online only. **Description:** Journal focusing on the field of biotechnology and related topics including microbiology, genetics, biochemistry, and chemistry.

1371 ■ Epigenetics
Landes Bioscience
1806 Rio Grande St.
Austin, TX 78701
Ph: (512)637-6050

Fax: (512)637-6079
E-mail: info@landesbioscience.com
URL: http://www.landesbioscience.com/journals/
epigenetics/

Price: $129 Individuals online; $350 Individuals print and online; $450 Other countries print and online; $1,500 Institutions online; $1,850 Institutions print and online; $1,950 Institutions, other countries print and online. **Description:** Journal devoted to practicing physicians, residents and students.

1372 ■ International Journal on Algae
Begell House Inc.
50 Cross Hwy.
Redding, CT 06896
Ph: (203)938-1300
Fax: (203)938-1304
E-mail: orders@begellhouse.com
URL: http://www.begellhouse.com/journals/
7dd4467e7de5b7ef

Frequency: Quarterly. **Price:** $1,057 Institutions. **Description:** Journal covering fundamental and applied aspects in algology.

1373 ■ International Journal of Computational Bioscience
ACTA Press
Bldg. B6, Ste. 101
Calgary, AB, Canada T3E 7J9
Ph: (403)288-1195
Fax: (403)247-6851
E-mail: journals@actapress.com
URL: http://www.actapress.com/Content_of_Journal
.aspx?journalID=148

Frequency: Annual. **Price:** $120 Individuals. **Description:** Journal featuring research articles that combine biological and computational research to enhance the scientific understanding of life.

1374 ■ Invertebrate Biology
American Microscopical Society
Dept. of Biol. Sciences
CSU, Long Beach
1250 Bellflower Blvd.
Long Beach, CA 90840
Ph: (562)985-5378
Fax: (562)985-8878
E-mail: bconn@berry.edu
URLs: http://www.amicros.org/; http://as.wiley.com/
WileyCDA/WileyTitle/productCd-IVB.html

Frequency: Quarterly. **Price:** $323 Institutions online or print; $371 Institutions print + online; £196 Institutions print or online; £226 Institutions print + online. **Description:** Features original research articles on invertebrate animals.

1375 ■ Journal of Bacteriology
ASM Journals
1752 North St. NW
Washington, DC 20036-2904
Ph: (202)737-3600
Fax: (202)942-9335
E-mail: journals@asmusa.org
URL: http://jb.asm.org

Frequency: Semimonthly. **Price:** $214 Members print; $284 Members print and online; $333 Members Canada, print; $403 Members Canada, print and online. **Description:** Contains research articles on structure and function, cell surfaces, eucaryotic cells, genetics and molecular biology, and bacteriophages.

1376 ■ Lab Animal: Information, Ideas, Methods, and Materials for the Animal Research Professional
Macmillan Publishers Ltd. - Nature Publishing Group
75 Varick St., 9th Fl.
New York, NY 10013-1917
Ph: (212)726-9200
Free: 888-331-6288
Fax: (212)696-9006
E-mail: editors@labanimal.com
URL: http://www.labanimal.com/laban/index.html

Frequency: Monthly. **Price:** $250 Individuals; $1,932

Institutions; £139 Individuals; £1,160 Institutions; C$270.60 Individuals; C$2,091.19 Institutions; €215 Individuals; €1,798 Individuals; ¥20,000 Individuals; ¥238,280 Institutions. **Description:** Life science magazine.

1377 ■ Nanomechanics Science and Technology: An International Journal
Begell House Inc.
50 Cross Hwy.
Redding, CT 06896
Ph: (203)938-1300
Fax: (203)938-1304
E-mail: orders@begellhouse.com
URL: http://www.begellhouse.com/journals/
11e12455066dab5d

Price: $800 Institutions. **Description:** Journal covering the areas of nano- and micromechanics.

1378 ■ Narrative Inquiry in Bioethics: A Journal of Qualitative Research
Johns Hopkins University Press
2715 N Charles St.
Baltimore, MD 21218-4363
Ph: (410)516-6900
Free: 800-537-5487
Fax: (410)516-6968
E-mail: jrnlcirc@press.jhu.edu
URL: http://www.press.jhu.edu/journals/narrative_in-
quiry_in_bioethics

Frequency: 3/yr. **Price:** $175 Institutions print; $50 Individuals print. **Description:** Journal publishing information on bioethics.

1379 ■ Nature Biotechnology
Macmillan Publishers Ltd. - Nature Publishing Group
75 Varick St., 9th Fl.
New York, NY 10013-1917
Ph: (212)726-9200
Free: 888-331-6288
Fax: (212)696-9006
E-mail: biotech@natureny.com
URL: http://www.nature.com/nbt/index.html

Frequency: Monthly. **Price:** $250 Individuals print + online; $425 Two years print + online. **Description:** Scientific research journal.

1380 ■ Ornithological Newsletter
Ornithological Societies of North America
5400 Bosque Blvd., Ste. 680
Waco, TX 76710
Ph: (254)399-9636
Fax: (254)776-3767
E-mail: business@osnabirds.org
URL: http://www.osnabirds.org

Description: Bimonthly. Provides information of interest to ornithologists. Recurring features include listings of available grants and awards, news of members, a calendar of events, activities of sponsoring societies, and notices of publications available. Notices of employment opportunities are also available on the Web version.

1381 ■ PALAIOS
SEPM Publications
University of Kansas
Paleontological Institute, Department of Geology
1475 Jawyhawk Blvd., Rm. 120
Lawrence, KS 66045-7613
Ph: (785)864-2737
Fax: (785)864-3636
E-mail: palois@ku.edu
URLs: http://palaios.ku.edu/; http://palaios
.geoscienceworld.org/

Frequency: Monthly. **Price:** $400 Individuals for U.S.; online version with CD-ROM; $500 Individuals for U.S.; print and online version with CD-ROM; $400 Other countries online version with CD-ROM; $500 Other countries print and online version with CD-ROM. **Description:** Journal providing information on the impact of life on Earth history as recorded in the paleontological and sedimentological records. Covers areas such as biogeochemistry, ichnology, sedimentology, stratigraphy, paleoecology, paleoclimatology, and paleoceanography.

1382 ■ Perspectives in Biology and Medicine

Johns Hopkins University Press
2715 N Charles St.
Baltimore, MD 21218-4363
Ph: (410)516-6900
Free: 800-537-5487
Fax: (410)516-6968
E-mail: jrnlcirc@press.jhu.edu
URL: http://www.press.jhu.edu/journals/perspectives
_in_biology_and_medicine

Frequency: Quarterly. **Price:** $50 Individuals print; $155 Institutions print; $100 Two years print; $45 Students print; $310 Institutions print, 2 years. **Description:** Peer-reviewed journal publishing articles of current interest in medicine and biology in a context with humanistic, social, and scientific concerns. Covers a wide range of biomedical topics such as neurobiology, biomedical ethics and history, genetics and evolution, and ecology.

1383 ■ Plant Science Bulletin

URL: http://www.botany.org

Description: Quarterly. Carries news of the Association, with some issues including brief articles of more general interest in the field. Recurring features include notices of awards, meetings, courses, and study and professional opportunities; annotated lists of botanical books; and book reviews.

1384 ■ Popular Science: The Whant New Magazine

Time4 Media
2 Park Ave., Fl. 9
New York, NY 10016-5600
Ph: (212)779-5000
Fax: (212)779-5599
URL: http://www.popsci.com/popsci

Frequency: Monthly. **Price:** $12 Individuals; $20 Two years; $26 Canada; $45 Other countries USA. **Description:** General interest science magazine.

1385 ■ Science

American Association for the Advancement of Science
1200 New York Ave. NW
Washington, DC 20005
Ph: (202)326-6400
Fax: (202)371-9526
E-mail: membership@aaas.org
URLs: http://www.scienceonline.org; http://www.sci-encemag.org

Frequency: Weekly. **Price:** $146 Members professional, print & online; $119 Individuals NPA postdoctoral, print & online; $99 Individuals postdoctoral/resident, print & online; $75 Students print & online; $310 Individuals patron, print & online; $115 Individuals emeritus, print & online; $161 Canada postdoctoral/resident, print & online; $149 in U.S.; $211.05 in Canada; $201 in Mexico/Caribbean; $231 in all other countries. **Description:** Contains research reports, book reviews, editorial, news, and comments.

1386 ■ Seed Technologist Newsletter

Association of Official Seed Analysts
653 Consitution Ave. NE
Washington, DC 20002
Ph: (202)870-2412
Fax: (607)273-1638
E-mail: aosa@aosaseed.com
URL: http://www.aosaseed.com

Frequency: 3/year. **Price:** $35/year. **Description:** Three issues/year. Relates activities of the Society, with reports from various chapters across the U.S. and Canada. Publishes technical information about testing seeds and ensuring seed quality. Recurring features include news of research, a calendar of events, reports of meetings, news of educational opportunities, job listings, book reviews, and notices of publications available.

1387 ■ The World Wide Web Journal of Biology

Epress Inc.
130 Union Terrace Ln.
Plymouth, MN 55441
E-mail: editor@epress.com
URL: http://www.epress.com/w3jbio/

Description: Journal on Bio-informatics.

EMPLOYER DIRECTORIES AND NETWORKING LISTS

1388 ■ American Men and Women of Science: A Biographical Dictionary of Today's Leaders in Physical, Biological, and Related Sciences

R.R. Bowker
630 Central Ave
New Providence, NJ 07974
Ph: (888)269-5372
Free: 888-269-5372
Fax: (908)464-3553
E-mail: info@bowker.com
URL: http://www.gale.cengage.com

Frequency: Biennial; even years; New edition expected 29th, June 2011. **Price:** $1,368 Individuals. **Covers:** Over 135,000 U.S. and Canadian scientists active in the physical, biological, mathematical, computer science, and engineering fields; includes references to previous edition for deceased scientists and nonrespondents. **Entries include:** Name, address, education, personal and career data, memberships, honors and awards, research interest. **Arrangement:** Alphabetical. **Indexes:** Discipline (in separate volume).

1389 ■ Federation of American Societies for Experimental Biology--Directory of Members

Federation of American Societies for Experimental Biology
9650 Rockville Pike
Bethesda, MD 20814
Ph: (301)634-7000
Free: 800-433-2732
Fax: (301)634-7001
E-mail: directoryinfo@faseb.org
URL: http://www.faseb.org

Frequency: Annual; Latest edition 2009-2010. **Price:** $70 Individuals hardcopy; $55 Individuals softcopy. **Covers:** About 63,000 members of The American Physiological Society, American Society for Biochemistry and Molecular Biology, American Society for Pharmacology and Experimental Therapeutics, American Society for Investigative Pathology, American Society for Nutritional Sciences, The American Association of Immunologists, Biophysical Society, American Association of Anatomists, The Protein Society, The American Society for Bone and Mineral Research, American Society for Clinical Investigation, The Endocrine Society, The American Society of Human Genetics, Society for Developmental Biology, American Peptide Society, Society for the Study of Reproduction and Radiation Research Society. **Entries include:** Name, address, title, affiliation, memberships in federation societies, highest degree, year elected to membership, phone, fax and electronic mail address. Membership directories of the Biophysical Society, The Protein Society, The American Society for Bone and Mineral Research, and American Society for Clinical Investigation are also available separately (see separate entries). **Arrangement:** Alphabetical. **Indexes:** Geographical.

1390 ■ Peterson's Graduate Programs in the Biological Sciences

Peterson's
461 From Rd.
Paramus, NJ 07652
Ph: (609)896-1800
Free: 800-338-3282

Fax: (402)458-3042
E-mail: custsvc@petersons.com
URL: http://www.petersons.com/

Frequency: Annual; latest edition 2013. **Price:** $54.95 Individuals. **Pages:** 1,152. **Covers:** Colleges and universities in the United States and Canada that offer more than 4,000 accredited graduate and professional programs in the biological and agricultural science fields. **Entries include:** School name, address, phone; name, title, and phone number of contact; admission requirements, description of school and programs. Publication is third in a series called 'Grad Guides.'. **Arrangement:** Classified by academic field. **Indexes:** School name, subject.

HANDBOOKS AND MANUALS

1391 ■ Opportunities in Biological Science Careers

The McGraw-Hill Companies Inc.
PO Box 182604
Columbus, OH 43272
Ph: (212)512-2000
Free: 877-833-5524
Fax: (614)759-3749
E-mail: customer.service@mcgraw-hill.com
URL: http://www.mcgraw-hill.com

Description: Charles A. Winter. 2004. $13.95 (paper). 160 pages. Identifies employers and outlines opportunities in plant and animal biology, biological specialties, biomedical sciences, applied biology, and other areas. Illustrated.

EMPLOYMENT AGENCIES AND SEARCH FIRMS

1392 ■ Amtec Human Capital

2749 Saturn St.
Brea, CA 92821
Ph: (714)993-1900
Fax: (714)993-2419
E-mail: info@amtechc.com
URL: http://www.amtechc.com

Description: Employment agency.

1393 ■ Biomedical Search Consultants

275 Wyman St., Ste. 110
Waltham, MA 02451
Ph: (781)890-8824
Fax: (781)998-1266
E-mail: kprovost@biomedicalsearch.com
URL: http://www.biomedicalsearchconsultants.com

Description: Employment agency.

1394 ■ Caliber Associates

6336 Greenwich Dr., Ste. C
San Diego, CA 92122
Ph: (858)551-7880
Fax: (858)551-7887
E-mail: info@caliberassociates.com
URL: http://www.caliberassociates.com

Description: Executive search firm.

1395 ■ CEO Resources Inc.

PO Box 2883
Framingham, MA 01703-2883
Ph: (508)877-2775
Fax: (508)877-8433
E-mail: info@ceoresourcesinc.com
URL: http://ceoresourcesinc.com

Description: Executive search firm.

1396 ■ Clark Executive Search Inc.

135 N Ferry Rd.
Shelter Island, NY 11964

Ph: (631)749-3540
E-mail: mail@clarksearch.com
URL: http://www.clarksearch.com
Description: Executive search firm.

1397 ■ CTR Group
11843 Canon Blvd.
Newport News, VA 23606
Ph: (757)462-5900
Free: 800-945-9095
Fax: (866)597-0055
URL: http://www.ctrc.com
Description: Executive search firm.

1398 ■ Daly & Company Inc.
175 Federal St.
Boston, MA 02110-2210
Ph: (617)262-2800
E-mail: contact@dalyco.com
URL: http://www.dalyco.com
Description: Executive search firm.

1399 ■ Diversified Search Inc.
2005 Market St., 33rd Fl.
Philadelphia, PA 19103-7041
Ph: (215)732-6666
Free: 800-423-3932
Fax: (215)568-8399
E-mail: usinfo@odgersberndtson.com
URL: http://www.diversifiedsearch.com
Description: Executive search firm. Branches in Burlington, MA and New York.

1400 ■ Empire International
1147 Lancaster Ave.
Berwyn, PA 19312
Ph: (610)647-7976
Free: 800-539-0231
Fax: (610)647-8488
E-mail: info@empire-internl.com
URL: http://www.empire-internl.com
Description: Executive search firm.

1401 ■ The Employment Place
719 Van Lennen Ave.
Cheyenne, WY 82009
Ph: (307)632-0534
Fax: (307)638-2104
E-mail: agrecruit@juno.com
Description: A twofold placement firm operates as a general employment agency offering services to all areas of employment. Also serves as Ag Recruiters offering services to the agricultural professional. Industries served: All areas including government agencies in the U.S.; also serve fields of plant science, animal science, engineering, agri-business, management, sales and service.

1402 ■ Eton Partners
1185 Springdale Rd.
Atlanta, GA 30306
Ph: (404)685-8788
E-mail: info@etonpartners.com
URL: http://etonpartners.com
Description: Executive search firm.

1403 ■ JPM International
26034 Acero
Mission Viejo, CA 92691
Ph: (949)699-4300
Free: 800-685-7856
Fax: (949)699-4333
E-mail: trish@jpmintl.com
URL: http://www.jpmintl.com
Description: Executive search firm and employment agency.

1404 ■ The Katonah Group Inc.
33 Flying Point Rd.
Southampton, NY 11968
Ph: (631)287-9001
Fax: (631)287-9773
E-mail: info@katonahgroup.com
URL: http://www.katonahgroup.com
Description: Company specializes in executive recruiting for companies in the fields of life sciences (genomic and proteomic instrumentation), bio-informatics, chem-informatics, medical devices, clinical diagnostics, and scientific and analytical instrumentation.

1405 ■ K.S. Frary & Associates
16 Schooner Ridge
Marblehead, MA 01945
Ph: (781)631-2464
E-mail: ksfrary@comcast.net
URL: http://www.ksfrary.com
Description: Executive search firm.

1406 ■ Professional Placement Associates, Inc.
287 Bowman Ave.
Purchase, NY 10577-2517
Ph: (914)251-1000
Fax: (914)251-1055
E-mail: careers@ppasearch.com
URL: http://www.ppasearch.com
Description: Executive search firm specializing in the health and medical field.

1407 ■ Team Placement Service Inc.
1414 Prince St., Ste. 202
Alexandria, VA 22314
Ph: (703)820-8618
Free: 800-495-6767
Fax: (703)820-3368
E-mail: info@teamplace.com
URL: http://www.teamplace.com
Description: Full-service personnel consultants provide placement for healthcare staff, physician and dentist, private practice, and hospitals. Conduct interviews, tests, and reference checks to select the top 20% of applicants. Survey applicants' skill levels, provide backup information on each candidate, select compatible candidates for consideration, and insure the hiring process minimizes potential legal liability. Industries served: healthcare and government agencies providing medical, dental, biotech, laboratory, hospitals, and physician search.

ONLINE JOB SOURCES AND SERVICES

1408 ■ AgCareers.com
URL: http://www.agcareers.com
Description: Serves as an agriculture employment search engine. Supplies human resource services to the agriculture, food, natural resources and biotechnology industry.

1409 ■ American Institute of Biological Sciences Classifieds
URL: http://www.aibs.org/classifieds
Description: Section of the American Institute of Biological Sciences website used for posting available positions, research awards and fellowships, and other classified ads.

1410 ■ American Society of Plant Biologists Job Bank
URL: http://my.aspb.org/networking
Description: A service of the American Society of Plant Biologists, intended to aid its members in locating jobs and job resources. Site lists new jobs weekly in its job bank. Fee: A fee of $150 is charged for all academic/government/industry permanent positions and for all positions, regardless of rank, posted by private companies. Postdoctoral positions; research/technical positions (non-Ph.D.); and assistantships, fellowships, and internships at universities and not-for-profit agencies are published for a fee of $25.

1411 ■ BiologyJobs.com
URL: http://www.biologyjobs.com
Description: Provides resource for job seekers and employers who are interested in the life sciences. Includes listings of resumes and job openings.

1412 ■ BiosciRegister.com
URL: http://www.biosciregister.com
Description: Serves as an online directory or reference database of suppliers of products and services used in the biotechnology and life sciences industries. Contains job listings.

1413 ■ BioSpace.com
URL: http://www.biospace.com
Description: Serves as an online community for industry news and careers for life science professionals. Provides biospace news, career events, recruitment and job seeking opportunities for professionals in the biotechnology and pharmaceutical industries.

1414 ■ Biotech Career Center
URL: http://www.biotechcareercenter.com
Description: Serves as a portal for scientists seeking career advancement and/or job opportunities in biotech companies. Provides links to biology career and information sites.

1415 ■ BiotechCrossing.com
URL: http://www.biotechcrossing.com
Description: Offers a collection of active biotech job listings. Includes the lists of employer career pages, job websites, association websites, newspaper classifieds and recruitment sites.

1416 ■ Discover8.com
URL: http://www.discover8.com
Description: Focuses on the dissemination and intelligent discussion of life science news, discoveries, hypotheses, and procedures. Features resume postings and career listings.

1417 ■ FASEB Career Resources
URL: http://www.faseb.org/MARC-and-Professional
-Development/Career-Resources.aspx
Description: A career opportunity site combined with a development service that attempts to pair applicants at all career levels with employers who hire biomedical scientists and technicians. Biomedical career development is highlighted through career resource tools. Main files include: Careers Online DataNet, Career Online Classified.

1418 ■ GrantsNet
URL: http://sciencecareers.sciencemag.org/funding
Description: Grant-locating site intended for scientists in training who may become vulnerable in an era of competitive funding. Includes a directory of over 600 programs with contact information within a searchable database.

1419 ■ HireRx.com
URL: http://www.hirerx.com
Description: E-recruiting and training company that is focused on solving workforce issues for biotechnology and pharmaceutical firms. Provides access to job openings, online training courses, and communities in their scientific or functional concentration.

1420 ■ Hum-Molgen.org
URL: http://hum-molgen.org
Description: Provides resources for the latest information in human molecular genetics. Features biotechnical sources, diagnostics, ethical, legal and social implications, meetings and conferences, and positions in bioscience and medicine. Provides the opportunity to communicate with scientists, physicians, and other genetics professionals worldwide.

1421 ■ Naturejobs.com
URL: http://www.nature.com/naturejobs/science/
Description: Lists jobs in the following disciplines of science: cell biology, biochemistry, bioinformatics, materials, and nanotechnology. Features scientific career information as well as news and advice.

TRADESHOWS

1422 ■ American Society for Biochemistry and Molecular Biology Annual Meeting
American Society for Biochemistry and Molecular Biology
11200 Rockville Pike, Ste. 302
Rockville, MD 20852-3110
Ph: (240)283-6600
Fax: (301)881-2080
E-mail: asbmb@asbmb.org
URL: http://www.asbmb.org
Frequency: Annual. **Primary Exhibits:** Biological chemistry and molecular biology equipment, supplies, and services.

1423 ■ American Society for Cell Biology Annual Meeting
American Society for Cell Biology
8120 Woodmont Ave., Ste. 750
Bethesda, MD 20814-2762
Ph: (301)347-9300
Fax: (301)347-9310
E-mail: ascbinfo@ascb.org
URL: http://www.ascb.org
Frequency: Annual. **Primary Exhibits:** Equipment, supplies, and services related to doing research in cell and molecular biology.

1424 ■ American Society of Cytopathology Annual Scientific Meeting
American Society of Cytopathology
100 W 10th St., Ste. 605
Wilmington, DE 19801-6604
Ph: (302)543-6583
Fax: (302)543-6597
E-mail: asc@cytopathology.org
URL: http://www.cytopathology.org
Frequency: Annual. **Primary Exhibits:** Cytopathology microscopes, analysis equipment and supplies, and publishers.

1425 ■ Biophysical Society Annual Meeting
Biophysical Society
11400 Rockville Pike Rd., Ste. 800
Rockville, MD 20852
Ph: (240)290-5600
Fax: (240)290-5555
E-mail: society@biophysics.org
URL: http://www.biophysics.org
Frequency: Annual. **Primary Exhibits:** Biomedical research equipment, supplies, and services, including instruments and publications.

1426 ■ Society for Developmental Biology Annual Meeting
Society for Developmental Biology
9650 Rockville Pike
Bethesda, MD 20814-3998
Ph: (301)634-7815
Fax: (301)634-7825
E-mail: sdb@sdbonline.org
URL: http://www.sdbonline.org
Frequency: Annual. **Primary Exhibits:** Exhibits related to problems of development and growth of organisms, scientific journals and scientific tools and post-doc. openings.

OTHER SOURCES

1427 ■ American Academy of Clinical Toxicology
6728 Old McLean Village Dr.
McLean, VA 22101
Ph: (703)556-9222
Fax: (703)556-8729
E-mail: admin@clintox.org
URL: http://www.clintox.org
Description: Physicians, veterinarians, pharmacists, nurses research scientists, and analytical chemists. Seeks to unite medical scientists and facilitate the exchange of information. Encourages the development of therapeutic methods and technology. Conducts professional training in poison information and emergency service personnel.

1428 ■ American Academy of Forensic Sciences
2906 Lafayette Ave.
Newport Beach, CA 92663
Ph: (949)230-7321
E-mail: damartell@aol.com
URL: http://www.aafs.org
Description: Represents criminalists, scientists, members of the bench and bar, pathologists, biologists, psychiatrists, examiners of questioned documents, toxicologists, odontologists, anthropologists, and engineers. Works to: encourage the study, improve the practice, elevate the standards, and advance the cause of the forensic sciences; improve the quality of scientific techniques, tests, and criteria; plan, organize, and administer meetings, reports, and other projects for the stimulation and advancement of these and related purposes. Maintains Forensic Sciences Job Listing; conducts selected research for the government; offers forensic expert referral service.

1429 ■ American Association of Anatomists
9650 Rockville Pike
Bethesda, MD 20814-3999
Ph: (301)634-7910
E-mail: sboynes@anatomy.org
URL: http://www.anatomy.org
Description: Represents biomedical researchers and educators focusing on anatomical form and function. Focuses on imaging, cell biology, genetics, molecular development, endocrinology, histology, neuroscience, forensics, microscopy, physical anthropology, and other areas. Promotes the three-dimensional understanding of structure as it relates to development and function, from molecule to organism through research and education.

1430 ■ American Institute of Biological Sciences
1313 Dolley Madison Blvd.
McLean, VA 22101
Ph: (703)790-1745
Fax: (703)790-2672
E-mail: adm@aibs.org
URL: http://www.aibs.org
Description: Professional member organization and federation of biological associations, laboratories, and museums whose members have an interest in the life sciences. Promotes unity and effectiveness of effort among persons engaged in biological research, education, and application of biological sciences, including agriculture, environment, and medicine. Seeks to further the relationships of biological sciences to other sciences and industries. Conducts roundtable series; provides names of prominent biologists who are willing to serve as speakers and curriculum consultants; provides advisory committees and other services to the Department of Energy, Environmental Protection Agency, National Science Foundation, Department of Defense, and National Aeronautics and Space Administration. Maintains educational consultant panel. **Members:** 6,000.

1431 ■ American Institute of Chemical Engineers - Society for Biological Engineering
3 Park Ave., 19th Fl.
New York, NY 10016
Ph: (212)591-8888
E-mail: bio@aiche.org
URL: http://www.aiche.org/SBE
Description: Promotes the integration of biology with engineering and its benefits through bioprocessing, biomedical, and biomolecular applications. Raises interest, understanding, and recognition of engineers' and scientists' roles in biological engineering. Provides opportunities for the successful interaction of engineers and scientists.

1432 ■ American Reef Coalition
PO Box 844
Kihei, HI 96753
Ph: (808)870-5817
E-mail: info@americanreef.org
URL: http://www.americanreef.org
Description: To protect coral reef ecosystems, ocean resources and wilderness through a variety of proven methods and by providing support to other nonprofit organizations and government agencies engaged in marine, wilderness and natural area research, conservation and education.

1433 ■ American Society for Biochemistry and Molecular Biology
11200 Rockville Pike, Ste. 302
Rockville, MD 20852-3110
Ph: (240)283-6600
Fax: (301)881-2080
E-mail: asbmb@asbmb.org
URL: http://www.asbmb.org
Description: Biochemists and molecular biologists who have conducted and published original investigations in biological chemistry and/or molecular biology. Operates placement service.

1434 ■ American Society for Cell Biology
8120 Woodmont Ave., Ste. 750
Bethesda, MD 20814-2762
Ph: (301)347-9300
Fax: (301)347-9310
E-mail: ascbinfo@ascb.org
URL: http://www.ascb.org
Description: Represents scientists with educational or research experience in cell biology or an allied field. Offers placement service.

1435 ■ American Society for Histocompatibility and Immunogenetics
15000 Commerce Pkwy., Ste. C
Mount Laurel, NJ 08054-2212
Ph: (856)638-0428
Fax: (856)439-0525
E-mail: info@ashi-hla.org
URL: http://www.ashi-hla.org
Description: Scientists, physicians, and technologists involved in research and clinical activities related to histocompatibility testing (a state of mutual tolerance that allows some tissues to be grafted effectively to others). Conducts proficiency testing and educational programs. Maintains liaison with regulatory agencies; offers placement services and laboratory accreditation. Has co-sponsored development of histocompatibility specialist and laboratory certification program.

1436 ■ American Society for Microbiology
1752 N St. NW
Washington, DC 20036-290
Ph: (202)942-9207
Fax: (202)942-9333
E-mail: finance@asmusa.org
URL: http://www.asm.org
Description: Scientific society of microbiologists. Promotes the advancement of scientific knowledge in order to improve education in microbiology. Encourages the highest professional and ethical standards, and the adoption of sound legislative and regulatory policies affecting the discipline of microbiology at all levels. Communicates microbiological scientific achievements to the public. Maintains numerous committees and 23 divisions, and placement services; compiles statistics.

1437 ■ American Society of Plant Biologists
15501 Monona Dr.
Rockville, MD 20855-2768
Ph: (301)251-0560
Fax: (301)279-2996
E-mail: info@aspb.org
URL: http://my.aspb.org

Description: Professional society of plant biologists, plant biochemists, and other plant scientists engaged in research and teaching. Offers placement service for members; conducts educational and public affairs programs.

1438 ■ Association of Applied IPM Ecologists
PO Box 1119
Coarsegold, CA 93614
Ph: (559)761-1064
E-mail: director@aaie.net
URL: http://aaie.net

Description: Professional agricultural pest management consultants, entomologists, and field personnel. Promotes the implementation of integrated pest management in agricultural and urban environments. Provides a forum for the exchange of technical information on pest control. Offers placement service.

1439 ■ Association for Computing Machinery
2 Penn Plz., Ste. 701
New York, NY 10121-0701
Ph: (212)626-0500
Free: 800-342-6626
Fax: (212)944-1318
E-mail: acmhelp@acm.org
URL: http://www.acm.org

Description: Biological, medical, behavioral, and computer scientists; hospital administrators; programmers and others interested in application of computer methods to biological, behavioral, and medical problems.

1440 ■ Biophysical Society
11400 Rockville Pike Rd., Ste. 800
Rockville, MD 20852
Ph: (240)290-5600
Fax: (240)290-5555
E-mail: society@biophysics.org
URL: http://www.biophysics.org

Description: Biophysicists, physical biochemists, and physical and biological scientists interested in the application of physical laws and techniques to the analysis of biological or living phenomena. Maintains placement service.

1441 ■ Black Entomologists
USDA, ARS
59 Lee Rd.
Stoneville, MS 38776
Ph: (662)686-3646
Fax: (662)686-5281
E-mail: eric.riddick@ars.usda.gov
URL: http://www.blackentomologists.org

Description: Serves the professional, scientific, social and cultural interests and needs of black men and women in entomology and related disciplines. Promotes the science of entomology and facilitates the advancement of entomology-related careers in the developing world. Fosters communication among black entomologists.

1442 ■ *Career Opportunities in Conservation and the Environment*
InfoBase Holdings Inc.
132 W 31st., 17 Fl.
New York, NY 10001-3406
Ph: (212)967-8800
Fax: (800)678-3633
E-mail: info@infobasepublishing.com
URL: http://www.ferguson.infobasepublishing.com

Description: 2007. $49.50. 304 pages. Covers job profiles on conservation and the environment, followed by the descriptions of certification, education,

special skills, and training required. **Includes:** Appendices of educational institutions, periodicals, directories, and associations. Appendices of educational institutions, periodicals, directories, and associations.

1443 ■ *Career Opportunities in Science*
InfoBase Holdings Inc.
132 W 31st., 17 Fl.
New York, NY 10001-3406
Ph: (212)967-8800
Fax: (800)678-3633
E-mail: info@infobasepublishing.com
URL: http://factsonfile.infobasepublishing.com

Frequency: Latest edition 2008. **Price:** $49.50 Individuals hardcover. **Pages:** 344. **Description:** Susan Echaore-McDavid. Second edition, 2008. 332 pages. **Covers:** More than 80 jobs, such as biochemist, molecular biologist, bioinformatic specialist, pharmacologist, computer engineer, geographic information systems specialist, science teacher, forensic scientist, patent agent, as well as physicist, astronomer, chemist, zoologist, oceanographer, and geologist. **Includes:** Appendices of educational institutions, periodicals, directories, and associations.

1444 ■ *Careers for Plant Lovers and Other Green Thumb Types*
The McGraw-Hill Companies Inc.
PO Box 182604
Columbus, OH 43272
Ph: (212)512-2000
Free: 877-833-5524
Fax: (614)759-3749
E-mail: customer.service@mcgraw-hill.com
URL: http://www.mcgraw-hill.com

Description: Blythe Camenson. Second edition, 2004. $13.95. 160 pages. **Includes:** Appendices of selected list botanical gardens and arboreta for internships, summer employment, and volunteer opportunities, as well as a list of U.S. National Park Service regional offices. Appendices of selected list botanical gardens and arboreta for internships, summer employment, and volunteer opportunities, as well as a list of U.S. National Park Service regional offices. **Entries include:** Organization name, address.

1445 ■ Cultural Vistas
440 Park Ave. S, 2nd Fl.
New York, NY 10016
Ph: (212)497-3500
Fax: (212)497-3535
E-mail: info@culturalvistas.org
URL: http://culturalvistas.org

Description: Providers worldwide of on-the-job training programs for students and professionals seeking international career development and life-changing experiences. Arranges workplace exchanges in hundreds of professional fields, bringing employers and trainees together from around the world. Client list ranges from small farming communities to Fortune 500 companies.

1446 ■ Ecological Research and Development Group
190 Main St.
Dover, DE 19901
Ph: (302)236-5383
E-mail: erdg@horseshoecrab.org
URL: http://www.horseshoecrab.org

Description: Promotes the conservation of horseshoe crab species. Provides educational programs to create an atmosphere of learning to inspire and nurture curiosity about the horseshoe crabs species and their habitat. Seeks solutions that prevent the extinction of the horseshoe crab species through scientific research and development.

1447 ■ Engineering Society of Detroit
20700 Civic Center Dr., Ste. 450
Southfield, MI 48076
Ph: (248)353-0735

Fax: (248)353-0736
E-mail: esd@esd.org
URL: http://ww2.esd.org/home.htm

Description: Engineers from all disciplines; scientists and technologists. Conducts technical programs and engineering refresher courses; sponsors conferences and expositions. Maintains speakers' bureau; offers placement services; although based in Detroit, MI, society membership is international. **Members:** 6,000.

1448 ■ Environmental Mutagen Society
1821 Michael Faraday Dr., Ste. 300
Reston, VA 20190
Ph: (703)438-8220
Fax: (703)438-3113
E-mail: emshq@ems-us.org
URL: http://www.ems-us.org

Description: Bioscientists in universities, governmental agencies, and industry. Promotes basic and applied studies of mutagenesis (the area of genetics dealing with mutation and molecular biology); disseminates information relating to environmental mutagenesis. Offers placement service.

1449 ■ Federation of American Societies for Experimental Biology
9650 Rockville Pike
Bethesda, MD 20814
Ph: (301)634-7000
Free: 800-433-2732
Fax: (301)634-7001
E-mail: info@faseb.org
URL: http://www.faseb.org

Description: Federation of scientific societies with a total of 40,000 members: the American Physiological Society; American Society for Biochemistry and Molecular Biology; American Society for Pharmacology and Experimental Therapeutics; American Society for Investigative Pathology; American Society for Nutritional Sciences; the American Association of Immunologists; the American Society for Bone and Mineral Research; American Society for Clinical Investigation; the Indocrine Society; the American Society of Human Genetics; Society for Developmental Biology; Biophysical Society; American Association of Anatomists; and the Protein Society. Maintains placement service.

1450 ■ Forensic Sciences Foundation
410 N 21st St.
Colorado Springs, CO 80904
Ph: (719)636-1100
Fax: (719)636-1993
E-mail: awarren@aafs.org
URL: http://fsf.aafs.org/

Description: Purposes are to: conduct research in the procedures and standards utilized in the practice of forensic sciences; develop and implement useful educational and training programs and methods of benefit to forensic sciences; conduct programs of public education concerning issues of importance to the forensic sciences; engage in activities which will promote, encourage, and assist the development of the forensic sciences. Provides referral service for forensic scientists. Compiles statistics. Operates the Forensic Sciences Foundation Press.

1451 ■ Korean-American Scientists and Engineers Association
1952 Gallows Rd., Ste. 300
Vienna, VA 22182
Ph: (703)748-1221
Fax: (703)748-1331
E-mail: sejong@ksea.org
URL: http://www.ksea.org

Description: Represents scientists and engineers holding single or advanced degrees. Promotes friendship and mutuality among Korean and American scientists and engineers; contributes to Korea's scientific, technological, industrial, and economic developments; strengthens the scientific, technological, and cultural bonds between Korea and the U.S. Sponsors symposium. Maintains speakers' bureau, placement service, and biographical archives. Compiles statistics. **Members:** 10,000.

1452 ■ Moroccan-American Society for Life Sciences
PO Box 324
Dunn Loring, VA 22027-0324
Ph: (202)413-6025
E-mail: board@us.biomatec.org
URL: http://us.biomatec.org

Description: Promotes advances and excellence in the life sciences. Serve as a bridge between scientific communities and organizations in the United States and Morocco. Conducts scientific events and activities.

1453 ■ National Oceanic Society
17300 Red Hill Ave., Ste. 280
Irvine, CA 92614
Ph: (949)500-5451
Fax: (949)675-1366

Description: Promotes the fundamental concepts of marine conservation and preservation. Supports the education, research and scientific study of marine environment. Assists governmental agencies in the monitoring and detection of activities that are hazardous and harmful to marine environment.

1454 ■ Ornithological Societies of North America
5400 Bosque Blvd., Ste. 680
Waco, TX 76710
Ph: (254)399-9636
Fax: (254)776-3767
E-mail: business@osnabirds.org
URL: http://www.osnabirds.org

Description: Comprises societies promoting ornithology; is a joint billing and membership service of the American Ornithologists' Union, the Association of Field Ornithologists, the Cooper Ornithological Society, the Raptor Research Foundation, The Waterbird Society, and the Wilson Ornithological Society.

1455 ■ Overseas Chinese Entomologists Association
136 Ag Hall
Stillwater, OK 74078-6015
Ph: (405)744-5395
E-mail: haobo.jiang@okstate.edu
URL: http://www.go-to-ocea.org

Description: Aims to advance the study and knowledge of entomology by facilitating communication and collaboration among Chinese entomologists

around the world. Provides academic-oriented services for members.

1456 ■ Radiation Research Society
380 Ice Center Ln., Ste. C
Bozeman, MT 59718
Free: 877-216-1919
Fax: (785)587-2451
E-mail: info@radres.org
URL: http://www.radres.org

Description: Professional society of biologists, physicists, chemists, and physicians contributing to knowledge of radiation and its effects. Promotes original research in the natural sciences relating to radiation; facilitates integration of different disciplines in the study of radiation effects.

1457 ■ Save the Frogs!
303 Potrero St., No. 51
Santa Cruz, CA 95060
Ph: (831)621-6215
Free: 877-753-7647
E-mail: contact@savethefrogs.com
URL: http://www.savethefrogs.com

Description: Seeks to protect amphibian populations and promote a society that respects and appreciates nature and wildlife. Educates the public about the necessity of protecting the world's amphibians and provides them with information and capabilities to protect amphibian populations. Conducts scientific research to stop amphibian extinction.

1458 ■ Society for In Vitro Biology
514 Daniels St., Ste. 411
Raleigh, NC 27605-1317
Ph: (919)562-0600
Fax: (919)562-0608
E-mail: sivb@sivb.org
URL: http://www.sivb.org

Description: Fosters exchange of knowledge of in vitro biology of cells, tissues and organs from both plant and animals (including humans). Focuses on biological research, development, and applications of significance to science and society. Accomplishes its mission through the society's publications; national and local conferences, meetings and workshops; and through support of teaching initiatives in cooperation with educational institutions. Creates an environment of scientific exchange and interdisciplinary synergy with the goal of advancing current and future systems for in vitro biology.

1459 ■ Society for Industrial Microbiology
3929 Old Lee Hwy., Ste. 92A
Fairfax, VA 22030-2421
Ph: (703)691-3357

Fax: (703)691-7991
E-mail: info@simhq.org
URL: http://www.simhq.org

Description: Mycologists, bacteriologists, biologists, chemists, engineers, zoologists, and others interested in biological processes as applied to industrial materials and processes concerning microorganisms. Serves as liaison between the specialized fields of microbiology. Maintains placement service; conducts surveys and scientific workshops in industrial microbiology.

1460 ■ Soil Science Society of America
5585 Guilfor Rd.
Madison, WI 53711
Ph: (608)273-8080
Fax: (608)273-2021
E-mail: headquarters@soils.org
URL: http://www.soils.org

Description: Professional soil scientists, including soil physicists, soil classifiers, land use and management specialists, chemists, microbiologists, soil fertility specialists, soil cartographers, conservationists, mineralogists, engineers, and others interested in fundamental and applied soil science.

1461 ■ Teratology Society
1821 Michael Faraday Dr., Ste. 300
Reston, VA 20190
Ph: (703)438-3104
Fax: (703)438-3113
E-mail: tshq@teratology.org
URL: http://www.teratology.org

Description: Individuals from academia, government, private industry, and the professions. Stimulates scientific interest in, and promotes the exchange of ideas and information about, problems of abnormal biological development and malformations at the fundamental or clinical level. Sponsors annual education course, and presentations. Establishes archives of society documents and history.

1462 ■ World Federation for Coral Reef Conservation
PO Box 311117
Houston, TX 77231
Ph: (281)309-1201
E-mail: contact@wfcrc.org
URL: http://www.wfcrc.org

Description: Works to stop the destruction of coral reefs by involving local citizens, scientists and recreational divers. Collaborates with like-minded organizations in implementing programs for coral reef decline management. Supports conservation efforts on coral reefs.

SOURCES OF HELP-WANTED ADS

1463 ■ AIE Perspectives Newsmagazine
American Institute of Engineers
4630 Appian Way, Ste. 206
El Sobrante, CA 94803-1875
Ph: (510)758-6240
Fax: (510)758-6240
E-mail: aie@aieonline.org
URL: http://www.members-aie.org
Frequency: Monthly. **Price:** included in membership dues. **Description:** Professional magazine covering engineering.

1464 ■ American Biotechnology Laboratory
International Scientific Communications Inc.
30 Controls Dr.
Shelton, CT 06484-0870
Ph: (650)243-5600
Fax: (203)926-9310
E-mail: iscpubs@iscpubs.com
URL: http://www.americanbiotechnologylaboratory.com
Frequency: 10/yr. **Description:** Biotechnology magazine.

1465 ■ Annual Review of Genetics
Annual Reviews
4139 El Camino Way
Palo Alto, CA 94306-4010
Ph: (650)493-4400
Free: 800-523-8635
Fax: (650)855-9815
E-mail: service@annualreviews.org
URL: http://www.annualreviews.org/journal/genet
Frequency: Annual. **Price:** $86 Individuals print & online; $263 Institutions print & online; $219 Institutions online; $219 Institutions print. **Description:** Periodical covering issues in genetics and the biological sciences.

1466 ■ Annual Review of Microbiology
Annual Reviews
4139 El Camino Way
Palo Alto, CA 94306-4010
Ph: (650)493-4400
Free: 800-523-8635
Fax: (650)855-9815
E-mail: service@annualreviews.org
URL: http://www.annualreviews.org/journal/micro
Frequency: Annual. **Price:** $86 Individuals print & online; $263 Institutions print & online; $219 Institutions online; $219 Institutions print. **Description:** Periodical covering microbiology and the biological sciences.

1467 ■ Biomedical Engineering News
Biomedical Engineering Society
8201 Corporate Dr., Ste. 1125
Landover, MD 20785-2224
Ph: (301)459-1999

Free: 877-871-2637
Fax: (301)459-2444
URL: http://www.bmes.org
Description: Monthly. Provides news and information on the Society; presents articles on bioengineering science. Recurring features include letters to the editor, news of research, a calendar of events, reports of meetings, news of educational opportunities, job listings, and columns titled Public Affairs, Student Chapter News, and Society News.

1468 ■ CBE--Life Sciences Education
American Society for Cell Biology
8120 Woodmont Ave., Ste. 750
Bethesda, MD 20814-2762
Ph: (301)347-9300
Fax: (301)347-9310
E-mail: ascbinfo@ascb.org
URL: http://www.lifescied.org/
Frequency: Quarterly. **Description:** Journal that focuses on life science education at the K-12, undergraduate, and graduate levels.

1469 ■ Cell
Cell Press
600 Technology Sq.
Cambridge, MA 02139
Ph: (617)661-7057
Free: 866-314-2355
Fax: (617)661-7061
E-mail: celleditor@cell.com
URL: http://www.cell.com
Frequency: 26/yr. **Price:** $212 U.S. and Canada individual, print and online; $320 Other countries individual, print and online; $212 U.S. and Canada online only, individual; $212 Other countries online only, individual; $1,425 U.S. and Canada institution, print only; $1,605 Institutions, other countries print only. **Description:** Peer-reviewed journal on molecular and cell biology.

1470 ■ Chemistry & Biology
Elsevier Science Inc.
Secondary Publishing Division
650 Ave. of the Americas
New York, NY 10011
Ph: (212)633-3980
Free: 888-437-4636
Fax: (212)633-3975
URL: http://www.elsevier.com/wps/find/journaldescription.cws_home/601281/description#description
Frequency: Monthly. **Price:** $2,137 Institutions print; $442 U.S. and other countries online only; $457 Other countries print + online; $442 U.S. and Canada print; $843 Institutions online. **Description:** Journal focused on genetic, computational, or theoretical information of chemistry and biology, substantiating experimental data.

1471 ■ Composites: Mechanics, Computations, Applications
Begell House Inc.
50 Cross Hwy.
Redding, CT 06896

Ph: (203)938-1300
Fax: (203)938-1304
E-mail: orders@begellhouse.com
URL: http://www.begellhouse.com/journals/36ff4a142dec9609
Price: $758 Institutions. **Description:** Journal featuring basic ideas in the mechanics of composite materials and structures between research workers and engineers.

1472 ■ Current Advances in Genetics & Molecular Biology
Elsevier Science Inc.
Secondary Publishing Division
650 Ave. of the Americas
New York, NY 10011
Ph: (212)633-3980
Free: 888-437-4636
Fax: (212)633-3975
URL: http://www.elsevier.com/journals/current-advances-in-genetics-and-molecular-biology/0741-1642
Frequency: Monthly. **Price:** ¥25,500 Individuals associate; $221 Individuals associate; €221 Individuals associate; $6,340 Institutions; ¥755,700 Institutions; €5,713 Institutions. **Description:** Journal covering current details of genetics and molecular biology.

1473 ■ Engineering
Scientific Research Publishing
PO Box 54821
Irvine, CA 92619-4821
E-mail: eng@scirp.org
URL: http://www.scirp.org/journal/eng/
Frequency: Monthly. **Price:** $468 Individuals. **Description:** Peer-reviewed journal publishing articles on the latest advancements in engineering.

1474 ■ Engineering in Life Sciences
John Wiley & Sons Inc.
111 River St.
Hoboken, NJ 07030-5774
Ph: (201)748-6000
Free: 800-225-5945
Fax: (201)748-6088
E-mail: info@wiley.com
URL: http://onlinelibrary.wiley.com/journal/10.1002/(ISSN)1618-2863
Frequency: Bimonthly. **Price:** €1,069 Institutions European, online only; $1,403 Institutions, Canada and Mexico online only; $1,403 Institutions, other countries online only; £717 Institutions European, online only; $1,403 Institutions online only. **Description:** Journal focusing on the field of biotechnology and related topics including microbiology, genetics, biochemistry, and chemistry.

1475 ■ Epigenetics
Landes Bioscience
1806 Rio Grande St.
Austin, TX 78701
Ph: (512)637-6050

Fax: (512)637-6079
E-mail: info@landesbioscience.com
URL: http://www.landesbioscience.com/journals/
epigenetics/

Price: $129 Individuals online; $350 Individuals print and online; $450 Other countries print and online; $1,500 Institutions online; $1,850 Institutions print and online; $1,950 Institutions, other countries print and online. **Description:** Journal devoted to practicing physicians, residents and students.

1476 ■ Forum on Immunopathological Diseases and Therapeutics
Begell House Inc.
50 Cross Hwy.
Redding, CT 06896
Ph: (203)938-1300
Fax: (203)938-1304
E-mail: orders@begellhouse.com
URL: http://www.begellhouse.com/journals/
1a654bf03faf67ac.html

Price: $800 Institutions. **Description:** Journal publishing articles on immunopathological diseases and therapeutics.

1477 ■ Graduating Engineer & Computer Careers
Career Recruitment Media
2 LAN Dr., Ste. 100
Westford, MA 01886
Ph: (978)692-5092
Fax: (978)692-4174
E-mail: hshulick@alloyeducation.com
URL: http://www.graduatingengineer.com

Frequency: Quarterly. **Price:** $16.95 Individuals. **Description:** Magazine focusing on employment, education, and career development for entry-level engineers and computer scientists.

1478 ■ International Journal of Computational Bioscience
ACTA Press
Bldg. B6, Ste. 101
Calgary, AB, Canada T3E 7J9
Ph: (403)288-1195
Fax: (403)247-6851
E-mail: journals@actapress.com
URL: http://www.actapress.com/Content_of_Journal
.aspx?journalID=148

Frequency: Annual. **Price:** $120 Individuals. **Description:** Journal featuring research articles that combine biological and computational research to enhance the scientific understanding of life.

1479 ■ Invertebrate Biology
American Microscopical Society
Dept. of Biol. Sciences
CSU, Long Beach
1250 Bellflower Blvd.
Long Beach, CA 90840
Ph: (562)985-5378
Fax: (562)985-8878
E-mail: bconn@berry.edu
URLs: http://www.amicros.org/; http://as.wiley.com/
WileyCDA/WileyTitle/productCd-IVB.html

Frequency: Quarterly. **Price:** $323 Institutions online or print; $371 Institutions print + online; £196 Institutions print or online; £226 Institutions print + online. **Description:** Features original research articles on invertebrate animals.

1480 ■ NABR Update
National Association for Biomedical Research
818 Connecticut Ave. NW, Ste. 900
Washington, DC 20006
Ph: (202)857-0540
Fax: (202)659-1902
E-mail: info@nabr.org
URL: http://www.nabr.org/

Frequency: 48/year. **Price:** included in membership dues; Included in membership. **Description:** Periodic. Apprises Association members of government, legal, and media-based activity regarding

biomedical research and the animal rights movement. Summarized news items are provided in the Association's sister publication, NABR Alert.

1481 ■ Narrative Inquiry in Bioethics: A Journal of Qualitative Research
Johns Hopkins University Press
2715 N Charles St.
Baltimore, MD 21218-4363
Ph: (410)516-6900
Free: 800-537-5487
Fax: (410)516-6968
E-mail: jrnlcirc@press.jhu.edu
URL: http://www.press.jhu.edu/journals/narrative_inquiry_in_bioethics

Frequency: 3/yr. **Price:** $175 Institutions print; $50 Individuals print. **Description:** Journal publishing information on bioethics.

1482 ■ NSBE Magazine: National Society of Black Engineers
NSBE Publications
205 Daingerfield Rd.
Alexandria, VA 22314
Ph: (703)549-2207
Fax: (703)683-5312
E-mail: info@nsbe.org
URL: http://www.nsbe.org/News-Media/Magazines/
About-NSBE-Magazine.aspx

Frequency: 3/yr. **Price:** $20 Individuals; $35 Other countries; $15 Students. **Description:** Journal providing information on engineering careers, self-development, and cultural issues for recent graduates with technical majors.

1483 ■ PALAIOS
SEPM Publications
University of Kansas
Paleontological Institute, Department of Geology
1475 Jawyhawk Blvd., Rm. 120
Lawrence, KS 66045-7613
Ph: (785)864-2737
Fax: (785)864-3636
E-mail: palois@ku.edu
URLs: http://palaios.ku.edu/; http://palaios
.geoscienceworld.org/

Frequency: Monthly. **Price:** $400 Individuals for U.S.; online version with CD-ROM; $500 Individuals for U.S.; print and online version with CD-ROM; $400 Other countries online version with CD-ROM; $500 Other countries print and online version with CD-ROM. **Description:** Journal providing information on the impact of life on Earth history as recorded in the paleontological and sedimentological records. Covers areas such as biogeochemistry, ichnology, sedimentology, stratigraphy, paleoecology, paleoclimatology, and paleoceanography.

1484 ■ PE
National Society of Professional Engineers
1420 King St.
Alexandria, VA 22314-2794
Ph: (703)684-2800
Fax: (703)836-4875
E-mail: memserv@nspe.org
URL: http://www.nspe.org/PEmagazine/index.html

Frequency: Semimonthly; 10/yr. **Price:** included in membership dues; $50 for nonmembers. **Description:** Covers matters of importance to engineering educators and students.

1485 ■ Perspectives in Biology and Medicine
Johns Hopkins University Press
2715 N Charles St.
Baltimore, MD 21218-4363
Ph: (410)516-6900
Free: 800-537-5487
Fax: (410)516-6968
E-mail: jrnlcirc@press.jhu.edu
URL: http://www.press.jhu.edu/journals/perspectives
_in_biology_and_medicine

Frequency: Quarterly. **Price:** $50 Individuals print; $155 Institutions print; $100 Two years print; $45

Students print; $310 Institutions print, 2 years. **Description:** Peer-reviewed journal publishing articles of current interest in medicine and biology in a context with humanistic, social, and scientific concerns. Covers a wide range of biomedical topics such as neurobiology, biomedical ethics and history, genetics and evolution, and ecology.

1486 ■ Reviews in Biomedical Engineering
IEEE - Engineering Management Society
IEEE Admission and Advancement
445 Hoes Ln.
Piscataway, NJ 08855-6804
Ph: (732)981-0060
Free: 800-678-4333
Fax: (732)981-9667
E-mail: office@rbme.embs.org
URL: http://rbme.embs.org/index.html

Description: Journal focusing on new developments and trends in the field of biomedical engineering.

1487 ■ SWE, Magazine of the Society of Women Engineers
Society of Women Engineers
203 N La Salle St., Ste. 1675
Chicago, IL 60601
Ph: (312)596-5223
Free: 877-SWE-INFO
Fax: (312)596-5252
E-mail: hq@swe.org
URL: http://societyofwomenengineers.swe.org/index
.php

Frequency: Quarterly. **Price:** $30 Nonmembers. **Description:** Magazine for engineering students and for women and men working in the engineering and technology fields. Covers career guidance, continuing development and topical issues.

1488 ■ Woman Engineer
Equal Opportunity Publications Inc.
445 Broad Hollow Rd., Ste. 425
Melville, NY 11747
Ph: (631)421-9421
Fax: (631)421-1352
E-mail: info@eop.com
URL: http://www.eop.com

Description: Annual. Magazine that is offered at no charge to qualified female engineering, computer-science, and information-technology students and professionals seeking to find employment and advancement in their careers.

1489 ■ The World Wide Web Journal of Biology
Epress Inc.
130 Union Terrace Ln.
Plymouth, MN 55441
E-mail: editor@epress.com
URL: http://www.epress.com/w3jbio/

Description: Journal on Bio-informatics.

EMPLOYER DIRECTORIES AND NETWORKING LISTS

1490 ■ AGT International Membership Directory
Association of Genetic Technologists
PO Box 19193
Lenexa, KS 66285
Ph: (913)895-4605
Fax: (913)895-4652
E-mail: agt-info@goamp.com
URL: http://www.agt-info.org/IntMembershipDir.aspx

Frequency: Monthly. **Covers:** About 520 laboratories studying heritable and acquired chromosomal disorders using cytogenetic, genetics, and cellular biology techniques. **Includes:** Summaries of procedure counts (by specimen type); number of reporting laboratories by procedure; cytogenetic technology training programs information; membership information. **Entries include:** Laboratory name, address, phone, areas of specialization, techniques, numbers and types of laboratory tests performed, and names of director and cytogenetic technologists. **Arrangement:** Geographical. **Indexes:** Director name, ACT member name.

1491 ■ Directory of Contract Staffing Firms
C.E. Publications Inc.
PO Box 3006
Bothell, WA 98041-3006
Ph: (425)806-5200
Fax: (425)806-5585
E-mail: staff@cjhunter.com
URL: http://www.cjhunter.com/dcsf/overview.html
Frequency: Annual. **Covers:** Nearly 1,300 contract firms actively engaged in the employment of engineering, IT/IS, and technical personnel for 'temporary' contract assignments throughout the world. **Entries include:** Company name, address, phone, name of contact, email, web address. **Arrangement:** Alphabetical. **Indexes:** Geographical.

1492 ■ Indiana Society of Professional Engineers--Directory
Indiana Society of Professional Engineers
c/o Lauraine M. Howe, Executive Director
PO Box 20806
Indianapolis, IN 46220
Ph: (317)255-2267
Fax: (317)255-2530
E-mail: indspe@gmail.com
URL: http://www.indspe.org
Frequency: Annual; fall. **Pages:** 150. **Covers:** Member registered engineers, land surveyors, engineering students, and engineers in training. **Entries include:** Member name, address, phone, type of membership, business information, specialty. **Arrangement:** Alpha by chapter area.

1493 ■ Plunkett's Engineering and Research Industry Almanac: The Only Complete Guide to the Business of Research, Development, and Engineering
Plunkett Research Ltd.
4102 Bellaire Blvd.
Houston, TX 77025-1004
Ph: (713)932-0000
Fax: (713)932-7080
E-mail: customersupport@plunkettresearch.com
URL: http://www.plunkettresearch.com
Frequency: Annual; Latest edition 2013; New edition expected June 2014. **Price:** $349.99 Individuals eBook, print and CD-ROM. **Pages:** 690. **Covers:** 500 of the largest companies involved in research, engineering and development in the biotech, electronics, aerospace and infotech industries. **Entries include:** Name, address, phone, fax, names and titles of key personnel, subsidiary and branch names and locations, financial data, salaries and benefits, description of products/services, overview of company culture/activities. **Indexes:** Industry, location, sales rank, profit rank.

1494 ■ Who's Who in Engineering
American Association of Engineering Societies
1801 Alexander Bell Dr.
Reston, VA 20191
Ph: (202)296-2237
Free: 888-400-2237
Fax: (202)296-1151
E-mail: dbateson@aaes.org
URL: http://www.aaes.org
Frequency: Triennial; Latest edition 9th. **Covers:** About 15,000 engineers who have received professional recognition for outstanding achievement. **Entries include:** Name, address; education and employment history; awards and achievements. **Arrangement:** Alphabetical. **Indexes:** Geographical, field of specialization.

HANDBOOKS AND MANUALS

1495 ■ The Biomedical Engineering Handbook
CRC
6000 Broken Sounds Pkwy. NW, Ste. 300
Boca Raton, FL 33487

Ph: (561)994-0555
Free: 800-272-7737
Fax: (800)374-3401
E-mail: orders@crcpress.com
URL: http://www.crcpress.com
Description: Joseph D. Bronzino, editor. Third edition, 2006. $229.95. 4,232 pages. Beginning with an overview of physiology and physiological modeling, simulation, and control, the book explores bioelectric phenomena, biomaterials, biomechanics, rehabilitation and human performance engineering, and ethical issues.

1496 ■ Career Development in Bioengineering and Biotechnology
Springer
233 Spring St.
New York, NY 10013
Ph: (212)460-1500
Fax: (212)460-1575
URL: http://www.springer.com
Description: Guruprasad Madhavan, Barbara Oakley, and Luis Kun (Editors.) 2009. $49.95. 485 pages. Provides a roadmap to the broad and varied career development opportunities in bioengineering, biotechnology, and related fields.

1497 ■ Career Opportunities in Biotechnology and Drug Development
Cold Spring Harbor Laboratory Press
500 Sunnyside Blvd.
Woodbury, NY 11797-2924
Ph: (516)422-4101
Free: 800-843-4388
Fax: (516)422-4097
E-mail: cshpress@cshl.org
URL: http://www.cshlpress.com
Description: Toby Freedman. 2009. $59.00 (hardcover). 409 pages. Provides an overview of careers in the life science industry. Features chapters that includes sections on preparing for a prospective career; educational requirements and personality characteristics needed; recommendations of books, magazines, and web site resources; and issues to consider regarding salary and compensation. Includes interviewing and job searching tips, as well as suggestions on writing a resume specifically for the industry.

1498 ■ Expert Resumes for Engineers
JIST Publishing
875 Montreal Way
Saint Paul, MN 55102-4245
Ph: (317)613-4200
Free: 800-648-5478
Fax: (800)328-4564
E-mail: info@jist.com
URL: http://www.jist.com
Description: Louise M. Kursmark and Wendy S. Enelow. 2009. $16.95 (softcover). 272 pages. Features a collection of written resume samples for all types of engineers including civil, mechanical, industrial, electrical, electronics, computer, and more. Contains tips and strategies for writing engineering resumes and finding the best jobs.

1499 ■ Great Jobs for Engineering Majors
The McGraw-Hill Companies Inc.
PO Box 182604
Columbus, OH 43272
Ph: (212)512-2000
Free: 877-833-5524
Fax: (614)759-3749
E-mail: customer.service@mcgraw-hill.com
URL: http://www.mcgraw-hill.com
Description: Geraldine O. Garner. Second edition, 2008. $16.95. 192 pages. Covers all the career options open to students majoring in engineering.

1500 ■ Introduction to Biomedical Engineering
Elsevier
3251 Riverport Ln.
Maryland Heights, MO 63043

Ph: (314)453-7010
Free: 800-545-2522
Fax: (314)453-7095
E-mail: usbkinfo@elsevier.com
URL: http://www.elsevier.com
Description: Susan M. Blanchard, Joseph D. Bronzino and John Denis Enderle, editors. Second edition. 2005. $108.00. 1144 pages. Provides a historical perspective of the major developments in the biomedical field.

1501 ■ Opportunities in Biological Science Careers
The McGraw-Hill Companies Inc.
PO Box 182604
Columbus, OH 43272
Ph: (212)512-2000
Free: 877-833-5524
Fax: (614)759-3749
E-mail: customer.service@mcgraw-hill.com
URL: http://www.mcgraw-hill.com
Description: Charles A. Winter. 2004. $13.95 (paper). 160 pages. Identifies employers and outlines opportunities in plant and animal biology, biological specialties, biomedical sciences, applied biology, and other areas. Illustrated.

EMPLOYMENT AGENCIES AND SEARCH FIRMS

1502 ■ Amtec Human Capital
2749 Saturn St.
Brea, CA 92821
Ph: (714)993-1900
Fax: (714)993-2419
E-mail: info@amtechc.com
URL: http://www.amtechc.com
Description: Employment agency.

1503 ■ Apple and Associates
PO Box 996
Chapin, SC 29036
Ph: (803)932-2000
E-mail: info@appleassoc.com
URL: http://www.appleassoc.com
Description: Provides staffing services to medical device, plastics, pharmaceutical and performance materials industries.

1504 ■ Battalia Winston International
555 Madison Ave.
New York, NY 10022
Ph: (212)308-8080
URL: http://www.battaliawinston.com
Description: Executive search firm. Branches in Los Angeles; Chicago; Wellesley Hills, MA; Edison, NJ.

1505 ■ Biomedical Search Consultants
275 Wyman St., Ste. 110
Waltham, MA 02451
Ph: (781)890-8824
Fax: (781)998-1266
E-mail: kprovost@biomedicalsearch.com
URL: http://www.biomedicalsearchconsultants.com
Description: Employment agency.

1506 ■ BioQuest Inc.
100 Spear St., Ste. 700
San Francisco, CA 94105
Ph: (415)777-2422
E-mail: resumes@bioquestinc.com
URL: http://www.bioquestinc.com
Description: Executive search firm focused in healthcare and life sciences.

1507 ■ Career Advocates International
1539 Ave. A
Katy, TX 77493

Ph: (281)371-3917
E-mail: hank@careeradvocates.org
URL: http://www.careeradvocates.org

Description: Provides permanent placement and temporary staffing for executive and staff level positions. Specializes in multiple niches including: sales and marketing, accounting and financial services, banking, communications, human resources, chemicals, oil and gas, medical and dental, legal, information technology, energy, technology, engineering, manufacturing, construction, and light industrial.

1508 ■ Centennial, Inc.
8044 Montgomery Rd., Ste. 260
Cincinnati, OH 45236
Ph: (513)366-3760
Fax: (513)366-3761
URL: http://www.centennialinc.com

Description: Serves as an executive search firm specializing in the areas of executive and general management, accounting and finance, human resources, information technology, manufacturing, engineering, marketing and advertising, not-for-profit, sales and business development, and supply chain and logistics.

1509 ■ The Coelyn Group
1 Park Plz., Ste. 600
Irvine, CA 92614
Ph: (949)553-8855
Fax: (866)436-2171
E-mail: contact@coelyngroup.com
URL: http://www.coelyngroup.com

Description: Executive search firm.

1510 ■ Cornell Global
PO Box 7113
Wilton, CT 06897
Ph: (203)762-0730
E-mail: info@cornellglobal.com
URL: http://www.cornellglobal.com

Description: Executive search firm with areas of expertise in the following areas: advertising, public relations, marketing, sales, finance and accounting, risk management, private equity and venture capital, construction, industrial, manufacturing, life sciences, publishing, information technology, engineering, human resources, legal, and logisitics.

1511 ■ CSI Executive Search LLC
9600 Great Hills Trail, Ste. 150W
Austin, TX 78759
Ph: (512)301-1119
Fax: (512)301-5559
E-mail: info@csi-executivesearch.com
URL: http://www.csi-executivesearch.com

Description: Executive search firm that specializes in the following arenas: accounting, engineering, healthcare, information technology, and legal.

1512 ■ D'Antoni Partners Inc.
122 W John Carpenter Fwy., Ste. 525
Irving, TX 75039
Ph: (972)719-4400
Fax: (972)719-4401
URL: http://www.dantonipartners.com

Description: Executive search firm.

1513 ■ Day & Associates
577 Airport Blvd., Ste. 130
Burlingame, CA 94010
Ph: (650)343-2660
Fax: (650)344-8460
E-mail: info@dayassociates.net
URL: http://www.dayassociates.net

Description: Executive search firm.

1514 ■ Executive Directions Inc.
PO Box 5742
Sarasota, FL 34277

Ph: (941)922-9180
E-mail: info@execdir.com
URL: http://www.execdir.com

Description: Executive search firm.

1515 ■ JPM International
26034 Acero
Mission Viejo, CA 92691
Ph: (949)699-4300
Free: 800-685-7856
Fax: (949)699-4333
E-mail: trish@jpmintl.com
URL: http://www.jpmintl.com

Description: Executive search firm and employment agency.

1516 ■ Lloyd Staffing
445 Broadhollow Rd., Ste. 119
Melville, NY 11747
Ph: (631)777-7600
Free: 888-292-6678
Fax: (631)777-7626
E-mail: info@lloydstaffing.com
URL: http://www.lloydstaffing.com

Description: Personnel agency and search firm.

1517 ■ Nesco Inc.
6140 Parkland Blvd., Ste. 110
Mayfield Heights, OH 44124-6106
Ph: (440)461-6000
Fax: (440)449-3111
E-mail: corporate@nescoresource.com
URL: http://www.nescoresource.com

Description: Offers staffing and consulting solutions in the fields of engineering, information technology, accounting and finance, manufacturing and distribution, and administrative and customer services.

1518 ■ O'Keefe and Partners
4 Corporate Dr., Ste 490
Shelton, CT 06484
Ph: (203)929-4222
E-mail: jvokeefe@okeefepartners.com
URL: http://www.okeefepartners.com

Description: Executive search firm.

1519 ■ Techtronix Technical Search
5401 N 76th St.
Milwaukee, WI 53217-0173
Ph: (414)466-3100
Fax: (414)466-3598

Description: Firm specializes in recruiting executives for the engineering, information systems, manufacturing, marketing, finance and human resources industries. Industries include electronic, manufacturing and finance.

ONLINE JOB SOURCES AND SERVICES

1520 ■ Biofind
URL: http://www.biofind.com

Description: Provides industry insights for the biotechnology industry. Tracks the latest news from around the biotechnology field. Features job opportunities.

1521 ■ BiomedicalEngineer.com
URL: http://www.biomedicalengineer.com

Description: Features biomedical engineering jobs and products to biomedical engineers.

1522 ■ BiosciRegister.com
URL: http://www.biosciregister.com

Description: Serves as an online directory or reference database of suppliers of products and services used in the biotechnology and life sciences industries. Contains job listings.

1523 ■ Biotech Career Center
URL: http://www.biotechcareercenter.com

Description: Serves as a portal for scientists seeking career advancement and/or job opportunities in biotech companies. Provides links to biology career and information sites.

1524 ■ Discover8.com
URL: http://www.discover8.com

Description: Focuses on the dissemination and intelligent discussion of life science news, discoveries, hypotheses, and procedures. Features resume postings and career listings.

1525 ■ Engineering Classifieds
URL: http://www.engineeringclassifieds.com

Description: Serves as a career site for engineering professionals. Provides services including job search agents, resume creation and posting.

1526 ■ EngineerJobs.com
URL: http://www.engineerjobs.com

Description: Provides job opportunities for engineering professionals in the following disciplines: aerospace, agricultural, biomedical, chemical, civil, electrical, environmental, industrial, manufacturing, marine, materials, mechanical, mining, nuclear, petroleum, process, project, quality, sales, software, solar, systems, and structural.

1527 ■ Engineer.net
URL: http://www.engineer.net

Description: Provides engineering employment tools such as job search, job posting, and engineering resumes.

1528 ■ FASEB Career Resources
URL: http://www.faseb.org/MARC-and-Professional
-Development/Career-Resources.aspx

Description: A career opportunity site combined with a development service that attempts to pair applicants at all career levels with employers who hire biomedical scientists and technicians. Biomedical career development is highlighted through career resource tools. Main files include: Careers Online DataNet, Career Online Classified.

1529 ■ Genetics Society of America: Positions Open
URL: http://www.genetics-gsa.org/careers/

Description: Listing of position announcements formerly published in Genetics. Members may e-mail job listings to the site to be posted.

1530 ■ Get Biomedical Engineer Jobs
URL: http://www.getbiomedicalengineerjobs.net

Description: Features employment opportunities for biomedical engineers.

1531 ■ GrantsNet
URL: http://sciencecareers.sciencemag.org/funding

Description: Grant-locating site intended for scientists in training who may become vulnerable in an era of competitive funding. Includes a directory of over 600 programs with contact information within a searchable database.

1532 ■ HireRx.com
URL: http://www.hirerx.com

Description: E-recruiting and training company that is focused on solving workforce issues for biotechnology and pharmaceutical firms. Provides access to job openings, online training courses, and communities in their scientific or functional concentration.

1533 ■ Hum-Molgen.org
URL: http://hum-molgen.org

Description: Provides resources for the latest information in human molecular genetics. Features biotechnical sources, diagnostics, ethical, legal and social implications, meetings and conferences, and positions in bioscience and medicine. Provides the opportunity to communicate with scientists, physicians, and other genetics professionals worldwide.

1534 ■ Naturejobs.com
URL: http://www.nature.com/naturejobs/science/

Description: Lists jobs in the following disciplines of science: cell biology, biochemistry, bioinformatics, materials, and nanotechnology. Features scientific career information as well as news and advice.

1535 ■ Spherion
URL: http://www.spherion.com

Description: Recruitment firm specializing in accounting and finance, sales and marketing, interim executives, technology, engineering, retail and human resources.

TRADESHOWS

1536 ■ American Society for Engineering Education Annual Conference and Exposition
American Society for Engineering Education
1818 N St. NW, Ste. 600
Washington, DC 20036-2479
Ph: (202)331-3500
Fax: (202)265-8504
E-mail: board@asee.org
URL: http://www.asee.org

Frequency: Annual. Primary Exhibits: Publications, engineering supplies and equipment, computers, software, and research companies all products and services related to engineering education.

1537 ■ Bio-IT World Conference & Expo
Cambridge Healthtech Institute
250 1st Ave., Ste. 300
Needham, MA 02494
Ph: (781)972-5400
Free: 888-999-6288
Fax: (781)972-5425
E-mail: chi@healthtech.com
URL: http://www.chicorporate.com

Frequency: Annual. Showcases the myriad applications of IT and informatics to biomedical research and the drug discovery enterprise. Attracts a highly influential audience consisting of senior level scientists, IT professionals and executives from organizations across the life sciences industry including pharmaceutical, biotechnology, health systems, academia, government and national laboratories.

OTHER SOURCES

1538 ■ American Association of Engineering Societies
1801 Alexander Bell Dr.
Reston, VA 20191
Ph: (202)296-2237
Free: 888-400-2237
Fax: (202)296-1151
E-mail: dbateson@aaes.org
URL: http://www.aaes.org

Description: Coordinates the efforts of the member societies in the provision of reliable and objective information to the general public concerning issues which affect the engineering profession and the field of engineering as a whole; collects, analyzes, documents, and disseminates data which will inform the general public of the relationship between engineering and the national welfare; provides a forum for the engineering societies to exchange and discuss their views on matters of common interest; and represents the U.S. engineering community abroad through representation in WFEO and UPADI.

1539 ■ American Indian Science and Engineering Society
PO Box 9828
Albuquerque, NM 87119-9828
Ph: (505)765-1052
Fax: (505)765-5608
E-mail: pam@aises.org
URL: http://www.aises.org

Description: Represents American Indian and non-Indian students and professionals in science, technology, and engineering fields; corporations representing energy, mining, aerospace, electronic, and computer fields. Seeks to motivate and encourage students to pursue undergraduate and graduate studies in science, engineering, and technology. Sponsors science fairs in grade schools, teacher training workshops, summer math/science sessions for 8th-12th graders, professional chapters, and student chapters in colleges. Offers scholarships. Adult members serve as role models, advisers, and mentors for students. Operates placement service.

1540 ■ American Institute of Chemical Engineers - Society for Biological Engineering
3 Park Ave., 19th Fl.
New York, NY 10016
Ph: (212)591-8888
E-mail: bio@aiche.org
URL: http://www.aiche.org/SBE

Description: Promotes the integration of biology with engineering and its benefits through bioprocessing, biomedical, and biomolecular applications. Raises interest, understanding, and recognition of engineers' and scientists' roles in biological engineering. Provides opportunities for the successful interaction of engineers and scientists.

1541 ■ American Institute of Engineers
4630 Appian Way, Ste. 206
El Sobrante, CA 94803-1875
Ph: (510)758-6240
Fax: (510)758-6240
E-mail: aie@aieonline.org
URL: http://www.aieonline.org

Description: Professional association for engineers, scientists, and mathematicians. Multi-disciplined, non-technical association who aims to improve the stature and image of engineers, scientists, and mathematicians. Provides endorsements, awards and opportunities for small business start-ups within the AIE Councils. Sponsors "LA Engineer", a comedy-drama television series; produces annual "Academy Hall of FAME (TV)".

1542 ■ Biomedical Engineering Career Alliance
4809 E Thistle Landing Dr., Ste. 100
Phoenix, AZ 85044
Ph: (480)726-7272
Fax: (480)726-7276
E-mail: charla@bmecareer.org
URL: http://www.bmeplanet.org

Description: Seeks to facilitate interactions between Biomedical Engineering/Bioengineering Programs and industry. Provides students from universities throughout the country access to industrial experiences and assists these students in achieving their goals of rewarding industrial careers. Enhances knowledge and builds positive perceptions of BME students in the biomedical industry.

1543 ■ Biomedical Engineering Society
8201 Corporate Dr., Ste. 1125
Landover, MD 20785-2224
Ph: (301)459-1999
Free: 877-871-2637
Fax: (301)459-2444
URL: http://www.bmes.org

Description: Biomedical, chemical, electrical, civil, agricultural and mechanical engineers, physicians, managers, and university professors representing all fields of biomedical engineering; students and corporations. Encourages the development, dis-

semination, integration, and utilization of knowledge in biomedical engineering.

1544 ■ Career Opportunities in Engineering
InfoBase Holdings Inc.
132 W 31st., 17 Fl.
New York, NY 10001-3406
Ph: (212)967-8800
Fax: (800)678-3633
E-mail: info@infobasepublishing.com
URL: http://www.ferguson.infobasepublishing.com

Description: 2006. $49.50. 336 pages. Provides an overview of engineering, followed by a selection of jobs profiled in detail, including the nature of the job, earnings, prospects for employment, what kind of training and skills it requires and sources for further information. Includes: Appendices of educational institutions, periodicals, directories, and associations. Appendices of educational institutions, periodicals, directories, and associations.

1545 ■ Engineering Society of Detroit
20700 Civic Center Dr., Ste. 450
Southfield, MI 48076
Ph: (248)353-0735
Fax: (248)353-0736
E-mail: esd@esd.org
URL: http://ww2.esd.org/home.htm

Description: Engineers from all disciplines; scientists and technologists. Conducts technical programs and engineering refresher courses; sponsors conferences and expositions. Maintains speakers' bureau; offers placement services; although based in Detroit, MI, society membership is international. Members: 6,000.

1546 ■ International Functional Electrical Stimulation Society
1854 Los Encinos Ave.
Glendale, CA 91208-2240
E-mail: manfred.bijak@meduniwien.ac.at
URL: http://www.ifess.org

Description: Represents academic leaders in the field of biomedical engineering, physical therapists, medical doctors, members of the electrical stimulation manufacturing community, and students and users of functional electrical stimulation (FES) technology. Promotes the research, application, and understanding of electrical stimulation as it is utilized in the field of medicine. Facilitates cooperation and fellowship among members.

1547 ■ National Action Council for Minorities in Engineering
440 Hamilton Ave., Ste. 302
White Plains, NY 10601-1813
Ph: (914)539-4010
Free: 800-888-9929
Fax: (914)539-4032
E-mail: ajohnson@nacme.org
URL: http://www.nacme.org

Description: Leads the national effort to increase access to careers in engineering and other science-based disciplines. Conducts research and public policy analysis, develops and operates national demonstration programs at precollege and university levels, and disseminates information through publications, conferences and electronic media. Serves as a privately funded source of scholarships for minority students in engineering.

1548 ■ National Association for Biomedical Research
818 Connecticut Ave. NW, Ste. 900
Washington, DC 20006
Ph: (202)857-0540
Fax: (202)659-1902
E-mail: info@nabr.org
URL: http://www.nabr.org

Description: Universities, medical and veterinary schools, teaching hospitals, professional societies, voluntary health agencies, pharmaceutical companies and other research-related firms that use laboratory animals for biomedical research, education, and testing. Monitors and, when appropriate, attempts to influence legislation and regulations on behalf of members who are dependent on animals for biomedical research, education, and testing.

1549 ■ National Society of Professional Engineers
1420 King St.
Alexandria, VA 22314-2794
Ph: (703)684-2800
Fax: (703)836-4875
E-mail: memserv@nspe.org
URL: http://www.nspe.org

Description: Represents professional engineers and engineers-in-training in all fields registered in accordance with the laws of states or territories of the U.S. or provinces of Canada; qualified graduate engineers, student members, and registered land surveyors. Is concerned with social, professional, ethical, and economic considerations of engineering as a profession; encompasses programs in public relations, employment practices, ethical considerations, education, and career guidance. Monitors legislative and regulatory actions of interest to the engineering profession.

1550 ■ Society for Biomaterials
15000 Commerce Pkwy., Ste. C
Mount Laurel, NJ 08054
Ph: (856)439-0826
Fax: (856)439-0525
E-mail: info@biomaterials.org
URL: http://www.biomaterials.org

Description: Bioengineers and materials scientists; dental, orthopedic, cardiac, and other surgeons and scientists interested in developing biomaterials as tissue replacements in patients; corporations interested in the research manufacture of biomaterials. Provides an interdisciplinary forum for research in biomaterials. Promotes research, development, and education in the biomaterials sciences.

1551 ■ Society of Hispanic Professional Engineers
13181 Crossroads Pkwy. N, Ste. 450
City of Industry, CA 91746-3496

Ph: (323)725-3970
E-mail: shpenational@shpe.org
URL: http://national.shpe.org

Description: Represents engineers, student engineers, and scientists. Aims to increase the number of Hispanic engineers by providing motivation and support to students. Sponsors competitions and educational programs. Maintains placement service and speakers' bureau; compiles statistics.
Members: 8,000.

1552 ■ Society for Industrial Microbiology
3929 Old Lee Hwy., Ste. 92A
Fairfax, VA 22030-2421
Ph: (703)691-3357
Fax: (703)691-7991
E-mail: info@simhq.org
URL: http://www.simhq.org

Description: Mycologists, bacteriologists, biologists, chemists, engineers, zoologists, and others interested in biological processes as applied to industrial materials and processes concerning microorganisms. Serves as liaison between the specialized fields of microbiology. Maintains placement service; conducts surveys and scientific workshops in industrial microbiology.

1553 ■ Society of Women Engineers
203 N La Salle St., Ste. 1675
Chicago, IL 60601
Ph: (312)596-5223
Free: 877-SWE-INFO
Fax: (312)596-5252
E-mail: hq@swe.org
URL: http://societyofwomenengineers.swe.org

Description: Educational and service organization representing both students and professional women in engineering and technical fields.

1554 ■ Tissue Engineering International and Regenerative Medicine Society
223 Park Pl.
San Ramon, CA 94583
Ph: (925)362-0998

Fax: (925)362-0808
E-mail: swilburn@termis.org
URL: http://www.termis.org

Description: Represents professionals in the field of tissue engineering and regenerative medicine. Promotes education and research within the field of tissue engineering and regenerative medicine. Provides a forum for discussion of challenges and therapeutic benefits of the application of tissue engineering and regenerative medicine technologies.

1555 ■ Women in Engineering ProActive Network
1901 E Asbury Ave., Ste. 220
Denver, CO 80208
Ph: (303)871-4643
Fax: (303)871-4628
URL: http://www.wepan.org

Description: Women in engineering professions. Includes key strategies such as education and training, research, collaboration, leadership, diversity, advocacy, networking, sustainability, accountability, and volunteerism in order to be a catalyst for change that enhances the success of women in the engineering professions.

1556 ■ World Association for Chinese Biomedical Engineers
210 Lothrop St., E1641 BST
Pittsburgh, PA 15213
Ph: (412)648-1494
Fax: (412)648-8548
E-mail: info@wacbe.org
URL: http://www.wacbe.org

Description: Networks the worldwide Chinese professionals and students in the field of biomedical engineering. Promotes basic and translational research in the field. Encourages students to become biomedical engineers. Facilitates the professional and career development of members. Promotes cooperation among and between industrialists and academics.

SOURCES OF HELP-WANTED ADS

1557 ■ *CopCareer.com*
URL: http://www.copcareer.com
Description: Online job posting site for law enforcement professionals, including border patrol agents.

1558 ■ *Homeland Response*
Intertec Publishing
5 Penn Plz., 13th Fl.
New York, NY 10001-1810
Ph: (212)613-9700
Free: 800-795-5445
Fax: (212)613-9749
E-mail: bethany.weaver@penton.com
URL: http://www.respondersafetyonline.com/
Frequency: Bimonthly. **Description:** Magazine covering homeland security.

1559 ■ *HSToday*
HSToday
6800 Fleetwood Rd., Ste. 114
McLean, VA 22101
URL: http://www.hstoday.us/
Frequency: Monthly. **Description:** Magazine covering topics of interest to homeland security professionals.

EMPLOYER DIRECTORIES AND NETWORKING LISTS

1560 ■ *What Can I Do Now--Public Safety*
InfoBase Holdings Inc.
132 W 31st., 17 Fl.
New York, NY 10001-3406
Ph: (212)967-8800
Fax: (800)678-3633
E-mail: info@infobasepublishing.com
URL: http://factsonfile.infobasepublishing.com
Price: $22.95 Individuals; $20.65 Libraries. **Pages:** 184. **Covers:** Border patrol officers, corrections officers, crime analysts, emergency medical technicians, FBI agents, firefighters, and police officers.

HANDBOOKS AND MANUALS

1561 ■ *Border Patrol Exam*
LearningExpress L.L.C.
2 Rector St., 26th Fl.
New York, NY 10006
Ph: (212)995-2566
Free: 800-295-9556
E-mail: customerservice@learningexpressllc.com
URL: http://www.learningexpressllc.com
Description: Shirley Tarbell and Byron Demmer. Fourth edition. $24.95. 179 pages. Contains instruc-

tion on all areas covered by the examination, as well as three practice tests. Includes information on the procedures and requirements for applying for a position as a border patrol agent.

ONLINE JOB SOURCES AND SERVICES

1562 ■ **911hotjobs.com Employment Portal**
URL: http://www.911hotjobs.com
Description: Online site for those seeking job opportunities in public safety. Testing requirements and job postings are available to those seeking employment in law enforcement, fire careers, and EMS services.

1563 ■ **Airportjobs.Us**
URL: http://www.airportjobs.us
Description: Helps job seekers find airport career opportunities with top companies. Allows employers and recruiters to match qualified candidates with open airport postions.

1564 ■ **Border Patrol Jobs**
URL: http://www.border-patrol-jobs.us
Description: Provides job listings for those seeking employment as border patrol personnel in the federal government.

1565 ■ **Department of Homeland Security Jobs**
URL: http://www.homeland-security-jobs.us
Description: Provides a searchable database of employment opportunities available in the U.S. Department of Homeland Security.

1566 ■ **Homeland Security Jobs**
URL: http://www.homeland-security-jobs.com
Description: Offers a searchable database of homeland security job opportunities.

1567 ■ **Honor First**
URL: http://www.honorfirst.com
Description: Serves as the unofficial website of the United States Border Patrol. Includes information on how to apply, pay and benefits, hiring process, study guides for the examination, and class schedules. Provides links to other sites with information on becoming a border patrol agent.

OTHER SOURCES

1568 ■ **National Border Patrol Council**
PO Box 678
Campo, CA 91906
Ph: (619)478-5145
Free: 888-583-7237
E-mail: nbpc-info@nbpc.net
URL: http://www.nbpc.net

Description: Represents employees of the U.S. Border Patrol. **Members:** 6,500.

1569 ■ **Transportation Security Administration**
601 S 12th St.
Arlington, VA 22202
Free: 866-289-9673
Fax: (571)227-1904
E-mail: tsa-contactcenter@dhs.gov
URL: http://www.tsa.gov
Description: Governmental agency that lists available jobs on its website, including those for border patrol agents.

1570 ■ **U.S. Border Patrol Supervisors' Association**
591 Telegraph Canyon Rd.
Chula Vista, CA 91910
URL: http://www.bpsups.org
Members: Border patrol supervisors. **Purpose:** Promotes opportunities for training, liaison with other law enforcement associations, and political action efforts for career and retirement goals. **Activities:** Maintains an online chat room and message board to promote networking among its members.

1571 ■ **U.S. Customs and Border Protection - Blaine Sector**
2410 Nature's Path Way
Blaine, WA 98230-9114
Ph: (360)332-9200
Fax: (360)332-9263
URL: http://www.cbp.gov/xp/cgov/border_security/
border_patrol/border_patrol_sectors/blaine_sector_wa
Activities: Services the states of Alaska, Oregon, and the western half of the state of Washington. Stations are located in Blaine, Washington; Lynden, Washington; Bellingham, Washington; Port Angeles, Washington; and Roseburg, Oregon. Information about employment opportunities may be obtained by contacting the recruiter at the Sector office.

1572 ■ **U.S. Customs and Border Protection - Buffalo Sector**
201 Lang Blvd.
Grand Island, NY 14072
Ph: (716)774-7200
URL: http://www.cbp.gov/xp/cgov/border_security/
border_patrol/border_patrol_sectors/buffalo_sector_ny
Activities: Covers 450 miles of border with Canada from the Ohio/Pennsylvania state line to Jefferson County, New York. Stations are located in Niagara Falls, New York; Buffalo, New York; Fulton, New York; and Watertown, New York. Information about employment opportunities may be obtained by contacting the recruiter at the Sector office.

1573 ■ **U.S. Customs and Border Protection - Del Rio Sector**
2401 Dodson Ave.
Del Rio, TX 78840

Ph: (830)778-7000
URL: http://www.cbp.gov/xp/cgov/border_security/
border_patrol/border_patrol_sectors/delrio_sec-
tor_tx

Activities: Covers 41 counties in the state of Texas. Stations are located in Abilene, Brackettville, Carrizo Springs, Comstock, Del Rio, Eagle Pass, Llano, Rocksprings, San Angelo, and Uvalde. Information about employment opportunities may be obtained by contacting the recruiter at the Sector office.

1574 ■ U.S. Customs and Border Protection - Detroit Sector

26000 South St., Bldg. 1516
Selfridge ANGB, MI 48045-4932
Ph: (586)239-2160
URL: http://www.cbp.gov/xp/cgov/border_security/
border_patrol/border_patrol_sectors/detroit_sec-
tor_mi

Activities: Area of responsibility includes Illinois, Indiana, Michigan, and Ohio. Stations are located in Detroit, Michigan; Port Huron, Michigan; Sault Ste. Marie, Michigan; and Trenton, Michigan. Information about employment opportunities may be obtained by contacting the recruiter at the Sector office.

1575 ■ U.S. Customs and Border Protection - El Centro Sector

211 W Aten Rd.
Imperial, CA 92251
Ph: (760)335-5700
URL: http://www.cbp.gov/xp/cgov/border_security/
border_patrol/border_patrol_sectors/elcentro_sec-
tor_ca

Activities: Covers the counties of Imperial and Riverside in California. Stations are located in Calexico, California; El Centro, California; Indio, California; and Riverside, California. Information about employment opportunities may be obtained by contacting the recruiter at the Sector office.

1576 ■ U.S. Customs and Border Protection - El Paso Sector

8901 Montana Ave.
El Paso, TX 79925-1212
Ph: (915)834-8350
URL: http://www.cbp.gov/xp/cgov/border_security/
border_patrol/border_patrol_sectors/elpaso_sec-
tor_tx

Activities: Covers the entire state of New Mexico and Hudspeth and El Paso counties in Texas, totaling 125,500 square miles of territory. Stations are located in El Paso, Texas; Fabens, Texas; Fort Hancock, Texas; Ysleta, Texas; Alamagordo, New Mexico; Albuquerque, New Mexico; Carlsbad, New Mexico; Deming, New Mexico; Las Cruces, New Mexico; Lordsburg, New Mexico; Truth or Consequences, New Mexico; and Santa Teresa, New Mexico. Information about employment opportunities may be obtained by contacting the recruiter at the Sector office.

1577 ■ U.S. Customs and Border Protection - Grand Forks Sector

1816 17th St. NE
Grand Forks, ND 58203
Ph: (701)772-3056
URL: http://www.cbp.gov/xp/cgov/border_security/
border_patrol/border_patrol_sectors/grandforks
_sector_nd

Activities: Covers the states of North Dakota, Minnesota, Wisconsin, South Dakota, Iowa, Nebraska, Kansas, and Missouri. Stations are located in Grand Forks, North Dakota; Bottineau, North Dakota; Duluth, Minnesota; International Falls, Minnesota; Pembina, North Dakota; Portal, North Dakota; and Warroad, Minnesota. Information about employment opportunities may be obtained by contacting the recruiter at the Sector office.

1578 ■ U.S. Customs and Border Protection - Havre Sector

2605 5th Ave., SE
Havre, MT 59501

Ph: (406)262-5600
URL: http://www.cbp.gov/xp/cgov/border_security/
border_patrol/border_patrol_sectors/havre_sec-
tor_mt

Activities: Patrols 452 miles of border area between Montana and Canada, Wyoming, Colorado, Utah, as well as part of Idaho. Stations are located in Havre, Montana; Plentywood, Montana; Shelby, Montana; and Twin Falls, Idaho. Information about employment opportunities may be obtained by contacting the recruiter at the Sector office.

1579 ■ U.S. Customs and Border Protection - Houlton Sector

96 Calais Rd.
Hodgdon, ME 04730
Ph: (207)532-6521
Free: 800-851-8727
URL: http://www.cbp.gov/xp/cgov/border_security/
border_patrol/border_patrol_sectors/houlton_sec-
tor_me

Activities: Covers the entire state of Maine. Stations are located in Calais, Fort Fairfield, Houlton, Van Buren, Jackman, and Rangeley. Information about employment opportunities may be obtained by contacting the recruiter at the Sector office.

1580 ■ U.S. Customs and Border Protection - Laredo Sector

207 W Del Mar Blvd.
Laredo, TX 78041
Ph: (956)764-3200
URL: http://www.cbp.gov/xp/cgov/border_security/
border_patrol/border_patrol_sectors/laredo_sec-
tor_tx

Activities: Encompasses 116 counties and covers 101,439 square miles of southwest and northeast Texas. Stations are located Zapata, Hebbronville, Cotulla, Dallas, San Antonio, and Laredo. Information about employment opportunities may be obtained by contacting the recruiter at the Sector office.

1581 ■ U.S. Customs and Border Protection - Marfa Sector

300 Madrid St.
Marfa, TX 79843
Ph: (432)729-5200
Free: 888-536-6204
URL: http://www.cbp.gov/xp/cgov/border_security/
border_patrol/border_patrol_sectors/marfa_sec-
tor_tx

Activities: Covers over 135,000 square miles encompassing over 118 counties in Texas and Oklahoma, the largest geographical area of any sector along the southwest border. Stations are located in Sierra Blanca, Van Horn, Marfa, Presidio, Alpine, Sanderson, Pecos, Ft. Stockton, Midland, and Lubbock. Information about employment opportunities may be obtained by contacting the recruiter at the Sector office.

1582 ■ U.S. Customs and Border Protection - Miami Sector

15720 Pines Blvd.
Pembroke Pines, FL 33027
Ph: (954)965-6300
URL: http://www.cbp.gov/xp/cgov/border_security/
border_patrol/border_patrol_sectors/miami_sec-
tor_fl

Activities: Covers the states of Florida, Georgia, North Carolina, and South Carolina. Stations are located in Pembroke Pines, Florida; West Palm Beach, Florida; Orlando, Florida; Jacksonville, Florida; and Tampa, Florida. Information about employment opportunities may be obtained by contacting the recruiter at the Sector office.

1583 ■ U.S. Customs and Border Protection - New Orleans Sector

PO Box 6218
New Orleans, LA 70174-6218

Ph: (504)376-2800
URL: http://www.cbp.gov/xp/cgov/border_security/
border_patrol/border_patrol_sectors/neworleans
_sector_la

Activities: Maintains jurisdiction over a seven-state area, which encompasses 592 counties and parishes and approximately 362,310 square miles. Stations are located in New Orleans, Louisiana; Lake Charles, Louisiana; Baton Rouge, Louisiana; Gulfport, Mississippi; Mobile, Alabama; and Little Rock, Arkansas. Information about employment opportunities may be obtained by contacting the recruiter at the Sector office.

1584 ■ U.S. Customs and Border Protection - Rio Grande Valley Sector

4400 South Expy. 281
Edinburg, TX 78542-2621
Ph: (956)289-4800
URL: http://www.cbp.gov/xp/cgov/border_security/
border_patrol/border_patrol_sectors/rio_grande
_valley_sector

Activities: Covers over 17,000 square miles in southeast Texas. Stations are located in Brownsville, Fort Brown Station I, Weslaco, Harlingen, McAllen, Rio Grande City, Falfurrias, Kingsville, and Corpus Christi. Information about employment opportunities may be obtained by contacting the recruiter at the Sector office.

1585 ■ U.S. Customs and Border Protection - San Diego Sector

2411 Boswell Rd.
Chula Vista, CA 91914-3519
Ph: (619)216-4000
URL: http://www.cbp.gov/xp/cgov/border_security/
border_patrol/border_patrol_sectors/sandiego_sec-
tor_ca

Activities: Covers San Diego County in the state of California. Stations are located in Brown Field (the nation's largest Border Patrol station), Boulevard, Campo, Chula Vista, El Cajon, Imperial Beach, San Clemente, and Muriett. Information about employment opportunities may be obtained by contacting the recruiter at the Sector office.

1586 ■ U.S. Customs and Border Protection - Spokane Sector

10710 N Newport Hwy.
Spokane, WA 99218
Ph: (509)353-2747
URL: http://www.cbp.gov/xp/cgov/border_security/
border_patrol/border_patrol_sectors/spokane_sec-
tor_wa

Activities: Patrols eastern Washington, Idaho, and western Montana up to the Continental Divide. Stations are located in Spokane, Washington; Colville, Washington; Curlew, Washington; Metaline Falls, Washington; Oroville, Washington; Pasco, Washington; Wenatchee, Washington; Eureka, Montana; Whitefish, Montana; and Bonners Ferry, Idaho. Information about employment opportunities may be obtained by contacting the recruiter at the Sector office.

1587 ■ U.S. Customs and Border Protection - Swanton Sector

155 Grand Ave.
Swanton, VT 05488
Ph: (802)868-3361
Free: 800-247-2434
URL: http://www.cbp.gov/xp/cgov/border_security/
border_patrol/border_patrol_sectors/swanton_sec-
tor_vt

Activities: Encompasses 24,000 square miles and includes the state of Vermont; Clinton, Essex, Franklin, St. Lawrence, and Herkimer counties in New York; and Coos, Grafton, and Carroll counties in New Hampshire. Stations are located in Ogdensburg, New York; Massena, New York; Burke, New York; Champlain, New York; Swanton, Vermont; Richford, Vermont; Newport, Vermont; and Beecher Falls, Vermont. Information about employment opportunities may be obtained by contacting the recruiter at the Sector office.

1588 ■ U.S. Customs and Border Protection - Tucson Sector
2430 S Swan Rd.
Tucson, AZ 85711
Ph: (520)748-3000
URL: http://www.cbp.gov/xp/cgov/border_security/ border_patrol/border_patrol_sectors/tucson_sec- tor_az

Activities: Covers the state of Arizona. Stations are located in Ajo, Casa Grande, Douglas, Naco, Nogales, Sonoita, Tucson, and Wilcox. Information about employment opportunities may be obtained by contacting the recruiter at the Sector office.

1589 ■ U.S. Customs and Border Protection - Yuma Sector
4035 South Ave. A
Yuma, AZ 85365
Ph: (928)341-6500
URL: http://www.cbp.gov/xp/cgov/border_security/ border_patrol/border_patrol_sectors/yuma_sec- tor_az

Activities: Patrols 126 miles of border with Mexico between the Yuma-Pima County line in Arizona and the Imperial Sand Dunes in California. Stations are located in Yuma, Arizona; Wellton, Arizona; and Blythe, California. Information about employment opportunities may be obtained by contacting the recruiter at the Sector office.

1590 ■ U.S. Department of Homeland Security - Customs and Border Protection
1000 - 2nd Ave., Ste. 2200
Seattle, WA 98104-1049
Ph: (206)553-6944
Fax: (206)553-1401
URL: http://www.cbp.gov

Activities: Provides news releases and fact sheets on border patrol initiatives.

1591 ■ U.S. Office of Personnel Management
1900 E St. NW
Washington, DC 20415-0001

Ph: (202)606-1800
URL: http://www.opm.gov

Description: The Office of Personnel Management (OPM) administers a merit system to ensure compliance with personnel laws and regulations and assists agencies in recruiting, examining, and promoting people on the basis of their knowledge and skills, regardless of their race, religion, sex, political influence, or other non-merit factors. OPM's role is to provide guidance to agencies in operating human resources programs which effectively support their missions and to provide an array of personnel services to applicants and employees. OPM supports Government program managers in their human resources management responsibilities and provide benefits to employees, retired employees, and their survivors. **Purpose:** The federal government's human resources agency. **Activities:** Provides information on the specific requirements necessary to qualify as a border patrol agent, including education, experience, testing, language, firearms use, medical, and age.

SOURCES OF HELP-WANTED ADS

1592 ■ *BIA News*
Brick Industry Association
1850 Centennial Park Dr., Ste. 301
Reston, VA 20191
Ph: (703)620-0010
Fax: (703)620-3928
E-mail: brickinfo@bia.org
URL: http://www.gobrick.com/html/pr.html
Frequency: Monthly. **Price:** $30 Individuals. **Description:** Trade publication covering issues for the brick industry.

1593 ■ *Builder: The Magazine of the National Association of Home Builders*
DoveTale Publishers
1 Thomas Cir. NW
Washington, DC 20005
Ph: (202)339-0744
Free: 877-275-8647
Fax: (202)785-1974
E-mail: builder@omeda.com
URLs: http://www.hanleywood.com/default.aspx ?page=magazines; http://www.builderonline.com
Frequency: 13/yr. **Price:** $29.95 U.S. and Canada; $54.95 U.S. and Canada 2 years; $192 Other countries. **Description:** Magazine covering housing and construction industry.

1594 ■ *Building Systems Magazine*
Active Interest Media
4125 Lafayette Ctr. Dr., Ste. 100
Chantilly, VA 20151
Ph: (703)222-9411
Fax: (703)222-3209
URLs: http://www.buildingsystems.com; http://www .aimmedia.com/article_display_19.html
Frequency: Bimonthly. **Description:** Magazine featuring innovative construction technologies for builders, developers and general contractors.

1595 ■ *Concrete Products*
Mining Media Inc.
8751 E Hampden Ave., Ste. B-1
Denver, CO 80231
Ph: (303)283-0640
Fax: (303)283-0641
E-mail: dmarsh@prismb2b.com
URL: http://concreteproducts.com
Frequency: Monthly. **Price:** Free; $96 Other countries print. **Description:** Magazine on concrete products and ready-mixed concrete.

1596 ■ *Constructor: The Construction Management Magazine*
Associated General Contractors of America
2300 Wilson Blvd., Ste. 400
Arlington, VA 22201
Ph: (703)548-3118

Free: 800-242-1767
Fax: (703)548-3119
E-mail: info@agc.org
URL: http://constructor.agc.org/
Frequency: Bimonthly. **Price:** $95 Individuals. **Description:** Management magazine for the Construction Industry.

1597 ■ *Custom Home Outdoors*
DoveTale Publishers
1 Thomas Cir. NW
Washington, DC 20005
Ph: (202)339-0744
Free: 877-275-8647
Fax: (202)785-1974
E-mail: hwmicustomerservice@hanleywood.com
URLs: http://www.customhomemediakit.com/r5/ showkiosk.asp?listing_id=2033096; http://www.cus-tomhomeonline.com
Frequency: Quarterly. **Price:** $36 Individuals; $66 Canada; $192 Other countries. **Description:** Magazine featuring latest trends and products for building professionals.

1598 ■ *Green Home Builder: America's Premier Green Homebuilding Resource*
Peninsula Publishing Inc.
1602 Monrovia Ave.
Newport Beach, CA 92663-2808
Ph: (949)631-0308
Fax: (949)631-2475
E-mail: nslevin@penpubinc.com
URL: http://www.greenhomebuildermag.com/
Frequency: Quarterly. **Description:** Magazine for home builders and home building industry.

1599 ■ *Masonry Magazine*
Mason Contractors Association of America
1481 Merchant Dr.
Algonquin, IL 60102
Ph: (224)678-9709
Free: 800-536-2225
Fax: (224)678-9714
E-mail: bennett@lionhrtpub.com
URL: http://www.masoncontractors.org
Description: Monthly. $43.00/2 years; $29.00/year. Covers every aspect of the mason contractor profession, from equipment and techniques to building codes and standards, training the future masonry labor force, business planning, promoting business, job interviewing, negotiation and legal issues.

1600 ■ *Professional Builder: The Magazine of the Housing and Light Construction Industry*
SGC Horizon L.L.C.
3030 W Salt Creek Ln., Ste. 201
Arlington Heights, IL 60005
Ph: (847)391-1000
Fax: (847)390-0408
URL: http://www.housingzone.com/ professionalbuilder

Frequency: Monthly. **Price:** Free. **Description:** The integrated engineering magazine of the building construction industry.

1601 ■ *Residential Concrete*
DoveTale Publishers
8726 W Higgins Rd.
Chicago, IL 60631
Ph: (773)284-2400
E-mail: hwmicustomerservice@hanleywood.com
URLs: http://www.hanleywood.com/default.aspx ?page=b2bresconcrete; http://www.concretecon-struction.net/industry-news.asp?sectionID=716&ar-ticleID=540600
Frequency: Bimonthly. **Price:** $30 Individuals; $46 Two years; $39 Canada and Mexico; $64 Two years Canada & Mexico; $93 Other countries; $162 Other countries two years. **Description:** Magazine featuring the use of concrete in residential concrete construction.

1602 ■ *Residential Design & Build*
Cygnus Business Media Inc.
1233 Janesville Ave.
Fort Atkinson, WI 53538
Ph: (847)454-2700
Fax: (847)454-2759
E-mail: info@cygnus.com
URLs: http://www.rdbmagazine.com; http://www .cygnusb2b.com/PropertyPub.cfm?PropertyID=177
Frequency: 9/yr. **Description:** Magazine providing advice and insight on the design/build project delivery method, as well as information on the latest design trends, new products and home building professionals.

1603 ■ *Tools of the Trade*
DoveTale Publishers
1 Thomas Cir. NW
Washington, DC 20005
Ph: (202)339-0744
Free: 877-275-8647
Fax: (202)785-1974
E-mail: hwmicustomerservice@hanleywood.com
URL: http://www.hanleywood.com/?page =toolsofthetrade&section=res_rem
Frequency: Bimonthly. **Price:** $36 Individuals; $66 Canada; $192 Other countries; $70 Two years. **Description:** Magazine featuring tools for commercial and residential construction.

EMPLOYER DIRECTORIES AND NETWORKING LISTS

1604 ■ *ABC Today--Associated Builders and Contractors National Membership Directory Issue*
Associated Builders and Contractors
440 1st St. NW, Ste. 200
Washington, DC 20001
E-mail: gotquestions@abc.org
URL: http://www.abc.org

Frequency: Annual; Latest Edition 2011. **Price:** $150 plus $7.00 shipping. **Publication includes:** List of approximately 19,000 member construction contractors and suppliers. **Entries include:** Company name, address, phone, name of principal executive, code to volume of business, business specialty. **Arrangement:** Classified by chapter, then by work specialty.

1605 ■ *ENR--Top 400 Construction Contractors Issue*
The McGraw-Hill Companies Inc.
PO Box 182604
Columbus, OH 43272
Ph: (212)512-2000
Free: 877-833-5524
Fax: (614)759-3749
E-mail: customer.service@mcgraw-hill.com
URL: http://enr.construction.com/toplists/Contractors/001-100.asp

Frequency: Annual; Latest edition 2011. **Price:** $35 Individuals. **Publication includes:** List of 400 United States contractors receiving largest dollar volumes of contracts in preceding calendar year. Separate lists of 50 largest design/construct management firms; 50 largest program and construction managers; 25 building contractors; 25 heavy contractors. **Entries include:** Company name, headquarters location, total value of contracts received in preceding year, value of foreign contracts, countries in which operated, construction specialties. **Arrangement:** By total value of contracts received.

Handbooks and Manuals

1606 ■ *Cement Mason*
National Learning Corporation
212 Michael Dr.
Syosset, NY 11791
Ph: (516)921-8888
Free: 800-632-8888
Fax: (516)921-8743
E-mail: info@passbooks.com
URL: http://www.passbooks.com

Price: $34.95 Paperback; $54.95 Hardcover. **Description:** 2012. Serves as exam and career preparation guide for cement masons.

1607 ■ *Construction*
InfoBase Holdings Inc.
132 W 31st., 17 Fl.
New York, NY 10001-3406
Ph: (212)967-8800
Fax: (800)678-3633
E-mail: info@infobasepublishing.com
URL: http://www.ferguson.infobasepublishing.com

Price: $30 Hardcover. **Description:** 2010. 128 pages. Contains profiles of 20 careers in the field of construction with emphasis on the nature of work, requirements, salary, and career outlook. Includes full-color photographs, index, glossary, resources, and side bars.

1608 ■ *Construction Technology Trainee Guide*
Prentice Hall
200 Old Tappan Rd.
Old Tappan, NJ 07675
Free: 800-223-1360
Fax: (800)445-6991
URL: http://www.prenticehall.com

Description: Third Edition, 2009. $186.67 (hardcover). 936 pages. Features a highly illustrated design, technical hints and tips from construction industry experts, and review questions.

Online Job Sources and Services

1609 ■ **Bricklayer Jobs**
URL: http://www.bricklayerjobs.org
Description: Features a searchable database of employment opportunities for bricklayers.

1610 ■ **Build Your Future Career Center**
URL: http://www.jobtarget.com/home/home.cfm?site_id=13781
Description: Features construction industry job listings. Includes resume bank that lists profiles voluntarily posted by job seekers.

1611 ■ **BuildZ Construction Jobs Network**
URL: http://buildz.net
Description: Provides listings of construction jobs throughout the U.S. Features news related to the construction industry.

1612 ■ **CementMasonConcreteFinisher.com**
URL: http://www.cementmasonconcretefinisher.com
Description: Features job listings for cement masons and concrete finishers.

1613 ■ **Construction Jobs Network**
URL: http://constructionjobs.net
Description: Provides job seekers access to construction employment opportunities for both construction management, construction professional and construction trade jobs. Features construction jobs, employer, and resume directories.

1614 ■ **ConstructionGigs.net**
URL: http://www.constructiongigs.net
Description: Provides an up-to-date listings of job opportunities and career resources for construction workers.

1615 ■ **IHireBuildingTrades**
URL: http://www.ihirebuildingtrades.com
Description: Serves as a job posting board that specializes in matching building jobs and construction candidates.

Tradeshows

1616 ■ **World of Concrete**
Hanley-Wood Exhibitions
6191 N State Hwy. 161, Ste. 500
Irving, TX 75038
Ph: (972)536-6300
Fax: (972)536-6301
URL: http://www.hanley-wood.com

Frequency: Annual. **Primary Exhibits:** Equipment and services for the construction industry.

Online and Database Services

1617 ■ **CareersForBuilders.com**
URL: http://www.careersforbuilders.com

Description: Features a searchable database of employment opportunities for different types of construction work. Includes career resources on job hunting tools and tips.

Other Sources

1618 ■ **Associated Builders and Contractors**
440 1st St. NW, Ste. 200
Washington, DC 20001
E-mail: gotquestions@abc.org
URL: http://www.abc.org

Description: Construction contractors, subcontractors, suppliers and associates. Aims to foster and perpetuate the principles of rewarding construction workers and management on the basis of merit. Sponsors management education programs and craft training; also sponsors apprenticeship and skill training programs. Disseminates technological and labor relations information.

1619 ■ **Associated General Contractors of America**
2300 Wilson Blvd., Ste. 400
Arlington, VA 22201
Ph: (703)548-3118
Free: 800-242-1767
Fax: (703)548-3119
E-mail: info@agc.org
URL: http://www.agc.org

Description: General construction contractors; subcontractors; industry suppliers; service firms. Provides market services through its divisions. Conducts special conferences and seminars designed specifically for construction firms. Compiles statistics on job accidents reported by member firms. Maintains 65 committees, including joint cooperative committees with other associations and liaison committees with federal agencies.

1620 ■ **Associated Specialty Contractors**
3 Bethesda Metro Ctr., Ste. 1100
Bethesda, MD 20814
E-mail: dgw@necanet.org
URL: http://www.assoc-spec-con.org

Description: Works to promote efficient management and productivity. Coordinates the work of specialized branches of the industry in management information, research, public information, government relations and construction relations. Serves as a liaison among specialty trade associations in the areas of public relations, government relations, and with other organizations. Seeks to avoid unnecessary duplication of effort and expense or conflicting programs among affiliates. Identifies areas of interest and problems shared by members, and develops positions and approaches on such problems. **Members:** 9.

1621 ■ **Mason Contractors Association of America**
1481 Merchant Dr.
Algonquin, IL 60102
Ph: (224)678-9709
Free: 800-536-2225
Fax: (224)678-9714
E-mail: bennett@lionhrtpub.com
URL: http://www.masoncontractors.org

Description: Masonry construction firms. Conducts specialized education and research programs. Compiles statistics.

1622 ■ **The Masonry Society**
105 S Sunset St., Ste. Q
Longmont, CO 80501-6172
Ph: (303)939-9700
Fax: (303)541-9215
E-mail: info@masonrysociety.org
URL: http://www.masonrysociety.org

Description: Represents individuals interested in the art and science of masonry. Serves as professional, technical, and educational association dedicated to the advancement and knowledge of masonry. Gathers and disseminates technical information.

1623 ■ **National Association of Home Builders - Systems Builder Council**
1201 15th St. NW
Washington, DC 20005
Ph: (202)266-8200
Free: 800-368-5242
Fax: (202)266-8400
URL: http://www.nahb.org/reference_list.aspx?sectionID=815

Description: Operates under the Building Systems Council of NAHB. Modular building manufacturers. Monitors state and federal housing legislation that impacts the building industry. Provides a forum for communication, networking and recruiting for those involved in manufacturing modular building systems. Addresses and solves problems specific to the council; offers consumer leads service.

1624 ■ **National Association of Women in Construction**
327 S Adams St.
Fort Worth, TX 76104
Ph: (817)877-5551

Free: 800-552-3506
Fax: (817)877-0324

E-mail: nawic@nawic.org
URL: http://www.nawic.org

Description: Seeks to enhance the success of women in the construction industry.

SOURCES OF HELP-WANTED ADS

1625 ■ *Advanced Imaging*
Cygnus Business Media Inc.
3030 Salt Creek Ln., Ste. 200
Arlington Heights, IL 60005
Free: 800-547-7377
E-mail: info@cygnus.com
URL: http://www.advancedimagingpro.com/magazine
.jsp
Frequency: 11/yr. **Description:** Magazine covering the full range of electronic imaging technology and its uses.

1626 ■ *AV Video & Multimedia Producer*
Access Intelligence L.L.C.
4 Choke Cherry Rd., 2nd Fl.
Rockville, MD 20850
Ph: (301)354-2000
Free: 800-777-5006
Fax: (301)309-3847
E-mail: info@accessintel.com
URL: http://www.accessintel.com/
Frequency: Monthly. **Description:** Magazine covering audio-visual, video and multimedia production, presentation, people, technology and techniques.

1627 ■ *Broadcasting & Cable*
Reed Elsevier Group plc - Reed Business Information
360 Park Ave. S
New York, NY 11010
Ph: (212)791-4208
E-mail: corporatecommunications@reedbusiness.
com
URLs: http://www.reedbusiness.com; http://www
.broadcastingcable.com
Frequency: 51/yr. **Price:** $199 Individuals; $249.99 Canada; $360.99 Other countries; $109 Individuals 6 months; $59 Individuals 3 months. **Description:** News magazine covering The Fifth Estate (radio, TV, cable, and satellite), and the regulatory commissions involved.

1628 ■ *Communications Engineering & Design: The Premier Magazine of Broadband Technology*
Communications Engineering & Design
PO Box 266007
Highlands Ranch, CO 80163-6007
Ph: (303)470-4800
Fax: (303)470-4890
URL: http://www.cedmagazine.com
Frequency: 10/year. **Price:** $64 Individuals; $85 Canada; $92 Other countries; $116 Two years; $153 Two years in Canada; $166 Two years elsewhere. **Description:** Technical/business publication serving the engineering/management community within broadband/cable TV networks, telecommunications carriers, data and interactive networks.

1629 ■ *Community Radio News*
National Federation of Community Broadcasters
1101 Pennsylvania Ave. NW, Ste. 600
Washington, DC 20004
Ph: (202)756-2268
E-mail: comments@nfcb.org
URL: http://www.nfcb.org
Evona Balcziunas, Editor. **Frequency:** Monthly; Monthly. **Price:** $75/year; Included in membership; $75 University Libraries. **Description:** Serves as a medium of communication for independent, community-licensed radio stations. Recurring features include job openings and a calendar of events/conferences for noncommercial broadcasters.

1630 ■ *Feminist Media Studies*
Routledge Journals - Taylor & Francis Group
270 Madison Ave.
New York, NY 10016-0601
Ph: (212)216-7800
Fax: (212)563-2269
URL: http://www.tandfonline.com/toc/rfms20/current
Frequency: 6/year. **Price:** $1,118 Institutions print + online; $197 Individuals print only; $979 Institutions online only. **Description:** Journal covering media and communication studies.

1631 ■ *FMedia!*
FM Atlas Publishing
241 Anderson Rd.
Esko, MN 55733-9413
Ph: (218)879-7676
Free: 800-605-2219
Fax: (218)879-8333
E-mail: fmatlas@aol.com
URL: http://members.aol.com/fmatlas/home.html
Frequency: Monthly. **Price:** $75 for broadcasters; $26 for individuals. **Description:** Lists information on the facilities and formats of FM radio, including new station grants and applications. Also provides official and unofficial news and comments, as well as FM Dxing and FM reception concerns. Recurring features include letters to the editor, news of research, job listings, and notices of publications available.

1632 ■ *Journal of the Audio Engineering Society*
Audio Engineering Society
60 E 42nd St., Rm. 2520
New York, NY 10165-2520
Ph: (212)661-8528
Free: 800-541-7299
Fax: (212)682-0477
URL: http://www.aes.org/journal
Frequency: Monthly; except Jan., Feb. and July, Aug. when it is published Bimonthly. **Price:** $50 Members; $280 Nonmembers print; $525 Nonmembers online; $695 Nonmembers print and online. **Description:** Newsletter reporting engineering developments and scientific progress in audio engineering for audio professionals, educators, executives, consumers, and students.

1633 ■ *Millimeter*
NewBay Media, LLC
28 E 28th St., 12th Fl.
New York, NY 10016
Ph: (212)378-0400
Fax: (917)281-4704
URL: http://digitalcontentproducer.com/mil/
Frequency: Monthly. **Description:** Magazine focusing on the process of motion picture and television production.

1634 ■ *Post: The International Magazine for Post Production Professionals*
Post Pro Publishing Inc.
One Park Ave.
New York, NY 10016
Ph: (212)951-6600
Fax: (212)951-6793
E-mail: info@advanstar.com
URL: http://www.postmagazine.com/
Frequency: Monthly. **Description:** Magazine serving the field of television, film, video production and post-production.

1635 ■ *Producers Masterguide: The International Film Directory & Guide*
Producers Masterguide
60 E 8th St., 34th Fl.
New York, NY 10003-6514
Ph: (212)777-4002
Fax: (212)777-4101
E-mail: nypc@earthlink.net
URL: http://www.producers.masterguide.com/cover
.html
Frequency: Annual. **Price:** $185 U.S.; $175 Canada; $205 Other countries. **Description:** An international film and TV production directory and guide for the professional motion picture, broadcast television, feature film, TV commercial, cable/satellite, digital and videotape industries in the U.S., Canada, the UK, the Caribbean Islands, Mexico, Australia, New Zealand, Europe, Israel, Morocco, the Far East, and South America.

1636 ■ *QST: Devoted Entirely to Amateur Radio*
Amateur Radio Relay League Inc.
225 Main St.
Newington, CT 06111-1400
Ph: (860)594-0200
Free: 888-277-5289
Fax: (860)594-0259
E-mail: qst@arrl.org
URL: http://www.arrl.org/qst/
Frequency: Monthly. **Price:** $34 Individuals. **Description:** Amateur radio magazine.

1637 ■ Radio and Records
Nielsen Business Media Inc.
770 Broadway
New York, NY 10003-9522
Ph: (646)654-4500
Free: 866-890-8541
Fax: (646)654-5584
E-mail: nbb@omeda.com
URL: http://www.radioandrecords.com

Frequency: Weekly. **Price:** $24.95 Individuals monthly, print & online; $299 Individuals print & online; $19.95 Individuals monthly, online. **Description:** Magazine covering every format of music radio, regulatory developments, news radio, talk radio, and satellite radio.

1638 ■ Telecommunications and Radio Engineering
Begell House Inc.
50 Cross Hwy.
Redding, CT 06896
Ph: (203)938-1300
Fax: (203)938-1304
E-mail: orders@begellhouse.com
URL: http://www.begellhouse.com/journals/0632a9d54950b268

Price: $4,518 Institutions. **Description:** Journal covering telecommunications and radio engineering.

1639 ■ TelevisionWeek
Crain Communications Inc.
6500 Wilshire Blvd., Ste. 2300
Los Angeles, CA 90048
Ph: (323)370-2417
E-mail: info@crain.com
URL: http://www.tvweek.com/

Frequency: Weekly. **Price:** $119 Individuals; $171 Canada incl. GST; $309 Other countries airmail. **Description:** Newspaper covering management, programming, cable and trends in the television and the media industry.

EMPLOYER DIRECTORIES AND NETWORKING LISTS

1640 ■ Actors' Yearbook
Bloomsbury Publishing PLC
50 Bedford Sq.
London WC1B 3DP, United Kingdom
Ph: 44 020 7631 5600
Fax: 020 7631 5800
E-mail: uk@bloomsbury.com
URL: http://www.bloomsbury.com/uk/actors-yearbook-2014-9781408185537/

Frequency: Latest Edition 2014. **Price:** $14.99 Individuals E-book; $13.49 Individuals Paperback. **Pages:** 496. **Covers:** Agents and production companies involved in television, film and theatre. **Entries include:** Name, address, phone, fax.

1641 ■ Bacon's Metro California Media
Cision US Inc.
332 S Michigan Ave., Ste. 900
Chicago, IL 60604-4393
Free: 866-639-5087
E-mail: info.us@cision.com
URL: http://us.cision.com/

Frequency: Annual; Latest edition 2012. **Price:** $445 Individuals per year. **Covers:** Consumer media in the state of California including newspapers, radio television & cable stations, magazines, and broadcast programs, ethnic media, news services & syndicates. **Entries include:** Name, address, phone, names of editors and creative staff, with titles or indication of assignments. **Arrangement:** Geographical, classified by type of outlet. **Indexes:** Alphabetical.

1642 ■ Bacon's Radio/TV/Cable Directory, Volume 1
Cision US Inc.
332 S Michigan Ave., Ste. 900
Chicago, IL 60604-4393

Free: 866-639-5087
E-mail: info.us@cision.com
URL: http://us.cision.com

Frequency: Annual; Latest edition 2012. **Price:** $650 Individuals. **Covers:** over 13,500 radio and television stations, including college radio and public television stations, and cable companies. **Entries include:** For radio and television stations--Call letters, address, phone, names and titles of key personnel, programs, times broadcast, name of contact, network affiliation, frequency or channel number, target audience data. For cable companies--Name, address, phone, description of activities. **Arrangement:** Geographical.

1643 ■ BIA's Television Yearbook
BIA/Kelsey
15120 Enterprise Ct.
Chantilly, VA 20151
Ph: (703)818-2425
Free: 800-331-5086
E-mail: sales@biakelsey.com
URL: http://www.bia.com/Broadcast-Media/Investing-In-Publications/Television

Frequency: Annual; Latest edition 2014. **Price:** $250 Individuals. **Pages:** 425. **Covers:** U.S. Television markets and their inclusive stations, television equipment manufacturers, and related service providers and trade associations. **Includes:** Annual market data, including television revenue, demographics, economic indicators, and viewing trends. **Entries include:** For stations--Call letters, address; name and phone of general manager, owner, and other key personnel; technical attributes, rep firm, network affiliation, last acquisition date and price and ratings for total day and prime time. For others--Company or organization name, address, phone, description. **Arrangement:** Classified by market. **Indexes:** Numerical by market rank; call letters.

1644 ■ Bowker's News Media Directory
R.R. Bowker
630 Central Ave
New Providence, NJ 07974
Ph: (888)269-5372
Free: 888-269-5372
Fax: (908)464-3553
E-mail: wpn@bowker.com
URL: http://www.bowker.com

Frequency: Annual; Latest edition 2009. **Price:** $668 Individuals softbound; three-volume set. **Covers:** In three separate volumes, syndicates and over 8,500 daily and weekly newspapers; 1,750 newsletters; over 16,800 radio and television stations; 5,500 magazines; 1,000 internal publications. **Entries include:** Name of publication or station, address, phone, fax, e-mail and URL, names of executives, editors, writers, etc., as appropriate. Broadcasting and magazine volumes include data on kinds of material accepted. Technical and mechanical requirements for publications are given. **Arrangement:** Magazines are classified by subject; newspapers and broadcasting stations geographical. **Indexes:** Newspaper department/editor by interest, metro area, feature syndicate subject; magazine subject, publication title; television director/personnel by subject, radio personnel and director by subject.

1645 ■ Broadcasting & Cable Yearbook: A Broadcasting and R.R. Bowker Publication
R.R. Bowker
630 Central Ave
New Providence, NJ 07974
Ph: (888)269-5372
Free: 888-269-5372
Fax: (908)464-3553
E-mail: info@bowker.com
URL: http://www.bowker.com

Frequency: Annual; latest edition 2010. **Price:** $395 Individuals softbound. **Covers:** Over 17,000 television and radio stations in the United States, its territories, and Canada; cable MSOs and their individual systems; television and radio networks, broadcast and cable group owners, station representatives; satellite networks and services, film companies,

advertising agencies, government agencies, trade associations, schools, and suppliers of professional and technical services, including books, serials, and videos; communications lawyers. **Entries include:** Company name, address, phone, fax, names of executives. Station listings include broadcast power, other operating details. **Arrangement:** Stations and systems are geographical, others are alphabetical. **Indexes:** Alphabetical.

1646 ■ Burrelle's Black/Hispanic Media Directory
BurrellesLuce
75 E Northfield Rd.
Livingston, NJ 07039
Ph: (973)992-6600
Free: 800-631-1160
Fax: (973)992-7675
E-mail: sross@burrellesluce.com
URL: http://www.burrellesluce.com

Frequency: Irregular; previous edition 1989; latest edition 1992. **Price:** $145 plus $4.00 shipping. **Pages:** 295. **Covers:** Newspapers, magazines, newsletters, radio and television programs, and other media serving the interests of the Black and Hispanic population. **Entries include:** Publication or station name, address, phone, names and titles of key personnel, description of publication or program. **Arrangement:** Geographical. **Indexes:** Geographical.

1647 ■ Christian Media Directory
James Lloyd Group
PO Box 448
Jacksonville, OR 97530
Ph: (541)899-8888
E-mail: james@christianmedianetwork.com
URL: http://www.christianmedianetwork.com

Frequency: Irregular. **Price:** $37.70 Individuals. **Covers:** Over 8,000 newspapers, periodicals, radio and television stations, video and film producers, and music record labels targeting a Christian audience. Provides market profiles and overview of television and music video networks. **Entries include:** Company or individual name, address, phone, fax, name of contact, description of service, programming, or product. **Arrangement:** Classified by line of business. **Indexes:** Product/service.

1648 ■ The Complete Television, Radio & Cable Industry Directory
Grey House Publishing
4919 Rte. 22
Amenia, NY 12501
Ph: (518)789-8700
Free: 800-562-2139
Fax: (518)789-0556
E-mail: books@greyhouse.com
URL: http://gold.greyhouse.com/page/datatype96

1649 ■ CPB Public Broadcasting Directory
Corporation for Public Broadcasting
401 9th St. NW
Washington, DC 20004
Ph: (202)879-9600
Free: 800-272-2190
Fax: (202)879-9699
E-mail: oigemail@cpb.org
URL: http://www.cpb.org/stations/isis

Frequency: Annual. **Covers:** Public television and radio stations, national and regional public broadcasting organizations and networks, state government agencies and commissions, and other related organizations. **Entries include:** For radio and television stations--Station call letters, frequency or channel, address, phone, licensee name, licensee type, date on air, antenna height, area covered, names and titles of key personnel. For organizations--Name, address, phone, name and title of key personnel. **Arrangement:** National and regional listings are alphabetical; state groups and the public radio and television stations are each geographical; other organizations and agencies are alphabetical. **Indexes:** Geographical, personnel, call letter, licensee type (all in separate indexes for radio and television).

1650 ■ *Film Producers, Studios, Agents, and Casting Directors Guide*
Hollywood Creative Directory
5055 Wilshire Blvd.
Los Angeles, CA 90036-4396
Ph: (323)525-2369
Free: 800-815-0503
Fax: (323)525-2398
E-mail: hcdsales@hcdonline.com
URL: http://www.loneeagle.com

Frequency: Annual. **Price:** $75 plus $7.50 shipping. **Pages:** 600. **Covers:** Approximately 5,000 television and motion picture producers, 1,700 studios executives and production companies, 1,800 agents and casting directors, and over 14,000 film credits. **Entries include:** For producers--Name, address, phone, films worked on; name, address, phone of contact. For studios--Name, address, phone, names and titles of key personnel. For agents--Agency name, address, phone, individual agents' names, job titles. For casting directors--Credits. **Arrangement:** Classified by line of business. **Indexes:** Film title, producer, studio executive, agent, casting director, academy awards and nominations by year.

1651 ■ *FINDERBINDER--Arizona: Arizona's Updated Media Directory*
Rita Sanders Advertising Public Relations
432 E Southern Ave.
Tempe, AZ 85282
Ph: (480)967-8714
Fax: (480)894-6216
E-mail: rita@ritasanders.com
URL: http://www.finderbinderaz.com

Frequency: Annual. **Price:** $314.07 Individuals online only; $399.88 Individuals print only; $464.86 Individuals print and online. **Pages:** 600. **Description:** "FINDERBINDER" directories are loose-leaf directories of broadcast and print media covering states or smaller areas published by companies, usually advertising and public relations firms, licensed to use the name and format by Finderbinder. Types of media covered include cable television systems; daily and weekly newspapers; religious, ethnic, and labor papers; business, trade, sports, recreation, and general interest publications; college papers; and radio and television stations in Arizona. **Entries include:** Publication or station name, names of management, editorial, and advertising personnel, deadlines, frequency or circulation as appropriate, and other data; cable TV listings. **Arrangement:** Classified by type of medium. **Indexes:** Publication or station name.

1652 ■ *FINDERBINDER--Cleveland*
Morgan & Co. Public Relations
Box 395
Richfield, OH 44286

Frequency: Annual. **Description:** "FINDERBINDER" directories are loose-leaf directories of broadcast and print media covering states or smaller areas published by Finderbinder. Types of media covered include daily and weekly local and outstate newspapers; religious, ethnic, and labor papers; business, trade, sports, recreation, and general interest publications; college papers; and radio and television stations in Cleveland and northeastern Ohio. **Entries include:** Publication or station name, names of management, editorial, and advertising personnel, deadlines, frequency or circulation as appropriate, and cable TV listings show homes served. **Arrangement:** Classified by type of medium. **Indexes:** Publication or station name.

1653 ■ *FINDERBINDER--Greater Detroit*
C & E Communications Inc.
PO Box 4952
East Lansing, MI 48826
Ph: (517)339-9160

Free: 877-515-9755
Fax: (517)339-7494
E-mail: info@michiganfinderbinder.com
URL: http://www.michiganfinderbinder.com

Frequency: Annual; September; bimonthly updates. **Price:** $250 Individuals set including outside Michigan. **Pages:** 300. **Description:** "FINDERBINDER" directories are loose-leaf directories of broadcast and print media covering states or smaller areas published by companies, usually advertising and public relations firms, licensed to use the name and format by Finderbinder. Types of media covered include cable television systems; daily and weekly newspapers; religious, ethnic, and labor papers; business, trade, sports, recreation, and general interest publications; college papers; and radio and television stations in the seven-county Detroit metro area. **Entries include:** Publication or station name, names of management, editorial, and advertising personnel, deadlines, frequency or circulation as appropriate, and other data; radio, TV, and cable TV listings give name of public service announcement (PSA) director, interview format programs. **Arrangement:** Classified by type of medium. **Indexes:** Publication or station name, geographical, cable by community.

1654 ■ *FINDERBINDER--Kansas City: Greater Kansas Cities News Media Directory*
E-mail: krisf@twowest.com
URL: http://www.twowest.com

Frequency: Annual; February. **Price:** $130 payment must accompany order. **Pages:** 330. **Description:** "FINDERBINDER" directories are loose-leaf directories of broadcast and print media covering states or smaller areas published by companies, usually advertising and public relations firms, licensed to use the name and format by Finderbinder. Types of media covered include cable television systems; daily and weekly newspapers; religious, ethnic, and labor papers; business, trade, sports, recreation, and general interest publications; college papers; and radio and television stations in the 14 county, Kansas City metropolitan area. **Entries include:** Publication or station name; names of management, editorial, and advertising personnel; deadlines, frequency or circulation as appropriate; advertising rates; public relations contacts, including fax numbers, and email addresses; cable TV listings show homes served. **Arrangement:** Classified by type of medium. **Indexes:** Publication or station name, geographic by county, by interests covered.

1655 ■ *FINDERBINDER--New Mexico*
Gary Beals Advertising and Public Relations
4679 Vista St.
San Diego, CA 92116
Ph: (619)284-1145

Description: "FINDERBINDER" directories are loose-leaf directories of broadcast and print media covering states or smaller areas published by companies, usually advertising and public relations firms, licensed to use the name and format by Finderbinder. Types of media covered include cable television systems; daily and weekly newspapers; religious, ethnic, and labor papers; business, trade, sports, recreation, and general interest publications; college papers; and radio and television stations in New Mexico. **Entries include:** Publication or station name, names of management, editorial, and advertising personnel, deadlines, frequency or circulation as appropriate, advertising rates, and other data; cable TV listings show homes served. **Arrangement:** Classified by type of medium. **Indexes:** Publication or station name.

1656 ■ *FINDERBINDER--Northeast Wisconsin*
Bishea, Meili & Associates Inc.
9141 N Briarwood Ct., Ste. 201
Milwaukee, WI 53217
Ph: (414)540-1407
Fax: (414)540-1417

Description: "FINDERBINDER" directories are

loose-leaf directories of broadcast and print media covering states or smaller areas published by companies, usually advertising and public relations firms, licensed to use the name and format by Finderbinder. Types of media covered include cable television systems; daily and weekly newspapers; religious, ethnic, and labor papers; business, trade, sports, recreation, and general interest publications; college papers; and radio and television stations in Northeast Wisconsin. **Entries include:** Publication or station name, names of management, editorial, and advertising personnel, deadlines, frequency or circulation as appropriate, advertising rates, and other data; cable TV listings show homes served. **Arrangement:** Classified by type of medium. **Indexes:** Publication or station name.

1657 ■ *FINDERBINDER--Oklahoma*
FINDERBINDER of Oklahoma
PO Box 3093
Edmond, OK 73083
Ph: (405)570-3569
E-mail: support@finderbinderok.com
URL: http://www.finderbinderok.com

Frequency: Annual. **Price:** $175 online. **Description:** "FINDERBINDER" directories are loose-leaf directories of broadcast and print media covering states or smaller areas published by companies, usually advertising and public relations firms, licensed to use the name and format by Finderbinder. Types of media covered include cable television systems; daily and weekly newspapers; religious, ethnic, and labor papers; business, trade, sports, recreation, and general interest publications; college papers; and radio and television stations in Oklahoma. **Entries include:** Publication or station name, names of management, editorial, and advertising personnel, deadlines, frequency or circulation as appropriate, and other data; cable TV listings show homes served. **Arrangement:** Classified by type of medium. **Indexes:** Publication or station name.

1658 ■ *FINDERBINDER--Outstate Michigan*
C & E Communications Inc.
PO Box 4952
East Lansing, MI 48826
Ph: (517)339-9160
Free: 877-515-9755
Fax: (517)339-7494
E-mail: info@michiganfinderbinder.com
URL: http://www.michiganfinderbinder.com

Frequency: Annual; Latest edition 16th. **Price:** $225 Individuals package; $180 Individuals binder only. **Pages:** 271. **Description:** "FINDERBINDER" directories are loose-leaf directories of broadcast and print media covering states or smaller areas published by companies, usually advertising and public relations firms, licensed to use the name and format by Finderbinder. Types of media covered include cable television systems; daily and weekly newspapers; religious, ethnic, and labor papers; business, trade, sports, recreation, and general interest publications; college papers; and radio and television stations outside the 7-county metropolitan Detroit area. **Entries include:** Publication title or station name, address, phone, names and titles of key personnel, deadlines, frequency, circulation; radio and TV stations also list name of public service announcement director and interview programs. **Arrangement:** Classified by market, then by medium. **Indexes:** Dailies, community papers, other print, radio, TV, and print by topics.

1659 ■ *FINDERBINDER--Pittsburgh*
Gary Beals Advertising and Public Relations
4679 Vista St.
San Diego, CA 92116
Ph: (619)284-1145

Description: "FINDERBINDER" directories are loose-leaf directories of broadcast and print media covering states or smaller areas published by companies, usually advertising and public relations firms, licensed to use the name and format by Finderbinder. Types of media covered include cable television systems; daily and weekly newspapers;

religious, ethnic, and labor papers; business, trade, sports, recreation, and general interest publications; college papers; and radio and television stations in Pittsburgh. **Entries include:** Publication or station name, names of management, editorial, and advertising personnel, deadlines, frequency or circulation as appropriate, advertising rates, and other data; cable TV listings show homes served. **Arrangement:** Classified by type of medium. **Indexes:** Publication or station name.

1660 ■ FINDERBINDER--Syracuse
Gary Beals Advertising and Public Relations
4679 Vista St.
San Diego, CA 92116
Ph: (619)284-1145

Description: "FINDERBINDER" directories are loose-leaf directories of broadcast and print media covering states or smaller areas published by companies, usually advertising and public relations firms, licensed to use the name and format by Finderbinder. Types of media covered include cable, advertising companies, cable television systems, billboard companies; daily and weekly newspapers; religious, ethnic, and labor papers; business, trade, sports, recreation, and general interest publications; college papers; and radio and television stations in Syracuse. **Entries include:** Publication or station name, names of management, editorial, and advertising personnel, deadlines, frequency or circulation as appropriate, advertising rates, and other data; cable TV listings show homes served. **Arrangement:** Classified by type of medium. **Indexes:** Publication or station name.

1661 ■ Gale Directory of Publications and Broadcast Media
Cengage Learning Inc.
200 1st Stamford Pl., Ste. 400
Stamford, CT 06902-6753
Ph: (203)965-8600
Free: 800-354-9706
Fax: (800)487-8488
E-mail: investors@cengage.com
URL: http://www.gale.cengage.com

Frequency: Annual; Latest edition April 2011. **Price:** $1,297 Individuals. **Covers:** Approximately 57,000 publications and broadcasting stations, including newspapers, magazines, journals, radio stations, television stations, radio/television/cable networks, syndicates and cable systems in the U.S. and Canada. Newsletters and directories are excluded. **Includes:** Appendices with maps and statistical tables, city descriptions, state descriptions with statistics, broadcast and cable networks, news and features syndicates. **Entries include:** For publications--Title, publishing and editorial addresses, phone, fax, description, names of editor, publisher, and advertising manager, base advertising rate, page specifications, subscription rate, circulation, frequency, ISSN, former names, additional contacts. For broadcast media--Call letters or cable system name, address, phone, fax, format, networks, owner, date founded, former call letters, operating hours, names and titles of key personnel, local programming, wattage, ad rates, additional contacts. **Arrangement:** Geographical. **Indexes:** Title; radio station format; publisher; geographic market; lists of agricultural, college, foreign language, Jewish, fraternal, black, women's, Hispanic, religious, general circulation, and trade and technical publications (by subject and/or geographical as needed); daily newspaper; daily periodical; free circulation newspaper; and shopping guides (each geographical); list of feature editors at daily newspapers with 50,000 or more circulation.

1662 ■ Hudson's Washington News Media Contacts Directory
Grey House Publishing
4919 Rte. 22
Amenia, NY 12501
Ph: (518)789-8700
Free: 800-562-2139
Fax: (518)789-0556
E-mail: books@greyhouse.com
URL: http://www.greyhouse.com/hudsons.htm

Frequency: Annual; Latest edition 2013. **Price:** $329 Individuals online and print. **Covers:** Nearly 5,000 editors, free-lance writers, and news correspondents, plus 4,624 United States, Canadian, and foreign newspapers, radio-TV networks and stations, magazines, and periodicals based or represented in Washington, D.C. **Entries include:** For publications and companies--Name, address, phone, and name of editor or key personnel. For individuals--Name, assignment. **Arrangement:** Classified by activity (e.g., correspondents), media type, etc; newspapers and radio-TV stations sections are arranged geographically; specialized periodicals section is arranged by subject. **Indexes:** Subject.

1663 ■ International Television and Video Almanac
Quigley Publishing Co.
64 Wintergreen Ln.
Groton, MA 01450
Ph: (978)448-0272
Free: 800-231-8239
Fax: (860)228-0157
E-mail: quigleypub@quigleypublishing.com
URL: http://quigleypublishing.com/

Frequency: Annual; January; latest edition 2013. **Price:** $235 Individuals. **Covers:** "Who's Who in Motion Pictures and Television and Home Video," television networks, major program producers, major group station owners, cable television companies, distributors, firms serving the television and home video industry, equipment manufacturers, casting agencies, literary agencies, advertising and publicity representatives, television stations, associations, list of feature films produced for television; statistics, industry's year in review, award winners, satellite and wireless cable provider, primetime programming, video producers, distributors, wholesalers. **Entries include:** Generally, company name, address, phone; manufacturer and service listings may include description of products and services and name of contact; producing, distributing, and station listings include additional detail, and contacts for cable and broadcast networks. **Arrangement:** Classified by service or activity. **Indexes:** Full.

1664 ■ Media Directory San Diego County
San Diego Chamber of Commerce
402 W Broadway, Ste. 1000
San Diego, CA 92101
Ph: (619)544-1300
E-mail: webinfo@sdchamber.org
URL: http://www.sdchamber.org

Frequency: Annual. **Price:** $5. **Pages:** 6. **Covers:** San Diego county newspapers, magazines, news bureaus, radio and television stations. **Entries include:** For publications--Name of publication, address, phone. For radio and television stations--Call letters, frequency, address, mailing address, phone. **Arrangement:** Classified by type of media.

1665 ■ Minority Employment Report
Federal Communications Commission - Wireless Telecommunications Bureau
445 12th St. SW
Washington, DC 20554
Free: 877-480-3201
E-mail: fccinfo@fcc.gov
URL: http://wireless.fcc.gov

Frequency: Annual; December. **Pages:** 1,480. **Covers:** Television and radio stations with ten or more full-time employees. **Entries include:** Station name (call letters or channel), city and state, class of station; total, female, and minority full-time employment in higher and lower pay occupations, and part-time employment for previous five years. **Arrangement:** By state and community.

1666 ■ The R & R Directory
Billboard.biz
Nielsen Business Media, PO Box 3595
Northbrook, IL 60065-3595
Ph: (847)559-7531
Free: 800-658-8372
E-mail: moreinfo@rronline.com
URL: http://cclamp.radioandrecords.com/Aboutus/FAQ.asp

Frequency: Semiannual; Spring and Fall. **Price:** $75. **Pages:** 500. **Covers:** More than 3,000 radio group owners, equipment manufacturers, jingle producers, TV production houses and spot producers, record companies, representative firms, research companies, consulting firms, media brokers, networks, program suppliers, trade associations, and other organizations involved in the radio and record industry. **Includes:** Ratings, demographic rankings, and format charts of all Arbitron rated radio markets. **Entries include:** Organization name, address, phone, fax, E-mail, name and title of contacts, branch offices or subsidiary names and locations. **Arrangement:** Alphabetical; classified by subject. **Indexes:** Company.

1667 ■ Radio Advertising Source
Kantar Media SRDS
1700 Higgins Rd., 5th Fl.
Des Plaines, IL 60018-5610
Ph: (847)375-5000
Free: 800-851-7737
E-mail: next@srds.com
URL: http://next.srds.com

Frequency: Annual; Latest edition 2014. **Price:** $809 Individuals Annual unlimited single-user access plus shipping. **Covers:** Over 10,500 AM and FM stations, networks, syndicators, group owners, and representative firms. **Includes:** Arbitron Average quarter-hour shares, metro market rankings persons 12+, Black and Hispanic population and SPARC cost-per-point. **Entries include:** Call letters, name of owning company, address, phone; names of representatives and station personnel; demonstration detail, station format, signal strength, programming opportunities, special features. **Arrangement:** Geographical by state, then Arbitron metro and non-metro area.

1668 ■ RTNDA Communicator--Directory Issues
Radio-Television Digital News Association
529 14th St. NW, Ste. 1240
Washington, DC 20045
Fax: (202)223-4007
URL: http://rtnda.org

Frequency: Semiannual; January and July. **Pages:** 90. **No. of Listings:** 3,000; membership includes Canada and some foreign countries. **Entries include:** Member name, address, phone; and name of radio or television station, network, or other news organization with which affiliated. **Arrangement:** Same information given in alphabetical and geographical arrangements.

1669 ■ Society of Motion Picture and Television Engineers--Directory for Members
Society of Motion Picture and Television Engineers
3 Barker Ave., 5th Fl.
White Plains, NY 10601
Ph: (914)761-1100
Fax: (914)761-3115
E-mail: journal@smpte.org
URL: http://www.smpte.org

Frequency: Annual; July. **Pages:** 200. **Covers:** 10,000 professional engineers and technicians in motion pictures, television, and allied arts and sciences; over 250 firms and organizations which are sustaining members. **Entries include:** For individual members--Name, affiliation and title, address, phone, membership classification. For sustaining members--Name, address, phone, extensive description of line of business or activities, name of contact. **Arrangement:** Each list is alphabetical. **Indexes:** Geographical.

1670 ■ Southern California Media Directory
Public Communicators of Los Angeles
1910 W Sunset Blvd., Ste. 860
Los Angeles, CA 90026-3247
Fax: (213)413-4026
URL: http://www.pcla.org

Frequency: Annual. **Pages:** 500 loose-leaf. **Covers:** 1,500 newspapers, magazines, radio and TV stations, and other media in eight-county southern California area; also covers suppliers of public relations products and services. **Entries include:** Media entries include publication name, address, phone, fax, e-mail and internet address, personnel (up to 30-40 editors, columnists, producers, etc.), circulation, and dates of publication. Supplier entries include company name, address, phone, fax, contact name, list of products or services. **Arrangement:** Geographical.

1671 ■ Talk Show Yearbook
Broadcast Interview Source Inc.
2233 Wisconsin Ave. NW, Ste. 301
Washington, DC 20007-4132
Ph: (202)333-5000
Free: 866-639-7735
Fax: (202)342-5411
E-mail: editor@yearbook.com
URL: http://www.expertclick.com

Frequency: Annual; winter. **Price:** $185 Individuals. **Pages:** 324. **Covers:** more than 700 contacts at radio and television talk shows. **Includes:** Reports on the top 100 markets in the country. **Entries include:** Name of contact, format, market, address, phone, fax, name of talk show, station call letters, ADI information. **Arrangement:** Geographical. **Indexes:** Station call letters or network name.

1672 ■ Television & Cable Factbook
Warren Communications News Inc.
2115 Ward Ct. NW
Washington, DC 20037
Ph: (202)872-9200
Free: 800-771-9202
Fax: (202)318-8350
URL: http://www.warren-news.com/factbook.htm

Frequency: Annual; Latest edition 2012. **Price:** $945 Individuals first copy, print or online; $295 Individuals second copy, print or online; $195 Individuals third copy, print or online & subsequent seats; $995 Individuals full online data, additional per seat. **Pages:** 4,500 4 volumes. **Covers:** Commercial and noncommercial television stations and networks, including educational, low-power and instructional TV stations, and translators; United States cable television systems; cable and television group owners; program and service suppliers; and brokerage and financing companies. **Entries include:** For stations-- Call letters, licensee name and address, studio address and phone; identification of owners, sales and legal representatives and chief station personnel; rates, technical data, map of service area, and Nielsen circulation data. For cable systems--Name, address, basic and pay subscribers, programming and fees, physical plant; names of personnel and ownership. **Arrangement:** Geographical by state, province, city, county, or country. **Indexes:** Call letters, product/service, name, general subject.

1673 ■ TV and Cable Source
Kantar Media SRDS
1700 Higgins Rd., 5th Fl.
Des Plaines, IL 60018-5610
Ph: (847)375-5000
Free: 800-851-7737
E-mail: next@srds.com
URL: http://next.srds.com

Frequency: Quarterly; Latest edition 2011. **Price:** $809 Annual unlimited single-user access plus shipping. **Covers:** All domestic and international commercial television stations and networks; public television stations, cable networks, systems, interconnects, rep firms, and group owners. Includes separate section showing production specifications of stations and systems. **Includes:** Market statistics,

such as population, household income, household expenditures, DMA ratings by TV and cable households, market maps, and SQAD cost-per-points. Also includes listings for Asia-Pacific, Europe, and Latin America. **Entries include:** Call letters, parent company, address, phone, representative, personnel, facilities, special features, programming. Production specifications section shows call letters or system name, address, and preferred specifications for ad copy. **Arrangement:** Classified by DMA ranking, then by call letters.

HANDBOOKS AND MANUALS

1674 ■ Careers in Communications
The McGraw-Hill Companies Inc.
PO Box 182604
Columbus, OH 43272
Ph: (212)512-2000
Free: 877-833-5524
Fax: (614)759-3749
E-mail: customer.service@mcgraw-hill.com
URL: http://www.mcgraw-hill.com

Description: Shonan Noronha. Fourth edition, 2004. $15.95 (paper). 192 pages. Examines the fields of journalism, photography, radio, television, film, public relations, and advertising. Gives concrete details on job locations and how to secure a job. Suggests many resources for job hunting.

1675 ■ Great Jobs for Music Majors
The McGraw-Hill Companies Inc.
PO Box 182604
Columbus, OH 43272
Ph: (212)512-2000
Free: 877-833-5524
Fax: (614)759-3749
E-mail: customer.service@mcgraw-hill.com
URL: http://www.mcgraw-hill.com

Description: Jan Goldberg. Second edition, 2004. $15.95 (paper). 180 pages.

1676 ■ Opportunities in Broadcasting Careers
The McGraw-Hill Companies Inc.
PO Box 182604
Columbus, OH 43272
Ph: (212)512-2000
Free: 877-833-5524
Fax: (614)759-3749
E-mail: customer.service@mcgraw-hill.com
URL: http://www.mcgraw-hill.com

Description: Elmo I. Ellis. 2004. $13.95. 176 pages. Discusses opportunities and job search techniques in broadcasting, television, and radio. Illustrated.

1677 ■ Radio Broadcast Technician
National Learning Corporation
212 Michael Dr.
Syosset, NY 11791
Ph: (516)921-8888
Free: 800-632-8888
Fax: (516)921-8743
E-mail: info@passbooks.com
URL: http://www.passbooks.com

Description: 2009. $34.95 (paper). Serves as an exam preparation guide for radio broadcast technicians.

1678 ■ Starting Your Career in Broadcasting: Working On and Off the Air in Radio and Television
Allworth Press
307 W 36th St., 11th Fl.
New York, NY 10018
Ph: (212)643-6816
Free: 800-491-2808
Fax: (212)643-6819
E-mail: pub@allworth.com
URL: http://www.allworth.com

Description: Chris Schneider. 2007. $19.95 (paper). 240 pages. Provides information on how to get into

the communications business. Includes chapters on specific on-air and behind-the-scenes jobs, academic programs in broadcasting, what news and program directors seek in job candidates, how an aspiring broadcaster can buy time on the air, weathering the ups and downs of a competitive industry, and how professionals of all kinds can host their own talk shows.

EMPLOYMENT AGENCIES AND SEARCH FIRMS

1679 ■ Baker Scott & Co.
1259 Rte. 46
Parsippany, NJ 07054
Ph: (973)263-3355
Fax: (973)263-9255
E-mail: exec.search@bakerscott.com
URL: http://www.bakerscott.com

Description: Consulting services include executive recruiting, employment attitude surveys and screening organization plans. Industries served: telecommunication, cable TV, broadcasting entertainment and financial institutions. The firm is integrated horizontally across functional discipline such as accounting, administration, call center, data processing, engineering, finance, general operations, marketing and technical and plant operations.

1680 ■ Warren and Morris Ltd.
463 15th St.
Del Mar, CA 92014
Ph: (858)461-0040
Fax: (858)481-6221
E-mail: cmorris@warrenmorrisltd.com
URL: http://www.warrenmorrisltd.com

Description: Offers the following services: Executive search and recruitment, providing clients with pre-screened, qualified candidates; and EEO management and labor relations consulting. Industries served: Cable TV and wireless communications, multimedia and competitive telephone.

1681 ■ Jim Young & Associates Inc.
1424 Clear Lake Rd.
Weatherford, TX 76086-5806
Ph: (817)599-7623
Free: 800-433-2160
Fax: (817)599-4483

Description: Specializes in the placement of cable television, telecommunications, cellular telephone, RF engineering and satellite communications personnel. Industries served: Cable television, telecommunications and cellular.

ONLINE JOB SOURCES AND SERVICES

1682 ■ Get Broadcast Technician Jobs
URL: http://www.getbroadcasttechnicianjobs.com

Description: Provides a searchable database of job postings for broadcast technicians.

1683 ■ Producer's Directory
IFILM Corp. - Hollywood Creative Directory Inc.
5055 Wilshire Blvd.
Hollywood, CA 90036-4396
Ph: (323)525-2369
Free: 800-815-0503
Fax: (323)525-2398
E-mail: hcdcustomerservice@hcdonline.com
URL: http://www.hcdonline.com

Price: 1 Year subscription: $199.95; Print version: $59.95. **Description:** Producer's Directory is an online source with information on film and television industry. Thoroughly researched and meticulously compiled, the PD lists up-to-date information on producers, studio and network executives. This Product covers: Over 7,800 names; Producers, Studio and Network Executives; Over 1,700 production companies, studios and networks; addresses, phone and fax numbers, staff and titles; selected credits and companies with studio deals. available as an online source, but also in print version, database is updated three times a year: March - July - November.

1684 ■ Society of Broadcast Engineers Job Line
URL: http://www.sbe.org/sections/jobs_online.php
Description: Job Line is one benefit of membership in the Society of Broadcast Engineers. Includes a resume service to distribute resumes to employers, job contact information, and descriptions of job openings. Also accessible via telephone.

TRADESHOWS

1685 ■ National Association of State Technology Directors Conference
National Association of State Technology Directors
2760 Research Park Dr.
Lexington, KY 40511-8482
Ph: (859)244-8187
E-mail: pjohson@csg.org
URL: http://www.nastd.org
Frequency: Annual. **Primary Exhibits:** Exhibits for state telecommunications systems.

1686 ■ SMPTE Technical Conference Exhibition
Society of Motion Picture and Television Engineers
3 Barker Ave., 5th Fl.
White Plains, NY 10601
Ph: (914)761-1100
Fax: (914)761-3115
E-mail: smpte@smpte.org
URL: http://www.smpte.org
Frequency: Annual; usually fall, October or November. **Primary Exhibits:** Equipment, lights, cameras, film, tape, and lenses.

1687 ■ Society of Broadcast Engineers Engineering Conference
Society of Broadcast Engineers
9102 N Meridian St., Ste. 150
Indianapolis, IN 46260
Ph: (317)846-9000
Fax: (317)846-9120
E-mail: mclappe@sbe.org
URL: http://www.sbe.org
Frequency: Annual. **Primary Exhibits:** Equipment, supplies, and services for the broadcast industry.

1688 ■ Southern States Communication Association Convention
Southern States Communication Association
c/o Dr. Carl M. Cates
Valdosta State University
1500 N Patterson St.
Valdosta, GA 31698
Ph: (229)333-5832
Fax: (229)245-3799
E-mail: ccates@valdosta.edu
URL: http://www.ssca.net
Frequency: Annual; late March to early April. **Primary Exhibits:** Communications equipment; textbooks.

OTHER SOURCES

1689 ■ Association for Educational Communications and Technology
320 W 8th St., Ste. 101
Bloomington, IN 47404
Ph: (812)335-7675
Free: 877-677-2328
Fax: (812)335-7678
E-mail: aect@aect.org
URL: http://www.aect.org/newsite

Description: Instructional technology professionals. Provides leadership in educational communications and technology by linking professionals holding a common interest in the use of educational technology and its application of the learning process.

1690 ■ *Baseball America--Radio, TV, & Cable Directory*
Baseball America Inc.
4319 S Alston Ave.
Durham, NC 27713-2488
Ph: (919)682-9635
Fax: (919)682-2880
E-mail: customerservice@baseballamerica.com
URL: http://www.baseballamerica.com
Frequency: Annual. **Covers:** Local broadcasters (radio, TV, and cable stations) of major league baseball games; radio stations which cover minor league baseball; and suppliers of baseball videos. **Entries include:** For broadcasters--Call letters, station numbers, and contact information. For suppliers--Contact information.

1691 ■ *A Career Handbook for TV, Radio, Film, Video and Interactive Media*
Bloomsbury Publishing PLC
50 Bedford Sq.
London WC1B 3DP, United Kingdom
Ph: 44 020 7631 5600
Fax: 020 7631 5800
E-mail: uk@bloomsbury.com
URL: http://www.bloomsbury.com/uk/a-career -handbook-for-tv-radio-film-video-and-interactive -media-9780713663204/
Frequency: Monthly. **Price:** £13.49 Individuals. **Covers:** TV, radio, film, video and interactive media specialists.

1692 ■ *Career Opportunities in Radio*
InfoBase Holdings Inc.
132 W 31st., 17 Fl.
New York, NY 10001-3406
Ph: (212)967-8800
Fax: (800)678-3633
E-mail: info@infobasepublishing.com
URL: http://www.infobasepublishing.com
Frequency: Published April, 2004. **Price:** $49.50 Individuals hardcover. **Pages:** 336. **Description:** Shelly Field. 2004. 326 pages. **Covers:** More than 70 jobs, such as on-air personality/disc jockey, business reporter, sportscaster, advertising account representative, billing specialist, publicist, studio engineer, program director, website content producer, and more. **Includes:** Appendices of educational institutions, periodicals, directories, unions, and associations.

1693 ■ *Career Opportunities in Television and Cable*
InfoBase Holdings Inc.
132 W 31st., 17 Fl.
New York, NY 10001-3406
Ph: (212)967-8800
Fax: (800)678-3633
E-mail: info@infobasepublishing.com
URL: http://www.ferguson.infobasepublishing.com
Description: 2006. $49.50. Covers job profiles in television and cable industry, followed by the descriptions of the nature of the job, earnings, prospects for employment, what kind of training and skills it requires, and sources of other relevant information.

1694 ■ Corporation for Public Broadcasting
401 9th St. NW
Washington, DC 20004
Ph: (202)879-9600
Free: 800-272-2190
Fax: (202)879-9699
E-mail: oigemail@cpb.org
URL: http://www.cpb.org
Description: Promotes and finances the growth and development of noncommercial radio and television. Makes grants to local public television and radio stations; program producers, and program distribution

networks; studies emerging technologies; works to provide adequate long-range financing from the U.S. government and other sources for public broadcasting. Supports children's services; compiles statistics; sponsors training programs.

1695 ■ Country Radio Broadcasters Inc.
819 18th Ave. S
Nashville, TN 37203
Ph: (615)327-4487
Fax: (615)329-4492
E-mail: bill@crb.org
URL: http://countryradioseminar.com
Description: Seeks to advance and promote the study of the science of broadcasting through the mutual exchange of ideas by conducting seminars and workshops, as well as providing scholarships to broadcasting students.

1696 ■ Health Science Communications Association
PO Box 31323
Omaha, NE 68131-0323
Ph: (402)915-5373
E-mail: hesca@hesca.org
URL: http://www.hesca.org
Description: Represents media managers, graphic artists, biomedical librarians, producers, faculty members of health science and veterinary medicine schools, health professional organizations, and industry representatives. Acts as a clearinghouse for information used by professionals engaged in health science communications. Coordinates Media Festivals Program that recognizes outstanding media productions in the health sciences. Offers placement service. **Members:** 400.

1697 ■ Media Alliance
1904 Franklin St., Ste. 818
Oakland, CA 94612
Ph: (510)832-9000
Fax: (510)238-8557
E-mail: information@media-alliance.org
URL: http://www.media-alliance.org
Description: Writers, photographers, editors, broadcast workers, public relations practitioners, videographers, filmmakers, commercial artists and other media workers and aspiring media workers. Supports free press and independent, alternative journalism that services progressive politics and social justice.

1698 ■ National Association of Black Owned Broadcasters
1201 Connecticut Ave. NW, Ste. 200
Washington, DC 20036
Ph: (202)463-8970
Fax: (202)429-0657
E-mail: nabobinfo@nabob.org
URL: http://www.nabob.org
Description: Black broadcast station owners; black formatted stations not owned or controlled by blacks; organizations having an interest in the black consumer market or black broadcast industry; individuals interested in becoming owners; and communications schools, departments and professional groups and associations. Represents the interests of existing and potential black radio and television stations. Works with the Office of Federal Procurement Policy to determine which government contracting major advertisers and advertising agencies are complying with government initiatives to increase the amount of advertising dollars received by minority-owned firms. Conducts lobbying activities; provides legal representation for the protection of minority ownership policies. Sponsors annual Communications Awards Dinner each March. Conducts workshops; compiles statistics.

1699 ■ National Association of Broadcasters
1771 N St. NW
Washington, DC 20036
Ph: (202)429-5300

Broadcast Technicians

■ 1704 ■

Free: 800-342-2460
E-mail: nab@nab.org
URL: http://www.nab.org

Description: Serves as the voice for the nation's radio and television broadcasters. Advances the interests of members in federal government, industry and public affairs; improves the quality and profitability of broadcasting; encourages content and technology innovation; and spotlights the important and unique ways stations serve their communities. Delivers value to its members through advocacy, education and innovation. Relies on the grassroots strength of its television and radio members and state broadcast associations. Helps broadcasters seize opportunities in the digital age. Offers broadcasters a variety of programs to help them grow in their careers, promote diversity in the workplace and strengthen their businesses.

1700 ■ National Cable and Telecommunications Association
25 Massachusetts Ave. NW, Ste. 100
Washington, DC 20001
Ph: (202)222-2300
Fax: (202)222-2514
E-mail: info@ncta.com
URL: http://www.ncta.com

Description: Franchised cable operators, programmers, and cable networks; associate members are cable hardware suppliers and distributors; affiliate members are brokerage and law firms and financial institutions; state and regional cable television associations cooperate, but are not affiliated, with the organization. Serves as national medium for exchange of experiences and opinions through research, study, discussion, and publications. Represents the cable industry before Congress, the Federal Communications Commission and various courts on issues of primary importance. Conducts research program in conjunction with National Academy of Cable Programming. Sponsors, in conjunction with Motion Picture Association of America, the Coalition Opposing Signal Theft, an organization designed to deter cable signal theft and to develop anti-piracy materials. Provides promotional aids and information on legal, legislative and regulatory matters. Compiles statistics.

1701 ■ National Federation of Community Broadcasters
1101 Pennsylvania Ave. NW, Ste. 600
Washington, DC 20004
Ph: (202)756-2268
E-mail: comments@nfcb.org
URL: http://www.nfcb.org

Description: Independent, community-licensed radio and radio production organizations.

1702 ■ National Religious Broadcasters
9510 Technology Dr.
Manassas, VA 20110
Ph: (703)330-7000
Fax: (703)330-7100
E-mail: info@nrb.org
URL: http://nrb.org

Description: Christian communicators. Fosters electronic media access for the Gospel; promotes standards of excellence; integrity and accountability; and provides networking and fellowship opportunities for members.

1703 ■ *Newsclip's Illinois Media*
Newsclip Inc.
363 W Erie St., Ste. 7E
Chicago, IL 60610
Ph: (312)751-7300
E-mail: customerservice@newsclip.com
URL: http://www.newsclip.com/press.htm

Frequency: Annual; Latest edition 2009. **Pages:** 360. **Covers:** About 1,200 newspapers, magazines, and radio, television, and cable television stations located in or serving Illinois. **Entries include:** For print media--Name of publication, address, phone; names of publisher, editors, and advertising managers; deadlines; photo requirements; publication dates; circulation areas and figures; advertising rates. For stations--Address, phone; names of general manager, news director, and advertising manager; station format; wire services used; newscast times; interview shows offered; names of producers and other contacts; prime time advertising rates; broadcast areas and hours. **Arrangement:** Classified by type of medium, then geographical. **Indexes:** Geographical.

1704 ■ Women in Cable Telecommunications
2000 K St. NW, Ste. 350
Washington, DC 20006
Ph: (202)827-4794
Fax: (202)450-5596
E-mail: membership@wict.org
URL: http://www.wict.org

Description: Empowers and educates women to achieve their professional goals by providing opportunities for leadership, networking and advocacy. **Members:** 5,000.

Job Hunter's Sourcebook, 14th Edition

127

SOURCES OF HELP-WANTED ADS

1705 ■ Accounting and Finance
Blackwell Publishing Inc.
350 Main St.
Malden, MA 02148
Ph: (781)388-8200
Free: 800-216-2522
Fax: (781)388-8210
E-mail: journaladsusa@bos.blackwellpublishing.com
URL: http://as.wiley.com/WileyCDA/WileyTitle/productCd-ACFI.html

Frequency: Quarterly. **Price:** $469 Institutions print + online, Australia/New Zealand; $408 Institutions print or online, Australia/New Zealand; $633 Institutions print + online; $551 Institutions print or online; £441 Institutions print + online; £383 Institutions print or online. **Description:** Journal focusing on accounting and finance.

1706 ■ Boomer Market Advisor
Summit Business Media
5081 Olympic Blvd.
Erlanger, KY 41018
Ph: (859)692-2100
Free: 800-543-0874
Fax: (859)692-2000
URLs: http://www.advisorone.com; http://https://highline-sub.halldata.com/site/HLM000747XEnew/init.do

Frequency: Monthly. **Price:** $120 Canada; $160 Other countries. **Description:** Magazine for financial planners who work with variable products.

1707 ■ Brookings Papers on Economic Activity
Brookings Institution Press
1775 Massachusetts Ave. NW
Washington, DC 20036
Ph: (202)797-6000
Free: 800-275-1447
Fax: (202)797-6195
E-mail: brookingspapers@brookings.edu
URL: http://www.brookings.edu/about/projects/bpea

Frequency: Semiannual. **Price:** $60 Individuals; $100 Institutions; $74 Other countries; $114 Institutions, other countries. **Description:** Publication covering economics and business.

1708 ■ Commercial Lending Review
Wolters Kluwer Law & Business - CCH
CCH Inc.
2700 Lake Cook Rd.
Riverwoods, IL 60015
Ph: (847)267-7000
Fax: (978)371-2961
E-mail: cust_serv@cch.com
URL: http://www.commerciallendingreview.com/

Frequency: Bimonthly. **Price:** $445 Individuals. **Description:** Journal covering all aspects of lending

for commercial banks, community and regional banks and other financial institutions.

1709 ■ Foundations and Trends in Finance
Now Publishers
PO Box 1024
Hanover, MA 02339-1001
Ph: (781)871-0245
E-mail: zac.rolnik@nowpublishers.com
URL: http://www.nowpublishers.com/product.aspx?product=FIN

Frequency: Irregular. **Price:** $400 Individuals online only; $470 Individuals print and online; €400 Other countries online only; €470 Other countries print and online. **Description:** Academic journal that covers corporate finance, financial markets, asset pricing, and derivatives.

1710 ■ Journal of Applied Finance
Financial Management Association International
University of South Florida
College of Business Administration
4202 E Fowler Ave., BSN 3331
Tampa, FL 33620-5500
Ph: (813)974-2084
Fax: (813)974-3318
E-mail: fma@coba.usf.edu
URL: http://69.175.2.130/~finman/Publications/JAF.htm

Frequency: Semiannual; in spring and fall. **Price:** $75 Individuals; $150 Individuals/2 years; $150 Individuals/3 years, special offer. **Description:** Features scientific debate on the theory, practice, and education of finance.

1711 ■ Journal of Public Budgeting and Finance
American Association for Budget and Program Analysis
PO Box 1157
Falls Church, VA 22041
Ph: (703)941-4300
Fax: (703)941-1535
E-mail: aabpa@aabpa.org
URL: http://www.aabpa.org/main/pubs.htm

Frequency: Quarterly. **Description:** Journal covering public finance.

1712 ■ Strategic Finance: Leadership Strategies in Accounting, Finance, and Information Management
Institute of Management Accountants
10 Paragon Dr., Ste. 1
Montvale, NJ 07645-1774
Ph: (201)573-9000
Free: 800-638-4427
Fax: (201)474-1600
E-mail: ima@imanet.org
URL: http://www.imanet.org/publications.asp

Frequency: Monthly. **Price:** $210 Nonmembers; $48 Members; $25 Students; $18 Single issue back issue. **Description:** Magazine reporting on corporate

finance, accounting, cash management, and budgeting.

1713 ■ Wilmott Magazine
John Wiley & Sons Inc.
111 River St.
Hoboken, NJ 07030-5774
Ph: (201)748-6000
Free: 800-225-5945
Fax: (201)748-6088
E-mail: info@wiley.com
URLs: http://www.wilmott.com; http://onlinelibrary.wiley.com/journal/10.1002/(ISSN)1541-8286

Frequency: Bimonthly. **Price:** €528 Institutions, other countries print only; £395 Institutions print only; $695 Institutions, other countries print only. **Description:** Journal focusing on the quantitative finance community and concentrating on practicalities.

EMPLOYER DIRECTORIES AND NETWORKING LISTS

1714 ■ Barron's Finance and Investment Handbook
Barron's Educational Series Inc.
250 Wireless Blvd.
Hauppauge, NY 11788
Ph: (631)434-3311
Free: 800-645-3476
Fax: (631)434-3723
E-mail: barrons@barronseduc.com
URL: http://barronseduc.stores.yahoo.net/0764162691.html

Frequency: Latest edition 8th; 2010. **Price:** $39.99 Individuals list price; $35.99 Individuals web price. **Pages:** 1,168. **Covers:** More than 6,000 publicly traded corporations in the U.S. and Canada. **Entries include:** Name, address, phone, fax of all brokerage and mutual funds firms, banks, savings and loan companies, insurance companies, federal and state regulators, and major investment publications.

1715 ■ Internet Guide to Personal Finance and Investment
Greenwood Electronic Media
c/o ABC-CLIO
130 Cremona Dr.
Santa Barbara, CA 93117
Ph: (805)968-1911
Free: 800-368-6868
Fax: (866)270-3856
E-mail: customerservice@abc-clio.com
URL: http://www.abc-clio.com/product.aspx?id=2147495461

Price: $75 Single issue Paperback. **Pages:** 364. **Covers:** Over 1,400 Web sites regarding personal finance and investment. **Entries include:** Name of Web site, URL, sponsor of site, and description of contents. **Indexes:** Website title; Sponsor; Subject.

HANDBOOKS AND MANUALS

1716 ■ *Assistant Budget Analyst*
National Learning Corporation
212 Michael Dr.
Syosset, NY 11791
Ph: (516)921-8888
Free: 800-632-8888
Fax: (516)921-8743
E-mail: info@passbooks.com
URL: http://www.passbooks.com
Description: 2009. $34.95 (paper). Serves as an exam preparation guide for assistant budget analysts.

1717 ■ *Associate Budget Analyst*
National Learning Corporation
212 Michael Dr.
Syosset, NY 11791
Ph: (516)921-8888
Free: 800-632-8888
Fax: (516)921-8743
E-mail: info@passbooks.com
URL: http://www.passbooks.com
Description: 2009. $39.95 (paper). Serves as an exam preparation guide for associate budget analysts.

1718 ■ *Opportunities in Financial Careers*
The McGraw-Hill Companies Inc.
PO Box 182604
Columbus, OH 43272
Ph: (212)512-2000
Free: 877-833-5524
Fax: (614)759-3749
E-mail: customer.service@mcgraw-hill.com
URL: http://www.mcgraw-hill.com
Description: Michael Sumichrast and Martin A. Sumichrast. 2004. $13.95 (paper). 160 pages. A guide to planning for and seeking opportunities in this challenging field.

1719 ■ *The Portable MBA in Finance and Accounting*
John Wiley & Sons, Inc.
1 Wiley Dr.
Somerset, NJ 08873
Free: 877-762-2974
Fax: (800)597-3299
E-mail: custserv@wiley.com
URL: http://www.wiley.com
Description: Theodore Grossman and John Leslie Livingstone. 2009. $34.95. 624 pages. Offers advice to businesses. Includes preparing budgets, implementing business plans, and evaluating acquisition targets.

EMPLOYMENT AGENCIES AND SEARCH FIRMS

1720 ■ Capitol Staffing Inc.
460 Briarwood Dr., Briarwood 1 Bldg., Ste. 110
Jackson, MS 39206
Ph: (601)957-1755
Fax: (601)957-3880
E-mail: info@capitolstaffing.com
URL: http://www.capitolstaffing.com
Description: Personnel consultancy that focuses on office administration, management, sales, accounting, medical, information technology, accounting, and engineering/technical fields. Industries served: insurance, finance, medical, communications, investment, industry, and small businesses.

ONLINE JOB SOURCES AND SERVICES

1721 ■ American Association of Finance and Accounting
URL: http://www.aafa.com
Description: Alliance of executive search firms specializing in the recruitment and placement of finance and accounting professionals. Contains career opportunities site with job board for both job seekers and hiring employers. One does not have to be a member to search for jobs.

1722 ■ Budget Analyst Jobs
URL: http://www.budgetanalystjobs.org
Description: Serves as a niche job board for budget analyst professionals. Offers employment opportunities and candidate recruiting.

1723 ■ The Digital Financier
URL: http://www.dfin.com
Description: Job postings from financial companies. Offers links to major job search websites. Has leads for further training and allows companies to post its own job links.

1724 ■ FinancialServicesCrossing.com
URL: http://www.financialservicescrossing.com
Description: Offers a collection of top financial services job openings carefully researched by analysts. Provides instant access to a comprehensive pool of listings in the industry of financial services.

1725 ■ Get Budget Analyst Jobs
URL: http://www.getbudgetanalystjobs.com
Description: Features job listings for budget analysts. Offers services for employment and staffing needs of hiring and recruitment managers.

OTHER SOURCES

1726 ■ *Career Opportunities in Banking, Finance, and Insurance*
InfoBase Holdings Inc.
132 W 31st., 17 Fl.
New York, NY 10001-3406
Ph: (212)967-8800
Fax: (800)678-3633
E-mail: info@infobasepublishing.com
URL: http://factsonfile.infobasepublishing.com
Frequency: Latest edition 2nd; Published February, 2007. **Price:** $49.50 Individuals hardcover. **Description:** Thomas P. Fitch. Second edition, 2007. 267 pages. Lists of colleges with programs supporting banking, finance, and industry; professional associations; professional certifications; regulatory agencies; and Internet resources for career planning. **Publication includes:** Lists of colleges with programs supporting banking, finance, and industry; professional associations; professional certifications; regulatory agencies; and Internet resources for career planning. Principal content of publication is job descriptions for professions in the banking, finance, and insurance industries. **Indexes:** Alphabetical.

SOURCES OF HELP-WANTED ADS

1727 ■ *Archetype*
Woodwork Institute
3188 Industrial Blvd.
West Sacramento, CA 95798-0247
Ph: (916)372-9943
Fax: (916)372-9950
E-mail: info@woodinst.com
URL: http://www.wicnet.org/publications/archetype
.asp
Frequency: Semiannual. **Description:** Journal of the Woodwork Institute.

1728 ■ *Builder and Developer*
Peninsula Publishing Inc.
1602 Monrovia Ave.
Newport Beach, CA 92663-2808
Ph: (949)631-0308
Fax: (949)631-2475
E-mail: nslevin@penpubinc.com
URL: http://www.bdmag.com
Frequency: 11/yr. **Description:** Magazine for home-builders.

1729 ■ *Builder: The Magazine of the National Association of Home Builders*
DoveTale Publishers
1 Thomas Cir. NW
Washington, DC 20005
Ph: (202)339-0744
Free: 877-275-8647
Fax: (202)785-1974
E-mail: builder@omeda.com
URLs: http://www.hanleywood.com/default.aspx
?page=magazines; http://www.builderonline.com
Frequency: 13/yr. **Price:** $29.95 U.S. and Canada; $54.95 U.S. and Canada 2 years; $192 Other countries. **Description:** Magazine covering housing and construction industry.

1730 ■ *Concrete & Masonry Construction Products*
DoveTale Publishers
1 Thomas Cir. NW
Washington, DC 20005
Ph: (202)339-0744
Free: 877-275-8647
Fax: (202)785-1974
E-mail: hwmicustomerservice@hanleywood.com
URL: http://www.hanleywoodopportunities.com/Index
.asp?Cat=cc&Pub=cmcp&Sect=Intro
Frequency: Bimonthly. **Price:** Free. **Description:** Publication that covers carpenter tips, tools, and up keep.

1731 ■ *Constructor: The Construction Management Magazine*
Associated General Contractors of America
2300 Wilson Blvd., Ste. 400
Arlington, VA 22201
Ph: (703)548-3118
Free: 800-242-1767
Fax: (703)548-3119
E-mail: info@agc.org
URL: http://constructor.agc.org/
Frequency: Bimonthly. **Price:** $95 Individuals. **Description:** Management magazine for the Construction Industry.

1732 ■ *Daily Journal of Commerce*
New Orleans Publishing Group Inc.
111 Veterans Blvd., Ste. 1440
Metairie, LA 70005
Ph: (504)834-9292
Fax: (504)832-3550
E-mail: mail@nopg.com
URLs: http://www.djc-gp.com; http://www.djcgulfcoast
.com
Frequency: Daily. **Price:** $525 Individuals online; $375 Individuals 6 months; $225 Individuals 3 months. **Description:** Trade newspaper covering construction news in Louisiana and Mississippi.

1733 ■ *Green Home Builder: America's Premier Green Homebuilding Resource*
Peninsula Publishing Inc.
1602 Monrovia Ave.
Newport Beach, CA 92663-2808
Ph: (949)631-0308
Fax: (949)631-2475
E-mail: nslevin@penpubinc.com
URL: http://www.greenhomebuildermag.com/
Frequency: Quarterly. **Description:** Magazine for home builders and home building industry.

1734 ■ *Journal of Light Construction*
DoveTale Publishers
1 Thomas Cir. NW
Washington, DC 20005
Ph: (202)339-0744
Free: 877-275-8647
Fax: (202)785-1974
E-mail: hwmicustomerservice@hanleywood.com
URL: http://www.jlconline.com
Description: Monthly. Contains articles, news, and information related to construction. Topics include building science, foundation and framing, heating, ventilation, and air conditioning (HVAC) and plumbing.

1735 ■ *Kitchen and Bath Design News*
Cygnus Business Media Inc.
1233 Janesville Ave.
Fort Atkinson, WI 53538
Free: 800-547-7377
E-mail: info@cygnus.com
URL: http://www.cygnusb2b.com/PropertyPub.cfm
?PropertyID=78
Frequency: Monthly. **Description:** Trade journal.

1736 ■ *Oxymag*
Elsevier Science Inc.
Secondary Publishing Division
650 Ave. of the Americas
New York, NY 10011
Ph: (212)633-3980
Free: 888-437-4636
Fax: (212)633-3975
URL: http://www.elsevier.com/wps/find/journalde-scription.cws_home/709679/description#description
Frequency: 6/yr. **Description:** Journal related to the construction field covering information in the manufacture of commercial, industrial, spark proof and decorative terrazzo floors, flooring for railroad boxcars, industrial fireproof coatings, fire-resistant marine interior deckings and a variety of building units.

1737 ■ *Panel World*
Hatton-Brown Publishers Inc.
225 Hanrick St.
Montgomery, AL 36102
Ph: (334)834-1170
Free: 800-669-5613
Fax: (334)834-4525
E-mail: dianne@hattonbrown.com
URL: http://www.panelworldmag.com
Frequency: Bimonthly. **Description:** Business magazine serving the worldwide veneer, plywood, and panel board industry.

1738 ■ *Professional Builder: The Magazine of the Housing and Light Construction Industry*
SGC Horizon L.L.C.
3030 W Salt Creek Ln., Ste. 201
Arlington Heights, IL 60005
Ph: (847)391-1000
Fax: (847)390-0408
URL: http://www.housingzone.com/
professionalbuilder
Frequency: Monthly. **Price:** Free. **Description:** The integrated engineering magazine of the building construction industry.

1739 ■ *Replacement Contractor*
DoveTale Publishers
1 Thomas Cir. NW
Washington, DC 20005
Ph: (202)339-0744
Free: 877-275-8647
Fax: (202)785-1974
E-mail: rcon@omeda.com
URLs: http://www.omeda.com/rcon/; http://www
.replacementcontractoronline.com/
Frequency: 4/yr. **Price:** $29.95 Individuals; $39.95 Canada; $49.95 Other countries. **Description:** Magazine for contractors engaged in roofing, siding, decking and window replacement.

1740 ■ *Residential Contractor: The U.S. Home Construction Industry Source*
Peninsula Publishing Inc.
1602 Monrovia Ave.
Newport Beach, CA 92663-2808
Ph: (949)631-0308
Fax: (949)631-2475
E-mail: nslevin@penpubinc.com
URL: http://www.residentialcontractormag.com/

Frequency: Quarterly. **Description:** Magazine for small volume residential builders, contractors, and specialty trades.

1741 ■ *Wood & Wood Products*
Vance Publishing Corp.
400 Knightsbridge Pkwy.
Lincolnshire, IL 60069-3613
Ph: (847)634-2600
Free: 800-255-5113
Fax: (847)634-4342
E-mail: info@vancepublishing.com
URLs: http://www.vancepublishing.com; http://woodworkingnetwork.com/IssueArchives.aspx?fid=WWN-WWP-ARCHIVES

Frequency: Monthly. **Description:** Magazine for furniture, cabinet, and woodworking industry.

Employer Directories and Networking Lists

1742 ■ *ABC Today--Associated Builders and Contractors National Membership Directory Issue*
Associated Builders and Contractors
440 1st St. NW, Ste. 200
Washington, DC 20001
E-mail: gotquestions@abc.org
URL: http://www.abc.org

Frequency: Annual; Latest Edition 2011. **Price:** $150 plus $7.00 shipping. **Publication includes:** List of approximately 19,000 member construction contractors and suppliers. **Entries include:** Company name, address, phone, name of principal executive, code to volume of business, business specialty. **Arrangement:** Classified by chapter, then by work specialty.

1743 ■ *ENR--Top 400 Construction Contractors Issue*
The McGraw-Hill Companies Inc.
PO Box 182604
Columbus, OH 43272
Ph: (212)512-2000
Free: 877-833-5524
Fax: (614)759-3749
E-mail: customer.service@mcgraw-hill.com
URL: http://enr.construction.com/toplists/Contractors/001-100.asp

Frequency: Annual; Latest edition 2011. **Price:** $35 Individuals. **Publication includes:** List of 400 United States contractors receiving largest dollar volumes of contracts in preceding calendar year. Separate lists of 50 largest design/construct management firms; 50 largest program and construction managers; 25 building contractors; 25 heavy contractors. **Entries include:** Company name, headquarters location, total value of contracts received in preceding year, value of foreign contracts, countries in which operated, construction specialties. **Arrangement:** By total value of contracts received.

Handbooks and Manuals

1744 ■ *Construction*
InfoBase Holdings Inc.
132 W 31st., 17 Fl.
New York, NY 10001-3406
Ph: (212)967-8800

Fax: (800)678-3633
E-mail: info@infobasepublishing.com
URL: http://www.ferguson.infobasepublishing.com

Price: $30 Hardcover. **Description:** 2010. 128 pages. Contains profiles of 20 careers in the field of construction with emphasis on the nature of work, requirements, salary, and career outlook. Includes full-color photographs, index, glossary, resources, and side bars.

1745 ■ *Construction Technology Trainee Guide*
Prentice Hall
200 Old Tappan Rd.
Old Tappan, NJ 07675
Free: 800-223-1360
Fax: (800)445-6991
URL: http://www.prenticehall.com

Description: Third Edition, 2009. $186.67 (hardcover). 936 pages. Features a highly illustrated design, technical hints and tips from construction industry experts, and review questions.

1746 ■ *Opportunities in Carpentry Careers*
The McGraw-Hill Companies Inc.
PO Box 182604
Columbus, OH 43272
Ph: (212)512-2000
Free: 877-833-5524
Fax: (614)759-3749
E-mail: customer.service@mcgraw-hill.com
URL: http://www.mcgraw-hill.com

Description: Roger Sheldon. 2007. $13.95 (paper). 221 pages. Discusses how to get started and covers the job market. Illustrated.

Online Job Sources and Services

1747 ■ *Build Your Future Career Center*
URL: http://www.jobtarget.com/home/home.cfm?site_id=13781

Description: Features construction industry job listings. Includes resume bank that lists profiles voluntarily posted by job seekers.

1748 ■ *BuildZ Construction Jobs Network*
URL: http://buildz.net

Description: Provides listings of construction jobs throughout the U.S. Features news related to the construction industry.

1749 ■ *CarpenterCareers.com*
URL: http://www.carpentercareers.com

Description: Free for job seekers and affordable for employers. Caters to different professionals in the carpentry industry. Allows job seekers to search for jobs in specific locations.

1750 ■ *CarpenterJobsite.com*
URL: http://www.carpenterjobsite.com

Description: Serves as an online career community for the carpentry industry. Provides new job openings for carpenters, latest research in the construction and extraction employment markets, and career articles.

1751 ■ *Construction Help Wanted*
URL: http://www.constructionhelpwanted.net

Description: Serves as an online resource for those seeking jobs in construction. Allows people to look for specified jobs according to location.

1752 ■ *Construction Jobs Network*
URL: http://constructionjobs.net

Description: Provides job seekers access to construction employment opportunities for both construction management, construction professional and construction trade jobs. Features construction jobs, employer, and resume directories.

1753 ■ *ConstructionGigs.net*
URL: http://www.constructiongigs.net

Description: Provides an up-to-date listings of job opportunities and career resources for construction workers.

1754 ■ *ConstructMyFuture.com*
URL: http://www.constructmyfuture.com

Description: Offers comprehensive information for students, parents, and educators on varied careers in construction. Includes a searchable database of colleges, universities and trade schools that offer degrees in construction fields.

1755 ■ *IHireBuildingTrades*
URL: http://www.ihirebuildingtrades.com

Description: Serves as a job posting board that specializes in matching building jobs and construction candidates.

1756 ■ *Locate Carpenter Jobs*
URL: http://www.locatecarpenterjobs.com

Description: Provides employment opportunities to carpenters nationwide.

1757 ■ *USA Construction Jobs*
URL: http://www.usaconstructionjobs.com

Description: Features job listings in construction and general labor.

Tradeshows

1758 ■ *Florida Industrial Woodworking Expo*
Trade Shows, Inc.
PO Box 2000
Claremont, NC 28610-2000
Ph: (828)459-9894
Fax: (828)459-1312
E-mail: tsi@tsiexpos.com

Frequency: Biennial. **Primary Exhibits:** Machinery, tooling, supplies, and services for the furniture, cabinet, casegoods, millwork, and industrial wood products industries.

1759 ■ *International Woodworking Machinery and Furniture Supply Fair - USA*
Schneider Publishing Company Inc.
11835 W Olympic Blvd., 12th Fl.
Los Angeles, CA 90064
Ph: (310)577-3700
Free: 877-577-3700
Fax: (310)577-3715
E-mail: info@schneiderpublishing.com
URL: http://www.schneiderpublishing.com

Frequency: Biennial. **Primary Exhibits:** Woodworking machinery and supplies for furniture, woodworking, kitchen cabinets, architectural woodwork, and specialty wood products. **Dates and Locations:** Atlanta, GA; World Congress Center.

1760 ■ *Mid-Atlantic Industrial Woodworking Expo*
Trade Shows, Inc.
PO Box 2000
Claremont, NC 28610-2000
Ph: (828)459-9894
Fax: (828)459-1312
E-mail: tsi@tsiexpos.com

Frequency: Annual. **Primary Exhibits:** Woodworking and furniture industry equipment, supplies, and services.

Online and Database Services

1761 ■ *CareersForBuilders.com*
URL: http://www.careersforbuilders.com

Description: Features a searchable database of

employment opportunities for different types of construction work. Includes career resources on job hunting tools and tips.

OTHER SOURCES

1762 ■ Associated Builders and Contractors
440 1st St. NW, Ste. 200
Washington, DC 20001
E-mail: gotquestions@abc.org
URL: http://www.abc.org
Description: Construction contractors, subcontractors, suppliers and associates. Aims to foster and perpetuate the principles of rewarding construction workers and management on the basis of merit. Sponsors management education programs and craft training; also sponsors apprenticeship and skill training programs. Disseminates technological and labor relations information.

1763 ■ Associated General Contractors of America
2300 Wilson Blvd., Ste. 400
Arlington, VA 22201
Ph: (703)548-3118
Free: 800-242-1767
Fax: (703)548-3119
E-mail: info@agc.org
URL: http://www.agc.org
Description: General construction contractors; subcontractors; industry suppliers; service firms. Provides market services through its divisions. Conducts special conferences and seminars designed specifically for construction firms. Compiles statistics on job accidents reported by member firms. Maintains 65 committees, including joint cooperative committees with other associations and liaison committees with federal agencies.

1764 ■ Associated Specialty Contractors
3 Bethesda Metro Ctr., Ste. 1100
Bethesda, MD 20814
E-mail: dgw@necanet.org
URL: http://www.assoc-spec-con.org

Description: Works to promote efficient management and productivity. Coordinates the work of specialized branches of the industry in management information, research, public information, government relations and construction relations. Serves as a liaison among specialty trade associations in the areas of public relations, government relations, and with other organizations. Seeks to avoid unnecessary duplication of effort and expense or conflicting programs among affiliates. Identifies areas of interest and problems shared by members, and develops positions and approaches on such problems. **Members:** 9.

1765 ■ Cabinet Makers Association
PO Box 14276
Milwaukee, WI 53214-0276
Ph: (414)377-1340
E-mail: director@cabinetmakers.org
URL: http://www.cabinetmakers.org

Description: Represents cabinetmakers and woodworkers from both the residential and commercial markets who get together and share their knowledge and experience to help one another. Aims to uphold professionalism in the industry by providing its members with networking opportunities, continuing education, and ongoing professional development.

1766 ■ *Careers for Crafty People and Other Dexterous Types*
The McGraw-Hill Companies Inc.
PO Box 182604
Columbus, OH 43272
Ph: (212)512-2000
Free: 877-833-5524
Fax: (614)759-3749
E-mail: customer.service@mcgraw-hill.com
URL: http://www.mcgraw-hill.com

Description: Mark Rowh. Third edition, 2006. $13.95 (paper). 160 pages. **Includes:** List of agencies in the

United States and Canada that offer information on education and training, as well as opportunities for practicing craft making in various geographical regions. List of agencies in the United States and Canada that offer information on education and training, as well as opportunities for practicing craft making in various geographical regions. **Entries include:** Name, address, URL.

1767 ■ National Association of Home Builders - Systems Builder Council
1201 15th St. NW
Washington, DC 20005
Ph: (202)266-8200
Free: 800-368-5242
Fax: (202)266-8400
URL: http://www.nahb.org/reference_list.aspx?sectionID=815

Description: Operates under the Building Systems Council of NAHB. Modular building manufacturers. Monitors state and federal housing legislation that impacts the building industry. Provides a forum for communication, networking for those involved in manufacturing modular building systems. Addresses and solves problems specific to the council; offers consumer leads service.

1768 ■ National Association of Women in Construction
327 S Adams St.
Fort Worth, TX 76104
Ph: (817)877-5551
Free: 800-552-3506
Fax: (817)877-0324
E-mail: nawic@nawic.org
URL: http://www.nawic.org

Description: Seeks to enhance the success of women in the construction industry.

Sources of Help-Wanted Ads

1769 ■ *Chow*
Cbs Interactive Inc.
235 2nd St.
San Francisco, CA 94105-3124
Ph: (415)344-2000
Fax: (415)395-9207
URL: http://www.chow.com
Frequency: Bimonthly. **Price:** $18.95 Individuals. **Description:** Magazine that covers food preparation techniques, recipes, columns on specialty food items, how-to articles and editorials.

1770 ■ *Foodservice East*
The Newbury Street Group Inc.
93 Massachusetts Ave., Ste. 306
Boston, MA 02115
Ph: (617)267-2224
Fax: (617)267-5554
URL: http://www.foodserviceeast.com/
Frequency: Bimonthly; 6/year. **Price:** $30 Individuals. **Description:** Compact Tabloid covering trends and analysis of the foodservice industry in the Northeast. A business-to-business publication featuring news, analysis and trends for the Northeast food service professional.

1771 ■ *Good Things to Eat*
URL: http://www.somegoodthingstoeat.com/
Frequency: Quarterly. **Price:** $9.95 Individuals; $28.50 Canada. **Description:** Magazine featuring food and recipes.

1772 ■ *The Gourmet Connection Magazine*
CAPCO Marketing
8417 Oswego Rd., Ste. 177
Baldwinsville, NY 13027-8813
Ph: (315)699-1687
Fax: (315)699-1689
E-mail: cookbook@capcomarketing.com
URL: http://tgcmagazine.com/
Description: Magazine on gourmet food and the finer things in life. Covers a wide range of topics from nutritional information, and diet tips, to recipes, and information on arranging parties.

1773 ■ *The National Culinary Review: Official Magazine of the American Culinary Federation*
American Culinary Federation
180 Center Place Way
Saint Augustine, FL 32095
Free: 800-624-9458
Fax: (904)825-4758
E-mail: acf@acfchefs.net
URL: http://www.acfchefs.org/Content/Navigation-Menu2/About/Media/Publications/default.htm
Frequency: Monthly. **Price:** $60 Individuals; $200

Other countries. **Description:** Trade magazine covering food and cooking.

1774 ■ *Plate*
Marketing & Technology Group Inc.
1415 N Dayton St.
Chicago, IL 60622
Ph: (312)266-3311
Fax: (312)266-3363
URL: http://www.plateonline.com
Frequency: Bimonthly; Monthly. **Description:** Provides regular columns and features on new foods, industry news, nutrition and food safety.

1775 ■ *Real Food: The magazine for the way we eat today*
Greenspring Media Group Inc.
600 US Trust Bldg., 730 2nd Ave. S
Minneapolis, MN 55402-1012
Ph: (612)371-5800
Free: 800-933-4398
Fax: (612)371-5801
E-mail: letters@mnmo.com
URL: http://www.realfoodmag.com/
Frequency: Quarterly. **Price:** $20 Individuals. **Description:** Magazine featuring food choices.

1776 ■ *Restaurant Hospitality: Ideas for Full Service Restaurants*
Intertec Publishing
5 Penn Plz., 13th Fl.
New York, NY 10001-1810
Ph: (212)613-9700
Free: 800-795-5445
Fax: (212)613-9749
E-mail: bethany.weaver@penton.com
URLs: http://restaurant-hospitality.com; http://www.penton.com
Frequency: Monthly. **Price:** Free. **Description:** Dedicated to the success of full service restaurants and edited for chefs and other commercial foodservice professionals. Includes new food and equipment products and trends, menu and recipe ideas, industry news, new technology, food safety, emerging new concepts, consumer attitudes and trends, labor and training, and profiles of successful operations.

1777 ■ *Simple & Delicious*
Reiman Publications L.L.C.
5400 S 60th St.
Greendale, WI 53129
Ph: (414)423-0100
Free: 800-344-6913
Fax: (414)423-3840
E-mail: subscriberservices@reimanpub.com
URL: http://www.tasteofhome.com/Simple---Delicious-Magazine
Frequency: Bimonthly. **Price:** $14.98 Individuals; $19.98 Canada. **Description:** Magazine covering recipes and kitchen shortcuts, 10-minute dishes, 5-ingredient recipes, 30-minute meals, and mix and match meal planner.

1778 ■ *Sizzle: The American Culinary Federation Quarterly for Students of Cooking*
American Culinary Federation
180 Center Place Way
Saint Augustine, FL 32095
Free: 800-624-9458
Fax: (904)825-4758
E-mail: acf@acfchefs.net
URL: http://www.acfchefs.org/Content/Navigation-Menu2/About/Media/Publications/default.htm
Frequency: Quarterly. **Price:** $19.95 Individuals; $34.95 Two years; $9.95 Individuals bulk; $150 Other countries. **Description:** Magazine for culinary students offering food trends, career information, and how-tos.

Handbooks and Manuals

1779 ■ *Careers for Gourmets and Others Who Relish Food*
The McGraw-Hill Companies Inc.
PO Box 182604
Columbus, OH 43272
Ph: (212)512-2000
Free: 877-833-5524
Fax: (614)759-3749
E-mail: customer.service@mcgraw-hill.com
URL: http://www.mhprofessional.com
Frequency: Latest edition 2nd, April 2002. **Price:** $12.95 Individuals E-book and Book. **Pages:** 192. **Publication includes:** List of government agencies, companies, colleges and universities, and other organizations that provide opportunities in or information about a variety of careers that involve food. **Entries include:** Organization name, address. Principal content of publication is a review of career opportunities for those who enjoy cooking.

1780 ■ *Catering on Campus: A Handbook on Catering in Colleges and Universities*
Colman Publishers
1147 Elmwood
Stockton, CA 95204
Ph: (209)464-9503
Fax: (209)262-4257
URL: http://www.paulfairbrook.com
Description: Paul Fairbrook. 2004. $50.00. Designed to help catering managers at colleges do a better job of selling and providing quality and profitable catering services.

1781 ■ *How to Start a Home-Based Catering Business*
Globe Pequot Press Inc.
246 Goose Ln.
Guilford, CT 06437
Ph: (203)458-4500
Free: 888-249-7586

Fax: (800)820-2329
E-mail: gpp.info@globepequot.com
URL: http://www.globepequot.com

Description: Denise Vivaldo. Sixth edition, 2010. $18.95. 256 pages. Part of the Home-Based Business Series.

1782 ■ On-Premise Catering: Hotels, Convention Centers, Arenas, Clubs, and More
John Wiley & Sons Inc.
111 River St.
Hoboken, NJ 07030-5774
Ph: (201)748-6000
Free: 800-225-5945
Fax: (201)748-6088
E-mail: info@wiley.com
URL: http://www.wiley.com

Description: Patti J. Shock, John M. Stefanelli and Cheryl Sgovio. 2011. $70.00. 496 pages. Covers the essential skills and knowledge a professional needs to succeed in the field. Serves as guide to catering in hotels, banquet halls, wedding facilities, and other venues. Features modern technological trends in the catering industry, such as online marketing, social media and digital proposals. Includes topics on modern decor and effective menu writing.

1783 ■ Opportunities in Restaurant Careers
The McGraw-Hill Companies Inc.
PO Box 182604
Columbus, OH 43272
Ph: (212)512-2000
Free: 877-833-5524
Fax: (614)759-3749
E-mail: customer.service@mcgraw-hill.com
URL: http://www.mcgraw-hill.com

Description: Carol Caprione Chmelynski. 2004. $13.95 (paper). 160 pages. Covers opportunities in the food service industry and details salaries, benefits, training opportunities, and professional associations. Special emphasis is put on becoming a successful restaurant manager by working up through the ranks. Illustrated.

1784 ■ The Professional Caterer's Handbook: How to Open and Operate a Financially Successful Catering Business
Atlantic Publishing Co.
1210 SW 23rd Pl.
Ocala, FL 34471-1825
Ph: (352)622-1825
Free: 800-814-1132
Fax: (352)622-1875
E-mail: sales@atlantic-pub.com
URL: http://www.atlantic-pub.com

Description: Douglas Robert Brown and Lora Arduser. 2005. $79.95. Comprehensive guide for planning, starting, and operating a catering business; includes companion CD-ROM. Covers marketing, management, budgeting, home-based catering, ways for restaurants to add catering services to existing businesses, forms, Web sites, and more.

ONLINE JOB SOURCES AND SERVICES

1785 ■ FoodIndustryJobs.com
URL: http://www.foodindustryjobs.com

Description: Job databank and resume submission service for food industry workers.

1786 ■ HCareers.com
URL: http://www.hcareers.com

Description: Connects employers and candidates within the hospitality industry. Enables candidates to search for jobs within a specific industry or location.

1787 ■ New Restaurant and Food Jobs
URL: http://www.newrestaurantandfoodjobs.com

Description: Provides an online listing of companies

with available restaurant and food jobs in all specialties.

TRADESHOWS

1788 ■ Annual Hotel, Motel, and Restaurant Supply Show of the Southeast
Leisure Time Unlimited, Inc.
708 Main St.
Myrtle Beach, SC 29577
Ph: (843)448-9483
Free: 800-261-5591
Fax: (843)626-1513
E-mail: ltushows@sc.rr.com
URL: http://www.leisuretimeunlimited.com/

Frequency: Annual. **Primary Exhibits:** Carpeting, furniture, coffee makers, produce companies, wine and beer and food companies, and services to motels, hotels, and restaurants. **Dates and Locations:** Myrtle Beach, SC; Convention Center.

1789 ■ Institute of Food Technologists Annual Meeting and Food Expo
Institute of Food Technologists
525 W Van Buren St., Ste. 1000
Chicago, IL 60607
Ph: (312)782-8424
Free: 800-438-3663
Fax: (312)782-8348
E-mail: info@ift.org
URL: http://www.ift.org

Frequency: Annual. **Primary Exhibits:** Food ingredients, equipment, laboratory equipment and supplies, and other services rendered to the food processing industry.

1790 ■ International Baking Industry Exposition
IBIE Exhibition Management
401 N. Michigan Ave.
Chicago, IL 60611
Ph: (312)644-6610
Fax: (312)644-0575
E-mail: pdwyer@smithbucklin.com
URL: http://ibie2013.org

Primary Exhibits: Baking equipment, supplies, and services.

1791 ■ Louisiana Foodservice Expo
Louisiana Restaurant Association
2700 N Arnoult Rd.
Metairie, LA 70002
Ph: (504)454-2277
Fax: (504)454-2299
E-mail: ericap@lra.org
URL: http://www.lra.org

Frequency: Annual. **Primary Exhibits:** Food service equipment, supplies, and services, food products, furniture, tableware. **Dates and Locations:** New Orleans, LA; Convention Center.

1792 ■ National Association of Catering Executives Experience Conference
National Association of Catering Executives
9891 Broken Land Pkwy., Ste. 301
Columbia, MD 21046
Ph: (410)290-5410
Fax: (410)290-5460
URL: http://www.nace.net

Frequency: Annual. Features educational program, social events, and networking opportunities among peers.

1793 ■ National Restaurant Association Restaurant and Hotel-Motel Show
National Restaurant Association Convention Office
2055 L St., NW
Washington, DC 20036
Ph: (202)331-5900
URL: http://www.restaurant.org

Frequency: Annual. **Primary Exhibits:** Food service

equipment, supplies, and services and food and beverage products for the hospitality industry. Includes international cuisine pavilion. **Dates and Locations:** Chicago, IL; McCormick Place.

OTHER SOURCES

1794 ■ Career Opportunities in the Food and Beverage Industry
InfoBase Holdings Inc.
132 W 31st., 17 Fl.
New York, NY 10001-3406
Ph: (212)967-8800
Fax: (800)678-3633
E-mail: info@infobasepublishing.com
URL: http://www.ferguson.infobasepublishing.com

Description: Barbara Sims-Bell. 2010. $18.95 (paper). 223 pages. Provides information about locating and landing 80 skilled and unskilled jobs in the food and beverage industry. **Includes:** Appendices of trade associations, recruiting organizations, and major agencies. Appendices of trade associations, recruiting organizations, and major agencies.

1795 ■ International Association of Culinary Professionals
1221 Avenue of the Americas, 42nd Fl.
New York, NY 10020
Ph: (646)358-4957
Free: 866-358-4951
Fax: (866)358-2524
E-mail: info@iacp.com
URL: http://www.iacp.com

Description: Represents cooking school owners, food writers, chefs, caterers, culinary specialists, directors, teachers, cookbook authors, food stylists, food photographers, student/apprentices, and individuals in related industries in 20 countries. Promotes the interests of cooking schools, teachers, and culinary professionals. Encourages the exchange of information and education. Promotes professional standards and accreditation procedures. Maintains a Foundation to award culinary scholarships and grants.

1796 ■ International Council on Hotel, Restaurant, and Institutional Education
2810 N Parham Rd., Ste. 230
Richmond, VA 23294
Ph: (804)346-4800
Fax: (804)346-5009
E-mail: publications@chrie.org
URL: http://www.chrie.org

Description: Schools and colleges offering specialized education and training in hospitals, recreation, tourism and hotel, restaurant, and institutional administration; individuals, executives, and students. Provides networking opportunities and professional development.

1797 ■ International Flight Services Association
1100 Johnson Ferry Rd., Ste. 300
Atlanta, GA 30342
Ph: (404)252-3663
Fax: (404)252-0774
E-mail: jpetty@kellencompany.com
URL: http://www.ifsanet.com

Description: Works to serve the needs and interests of the airline and railway personnel, in-flight and railway caterers and suppliers responsible for providing passenger foodservice on regularly scheduled travel routes.

1798 ■ Les Amis d'Escoffier Society of New York
787 Ridgewood Rd.
Millburn, NJ 07041-1541
Ph: (212)414-5820
Fax: (973)379-3117
URL: http://www.escoffier-society.com

Description: An educational organization of professionals in the food and wine industries. Maintains museum, speakers' bureau, hall of fame, and placement service. Sponsors charitable programs. **Members:** 1,650.

1799 ■ National Association of Catering Executives
9891 Broken Land Pkwy., Ste. 301
Columbia, MD 21046
Ph: (410)290-5410
Fax: (410)290-5460
URL: http://www.nace.net

Description: Serves the catering and special events industries. Promotes career success of members and professionalism in the industry. Offers educational programs, certification, and networking opportunities for members.

1800 ■ National Restaurant Association
2055 L St. NW
Washington, DC 20036
Ph: (202)331-5900
Free: 800-424-5156
Fax: (202)331-2429
URL: http://www.restaurant.org

Description: Represents restaurants, cafeterias, clubs, contract foodservice management, drive-ins, caterers, institutional food services and other members of the foodservice industry; also represents establishments belonging to non-affiliated state and local restaurant associations in governmental affairs. Supports foodservice education and research in several educational institutions. Is affiliated with the Educational Foundation of the National Restaurant Association to provide training and education for operators, food and equipment manufacturers, distributors and educators. Has 300,000 member locations.

SOURCES OF HELP-WANTED ADS

1801 ■ *Chef: The Food Magazine for Professionals*
Talcott Communication Corp.
233 N Michigan Ave., Ste. 1780
Chicago, IL 60601
Ph: (312)849-2220
Free: 800-229-1967
Fax: (312)849-2174
E-mail: chef@talcott.com
URL: http://www.chefmagazine.com

Frequency: 11/yr. **Price:** $32 Individuals; $47 Two years; $64 Individuals 3 years; $43 Canada; $96 Other countries. **Description:** Food information for chefs.

1802 ■ *Chow*
Cbs Interactive Inc.
235 2nd St.
San Francisco, CA 94105-3124
Ph: (415)344-2000
Fax: (415)395-9207
URL: http://www.chow.com

Frequency: Bimonthly. **Price:** $18.95 Individuals. **Description:** Magazine that covers food preparation techniques, recipes, columns on specialty food items, how-to articles and editorials.

1803 ■ *Field & Feast: The Magazine of Food, Agriculture & Health*
Field & Feast
PO Box 205
Four Lakes, WA 99014
E-mail: fieldandfeast@aol.com
URL: http://www.fieldandfeast.net

Frequency: Quarterly. **Price:** $19 Individuals. **Description:** Magazine that offers information on organic food cultivation and its health benefits.

1804 ■ *Foodservice East*
The Newbury Street Group Inc.
93 Massachusetts Ave., Ste. 306
Boston, MA 02115
Ph: (617)267-2224
Fax: (617)267-5554
URL: http://www.foodserviceeast.com/

Frequency: Bimonthly; 6/year. **Price:** $30 Individuals. **Description:** Compact Tabloid covering trends and analysis of the foodservice industry in the Northeast. A business-to-business publication featuring news, analysis and trends for the Northeast food service professional.

1805 ■ *Good Things to Eat*
URL: http://www.somegoodthingstoeat.com/

Frequency: Quarterly. **Price:** $9.95 Individuals; $28.50 Canada. **Description:** Magazine featuring food and recipes.

1806 ■ *The Gourmet Connection Magazine*
CAPCO Marketing
8417 Oswego Rd., Ste. 177
Baldwinsville, NY 13027-8813
Ph: (315)699-1687
Fax: (315)699-1689
E-mail: cookbook@capcomarketing.com
URL: http://tgcmagazine.com/

Description: Magazine on gourmet food and the finer things in life. Covers a wide range of topics from nutritional information, and diet tips, to recipes, and information on arranging parties.

1807 ■ *Hotel & Motel Management*
Questex Media Group L.L.C.
600 Superior Ave. E, Ste. 1100
Cleveland, OH 44114
Ph: (216)706-3791
Fax: (216)706-3711
E-mail: sales@questex.com
URL: http://www.hotelmanagement.net/hotel
-management/hotel-management-archive

Frequency: 21/yr. **Price:** $58.85 Individuals; $81.40 Canada and Mexico; $143 Other countries; $75 Individuals additional airmail shipping. **Description:** Magazine (tabloid) covering the global lodging industry.

1808 ■ *The National Culinary Review: Official Magazine of the American Culinary Federation*
American Culinary Federation
180 Center Place Way
Saint Augustine, FL 32095
Free: 800-624-9458
Fax: (904)825-4758
E-mail: acf@acfchefs.net
URL: http://www.acfchefs.org/Content/Navigation-
Menu2/About/Media/Publications/default.htm

Frequency: Monthly. **Price:** $60 Individuals; $200 Other countries. **Description:** Trade magazine covering food and cooking.

1809 ■ *Plate*
Marketing & Technology Group Inc.
1415 N Dayton St.
Chicago, IL 60622
Ph: (312)266-3311
Fax: (312)266-3363
URL: http://www.plateonline.com

Frequency: Bimonthly; Monthly. **Description:** Provides regular columns and features on new foods, industry news, nutrition and food safety.

1810 ■ *Real Food: The magazine for the way we eat today*
Greenspring Media Group Inc.
600 US Trust Bldg., 730 2nd Ave. S
Minneapolis, MN 55402-1012
Ph: (612)371-5800
Free: 800-933-4398

Fax: (612)371-5801
E-mail: letters@mnmo.com
URL: http://www.realfoodmag.com/

Frequency: Quarterly. **Price:** $20 Individuals. **Description:** Magazine featuring food choices.

1811 ■ *Restaurant Hospitality: Ideas for Full Service Restaurants*
Intertec Publishing
5 Penn Plz., 13th Fl.
New York, NY 10001-1810
Ph: (212)613-9700
Free: 800-795-5445
Fax: (212)613-9749
E-mail: bethany.weaver@penton.com
URLs: http://restaurant-hospitality.com; http://www
.penton.com

Frequency: Monthly. **Price:** Free. **Description:** Dedicated to the success of full service restaurants and edited for chefs and other commercial foodservice professionals. Includes new food and equipment products and trends, menu and recipe ideas, industry news, new technology, food safety, emerging new concepts, consumer attitudes and trends, labor and training, and profiles of successful operations.

1812 ■ *Restaurant Startup & Growth: Good Restaurateurs Are Always Learning*
Smooth Propeller Corp.
5215 NW Crooked Rd.
Parkville, MO 64152-3447
Ph: (816)741-5151
Fax: (816)741-6458
E-mail: rsg@spc-mag.com
URL: http://www.restaurantowner.com/mag/

Frequency: Monthly. **Description:** Magazine about starting and operating a restaurant business.

1813 ■ *Simple & Delicious*
Reiman Publications L.L.C.
5400 S 60th St.
Greendale, WI 53129
Ph: (414)423-0100
Free: 800-344-6913
Fax: (414)423-3840
E-mail: subscriberservices@reimanpub.com
URL: http://www.tasteofhome.com/Simple---Delicious
-Magazine

Frequency: Bimonthly. **Price:** $14.98 Individuals; $19.98 Canada. **Description:** Magazine covering recipes and kitchen shortcuts, 10-minute dishes, 5-ingredient recipes, 30-minute meals, and mix and match meal planner.

1814 ■ *Sizzle: The American Culinary Federation Quarterly for Students of Cooking*
American Culinary Federation
180 Center Place Way
Saint Augustine, FL 32095
Free: 800-624-9458

Fax: (904)825-4758
E-mail: acf@acfchefs.net
URL: http://www.acfchefs.org/Content/Navigation-
Menu2/About/Media/Publications/default.htm

Frequency: Quarterly. **Price:** $19.95 Individuals;
$34.95 Two years; $9.95 Individuals bulk; $150 Other
countries. **Description:** Magazine for culinary
students offering food trends, career information, and
how-tos.

HANDBOOKS AND MANUALS

**1815 ▪ *Becoming a Culinary Arts
Professionals***
LearningExpress L.L.C.
2 Rector St., 26th Fl.
New York, NY 10006
Ph: (212)995-2566
Free: 800-295-9556
E-mail: customerservice@learningexpressllc.com
URL: http://www.learningexpressllc.com

Description: LearningExpress Editors. 2010. $16.95
(paper). 208 pages. Details how to navigate the
hundreds of paths to a culinary career available in
the United States. Provides many culinary career options and addresses how to develop new skills or
refine current skills and how to understand the
certification process.

**1816 ▪ *Careers for Gourmets and Others
Who Relish Food***
The McGraw-Hill Companies Inc.
PO Box 182604
Columbus, OH 43272
Ph: (212)512-2000
Free: 877-833-5524
Fax: (614)759-3749
E-mail: customer.service@mcgraw-hill.com
URL: http://www.mhprofessional.com

Frequency: Latest edition 2nd, April 2002. **Price:**
$12.95 Individuals E-book and Book. **Pages:** 192.
Publication includes: List of government agencies,
companies, colleges and universities, and other
organizations that provide opportunities in or information about a variety of careers that involve food.
Entries include: Organization name, address.
Principal content of publication is a review of career
opportunities for those who enjoy cooking.

**1817 ▪ *The Cook's Book: Techniques and
Tips from the World's Master Chefs***
Dorling Kindersley Publishing, Inc.
375 Hudson St., 2nd Fl.
New York, NY 10014
Ph: (646)674-4047
Free: 800-788-6262
Fax: (646)674-4020
URL: http://us.dk.com

Description: Jill Norman. 2005. $50.00. 648 pages.
Tips for home cooks from top chefs around the world;
includes concise directions and color photography.

1818 ▪ *Opportunities in Restaurant Careers*
The McGraw-Hill Companies Inc.
PO Box 182604
Columbus, OH 43272
Ph: (212)512-2000
Free: 877-833-5524
Fax: (614)759-3749
E-mail: customer.service@mcgraw-hill.com
URL: http://www.mcgraw-hill.com

Description: Carol Caprione Chmelynski. 2004.
$13.95 (paper). 160 pages. Covers opportunities in
the food service industry and details salaries,
benefits, training opportunities, and professional associations. Special emphasis is put on becoming a
successful restaurant manager by working up
through the ranks. Illustrated.

**1819 ▪ *Purchasing for Chefs: A Concise
Guide***
John Wiley & Sons Inc.
111 River St.
Hoboken, NJ 07030-5774
Ph: (201)748-6000
Free: 800-225-5945
Fax: (201)748-6088
E-mail: info@wiley.com
URL: http://www.wiley.com

Description: Andrew H. Feinstein and John M. Stefanelli. 2010. $51.95. 256 pages. Guide details
purchasing principles to chefs and hospitality managers for obtaining goods and services for their business.

EMPLOYMENT AGENCIES AND SEARCH FIRMS

1820 ▪ Boutique Search Firm
1173 Rodeo Dr.
Los Angeles, CA 90035
Ph: (310)552-2221
Fax: (310)552-2224
URL: http://www.boutiquesearchfirm.com

Description: Serves as a recruiting firm specializing
in hospitality management. Offers jobs in luxury
hotels and resorts worldwide.

1821 ▪ Chefs' Professional Agency
870 Market St., 863
San Francisco, CA 94102
Ph: (415)392-1563
E-mail: hospitality@chefsprofessional.com
URL: http://chefsprofessional.com

Description: Locates talent for restaurants, hotels,
clubs and resorts. Provides resume kits, career tools,
and other candidate resources while also providing
resources for employers.

1822 ▪ dd factor
2615 190th St., Ste. 221
Redondo Beach, CA 90278
Ph: (310)376-0870
Fax: (310)376-1840
URL: http://ddfactor.com

Description: Operates as a hospitality search firm
that specializes in chefs, sous chefs, and kitchen
managers.

1823 ▪ Food Management Search
235 State St., Ste. 326
Springfield, MA 01103
Ph: (413)732-2666
Fax: (413)732-6466
E-mail: recruiters@foodmanagementsearch.com
URL: http://foodmanagementsearch.com/index.cfm

Description: Specializes in contingency recruiting
projects exclusively in the food manufacturing and
food service industries. Provides positions covering
food production/manufacturing, supply chain, food
service, sales and marketing.

1824 ▪ Global Hospitality
3579 E Foothill Blvd., Ste. 229
Pasadena, CA 91107
Ph: (626)836-1222
Fax: (626)836-1223
E-mail: mail@globalhospitality.com
URL: http://www.globalhospitality.com

Description: Executive search firm that specializes
in identifying, evaluating, and placing leadership and
management talent in the hospitality industry.

1825 ▪ HospitalityStaff.com
3195 Tamiami Trail, Ste. 204
Port Charlotte, FL 33952
Ph: (941)743-8540
Free: 800-987-1555
Fax: (941)743-9684
URL: http://www.hospitalitystaff.com

Description: Serves as a placement agency,
specializing in the supply of temporary and
permanent staff to the hospitality industry.

1826 ▪ Prospection Group
PO Box 1999
Santa Monica, CA 90406
Ph: (310)398-3795
URL: http://www.prospectiongroup.com

Description: Executive search firm for the hospitality
industry. Searches for hospitality executives ranging
from the level of general management to private
chefs.

ONLINE JOB SOURCES AND SERVICES

1827 ▪ BestfoodJobs.com
URL: http://www.bestfoodjobs.com

Description: Provides information on employment
opportunities for the restaurant and food service
industry.

1828 ▪ ChefCrossing.com
URL: http://www.chefcrossing.com

Description: Shows job listings from employer
career pages, job websites, association websites,
newspaper classified ads and recruiter sites.

1829 ▪ ChefJobs.com
URL: http://www.chefjobs.com

Description: Provides resources to career and
recreational culinary education programs worldwide.

1830 ▪ ChefJobsNetwork.com
URL: http://chefjobsnetwork.com

Description: Provides employment opportunities for
professionals in the culinary industry.

1831 ▪ Escoffier.com
URL: http://escoffier.com

Description: Offers a collection of chef job openings,
recreational culinary educational resources, resume
writing services and career advice for job seekers.

1832 ▪ FoodIndustryJobs.com
URL: http://www.foodindustryjobs.com

Description: Job databank and resume submission
service for food industry workers.

1833 ▪ Foodservice.com
URL: http://www.foodservice.com

Description: Serves as an online community of
foodservice professionals. Provides services such as
a virtual foodshow, employment center, market
reports, daily industry news and editorials, discussion
forums, culinary school connections, and the weekly
foodservice.com express e-Newsletter.

1834 ▪ Get Chef Jobs
URL: http://www.getchefjobs.com

Description: Serves as an online job search
resource for professional chefs.

1835 ▪ HCareers.com
URL: http://www.hcareers.com

Description: Connects employers and candidates
within the hospitality industry. Enables candidates to
search for jobs within a specific industry or location.

1836 ▪ HotelJobs.com
URL: http://www.hoteljobs.com

Description: Provides job postings and resume
database for hotel, casino and cruise ship professionals and recruiters.

1837 ▪ New Restaurant and Food Jobs
URL: http://www.newrestaurantandfoodjobs.com

Description: Provides an online listing of companies

with available restaurant and food jobs in all specialties.

1838 ■ PastryBakerChef.com
URL: http://www.pastrybakerchef.com

Description: Features employment opportunities for bakers and pastry chefs.

1839 ■ RestaurantOperator.com
URL: http://www.restaurantoperator.com

Description: Exists as a virtual community created for the benefit of restaurant operators and employees. Offers a variety of services that encompass all facets of the restaurant business. Provides services on product information, distributor and supplier information, professional services, associations and trade show listings, publications, restaurants for sale, business opportunities, and an employment center.

1840 ■ StarChefs.com
URL: http://www.starchefs.com

Description: Contains job board, resume writing service and career advice for job seekers in the culinary arts. Seekers can sign up for free e-mail account and receive job notifications through this service.

TRADESHOWS

1841 ■ ACF National Convention and Trade Show
American Culinary Federation
180 Center Place Way
Saint Augustine, FL 32095
Free: 800-624-9458
Fax: (904)825-4758
E-mail: acf@acfchefs.net
URL: http://www.acfchefs.org

Frequency: Annual. Includes exhibits featuring apparel, equipment, cookware, books and media, seasonings, packaged goods, and similar merchandise. Provides networking opportunities for attendees.

1842 ■ Denver Food and Kitchen Expo
Professional Chefs Association
PO Box 453
Frederick, CO 80530-0453
Ph: (720)379-8759
E-mail: support@professionalchef.com
URL: http://www.professionalchef.com

Annual. Features all things related to food, kitchens, and cooking.

1843 ■ International Baking Industry Exposition
IBIE Exhibition Management
401 N. Michigan Ave.
Chicago, IL 60611
Ph: (312)644-6610
Fax: (312)644-0575
E-mail: pdwyer@smithbucklin.com
URL: http://ibie2013.org

Primary Exhibits: Baking equipment, supplies, and services.

1844 ■ National Restaurant Association Restaurant and Hotel-Motel Show
National Restaurant Association Convention Office
2055 L St., NW
Washington, DC 20036
Ph: (202)331-5900
URL: http://www.restaurant.org

Frequency: Annual. **Primary Exhibits:** Food service equipment, supplies, and services and food and beverage products for the hospitality industry. Includes international cuisine pavilion. **Dates and Locations:** Chicago, IL; McCormick Place.

OTHER SOURCES

1845 ■ American Culinary Federation
180 Center Place Way
Saint Augustine, FL 32095
Free: 800-624-9458
Fax: (904)825-4758
E-mail: acf@acfchefs.net
URL: http://www.acfchefs.org

Description: Aims to promote the culinary profession and provide on-going educational training and networking for members. Provides opportunities for competition, professional recognition, and access to educational forums with other culinary experts at local, regional, national, and international events. Operates the National Apprenticeship Program for Cooks and pastry cooks. Offers programs that address certification of the individual chef's skills, accreditation of culinary programs, apprenticeship of cooks and pastry cooks, professional development, and the fight against childhood hunger.

1846 ■ Asian Chefs Association
3145 Geary Blvd., No. 112
San Francisco, CA 94118
Ph: (408)634-9462
E-mail: contactus@acasf.com
URL: http://www.acasf.com

Description: Aims to increase public and media awareness of Asian-inspired cuisine. Educates chefs about the various aspects of the restaurant and culinary business. Promotes the art of Asian-inspired cuisine. Provides a forum for Asian chefs.

1847 ■ *Career Opportunities in the Food and Beverage Industry*
InfoBase Holdings Inc.
132 W 31st., 17 Fl.
New York, NY 10001-3406
Ph: (212)967-8800
Fax: (800)678-3633
E-mail: info@infobasepublishing.com
URL: http://www.ferguson.infobasepublishing.com

Description: Barbara Sims-Bell. 2010. $18.95 (paper). 223 pages. Provides information about locating and landing 80 skilled and unskilled jobs in the food and beverage industry. **Includes:** Appendices of trade associations, recruiting organizations, and major agencies. Appendices of trade associations, recruiting organizations, and major agencies.

1848 ■ Cultural Vistas
440 Park Ave. S, 2nd Fl.
New York, NY 10016
Ph: (212)497-3500
Fax: (212)497-3535
E-mail: info@culturalvistas.org
URL: http://culturalvistas.org

Description: Providers worldwide of on-the-job training programs for students and professionals seeking international career development and life-changing experiences. Arranges workplace exchanges in hundreds of professional fields, bringing employers and trainees together from around the world. Client list ranges from small farming communities to Fortune 500 companies.

1849 ■ International Association of Culinary Professionals
1221 Avenue of the Americas, 42nd Fl.
New York, NY 10020
Ph: (646)358-4957
Free: 866-358-4951
Fax: (866)358-2524
E-mail: info@iacp.com
URL: http://www.iacp.com

Description: Represents cooking school owners, food writers, chefs, caterers, culinary specialists, directors, teachers, cookbook authors, food stylists, food photographers, student/apprentices, and individuals in related industries in 20 countries. Promotes the interests of cooking schools, teachers,

and culinary professionals. Encourages the exchange of information and education. Promotes professional standards and accreditation procedures. Maintains a Foundation to award culinary scholarships and grants.

1850 ■ International Council on Hotel, Restaurant, and Institutional Education
2810 N Parham Rd., Ste. 230
Richmond, VA 23294
Ph: (804)346-4800
Fax: (804)346-5009
E-mail: publications@chrie.org
URL: http://www.chrie.org

Description: Schools and colleges offering specialized education and training in hospitals, recreation, tourism and hotel, restaurant, and institutional administration; individuals, executives, and students. Provides networking opportunities and professional development.

1851 ■ Les Amis d'Escoffier Society of New York
787 Ridgewood Rd.
Millburn, NJ 07041-1541
Ph: (212)414-5820
Fax: (973)379-3117
URL: http://www.escoffier-society.com

Description: An educational organization of professionals in the food and wine industries. Maintains museum, speakers' bureau, hall of fame, and placement service. Sponsors charitable programs. **Members:** 1,650.

1852 ■ National Restaurant Association
2055 L St. NW
Washington, DC 20036
Ph: (202)331-5900
Free: 800-424-5156
Fax: (202)331-2429
URL: http://www.restaurant.org

Description: Represents restaurants, cafeterias, clubs, contract foodservice management, drive-ins, caterers, institutional food services and other members of the foodservice industry; also represents establishments belonging to non-affiliated state and local restaurant associations in governmental affairs. Supports foodservice education and research in several educational institutions. Is affiliated with the Educational Foundation of the National Restaurant Association to provide training and education for operators, food and equipment manufacturers, distributors and educators. Has 300,000 member locations.

1853 ■ Professional Chefs Association
PO Box 453
Frederick, CO 80530-0453
Ph: (720)379-8759
E-mail: support@professionalchef.com
URL: http://www.professionalchef.com

Description: Represents the interests of chefs and those associated with the food service industry. Promotes culinary excellence through the exchange of knowledge among chefs. Offers online education courses and certification programs.

1854 ■ Research Chefs Association
1100 Johnson Ferry Rd., Ste. 300
Atlanta, GA 30342
Ph: (678)298-1178
Fax: (404)836-5595
E-mail: rca@kellencompany.com
URL: http://www.culinology.com/

Description: Represents the interests of chefs, food scientists, and other industry professionals in the food research and development industry. Offers resources of culinary and technical information for professionals in the field.

1855 ■ United States Personal Chef Association
7680 Universal Blvd., Ste. 550
Orlando, FL 32819

Free: 800-995-2138
E-mail: info@uspca.com

URL: http://www.uspca.com
Description: Strives to set standards and create

guidelines for the industry. Promotes ongoing education.

SOURCES OF HELP-WANTED ADS

1856 ■ **AIE Perspectives Newsmagazine**
American Institute of Engineers
4630 Appian Way, Ste. 206
El Sobrante, CA 94803-1875
Ph: (510)758-6240
Fax: (510)758-6240
E-mail: aie@aieonline.org
URL: http://www.members-aie.org

Frequency: Monthly. **Price:** included in membership dues. **Description:** Professional magazine covering engineering.

1857 ■ **Chemical Engineering**
Access Intelligence L.L.C.
4 Choke Cherry Rd., 2nd Fl.
Rockville, MD 20850
Ph: (301)354-2000
Free: 800-777-5006
Fax: (301)309-3847
E-mail: info@accessintel.com
URL: http://www.che.com

Frequency: Monthly. **Price:** $109.97 Individuals print; $136.97 Canada; $239 Other countries. **Description:** Chemical process industries magazine.

1858 ■ **Chemical Engineering Communications**
Taylor & Francis Group Journals
c/o William N. Gill, Ed.-in-Ch.
Chemical Engineering Department
Ricketts Bldg.
Rensselaer Polytechnic Institute
Troy, NY 12180-3590
Ph: (215)625-8900
Free: 800-354-1420
Fax: (215)625-2940
E-mail: customerservice@taylorandfrancis.com
URL: http://www.tandfonline.com/toc/gcec20/current

Frequency: Monthly. **Price:** $2,518 Individuals print only; $5,510 Institutions online only; $6,122 Institutions print and online. **Description:** Journal focusing on the results of basic and applied research in chemical engineering.

1859 ■ **Chemical Engineering Progress**
Center for Chemical Process Safety
3 Park Ave., 19th Fl.
New York, NY 10016-5991
Ph: (646)495-1370
Free: 800-242-4363
Fax: (646)495-1504
E-mail: ccps@aiche.org
URL: http://www.aiche.org/CEP/index.aspx

Frequency: Monthly. **Price:** $170 Nonmembers in North America; $295 Nonmembers international; $210 Nonmembers with online; in North America; $335 Nonmembers with online; international. **Description:** Chemical process industries magazine.

1860 ■ **Chemical Engineering and Technology**
John Wiley & Sons Inc.
111 River St.
Hoboken, NJ 07030-5774
Ph: (201)748-6000
Free: 800-225-5945
Fax: (201)748-6088
E-mail: info@wiley.com
URL: http://onlinelibrary.wiley.com/journal/10.1002/ (ISSN)1521-4125

Frequency: Monthly. **Price:** $5,036 Institutions print only; $5,036 Institutions, other countries print only; $5,792 Institutions print with online; €3,924 Institutions print only, rest of Europe; £2,570 Institutions print only. **Description:** Journal focusing on all aspects of chemical and process engineering.

1861 ■ **The Chemical Record**
John Wiley & Sons Inc.
111 River St.
Hoboken, NJ 07030-5774
Ph: (201)748-6000
Free: 800-225-5945
Fax: (201)748-6088
E-mail: info@wiley.com
URL: http://onlinelibrary.wiley.com/journal/10.1002/ (ISSN)1528-0691

Frequency: Bimonthly. **Price:** $123 U.S., Canada, and Mexico print only; $735 Institutions print & online; $153 Other countries print only; $639 Institutions print only; $639 Institutions, Canada and Mexico print only; $639 Institutions, other countries print only. **Description:** Journal publishing overviews of new developments at the cutting edge of chemistry of interest to a wide audience of chemists.

1862 ■ **The Chemist**
American Institute of Chemists
315 Chestnut St.
Philadelphia, PA 19106-2702
Ph: (215)873-8224
Fax: (215)629-5224
E-mail: info@theaic.org
URL: http://www.theaic.org

Description: Quarterly. Covers news items relating to the chemical profession and membership in the Institute. Reports on legislation, licensure, earnings, awards, and professional education. Recurring features include news of employment opportunities and news of members. Published alternate months as a magazine.

1863 ■ **Chemistry & Biology**
Elsevier Science Inc.
Secondary Publishing Division
650 Ave. of the Americas
New York, NY 10011
Ph: (212)633-3980
Free: 888-437-4636
Fax: (212)633-3975
URL: http://www.elsevier.com/wps/find/journalde-scription.cws_home/601281/description#description

Frequency: Monthly. **Price:** $2,137 Institutions print; $442 U.S. and other countries online only; $457 Other countries print + online; $442 U.S. and Canada print; $843 Institutions online. **Description:** Journal focused on genetic, computational, or theoretical information of chemistry and biology, substantiating experimental data.

1864 ■ **Composites: Mechanics, Computations, Applications**
Begell House Inc.
50 Cross Hwy.
Redding, CT 06896
Ph: (203)938-1300
Fax: (203)938-1304
E-mail: orders@begellhouse.com
URL: http://www.begellhouse.com/journals/ 36ff4a142dec9609

Price: $758 Institutions. **Description:** Journal featuring basic ideas in the mechanics of composite materials and structures between research workers and engineers.

1865 ■ **The Electrochemical Society Interface**
Electrochemical Society
c/o Krishan Rajeshwar, Ed.
University of Texas at Arlington
Department of Chemistry & Biochemistry
502 Yates St.
Arlington, TX 76019
Ph: (817)272-3810
Fax: (817)272-3808
E-mail: interface@electrochem.org
URL: http://www.electrochem.org/dl/interface/

Frequency: Quarterly. **Price:** $69 Individuals tier 1, print & online; $84 Canada tier 1, print & online; $92 Other countries tier 1, print & online. **Description:** Publication featuring news and articles of interest to members of the Electrochemical Society.

1866 ■ **Engineering**
Scientific Research Publishing
PO Box 54821
Irvine, CA 92619-4821
E-mail: eng@scirp.org
URL: http://www.scirp.org/journal/eng/

Frequency: Monthly. **Price:** $468 Individuals. **Description:** Peer-reviewed journal publishing articles on the latest advancements in engineering.

1867 ■ **Engineering in Life Sciences**
John Wiley & Sons Inc.
111 River St.
Hoboken, NJ 07030-5774
Ph: (201)748-6000
Free: 800-225-5945
Fax: (201)748-6088
E-mail: info@wiley.com
URL: http://onlinelibrary.wiley.com/journal/10.1002/ (ISSN)1618-2863

Frequency: Bimonthly. **Price:** €1,069 Institutions

European, online only; $1,403 Institutions, Canada and Mexico online only; $1,403 Institutions, other countries online only; £717 Institutions European, online only; $1,403 Institutions online only. **Description:** Journal focusing on the field of biotechnology and related topics including microbiology, genetics, biochemistry, and chemistry.

1868 ■ *Graduating Engineer & Computer Careers*
Career Recruitment Media
2 LAN Dr., Ste. 100
Westford, MA 01886
Ph: (978)692-5092
Fax: (978)692-4174
E-mail: hshulick@alloyeducation.com
URL: http://www.graduatingengineer.com
Frequency: Quarterly. **Price:** $16.95 Individuals. **Description:** Magazine focusing on employment, education, and career development for entry-level engineers and computer scientists.

1869 ■ *Journal of Chemical Theory and Computation*
American Chemical Society
1155 16th St. NW
Washington, DC 20036
Ph: (202)872-4600
Free: 800-227-5558
E-mail: help@acs.org
URL: http://pubs.acs.org/journal/jctcce
Frequency: 6/yr. **Price:** $1,367 Institutions North America; $1,499 Institutions, other countries. **Description:** Journal presenting new theories, methodology, and/or important applications in quantum chemistry, molecular dynamics, and statistical mechanics.

1870 ■ *Modern Plastics Worldwide*
UBM Canon
3300 E 1st Ave., Ste. 370
Denver, CO 80206
Ph: (303)321-2322
Fax: (303)321-3552
E-mail: info@ubm.com
URL: http://www.modplas.com
Frequency: Monthly. **Price:** $59 Individuals; $99 Two years U.S. and possessions; $110 Canada; $199 Two years for Canada; $150 Other countries; $250 Two years. **Description:** Magazine for the plastics industry.

1871 ■ *Nanomechanics Science and Technology: An International Journal*
Begell House Inc.
50 Cross Hwy.
Redding, CT 06896
Ph: (203)938-1300
Fax: (203)938-1304
E-mail: orders@begellhouse.com
URL: http://www.begellhouse.com/journals/
11e12455066dab5d
Price: $800 Institutions. **Description:** Journal covering the areas of nano- and micromechanics.

1872 ■ *Nanoparticle News*
BCC Research
35 Walnut St., Ste. 100
Wellesley, MA 02481
Ph: (781)489-7301
Free: 866-285-7215
Fax: (781)253-3933
E-mail: info@bccresearch.com
URL: http://www.bccresearch.com/report/index.php
?rcode=nan
Frequency: Monthly. **Price:** $675 Single issue web access and archive (2 user license); $640 Single issue print, online, archive (outside North America); $495 Single issue web access and archive; $590 Single issue print, web access and archive (North America); $1,485 Individuals online (enterprise license); $990 Individuals online (Department license); $750 Individuals online (5 user license).

Description: Publication covering issues in the chemical industry.

1873 ■ *NSBE Magazine: National Society of Black Engineers*
NSBE Publications
205 Daingerfield Rd.
Alexandria, VA 22314
Ph: (703)549-2207
Fax: (703)683-5312
E-mail: info@nsbe.org
URL: http://www.nsbe.org/News-Media/Magazines/
About-NSBE-Magazine.aspx
Frequency: 3/yr. **Price:** $20 Individuals; $35 Other countries; $15 Students. **Description:** Journal providing information on engineering careers, self-development, and cultural issues for recent graduates with technical majors.

1874 ■ *PALAIOS*
SEPM Publications
University of Kansas
Paleontological Institute, Department of Geology
1475 Jawyhawk Blvd., Rm. 120
Lawrence, KS 66045-7613
Ph: (785)864-2737
Fax: (785)864-3636
E-mail: palois@ku.edu
URLs: http://palaios.ku.edu/; http://palaios
.geoscienceworld.org/
Frequency: Monthly. **Price:** $400 Individuals for U.S.; online version with CD-ROM; $500 Individuals for U.S.; print and online version with CD-ROM; $400 Other countries online version with CD-ROM; $500 Other countries print and online version with CD-ROM. **Description:** Journal providing information on the impact of life on Earth history as recorded in the paleontological and sedimentological records. Covers areas such as biogeochemistry, ichnology, sedimentology, stratigraphy, paleoecology, paleoclimatology, and paleoceanography.

1875 ■ *PE*
National Society of Professional Engineers
1420 King St.
Alexandria, VA 22314-2794
Ph: (703)684-2800
Fax: (703)836-4875
E-mail: memserv@nspe.org
URL: http://www.nspe.org/PEmagazine/index.html
Frequency: Semimonthly; 10/yr. **Price:** included in membership dues; $50 for nonmembers. **Description:** Covers matters of importance to engineering educators and students.

1876 ■ *Plastics Engineering*
Society of Plastics Engineers
13 Church Hill Rd.
Newtown, CT 06470
Ph: (203)775-0471
Fax: (203)775-8490
E-mail: info@4spe.org
URLs: http://www.4spe.org/pub; http://
plasticsengineering.org/home
Frequency: 10/year. **Price:** $142 Nonmembers; $242 Nonmembers outside North America; $180 Institutions corporate library; $280 Institutions corporate library outside North America; included in membership dues; $160/year for nonmembers. **Description:** Plastics trade magazine.

1877 ■ *Plastics News: Crains' International Newspaper for the Plastics Industry*
Crain Communications Inc.
77 Franklin St., Ste. 809
Boston, MA 02110-1510
Ph: (617)292-3385
E-mail: info@crain.com
URL: http://www.plasticsnews.com
Frequency: Weekly. **Price:** $89 U.S. print + web; $160 Two years print + web; $292 Other countries print + web; $89 Individuals web only; $139 Canada print + web; $250 Canada two years, print + web.

Description: Magazine (tabloid) for the plastics industry providing business news.

1878 ■ *Powder and Bulk Engineering*
CSC Publishing Inc.
1155 Northland Dr.
Saint Paul, MN 55120
Ph: (651)287-5650
Fax: (651)287-5600
E-mail: info@cscpub.com
URL: http://www.powderbulk.com/Content/Default
.aspx
Frequency: Monthly. **Price:** $100 Individuals outside North America, or digital format. **Description:** Journal serving chemical, food, plastics, pulp and paper, and electronic industries.

1879 ■ *Rubber World: The*
Rubber World
1867 W Market St.
Akron, OH 44313-6901
Ph: (330)864-2122
Fax: (330)864-5298
E-mail: jhl@rubberworld.com
URL: http://www.rubberworld.com/
Frequency: 16/yr. **Price:** $34 Individuals; $39 Canada; $89 Other countries airmail. **Description:** Rubber manufacturing magazine.

1880 ■ *Structure Magazine*
American Consulting Engineers Council
1015 15th St. NW, 8th Fl.
Washington, DC 20005-2605
Ph: (202)347-7474
Fax: (202)898-0068
E-mail: acec@acec.org
URL: http://structuremag.org
Frequency: Annual. **Price:** $75 Nonmembers for U.S residents; $40 Students; $90 Canada individual; $135 Other countries; $60 Canada students; $90 Other countries students. **Description:** Magazine focused on providing tips, tools, techniques, and innovative concepts for structural engineers.

1881 ■ *SWE, Magazine of the Society of Women Engineers*
Society of Women Engineers
203 N La Salle St., Ste. 1675
Chicago, IL 60601
Ph: (312)596-5223
Free: 877-SWE-INFO
Fax: (312)596-5252
E-mail: hq@swe.org
URL: http://societyofwomenengineers.swe.org/index
.php
Frequency: Quarterly. **Price:** $30 Nonmembers. **Description:** Magazine for engineering students and for women and men working in the engineering and technology fields. Covers career guidance, continuing development and topical issues.

1882 ■ *Woman Engineer*
Equal Opportunity Publications Inc.
445 Broad Hollow Rd., Ste. 425
Melville, NY 11747
Ph: (631)421-9421
Fax: (631)421-1352
E-mail: info@eop.com
URL: http://www.eop.com
Description: Annual. Magazine that is offered at no charge to qualified female engineering, computer-science, and information-technology students and professionals seeking to find employment and advancement in their careers.

EMPLOYER DIRECTORIES AND NETWORKING LISTS

1883 ■ *American Men and Women of Science: A Biographical Dictionary of Today's Leaders in Physical, Biological, and Related Sciences*
R.R. Bowker
630 Central Ave
New Providence, NJ 07974

Ph: (888)269-5372
Free: 888-269-5372
Fax: (908)464-3553
E-mail: info@bowker.com
URL: http://www.gale.cengage.com

Frequency: Biennial; even years; New edition expected 29th, June 2011. **Price:** $1,368 Individuals. **Covers:** Over 135,000 U.S. and Canadian scientists active in the physical, biological, mathematical, computer science, and engineering fields; includes references to previous edition for deceased scientists and nonrespondents. **Entries include:** Name, address, education, personal and career data, memberships, honors and awards, research interest. **Arrangement:** Alphabetical. **Indexes:** Discipline (in separate volume).

1884 ■ Chemical Week--Buyers Guide Issue
Chemical Week Associates
2 Grand Central Tower
140 E 45th St., 40th Fl.
New York, NY 10017
Ph: (212)884-9528
Free: 800-774-5733
Fax: (212)883-9514
E-mail: webmaster@chemweek.com
URL: http://www.chemweek.com/buyersguide/public

Frequency: Annual; Latest edition 2012. **Price:** $115 Included in subscription, per year; $25 Individuals. **Publication includes:** About 4,200 manufacturers and suppliers of chemical raw materials to the chemical process industries; 400 manufacturers of packaging materials; and suppliers of products and services to the chemical process industries, including hazardous waste/environmental services, computer services, plant design, construction, consulting, shipping, and transportation. **Entries include:** Over 17,000 product/service listings, Company name, address, phone; local addresses and phone numbers for up to 25 sales locations. **Arrangement:** Separate alphabetical sections for chemical, packaging, and hazardous waste/environmental services. **Indexes:** Product (all sections); trade name (chemical and packaging sections only).

1885 ■ Consulting Services
Association of Consulting Chemists and Chemical Engineers
PO Box 902
Murray Hill, NJ 07974-0902
Ph: (908)464-3182
Fax: (908)464-3182
E-mail: accce@chemconsult.org
URL: http://www.chemconsult.org

Frequency: Biennial; even years. **Price:** $30 Individuals postpaid. **Pages:** 200. **Covers:** About 160 member consultants in chemistry, chemical engineering, metallurgy, etc. **Entries include:** Individual name, address, certificate number, qualifications, affiliation, experience, facilities, staff. **Arrangement:** Classified by area of expertise. **Indexes:** Personal name, geographical.

1886 ■ Directory of Chemical Producers--United States
SRI International - IHS Chemical: Chemical Insight & Forecasting
333 Ravenswood Ave.
Menlo Park, CA 94025-3493
Ph: (303)858-6355
Free: 800-688-7391
Fax: (650)859-4111
E-mail: sric-dcp@ihs.com
URL: http://www.ihs.com/products/chemical/companies/producers.aspx?pu=1&rd=chemihs

Frequency: Annual; latest edition April, 2011. **Price:** $2,050 U.S. new subscription; $1,635 U.S. renewing subscription; $2,100 Online. **Pages:** 1,050. **Covers:** Over 1,255 United States basic chemical producers manufacturing 7,085 chemicals in commercial quantities at more than 3,205 plant locations. **Includes:** Plant-by-plant capacities for over 150 major chemicals. **Entries include:** For companies-- Company name, division or subsidiary names,

corporate address, phone, fax, telex, location of each subsidiary, division, and manufacturing plant, and the products made at each plant location. For products-- Producer name and plant locations, alternate product names (if any). Subscription price includes bound volume, plus access to the directory staff for inquiries. **Arrangement:** Companies are alphabetical; products are alphabetical and by group (dyes, pesticides, etc.); manufacturing plants are geographical. **Indexes:** Geographical, product.

1887 ■ Directory of Contract Staffing Firms
C.E. Publications Inc.
PO Box 3006
Bothell, WA 98041-3006
Ph: (425)806-5200
Fax: (425)806-5585
E-mail: staff@cjhunter.com
URL: http://www.cjhunter.com/dcsf/overview.html

Frequency: Annual. **Covers:** Nearly 1,300 contract firms actively engaged in the employment of engineering, IT/IS, and technical personnel for 'temporary' contract assignments throughout the world. **Entries include:** Company name, address, phone, name of contact, email, web address. **Arrangement:** Alphabetical. **Indexes:** Geographical.

1888 ■ Directory of World Chemical Producers
Chemical Information Services Inc.
9101 LBJ Fwy., Ste. 310
Dallas, TX 75243
Ph: (214)349-6200
Fax: (214)349-6286
E-mail: info@chemicalinfo.com
URL: http://chemicalinfo.com/database-products/dwcp

Frequency: Annual. **Price:** $1,500 Individuals book; $4,750 Individuals CD format. **Pages:** 2,450. **Covers:** Over 20,000 producers of all classes of chemicals worldwide; including bulk pharmaceuticals, fire chemicals, agrochemicals, dyes, pigments, cosmetic, food ingredients, intermediates, etc. **Entries include:** Company name, address, phone, fax, telex, E-mail address, websites, contact information. **Arrangement:** Product, CAS#, geographical.

1889 ■ Indiana Society of Professional Engineers--Directory
Indiana Society of Professional Engineers
c/o Lauraine M. Howe, Executive Director
PO Box 20806
Indianapolis, IN 46220
Ph: (317)255-2267
Fax: (317)255-2530
E-mail: indspe@gmail.com
URL: http://www.indspe.org

Frequency: Annual; fall. **Pages:** 150. **Covers:** Member registered engineers, land surveyors, engineering students, and engineers in training. **Entries include:** Member name, address, phone, type of membership, business information, specialty. **Arrangement:** Alpha by chapter area.

1890 ■ Who's Who in Engineering
American Association of Engineering Societies
1801 Alexander Bell Dr.
Reston, VA 20191
Ph: (202)296-2237
Free: 888-400-2237
Fax: (202)296-1151
E-mail: dbateson@aaes.org
URL: http://www.aaes.org

Frequency: Triennial; Latest edition 9th. **Covers:** About 10,000 engineers who have received professional recognition for outstanding achievement. **Entries include:** Name, address; education and employment history; awards and achievements. **Arrangement:** Alphabetical. **Indexes:** Geographical, field of specialization.

HANDBOOKS AND MANUALS

1891 ■ Expert Resumes for Engineers
JIST Publishing
875 Montreal Way
Saint Paul, MN 55102-4245
Ph: (317)613-4200
Free: 800-648-5478
Fax: (800)328-4564
E-mail: info@jist.com
URL: http://www.jist.com

Description: Louise M. Kursmark and Wendy S. Enelow. 2009. $16.95 (softcover). 272 pages. Features a collection of written resume samples for all types of engineers including civil, mechanical, industrial, electrical, electronics, computer, and more. Contains tips and strategies for writing engineering resumes and finding the best jobs.

1892 ■ Great Jobs for Chemistry Majors
The McGraw-Hill Companies Inc.
PO Box 182604
Columbus, OH 43272
Ph: (212)512-2000
Free: 877-833-5524
Fax: (614)759-3749
E-mail: customer.service@mcgraw-hill.com
URL: http://www.mcgraw-hill.com

Description: Mark Rowh. Second edition, 2005. $15.95 (paper). 208 pages.

1893 ■ Great Jobs for Engineering Majors
The McGraw-Hill Companies Inc.
PO Box 182604
Columbus, OH 43272
Ph: (212)512-2000
Free: 877-833-5524
Fax: (614)759-3749
E-mail: customer.service@mcgraw-hill.com
URL: http://www.mcgraw-hill.com

Description: Geraldine O. Garner. Second edition, 2008. $16.95. 192 pages. Covers all the career options open to students majoring in engineering.

EMPLOYMENT AGENCIES AND SEARCH FIRMS

1894 ■ Apple and Associates
PO Box 996
Chapin, SC 29036
Ph: (803)932-2000
E-mail: info@appleassoc.com
URL: http://www.appleassoc.com

Description: Provides staffing services to medical device, plastics, pharmaceutical and performance materials industries.

1895 ■ The Baer Group
900 Ashwood Pkwy., Ste. 300
Atlanta, GA 30346
Ph: (770)557-4900
Fax: (770)557-3499
E-mail: info@baergroup.com
URL: http://www.baergroup.com

Description: Executive search firm.

1896 ■ Capstone Inc.
971 Albany Shaker Rd.
Latham, NY 12110
Ph: (518)783-9300
E-mail: amyj@capstone-inc.com
URL: http://www.capstone-inc.com

Description: Executive search firm.

1897 ■ Career Advocates International
1539 Ave. A
Katy, TX 77493

Ph: (281)371-3917
E-mail: hank@careeradvocates.org
URL: http://www.careeradvocates.org

Description: Provides permanent placement and temporary staffing for executive and staff level positions. Specializes in multiple niches including: sales and marketing, accounting and financial services, banking, communications, human resources, chemicals, oil and gas, medical and dental, legal, information technology, energy, technology, engineering, manufacturing, construction, and light industrial.

1898 ■ Centennial, Inc.
8044 Montgomery Rd., Ste. 260
Cincinnati, OH 45236
Ph: (513)366-3760
Fax: (513)366-3761
URL: http://www.centennialinc.com

Description: Serves as an executive search firm specializing in the areas of executive and general management, accounting and finance, human resources, information technology, manufacturing, engineering, marketing and advertising, not-for-profit, sales and business development, and supply chain and logistics.

1899 ■ Cochran, Cochran & Yale LLC
955 E Henrietta Rd.
Rochester, NY 14623
Ph: (585)424-6060
E-mail: roch@ccy.com
URL: http://www.ccy.com

Description: Executive search firm. Branches in Denver, CO and Williamsville, NY.

1900 ■ Conboy Sur Morice & Associates
15 Churchville Rd., No. 170
Bel Air, MD 21014-3837
E-mail: wks@csma-cons.com
URL: http://www.csma-cons.com

Description: Executive search firm.

1901 ■ CSI Executive Search LLC
9600 Great Hills Trail, Ste. 150W
Austin, TX 78759
Ph: (512)301-1119
Fax: (512)301-5559
E-mail: info@csi-executivesearch.com
URL: http://www.csi-executivesearch.com

Description: Executive search firm that specializes in the following arenas: accounting, engineering, healthcare, information technology, and legal.

1902 ■ ENTEGEE Inc.
70 Blanchard Rd., Ste. 102
Burlington, MA 01803-5100
Free: 800-368-3433
E-mail: corporate@entegee.com
URL: http://www.entegee.com

Description: Specializes in recruiting experienced professionals in the engineering and technical industries. Features a searchable database of employment opportunities in the engineering and technical fields.

1903 ■ Executive Directions Inc.
PO Box 5742
Sarasota, FL 34277
Ph: (941)922-9180
E-mail: info@execdir.com
URL: http://www.execdir.com

Description: Executive search firm.

1904 ■ Executive Recruiters Agency
PO Box 21810
Little Rock, AR 72211
Ph: (501)224-7000
Fax: (501)224-8534
E-mail: jobs@execrecruit.com
URL: http://www.execrecruit.com

Description: Personnel service firm.

1905 ■ Global Employment Solutions Inc.
10375 Park Meadows Dr., Ste. 475
Littleton, CO 80124-6724
Ph: (303)216-9500
Fax: (303)216-9533
URL: http://www.gesnetwork.com

Description: Employment agency.

1906 ■ International Search
9717 E 42nd St.
Tulsa, OK 74147-0898
Ph: (918)627-9070
Fax: (918)524-8604

Description: Personnel consulting group provides placement expertise in engineering, accounting, and data processing. Industries served: Energy, manufacturing, oil and gas, and services.

1907 ■ Ken Clark International
2000 Lenox Dr., Ste. 200
Lawrenceville, NJ 08648
Ph: (609)308-5200
Fax: (609)308-5250
E-mail: info-princeton@kenclark.com
URL: http://www.kenclark.com

Description: Executive search firm. Branches in Newport Beach, CA; Deerfield, IL; Waltham, MA; and Wayne, PA.

1908 ■ Houser Martin Morris
110th Ave. NE, 110 Atrium Pl., Ste. 580
Bellevue, WA 98004
Ph: (425)453-2700
Fax: (425)453-8726
E-mail: info@houser.com
URL: http://www.houser.com

Description: Focus is in the areas of retained executive search, professional, and technical recruiting. Areas of specialization include software engineering, sales and marketing, information technology, legal, human resources, accounting and finance, manufacturing, factory automation and engineering.

1909 ■ Nesco Inc.
6140 Parkland Blvd., Ste. 110
Mayfield Heights, OH 44124-6106
Ph: (440)461-6000
Fax: (440)449-3111
E-mail: corporate@nescoresource.com
URL: http://www.nescoresource.com

Description: Offers staffing and consulting solutions in the fields of engineering, information technology, accounting and finance, manufacturing and distribution, and administrative and customer services.

1910 ■ Pate Resources Group Inc.
505 Orleans St., Ste. 300
Beaumont, TX 77701-3224
Ph: (409)833-4514
Fax: (409)833-4646

Description: Offers executive search and recruiting services to professionals who include physicians, health care administrators, accountants, financial managers; chemical, mechanical, industrial, and electrical engineers; sales and marketing managers, human resources administrators, and general managers and top executives in numerous disciplines. Industries served: health care, petrochemicals, accounting, utility, legal and municipalities.

1911 ■ Polly Brown Associates
150 E 57th St., Ste. 25A
New York, NY 10022
E-mail: pbrown@pollybrownassociates.com
URL: http://www.pollybrownassociates.com

Description: Executive search firm.

1912 ■ Quality Search Personnel Inc.
1820 Graham Dr.
Chesterton, IN 46304
Ph: (219)926-7772

Fax: (219)926-7773
E-mail: info@qsjobs.com
URL: http://www.qsjobs.com

Description: Technical recruiting specialists for placing technical and engineering personnel. The current concentration of assignments involves technical and engineering positions with a specialization in packaging and quality control. Assignments are primarily taken on a contingency basis. Industries served: consumer products, food, pharmaceutical and cosmetic, chemical, computer, heavy and light industrial.

ONLINE JOB SOURCES AND SERVICES

1913 ■ American Chemical Society Career Sources
URL: http://www.acs.org/content/acs/en.html

Description: Offers online interviewing between employers and potential employees, postings for positions available and situations wanted, and regularly updated career advice and information for American Chemical Society members only.

1914 ■ ChemicalEngineer.com
URL: http://www.chemicalengineer.com

Description: Serves as an employment center where job seekers can find many job opportunities in the field of chemical engineering.

1915 ■ EnergyCentralJobs.com
URL: http://www.energycentraljobs.com

Description: Serves as an on-line job resource for candidates and power companies worldwide. Maintains a job search database dedicated to the power, nuclear, oil and gas career fields.

1916 ■ Engineering Classifieds
URL: http://www.engineeringclassifieds.com

Description: Serves as a career site for engineering professionals. Provides services including job search agents, resume creation and posting.

1917 ■ EngineerJobs.com
URL: http://www.engineerjobs.com

Description: Provides job opportunities for engineering professionals in the following disciplines: aerospace, agricultural, biomedical, chemical, civil, electrical, environmental, industrial, manufacturing, marine, materials, mechanical, mining, nuclear, petroleum, process, project, quality, sales, software, solar, systems, and structural.

1918 ■ Engineer.net
URL: http://www.engineer.net

Description: Provides engineering employment tools such as job search, job posting, and engineering resumes.

1919 ■ PowerPlantPro.com
URL: http://www.powerplantpro.com/main/sendform/4/18/3472

Description: Dedicated to professionals in the power and energy industry. Features career advice and employer listings.

1920 ■ Spherion
URL: http://www.spherion.com

Description: Recruitment firm specializing in accounting and finance, sales and marketing, interim executives, technology, engineering, retail and human resources.

1921 ■ ThinkEnergyGroup.com
URL: http://www.thinkenergygroup.com

Description: Serves as a job board for professionals looking for positions in engineering, power plant, energy, and technical fields. Contains advice and tips on interviews, job searching, resume writing, hiring, and management. Provides choices of work location, pay rates in the field of expertise and contract, temp-to-hire, and direct hiring options.

TRADESHOWS

1922 ■ ACS National Meeting and Exposition
American Chemical Society
1155 16th St. NW
Washington, DC 20036
Ph: (202)872-4600
Free: 800-227-5558
E-mail: help@acs.org
URL: http://www.acs.org/content/acs/en.html

Primary Exhibits: Products related to all chemical disciplines.

1923 ■ American Chemical Society Southeastern Regional Meeting and Conference
American Chemical Society
1155 16th St. NW
Washington, DC 20036
Ph: (202)872-4600
Free: 800-227-5558
E-mail: help@acs.org
URL: http://www.acs.org/content/acs/en.html

Primary Exhibits: Chemical equipment, supplies, and services.

1924 ■ American Society for Engineering Education Annual Conference and Exposition
American Society for Engineering Education
1818 N St. NW, Ste. 600
Washington, DC 20036-2479
Ph: (202)331-3500
Fax: (202)265-8504
E-mail: board@asee.org
URL: http://www.asee.org

Frequency: Annual. **Primary Exhibits:** Publications, engineering supplies and equipment, computers, software, and research companies all products and services related to engineering education.

1925 ■ AOCS Annual Meeting & Expo
American Oil Chemist Society
2710 S Boulder
Urbana, IL 61802-6996
Ph: (217)359-2344
Fax: (217)351-8091
E-mail: general@aocs.org
URL: http://www.aocs.org

Frequency: Annual. **Primary Exhibits:** Fat and oil processing plant equipment, supplies, and services; laboratory instrumentation; chemical ingredients for foods, detergents, and personal care products; and publications.

OTHER SOURCES

1926 ■ American Academy of Environmental Engineers and Scientists
130 Holiday Ct., Ste. 100
Annapolis, MD 21401
Ph: (410)266-3311
Fax: (410)266-7653
E-mail: info@aaees.org
URL: http://www.aaees.org

Description: Environmentally oriented registered professional engineers certified by examination as Diplomates of the Academy. Seeks to improve the standards of environmental engineering. Certifies those with special knowledge of environmental engineering. Furnishes lists of those certified to the public. Maintains speakers' bureau. Recognizes areas of specialization: Air Pollution Control; General Environmental; Hazardous Waste Management; Industrial Hygiene; Radiation Protection; Solid Waste Management; Water Supply and Wastewater.

Requires written and oral examinations for certification. Works with other professional organizations on environmentally oriented activities. Identifies potential employment candidates through Talent Search Service.

1927 ■ American Association of Engineering Societies
1801 Alexander Bell Dr.
Reston, VA 20191
Ph: (202)296-2237
Free: 888-400-2237
Fax: (202)296-1151
E-mail: dbateson@aaes.org
URL: http://www.aaes.org

Description: Coordinates the efforts of the member societies in the provision of reliable and objective information to the general public concerning issues which affect the engineering profession and the field of engineering as a whole; collects, analyzes, documents, and disseminates data which will inform the general public of the relationship between engineering and the national welfare; provides a forum for the engineering societies to exchange and discuss their views on matters of common interest; and represents the U.S. engineering community abroad through representation in WFEO and UPADI.

1928 ■ American Chemical Society
1155 16th St. NW
Washington, DC 20036
Ph: (202)872-4600
Free: 800-227-5558
E-mail: help@acs.org
URL: http://www.acs.org/content/acs/en.html

Description: Scientific and educational society of chemists and chemical engineers. Conducts: studies and surveys; special programs for disadvantaged persons; legislation monitoring, analysis, and reporting; courses for graduate chemists and chemical engineers; radio and television programming. Offers career guidance counseling; administers the Petroleum Research Fund and other grants and fellowship programs. Operates Employment Clearing Houses. Compiles statistics. Maintains speakers' bureau and 33 divisions. **Members:** 161,783.

1929 ■ American Indian Science and Engineering Society
PO Box 9828
Albuquerque, NM 87119-9828
Ph: (505)765-1052
Fax: (505)765-5608
E-mail: pam@aises.org
URL: http://www.aises.org

Description: Represents American Indian and non-Indian students and professionals in science, technology, and engineering fields; corporations representing energy, mining, aerospace, electronic, and computer fields. Seeks to motivate and encourage students to pursue undergraduate and graduate studies in science, engineering, and technology. Sponsors science fairs in grade schools, teacher training workshops, summer math/science sessions for 8th-12th graders, professional chapters, and student chapters in colleges. Offers scholarships. Adult members serve as role models, advisers, and mentors for students. Operates placement service.

1930 ■ American Institute of Chemists
315 Chestnut St.
Philadelphia, PA 19106-2702
Ph: (215)873-8224
Fax: (215)629-5224
E-mail: info@theaic.org
URL: http://www.theaic.org

Description: Represents chemists and chemical engineers. Promotes advancement of chemical professions in the U.S.; protects public welfare by establishing and enforcing high practice standards; represents professional interests of chemists and chemical engineers. Sponsors National Certification Commission in Chemistry and Chemical Engineering and AIC Foundation.

1931 ■ American Institute of Engineers
4630 Appian Way, Ste. 206
El Sobrante, CA 94803-1875
Ph: (510)758-6240
Fax: (510)758-6240
E-mail: aie@aieonline.org
URL: http://www.aieonline.org

Description: Professional association for engineers, scientists, and mathematicians. Multi-disciplined, non-technical association who aims to improve the stature and image of engineers, scientists, and mathematicians. Provides endorsements, awards and opportunities for small business start-ups within the AIE Councils. Sponsors "LA Engineer", a comedy-drama television series; produces annual "Academy Hall of FAME (TV)".

1932 ■ American Oil Chemists' Society
2710 S Boulder
Urbana, IL 61803-7190
Ph: (217)359-2344
Fax: (217)351-8091
E-mail: general@aocs.org
URL: http://www.aocs.org

Description: Chemists, biochemists, chemical engineers, research directors, plant personnel, and others in laboratories and chemical process industries concerned with animal, marine, and vegetable oils and fats, and their extraction, refining, safety, packaging, quality control, and use in consumer and industrial products such as foods, drugs, paints, waxes, lubricants, soaps, and cosmetics. Sponsors short courses; certifies referee chemists; distributes cooperative check samples; sells official reagents. Maintains 100 committees. Operates job placement service for members only. **Members:** 4,700.

1933 ■ *Career Opportunities in Engineering*
InfoBase Holdings Inc.
132 W 31st., 17 Fl.
New York, NY 10001-3406
Ph: (212)967-8800
Fax: (800)678-3633
E-mail: info@infobasepublishing.com
URL: http://www.ferguson.infobasepublishing.com

Description: 2006. $49.50. 336 pages. Provides an overview of engineering, followed by a selection of jobs profiled in detail, including the nature of the job, earnings, prospects for employment, what kind of training and skills it requires and sources for further information. **Includes:** Appendices of educational institutions, periodicals, directories, and associations. Appendices of educational institutions, periodicals, directories, and associations.

1934 ■ Center for Chemical Process Safety
3 Park Ave., 19th Fl.
New York, NY 10016-5991
Ph: (646)495-1370
Free: 800-242-4363
Fax: (646)495-1504
E-mail: ccps@aiche.org
URL: http://www.aiche.org/ccps

Description: Chemical and hydrocarbon manufacturers; engineering firms. Purpose is to study process safety issues in the chemical and hydrocarbon industries and publish and disseminate the results. Is concerned with safety in the manufacture, handling, and storage of toxic and reactive materials and those scientific and engineering practices that can prevent episodic events involving the release of potentially hazardous materials. Conducts research on hazard evaluation procedures, bulk storage and handling of toxic or reactive materials, plant operating procedures, safety training, and dispersion modeling. Seeks to enhance the personal, professional, and technical development of engineers in process plant safety.

1935 ■ Cultural Vistas
440 Park Ave. S, 2nd Fl.
New York, NY 10016
Ph: (212)497-3500

Fax: (212)497-3535
E-mail: info@culturalvistas.org
URL: http://culturalvistas.org

Description: Providers worldwide of on-the-job training programs for students and professionals seeking international career development and life-changing experiences. Arranges workplace exchanges in hundreds of professional fields, bringing employers and trainees together from around the world. Client list ranges from small farming communities to Fortune 500 companies.

1936 ■ Engineering Society of Detroit
20700 Civic Center Dr., Ste. 450
Southfield, MI 48076
Ph: (248)353-0735
Fax: (248)353-0736
E-mail: esd@esd.org
URL: http://ww2.esd.org/home.htm

Description: Engineers from all disciplines; scientists and technologists. Conducts technical programs and engineering refresher courses; sponsors conferences and expositions. Maintains speakers' bureau; offers placement services; although based in Detroit, MI, society membership is international. **Members:** 6,000.

1937 ■ Iranian Chemists' Association of the American Chemical Society
35 Meadowbrook Ln.
Woodbury, CT 06798
Ph: (203)573-3220
Fax: (203)573-3660
E-mail: banijamali@ica-acs.org
URL: http://www.ica-acs.org

Description: Encourages and enhances the interchange and sharing of scientific knowledge and friendship among chemists and chemistry-related professionals of Iranian descent. Provides opportunities for members to assist each other in pursuit of academic and professional development and growth. Promotes awareness of scientific contributions made by Iranian scientists.

1938 ■ ISA -The International Society of Automation
67 Alexander Dr.
Research Triangle Park, NC 27709
Ph: (919)549-8411
Fax: (919)549-8288
E-mail: info@isa.org
URL: http://www.isa.org

Description: Sets the standard for automation by helping over 30,000 worldwide members and other professionals solve difficult technical problems, while enhancing their leadership and personal career capabilities. Develops standards; certifies industry professionals; provides education and training; publishes books and technical articles; and hosts the largest conference and exhibition for automation

professionals in the Western Hemisphere. Is the founding sponsor of The Automation Federation.

1939 ■ Korean-American Scientists and Engineers Association
1952 Gallows Rd., Ste. 300
Vienna, VA 22182
Ph: (703)748-1221
Fax: (703)748-1331
E-mail: sejong@ksea.org
URL: http://www.ksea.org

Description: Represents scientists and engineers holding single or advanced degrees. Promotes friendship and mutuality among Korean and American scientists and engineers; contributes to Korea's scientific, technological, industrial, and economic developments; strengthens the scientific, technological, and cultural bonds between Korea and the U.S. Sponsors symposium. Maintains speakers' bureau, placement service, and biographical archives. Compiles statistics. **Members:** 10,000.

1940 ■ National Action Council for Minorities in Engineering
440 Hamilton Ave., Ste. 302
White Plains, NY 10601-1813
Ph: (914)539-4010
Free: 800-888-9929
Fax: (914)539-4032
E-mail: ajohnson@nacme.org
URL: http://www.nacme.org

Description: Leads the national effort to increase access to careers in engineering and other science-based disciplines. Conducts research and public policy analysis, develops and operates national demonstration programs at precollege and university levels, and disseminates information through publications, conferences and electronic media. Serves as a privately funded source of scholarships for minority students in engineering.

1941 ■ National Organization for the Professional Advancement of Black Chemists and Chemical Engineers
PO Box 77040
Washington, DC 20013
Ph: (240)228-1763
Free: 800-776-1419
E-mail: president@nobcche.org
URL: http://www.nobcche.org

Description: Black professionals in science and chemistry. Seeks to aid black scientists and chemists in reaching their full professional potential; encourages black students to pursue scientific studies and employment; promotes participation of blacks in scientific research. Provides volunteers to teach science courses in selected elementary schools; sponsors scientific field trips for students; maintains speakers' bureau for schools. Conducts technical seminars in Africa. Sponsors competitions; presents awards for significant achievements to individuals in

the field. Maintains placement service; compiles statistics.

1942 ■ National Society of Professional Engineers
1420 King St.
Alexandria, VA 22314-2794
Ph: (703)684-2800
Fax: (703)836-4875
E-mail: memserv@nspe.org
URL: http://www.nspe.org

Description: Represents professional engineers and engineers-in-training in all fields registered in accordance with the laws of states or territories of the U.S. or provinces of Canada; qualified graduate engineers, student members, and registered land surveyors. Is concerned with social, professional, ethical, and economic considerations of engineering as a profession; encompasses programs in public relations, employment practices, ethical considerations, education, and career guidance. Monitors legislative and regulatory actions of interest to the engineering profession.

1943 ■ Society of Hispanic Professional Engineers
13181 Crossroads Pkwy. N, Ste. 450
City of Industry, CA 91746-3496
Ph: (323)725-3970
E-mail: shpenational@shpe.org
URL: http://national.shpe.org

Description: Represents engineers, student engineers, and scientists. Aims to increase the number of Hispanic engineers by providing motivation and support to students. Sponsors competitions and educational programs. Maintains placement service and speakers' bureau; compiles statistics. **Members:** 8,000.

1944 ■ Society of Women Engineers
203 N La Salle St., Ste. 1675
Chicago, IL 60601
Ph: (312)596-5223
Free: 877-SWE-INFO
Fax: (312)596-5252
E-mail: hq@swe.org
URL: http://societyofwomenengineers.swe.org

Description: Educational and service organization representing both students and professional women in engineering and technical fields.

1945 ■ Women in Engineering ProActive Network
1901 E Asbury Ave., Ste. 220
Denver, CO 80208
Ph: (303)871-4643
Fax: (303)871-4628
URL: http://www.wepan.org

Description: Women in engineering professions. Includes key strategies such as education and training, research, collaboration, leadership, diversity, advocacy, networking, sustainability, accountability, and volunteerism in order to be a catalyst for change that enhances the success of women in the engineering professions.

Sources of Help-Wanted Ads

1946 ■ *American Biotechnology Laboratory*
International Scientific Communications Inc.
30 Controls Dr.
Shelton, CT 06484-0870
Ph: (650)243-5600
Fax: (203)926-9310
E-mail: iscpubs@iscpubs.com
URL: http://www.americanbiotechnologylaboratory
.com

Frequency: 10/yr. **Description:** Biotechnology magazine.

1947 ■ *Biochemistry and Molecular Biology Education*
John Wiley & Sons Inc.
111 River St.
Hoboken, NJ 07030-5774
Ph: (201)748-6000
Free: 800-225-5945
Fax: (201)748-6088
E-mail: info@wiley.com
URL: http://onlinelibrary.wiley.com/journal/10.1002/
(ISSN)1539-3429

Frequency: Bimonthly. **Price:** $618 Institutions print only; $702 Institutions, Canada and Mexico print only; $744 Institutions, other countries print only. **Description:** Journal covering the field of biochemistry, molecular biology, and related sciences.

1948 ■ *Chemical Engineering Communications*
Taylor & Francis Group Journals
c/o William N. Gill, Ed.-in-Ch.
Chemical Engineering Department
Ricketts Bldg.
Rensselaer Polytechnic Institute
Troy, NY 12180-3590
Ph: (215)625-8900
Free: 800-354-1420
Fax: (215)625-2940
E-mail: customerservice@taylorandfrancis.com
URL: http://www.tandfonline.com/toc/gcec20/current

Frequency: Monthly. **Price:** $2,518 Individuals print only; $5,510 Institutions online only; $6,122 Institutions print and online. **Description:** Journal focusing on the results of basic and applied research in chemical engineering.

1949 ■ *Chemical Engineering and Technology*
John Wiley & Sons Inc.
111 River St.
Hoboken, NJ 07030-5774
Ph: (201)748-6000
Free: 800-225-5945

Fax: (201)748-6088
E-mail: info@wiley.com
URL: http://onlinelibrary.wiley.com/journal/10.1002/
(ISSN)1521-4125

Frequency: Monthly. **Price:** $5,036 Institutions print only; $5,036 Institutions, other countries print only; $5,792 Institutions print with online; €3,924 Institutions print only, rest of Europe; £2,570 Institutions print only. **Description:** Journal focusing on all aspects of chemical and process engineering.

1950 ■ *Chemical Processing*
Putman Media Inc.
555 W Pierce Rd., Ste. 301
Itasca, IL 60143-2649
Ph: (630)467-1301
Fax: (630)467-1120
E-mail: controlroundup@putman.net
URL: http://www.chemicalprocessing.com

Frequency: Monthly. **Description:** Magazine for the chemical process industry.

1951 ■ *The Chemical Record*
John Wiley & Sons Inc.
111 River St.
Hoboken, NJ 07030-5774
Ph: (201)748-6000
Free: 800-225-5945
Fax: (201)748-6088
E-mail: info@wiley.com
URL: http://onlinelibrary.wiley.com/journal/10.1002/
(ISSN)1528-0691

Frequency: Bimonthly. **Price:** $123 U.S., Canada, and Mexico print only; $735 Institutions print & online; $153 Other countries print only; $639 Institutions print only; $639 Institutions, Canada and Mexico print only; $639 Institutions, other countries print only. **Description:** Journal publishing overviews of new developments at the cutting edge of chemistry of interest to a wide audience of chemists.

1952 ■ *The Chemist*
American Institute of Chemists
315 Chestnut St.
Philadelphia, PA 19106-2702
Ph: (215)873-8224
Fax: (215)629-5224
E-mail: info@theaic.org
URL: http://www.theaic.org

Description: Quarterly. Covers news items relating to the chemical profession and membership in the Institute. Reports on legislation, licensure, earnings, awards, and professional education. Recurring features include news of employment opportunities and news of members. Published alternate months as a magazine.

1953 ■ *Chemistry & Biology*
Elsevier Science Inc.
Secondary Publishing Division
650 Ave. of the Americas
New York, NY 10011

Ph: (212)633-3980
Free: 888-437-4636
Fax: (212)633-3975
URL: http://www.elsevier.com/wps/find/journalde-
scription.cws_home/601281/description#description

Frequency: Monthly. **Price:** $2,137 Institutions print; $442 U.S. and other countries online only; $457 Other countries print + online; $442 U.S. and Canada print; $843 Institutions online. **Description:** Journal focused on genetic, computational, or theoretical information of chemistry and biology, substantiating experimental data.

1954 ■ *The Electrochemical Society Interface*
Electrochemical Society
c/o Krishan Rajeshwar, Ed.
University of Texas at Arlington
Department of Chemistry & Biochemistry
502 Yates St.
Arlington, TX 76019
Ph: (817)272-3810
Fax: (817)272-3808
E-mail: interface@electrochem.org
URL: http://www.electrochem.org/dl/interface/

Frequency: Quarterly. **Price:** $69 Individuals tier 1, print & online; $84 Canada tier 1, print & online; $92 Other countries tier 1, print & online. **Description:** Publication featuring news and articles of interest to members of the Electrochemical Society.

1955 ■ *Engineering in Life Sciences*
John Wiley & Sons Inc.
111 River St.
Hoboken, NJ 07030-5774
Ph: (201)748-6000
Free: 800-225-5945
Fax: (201)748-6088
E-mail: info@wiley.com
URL: http://onlinelibrary.wiley.com/journal/10.1002/
(ISSN)1618-2863

Frequency: Bimonthly. **Price:** €1,069 Institutions European, online only; $1,403 Institutions, Canada and Mexico online only; $1,403 Institutions, other countries online only; £717 Institutions European, online only; $1,403 Institutions online only. **Description:** Journal focusing on the field of biotechnology and related topics including microbiology, genetics, biochemistry, and chemistry.

1956 ■ *Journal of Chemical Theory and Computation*
American Chemical Society
1155 16th St. NW
Washington, DC 20036
Ph: (202)872-4600
Free: 800-227-5558
E-mail: help@acs.org
URL: http://pubs.acs.org/journal/jctcce

Frequency: 6/yr. **Price:** $1,367 Institutions North America; $1,499 Institutions, other countries. **Description:** Journal presenting new theories, methodology, and/or important applications in quantum chemistry, molecular dynamics, and statistical mechanics.

1957 ■ MainStream / Streamline
American Water Works Association
6666 W Quincy Ave.
Denver, CO 80235-3098
Ph: (303)794-7711
Free: 800-926-7337
Fax: (303)347-0804
URL: http://www.awwa.org

Mary A. Parmelee, Editor, mparmele@awwa.org. **Frequency:** Biweekly, online; print issue is published quarterly. **Price:** Included in membership; $16, nonmembers U.S. and Canada; $22, nonmembers. **Description:** Recurring features include a calendar of events, news of educational opportunities, and education and job opportunities in the industry.

1958 ■ Modern Plastics Worldwide
UBM Canon
3300 E 1st Ave., Ste. 370
Denver, CO 80206
Ph: (303)321-2322
Fax: (303)321-3552
E-mail: info@ubm.com
URL: http://www.modplas.com

Frequency: Monthly. **Price:** $59 Individuals; $99 Two years U.S. and possessions; $110 Canada; $199 Two years for Canada; $150 Other countries; $250 Two years. **Description:** Magazine for the plastics industry.

1959 ■ Nanomechanics Science and Technology: An International Journal
Begell House Inc.
50 Cross Hwy.
Redding, CT 06896
Ph: (203)938-1300
Fax: (203)938-1304
E-mail: orders@begellhouse.com
URL: http://www.begellhouse.com/journals/11e12455066dab5d

Price: $800 Institutions. **Description:** Journal covering the areas of nano- and micromechanics.

1960 ■ Nanoparticle News
BCC Research
35 Walnut St., Ste. 100
Wellesley, MA 02481
Ph: (781)489-7301
Free: 866-285-7215
Fax: (781)253-3933
E-mail: info@bccresearch.com
URL: http://www.bccresearch.com/report/index.php?rcode=nan

Frequency: Monthly. **Price:** $675 Single issue web access and archive (2 user license); $640 Single issue print, online, archive (outside North America); $495 Single issue web access and archive; $590 Single issue print, web access and archive (North America); $1,485 Individuals online (enterprise license); $990 Individuals online (Department license); $750 Individuals online (5 user license). **Description:** Publication covering issues in the chemical industry.

1961 ■ Nature Biotechnology
Macmillan Publishers Ltd. - Nature Publishing Group
75 Varick St., 9th Fl.
New York, NY 10013-1917
Ph: (212)726-9200
Free: 888-331-6288
Fax: (212)696-9006
E-mail: biotech@natureny.com
URL: http://www.nature.com/nbt/index.html

Frequency: Monthly. **Price:** $250 Individuals print + online; $425 Two years print + online. **Description:** Scientific research journal.

1962 ■ PALAIOS
SEPM Publications
University of Kansas
Paleontological Institute, Department of Geology
1475 Jawyhawk Blvd., Rm. 120
Lawrence, KS 66045-7613
Ph: (785)864-2737
Fax: (785)864-3636
E-mail: palois@ku.edu
URLs: http://palaios.ku.edu/; http://palaios.geoscienceworld.org/

Frequency: Monthly. **Price:** $400 Individuals for U.S.; online version with CD-ROM; $500 Individuals for U.S.; print and online version with CD-ROM; $400 Other countries online version with CD-ROM; $500 Other countries print and online version with CD-ROM. **Description:** Journal providing information on the impact of life on Earth history as recorded in the paleontological and sedimentological records. Covers areas such as biogeochemistry, ichnology, sedimentology, stratigraphy, paleoecology, paleoclimatology, and paleoceanography.

1963 ■ Paper, Film & Foil Converter
Intertec Publishing
330 N Wabash, Ste. 2300
Chicago, IL 60611-3698
Ph: (312)595-1080
Free: 800-458-0479
Fax: (913)514-3924
E-mail: bethany.weaver@penton.com
URL: http://pffc-online.com/

Frequency: Monthly. **Description:** Magazine focusing on flexible packaging, paperboard, and film.

1964 ■ Plastics Engineering
Society of Plastics Engineers
13 Church Hill Rd.
Newtown, CT 06470
Ph: (203)775-0471
Fax: (203)775-8490
E-mail: info@4spe.org
URLs: http://www.4spe.org/pub; http://plasticsengineering.org/home

Frequency: 10/year. **Price:** $142 Nonmembers; $242 Nonmembers outside North America; $180 Institutions corporate library; $280 Institutions corporate library outside North America; included in membership dues; $160/year for nonmembers. **Description:** Plastics trade magazine.

1965 ■ Powder and Bulk Engineering
CSC Publishing Inc.
1155 Northland Dr.
Saint Paul, MN 55120
Ph: (651)287-5650
Fax: (651)287-5600
E-mail: info@cscpub.com
URL: http://www.powderbulk.com/Content/Default.aspx

Frequency: Monthly. **Price:** $100 Individuals outside North America, or digital format. **Description:** Journal serving chemical, food, plastics, pulp and paper, and electronic industries.

1966 ■ Science
American Association for the Advancement of Science
1200 New York Ave. NW
Washington, DC 20005
Ph: (202)326-6400
Fax: (202)371-9526
E-mail: membership@aaas.org
URLs: http://www.scienceonline.org; http://www.sciencemag.org

Frequency: Weekly. **Price:** $146 Members professional, print & online; $119 Individuals NPA postdoctoral, print & online; $99 Individuals postdoctoral/resident, print & online; $75 Students print & online; $310 Individuals patron, print & online; $115 Individuals emeritus, print & online; $161 Canada postdoctoral/resident, print & online; $136.50 Students, Canada print & online; $149 in U.S.; $211.05 in Canada; $201 in Mexico/Caribbean; $231 in all other

countries. **Description:** Contains research reports, book reviews, editorial, news, and comments.

EMPLOYER DIRECTORIES AND NETWORKING LISTS

1967 ■ American Men and Women of Science: A Biographical Dictionary of Today's Leaders in Physical, Biological, and Related Sciences
R.R. Bowker
630 Central Ave
New Providence, NJ 07974
Ph: (888)269-5372
Free: 888-269-5372
Fax: (908)464-3553
E-mail: info@bowker.com
URL: http://www.gale.cengage.com

Frequency: Biennial; even years; New edition expected 29th, June 2011. **Price:** $1,368 Individuals. **Covers:** Over 135,000 U.S. and Canadian scientists active in the physical, biological, mathematical, computer science, and engineering fields; includes references to previous edition for deceased scientists and nonrespondents. **Entries include:** Name, address, education, personal and career data, memberships, honors and awards, research interest. **Arrangement:** Alphabetical. **Indexes:** Discipline (in separate volume).

1968 ■ Chemical Week--Buyers Guide Issue
Chemical Week Associates
2 Grand Central Tower
140 E 45th St., 40th Fl.
New York, NY 10017
Ph: (212)884-9528
Free: 800-774-5733
Fax: (212)883-9514
E-mail: webmaster@chemweek.com
URL: http://www.chemweek.com/buyersguide/public

Frequency: Annual; Latest edition 2012. **Price:** $115 Included in subscription, per year; $25 Individuals. **Publication includes:** About 4,200 manufacturers and suppliers of chemical raw materials to the chemical process industries; 400 manufacturers of packaging materials; and suppliers of products and services to the chemical process industries, including hazardous waste/environmental services, computer services, plant design, construction, consulting, shipping, and transportation. **Entries include:** Over 17,000 product/service listings, Company name, address, phone; local addresses and phone numbers for up to 25 sales locations. **Arrangement:** Separate alphabetical sections for chemical, packaging, and hazardous waste/environmental services. **Indexes:** Product (all sections); trade name (chemical and packaging sections only).

1969 ■ Consulting Services
Association of Consulting Chemists and Chemical Engineers
PO Box 902
Murray Hill, NJ 07974-0902
Ph: (908)464-3182
Fax: (908)464-3182
E-mail: accce@chemconsult.org
URL: http://www.chemconsult.org

Frequency: Biennial; even years. **Price:** $30 Individuals postpaid. **Pages:** 200. **Covers:** About 160 member consultants in chemistry, chemical engineering, metallurgy, etc. **Entries include:** Individual name, address, certificate number, qualifications, affiliation, experience, facilities, staff. **Arrangement:** Classified by area of expertise. **Indexes:** Personal name, geographical.

1970 ■ Directory of Chemical Producers--United States
SRI International - IHS Chemical: Chemical Insight & Forecasting
333 Ravenswood Ave.
Menlo Park, CA 94025-3493

Ph: (303)858-6355
Free: 800-688-7391
Fax: (650)859-4111
E-mail: sric-dcp@ihs.com
URL: http://www.ihs.com/products/chemical/companies/producers.aspx?pu=1&rd=chemihs

Frequency: Annual; latest edition April, 2011. **Price:** $2,050 U.S. new subscription; $1,635 U.S. renewing subscription; $2,100 Online. **Pages:** 1,050. **Covers:** Over 1,255 United States basic chemical producers manufacturing 7,085 chemicals in commercial quantities at more than 3,205 plant locations. **Includes:** Plant-by-plant capacities for over 150 major chemicals. **Entries include:** For companies-- Company name, division or subsidiary names, corporate address, phone, fax, telex, location of each subsidiary, division, and manufacturing plant, and the products made at each plant location. For products-- Producer name and plant locations, alternate product names (if any). Subscription price includes bound volume, plus access to the directory staff for inquiries. **Arrangement:** Companies are alphabetical; products are alphabetical and by group (dyes, pesticides, etc.); manufacturing plants are geographical. **Indexes:** Geographical, product.

1971 ■ Physical and Earth Sciences Graduate Program Directories
EducationDynamics LLC - Prospecting Services Div. - GradSchools.com
1350 Edgmont Ave., Ste. 1100
Chester, PA 19013
Ph: (484)766-2910
Free: 866-GRAD-COM
Fax: (610)499-9205
E-mail: info@edudirectories.com
URL: http://www.gradschools.com

HANDBOOKS AND MANUALS

1972 ■ *Career Management for Chemists*
Springer-Verlag New York, Inc.
233 Spring St.
New York, NY 10013
Ph: (212)460-1500
Free: 877-687-7476
Fax: (212)460-1575
E-mail: service-ny@springer.com
URL: http://www.springer.com/life+sci/agriculture/book/978-3-540-20755-9

Description: John Fetzer. 2004. $54.95. Illustrated. 266 pages. Vocational guide for Chemists.

1973 ■ *Great Jobs for Chemistry Majors*
The McGraw-Hill Companies Inc.
PO Box 182604
Columbus, OH 43272
Ph: (212)512-2000
Free: 877-833-5524
Fax: (614)759-3749
E-mail: customer.service@mcgraw-hill.com
URL: http://www.mcgraw-hill.com

Description: Mark Rowh. Second edition, 2005. $15.95 (paper). 208 pages.

1974 ■ *Principal Chemist*
National Learning Corporation
212 Michael Dr.
Syosset, NY 11791
Ph: (516)921-8888
Free: 800-632-8888
Fax: (516)921-8743
E-mail: info@passbooks.com
URL: http://www.passbooks.com

Description: 2009. $34.95 (paper). Serves as an exam preparation guide for principal chemists.

1975 ■ *Theoretical and Quantum Mechanics: Fundamentals for Chemists*
Springer Publishing Co.
11 W 42nd St., 15th Fl.
New York, NY 10036

Ph: (212)431-4370
Free: 877-687-7476
Fax: (212)941-7842
E-mail: cs@springerpub.com
URL: http://www.springerpub.com

Description: Stefan Ivanov. 2006. $199. 513 pages. Offers an introduction into theoretical and quantum mechanics for chemists. The book focuses on the atom and bridges the gap between classical physics, general and inorganic chemistry, and quantum mechanics.

1976 ■ *What's Cooking in Chemistry?: How Leading Chemists Succeed in the Kitchen*
John Wiley & Sons, Inc.
1 Wiley Dr.
Somerset, NJ 08873
Free: 877-762-2974
Fax: (800)597-3299
E-mail: custserv@wiley.com
URL: http://www.wiley.com

Description: Hubertus P. Bell, Tim Feuerstein, Carlos E. Guntner, Soren Holsken and Jan Klaas Lohmann. 2009. $19.95. Illustrated. 243 pages.

EMPLOYMENT AGENCIES AND SEARCH FIRMS

1977 ■ Amtec Human Capital
2749 Saturn St.
Brea, CA 92821
Ph: (714)993-1900
Fax: (714)993-2419
E-mail: info@amtechc.com
URL: http://www.amtechc.com

Description: Employment agency.

1978 ■ Apple and Associates
PO Box 996
Chapin, SC 29036
Ph: (803)932-2000
E-mail: info@appleassoc.com
URL: http://www.appleassoc.com

Description: Provides staffing services to medical device, plastics, pharmaceutical and performance materials industries.

1979 ■ Biomedical Search Consultants
275 Wyman St., Ste. 110
Waltham, MA 02451
Ph: (781)890-8824
Fax: (781)998-1266
E-mail: kprovost@biomedicalsearch.com
URL: http://www.biomedicalsearchconsultants.com

Description: Employment agency.

1980 ■ The Brentwood Group Inc.
170 Kinnelon Rd.
Kinnelon, NJ 07405
Ph: (973)283-1000
Fax: (973)850-6103
E-mail: officemanager@thebrentwoodgroup.com
URL: http://www.thebrentwoodgroup.com

Description: Executive search firm.

1981 ■ Professional Placement Associates, Inc.
287 Bowman Ave.
Purchase, NY 10577-2517
Ph: (914)251-1000
Fax: (914)251-1055
E-mail: careers@ppasearch.com
URL: http://www.ppasearch.com

Description: Executive search firm specializing in the health and medical field.

1982 ■ Team Placement Service Inc.
1414 Prince St., Ste. 202
Alexandria, VA 22314
Ph: (703)820-8618

Free: 800-495-6767
Fax: (703)820-3368
E-mail: info@teamplace.com
URL: http://www.teamplace.com

Description: Full-service personnel consultants provide placement for healthcare staff, physician and dentist, private practice, and hospitals. Conduct interviews, tests, and reference checks to select the top 20% of applicants. Survey applicants' skill levels, provide backup information on each candidate, select compatible candidates for consideration, and insure the hiring process minimizes potential legal liability. Industries served: healthcare and government agencies providing medical, dental, biotech, laboratory, hospitals, and physician search.

ONLINE JOB SOURCES AND SERVICES

1983 ■ American Chemical Society Career Sources
URL: http://www.acs.org/content/acs/en.html

Description: Offers online interviewing between employers and potential employees, postings for positions available and situations wanted, and regularly updated career advice and information for American Chemical Society members only.

1984 ■ American Oil Chemists Society Career Opportunities
URL: http://www.aocs.org/membership/jobtarget.cfm

Description: Section of the AOCS homepage intended to aid members in finding jobs in the oil chemistry field. Job areas include analytical, health and nutrition, processing, surfactants and detergents, general fats and oils/chemistry, and others. Jobs may be posted and searched.

1985 ■ ChemIndustry.com
URL: http://www.chemindustry.com

Description: Directory and search engine for chemical and related industry professionals. Provides specialized search services for chemical names, jobs, market research and consultants.

1986 ■ Chemist Jobs
URL: http://www.chemistjobs.us

Description: Features nationwide chemist job listings and cost-effective job posting for employers.

1987 ■ ChemistryCrossing.com
URL: http://www.chemistrycrossing.com

Description: Provides employment opportunities for chemists. Locates and classifies jobs on every source and provides specialized research to job seekers, recruiters and other job sites throughout North America.

1988 ■ Discover8.com
URL: http://www.discover8.com

Description: Focuses on the dissemination and intelligent discussion of life science news, discoveries, hypotheses, and procedures. Features resume postings and career listings.

1989 ■ Hum-Molgen.org
URL: http://hum-molgen.org

Description: Provides resources for the latest information in human molecular genetics. Features biotechnical sources, diagnostics, ethical, legal and social implications, meetings and conferences, and positions in bioscience and medicine. Provides the opportunity to communicate with scientists, physicians, and other genetics professionals worldwide.

1990 ■ iHireChemists.com
URL: http://www.ihirechemists.com

Description: Features job listings for chemists. Helps job seekers find employment opportunities and connect with hiring managers in all locations throughout the United States.

1991 ■ ThinkEnergyGroup.com
URL: http://www.thinkenergygroup.com

Description: Serves as a job board for professionals looking for positions in engineering, power plant, energy, and technical fields. Contains advice and tips on interviews, job searching, resume writing, hiring, and management. Provides choices of work location, pay rates in the field of expertise and contract, temp-to-hire, and direct hiring options.

TRADESHOWS

1992 ■ AOAC International Annual Meeting and Exposition
AOAC International
481 N Frederick Ave., Ste. 500
Gaithersburg, MD 20877-2417
Ph: (301)924-7077
Free: 800-379-2622
Fax: (301)924-7089
E-mail: aoac@aoac.org
URL: http://www.aoac.org

Frequency: Annual. **Primary Exhibits:** Scientific and laboratory supplies and publications exhibits and posters.

OTHER SOURCES

1993 ■ AACC International
3340 Pilot Knob Rd.
Saint Paul, MN 55121
Ph: (651)454-7250
Free: 800-328-7560
Fax: (651)454-0766
E-mail: aacc@scisoc.org
URL: http://www.aaccnet.org

Description: Serves as professional society of scientists and other individuals in the grain processing industry (milling, baking, convenience foods, and feeds). Encourages research on cereal grains, oil seeds, pulses, and related materials, and studies their processing, utilization, and products. Seeks to develop and standardize analytical methods used in cereal and seed chemistry and to disseminate scientific and technical information through workshops and publications. Offers honors for outstanding research. Maintains over 20 technical subcommittees. Conducts short courses for continuing education and annual sanitation certification program.

1994 ■ American Academy of Clinical Toxicology
6728 Old McLean Village Dr.
McLean, VA 22101
Ph: (703)556-9222
Fax: (703)556-8729
E-mail: admin@clintox.org
URL: http://www.clintox.org

Description: Physicians, veterinarians, pharmacists, nurses research scientists, and analytical chemists. Seeks to unite medical scientists and facilitate the exchange of information. Encourages the development of therapeutic methods and technology. Conducts professional training in poison information and emergency service personnel.

1995 ■ American Association of Textile Chemists and Colorists
PO Box 12215
Research Triangle Park, NC 27709-2215
Ph: (919)549-8141
Fax: (919)549-8933
E-mail: danielsj@aatcc.org
URL: http://www.aatcc.org

Description: Professional association for textile design, processing and testing. Works as an authority for industry standard test methods and evaluation procedures.

1996 ■ American Chemical Society
1155 16th St. NW
Washington, DC 20036
Ph: (202)872-4600
Free: 800-227-5558
E-mail: help@acs.org
URL: http://www.acs.org/content/acs/en.html

Description: Scientific and educational society of chemists and chemical engineers. Conducts: studies and surveys; special programs for disadvantaged persons; legislation monitoring, analysis, and reporting; courses for graduate chemists and chemical engineers; radio and television programming. Offers career guidance counseling; administers the Petroleum Research Fund and other grants and fellowship programs. Operates Employment Clearing Houses. Compiles statistics. Maintains speakers' bureau and 33 divisions. **Members:** 161,783.

1997 ■ American Crystallographic Association
PO Box 96
Buffalo, NY 14205-0096
Ph: (716)898-8690
Fax: (716)898-8695
E-mail: marcia@hwi.buffalo.edu
URL: http://www.amercrystalassn.org

Description: Chemists, biochemists, physicists, mineralogists, and metallurgists interested in crystallography and in the application of X-ray, electron, and neutron diffraction. Promotes the study of the arrangement of atoms in matter, its causes, its nature, and its consequences, and of the tools and methods used in such studies. Maintains employment clearinghouse for members and employers.

1998 ■ American Institute of Chemists
315 Chestnut St.
Philadelphia, PA 19106-2702
Ph: (215)873-8224
Fax: (215)629-5224
E-mail: info@theaic.org
URL: http://www.theaic.org

Description: Represents chemists and chemical engineers. Promotes advancement of chemical professions in the U.S.; protects public welfare by establishing and enforcing high practice standards; represents professional interests of chemists and chemical engineers. Sponsors National Certification Commission in Chemistry and Chemical Engineering and AIC Foundation.

1999 ■ American Microchemical Society
c/o Herk Felder, Treasurer
2 June Way
Middlesex, NJ 08846
E-mail: hal1116@netscape.com
URL: http://www.microchem.org

Description: Promotes interest in the practice and teaching of microchemistry. Participates in exhibits and symposia. Maintains placement service. **Members:** 150.

2000 ■ American Oil Chemists' Society
2710 S Boulder
Urbana, IL 61803-7190
Ph: (217)359-2344
Fax: (217)351-8091
E-mail: general@aocs.org
URL: http://www.aocs.org

Description: Chemists, biochemists, chemical engineers, research directors, plant personnel, and others in laboratories and chemical process industries concerned with animal, marine, and vegetable oils and fats, and their extraction, refining, safety, packaging, quality control, and use in consumer and industrial products such as foods, drugs, paints, waxes, lubricants, soaps, and cosmetics. Sponsors short courses; certifies referee chemists; distributes cooperative check samples; sells official reagents. Maintains 100 committees. Operates job placement service for members only. **Members:** 4,700.

2001 ■ American Society for Biochemistry and Molecular Biology
11200 Rockville Pike, Ste. 302
Rockville, MD 20852-3110
Ph: (240)283-6600
Fax: (301)881-2080
E-mail: asbmb@asbmb.org
URL: http://www.asbmb.org

Description: Biochemists and molecular biologists who have conducted and published original investigations in biological chemistry and/or molecular biology. Operates placement service.

2002 ■ American Society of Brewing Chemists
3340 Pilot Knob Rd.
Saint Paul, MN 55121-2097
Ph: (651)454-7250
Fax: (651)454-0766
E-mail: asbc@scisoc.org
URL: http://www.asbcnet.org

Description: Serves as a group of individual and corporate members worldwide representing large and small brewers, consultants, government agencies, academics, distillers, vintners and those working in allied industries (suppliers of malt, hops, enzymes, brewing syrups, chill proofing, filtration aids, CO2 packaging materials, etc.). Strives to improve and bring uniformity to the brewing industry on a technical level. Provides problem solving on industry-wide issues using chemistry and microbiology and professional development opportunities.

2003 ■ American Society for Neurochemistry
9037 Ron Den Ln.
Windermere, FL 34786
Ph: (407)909-9064
Fax: (407)876-0750
E-mail: amazing@iag.net
URL: http://www.asneurochem.org

Description: Represents investigators in the field of neurochemistry and scientists who are qualified specialists in other disciplines and are interested in the activities of the society. Aims to advance and promote the science of neurochemistry and related neurosciences and to increase and enhance neurochemical knowledge; to facilitate the dissemination of information concerning neurochemical research; to encourage the research of individual neurochemists. Conducts roundtables; distributes research communications. Maintains placement service.

2004 ■ American Society of Plant Biologists
15501 Monona Dr.
Rockville, MD 20855-2768
Ph: (301)251-0560
Fax: (301)279-2996
E-mail: info@aspb.org
URL: http://my.aspb.org

Description: Professional society of plant biologists, plant biochemists, and other plant scientists engaged in research and teaching. Offers placement service for members; conducts educational and public affairs programs.

2005 ■ American Water Works Association
6666 W Quincy Ave.
Denver, CO 80235-3098
Ph: (303)794-7711
Free: 800-926-7337
Fax: (303)347-0804
URL: http://www.awwa.org

Description: Water utility managers, superintendents, engineers, chemists, bacteriologists, and other individuals interested in public water supply; municipal- and investor-owned water departments; boards of health; manufacturers of waterworks equipment; government officials and consultants interested in water supply. Offers placement service via member newsletter.

2006 ■ Association of Consulting Chemists and Chemical Engineers
PO Box 902
Murray Hill, NJ 07974-0902
Ph: (908)464-3182
Fax: (908)464-3182
E-mail: accce@chemconsult.org
URL: http://www.chemconsult.org
Description: Serves the chemical and related industries through its expertise on a wide variety of technical and business knowledge. Provides experienced counseling for new members.

2007 ■ Biomedical Engineering Society
8201 Corporate Dr., Ste. 1125
Landover, MD 20785-2224
Ph: (301)459-1999
Free: 877-871-2637
Fax: (301)459-2444
URL: http://www.bmes.org
Description: Biomedical, chemical, electrical, civil, agricultural and mechanical engineers, physicians, managers, and university professors representing all fields of biomedical engineering; students and corporations. Encourages the development, dissemination, integration, and utilization of knowledge in biomedical engineering.

2008 ■ *Career Opportunities in Science*
InfoBase Holdings Inc.
132 W 31st., 17 Fl.
New York, NY 10001-3406
Ph: (212)967-8800
Fax: (800)678-3633
E-mail: info@infobasepublishing.com
URL: http://factsonfile.infobasepublishing.com
Frequency: Latest edition 2008. **Price:** $49.50 Individuals hardcover. **Pages:** 344. **Description:** Susan Echaore-McDavid. Second edition, 2008. 332 pages. **Covers:** More than 80 jobs, such as biochemist, molecular biologist, bioinformatic specialist, pharmacologist, computer engineer, geographic information systems specialist, science teacher, forensic scientist, patent agent, as well as physicist, astronomer, chemist, zoologist, oceanographer, and geologist. **Includes:** Appendices of educational institutions, periodicals, directories, and associations.

2009 ■ Council for Chemical Research
1550 M St. NW, Ste. 300
Washington, DC 20005
Ph: (202)429-3971
Fax: (202)429-3976
E-mail: pmendez@ccrhq.org
URL: http://www.ccrhq.org
Description: Represents universities that grant advanced degrees in chemistry or chemical engineering; chemical companies, government laboratories, and independent research laboratories that employ chemists and chemical engineers in research and development. Aims to promote more effective interactions between university chemistry and chemical engineering departments and the research function of industry and government and to support basic research in chemistry and chemical engineering. Strives for continued vitality of chemical science, engineering, and technology in the U.S., and the greater recognition of the global nature of the chemical research enterprise. Sponsors charitable programs; produces educational materials; compiles statistics. Maintains speakers' bureau.

2010 ■ Cultural Vistas
440 Park Ave. S, 2nd Fl.
New York, NY 10016
Ph: (212)497-3500
Fax: (212)497-3535
E-mail: info@culturalvistas.org
URL: http://culturalvistas.org
Description: Providers worldwide of on-the-job training programs for students and professionals seeking international career development and life-changing experiences. Arranges workplace exchanges in hundreds of professional fields, bringing employers and trainees together from around the world. Client list ranges from small farming communities to Fortune 500 companies.

2011 ■ Electrochemical Society
65 S Main St., Bldg. D
Pennington, NJ 08534-2827
Ph: (609)737-1902
Fax: (609)737-2743
E-mail: ecs@electrochem.org
URL: http://www.electrochem.org
Description: Serves as technical society of electrochemists, chemists, chemical and electrochemical engineers, metallurgists and metallurgical engineers, physical chemists, physicists, electrical engineers, research engineers, teachers, technical sales representatives, and patent attorneys. Seeks to advance the science and technology of electrochemistry, electronics, electrothermics, electrometallurgy, and applied subjects.

2012 ■ Engineering Society of Detroit
20700 Civic Center Dr., Ste. 450
Southfield, MI 48076
Ph: (248)353-0735
Fax: (248)353-0736
E-mail: esd@esd.org
URL: http://ww2.esd.org/home.htm
Description: Engineers from all disciplines; scientists and technologists. Conducts technical programs and engineering refresher courses; sponsors conferences and expositions. Maintains speakers' bureau; offers placement services; although based in Detroit, MI, society membership is international. **Members:** 6,000.

2013 ■ Federation of Analytical Chemistry and Spectroscopy Societies
c/o Greg Klunder, LLNL, President
PO Box 808-L-091
Livermore, CA 94551
Ph: (925)423-5083
E-mail: klunder@llnl.gov
URL: http://www.facss.org
Description: Professional societies representing 9,000 analytical chemists and spectroscopists. Members are: Analysis Instrumentation Division of the Instrument Society of America; Association of Analytical Chemists; Coblentz Society; Division of Analytical Chemistry of the American Chemical Society; Division of Analytical Chemistry of the Royal Society of Chemistry; Society for Applied Spectroscopy. Aims to provide a forum to address the challenges of analytical chemistry, chromatography, and spectroscopy. Reviews technical papers; maintains placement service.

2014 ■ Geochemical Society
Washington University
Earth and Planetary Sciences Dept.
1 Brookings Dr.
Saint Louis, MO 63130
Ph: (314)935-4131
Fax: (314)935-4121
E-mail: gsoffice@geochemsoc.org
URL: http://www.geochemsoc.org
Description: Professional society of geochemists, chemists, geologists, physicists, biologists, oceanographers, mathematicians, meteorologists, and other scientists interested in the application of chemistry to the solution of geological and cosmological problems. The Organic Geochemistry Division focuses on biogeochemistry and organic processes at the Earth's surface and subsurface.

2015 ■ Iranian Chemists' Association of the American Chemical Society
35 Meadowbrook Ln.
Woodbury, CT 06798
Ph: (203)573-3220
Fax: (203)573-3660
E-mail: banijamali@ica-acs.org
URL: http://www.ica-acs.org
Description: Encourages and enhances the interchange and sharing of scientific knowledge and friendship among chemists and chemistry-related professionals of Iranian descent. Provides opportunities for members to assist each other in pursuit of academic and professional development and growth. Promotes awareness of scientific contributions made by Iranian scientists.

2016 ■ Korean-American Scientists and Engineers Association
1952 Gallows Rd., Ste. 300
Vienna, VA 22182
Ph: (703)748-1221
Fax: (703)748-1331
E-mail: sejong@ksea.org
URL: http://www.ksea.org
Description: Represents scientists and engineers holding single or advanced degrees. Promotes friendship and mutuality among Korean and American scientists and engineers; contributes to Korea's scientific, technological, industrial, and economic developments; strengthens the scientific, technological, and cultural bonds between Korea and the U.S. Sponsors symposium. Maintains speakers' bureau, placement service, and biographical archives. Compiles statistics. **Members:** 10,000.

2017 ■ National Organization for the Professional Advancement of Black Chemists and Chemical Engineers
PO Box 77040
Washington, DC 20013
Ph: (240)228-1763
Free: 800-776-1419
E-mail: president@nobcche.org
URL: http://www.nobcche.org
Description: Black professionals in science and chemistry. Seeks to aid black scientists and chemists in reaching their full professional potential; encourages black students to pursue scientific studies and employment; promotes participation of blacks in scientific research. Provides volunteers to teach science courses in selected elementary schools; sponsors scientific field trips for students; maintains speakers' bureau for schools. Conducts technical seminars in Africa. Sponsors competitions; presents awards for significant achievements to individuals in the field. Maintains placement service; compiles statistics.

2018 ■ National Registry of Certified Chemists
125 Rose Ann Ln.
West Grove, PA 19390-8946
Ph: (610)322-0657
Fax: (800)858-6273
E-mail: rphifer@nrcc6.org
URL: http://www.nrcc6.org
Description: Certifies programs for chemical hygiene officers, clinical chemists, clinical chemistry technologists, environmental analytical chemists, environmental analytical technicians, and toxicological chemists based on education, experience, and examination. **Members:** 500.

2019 ■ Radiation Research Society
380 Ice Center Ln., Ste. C
Bozeman, MT 59718
Free: 877-216-1919
Fax: (785)587-2451
E-mail: info@radres.org
URL: http://www.radres.org
Description: Professional society of biologists, physicists, chemists, and physicians contributing to knowledge of radiation and its effects. Promotes original research in the natural sciences relating to radiation; facilitates integration of different disciplines in the study of radiation effects.

2020 ■ Radiochemistry Society
PO Box 3091
Richland, WA 99354
Ph: (509)460-7474

Free: 800-371-0542
E-mail: rad-info@radiochemistry.org
URL: http://www.radiochemistry.org

Description: Aims to promote education and public outreach for the safe use, handling and benefits of radioisotopes in security, energy, agriculture, environment, food safety and medicine. Conducts seminars, trainings, scholarships, meetings and exchange of scientific information.

2021 ■ Society of Cosmetic Chemists
120 Wall St., Ste. 2400
New York, NY 10005-4088
Ph: (212)668-1500
Fax: (212)668-1504
E-mail: scc@scconline.org
URL: http://www.scconline.org

Description: Serves a professional society of scientists involved in the cosmetic industry. Sponsors educational institution support programs to stimulate growth of cosmetic science-related programs. Maintains placement service.

2022 ■ Society of Flavor Chemists
3301 Rte. 66, Bldg. C, Ste. 205
Neptune, NJ 07753
Ph: (732)922-3393
Fax: (732)922-3590
E-mail: administrator@flavorchemist.org
URL: http://www.flavorchemist.org

Description: Works to advance the field of flavor technology and related sciences. Encourages the exchange of ideas and personal contacts among flavor chemists.

2023 ■ Society for In Vitro Biology
514 Daniels St., Ste. 411
Raleigh, NC 27605-1317

Ph: (919)562-0600
Fax: (919)562-0608
E-mail: sivb@sivb.org
URL: http://www.sivb.org

Description: Fosters exchange of knowledge of in vitro biology of cells, tissues and organs from both plant and animals (including humans). Focuses on biological research, development, and applications of significance to science and society. Accomplishes its mission through the society's publications; national and local conferences, meetings and workshops; and through support of teaching initiatives in cooperation with educational institutions. Creates an environment of scientific exchange and interdisciplinary synergy with the goal of advancing current and future systems for in vitro biology.

2024 ■ Society of Rheology
American Institute of Physics
2 Huntington Quadrangle
Ste. 1, NO. 1
Melville, NY 11747-4502
Ph: (516)576-2397
Fax: (516)576-2223
E-mail: rheology@aip.org
URL: http://www.rheology.org

Description: Professional society of chemical engineers, chemists, physicists, biologists, and others interested in the theory and precise measurement of the deformation and flow of matter and application of the physical data in fields such as biology, food, high polymers and plastics, metals, petroleum products, rubber, paint, printing ink, ceramics and glass, starch, floor preparations, and cosmetics.

2025 ■ Soil Science Society of America
5585 Guilfor Rd.
Madison, WI 53711

Ph: (608)273-8080
Fax: (608)273-2021
E-mail: headquarters@soils.org
URL: http://www.soils.org

Description: Professional soil scientists, including soil physicists, soil classifiers, land use and management specialists, chemists, microbiologists, soil fertility specialists, soil cartographers, conservationists, mineralogists, engineers, and others interested in fundamental and applied soil science.

2026 ■ Water Environment Federation
601 Wythe St.
Alexandria, VA 22314-1994
Free: 800-666-0206
Fax: (703)684-2492
E-mail: inquiry@wef.org
URL: http://www.wef.org

Description: Technical societies representing chemists, biologists, ecologists, geologists, operators, educational and research personnel, industrial wastewater engineers, consultant engineers, municipal officials, equipment manufacturers, and university professors and students dedicated to the enhancement and preservation of water quality and resources. Seeks to advance fundamental and practical knowledge concerning the nature, collection, treatment, and disposal of domestic and industrial wastewaters, and the design, construction, operation, and management of facilities for these purposes. Disseminates technical information; and promotes good public relations and regulations that improve water quality and the status of individuals working in this field. Conducts educational and research programs.

SOURCES OF HELP-WANTED ADS

2027 ■ *Education & Treatment of Children*
West Virginia University Press
139 Stansbury Hall
Morgantown, WV 26506
Ph: (304)293-8400
Fax: (304)293-6585
E-mail: press@wvu.edu
URLs: http://wvupressonline.com/journals; http://www
.educationandtreatmentofchildren.net

Frequency: Quarterly. **Price:** $100 Institutions; $50 Individuals; $115 Institutions elsewhere; $65 Individuals elsewhere. **Description:** Periodical featuring information concerning the development of services for children and youth. Includes reports written for educators and other child care and mental health providers focused on teaching, training, and treatment effectiveness.

PLACEMENT AND JOB REFERRAL SERVICES

2028 ■ *4Nannies.com*
2 Pidgeon Hill Dr., No. 550
Potomac Falls, VA 20165
Free: 800-810-2611
E-mail: support@4nannies.com
URL: http://www.4nannies.com

Description: Exists as an online nanny resource serving both nannies seeking jobs and families seeking nannies through its family-nanny job matching system. Recruits nanny candidates seeking immediate employment and delivers an extensive pool of candidates to choose from.

2029 ■ *ABC Nannies & Domestics, Inc.*
400 South Colorado Blvd., Ste. 310
Glendale, CO 80246
Ph: (303)321-3866
Free: 888-33-NANNY
Fax: (303)321-1395
E-mail: info@abcnannies.com
URL: http://www.abcnannies.com

Description: Specializes in nanny and domestic placements. Sponsors quarterly functions such as education seminars, picnics and other events for nannies and domestics.

2030 ■ *NannyClassifieds.com*
410 W Grand Pkwy. S, Ste. 250
Katy, TX 77494
URL: http://www.nannyclassifieds.com

Description: Exists as an agency that serves the needs of both nannies and working parents through affordable child care services and solutions. Partners with many other nanny and parenting sites to recruit nannies and get their ads the most exposure on the web. Features services and resources such as background screening, nanny payroll tax calculator and other more.

HANDBOOKS AND MANUALS

2031 ■ *Basic Training for Residential Childcare Workers: A Practical Guide for Improving Service to Children*
Charles C. Thomas Publisher Ltd.
2600 S 1st St.
Springfield, IL 62704-4730
Ph: (217)789-8980
Free: 800-258-8980
Fax: (217)789-9130
E-mail: books@ccthomas.com
URL: http://www.ccthomas.com

Description: Beverly Boone. 2011. $36.95 (paper). 224 pages. Contains solid, easy to understand and follow information for residential childcare workers and trainers. Includes exercises designed to help the reader put the material covered into actual use and practice.

2032 ■ *Child and Adult Care Professionals*
The McGraw-Hill Companies Inc.
PO Box 182604
Columbus, OH 43272
Ph: (212)512-2000
Free: 877-833-5524
Fax: (614)759-3749
E-mail: customer.service@mcgraw-hill.com
URL: http://www.mcgraw-hill.com

Description: Karen Stephens and Maxine Hammonds-Smith. Student edition, 2004. $66.64. Illustrated. 688 pages.

2033 ■ *Opportunities in Child Care Careers*
The McGraw-Hill Companies Inc.
PO Box 182604
Columbus, OH 43272
Ph: (212)512-2000
Free: 877-833-5524
Fax: (614)759-3749
E-mail: customer.service@mcgraw-hill.com
URL: http://www.mcgraw-hill.com

Description: Renee Wittenberg. 2006. $13.95 (paper). 160 pages. Discusses various job opportunities and how to secure a position. Illustrated.

2034 ■ *Working with Young Children: Teacher's Resource*
Goodheart Willcox Publisher
18604 W Creek Dr.
Tinley Park, IL 60477-6243
Ph: (708)687-5000
Free: 800-323-0440
Fax: (888)409-3900
E-mail: custserv@g-w.com
URL: http://www.g-w.com

Description: Judy Herr. Seventh edition, 2012. $248.00 (Compact Disc). Educational format.

EMPLOYMENT AGENCIES AND SEARCH FIRMS

2035 ■ *Hometown Nannies Plus*
250 Post Rd. E, Ste. 110
Westport, CT 06880-3616
Ph: (203)227-3924
E-mail: jobs@hometownnannies.com
URL: http://www.hometownnannies.com

Description: Serves as a full-service domestic placement employment agency that seeks to provide excellence in the referral and placement of child, home, estate, and elder care professionals. Works with family in assessing their job requirements so they can hire and retain the most viable domestic employees possible. Works with job seekers to help them focus their experience, strengths, goals, needs and concerns in their search for a specific type of job with a compatible family in a positive work environment.

ONLINE JOB SOURCES AND SERVICES

2036 ■ *AllAboutNannyCare.com*
URL: http://nannybizreviews.com

Description: Provides expert assistance in recruitment, screening and retention of quality in-home caregivers and the creation of successful nanny/family relationships. Provides a variety of resources and connection to the larger childcare community. Offers a variety of exclusive tools to help caregivers and families find the right job/nanny match.

2037 ■ *ChildcareJob.org*
URL: http://childcarejob.org

Description: Offers a searchable database of employment opportunities for child care workers. Enables job seekers to post their resumes online. Facilitates the employers' search for potential candidates through its find-a-resume feature.

2038 ■ *ChildcareJobs.net*
URL: http://www.childcarejobs.net

Description: Features job opportunities, resume search, postings and employment for childcare workers.

2039 ■ *GreatAupair.com*
URL: http://www.greataupair.com

Description: Exists as a website created for matching nannies and au pairs with families worldwide. Offers a way for host families, nannies and au pairs to easily find their matches.

2040 ■ The Houseparent Network
URL: http://www.houseparent.net

Description: Serves as an online career resource for houseparents and residential child care workers.

2041 ■ NannyJobs.com
URL: http://www.nannyjobs.com

Description: Provides free access to nanny jobs available across the nation. Offers resources and tools, including career information, conferences and event dates for nannies, and more.

2042 ■ NannyLocators.com
URL: http://www.nannylocators.com

Description: Allows posting of nanny availabilities and job-wanted ads. Includes key points on evaluating salary offers and other nanny job information.

2043 ■ NannyNeeded.com
URL: http://www.nannyneeded.com

Description: Provides a database of nanny jobs and nanny services. Offers listings and specific requirements of the jobs.

2044 ■ NannyNetwork.com
URL: http://www.nannynetwork.com

Description: Serves as an online resource for nanny placement and referral agencies. Provides information pertaining to nanny recruitment, nanny employment and nanny retention.

OTHER SOURCES

2045 ■ Association of Premier Nanny Agencies
400 S Colorado Blvd., Ste. 300
Denver, CO 80246
E-mail: admin@theapna.org
URL: http://www.theapna.org

Description: Aims to establish and enforce standards of professional practices within the nanny placement industry. Seeks to address issues and concerns pertinent to domestic services.

2046 ■ *Careers for Kids at Heart and Others Who Adore Children*
The McGraw-Hill Companies Inc.
PO Box 182604
Columbus, OH 43272
Ph: (212)512-2000
Free: 877-833-5524
Fax: (614)759-3749
E-mail: customer.service@mcgraw-hill.com
URL: http://www.mcgraw-hill.com

Description: Marjorie Eberts and Margaret Gisler. Third edition, 2006. $13.95 (paper). 160 pages.
Publication includes: Lists of U.S. organizations that offer information on careers in child care, nannies, babysitting, teaching, sports and recreation, children's health, and arts and entertainment.
Entries include: For organizations: name, address, website address.

2047 ■ International Nanny Association
PO Box 18126
Charlotte, NC 28218
Free: 888-878-1477
Fax: (508)638-6462
E-mail: info@nanny.org
URL: http://www.nanny.org

Description: An educational association for nannies and those who educate, place, employ, and support professional in-home child care. Membership is open to those who are directly involved with the in-home child care profession, including nannies, nanny employers, nanny placement agency owners (and staff), nanny educators, and providers of special services related to the nanny profession.

2048 ■ National Association for the Education of Young Children
1313 L St. NW, Ste. 500
Washington, DC 20005
Ph: (202)232-8777
Free: 800-424-2460
Fax: (202)328-1846
E-mail: naeyc@naeyc.org
URL: http://www.naeyc.org

Description: Teachers and directors of preschool and primary schools, kindergartens, child care centers, and early other learning programs for young childhood; early childhood education and child development educators, trainers, and researchers and other professionals dedicated to young children's healthy development.

SOURCES OF HELP-WANTED ADS

2049 ■ *Chiropractic Economics*
Doyle Group
5150 Palm Valley Rd., Ste. 103
Ponte Vedra Beach, FL 32082
Ph: (904)285-6020
Fax: (904)285-9944
URL: http://www.chiroeco.com

Description: 18/year. $39.95/year. Provides news and information to practicing chiropractors with a focus on office management; patient relations; personal development; financial planning; legal, clinical, and research data; and wellness/nutrition.

EMPLOYER DIRECTORIES AND NETWORKING LISTS

2050 ■ **Health Professionals Directory**
Sussex Directories Inc.
10 Market St., Ste. 750
Camana Bay
Grand Cayman, Cayman Islands
URL: http://sussexdirectories.com

HANDBOOKS AND MANUALS

2051 ■ *Opportunities in Chiropractic Careers*
The McGraw-Hill Companies Inc.
PO Box 182604
Columbus, OH 43272
Ph: (212)512-2000
Free: 877-833-5524
Fax: (614)759-3749
E-mail: customer.service@mcgraw-hill.com
URL: http://www.mcgraw-hill.com

Description: Bart Green, Claire Johnson, and Louis Sportelli. 2004. $13.95 (paper). 160 pages. A guide to planning for and building a career in the field. Illustrated.

2052 ■ *Resumes for Health and Medical Careers*
The McGraw-Hill Companies Inc.
PO Box 182604
Columbus, OH 43272
Ph: (212)512-2000
Free: 877-833-5524
Fax: (614)759-3749
E-mail: customer.service@mcgraw-hill.com
URL: http://www.mcgraw-hill.com

Description: Third edition. 2008. $12.95 (paper). 144 pages.

EMPLOYMENT AGENCIES AND SEARCH FIRMS

2053 ■ **Chiropractic Staffing Services**
1358 Sandpiper Dr.
Corpus Christi, TX 78412
Ph: (361)993-3567
Fax: (361)334-0379
E-mail: info@chiropracticstaffing.com
URL: http://www.chiropracticstaffing.com

Description: Provides permanent and temporary clinical staffing and consulting services to a wide range of clients. Reviews, screens and trains every chiropractic physician and technician to suit the client's workplace environment, patient profiles, and patient needs.

2054 ■ **Michael McGurn, D.C. and Associates**
450-106 SR 13 N, No. 173
Jacksonville, FL 32259
Free: 800-501-6111
Fax: (904)829-5175
E-mail: mma@mmachiropractors.com
URL: http://www.mmachiropractors.com

Description: Provides temporary and associate placement services for chiropractors in the United States. Conducts screening of substitute and associate doctors by investigating state board complaints, malpractice and criminal history.

ONLINE JOB SOURCES AND SERVICES

2055 ■ **ChiroEco.com**
URL: http://www.chiroeco.com

Description: Provides online information and resources for the chiropractic community. Features chiropractic news, articles, videos, and job board.

2056 ■ **chiropractorjobs.us**
URL: http://www.chiropractorjobs.net

Description: Serves as a job board that focuses exclusively on chiropractor employment opportunities and candidate recruiting.

2057 ■ **ExploreHealthCareers.org**
URL: http://explorehealthcareers.org/en/home

Description: Provides employment information in health professions. Includes links to health-related education/training programs, financial aid resources, specialized learning opportunities, and current issues in health care.

2058 ■ **HEALTHeCAREERS Network**
URL: http://www.healthecareers.com

Description: Career search site for jobs in all health care specialties; educational resources; visa and licensing information for relocation; interesting articles; relocation tools; links to professional organizations and general resources.

2059 ■ **ProHealthJobs.com**
URL: http://prohealthjobs.com/jobboard

Description: Career resources site for the medical and health care field. Lists professional opportunities, product information, continuing education and open positions.

TRADESHOWS

2060 ■ **California Chiropractic Association Annual Convention & Marketplace**
California Chiropractic Association
1451 River Park Dr., Ste. 230
Sacramento, CA 95815-4521
Ph: (916)648-2727
Fax: (916)648-2738
E-mail: cca@calchiro.org
URL: http://www.calchiro.org

Frequency: Annual. **Primary Exhibits:** Publications, office equipment and supplies, computers, health foods, insurance companies, and x-ray equipment; nutritional, chiropractic equipment, physical therapy, orthopedics.

2061 ■ **Florida Chiropractic Association National Convention and Expo**
Florida Chiropractic Association
30 Remington Rd., Ste. 1
Oakland, FL 34787
Ph: (407)654-3225
Fax: (407)656-5433
URL: http://www.fcachiro.org

Frequency: Annual. **Primary Exhibits:** Chiropractic examining/adjusting tables; X-ray equipment and products; diagnostic equipment and supplies; office furniture; computer systems and software; nutritional supplements; physical therapy equipment; orthopedic appliances; medical books; patient educational material, and uniforms.

2062 ■ **North American Spine Society Annual Meeting**
North American Spine Society
7075 Veterans Blvd.
Burr Ridge, IL 60527
Ph: (630)230-3600
Free: 866-960-6277
Fax: (630)230-3700
E-mail: info@spine.org
URL: http://www.spine.org

Frequency: Annual. **Primary Exhibits:** Products & services directly and indirectly related to spinal diagnosis, treatment and surgery, the general practice of medicine aid peripheral products and services.

OTHER SOURCES

2063 ■ American Chiropractic Association
1701 Clarendon Blvd.
Arlington, VA 22209
Ph: (703)276-8800
Fax: (703)243-2593
E-mail: memberinfo@acatoday.org
URL: http://www.acatoday.org

Description: Enhances the philosophy, science, and art of chiropractic, and the professional welfare of individuals in the field. Promotes legislation defining chiropractic health care and improves the public's awareness and utilization of chiropractic. Conducts chiropractic survey and statistical study; maintains library. Sponsors Correct Posture Week in May and Spinal Health Month in October. Chiropractic colleges have student groups.

2064 ■ American College of Chiropractic Orthopedists
c/o Joseph F. Ferstl, President
1557 Weatherstone Ln.
Elgin, IL 60123
Ph: (847)741-3355
Fax: (847)741-3597
E-mail: ferstlchiro@msn.com
URL: http://www.accoweb.org

Description: Certified and non-certified chiropractic orthopedists; students enrolled in a postgraduate chiropractic orthopedic program. Seeks to establish and maintain optimal educational and clinical standards within the field of chiropractic orthopedics. Sponsors educational programs.

2065 ■ Association for Catholic Chiropractors
2049 Kolb Ridge Ct.
Marietta, GA 30008
E-mail: afcchiro@bellsouth.net
URL: http://afcc.homestead.com

Description: Promotes the Catholic faith through the art, science and practice of the chiropractic profession. Supports the chiropractic community-at-large in establishing ethical health care practice principles that will reflect the Church's teachings. Provides spiritual guidance to Catholic chiropractors to help them follow a Christ centered professional and personal life.

2066 ■ *Career Opportunities in Health Care*
InfoBase Holdings Inc.
132 W 31st., 17 Fl.
New York, NY 10001-3406
Ph: (212)967-8800
Fax: (800)678-3633
E-mail: info@infobasepublishing.com
URL: http://www.ferguson.infobasepublishing.com

Description: Shelly Field. 2007. Third edition. $49.50. 304 pages. **Includes:** Appendices provide lists of educational institutions, periodicals, directories, associations, and unions. Appendices provide lists of educational institutions, periodicals, directories, associations, and unions.

2067 ■ Chiropractic Diplomatic Corps
17602 17th St., Ste. 102
Tustin, CA 92780
Free: 888-243-2322
E-mail: info@chiropracticdiplomatic.com
URL: http://www.chiropracticdiplomatic.com

Description: Seeks to advance chiropractic training and services throughout the world. Aims to establish cooperative alliances with international organizations that are involved with the delivery of chiropractic care.

2068 ■ Chiropractic Orthopedists of North America
2048 Montrose Ave.
Montrose, CA 91020

Ph: (818)249-8326
E-mail: rakechiro@ca.rr.com
URL: http://www.conanet.org

Description: Assists in the advancement of chiropractic using scientific and evidence-based research and information. Maintains highest standards of moral and ethical conduct among members. Promotes chiropractic orthopedics with other branches of the healing arts and professions.

2069 ■ Christian Chiropractors Association
2550 Stover St., No. B-102
Fort Collins, CO 80525
Ph: (970)482-1404
Free: 800-999-1970
Fax: (970)482-1538
URL: http://www.christianchiropractors.org

Description: Works to spread the Gospel of Christ throughout the U.S. and abroad. Offers Christian fellowship and works to unify Christian chiropractors around the essentials of the faith, "leaving minor points of doctrine to the conscience of the individual believer." Focuses on world missions; organizing short-term trips and aiding in the placement of Christian chiropractors as missionaries. **Members:** 1,250.

2070 ■ Council of Chiropractic Acupuncture
291 Main Rd.
Holden, ME 04429
Ph: (207)989-0000
URL: http://councilofchiropracticacupuncture.org

Description: Aims to provide excellent educational opportunities to elevate the quality of care, life and practice of chiropractic acupuncture. Serves as a platform for professional communication regarding the practice of acupuncture in the chiropractic profession.

2071 ■ Council on Chiropractic Education
8049 N 85th Way
Scottsdale, AZ 85258-4321
Ph: (480)443-8877
Free: 888-443-3506
Fax: (480)483-7333
E-mail: cce@cce-usa.org
URL: http://www.cce-usa.org

Description: Advocates high standards in chiropractic education; establishes criteria of institutional excellence for educating chiropractic physicians; acts as national accrediting agency for chiropractic colleges. Conducts workshops for college teams, consultants, and chiropractic college staffs. **Members:** 13.

2072 ■ Council on Chiropractic Guidelines and Practice Parameters
PO Box 2542
Lexington, SC 29071
Ph: (803)356-6809
Fax: (803)356-6826
E-mail: ccgpp@sc.rr.com
URL: http://www.ccgpp.org

Description: Advances the development, evaluation and dissemination of clinical practice guidelines and parameters for quality health-care improvement. Promotes the improvement of the quality of chiropractic services and of the professional reputation of doctors of chiropractic. Enhances the intellectual, academic and clinical integrity of chiropractic practice.

2073 ■ Council of Chiropractic Physiological Therapeutics and Rehabilitation
11600 Wilshire Blvd., Ste. 412
Los Angeles, CA 90025
Ph: (740)653-2973
Fax: (740)653-3249
E-mail: jsimon@rrohio.com
URL: http://www.ccptr.org

Description: Represents chiropractors who use physiotherapy and rehabilitation in their practice and

are dedicated to furthering the extended use of physiotherapy in the chiropractic field. **Members:** 200.

2074 ■ Council on Chiropractic Practice
2950 N Dobson Rd., Ste. 1
Chandler, AZ 85224
E-mail: ccp@ccp-guidelines.org
URL: http://ccp-guidelines.org

Description: Strives to develop evidence-based guidelines, conduct research and perform other functions to enhance chiropractic practice for the benefit of the consumer. Provides practice guidelines which serve the needs of the consumer and are consistent with chiropractic practice.

2075 ■ Councils on Chiropractic Education International
PO Box 4943
Pocatello, ID 83205
Ph: (208)241-4855
E-mail: ccei@cceintl.org
URL: http://www.cceintl.org

Description: Represents chiropractic accrediting bodies worldwide. Promotes excellence in chiropractic education through emphasis on quality in International Chiropractic Accreditation Standards. Advocates quality education through the dissemination and promotion of information to governments, professional organizations and others.

2076 ■ Holistic Dental Association
1825 Ponce de Leon Blvd., No. 148
Coral Gables, FL 33134
Ph: (305)356-7338
Fax: (305)468-6359
E-mail: director@holisticdental.org
URL: http://www.holisticdental.org

Description: Represents dentists, chiropractors, dental hygienists, physical therapists, and medical doctors. Aims to provide a holistic approach to better dental care for patients, and to expand techniques, medications, and philosophies that pertain to extractions, anesthetics, fillings, crowns, and orthodontics. Encourages the use of homeopathic medications, acupuncture, cranial osteopathy, nutritional techniques, and physical therapy in treating patients in addition to conventional treatments. Sponsors training and educational seminars. **Members:** 200.

2077 ■ International Chiropractors Association
6400 Arlington Blvd., Ste. 800
Falls Church, VA 22042
Ph: (703)528-5000
Free: 800-423-4690
Fax: (703)528-5023
E-mail: chiro@chiropractic.org
URL: http://www.chiropractic.org

Description: Serves as professional society of chiropractors, chiropractic educators, students, and laypersons. Sponsors professional development programs and practice management seminars.

2078 ■ Journey to Solidarity
301 Cottage Grove Ave. SE
Cedar Rapids, IA 52403
Fax: (888)860-9263
E-mail: jay@journeytosolidarity.org
URL: http://journeytosolidarity.org

Description: Seeks to improve the health and well-being of people in developing countries. Promotes chiropractic and wellness care as a profession and healing art to communities in need. Strives to grow the chiropractic profession by facilitating young students so they can get an education and return to their own countries.

2079 ■ Non-Profit Chiropractic Organization
601 Brady St., Ste. 201
Davenport, IA 52803
Ph: (708)459-8080
E-mail: info@npco.org
URL: http://www.npco.org

Description: Provides chiropractic healthcare services to people in underdeveloped countries.

Seeks to educate the public about chiropractic through the implementation of various programs.

2080 ■ Professional Football Chiropractic
PO Box 842
Sumner, WA 98390

Ph: (253)948-6039
Fax: (253)435-1053
E-mail: footballchiros@gmail.com
URL: http://www.profootballchiros.com

Description: Provides chiropractic health care to professional football athletes. Enhances the perception of chiropractic in sports and with the general public through education and communication. Initiates an understanding of chiropractic for athletes, coaches, administrative and healthcare staff.

SOURCES OF HELP-WANTED ADS

2081 ■ AIE Perspectives Newsmagazine
American Institute of Engineers
4630 Appian Way, Ste. 206
El Sobrante, CA 94803-1875
Ph: (510)758-6240
Fax: (510)758-6240
E-mail: aie@aieonline.org
URL: http://www.members-aie.org
Frequency: Monthly. **Price:** included in membership dues. **Description:** Professional magazine covering engineering.

2082 ■ American City and County
Penton
9800 Metcalf Ave.
Overland Park, KS 66212
Ph: (913)341-1300
Free: 866-748-4926
Fax: (913)967-1905
E-mail: corporatecustomerservice@penton.com
URL: http://americancityandcounty.com
Frequency: Monthly. **Description:** Municipal and county administration magazine.

2083 ■ ASCE News
American Society of Civil Engineers - Architectural Engineering Institute
1801 Alexander Bell Dr.
Reston, VA 20191-4400
Free: 800-548-2723
E-mail: aei@asce.org
URL: http://asce-news.asce.org
Description: Monthly. Reports on activities of the society and news of the civil engineering profession.

2084 ■ AWWA Streamlines
American Water Works Association
6666 W Quincy Ave.
Denver, CO 80235-3098
Ph: (303)794-7711
Free: 800-926-7337
Fax: (303)347-0804
URL: http://www.awwa.org/publications/streamlines-current.cfm
Description: Biweekly, online; print issue is quarterly. Carries news of the Association and features about the drinking water industry, including regulations, legislation, conservation, treatment, quality, distribution, management, and utility operations. Recurring features include letters to the editor, a calendar of events, reports of meetings, news of educational opportunities, notices of publications available, education and job opportunities in the industry and legislative news.

2085 ■ Better Roads
James Informational Media Inc.
2340 S River Rd., No. 202
Des Plaines, IL 60018

Ph: (847)636-5060
Fax: (847)636-5077
E-mail: kirk@jiminc.com
URL: http://www.betterroads.com
Frequency: Monthly. **Price:** Free. **Description:** Magazine serving federal, state, county, city, and township officials involved in road, street, bridge, and airport construction, maintenance and safety.

2086 ■ Civil Engineering
U.S. Department of Commerce - Technology Administration - National Technical Information Service
5301 Shawnee Rd.
Alexandria, VA 22312
Ph: (703)605-6040
Free: 800-553-NTIS
Fax: (703)605-6900
E-mail: info@ntis.gov
URL: http://www.ntis.gov
Description: Biweekly. $255/year. Publishes abstracts with full bibliographic citations in the areas of highway engineering, civil engineering, soil and rock mechanics, flood control, and construction equipment, materials and supplies. Alerts readers to related published materials available from NTIS and other sources. Also available via e-mail.

2087 ■ Civil Engineering-ASCE
American Society of Civil Engineers - Architectural Engineering Institute
1801 Alexander Bell Dr.
Reston, VA 20191-4400
Free: 800-548-2723
E-mail: aei@asce.org
URL: http://pubs.asce.org/magazines/CEMag/
Frequency: Monthly. **Price:** $230 Institutions; $275 Institutions, other countries; $230 Individuals; $275 Other countries; $30 Members domestic; $69 Other countries member; $30 Students member; domestic; $69 Students member; international. **Description:** Professional magazine.

2088 ■ Consulting-Specifying Engineer
CFE Media LLC
1111 W 22nd St., Ste. 250
Oak Brook, IL 60523
Ph: (630)571-4070
Fax: (630)214-4504
URLs: http://www.csemag.com; http://mediakit.cfe-media.com/cseimk/csewebcasts.html
Frequency: 13/yr. **Description:** The integrated engineering magazine of the building construction industry.

2089 ■ Engineering
Scientific Research Publishing
PO Box 54821
Irvine, CA 92619-4821
E-mail: eng@scirp.org
URL: http://www.scirp.org/journal/eng/
Frequency: Monthly. **Price:** $468 Individuals.

Description: Peer-reviewed journal publishing articles on the latest advancements in engineering.

2090 ■ ENR: Engineering News-Record: The Construction Weekly
The McGraw-Hill Companies Inc.
2 Penn Plz., 9th Fl.
New York, NY 10121
Ph: (212)904-3507
Fax: (212)904-2820
E-mail: customer.service@mcgraw-hill.com
URL: http://enr.construction.com/Default.asp
Frequency: Weekly. **Price:** $87 Individuals print and online. **Description:** Magazine focusing on engineering and construction.

2091 ■ Graduating Engineer & Computer Careers
Career Recruitment Media
2 LAN Dr., Ste. 100
Westford, MA 01886
Ph: (978)692-5092
Fax: (978)692-4174
E-mail: hshulick@alloyeducation.com
URL: http://www.graduatingengineer.com
Frequency: Quarterly. **Price:** $16.95 Individuals. **Description:** Magazine focusing on employment, education, and career development for entry-level engineers and computer scientists.

2092 ■ ITE Journal
Institute of Transportation Engineers
1627 Eye St. NW, Ste. 600
Washington, DC 20006
Ph: (202)289-0222
Fax: (202)289-7722
E-mail: ite_staff@ite.org
URL: http://www.ite.org/itejournal/
Frequency: Monthly. **Price:** $65 U.S., Canada, and Mexico; $85 Other countries; $160 U.S., Canada, and Mexico 3 years; $200 Other countries 3 years; $5 Single issue back issue. **Description:** Technical magazine focusing on the plan, design, and operation of surface transportation systems.

2093 ■ Masonry Magazine
Mason Contractors Association of America
1481 Merchant Dr.
Algonquin, IL 60102
Ph: (224)678-9709
Free: 800-536-2225
Fax: (224)678-9714
E-mail: bennett@lionhrtpub.com
URL: http://www.masoncontractors.org
Description: Monthly. $43.00/2 years; $29.00/year. Covers every aspect of the mason contractor profession, from equipment and techniques to building codes and standards, training the future masonry labor force, business planning, promoting business, job interviewing, negotiation and legal issues.

2094 ■ *The Military Engineer*
Society of American Military Engineers
607 Prince St.
Alexandria, VA 22314-3117
Ph: (703)549-3800
Fax: (703)684-0231
E-mail: rwolff@same.org
URL: http://www.same.org/i4a/pages/index.cfm
?pageid=4273

Frequency: Bimonthly. **Price:** $88 U.S. and Canada individuals, second class mail; $168 U.S. and Canada two years; $222 U.S. and Canada three years; $188 Other countries air mail, individuals; $358 Other countries two years, air mail; $458 Other countries three years, air mail; $22 Students U.S., Canada, and foreign (regular mail). **Description:** Journal on military and civil engineering.

2095 ■ *Minority Engineer Magazine*
Employment Opportunity Publications
445 Broad Hollow Rd., Ste. 425
Melville, NY 11747
Ph: (631)421-9421
Fax: (631)421-1352
E-mail: info@eop.com
URL: http://www.eop.com/mags-ME.php

Description: $18.00/year for non-minority engineering student or professional; $34.00/2 years for non-minority engineering student or professional; $49.00/3 years for non-minority engineering student or professional. Provides job listings, company profiles, and articles geared toward the engineering student and professional.

2096 ■ *The Municipality*
League of Wisconsin Municipalities
122 W Washington Ave., Ste. 300
Madison, WI 53703-2715
Ph: (608)267-2380
Free: 800-991-5502
Fax: (608)267-0645
E-mail: jmstaral@lwm-info.org
URL: http://www.lwm-info.org/

Frequency: Monthly. **Price:** $25/year. **Description:** Magazine for officials of Wisconsin's local municipal governments.

2097 ■ *NSBE Magazine: National Society of Black Engineers*
NSBE Publications
205 Daingerfield Rd.
Alexandria, VA 22314
Ph: (703)549-2207
Fax: (703)683-5312
E-mail: info@nsbe.org
URL: http://www.nsbe.org/News-Media/Magazines/
About-NSBE-Magazine.aspx

Frequency: 3/yr. **Price:** $20 Individuals; $35 Other countries; $15 Students. **Description:** Journal providing information on engineering careers, self-development, and cultural issues for recent graduates with technical majors.

2098 ■ *PE*
National Society of Professional Engineers
1420 King St.
Alexandria, VA 22314-2794
Ph: (703)684-2800
Fax: (703)836-4875
E-mail: memserv@nspe.org
URL: http://www.nspe.org/PEmagazine/index.html

Frequency: Semimonthly; 10/yr. **Price:** included in membership dues; $50 for nonmembers. **Description:** Covers matters of importance to engineering educators and students.

2099 ■ *Public Works*
DoveTale Publishers
1 Thomas Cir. NW
Washington, DC 20005
Ph: (202)339-0744
Free: 877-275-8647

Fax: (202)785-1974
E-mail: hwmicustomerservice@hanleywood.com
URL: http://www.pwmag.com

Frequency: 13/yr. **Price:** $60 Individuals; $75 Canada; $90 Other countries. **Description:** Trade magazine covering the public works industry nationwide for city, county, and state.

2100 ■ *Roads & Bridges Magazine*
Scranton Gillette Communications Inc.
3030 W Salt Creek Ln., Ste. 201
Arlington Heights, IL 60005-5025
Ph: (847)391-1000
Fax: (847)390-0408
E-mail: hgillette@sgcmail.com
URL: http://www.roadsbridges.com

Frequency: Monthly. **Description:** Magazine containing information on highway, road, and bridge design, construction, and maintenance for government agencies, contractors, and consulting engineers.

2101 ■ *SWE, Magazine of the Society of Women Engineers*
Society of Women Engineers
203 N La Salle St., Ste. 1675
Chicago, IL 60601
Ph: (312)596-5223
Free: 877-SWE-INFO
Fax: (312)596-5252
E-mail: hq@swe.org
URL: http://societyofwomenengineers.swe.org/index
.php

Frequency: Quarterly. **Price:** $30 Nonmembers. **Description:** Magazine for engineering students and for women and men working in the engineering and technology fields. Covers career guidance, continuing development and topical issues.

2102 ■ *Western City*
League of California Cities
1400 K St., 4th Fl.
Sacramento, CA 95814
Ph: (916)658-8200
Free: 800-262-1801
Fax: (916)658-8240
E-mail: okabel@cacities.org
URL: http://www.westerncity.com

Frequency: Monthly. **Price:** $39 Individuals; $63 Two years; $52 Other countries; $26.50 Students. **Description:** Municipal interest magazine.

2103 ■ *Woman Engineer*
Equal Opportunity Publications Inc.
445 Broad Hollow Rd., Ste. 425
Melville, NY 11747
Ph: (631)421-9421
Fax: (631)421-1352
E-mail: info@eop.com
URL: http://www.eop.com

Description: Annual. Magazine that is offered at no charge to qualified female engineering, computer-science, and information-technology students and professionals seeking to find employment and advancement in their careers.

Employer Directories and Networking Lists

2104 ■ *Directory of Contract Staffing Firms*
C.E. Publications Inc.
PO Box 3006
Bothell, WA 98041-3006
Ph: (425)806-5200
Fax: (425)806-5585
E-mail: staff@cjhunter.com
URL: http://www.cjhunter.com/dcsf/overview.html

Frequency: Annual. **Covers:** Nearly 1,300 contract firms actively engaged in the employment of engineering, IT/IS, and technical personnel for 'temporary' contract assignments throughout the

world. **Entries include:** Company name, address, phone, name of contact, email, web address. **Arrangement:** Alphabetical. **Indexes:** Geographical.

2105 ■ *ENR--Top 500 Design Firms Issue*
The McGraw-Hill Companies Inc.
PO Box 182604
Columbus, OH 43272
Ph: (212)512-2000
Free: 877-833-5524
Fax: (614)759-3749
E-mail: customer.service@mcgraw-hill.com
URL: http://enr.construction.com/toplists/
sourcebooks/2010/designfirms/

Frequency: Annual; latest edition 2010. **Price:** $82 Individuals yearly subscription; $87 Individuals print and online. **Publication includes:** List of 500 leading architectural, engineering, and specialty design firms selected on basis of annual billings. **Entries include:** Company name, headquarters location, type of firm, current and prior year rank in billings, types of services, countries in which operated in preceding year. **Arrangement:** Ranked by billings.

2106 ■ *Indiana Society of Professional Engineers--Directory*
Indiana Society of Professional Engineers
c/o Lauraine M. Howe, Executive Director
PO Box 20806
Indianapolis, IN 46220
Ph: (317)255-2267
Fax: (317)255-2530
E-mail: indspe@gmail.com
URL: http://www.indspe.org

Frequency: Annual; fall. **Pages:** 150. **Covers:** Member registered engineers, land surveyors, engineering students, and engineers in training. **Entries include:** Member name, address, phone, type of membership, business information, specialty. **Arrangement:** Alpha by chapter area.

2107 ■ *Who's Who in Engineering*
American Association of Engineering Societies
1801 Alexander Bell Dr.
Reston, VA 20191
Ph: (202)296-2237
Free: 888-400-2237
Fax: (202)296-1151
E-mail: dbateson@aaes.org
URL: http://www.aaes.org

Frequency: Triennial; Latest edition 9th. **Covers:** About 15,000 engineers who have received professional recognition for outstanding achievement. **Entries include:** Name, address; education and employment history; awards and achievements. **Arrangement:** Alphabetical. **Indexes:** Geographical, field of specialization.

Handbooks and Manuals

2108 ■ *Changing Our World: True Stories of Women Engineers*
American Society of Civil Engineers - Architectural Engineering Institute
1801 Alexander Bell Dr.
Reston, VA 20191-4400
Free: 800-548-2723
E-mail: aei@asce.org
URL: http://www.asce.org/aei

Description: Sybil E. Hatch. 2006. $54.00. 232 pages.

2109 ■ *Civil Engineer's Handbook of Professional Practice*
John Wiley & Sons Inc.
111 River St.
Hoboken, NJ 07030-5774
Ph: (201)748-6000
Free: 800-225-5945
Fax: (201)748-6088
E-mail: info@wiley.com
URL: http://www.wiley.com

Description: Karen Hansen and Kent Zenobia. 2011. $134.95 (hardcover). 744 pages. Features quotes, techniques, case examples, problems and information that assist in addressing challenges faced by civil engineers. Focuses on business and management aspects of a civil engineer's job.

2110 ■ Engineering, Mechanics, and Architecture
InfoBase Holdings Inc.
132 W 31st., 17 Fl.
New York, NY 10001-3406
Ph: (212)967-8800
Fax: (800)678-3633
E-mail: info@infobasepublishing.com
URL: http://www.ferguson.infobasepublishing.com

Description: Kelly Wiles. 2010. $39.95. 160 pages (hardcover). Serves as a guide for readers interested in switching jobs. Contains useful advice, career tips, interviews and self-assessment questions.

2111 ■ Expert Resumes for Engineers
JIST Publishing
875 Montreal Way
Saint Paul, MN 55102-4245
Ph: (317)613-4200
Free: 800-648-5478
Fax: (800)328-4564
E-mail: info@jist.com
URL: http://www.jist.com

Description: Louise M. Kursmark and Wendy S. Enelow. 2009. $16.95 (softcover). 272 pages. Features a collection of written resume samples for all types of engineers including civil, mechanical, industrial, electrical, electronics, computer, and more. Contains tips and strategies for writing engineering resumes and finding the best jobs.

2112 ■ Great Jobs for Engineering Majors
The McGraw-Hill Companies Inc.
PO Box 182604
Columbus, OH 43272
Ph: (212)512-2000
Free: 877-833-5524
Fax: (614)759-3749
E-mail: customer.service@mcgraw-hill.com
URL: http://www.mcgraw-hill.com

Description: Geraldine O. Garner. Second edition. 2008. $16.95. 192 pages. Covers all the career options open to students majoring in engineering.

2113 ■ Preparing for Design-Build Projects: A Primer for Owners, Engineers, and Contractors
American Society of Civil Engineers - Architectural Engineering Institute
1801 Alexander Bell Dr.
Reston, VA 20191-4400
Free: 800-548-2723
E-mail: aei@asce.org
URL: http://www.asce.org/aei

Description: Douglas D. Gransberg, James E. Koch and Keith R. Molenaar. 2006. $64.00. 296 pages.

EMPLOYMENT AGENCIES AND SEARCH FIRMS

2114 ■ Civil Search International
324 S Bracken Ln., Ste. 2
Chandler, AZ 85224
Ph: (480)820-8663
Free: 800-737-8182
Fax: (480)820-8709
URL: http://www.csijobs.com

Description: Executive recruiting firm that specializes in the placement of civil engineers. Additional services include preparation of job orders as well as reviewing of prospective candidates.

2115 ■ Claremont-Branan, Inc.
1298 Rockbridge Rd., Ste. B
Stone Mountain, GA 30087
Free: 800-875-1292
URL: http://cbisearch.com

Description: Employment agency. Executive search firm.

2116 ■ Engineer One Inc.
2315 Laurel Lake Rd.
Knoxville, TN 37932
Ph: (865)692-0404
Fax: (865)691-0110
E-mail: engineerone@engineerone.com
URL: http://www.engineerone.com

Description: Engineering employment service specializing in engineering and management in the chemical process, power utilities, manufacturing, mechanical, electrical, and electronic industries. Maintains an Information Technology Division that works nationwide across all industries. Also provides systems analysis consulting services specializing in VAX based systems.

2117 ■ ENTEGEE Inc.
70 Blanchard Rd., Ste. 102
Burlington, MA 01803-5100
Free: 800-368-3433
E-mail: corporate@entegee.com
URL: http://www.entegee.com

Description: Specializes in recruiting experienced professionals in the engineering and technical industries. Features a searchable database of employment opportunities in the engineering and technical fields.

2118 ■ Global Employment Solutions Inc.
10375 Park Meadows Dr., Ste. 475
Littleton, CO 80124-6724
Ph: (303)216-9500
Fax: (303)216-9533
URL: http://www.gesnetwork.com

Description: Employment agency.

2119 ■ International Staffing Consultants Inc.
31655 2nd Ave.
Laguna Beach, CA 92651
Ph: (949)255-5857
Fax: (949)767-5959
E-mail: iscinc@iscworld.com
URL: http://www.iscworld.com

Description: Employment agency. Provides placement on regular or temporary basis. Affiliate office in London.

2120 ■ Metzner Group
10130 Harmony Rd.
Myersville, MD 21773
Ph: (301)293-4206
Fax: (301)293-4207
E-mail: carol@themetznergroup.com
URL: http://www.themetznergroup.com

Description: Specializes in the recruitment of architects, civil engineers, environmental engineers and planners for the A/E/P communities.

2121 ■ Precision Executive Search
977 E Schuylkill Rd., Ste. 201
Pottstown, PA 19465
Ph: (610)704-4942
E-mail: mbarcus@precision-recruiters.com
URL: http://precision-recruiters.com

Description: Executive search firm specializing in the civil engineering, surveying, planning, and landscape architecture industries.

2122 ■ Principal Resource Group
313 Railroad Ave., Ste. 203
Nevada City, CA 95959
Ph: (530)478-6478

Fax: (530)478-6477
E-mail: pat@prgnc.com
URL: http://www.prgnc.com

Description: Executive recruiting firm dedicated to the engineering community. Specializes in various disciplines in civil engineering. Provides personalized and confidential services to professionals with all levels of experience in the civil engineering and technology industries.

2123 ■ Recruiting Partners
3494 Camino Tassajara Rd., No. 404
Danville, CA 94506
Ph: (925)964-0249
E-mail: info@recruitingpartners.com
URL: http://www.recruitingpartners.com

Description: Serves as an executive and technical recruiting firm that specializes in accounting, legal, information technology, engineering, executive management and technical writing.

2124 ■ TRS Staffing Solutions USA
3 Polaris Way
Aliso Viejo, CA 92656
Ph: (949)349-3630
Free: 800-248-8774
Fax: (949)349-7196
E-mail: info-av@trsstaffing.com
URL: http://www.trsstaffing.com/us

Description: Specializes in engineering recruitment. Maintains a pool of experienced technical, engineering and professional services personnel.

ONLINE JOB SOURCES AND SERVICES

2125 ■ A/E/C JobBank
URL: http://www.aecjobbank.com

Description: Helps job seekers find employment opportunities in the construction industry. Allows employers and recruiters to post construction jobs and source top resumes.

2126 ■ AEJob.com
URL: http://aejob.com

Description: Provides lists of architectural jobs, engineering jobs and environmental consulting jobs nationwide.

2127 ■ CivilEngineeringCentral.com
URL: http://www.civilengineeringcentral.com

Description: Serves as niche for job board and resume database devoted exclusively to the civil engineering community-from the professionals who visit the site, to the companies, agencies or job recruiters who advertise job opportunities on the site. Offers unique opportunity to reach premier civil engineering professionals without the waste.

2128 ■ CivilEngineeringCrossing.com
URL: http://www.civilengineeringcrossing.com

Description: Locates jobs inside user's niche, conducting a more streamlined job search. Provides instant access to a comprehensive pool of listings based on particular area of focus.

2129 ■ CivilEngineeringJobs.com
URL: http://www.civilengineeringjobs.com/index.htm

Description: Provides job listings, employment information and career resources for civil engineers. Offers help with all civil engineering disciplines including water resources, environmental, research, and others.

2130 ■ CivilEngineerJobSource.com
URL: http://www.civilengineerjobsource.com

Description: Provides direct links to job and career sections of civil engineering firms throughout the United States.

2131 ■ CivilEngineerUSA.com
URL: http://www.civilengineerusa.com

Description: Serves as a career site for civil engineering professionals. Provides listings of jobs, career opportunities, and products to civil engineers and resources for both job seekers and employers.

2132 ■ Construction Jobs Network
URL: http://constructionjobs.net

Description: Provides job seekers access to construction employment opportunities for both construction management, construction professional and construction trade jobs. Features construction jobs, employer, and resume directories.

2133 ■ ConstructionJobs.com
URL: http://www.constructionjobs.com/index_eng.cfm

Description: Serves as an employment job board and resume database built exclusively for the construction, design, and building industries. Provides targeted candidate searches by geographic region, specific industries, job titles, education, and experience.

2134 ■ ConstructMyFuture.com
URL: http://www.constructmyfuture.com

Description: Offers comprehensive information for students, parents, and educators on varied careers in construction. Includes a searchable database of colleges, universities and trade schools that offer degrees in construction fields.

2135 ■ EnergyCentralJobs.com
URL: http://www.energycentraljobs.com

Description: Serves as an on-line job resource for candidates and power companies worldwide. Maintains a job search database dedicated to the power, nuclear, oil and gas career fields.

2136 ■ Engineering Classifieds
URL: http://www.engineeringclassifieds.com

Description: Serves as a career site for engineering professionals. Provides services including job search agents, resume creation and posting.

2137 ■ EngineerJobs.com
URL: http://www.engineerjobs.com

Description: Provides job opportunities for engineering professionals in the following disciplines: aerospace, agricultural, biomedical, chemical, civil, electrical, environmental, industrial, manufacturing, marine, materials, mechanical, mining, nuclear, petroleum, process, project, quality, sales, software, solar, systems, and structural.

2138 ■ Engineer.net
URL: http://www.engineer.net

Description: Provides engineering employment tools such as job search, job posting, and engineering resumes.

2139 ■ ENR Industry Jobs Site
URL: http://industry-jobs.enr.com/main/default.asp

Description: Provides job searching and recruitment services in the field of architecture, engineering and construction (AEC) industry. Offers comprehensive database of career opportunities for job seekers and resume of top AEC professionals for employers.

2140 ■ HeavyCivilJobs.com
URL: http://heavyciviljobs.com

Description: Serves as an online tool that helps construction workers and civil engineers the opportunity to look for a job in heavy civil disciplines.

2141 ■ iCivilEngineer.com
URL: http://www.icivilengineer.com

Description: Serves as a portal for civil engineering professionals and students. Offers civil engineering news, resources, and career center.

2142 ■ PowerPlantPro.com
URL: http://www.powerplantpro.com/main/sendform/4/18/3472

Description: Dedicated to professionals in the power and energy industry. Features career advice and employer listings.

2143 ■ Referwork Jobs
URL: http://www.referwork-jobs.com

Description: Provides a searchable database of major jobs in construction and related specialties.

2144 ■ Spherion
URL: http://www.spherion.com

Description: Recruitment firm specializing in accounting and finance, sales and marketing, interim executives, technology, engineering, retail and human resources.

2145 ■ ThinkEnergyGroup.com
URL: http://www.thinkenergygroup.com

Description: Serves as a job board for professionals looking for positions in engineering, power plant, energy, and technical fields. Contains advice and tips on interviews, job searching, resume writing, hiring, and management. Provides choices of work location, pay rates in the field of expertise and contract, temp-to-hire, and direct hiring options.

2146 ■ USA Construction Jobs
URL: http://www.usaconstructionjobs.com

Description: Features job listings in construction and general labor.

TRADESHOWS

2147 ■ Structures Congress
American Society of Civil Engineers - Architectural Engineering Institute
1801 Alexander Bell Dr.
Reston, VA 20191-4400
Free: 800-548-2723
E-mail: aei@asce.org
URL: http://www.asce.org/aei

Frequency: Annual. **Primary Exhibits:** Civil engineering equipment, supplies, and services, including practical design information, landmark bridges, disproportionate collapse, performance-based design, wind design, codes and standards, business and international engineering.

OTHER SOURCES

2148 ■ Acoustical Society of America
2 Huntington Quadrangle, Ste. 1N01
Melville, NY 11747-4505
Ph: (516)576-2360
Fax: (516)576-2377
E-mail: asa@aip.org
URL: http://acousticalsociety.org

Description: Represents members from various fields related to sound including physics, electrical, mechanical and aeronautical engineering, oceanography, biology, physiology, psychology, architecture, speech, noise and noise control, and music. Aims to increase and diffuse the knowledge of acoustics and its practical applications. Organizes meetings, provides reprints of out-of-print classic texts in acoustics, and translation books.

2149 ■ American Academy of Environmental Engineers and Scientists
130 Holiday Ct., Ste. 100
Annapolis, MD 21401
Ph: (410)266-3311
Fax: (410)266-7653
E-mail: info@aaees.org
URL: http://www.aaees.org

Description: Environmentally oriented registered professional engineers certified by examination as Diplomates of the Academy. Seeks to improve the standards of environmental engineering. Certifies those with special knowledge of environmental engineering. Furnishes lists of those certified to the public. Maintains speakers' bureau. Recognizes areas of specialization: Air Pollution Control; General Environmental; Hazardous Waste Management; Industrial Hygiene; Radiation Protection; Solid Waste Management; Water Supply and Wastewater. Requires written and oral examinations for certification. Works with other professional organizations on environmentally oriented activities. Identifies potential employment candidates through Talent Search Service.

2150 ■ American Association of Blacks in Energy
1625 K St. NW, Ste. 405
Washington, DC 20006
Ph: (202)371-9530
Fax: (202)371-9218
E-mail: info@aabe.org
URL: http://www.aabe.org

Description: Seeks to increase the knowledge, understanding, and awareness of the minority community in energy issues by serving as an energy information source for policymakers, recommending blacks and other minorities to appropriate energy officials and executives, encouraging students to pursue professional careers in the energy industry, and advocating the participation of blacks and other minorities in energy programs and policymaking activities. Updates members on key legislation and regulations being developed by the Department of Energy, the Department of Interior, the Department of Commerce, the Small Business Administration, and other federal and state agencies.

2151 ■ American Association of Engineering Societies
1801 Alexander Bell Dr.
Reston, VA 20191
Ph: (202)296-2237
Free: 888-400-2237
Fax: (202)296-1151
E-mail: dbateson@aaes.org
URL: http://www.aaes.org

Description: Coordinates the efforts of the member societies in the provision of reliable and objective information to the general public concerning issues which affect the engineering profession and the field of engineering as a whole; collects, analyzes, documents, and disseminates data which will inform the general public of the relationship between engineering and the national welfare; provides a forum for the engineering societies to exchange and discuss their views on matters of common interest; and represents the U.S. engineering community abroad through representation in WFEO and UPADI.

2152 ■ American Concrete Institute
38800 Country Club Dr.
Farmington Hills, MI 48331-3439
Ph: (248)848-3700
Fax: (248)848-3701
E-mail: ann.daugherty@acifoundation.org
URL: http://www.concrete.org

Description: Comprised of engineers, architects, contractors, educators, and others interested in improving techniques of design construction and maintenance of concrete products and structures. Advances engineering and technical education, scientific investigation and research, and development of standards for design and construction incorporating concrete and related materials. Gathers, correlates, and disseminates information for the improvement of the design, construction, manufacture, use and maintenance of concrete products and structures. **Members:** 20,000.

2153 ■ American Engineering Association
c/o Harold Ruchelman
533 Waterside Blvd.
Monroe Township, NJ 08831

Ph: (201)664-6954
E-mail: aea@aea.org
URL: http://www.aea.org

Description: Members consist of Engineers and engineering professionals. Purpose to advance the engineering profession and U.S. engineering capabilities. Issues of concern include age discrimination, immigration laws, displacement of U.S. Engineers by foreign workers, trade agreements, off shoring of U.S. Engineering and manufacturing jobs, loss of U.S. manufacturing and engineering capability, and recruitment of foreign students. Testifies before Congress. Holds local Chapter meetings.

2154 ■ American Indian Science and Engineering Society
PO Box 9828
Albuquerque, NM 87119-9828
Ph: (505)765-1052
Fax: (505)765-5608
E-mail: pam@aises.org
URL: http://www.aises.org

Description: Represents American Indian and non-Indian students and professionals in science, technology, and engineering fields; corporations representing energy, mining, aerospace, electronic, and computer fields. Seeks to motivate and encourage students to pursue undergraduate and graduate studies in science, engineering, and technology. Sponsors science fairs in grade schools, teacher training workshops, summer math/science sessions for 8th-12th graders, professional chapters, and student chapters in colleges. Offers scholarships. Adult members serve as role models, advisers, and mentors for students. Operates placement service.

2155 ■ American Institute of Engineers
4630 Appian Way, Ste. 206
El Sobrante, CA 94803-1875
Ph: (510)758-6240
Fax: (510)758-6240
E-mail: aie@aieonline.org
URL: http://www.aieonline.org

Description: Professional association for engineers, scientists, and mathematicians. Multi-disciplined, non-technical association who aims to improve the stature and image of engineers, scientists, and mathematicians. Provides endorsements, awards and opportunities for small business start-ups within the AIE Councils. Sponsors "LA Engineer", a comedy-drama television series; produces annual "Academy Hall of FAME (TV)".

2156 ■ American Road and Transportation Builders Association
1219 28th St. NW
Washington, DC 20007-3389
Ph: (202)289-4434
Fax: (202)289-4435
E-mail: general@artba.org
URL: http://www.artba.org

Description: Advances the interests of the transportation construction industry. Promotes the growth and protection of transportation infrastructure investment to meet the public and business demand for safe and efficient travel. Works to ensure its members' views and business concerns are addressed before Congress, the White House, federal agencies and news media.

2157 ■ American Society of Civil Engineers - Architectural Engineering Institute
1801 Alexander Bell Dr.
Reston, VA 20191-4400
Free: 800-548-2723
E-mail: aei@asce.org
URL: http://www.asce.org/aei

Description: Seeks to advance the state-of-the-art and state-of-the-practice of the building industry worldwide by facilitating effective and timely technology transfer. Provides a multidisciplinary forum for building industry professionals to examine technical,

scientific and professional issues of common interest.

2158 ■ Asian American Architects and Engineers
1167 Mission St., 4th Fl.
San Francisco, CA 94103
E-mail: info@aaaenc.org
URL: http://www.aaaenc.org

Description: Minorities. Provides contracts and job opportunities for minorities in the architectural and engineering fields. Serves as a network for the promotion in professional fields. **Members:** 120.

2159 ■ *Career Opportunities in Engineering*
InfoBase Holdings Inc.
132 W 31st., 17 Fl.
New York, NY 10001-3406
Ph: (212)967-8800
Fax: (800)678-3633
E-mail: info@infobasepublishing.com
URL: http://www.ferguson.infobasepublishing.com

Description: 2006. $49.50. 336 pages. Provides an overview of engineering, followed by a selection of jobs profiled in detail, including the nature of the job, earnings, prospects for employment, what kind of training and skills it requires and sources for further information. **Includes:** Appendices of educational institutions, periodicals, directories, and associations. Appendices of educational institutions, periodicals, directories, and associations.

2160 ■ Cultural Vistas
440 Park Ave. S, 2nd Fl.
New York, NY 10016
Ph: (212)497-3500
Fax: (212)497-3535
E-mail: info@culturalvistas.org
URL: http://culturalvistas.org

Description: Providers worldwide of on-the-job training programs for students and professionals seeking international career development and life-changing experiences. Arranges workplace exchanges in hundreds of professional fields, bringing employers and trainees together from around the world. Client list ranges from small farming communities to Fortune 500 companies.

2161 ■ Engineering Society of Detroit
20700 Civic Center Dr., Ste. 450
Southfield, MI 48076
Ph: (248)353-0735
Fax: (248)353-0736
E-mail: esd@esd.org
URL: http://ww2.esd.org/home.htm

Description: Engineers from all disciplines; scientists and technologists. Conducts technical programs and engineering refresher courses; sponsors conferences and expositions. Maintains speakers' bureau; offers placement services; although based in Detroit, MI, society membership is international. **Members:** 6,000.

2162 ■ Intelligent Transportation Society of America
1100 17th St. NW, Ste. 1200
Washington, DC 20036
Ph: (202)484-4847
Free: 800-374-8472
Fax: (202)484-3483
E-mail: info@itsa.org
URL: http://www.itsa.org

Description: Includes private corporations, public agencies, and academic institutions involved in the research, development, and design of intelligent transportation systems technologies that enhance safety, increase mobility, and sustain the environment.

2163 ■ Korean-American Scientists and Engineers Association
1952 Gallows Rd., Ste. 300
Vienna, VA 22182
Ph: (703)748-1221

Fax: (703)748-1331
E-mail: sejong@ksea.org
URL: http://www.ksea.org

Description: Represents scientists and engineers holding single or advanced degrees. Promotes friendship and mutuality among Korean and American scientists and engineers; contributes to Korea's scientific, technological, industrial, and economic developments; strengthens the scientific, technological, and cultural bonds between Korea and the U.S. Sponsors symposium. Maintains speakers' bureau, placement service, and biographical archives. Compiles statistics. **Members:** 10,000.

2164 ■ National Action Council for Minorities in Engineering
440 Hamilton Ave., Ste. 302
White Plains, NY 10601-1813
Ph: (914)539-4010
Free: 800-888-9929
Fax: (914)539-4032
E-mail: ajohnson@nacme.org
URL: http://www.nacme.org

Description: Leads the national effort to increase access to careers in engineering and other science-based disciplines. Conducts research and public policy analysis, develops and operates national demonstration programs at precollege and university levels, and disseminates information through publications, conferences and electronic media. Serves as a privately funded source of scholarships for minority students in engineering.

2165 ■ National Association of Traffic Accident Reconstructionists and Investigators
PO Box 2588
West Chester, PA 19382
Ph: (610)696-1919
E-mail: natari@natari.org
URL: http://www.natari.org

Description: Represents engineers, attorneys, police officers, private investigators, medical examiners, and other individuals involved in the analysis of motor vehicle traffic accidents. Gathers and disseminates information on techniques and equipment of potential use to members; reviews literature in the field. Participating Organization of the Accreditation Commission for Traffic Accident Reconstruction.

2166 ■ Society of Hispanic Professional Engineers
13181 Crossroads Pkwy. N, Ste. 450
City of Industry, CA 91746-3496
Ph: (323)725-3970
E-mail: shpenational@shpe.org
URL: http://national.shpe.org

Description: Represents engineers, student engineers, and scientists. Aims to increase the number of Hispanic engineers by providing motivation and support to students. Sponsors competitions and educational programs. Maintains placement service and speakers' bureau; compiles statistics. **Members:** 8,000.

2167 ■ Society of Women Engineers
203 N La Salle St., Ste. 1675
Chicago, IL 60601
Ph: (312)596-5223
Free: 877-SWE-INFO
Fax: (312)596-5252
E-mail: hq@swe.org
URL: http://societyofwomenengineers.swe.org

Description: Educational and service organization representing both students and professional women in engineering and technical fields.

2168 ■ Water Environment Federation
601 Wythe St.
Alexandria, VA 22314-1994
Free: 800-666-0206
Fax: (703)684-2492
E-mail: inquiry@wef.org
URL: http://www.wef.org

Description: Technical societies representing chemists, biologists, ecologists, geologists, operators, educational and research personnel, industrial wastewater engineers, consultant engineers, municipal officials, equipment manufacturers, and university professors and students dedicated to the enhancement and preservation of water quality and resources. Seeks to advance fundamental and practical knowledge concerning the nature, collection, treatment, and disposal of domestic and industrial wastewaters, and the design, construction, operation, and management of facilities for these purposes. Disseminates technical information; and promotes good public relations and regulations that improve water quality and the status of individuals working in this field. Conducts educational and research programs.

2169 ■ Women in Engineering ProActive Network
1901 E Asbury Ave., Ste. 220
Denver, CO 80208
Ph: (303)871-4643
Fax: (303)871-4628
URL: http://www.wepan.org

Description: Women in engineering professions. Includes key strategies such as education and training, research, collaboration, leadership, diversity, advocacy, networking, sustainability, accountability, and volunteerism in order to be a catalyst for change that enhances the success of women in the engineering professions.

SOURCES OF HELP-WANTED ADS

2170 ■ *ASCnet Quarterly*
Applied Systems Client Network
801 Douglas Ave., Ste. 205
Altamonte Springs, FL 32714
Ph: (407)869-0404
Free: 800-605-1045
Fax: (407)869-0418
E-mail: info@ascnet.org
URL: http://www.ascnet.org/AM/Template.cfm?Section=About
Frequency: Quarterly. **Price:** $24 Individuals.
Description: Professional magazine covering technical information, association news, and industry information for insurance professionals.

2171 ■ *Best's Review*
A.M. Best Company Inc.
Ambest Rd.
Oldwick, NJ 08858-7000
Ph: (908)439-2200
Fax: (908)439-3385
E-mail: customer_service@ambest.com
URLs: http://www.ambest.com/sales/newsoverview
.asp#br; http://www.ambest.com/review/default.asp
Frequency: Monthly. **Price:** $50 Individuals.
Description: Magazine covering issues and trends for the management personnel of life/health insurers, the agents, and brokers who market their products.

2172 ■ **Business Insurance**
Crain Communications Inc.
1155 Gratiot Ave.
Detroit, MI 48207-2732
Ph: (313)446-6000
E-mail: info@crain.com
URL: http://www.businessinsurance.com
Frequency: Weekly. **Price:** $399 Individuals print; $149 Individuals print & digital; $69 Individuals digital edition. **Description:** International newsweekly reporting on corporate risk and employee benefit management news.

2173 ■ *Claims: Covering the Business of Loss*
Claims
15112 64th Ave. W
Edmonds, WA 98026
Ph: (425)745-6394
URL: http://www.propertycasualty360.com/Claims
-Magazine
Frequency: Monthly. **Price:** $72 Individuals; $93 Canada; $131 Other countries. **Description:** Magazine for the property-casualty insurance claims industry.

EMPLOYER DIRECTORIES AND NETWORKING LISTS

2174 ■ *Best's Insurance Reports*
A.M. Best Company Inc.
Ambest Rd.
Oldwick, NJ 08858-7000

Ph: (908)439-2200
Fax: (908)439-3385
E-mail: customer_service@ambest.com
URL: http://www.ambest.com
Frequency: Annual; Latest edition 2014. **Pages:** 3,345 Life-health; 5,166 property-casualty. **Description:** Published in three editions: Life-health insurance, covering about 1,750 companies, property-casualty insurance, covering over 3,200 companies; and international, covering more than 1,200 insurers. Each edition lists state insurance commissioners and related companies and agencies (mutual funds, worker compensation funds, underwriting agencies, etc.). **Includes:** Review of financial performance, 5 years of exclusive Best's Ratings. **Entries include:** For each company--Company name, address, phone; history; states in which licensed; names of officers and directors; financial data; financial analysis and Best's rating. **Arrangement:** Alphabetical.

2175 ■ *Business Insurance--Third-Party Claims Administrators Issue*
Crain Communications Inc.
150 N Michigan Ave.
Chicago, IL 60601-7553
Ph: (312)649-5200
Free: 800-678-9595
Fax: (312)280-3150
E-mail: info@crain.com
URLs: http://businessinsurance.datajoe.com/app/
ecom/pub_products.php; http://www.businessinsurance.com
Frequency: Annual; Latest edition 2009. **Publication includes:** List of approximately 150 third-party claims administration, adjusting, and auditing firms that process claims for self-insured clients, including employee benefit and property/casualty claims. **Entries include:** Company name, address, phone, fax, number of employees, number of claims processing staff, number of clients, method of compensation, prior year's revenues (when available), along with percent attributed to claims administration, adjusting and auditing for self-insured clients; claims volume by number of projects conducted; specialty or area of expertise. **Arrangement:** Alphabetical by company.

2176 ■ *Insurance Phone Book*
Communication Publications & Resources
2807 N Parham Rd., Ste. 200
Richmond, VA 23294
Free: 800-780-4066
E-mail: customerservice@briefings.com
URLs: http://www.douglaspublications.com; http://
www.thesalesmansguide.com
Frequency: Annual; latest edition 2009-2010. **Price:** $195 directory price; $389 directory/CD combo price. **Covers:** About 3,700 life, accident and health, worker's compensation, auto, fire and casualty, marine, surety, and other insurance companies; 2,300 executive contacts from presidents and CEOs to claims and customer service managers. **Entries include:** Company name, address, phone, fax, toll-

free number, type of insurance provided. **Arrangement:** Alphabetical.

2177 ■ *Kirschner's Insurance Directories: Red Book*
URLs: http://www.nationalunderwriter.com; http://
www.kirschners.com
Frequency: Annual; Latest edition 2007. **Pages:** 500 minimum page count per edition; 1000 maximum page count per edition. **Covers:** Insurance agents and agencies in all 50 states and the District of Columbia. Published in 24 separate editions for Southern California, Northern California, Pacific Northwest (AK, ID, HI, OR, WA, MT), Michigan, Illinois, New England states (CT, ME, MA, NH, RI, VT), Ohio, Rocky Mountain states (AZ, CO, NV, NM, UT, WY), South Central states (GA, AL, MS), Indiana, Texas, Kentucky/Tennessee, East Central states (VA, WV, NC, SC), South Central West states (AR, OK, LA), Wisconsin, Central states (KS, MO, NE), North Central states (IA, MN, ND, SD), Mid-Atlantic states (DE, MD, NJ, DC), Pennsylvania, Florida. **Entries include:** For companies--Name, address, key personnel (with addresses and phone numbers). **Arrangement:** Separate alphabetical sections for insurance companies, wholesalers, field agents, and agencies. **Indexes:** Type of insurance.

2178 ■ *Mergent Bank and Finance Manual*
Mergent Inc.
580 Kingsley Park Dr.
Fort Mill, SC 29715
Ph: (704)527-2700
Free: 800-937-1398
Fax: (704)559-6837
E-mail: info@mergent.com
URL: http://www.mergent.com
Frequency: Annual; July; supplements in 'Mergent Bank & Finance News Reports'. **Price:** $2,095 per year, including supplements. **Pages:** 35,688 4 volumes. **Covers:** In four volumes, over 12,000 national, state, and private banks, savings and loans, mutual funds, unit investment trusts, and insurance and real estate companies in the United States. **Entries include:** Company name, headquarters and branch offices, phones, names and titles of principal executives, directors, history, Moody's rating, and extensive financial and statistical data. **Arrangement:** Classified by type of business. **Indexes:** Company name.

2179 ■ *National Association of Catastrophe Adjusters--Membership Roster*
National Association of Catastrophe Adjusters
PO Box 821864
North Richland Hills, TX 76182
Ph: (817)498-3466
Fax: (817)498-0480
E-mail: naca@nacatadj.org
URL: http://www.nacatadj.org
Frequency: Annual; March; Latest Edition 2013-2014. **Pages:** 152. **Covers:** About 400 insurance catastrophe claims adjusters and adjusting firms;

about 150 related insurance firms (associate members). **Entries include:** Name, address, phone, spouse's name. **Arrangement:** Separate geographical sections for regular associate and business associate members. **Indexes:** Alphabetical; geographical.

2180 ■ *Yearbook*

American Association of Managing General Agents
610 Freedom Business Ctr., Ste. 100
King of Prussia, PA 19406
Ph: (610)992-0022
Fax: (610)992-0021
E-mail: bernie@aamga.org
URL: http://www.aamga.org

Frequency: Annual; Latest edition 2006. **Pages:** 468. **Covers:** 250 managing general agents of insurance companies and their more than 500 branch offices; coverage includes Canada. **Entries include:** Name, address, names and titles of principal and contact, insurance companies represented. **Arrangement:** Geographical.

HANDBOOKS AND MANUALS

2181 ■ *Associate Claim Examiner*

National Learning Corporation
212 Michael Dr.
Syosset, NY 11791
Ph: (516)921-8888
Free: 800-632-8888
Fax: (516)921-8743
E-mail: info@passbooks.com
URL: http://www.passbooks.com

Description: 2009. $29.95 (paper). Serves as an exam preparation guide for associate claim examiners.

2182 ■ *Opportunities in Insurance Careers*

The McGraw-Hill Companies Inc.
PO Box 182604
Columbus, OH 43272
Ph: (212)512-2000
Free: 877-833-5524
Fax: (614)759-3749
E-mail: customer.service@mcgraw-hill.com
URL: http://www.mcgraw-hill.com

Description: Robert M. Schrayer. Revised, 2007. $14.95 (paper). 160 pages. A guide to planning for and seeking opportunities in the field. Contains bibliography and illustrations.

EMPLOYMENT AGENCIES AND SEARCH FIRMS

2183 ■ **International Insurance Personnel, Inc.**

300 W Wieuca Rd., Bldg. 2, Ste. 101
Atlanta, GA 30342
Ph: (404)255-9710

Fax: (404)255-9864
E-mail: iipjulie@bellsouth.net
URL: http://realpages.com/sites/intlinspersonnel/index.html

Description: Employment agency specializing in the area of insurance.

2184 ■ **Lear & Associates, Inc.**

43 E Pine St.
Orlando, FL 32801
Ph: (407)645-4611
Fax: (407)645-5735
E-mail: info@learsearch.com
URL: http://www.learsearch.com

Description: Serves as recruitment firm specializing in the insurance industry.

2185 ■ **Pinnacle Group, Inc.**

6 Greenleaf Woods, Ste. 201
Portsmouth, NH 03801
Ph: (603)427-1700
Free: 800-308-7205
Fax: (603)427-0526
E-mail: info@pinnaclejobs.com
URL: http://www.pinnaclejobs.com

Description: Provides recruiting services to insurance, consulting and investment firms. Offers career opportunities from entry-level to senior management.

2186 ■ **Questor Consultants, Inc.**

2515 N Broad St.
Colmar, PA 18915
Ph: (215)997-9262
Fax: (215)997-9226
E-mail: sbevivino@questorconsultants.com
URL: http://www.questorconsultants.com

Description: Executive search firm specializing in the insurance and legal fields.

ONLINE JOB SOURCES AND SERVICES

2187 ■ **Great Insurance Jobs**

URL: http://www.greatinsurancejobs.com

Description: Contains varied insurance positions. Job seekers may browse employee profiles, post resumes, and read descriptions of hundreds of recently-posted insurance jobs.

2188 ■ **InsuranceIndustryCentral.com**

URL: http://www.insuranceindustrycentral.com

Description: Features insurance jobs and products to the insurance community.

2189 ■ **National Insurance Recruiters Association**

URL: http://www.insurancerecruiters.com

Description: Contains lists of recruiters (listed by department and line of business) and available insurance positions.

2190 ■ **UltimateInsuranceJobs.com**

URL: http://www.ultimateinsurancejobs.com/index.asp

Description: Provides insurance job listings,

recruiter directory, and resources. Offers job seekers the opportunity to post and edit their resumes, and employers the opportunity to search through insurance resumes.

OTHER SOURCES

2191 ■ **Insurance Information Institute**

110 William St.
New York, NY 10038
Ph: (212)346-5500
E-mail: members@iii.org
URL: http://www.iii.org

Description: Property and casualty insurance companies. Provides information and educational services to mass media, educational institutions, trade associations, businesses, government agencies, and the public.

2192 ■ **International Association of Insurance Professionals**

8023 E 63rd Pl., Ste. 540
Tulsa, OK 74133
Ph: (918)294-3700
Free: 800-766-6249
Fax: (918)294-3711
URL: http://naiw.site-ym.com

Description: Insurance industry professionals. Promotes continuing education and networking for the professional advancement of its members. Offers education programs, meetings, services, and leadership opportunities. Provides a forum to learn about other disciplines in the insurance industry.

2193 ■ **LOMA**

2300 Windy Ridge Pkwy., Ste. 600
Atlanta, GA 30339-8443
Ph: (770)951-1770
E-mail: askloma@loma.org
URL: http://www.loma.org

Description: Life and health insurance companies and financial services in the U.S. and Canada; and overseas in 45 countries; affiliate members are firms that provide professional support to member companies. Provides research, information, training, and educational activities in areas of operations and systems, human resources, financial planning and employee development. Administers FLMI Insurance Education Program, which awards FLMI (Fellow, Life Management Institute) designation to those who complete the ten-examination program.

2194 ■ **National Association of Public Insurance Adjusters**

21165 Whitfield Pl., No. 105
Potomac Falls, VA 20165
Ph: (703)433-9217
Fax: (703)433-0369
E-mail: info@napia.com
URL: http://www.napia.com

Description: Professional society of public insurance adjusters. Sponsors certification and professional education programs. **Members:** 500.

SOURCES OF HELP-WANTED ADS

2195 ■ *AAB Bulletin*
American Association of Bioanalysts
906 Olive St., Ste. 1200
Saint Louis, MO 63101-1448
Ph: (314)241-1445
Fax: (314)241-1449
URL: http://www.aab.org
Mark S. Birenbaum, Ph.D., Editor. **Frequency:** Quarterly; Quarterly. **Price:** included in membership dues; Included in membership. **Description:** Recurring features include interviews, news of research, a calendar of events, reports of meetings, news of educational opportunities, and job listings.

2196 ■ *ADVANCE for Medical Laboratory Professionals: The Nation's Medical Laboratory Biweekly*
Merion Publications Inc.
2900 Horizon Dr.
King of Prussia, PA 19406-0956
Ph: (610)278-1400
Free: 800-355-5627
E-mail: advance@merion.com
URL: http://laboratorian.advanceweb.com/Default
.aspx
Frequency: Biweekly. **Price:** Free. **Description:** Magazine that reaches technologists and laboratory managers with professional news and employment opportunities.

2197 ■ *American Laboratory News*
International Scientific Communications Inc.
30 Controls Dr.
Shelton, CT 06484-0870
Ph: (650)243-5600
Fax: (203)926-9310
E-mail: iscpubs@iscpubs.com
URL: http://www.americanlaboratory.com
Frequency: Monthly. **Description:** Trade magazine for scientists.

2198 ■ *ASPB News*
American Society of Plant Biologists
15501 Monona Dr.
Rockville, MD 20855-2768
Ph: (301)251-0560
Fax: (301)279-2996
E-mail: info@aspb.org
URL: http://www.aspb.org/newsletter
Description: Bimonthly. $30/year for nonmember. Offers news of interest to plant physiologists, biochemists, horticulturists, and plant molecular and cell biologists engaged in research and teaching. Alerts members to public policy issues, educational opportunities, meetings, seminars, and conventions pertinent to the field. Recurring features include letters to the editor, reports of meetings, job listings, a calendar of events, news from regional sections, and teaching ideas.

2199 ■ *CAP Today*
College of American Pathologists
325 Waukegan Rd.
Northfield, IL 60093-2750
Ph: (847)832-7000
Free: 800-323-4040
Fax: (847)832-8000
E-mail: capfdn@cap.org
URL: http://www.cap.org
Frequency: Monthly. **Price:** $110 Individuals; $30 U.S. and Canada; $135 Individuals Canada; $135 Other countries; $40 Other countries single copy. **Description:** Magazine covering advances in pathology tests and equipment, clinical lab management and operations trends, and related regulatory and legislative changes.

2200 ■ *Cell*
Cell Press
600 Technology Sq.
Cambridge, MA 02139
Ph: (617)661-7057
Free: 866-314-2355
Fax: (617)661-7061
E-mail: celleditor@cell.com
URL: http://www.cell.com
Frequency: 26/yr. **Price:** $212 U.S. and Canada individual, print and online; $320 Other countries individual, print and online; $212 U.S. and Canada online only, individual; $212 Other countries online only, individual; $1,425 U.S. and Canada institution, print only; $1,605 Institutions, other countries print only. **Description:** Peer-reviewed journal on molecular and cell biology.

2201 ■ *Clinical Laboratory News*
American Association of Clinical Chemistry
1850 K St. NW, Ste. 625
Washington, DC 20006-2215
Ph: (202)857-0717
Free: 800-892-1400
Fax: (202)887-5093
E-mail: info@aacc.org
URL: http://www.aacc.org/publications/cln/Pages/
default.aspx
Frequency: Monthly. **Description:** Scholarly magazine providing current news in the field of clinical laboratory science.

2202 ■ *Laboratory Medicine: An Official Publication of the American Society for Clinical Pathology*
American Society for Clinical Pathology
33 W Monroe St., Ste. 1600
Chicago, IL 60603
Ph: (312)541-4999
Free: 800-267-2727
Fax: (312)541-4998
E-mail: labmed@ascp.org
URL: http://labmed.ascpjournals.org/
Frequency: Monthly. **Price:** $95 Individuals online; $120 Individuals print and online; $120 Institutions online; $145 Institutions print and online. **Description:** Professional journal covering medical technology and pathology.

2203 ■ *Medical Laboratory Observer*
Nelson Publishing Inc.
2500 Tamiami Trl. N
Nokomis, FL 34275
Ph: (941)966-9521
Fax: (941)966-2590
E-mail: webteam@nelsonpub.com
URL: http://www.mlo-online.com
Frequency: Monthly. **Price:** Free. **Description:** Magazine for clinical laboratory professionals.

2204 ■ *MEEN Diagnostic and Invasive Technology*
Reilly Publishing Co.
16 E. Schaumburg Rd.
Schaumburg, IL 60194-3536
Ph: (847)882-6336
Fax: (847)519-0166
E-mail: rcgroup@flash.net
URLs: http://www.dicardiology.net/; http://www.itnon-line.net
Frequency: Bimonthly; 9/yr. **Price:** $90 Canada and Mexico; $120 Other countries. **Description:** Trade magazine serving users and buyers of diagnostic and invasive cardiology technology.

2205 ■ *Vantage Point*
Clinical Laboratory Management Association
330 N Wabash Ave., Ste. 2000
Chicago, IL 60611
Ph: (312)321-5111
Fax: (312)673-6927
E-mail: info@clma.org
URL: http://www.clma.org
Description: Semimonthly. Features general, health care, and laboratory management tips, trends, and legislative news. Recurring features include news of educational opportunities, job listings, and columns titled Manager's Workshop, Healthcare Management Briefs, Career Corner, Online Update and Legislative Update.

EMPLOYER DIRECTORIES AND NETWORKING LISTS

2206 ■ *AGT International Membership Directory*
Association of Genetic Technologists
PO Box 19193
Lenexa, KS 66285
Ph: (913)895-4605
Fax: (913)895-4652
E-mail: agt-info@goamp.com
URL: http://www.agt-info.org/IntMembershipDir.aspx
Frequency: Monthly. **Covers:** About 520 laboratories studying heritable and acquired

chromosomal disorders using cytogenetic, genetics, and cellular biology techniques. **Includes:** Summaries of procedure counts (by specimen type); number of reporting laboratories by procedure; cytogenetic technology training programs information; membership information. **Entries include:** Laboratory name, address, phone, areas of specialization, techniques, numbers and types of laboratory tests performed, and names of director and cytogenetic technologists. **Arrangement:** Geographical. **Indexes:** Director name, ACT member name.

2207 ■ *Directory of Accredited Laboratories*
American Association for Laboratory Accreditation
5301 Buckeystown Pke., Ste. 350
Frederick, MD 21704-8307
Ph: (301)644-3248
Fax: (240)454-9449
E-mail: punger@a2la.org
URL: http://www.a2la.org
Frequency: Weekly. **Price:** Free. **Pages:** 1,432. **Covers:** Over 1,600 testing and calibration laboratories and inspection agencies accredited for technical competence as measured against national and international standards in the following fields of testing: metrology, acoustics and vibration, construction materials, biology, chemistry, electricity, environmental, geotechnical, mechanical, thermal, and nondestructive. **Entries include:** Name of laboratory, address, phone, contact, certificate number, current period of accreditation, fields of accreditation technologies and methodologies. **Arrangement:** Alphabetical. **Indexes:** Fields of accreditation.

2208 ■ *Directory of Hospital Personnel*
Grey House Publishing
4919 Rte. 22
Amenia, NY 12501
Ph: (518)789-8700
Free: 800-562-2139
Fax: (518)789-0556
E-mail: books@greyhouse.com
URL: http://www.greyhouse.com/hospital_personnel.htm
Frequency: Annual; Latest edition 2011. **Price:** $325 Individuals Softcover. **Pages:** 2,300. **Covers:** 200,000 executives at 6,000 U.S. Hospitals. **Entries include:** Name of hospital, address, phone, number of beds, type and JCAHO status of hospital, names and titles of key department heads and staff, medical and nursing school affiliations; number of residents, interns, and nursing students. **Arrangement:** Geographical. **Indexes:** Hospital name, personnel, hospital size.

2209 ■ *Hospital Blue Book*
Billian Publishing Inc. and Trans World Publishing Inc.
2100 River Edge Pkwy., Ste. 1200
Atlanta, GA 30328
Ph: (770)955-5656
Free: 800-800-5668
Fax: (770)952-0669
E-mail: info@billian.com
URL: http://www.billianshealthdata.com/Products/HealthDATA_Hospital_Blue_Book
Frequency: Annual; Latest edition 2012. **Price:** $250 Individuals national edition; $575 Individuals subscription. **Covers:** More than 6,500 hospitals; some listings also appear in a separate southern edition of this publication. **Entries include:** Name of hospital, accreditation, mailing address, phone, fax, number of beds, type of facility (nonprofit, general, state, etc.); list of administrative personnel and chiefs of medical services, with specific titles. **Arrangement:** Geographical.

2210 ■ *Medical and Health Information Directory: A Guide to Organizations, Agencies, Institutions, Programs, Publications, Services, and Other Resources Concerned with Clinical Medicine*
Cengage Learning Inc.
200 1st Stamford Pl., Ste. 400
Stamford, CT 06902-6753

Ph: (203)965-8600
Free: 800-354-9706
Fax: (800)487-8488
E-mail: investors@cengage.com
URL: http://www.gale.cengage.com
Frequency: Annual; Latest edition April 2011. **Price:** $1,190 Individuals set; $501 Individuals per volume. **Covers:** In volume 1, more than 33,000 medical and health oriented associations, organizations, institutions, and government agencies, including health maintenance organizations (HMOs), preferred provider organizations (PPOs), insurance companies, pharmaceutical companies, research centers, and medical and allied health schools. In Volume 2, over 20,000 medical book publishers; medical periodicals, directories, audiovisual producers and services, medical libraries and information centers, electronic resources, and health-related internet search engines. In Volume 3, more than 40,500 clinics, treatment centers, care programs, and counseling/diagnostic services for 34 subject areas. **Entries include:** Institution, service, or firm name, address, phone, fax, email and URL; many include names of key personnel and, when pertinent, descriptive annotation. Volume 3 was formerly listed separately as Health Services Directory. **Arrangement:** Classified by organization activity, service, etc. **Indexes:** Each volume has a complete alphabetical name and keyword index.

HANDBOOKS AND MANUALS

2211 ■ *Opportunities in Health and Medical Careers*
The McGraw-Hill Companies Inc.
PO Box 182604
Columbus, OH 43272
Ph: (212)512-2000
Free: 877-833-5524
Fax: (614)759-3749
E-mail: customer.service@mcgraw-hill.com
URL: http://www.mcgraw-hill.com
Description: I. Donald Snook, Jr. and Leo D'Orazio. 2004. $14.95 (paper). 157 pages. Covers the full range of medical and health occupations. Illustrated.

2212 ■ *Opportunities in Medical Imaging Careers*
The McGraw-Hill Companies Inc.
PO Box 182604
Columbus, OH 43272
Ph: (212)512-2000
Free: 877-833-5524
Fax: (614)759-3749
E-mail: customer.service@mcgraw-hill.com
URL: http://www.mcgraw-hill.com
Description: Clifford J. Sherry. 2006. $13.95. 160 pages.

2213 ■ *Resumes for Health and Medical Careers*
The McGraw-Hill Companies Inc.
PO Box 182604
Columbus, OH 43272
Ph: (212)512-2000
Free: 877-833-5524
Fax: (614)759-3749
E-mail: customer.service@mcgraw-hill.com
URL: http://www.mcgraw-hill.com
Description: Third edition, 2008. $12.95 (paper). 144 pages.

EMPLOYMENT AGENCIES AND SEARCH FIRMS

2214 ■ CHG Healthcare Services Inc.
6440 S Millrock Dr., Ste. 175
Salt Lake City, UT 84121-5892

Free: 800-466-0637
E-mail: info@chghealthcare.com
URL: http://www.chghealthcare.com
Description: Provides healthcare staffing and recruiting services covering certified registered nurse anesthetist, dosimetrist, imaging and radiation therapy, laboratory technology, medical physicist, nurse practitioner, nursing, pharmacy, physician, physician assistant, rehab therapy and respiratory therapy.

2215 ■ The Coelyn Group
1 Park Plz., Ste. 600
Irvine, CA 92614
Ph: (949)553-8855
Fax: (866)436-2171
E-mail: contact@coelyngroup.com
URL: http://www.coelyngroup.com
Description: Executive search firm.

2216 ■ Durakis Executive Search
PO Box 1523
Columbia, MD 21044
Ph: (410)740-7078
URL: http://www.durakis.com
Description: Executive search firm.

2217 ■ Flannery & Associates, LLC
N27 W23953 Paul Rd., Ste. 204
Pewaukee, WI 53072
Ph: (262)523-1206
Fax: (262)523-1873
E-mail: peter@flannerysearch.com
URL: http://flannerysearch.com
Description: Executive search firm.

ONLINE JOB SOURCES AND SERVICES

2218 ■ AgCareers.com
URL: http://www.agcareers.com
Description: Serves as an agriculture employment search engine. Supplies human resource services to the agriculture, food, natural resources and biotechnology industry.

2219 ■ BiosciRegister.com
URL: http://www.biosciregister.com
Description: Serves as an online directory or reference database of suppliers of products and services used in the biotechnology and life sciences industries. Contains job listings.

2220 ■ HEALTHeCAREERS Network
URL: http://www.healthecareers.com
Description: Career search site for jobs in all health care specialties; educational resources; visa and licensing information for relocation; interesting articles; relocation tools; links to professional organizations and general resources.

2221 ■ Hospital Jobs OnLine
URL: http://www.hospitaljobsonline.com
Description: Serves as a niche healthcare job board designed exclusively for hospitals, healthcare companies, and healthcare job seekers.

2222 ■ MedicalTechnologistsCentral.com
URL: http://www.medicaltechnologistscentral.com
Description: Offers medical technologist jobs and products in the healthcare industry.

2223 ■ MedTechJobsite.com
URL: http://www.medtechjobsite.com
Description: Provides new job openings for medical techs, in addition to insightful research into the healthcare and medical employment market, and a career articles section, written and frequented by industry professionals.

2224 ■ ProHealthJobs.com
URL: http://prohealthjobs.com/jobboard

Description: Career resources site for the medical and health care field. Lists professional opportunities, product information, continuing education and open positions.

2225 ■ TechniciansNow.com
URL: http://www.techniciansnow.com

Description: Provides an avenue to showcase jobs and products vital to the mechanical and technical trade communities.

TRADESHOWS

2226 ■ American Association of Blood Banks Annual Meeting and TXPO
American Association of Blood Banks
8101 Glenbrook Rd.
Bethesda, MD 20814-2749
Ph: (301)907-6977
Fax: (301)907-6895
E-mail: aabb@aabb.org
URL: http://www.aabb.org

Frequency: Annual. **Primary Exhibits:** Products related to blood banking and transfusion medicine: gloves, donor coaches, chairs, recruitment articles.

2227 ■ APIC Annual Meeting and Educational Conference
Association for Professionals in Infection Control and Epidemiology
1275 K St. NW, Ste. 1000
Washington, DC 20005-4006
Ph: (202)789-1890
Free: 800-650-9570
Fax: (202)789-1899
E-mail: apicinfo@apic.org
URL: http://www.apic.org

Frequency: Annual. **Primary Exhibits:** Pharmaceuticals, disinfectants, soaps, data processing software, sterilization devices, chemicals, housekeeping equipment and supplies, and related products.

OTHER SOURCES

2228 ■ Accrediting Bureau of Health Education Schools
7777 Leesburg Pike, Ste. 314 N
Falls Church, VA 22043
Ph: (703)917-9503
Fax: (703)917-4109
E-mail: info@abhes.org
URL: http://www.abhes.org

Description: Serves as a nationally recognized accrediting agency of health education institutions and schools conducting medical laboratory technician and medical assistant education programs. Establishes criteria and standards for the administration and operation of health education institutions. Seeks to enhance the profession through the improvement of schools, courses, and the competence of graduates. Schools must apply voluntarily for accreditation; once accredited, they must report to the bureau annually and be reexamined at least every 6 years. Has accredited 15 programs for medical laboratory technicians, 124 medical assistants, and 80 institutions of allied health.

2229 ■ American Association of Bioanalysts
906 Olive St., Ste. 1200
Saint Louis, MO 63101-1448
Ph: (314)241-1445
Fax: (314)241-1449
URL: http://www.aab.org

Description: Professional organization of directors, owners, managers, supervisors, technologists and technicians of bioanalytical clinical laboratories devoting their efforts to clinical laboratory procedure

and testing. Sponsors Proficiency Testing Service open to individuals engaged in the clinical laboratory field. Provides specialized education and representation before federal and state legislatures and regulatory agencies.

2230 ■ American Association for Clinical Chemistry
1850 K St. NW, Ste. 625
Washington, DC 20006
Free: 800-892-1400
Fax: (202)887-5093
E-mail: custserv@aacc.org
URL: http://www.aacc.org

Description: Clinical laboratory scientists and others engaged in the practice of clinical laboratory science in independent laboratories, hospitals, and allied institutions. Sponsors education programs; publishes books. **Members:** 9,000.

2231 ■ American Medical Technologists
10700 W Higgins Rd., Ste. 150
Rosemont, IL 60018
Ph: (847)823-5169
Free: 800-275-1268
Fax: (847)823-0458
E-mail: membership@amt1.com
URL: http://www.amt1.com

Description: Represents medical technologists, medical laboratory technicians, medical assistants, medical administrative specialists, dental assistants, office laboratory technicians, phlebotomy technicians, laboratory consultants, and allied health instructors. Provides allied health professionals with professional certification services and membership programs to enhance their professional and personal growth. Aims to issue certification credentials to medical and dental assistants, clinical laboratory personnel, laboratory consultants, and allied health instructors.

2232 ■ American Society for Clinical Laboratory Science
1861 International Dr., Ste. 200
McLean, VA 22102
Ph: (571)748-3770
E-mail: ascls@ascls.org
URL: http://www.ascls.org

Description: Primarily clinical laboratory personnel who have an associate or baccalaureate degree and clinical training and specialists who hold at least a master's degree in one of the major fields of clinical laboratory science such as bacteriology, mycology, or biochemistry; also includes technicians, specialists, and educators with limited certificates and students enrolled in approved programs of clinical laboratory studies and military medical technology schools. Promotes and maintains high standards in clinical laboratory methods and research and advances standards of education and training of personnel. Conducts educational program of seminars and workshops. Approves programs of continuing education and maintains records on participation in continuing education programs for members.

2233 ■ American Society of Cytopathology
100 W 10th St., Ste. 605
Wilmington, DE 19801-6604
Ph: (302)543-6583
Fax: (302)543-6597
E-mail: asc@cytopathology.org
URL: http://www.cytopathology.org

Description: Represents physicians, cytotechnologists, and scientists dedicated to the cytologic method of diagnostic pathology.

2234 ■ American Society of Plant Biologists
15501 Monona Dr.
Rockville, MD 20855-2768
Ph: (301)251-0560
Fax: (301)279-2996
E-mail: info@aspb.org
URL: http://my.aspb.org

Description: Professional society of plant biologists, plant biochemists, and other plant scientists engaged

in research and teaching. Offers placement service for members; conducts educational and public affairs programs.

2235 ■ *Career Opportunities in Forensic Science*
InfoBase Holdings Inc.
132 W 31st., 17 Fl.
New York, NY 10001-3406
Ph: (212)967-8800
Fax: (800)678-3633
E-mail: info@infobasepublishing.com
URL: http://www.ferguson.infobasepublishing.com

Description: 2008. $49.50. 336 pages. Includes a total of 82 job profiles in the field of forensic science. **Includes:** Appendices of educational institutions, certification programs, periodicals, directories, and associations. Appendices of educational institutions, certification programs, periodicals, directories, and associations.

2236 ■ *Career Opportunities in Health Care*
InfoBase Holdings Inc.
132 W 31st., 17 Fl.
New York, NY 10001-3406
Ph: (212)967-8800
Fax: (800)678-3633
E-mail: info@infobasepublishing.com
URL: http://www.ferguson.infobasepublishing.com

Description: Shelly Field. 2007. Third edition. $49.50. 304 pages. **Includes:** Appendices provide lists of educational institutions, periodicals, directories, associations, and unions. Appendices provide lists of educational institutions, periodicals, directories, associations, and unions.

2237 ■ *Career Opportunities in Science*
InfoBase Holdings Inc.
132 W 31st., 17 Fl.
New York, NY 10001-3406
Ph: (212)967-8800
Fax: (800)678-3633
E-mail: info@infobasepublishing.com
URL: http://factsonfile.infobasepublishing.com

Frequency: Latest edition 2008. **Price:** $49.50 Individuals hardcover. **Pages:** 344. **Description:** Susan Echaore-McDavid. Second edition, 2008. 332 pages. **Covers:** More than 80 jobs, such as biochemist, molecular biologist, bioinformatic specialist, pharmacologist, computer engineer, geographic information systems specialist, science teacher, forensic scientist, patent agent, as well as physicist, astronomer, chemist, zoologist, oceanographer, and geologist. **Includes:** Appendices of educational institutions, periodicals, directories, and associations.

2238 ■ Clinical Laboratory Management Association
330 N Wabash Ave., Ste. 2000
Chicago, IL 60611
Ph: (312)321-5111
Fax: (312)673-6927
E-mail: info@clma.org
URL: http://www.clma.org

Description: Semimonthly. Features general, health care, and laboratory management tips, trends, and legislative news. Recurring features include news of educational opportunities, job listings, and columns titled Manager's Workshop, Healthcare Management Briefs, Career Corner, Online Update and Legislative Update.

2239 ■ Commission on Accreditation of Allied Health Education Programs
1361 Park St.
Clearwater, FL 33756
Ph: (727)210-2350
Fax: (727)210-2354
E-mail: megivern@caahep.org
URL: http://www.caahep.org

Description: Serves as a nationally recognized accrediting agency for allied health programs in 23 occupational areas. **Members:** 80.

2240 ■ Endocrine Society
8401 Connecticut Ave., Ste. 900
Chevy Chase, MD 20815-5817
Ph: (301)941-0200

Free: 888-363-6274
Fax: (301)941-0259
E-mail: societyservices@endo-society.org
URL: http://www.endo-society.org

Description: Promotes excellence in research, education, and clinical practice in endocrinology and related disciplines. Maintains placement service.

SOURCES OF HELP-WANTED ADS

2241 ■ *Journal of Environmental Pathology, Toxicology and Oncology*
Begell House Inc.
50 Cross Hwy.
Redding, CT 06896
Ph: (203)938-1300
Fax: (203)938-1304
E-mail: orders@begellhouse.com
URL: http://www.begellhouse.com/journals/0ff459a57a4c08d0

Price: $1,005 Institutions. **Description:** Journal covering research and reviews of factors and conditions that affect human and animal carcinogenesis.

HANDBOOKS AND MANUALS

2242 ■ *Career Opportunities in Biotechnology and Drug Development*
Cold Spring Harbor Laboratory Press
500 Sunnyside Blvd.
Woodbury, NY 11797-2924
Ph: (516)422-4101
Free: 800-843-4388
Fax: (516)422-4097
E-mail: cshpress@cshl.org
URL: http://www.cshlpress.com

Description: Toby Freedman. 2009. $59.00 (hardcover). 409 pages. Provides an overview of careers in the life science industry. Features chapters that includes sections on preparing for a prospective career; educational requirements and personality characteristics needed; recommendations of books, magazines, and web site resources; and issues to consider regarding salary and compensation. Includes interviewing and job searching tips, as well as suggestions on writing a resume specifically for the industry.

EMPLOYMENT AGENCIES AND SEARCH FIRMS

2243 ■ **PMD Research, Inc.**
PO Box 61231
Raleigh, NC 27661-1231
Fax: (919)877-9937
E-mail: info@pmdresearch.com
URL: http://www.pmdresearch.com

Description: Maintains an extensive network between experienced clinical research professionals and the business systems that match career opportunities.

OTHER SOURCES

2244 ■ **International Cellular Medicine Society**
PO Box 371034
Las Vegas, NV 89137
Ph: (702)664-0017
Fax: (866)878-7717
E-mail: rdavis@cellmedicinesociety.com
URL: http://www.cellmedicinesociety.org

Description: Aims to advance the field of adult cell based medicine through developing international best practice standards that ensure patient safety, facilitate physician education, and provide peer oversight. Strives to provide unbiased, objective information regarding the medical use of autologous adult stem cells.

2245 ■ **International Society for Cardiovascular Translational Research**
3420 S Mercy Rd., Ste. 312
Gilbert, AZ 85297
Ph: (858)774-0206
E-mail: ndib@isctr.org
URL: http://www.isctr.org

Description: Strives to provide an environment for collaboration and guidance among basic and clinical scientists. Promotes research and development of guidelines for training and certification in translational research. Influences health care policy and educates the public about discoveries in cardiovascular translational research.

2246 ■ **International Society of Gastrointestinal Oncology**
200 Broadhollow Rd., Ste. 207
Melville, NY 11747
Ph: (631)390-8390
Fax: (631)393-5026
E-mail: malcolm.moore@uhn.ca
URL: http://www.isgio.org

Description: Facilitates gastrointestinal cancer research and education. Promotes dissemination of new gastrointestinal oncology-related knowledge and discovery. Provides a platform to build international and regional consensuses on therapy and research in gastrointestinal oncology.

2247 ■ **Society for Heart Brain Medicine**
9500 Euclid Ave.
Mail Code JJ40
Cleveland, OH 44195
Ph: (216)636-2424
Fax: (216)636-0271
E-mail: info@heartbrain.org

Description: Educates clinicians and scientists about the physiology, pathophysiology and medical aspects of heart-brain interactions. Promotes and fosters research into the heart-brain relationship. Educates the public about the physiology, pathophysiology and medical aspects of heart-brain interactions.

2248 ■ **Society for Translational Oncology**
318 Blackwell St., Ste. 270
Durham, NC 27701
Ph: (919)433-0489
E-mail: admin@sto-online.org
URL: http://sto-online.org

Description: Aims to speed up the discovery and translation of treatments in the field of cancer medicine. Brings knowledge and strategies for critical new developments in cancer treatment to the practice of the community oncologist. Provides educational activities to improve physician competencies and strategies for screening, prevention, diagnosis, treatment and management of patients with cancer.

SOURCES OF HELP-WANTED ADS

2249 ■ *AATSEEL Newsletter*
American Association of Teachers of Slavic and East European Languages
PO Box 1116
San Juan Bautista, CA 95045-1116
Ph: (831)578-0290
Fax: (831)886-2486
URL: http://www.aatseel.org
Description: 4/academic year. Carries articles of interest to teachers of Slavic languages. Reports on study programs, teaching innovations, and Association news. Recurring features include news of members, notices of employment opportunities, a calendar of events, reviews of materials, and columns titled Chapter Minutes, Computer Information, Communicative Corner, and Russian Language Features.

2250 ■ *About Campus*
John Wiley & Sons Inc.
111 River St.
Hoboken, NJ 07030-5774
Ph: (201)748-6000
Free: 800-225-5945
Fax: (201)748-6088
E-mail: info@wiley.com
URL: http://onlinelibrary.wiley.com/journal/10.1002/ (ISSN)1536-0687
Frequency: Bimonthly. **Price:** $219 Institutions print only; $279 Institutions, Canada and Mexico print only; $330 Institutions, other countries print only; $60 U.S., Canada, and Mexico print only; $96 Other countries print only. **Description:** Journal focused on the critical issues faced by both student affairs and academic affairs staff as they work on helping students learn.

2251 ■ *Academician Magazine*
National Association of State Approved Colleges and Universities
808 17th St. NW, Ste. 410
Washington, DC 20006
Ph: (202)293-0090
URL: http://www.nasadad.com
Frequency: Monthly. **Description:** Magazine covering higher education.

2252 ■ *American Academic*
American Federation of Teachers
555 New Jersey Ave. NW
Washington, DC 20001
Ph: (202)879-4400
URL: http://www.aft.org/pubs-reports/american_academic/index.htm
Description: Higher education policy journal.

2253 ■ *American School & University: Shaping Facilities & Business Decisions*
Penton
9800 Metcalf Ave.
Overland Park, KS 66212
Ph: (913)341-1300
Free: 866-748-4926
Fax: (913)967-1905
E-mail: corporatecustomerservice@penton.com
URLs: http://asumag.com/; http://www.schooldesigns.com
Frequency: Monthly. **Description:** Trade magazine.

2254 ■ *Annals of Medicine*
Informa Healthcare
52 Vanderbilt Ave., 7th Fl.
New York, NY 10017-3846
Ph: (212)520-2777
E-mail: healthcare.enquiries@informa.com
URL: http://informahealthcare.com/ann
Frequency: 4/yr. **Price:** £961 Institutions; $1,579 Institutions; €1,259 Institutions. **Description:** Journal covering health science and medical education.

2255 ■ *Change: The Magazine of Higher Learning*
Heldref Publications
325 Chestnut St., Ste. 800
Philadelphia, PA 19106
Ph: (215)625-8900
Free: 800-354-1420
E-mail: ch@heldref.org
URL: http://www.heldref.org/change.php
Frequency: Bimonthly. **Price:** €52 Individuals print only; £39 Institutions print only; $64 Individuals print and online; $207 Institutions print and online. **Description:** Magazine dealing with contemporary issues in higher learning.

2256 ■ *The Chronicle of Higher Education*
The Chronicle of Higher Education
1255 23rd St. NW, Ste. 700
Washington, DC 20037
Ph: (202)466-1000
Free: 800-728-2803
Fax: (202)452-1033
E-mail: editor@chronicle.com
URL: http://chronicle.com
Frequency: Weekly. **Price:** $82.50 Individuals 43 issues; $45 Individuals 21 issues; $140 Individuals 86 issues. **Description:** Higher education magazine (tabloid).

2257 ■ *Collegiate Aviation News Newsletter*
University Aviation Association
2415 Moore's Mill Rd., Ste. 265-216
Auburn, AL 36830-6444
Ph: (334)844-2434
Fax: (334)844-2432
E-mail: uaamail@uaa.aero
URL: http://www.uaa.aero/
Description: Quarterly. $42/yr. for non-members. Provides information on Association activities and projects, events of other aviation organizations that bear on higher education, and the future impact of collegiate aviation education. Recurring features include feature articles on outstanding individual and

institutional members, statistics, a calendar of events, news of members, news of research, an editorial, letters to the editor, book reviews, employment information, and the president's report.

2258 ■ *Columbia Journalism Review*
Columbia Journalism Review
2950 Broadway, Journalism Bldg.
Columbia University
New York, NY 10027
Ph: (212)854-1881
Fax: (212)854-8367
E-mail: letters@cjr.org
URL: http://www.cjr.org/
Frequency: Bimonthly. **Price:** $19.95 Individuals; $27.95 Other countries. **Description:** Magazine focusing on journalism.

2259 ■ *Community Colleges Journal*
American Association of Community Colleges
1 Dupont Cir. NW, Ste. 410
Washington, DC 20036-1145
Ph: (202)728-0200
Fax: (202)833-2467
E-mail: aaccpub@pmds.com
URL: http://www.aacc.nche.edu/Publications/CCJ/Pages/default.aspx
Frequency: 6/yr. **Price:** $36 Nonmembers; $36 Members. **Description:** Educational magazine.

2260 ■ *Connections*
Association of Jesuit Colleges and Universities
One Dupont Cir., Ste. 405
Washington, DC 20036
Ph: (202)862-9893
Fax: (202)862-8523
E-mail: dhowes@ajcunet.edu
URL: http://www.ajcunet.edu
Description: Monthly, except June, July and August. Furnishes information on legislative action affecting higher education and on Jesuit colleges and universities in the U.S. Recurring features include news of research, calendar of events, reports of meetings, notices of publications available, and columns titled Federal Relations, New Programs, and News from the Campuses. Only available online.

2261 ■ *Education & Treatment of Children*
West Virginia University Press
139 Stansbury Hall
Morgantown, WV 26506
Ph: (304)293-8400
Fax: (304)293-6585
E-mail: press@wvu.edu
URLs: http://wvupressonline.com/journals; http://www.educationandtreatmentofchildren.net
Frequency: Quarterly. **Price:** $100 Institutions; $50 Individuals; $115 Institutions elsewhere; $65 Individuals elsewhere. **Description:** Periodical featuring information concerning the development of services for children and youth. Includes reports written for educators and other child care and mental health

providers focused on teaching, training, and treatment effectiveness.

2262 ■ Educational Researcher
American Educational Research Association
1430 K St. NW, Ste. 1200
Washington, DC 20005-2504
Ph: (202)238-3200
Fax: (202)238-3250
E-mail: webmaster@aera.net
URL: http://www.aera.net/Publications/Journals/iEducationalResearcheri/tabid/12609/Default.aspx
Frequency: Monthly; 9/year. **Price:** $48 Individuals plus foreign mailing charges; $150 Institutions plus foreign mailing charges; $50/year for individuals; $309/year for institutions. **Description:** Educational research journal.

2263 ■ Environmental Education Research
Routledge Journals - Taylor & Francis Group
270 Madison Ave.
New York, NY 10016-0601
Ph: (212)216-7800
Fax: (212)563-2269
URL: http://www.tandfonline.com/toc/ceer20/current
Frequency: 6/year. **Price:** $1,594 Institutions print + online; $1,395 Institutions online only; $424 Individuals print only. **Description:** Journal covering all aspects of environmental education.

2264 ■ Essays in Education
University of South Carolina
471 University Pky.
Aiken, SC 29801
Ph: (803)648-6851
E-mail: info@sc.edu
URL: http://www.usca.edu/essays/
Frequency: Monthly. **Description:** Journal covering issues that impact and influence education.

2265 ■ The International Electronic Journal of Health Education
American Alliance for Health, Physical Education, Recreation and Dance
1900 Association Dr.
Reston, VA 20191-1598
Ph: (703)476-3400
Free: 800-213-7193
Fax: (703)476-9527
E-mail: membership@aahperd.org
URL: http://www.aahperd.org/aahe/publications/iejhe/
Frequency: Annual. **Price:** Free. **Description:** Journal promoting health through education and other systematic strategies.

2266 ■ International Journal of Early Years Education
Routledge Journals - Taylor & Francis Group
270 Madison Ave.
New York, NY 10016-0601
Ph: (212)216-7800
Fax: (212)563-2269
URL: http://www.tandfonline.com/toc/ciey20/current
Frequency: 4/yr. **Price:** $795 Institutions online only; $908 Institutions print + online; $314 Individuals print only. **Description:** Journal focusing on education world-wide.

2267 ■ International Journal of Inclusive Education
Routledge Journals - Taylor & Francis Group
270 Madison Ave.
New York, NY 10016-0601
Ph: (212)216-7800
Fax: (212)563-2269
URL: http://www.tandfonline.com/toc/tied20/current
Frequency: 10/yr. **Price:** $722 Individuals print only; $1,353 Institutions online only; $1,546 Individuals print + online. **Description:** Journal providing information on the nature of schools, universities and technical colleges for the educators and educational policy-makers.

2268 ■ International Journal of Leadership in Education
Routledge
c/o Duncan Waite, PhD, Ed.
Texas State University
601 University Dr.
San Marcos, TX 78666
Ph: (512)245-8918
E-mail: ijle@txstate.edu
URL: http://www.tandfonline.com/toc/tedl20/current
Frequency: Quarterly. **Price:** $277 Individuals print only; $690 Institutions online only; $788 Institutions print and online; £408 Institutions print and online; £367 Institutions online only; £142 Individuals print only. **Description:** Journal dealing with leadership in education.

2269 ■ International Journal of Whole Schooling
Whole Schooling Press
Wayne State University
217 Education
Detroit, MI 48202
Ph: (313)577-1607
E-mail: wholeschooling@twmi.rr.com
URL: http://www.wholeschooling.net/Journal_of_Whole_Schooling/IJWSIndex.html
Price: Free. **Description:** International, refereed academic journal dedicated to exploring ways to improve learning and schooling for all children.

2270 ■ Journal of Cases in Educational Leadership
Pine Forge Press
2455 Teller Rd.
Thousand Oaks, CA 91320-2234
Ph: (805)499-4224
Free: 800-818-7243
Fax: (805)499-0871
E-mail: sales@pfp.sagepub.com
URLs: http://jel.sagepub.com; http://www.sagepub.com/journals/Journal201765
Frequency: Quarterly. **Price:** $479 Institutions online; $103 Individuals online. **Description:** Journal covering cases appropriate for use in programs that prepare educational leaders.

2271 ■ Journal of College Teaching & Learning
The Clute Institute for Academic Research
6901 S Pierce St., Ste. 239
Littleton, CO 80128
Ph: (303)904-4750
Fax: (303)259-2420
E-mail: staff@cluteinstitute.com
URL: http://journals.cluteonline.com/index.php/TLC
Frequency: Monthly. **Price:** $495 Institutions with airmail postage. **Description:** Refereed academic journal covering all areas of college level teaching, learning and administration.

2272 ■ Journal of Curriculum and Supervision
Association for Supervision and Curriculum Development
1703 N Beauregard St.
Alexandria, VA 22311-1714
Ph: (703)578-9600
Free: 800-933-2723
Fax: (703)575-5400
URL: http://www.ascd.org/publications/jcs/fall2002/On_Community.aspx
Frequency: Quarterly. **Price:** $39/year for members; $49/year for nonmembers. **Description:** Includes abstracts of selected doctoral dissertations.

2273 ■ Journal of Higher Education Outreach and Engagement
University of Georgia - Institute of Higher Education
Meigs Hall
Athens, GA 30602
Ph: (706)542-3464

Fax: (706)542-7588
E-mail: ihe@uga.edu
URL: http://openjournals.libs.uga.edu/index.php/jheoe/
Frequency: Semiannual; Quarterly. **Price:** $60 Individuals; $95 Other countries; $30 Students; $65 Students, other countries; $100 Institutions; $199 Institutions, other countries. **Description:** Journal covering higher education outreach and engagement for scholars, practitioners, and professionals.

2274 ■ Journal of Language, Identity, and Education
Routledge Journals - Taylor & Francis Group
270 Madison Ave.
New York, NY 10016-0601
Ph: (212)216-7800
Fax: (212)563-2269
URL: http://www.tandfonline.com/toc/hlie20/current
Frequency: 5/yr. **Price:** $611 Institutions print + online; $535 Institutions online only; $84 Individuals print + online. **Description:** Scholarly, interdisciplinary journal covering issues in language, identity and education worldwide for academics, educators and policy specialists in a variety of disciplines, and others.

2275 ■ Journal of Latinos and Education
Routledge Journals - Taylor & Francis Group
c/o Enrique G. Murillo, Jr., Editor
California State University
College of Education
Center for Equity in Education, 5500 University Pky.
San Bernardino, CA 92407-2397
Ph: (212)216-7800
Fax: (212)563-2269
URL: http://www.tandf.co.uk/journals/titles/15348431.asp
Frequency: Quarterly. **Price:** $557 Institutions print + online; $487 Institutions online only. **Description:** Scholarly, multidisciplinary journal covering educational issues that impact Latinos for researchers, teaching professionals, academics, scholars, institutions, and others.

2276 ■ Journal of STEM Education: Innovations and Research
Auburn University
9088 Haley Ctr.
Auburn, AL 36849
Ph: (334)844-9088
Fax: (334)844-9027
URL: http://ojs.jstem.org/index.php?journal=JSTEM
Frequency: Semiannual. **Description:** Journal for educators in Science, Technology, Engineering, and Mathematics (STEM) education.

2277 ■ Leadership and Policy in Schools
Routledge Journals - Taylor & Francis Group
270 Madison Ave.
New York, NY 10016-0601
Ph: (212)216-7800
Fax: (212)563-2269
URL: http://www.tandfonline.com/toc/nlps20/current
Frequency: Quarterly. **Price:** $658 Institutions print and online; $304 Individuals print only; $576 Institutions online only. **Description:** Journal providing information about leadership and policy in primary and secondary education.

2278 ■ NAIA News
National Association of Intercollegiate Athletics
1200 Grand Blvd.
Kansas City, MO 64106
Ph: (816)595-8000
Fax: (816)595-8200
E-mail: info@naia.org
URL: http://naia.cstv.com
Frequency: Daily. **Description:** Daily. Provides news and information on the Association, which strives to "develop intercollegiate athletic programs as an integral part of the total educational program of the college rather than as a separate commercial or

promotional adjunct." Aims toward uniformity and equity in policies and practices. Recurring features include news of members and events, notices of awards, and job listings.

2279 ■ NewsNet, the Newsletter of the ASEEES
Association for Slavic, East European, and Eurasian Studies
University of Pittsburgh
203C Bellefield Hall
Pittsburgh, PA 15260-6424
Ph: (412)648-9911
Fax: (412)648-9815
E-mail: aseees@pitt.edu
URL: http://www.aseees.org
Description: Bimonthly. Reports on Association activities and on Slavic study research in institutions throughout the world. Alerts readers to research grants, internships, and fellowship opportunities as well as to employment opportunities in universities across the country. Announces awards, upcoming conferences, courses, new scholarly publications, and annual research.

2280 ■ OECD Observer
Organisation for Economic Co-operation and Development - Publications and Information Center
2001 L St. NW, Ste. 650
Washington, DC 20036-4922
Ph: (202)785-6323
Free: 800-456-6323
Fax: (202)785-0350
E-mail: observer@oecd.org
URLs: http://www.oecdobserver.org; http://www.oecd-bookshop.org/oecd/display.asp?k=sub
-01011s1&CID=&LANG=EN&ds= theoecdobserver
Price: $101 Individuals print + online; €73 Individuals print + online; £57 Individuals print + online; ¥9,500 Individuals print + online. **Description:** Magazine on economic affairs, science, and technology.

2281 ■ Oxford Review of Education
Routledge Journals - Taylor & Francis Group
270 Madison Ave.
New York, NY 10016-0601
Ph: (212)216-7800
Fax: (212)563-2269
URL: http://www.tandfonline.com/toc/core20/current
Frequency: 6/yr. **Price:** $529 Individuals print only; $1,243 Institutions online only; $1,420 Institutions print and online. **Description:** Journal covering advance study of education.

2282 ■ The Physics Teacher
American Association of Physics Teachers
Dept. of Physics & Astronomy
Appalachian State University
Boone, NC 28608-2142
Ph: (301)209-3311
Fax: (301)209-0845
E-mail: webmaster@aapt.org
URLs: http://tpt.aapt.org; http://www.aapt.org/Publications/
Frequency: 9/yr. **Price:** $628 Nonmembers domestic; $688 Nonmembers international. **Description:** Scientific education magazine.

2283 ■ School Effectiveness and School Improvement: An International Journal of Research, Policy and Practice
Routledge
711 3rd Ave., 8th Fl.
New York, NY 10017
Ph: (212)216-7800
Free: 800-634-7064
Fax: (212)564-7854
E-mail: book.orders@tandf.co.uk
URL: http://www.tandf.co.uk/journals/titles/09243453.asp
Frequency: Quarterly. **Price:** £387 Institutions print and online; £348 Institutions online only; £186 Individuals print only; $660 Institutions print and on-

line; $594 Institutions online only; $312 Individuals print only. **Description:** Journal focusing on educational progress of all students.

2284 ■ Teaching and Learning in Nursing
Elsevier Science Inc.
Secondary Publishing Division
650 Ave. of the Americas
New York, NY 10011
Ph: (212)633-3980
Free: 888-437-4636
Fax: (212)633-3975
URL: http://www.jtln.org
Frequency: Quarterly; Monthly. **Price:** $99 Individuals U.S.; $145 Individuals Mexico, Canada, other countries, print and online .**Description:** Includes articles concerning advancement of Associate Degree Nursing education and practice.

2285 ■ Technology and Engineering Teacher: The Voice of Technology Education
International Technology and Engineering Educators Association
1914 Association Dr., Ste. 201
Reston, VA 20191-1539
Ph: (703)860-2100
Fax: (703)860-0353
E-mail: iteea@iteea.org
URL: http://www.iteaconnect.org/Publications/ttt.htm
Frequency: 8/yr. **Price:** $35 Individuals professional U.S., 2 years; $70 Individuals professional U.S.; $30 Students undergrad student- first time member; $35 Students full-time grad/renewing undergrad student; $55 Students bridge - one-time student to professional; $410 Institutions group membership, 2 years; $210 Institutions group membership; $690 Individuals group membership, 2 years; $350 Individuals group membership; $270 Individuals group membership, 2 years. **Description:** Magazine on technology education.

2286 ■ Theory and Research in Education
Pine Forge Press
2455 Teller Rd.
Thousand Oaks, CA 91320-2234
Ph: (805)499-4224
Free: 800-818-7243
Fax: (805)499-0871
E-mail: sales@pfp.sagepub.com
URL: http://www.sagepub.com/journalsProdDesc.nav?prodId=Journal201652
Frequency: 3/year. **Price:** $635 Institutions print and online; $572 Institutions online; $622 Institutions print; $91 Individuals print; $228 Institutions single print issue; $39 Individuals single print issue. **Description:** Interdisciplinary journal covering normative and theoretical issues concerning education including multi-faceted philosophical analysis of moral, social, political and epistemological problems and issues arising from educational practice.

2287 ■ Weatherwise: The Magazine About the Weather
Routledge
711 3rd Ave., 8th Fl.
New York, NY 10017
Ph: (212)216-7800
Free: 800-634-7064
Fax: (212)564-7854
E-mail: book.orders@tandf.co.uk
URLs: http://www.weatherwise.org/; http://www.tand-fonline.com/loi/vwws20?open=35
Frequency: Bimonthly. **Price:** $48 Individuals print and online; $162 Institutions print and online; $162 Institutions print only. **Description:** Popular weather magazine for students, teachers, and professionals.

2288 ■ Wisconsin Lawyer
State Bar of Wisconsin
PO Box 7158
Madison, WI 53707-7158
Ph: (608)257-3838
Free: 800-728-7788

Fax: (608)257-5502
E-mail: wislawyer@wisbar.org
URL: http://www.wisbar.org/AM/Template.cfm?Section=Wisconsin_Lawyer
Frequency: Monthly. **Price:** $35 Members; $53 Nonmembers; $3.50 Single issue. **Description:** Official monthly publication of the State Bar of Wisconsin.

EMPLOYER DIRECTORIES AND NETWORKING LISTS

2289 ■ Accredited Institutions of Postsecondary Education: Programs - Candidates
Greenwood Electronic Media
c/o ABC-CLIO
130 Cremona Dr.
Santa Barbara, CA 93117
Ph: (805)968-1911
Free: 800-368-6868
Fax: (866)270-3856
E-mail: customerservice@abc-clio.com
URL: http://www.abc-clio.com/series.aspx?id=51746
Frequency: Annual; latest edition 2006. **Price:** $89.95 Individuals list price; £49.95 Individuals. **Pages:** 984. **Covers:** More than 7,000 accredited institutions and programs of postsecondary education in the United States and U.S. -chartered schools in 14 countries. **Includes:** Section listing the public systems of higher education in each of the 50 states, featuring central administrative office and all branches. **Entries include:** Institution name, address, phone, whether public or private, any religious affiliation, type of institution and student body, branch campuses or affiliated institutions, date of first accreditation and latest reaffirmation of accrediting body, accredited programs in professional fields, level of degrees offered, name of chief executive officer, size and composition of enrollment, type of academic calendar. **Arrangement:** Geographical. **Indexes:** Institution.

2290 ■ Association of American University Presses--Directory
Association of American University Presses
28 W 36th St., Ste. 602
New York, NY 10018
Ph: (212)989-1010
Fax: (212)989-0275
E-mail: info@aaupnet.org
URL: http://www.aaupnet.org
Frequency: Annual; Latest edition 2012. **Price:** $30 Individuals. **Pages:** 230. **Covers:** 124 presses and affiliates worldwide. **Entries include:** Press name, address, phone, e-mail, URL; titles and names of complete editorial and managerial staffs; editorial program; mailing, warehouse, printing, and/or customer service addresses; other details. **Arrangement:** Classified by press affiliation, alphabetical by press name. **Indexes:** Personal name.

2291 ■ Chronicle Four-Year College Databook
Chronicle Guidance Publications Inc.
66 Aurora St.
Moravia, NY 13118-3569
Ph: (315)497-0330
Free: 800-899-0454
Fax: (315)497-0339
E-mail: CustomerService@ChronicleGuidance.com
URL: http://www.chronicleguidance.com
Frequency: Annual; latest edition 2009-2010. **Price:** $26.75 Individuals softbound. **Pages:** 644. **Covers:** More than 825 baccalaureate, master's, doctoral, and first professional programs offered by more than 2,528 colleges and universities in the United States. **Includes:** College admissions information. **Entries include:** College charts section gives college name, address, phone; accreditation, enrollment, admissions, costs, financial aid; accreditation associations' names, addresses, and phone numbers. Appendices

gives details on admissions and other information special to each college. **Arrangement:** Part I, classified by college major; part II, geographical. **Indexes:** College name.

2292 ■ *Employment Information in the Mathematical Sciences*
American Mathematical Society
201 Charles St.
Providence, RI 02904-2294
Ph: (401)455-4000
Free: 800-321-4267
Fax: (401)331-3842
E-mail: eims-info@ams.org
URL: http://www.ams.org/profession/employment
-services/eims/eims-home

Frequency: Five times a year. **Price:** $190 Individuals list price; $114 Individuals. **Covers:** Colleges and universities with departments in the mathematical sciences, and non-academic and foreign organizations with employment openings. **Entries include:** For departments--Name, address, name and title of contact; job title, job description, salary (if applicable). **Arrangement:** Classified as academic or nonacademic, then geographical.

2293 ■ *Fulbright Scholar Program Grants for U.S. Faculty and Professionals*
Institute of International Education - Council for International Exchange of Scholars
1400 K St. NW, Ste. 700
Washington, DC 20005
Ph: (202)686-4000
Fax: (202)686-4029
E-mail: scholars@iie.org
URL: http://www.cies.org/

Frequency: Annual; March. **Price:** Free. **Pages:** 160. **Covers:** about 800 grants available for postdoctoral university lecturing and advanced research by American citizens in more than 140 countries. **Entries include:** Periods in which grants are tenable; number of grants available for the country; language or other requirement; fields in which lectures and research are desired; stipend, housing; additional income for dependents, applications and reference forms. **Arrangement:** Geographical. **Indexes:** Professional, discipline.

2294 ■ *Higher Education Directory*
Higher Education Publications Inc.
1801 Robert Fulton Dr., Ste. 555
Reston, VA 20191-4387
Ph: (571)313-0478
Free: 888-349-7715
Fax: (571)313-0526
E-mail: info@hepinc.com
URL: http://www.hepinc.com

Frequency: Annual; latest edition 2011. **Price:** $75 Individuals includes shipping and handling. **Pages:** 1,104. **Covers:** Over 4,364 degree granting colleges and universities accredited by approved agencies recognized by the U.S. Secretary of Education and by the Council of Higher Education Accreditation (CHEA); 103 systems offices; over 550 related associations and state government agencies; recognized accrediting agencies. **Entries include:** For institutions--Name, address, congressional district, phone, fax, year established; Carnegie classification; enrollment; type of student body; religious or other affiliation; undergraduate tuition and fees; type of academic calendar; highest degree offered; accreditations; IRS status; names, titles and job classification codes for academic and administrative officers. For associations and state agencies--Name, address, phone, name of chief executive officer. Same content and coverage as the base volume of the Department of Education's publication "Directory of Postsecondary Institutions" (see separate entry). **Arrangement:** Geographical, alphabetical by state. **Indexes:** Administrator name (with phone and e-mail addresses), accreditation, FICE numbers, college or university name.

2295 ■ *Mathematical Sciences Professional Directory*
American Mathematical Society
201 Charles St.
Providence, RI 02904-2294
Ph: (401)455-4000
Free: 800-321-4267
Fax: (401)331-3842
E-mail: cust-serv@ams.org
URLs: http://www.ams.org; http://www.ams.org/no-
tices/200807/tx080700873p.pdf; http://www.ams
.org/profession/profdir/profdir

Frequency: Annual; Latest edition 2010. **Price:** $44 Institutions; $55 Individuals softcover. **Covers:** 37 professional organizations concerned with mathematics, government agencies, academic institutions with department in the mathematical sciences, nonacademic organizations, and individuals. **Entries include:** For professional organizations and government agencies--Name, address, names and titles of key personnel. For institutions--Name, address; name, title, and address of department chair. **Arrangement:** Classified by type of organization; institutions are then geographical; others, alphabetical. **Indexes:** University or college name.

2296 ■ *Modern Language Association of America--Job Information List*
Modern Language Association of America
26 Broadway, 3rd Fl.
New York, NY 10004-1789
Ph: (646)576-5000
Fax: (646)458-0030
E-mail: jileditor@mla.org
URL: http://www.mla.org/jil

Frequency: Quarterly; February, April, October, and December. **Covers:** Available positions for college teachers of English and foreign languages in four-year colleges and universities; February issue includes separate section of openings in two-year institutions. Separate editions for English and American language and literature and for foreign language openings. **Entries include:** Department chair statement, including institution name; contact name, address, phone; definite or possible openings; related information for job seekers (change in deadline date, or job description, notice of a vacancy filled, etc.). **Arrangement:** First section--Statements of department chairmen. Second section (in October and February only)--List of departments reporting no vacancies.

2297 ■ *National Directory of College Athletics: The Yellow Pages of College Sports*
Collegiate Directories Inc.
PO Box 450640
Cleveland, OH 44145
Ph: (440)835-1172
Free: 800-426-2232
Fax: (440)835-8835
E-mail: info@collegiatedirectories.com
URL: http://www.collegiatedirectories.com/

Frequency: Annual; Latest edition 2013-2014. **Price:** $54.95 Individuals plus 6 shipping and handling; $29.95 Online. **Description:** Athletic departments of 2,100 senior and junior colleges in the United States and Canada. **Covers:** Athletic departments of 2,100 senior and junior colleges in the United States and Canada. **Entries include:** School name, address, enrollment, colors, team nicknames, stadium and/or gym capacity; names of president, men's athletic director, athletic administrative staff, physical education director and coaches for each sport; athletic department phones, faxes, etc.; association affiliations. **Arrangement:** Alphabetical. **Indexes:** Schools by program and division; Alphabetical by advertisers and products.

2298 ■ *National Faculty Directory*
Cengage Learning Inc.
200 1st Stamford Pl., Ste. 400
Stamford, CT 06902-6753
Ph: (203)965-8600

Free: 800-354-9706
Fax: (800)487-8488
E-mail: investors@cengage.com
URL: http://www.gale.cengage.com

Frequency: Annual; Latest edition 43rd; October, 2011. **Price:** $1,391 Individuals. **Covers:** More than 900,000 (60,000 more in supplement) teaching faculty members at over 4,600 junior colleges, colleges, and universities in the United States and those in Canada that give instruction in English. **Includes:** Geographical list of schools covered. **Entries include:** Name, department name, institution, address, and phone and fax numbers. Directory combines main edition and supplement. **Arrangement:** Alphabetical.

2299 ■ *Patterson's Schools Classified*
Educational Directories Inc.
PO Box 68097
Schaumburg, IL 60168-0097
Ph: (847)891-1250
Free: 800-357-6183
Fax: (847)891-0945
E-mail: info@ediusa.com
URL: http://www.ediusa.com

Frequency: Annual; Latest edition 2011. **Price:** $23 Individuals plus $7 shipping charges. **Pages:** 258. **Covers:** Over 6,000 accredited colleges, universities, community colleges, junior colleges, career schools and teaching hospitals. **Entries include:** School name, address, phone, URL, e-mail, name of administrator or admissions officer, description, professional accreditation (where applicable). Updated from previous year's edition of 'Patterson's American Education' (see separate entry). **Arrangement:** Classified by area of study, then geographical by state. **Indexes:** Alphabetical by name.

2300 ■ *School Guide*
School Guide Publications
210 North Ave.
New Rochelle, NY 10801
Ph: (914)632-7771
Free: 800-433-7771
E-mail: mridder@schoolguides.com
URL: http://distance.schoolguides.com

Frequency: Annual; Latest edition 2008. **Pages:** 290. **Covers:** Over 3,000 colleges, vocational schools, and nursing schools in the United States. **Entries include:** Institution name, address, phone, courses offered, degrees awarded. **Arrangement:** Classified by type of institution, then geographical. **Indexes:** Subject.

2301 ■ *Who's Who in American Law*
Marquis Who's Who L.L.C.
300 Connell Dr., Ste. 2000
Berkeley Heights, NJ 07922
Ph: (908)673-1000
Free: 800-473-7020
Fax: (908)673-1179
E-mail: law@marquiswhoswho.com
URL: http://www.marquiswhoswho.com

Frequency: Biennial; Latest edition 17th; 20011-2012. **Price:** $365 Individuals. **Pages:** 1,138. **Covers:** Over 19,000 lawyers, judges, law school deans and professors, and other legal professionals. **Entries include:** Name, home and office addresses, place and date of birth, educational background, career history, civic positions, professional memberships, publications, awards, special achievements. **Arrangement:** Alphabetical. **Indexes:** Fields of practice, professional area.

HANDBOOKS AND MANUALS

2302 ■ *Academic Job Search Handbook*
University of Pennsylvania Press
3905 Spruce St.
Philadelphia, PA 19104-4112
Ph: (215)898-6261
Free: 800-573-5487

Fax: (215)898-0404
E-mail: custserv@pobox.upenn.edu
URL: http://www.upenn.edu/pennpress

Description: Julia Miller Vick and Jennifer S. Furlong. 2008. $18.95 (paper). 296 pages. Includes information on aspects of the search that are common to all levels, with tips for those seeking their first or second faculty position. Provides advice and addresses topics in the job market, including the challenges faced by dual-career couples, job search issues for pregnant candidates, and advice on how to deal with gaps in a CV.

2303 ■ Educational Pathways: A Faculty Development Resource
Cengage Learning Inc.
200 1st Stamford Pl., Ste. 400
Stamford, CT 06902-6753
Ph: (203)965-8600
Free: 800-354-9706
Fax: (800)487-8488
E-mail: investors@cengage.com
URL: http://www.cengage.com

Description: Kathryn Kalanick. 2007. $73.49. 368 pages. Provides a three-track approach to address the training needs of instructors and educators by following the experiences of three educators from various backgrounds.

2304 ■ Great Jobs for English Majors
The McGraw-Hill Companies Inc.
PO Box 182604
Columbus, OH 43272
Ph: (212)512-2000
Free: 877-833-5524
Fax: (614)759-3749
E-mail: customer.service@mcgraw-hill.com
URL: http://www.mcgraw-hill.com

Description: Julie DeGalan and Stephen Lambert. Third edition, 2006. $15.95 (paper). 192 pages.

2305 ■ Great Jobs for History Majors
The McGraw-Hill Companies Inc.
PO Box 182604
Columbus, OH 43272
Ph: (212)512-2000
Free: 877-833-5524
Fax: (614)759-3749
E-mail: customer.service@mcgraw-hill.com
URL: http://www.mcgraw-hill.com

Description: Julie DeGalan and Stephen Lambert. 2007. $16.95 (paper). 192 pages.

2306 ■ Great Jobs for Liberal Arts Majors
The McGraw-Hill Companies Inc.
PO Box 182604
Columbus, OH 43272
Ph: (212)512-2000
Free: 877-833-5524
Fax: (614)759-3749
E-mail: customer.service@mcgraw-hill.com
URL: http://www.mcgraw-hill.com

Description: Blythe Camenson. Second edition, 2007. $16.95 (paper). 192 pages.

2307 ■ Great Jobs for Music Majors
The McGraw-Hill Companies Inc.
PO Box 182604
Columbus, OH 43272
Ph: (212)512-2000
Free: 877-833-5524
Fax: (614)759-3749
E-mail: customer.service@mcgraw-hill.com
URL: http://www.mcgraw-hill.com

Description: Jan Goldberg. Second edition, 2004. $15.95 (paper). 180 pages.

2308 ■ Great Jobs for Sociology Majors
The McGraw-Hill Companies Inc.
PO Box 182604
Columbus, OH 43272
Ph: (212)512-2000
Free: 877-833-5524

Fax: (614)759-3749
E-mail: customer.service@mcgraw-hill.com
URL: http://www.mcgraw-hill.com

Description: Stephen Lambert. Second edition, 2008. $16.95 (paper). 192 pages.

2309 ■ Great Jobs for Theater Majors
The McGraw-Hill Companies Inc.
PO Box 182604
Columbus, OH 43272
Ph: (212)512-2000
Free: 877-833-5524
Fax: (614)759-3749
E-mail: customer.service@mcgraw-hill.com
URL: http://www.mcgraw-hill.com

Description: Jan Goldberg and Julie DeGalan. 2005. $15.95 (paper). 192 pages.

2310 ■ Idea-Based Learning
Kumarian Press Inc.
22883 Quicksilver Dr.
Sterling, VA 20166-2012
Ph: (703)661-1504
Free: 800-232-0223
Fax: (703)661-1547
E-mail: kpbooks@kpbooks.com
URL: http://www.kpbooks.com

Description: Edmund J. Hansen. 2011. $75.00 (hardback); $24.95 (paperback). Serves as guide in developing college instruction that has clear purpose, is well integrated into the curriculum, and improves student learning.

2311 ■ Job Search in Academe: How to Get the Position You Deserve
Kumarian Press Inc.
22883 Quicksilver Dr.
Sterling, VA 20166-2012
Ph: (703)661-1504
Free: 800-232-0223
Fax: (703)661-1547
E-mail: kpbooks@kpbooks.com
URL: http://www.kpbooks.com

Description: Dawn M. Formo and Cheryl Reed. 2011. $49.95 (cloth) and $22.50 (paper). 268 pages. Covers the process for Masters and PhDs level jobseekers of all disciplines: from identifying sources of information about positions, to advising on the preparation of effective CVs and portfolios, through guidance on the process of interview to final negotiation of terms. Includes sample application letters and vitae.

2312 ■ Opportunities in Overseas Careers
The McGraw-Hill Companies Inc.
PO Box 182604
Columbus, OH 43272
Ph: (212)512-2000
Free: 877-833-5524
Fax: (614)759-3749
E-mail: customer.service@mcgraw-hill.com
URL: http://www.mcgraw-hill.com

Description: Blythe Camenson. 2004. $13.95 (paper). 173 pages.

2313 ■ Opportunities in Teaching Careers
The McGraw-Hill Companies Inc.
PO Box 182604
Columbus, OH 43272
Ph: (212)512-2000
Free: 877-833-5524
Fax: (614)759-3749
E-mail: customer.service@mcgraw-hill.com
URL: http://www.mcgraw-hill.com

Description: Janet Fine. 2005. $13.95 (paper). 160 pages. Discusses licensing and accreditation programs, sources of placement information, jobseeking correspondence, selection procedures, and paths to advancement. Also covers professional associations, non-traditional teaching opportunities, and jobs abroad.

2314 ■ A Survival Guide for New Faculty Members: Outlining the Keys to Success for Promotion and Tenure
Charles C. Thomas Publisher Ltd.
2600 S 1st St.
Springfield, IL 62704-4730
Ph: (217)789-8980
Free: 800-258-8980
Fax: (217)789-9130
E-mail: books@ccthomas.com
URL: http://www.ccthomas.com

Description: Jeffrey P. Bakken and Cynthia G. Simpson. 2011. $35.95 (paper). 258 pages. Serves as a guide for new faculty members in higher education. Contains practical, down-to-earth advice and suggestions for successfully working through to tenure and promotion.

EMPLOYMENT AGENCIES AND SEARCH FIRMS

2315 ■ Boston Search Group Inc.
224 Clarendon St., Ste. 41
Boston, MA 02116-3729
Ph: (617)266-4333
Fax: (781)735-0562
E-mail: ralph@bsgtv.com
URL: http://www.bostonsearchgroup.com

Description: Executive search firm.

2316 ■ The Dalley Hewitt Company
PO Box 19973
Atlanta, GA 30325
Ph: (404)992-5065
Fax: (404)355-6136
E-mail: rives@dalleyhewitt.com
URL: http://www.dalleyhewitt.com

Description: Executive search firm.

2317 ■ Deerfield Associates
572 Washington St., Ste. 15
Wellesley, MA 02482
Ph: (781)237-2800
E-mail: doug@deerfieldassociates.com
URL: http://www.deerfieldassociates.com

Description: Executive search firm.

2318 ■ The Development Resource Group
130 E 40th St., Ste. 800
New York, NY 10016
Ph: (212)983-1600
Fax: (212)983-1687
E-mail: search@drgnyc.com
URL: http://www.drgnyc.com

Description: Executive search firm.

2319 ■ Dunn Associates
229 Limberline Dr.
Greensburg, PA 15601
Ph: (724)832-9822
E-mail: maddunn@aol.com
URL: http://www.dunnassociatesinc.com

Description: Executive search firm.

2320 ■ EFL Associates
11440 Tomahawk Creek Pkwy.
Leawood, KS 66211
Ph: (913)234-1560
URL: http://www.cbiz.com/eflassociates

Description: Executive search firm. Locations in Englewood, CO and Lake Forest, IL.

2321 ■ Ford Webb Associates Inc.
60 Thoreau St.
Concord, MA 01742
Ph: (978)371-4900
Fax: (978)334-5544
E-mail: info@fordwebb.com
URL: http://www.fordwebb.com

Description: Executive search firm.

2322 ■ Perez-Arton Consultants Inc.
23 Spring St., Ste. 304
Ossining, NY 10562
Ph: (914)762-2100

Description: Provides executive searches for major academic and administrative units. Conducts institutional evaluations and executive staff assessments. Firm works for colleges, universities and education-related non-profits only.

2323 ■ Witt/Kieffer
2015 Spring Rd., Ste. 510
Oak Brook, IL 60523
Ph: (630)990-1370
Fax: (630)990-1382
E-mail: info@wittkieffer.com
URL: http://www.wittkieffer.com

Description: Executive search firm with five locations throughout the United States.

ONLINE JOB SOURCES AND SERVICES

2324 ■ Academic Careers Online
URL: http://www.academiccareers.com

Description: Serves as an academic job site for teaching jobs, education jobs, research jobs, and professional jobs in education and academia.

2325 ■ Academic Employment Network
URL: http://academploy.com

Description: Online position announcement service. Lists available positions in colleges, primary and secondary educational institutions for faculty, staff, and administrative professionals. Fee: Free searching and browsing features.

2326 ■ Academic360.com
URL: http://www.academic360.com

Description: Site is a collection of internet resources gathered for the academic job hunter. Contains links to over 1,400 colleges and universities that advertise job openings online. Positions listed are not limited to teaching positions.

2327 ■ AcademicKeys.com
URL: http://www.academickeys.com

Description: Provides resources for job seekers who are looking for academic employment. Offers higher education jobs and jobs at universities, colleges, and other institutions of higher education.

2328 ■ Adjunctnation.com
URL: http://www.adjunctnation.com

Description: Focuses on faculty job postings within higher education for both part-time, as well as full-time temporary college faculty appointments.

2329 ■ ChristianUniversityJobs.com
URL: http://www.christianuniversityjobs.com

Description: Features an online job search database focused on higher education jobs in Christian schools including universities, colleges, seminaries, and theological schools.

2330 ■ HigherEdJobs.com
URL: http://www.higheredjobs.com

Description: Exists as a job database focused exclusively on college and university positions. Provides a recruitment tool that adds value to the job seeker and recruiter by offering cost-effective, innovative, useful, and timely services.

2331 ■ National Educators Employment Review
URL: http://www.thereview.com

Description: Matches qualified educators with employment for teachers, specialists, and administrators from kindergarten through college.

2332 ■ TedJob.com
URL: http://www.tedjob.com

Price: Free. **Description:** Serves as a higher-education job marketplace designed to meet the unique, recruitment requirements for universities, colleges, and other academic organizations.

2333 ■ UniversityJobs.com
URL: http://www.universityjobs.com

Description: Provides an online recruitment solution for colleges and universities to hire new faculty and administrators or staff.

2334 ■ UnivJobs.com
URL: http://www.univjobs.com

Description: Serves as a site to find jobs at universities and colleges nationwide. Provides information on faculty, staff, and student positions at university and college campuses in all 50 states.

TRADESHOWS

2335 ■ American Association of Physics Teachers Winter Meeting
American Association of Physics Teachers
1 Physics Ellipse
College Park, MD 20740-3845
Ph: (301)209-3311
Fax: (301)209-0845
E-mail: webmaster@aapt.org
URL: http://www.aapt.org

Frequency: Annual. **Primary Exhibits:** Physics textbooks, apparatus, and software.

2336 ■ American Society for Engineering Education Annual Conference and Exposition
American Society for Engineering Education
1818 N St. NW, Ste. 600
Washington, DC 20036-2479
Ph: (202)331-3500
Fax: (202)265-8504
E-mail: board@asee.org
URL: http://www.asee.org

Frequency: Annual. **Primary Exhibits:** Publications, engineering supplies and equipment, computers, software, and research companies all products and services related to engineering education.

2337 ■ American Technical Education Association National Conference on Technical Education
American Technical Education Association
North Dakota State College of Science
800 N 6th St.
Wahpeton, ND 58076-0002
Ph: (701)671-2301
Fax: (701)671-2260
URL: http://www.ateaonline.org/

Frequency: Annual. **Primary Exhibits:** Supplies and services related to post secondary technical education.

2338 ■ Association for Education in Journalism and Mass Communication Annual Convention
Association for Education in Journalism and Mass Communication
234 Outlet Pointe Blvd., Ste. A
Columbia, SC 29210-5667
Ph: (803)798-0271
Fax: (803)772-3509
E-mail: aejmchq@aol.com
URL: http://www.aejmc.org

Frequency: Annual. **Primary Exhibits:** Publications, information retrieval services, and special programs.

2339 ■ Council of Graduate Schools Annual Meeting
Council of Graduate Schools
1 Dupont Cir. NW, Ste. 230
Washington, DC 20036
Ph: (202)223-3791
Fax: (202)331-7157
E-mail: general_inquiries@cgs.nche.edu
URL: http://www.cgsnet.org

Frequency: Annual. **Primary Exhibits:** Exhibits related to the improvement and advancement of graduate education.

2340 ■ National Association for Bilingual Education Conference
National Association for Bilingual Education
8701 Georgia Ave., Ste. 700
Silver Spring, MD 20910
Ph: (240)450-3700
Fax: (240)450-3799
E-mail: nabe@nabe.org
URL: http://www.nabe.org

Frequency: Annual. Features speakers, sessions, product exhibits, and job fair.

2341 ■ National Association for Developmental Education Conference
National Association for Developmental Education
500 N Estrella Pkwy., Ste. B2
PMB 412
Goodyear, AZ 85338
Free: 877-233-9455
Fax: (623)792-5747
E-mail: office@nade.net
URL: http://www.nade.net

Frequency: Annual. Offers an opportunity for personal and professional growth. Includes job fair. 2014 March 5-8; Dallas, TX; Hilton Anatole.

2342 ■ Southwestern Federation of Administrative Disciplines Convention
Southwestern Federation of Administrative Disciplines
2700 Bay Area Blvd.
Houston, TX 77058

Frequency: Annual. **Primary Exhibits:** Educational materials and services.

2343 ■ UCEA Annual Conference
Frequency: Annual. **Primary Exhibits:** Exhibits related to continuing education and online learning at institutions of higher learning.

OTHER SOURCES

2344 ■ Academy of International Business
Michigan State University
The Eli Broad College of Business
645 N Shaw Ln., Rm. 7
East Lansing, MI 48824-1121
Ph: (517)432-1452
Fax: (517)432-1009
E-mail: aib@aib.msu.edu
URL: http://aib.msu.edu

Description: Consists primarily of university professors, doctoral students, researchers, writers, consultants, executives, and policy setters in the international business/trade research and education fields. Facilitates information exchange among people in academia, business, and government and encourages research activities that advance the knowledge of international business operations and increase the available body of teaching materials. Compiles an inventory of collegiate courses in international business, a survey of research projects, and statistics.

2345 ■ Academy of Legal Studies in Business
c/o Robert E. Thomas
University of Florida
College of Business Administration
100 Bryan Hall
Gainesville, FL 32611

Ph: (215)898-9369
E-mail: carolmiller@missouristate.edu
URL: http://www.alsb.org

Description: Teachers of business law and legal environment in colleges and universities. Promotes and encourages business law scholarship and teaching outside of the law school environment.

2346 ■ Academy of Management
PO Box 3020
Briarcliff Manor, NY 10510
Ph: (914)923-2607
Fax: (914)923-2615
E-mail: membership@aom.org
URL: http://www.aom.org

Description: Professors in accredited universities and colleges who teach management; selected business executives who have made significant written contributions to the literature in the field of management and organization. Offers placement service.

2347 ■ Academy of Marketing Science
PO Box 3072
Ruston, LA 71272
Ph: (318)257-2612
Fax: (318)257-4253
E-mail: ams@latech.edu
URL: http://www.ams-web.org

Description: Marketing academicians and practitioners; individuals interested in fostering education in marketing science. Aims to promote the advancement of knowledge and the furthering of professional standards in the field of marketing. Explores the special application areas of marketing science and its responsibilities as an economic, ethical, and social force; promotes research and the widespread dissemination of findings. Facilitates exchange of information and experience among members, and the transfer of marketing knowledge and technology to developing countries; promotes marketing science on an international level. Provides a forum for discussion and refinement of concepts, methods and applications, and the opportunity to publish papers in the field. Assists member educators in the development of improved teaching methods, devices, directions, and materials. Offers guidance and direction in marketing practice and reviewer assistance on scholarly works. Contributes to the solution of marketing problems encountered by individual firms, industries, and society as a whole. Encourages members to utilize their marketing talents to the fullest through redirection, reassignment, and relocation. Sponsors competitions.

2348 ■ American Academy of Religion
825 Houston Mill Rd. NE, Ste. 300
Atlanta, GA 30329-4205
Ph: (404)727-3049
Fax: (404)727-7959
E-mail: jfitzmier@aarweb.org
URL: http://www.aarweb.org

Description: Professional society of scholars and teachers in the field of religion. Encourages scholarship, research, and publications in the study of religion, and stimulates effective teaching. Hosts annual meeting, publishes academic journal, offers research grants and placement services to members; compiles statistics.

2349 ■ American Alliance for Health, Physical Education, Recreation and Dance
1900 Association Dr.
Reston, VA 20191-1598
Ph: (703)476-3400
Free: 800-213-7193
Fax: (703)476-9527
E-mail: membership@aahperd.org
URL: http://www.aahperd.org

Description: Students and educators in physical education, dance, health, athletics, safety education, recreation, and outdoor education. Sponsors placement service.

2350 ■ American Association of Blind Teachers
c/o John Buckley
1025 Ree Way
Knoxville, TN 37909
Ph: (865)692-4888
E-mail: johnbuckley25@comcast.net
URL: http://www.blindteachers.net

Description: Public school teachers, teachers of the visually impaired, college and university professors, and teachers in residential schools for the blind. Promotes employment and professional goals of blind persons entering the teaching profession or those established in their respective teaching fields. Serves as a vehicle for the dissemination of information and the exchange of ideas addressing special problems of members.

2351 ■ American Association of Community Colleges
1 Dupont Cir. NW, Ste. 410
Washington, DC 20036-1145
Ph: (202)728-0200
Fax: (202)833-2467
E-mail: aaccpub@pmds.com
URL: http://www.aacc.nche.edu

Description: Community colleges; individual associates interested in community college development; corporate, educational, foundation, and international associate members. Office of Federal Relations monitors federal educational programming and legislation. Compiles statistics through data collection and policy analysis. Conducts seminars and professional training programs.

2352 ■ American Association for Employment in Education
947 E Johnstown Rd., No. 170
Gahanna, OH 43230
Ph: (614)485-1111
Fax: (360)244-7802
E-mail: execdir@aaee.org
URL: http://www.aaee.org/cwt/external/wcpages/index.aspx

Description: Represents colleges, universities, and other post-secondary educational institutions, which are not-for-profit. Prepares teachers and other educational personnel for service in public and private educational institutions, organizations and agencies. Provides information or services relating to career planning, placement, and recruitment activities in education.

2353 ■ American Association of Teachers of French
Southern Illinois University
Mail Code 4510
Carbondale, IL 62901
Ph: (618)453-5731
Fax: (618)453-5733
E-mail: aatf@frenchteachers.org
URL: http://www.frenchteachers.org

Description: Teachers of French in public and private elementary and secondary schools, colleges and universities. Sponsors National French Week each November to take French out of the classroom and into the schools and community. Conducts National French Contest in elementary and secondary schools and awards prizes at all levels. Maintains Materials Center with promotional and pedagogical materials; National French Honor Society (high school), Placement Bureau, summer scholarships.

2354 ■ American Association of Teachers of German
112 Haddontowne Ct., No. 104
Cherry Hill, NJ 08034-3668
Ph: (856)795-5553
Fax: (856)795-9398
E-mail: info@aatg.org
URL: http://www.aatg.org

Description: Represents teachers of German at all levels; individuals interested in German language and culture. Offers in-service teacher-training

workshops, materials, student honor society, national German examination and stipends/scholarships.

2355 ■ American Association of Teachers of Spanish and Portuguese
900 Ladd Rd.
Walled Lake, MI 48390
Ph: (248)960-2180
Fax: (248)960-9570
E-mail: aatspoffice@aatsp.org
URL: http://www.aatsp.org

Description: Teachers of Spanish and Portuguese languages and literatures and others interested in Hispanic culture. Operates placement bureau and maintains pen pal registry. Sponsors honor society, Sociedad Honoraria Hispanica and National Spanish Examinations for secondary school students.

2356 ■ American Association of University Professors
1133 19th St. NW, Ste. 200
Washington, DC 20036
Ph: (202)737-5900
Fax: (202)737-5526
E-mail: aaup@aaup.org
URL: http://www.aaup.org/aaup

Description: Serves as a group of college and university teachers, research scholars, and academic librarians. Aims to advance academic freedom and shared governance, to define fundamental professional values and standards for higher education, and to ensure higher education's contribution to the common good. Develops standards and procedures to maintain quality in education and academic freedom in colleges and universities.

2357 ■ American Association for Women in Community Colleges
PO Box 3098
Gaithersburg, MD 20885
Ph: (301)442-3374
E-mail: info@aawccnatl.org
URL: http://www.aawccnatl.org

Description: Women faculty members, administrators, staff members, students, and trustees of community colleges. Objectives are to: develop communication and disseminate information among women in community, junior, and technical colleges; encourage educational program development; obtain grants for educational projects for community college women. Disseminates information on women's issues and programs. Conducts regional and state professional development workshops and forums. Recognizes model programs that assist women in community colleges. An affiliate council of the American Association of Community Colleges.

2358 ■ American Catholic Philosophical Association
University of St. Thomas
Center for Thomistic Studies
3800 Montrose Blvd.
Houston, TX 77006-4626
Ph: (713)942-3483
Free: 800-444-2419
Fax: (713)525-6964
E-mail: acpa@stthom.edu
URL: http://www.acpaweb.org

Description: College and university teachers of philosophy; students engaged in research; writers and others interested in philosophical knowledge.

2359 ■ American Classical League
Miami University
422 Wells Mills Dr.
Oxford, OH 45056
Ph: (513)529-7741
Fax: (513)529-7742
E-mail: info@aclclassics.org
URL: http://www.aclclassics.org

Description: Teachers of classical languages in high schools and colleges. Works to promote the teaching of Latin and other classical languages. Presents scholarship. Maintains placement service, teaching materials, and resource center at Miami University in Oxford, OH to sell teaching aids to Latin and Greek teachers.

2360 ■ American College Personnel Association
1 Dupont Cir. NW, Ste. 300
Washington, DC 20036-1188
Ph: (202)835-2272
Fax: (202)296-3286
E-mail: info@acpa.nche.edu
URL: http://www2.myacpa.org/

Description: Represents individuals employed in higher education and involved in student personnel work, including administration, counseling, research, and teaching. Fosters student development in higher education in areas of service, advocacy, and standards by offering professional programs for educators committed to the overall development of post-secondary students. Sponsors professional and educational activities in cooperation with other organizations. Offers placement services.

2361 ■ American Mathematical Society
201 Charles St.
Providence, RI 02904-2294
Ph: (401)455-4000
Free: 800-321-4267
Fax: (401)331-3842
E-mail: cust-serv@ams.org
URL: http://www.ams.org

Description: Professional society of mathematicians and educators. Promotes the interests of mathematical scholarship and research. Holds institutes, seminars, short courses, and symposia to further mathematical research; awards prizes. Offers placement services; compiles statistics.

2362 ■ American Philosophical Association
University of Delaware
31 Amstel Ave.
Newark, DE 19716
Ph: (302)831-1112
Fax: (302)831-8690
E-mail: aferrer@udel.edu
URL: http://www.apaonline.org

Description: College and university teachers of philosophy and others with an interest in philosophy. Facilitates exchange of ideas in philosophy, encourages creative and scholarly activity in philosophy, and fosters the professional work of teachers of philosophy. Participates in international congresses of philosophy and maintains affiliations with national and international philosophical organizations. Maintains placement service; sponsors competitions. Oversees selection of Romanell, Schutz and Carus lecturers and other prizes and awards.

2363 ■ American Political Science Association
1527 New Hampshire Ave. NW
Washington, DC 20036-1206
Ph: (202)483-2512
Fax: (202)483-2657
E-mail: apsa@apsanet.org
URL: http://www.apsanet.org

Description: College and university teachers of political science, public officials, research workers, and businessmen. Encourages the impartial study and promotes the development of the art and science of government. Develops research projects of public interest and educational programs for political scientists and journalists; seeks to improve the knowledge of and increase citizen participation in political and governmental affairs. Serves as clearinghouse for teaching and research positions in colleges, universities, and research bureaus in the U.S. and abroad and for positions open to political scientists in government and private business; conducts Congressional Fellowship Program. Conducts Committee on Professional Ethic, and Rights and Freedom. Offers placement service.

2364 ■ Art Directors Club
106 W 29th St.
New York, NY 10001
Ph: (212)643-1440
Fax: (212)643-4266
E-mail: info@adcglobal.org
URL: http://www.adcglobal.org

Description: Art directors of advertising magazines and agencies, visual information specialists, and graphic designers; associate members are artists, cinematographers, photographers, copywriters, educators, journalists, and critics. Promotes and stimulates interest in the practice of art direction. Sponsors Annual Exhibition of Advertising, Editorial and Television Art and Design; International Traveling Exhibition. Provides educational, professional, and entertainment programs; on-premise art exhibitions; portfolio review program. Conducts panels for students and faculty. **Members:** 1,100.

2365 ■ Association of American Law Schools
1614 20th St. NW
Washington, DC 20009-1001
Ph: (202)296-8851
Fax: (202)296-8869
E-mail: aals@aals.org
URL: http://www.aals.org

Description: Law schools association. Seeks to improve the legal profession through legal education. Interacts for law professors with state and federal government, other legal education and professional associations, and other national higher education and learned society organizations. Compiles statistics; sponsors teacher placement service. Presents professional development programs.

2366 ■ Association of Departments of English
26 Broadway, 3rd Fl.
New York, NY 10004-1789
Ph: (646)576-5137
Fax: (646)835-4056
E-mail: dlaurence@mla.org
URL: http://www.ade.org

Description: Administrators of college and university departments of English, humanities, rhetoric, and communications. Works to improve the teaching of English and the administration of English departments. Conducts studies and surveys of literature and writing courses. Sponsors sessions at major English conventions and conferences nationwide. Sponsored by Modern Language Association of America.

2367 ■ Association for Education in Journalism and Mass Communication
234 Outlet Pointe Blvd., Ste. A
Columbia, SC 29210-5667
Ph: (803)798-0271
Fax: (803)772-3509
E-mail: aejmchq@aol.com
URL: http://www.aejmc.org

Description: Professional organization of college and university journalism and communication teachers. Works to improve methods and standards of teaching and stimulate research. Compiles statistics on enrollments and current developments in journalism education. Maintains a listing of journalism and communication teaching positions available and teaching positions wanted, revised bimonthly.

2368 ■ Association for Institutional Research
1435 E Piedmont Dr., Ste. 211
Tallahassee, FL 32308
Ph: (850)385-4155
Fax: (850)385-5180
E-mail: rswing@airweb.org
URL: http://www.airweb.org

Description: Serves as a professional organization for institutional researchers that provides educational resources and professional-development opportunities. Supports its members in the process of facilitat-

ing quality, data-informed decisions for the enhancement of higher education.

2369 ■ Association for Library and Information Science Education
65 E Wacker Pl., Ste. 1900
Chicago, IL 60601-7246
Ph: (312)795-0996
Fax: (312)419-8950
E-mail: contact@alise.org
URL: http://www.alise.org

Description: Graduate schools offering degree programs in library science and their faculties. Seeks to: promote excellence in education for library and information science as a means of increasing the effectiveness of library and information services; provide a forum for the active interchange of ideas and information among library educators; promote research related to teaching and to library and information science; formulate and promulgate positions on matters related to library education. Offers employment program at annual conference.

2370 ■ Association for Slavic, East European, and Eurasian Studies
University of Pittsburgh
203C Bellefield Hall
Pittsburgh, PA 15260-6424
Ph: (412)648-9911
Fax: (412)648-9815
E-mail: aseees@pitt.edu
URL: http://www.aseees.org

Description: Scholars and others in teaching, research, administration, and government. Seeks to advance study, publication, and teaching relating to Russia, Eurasia, and Eastern Europe.

2371 ■ Association for the Study of Higher Education
4505 S Maryland Pkwy.
Las Vegas, NV 89154
Ph: (702)895-2737
Fax: (702)895-4269
E-mail: ashe@unlv.edu
URL: http://www.ashe.ws

Description: Professors, researchers, administrators, policy analysts, graduate students, and others concerned with the study of higher education. Aims to advance the study of higher education and facilitate and encourage discussion of priority issues for research in the study of higher education.

2372 ■ Association of University Professors of Ophthalmology
PO Box 193030
San Francisco, CA 94119
Ph: (415)561-8548
Fax: (415)561-8531
E-mail: aupo@aao.org
URL: http://www.aupo.org

Description: Heads of departments or divisions of ophthalmology in accredited medical schools throughout the U.S. and Canada; directors of ophthalmology residency programs in institutions not connected to medical schools. Promotes medical education, research, and patient care relating to ophthalmology. Operates Ophthalmology Matching Program and faculty placement service, which aids ophthalmologists interested in being associated with university ophthalmology programs to locate such programs. **Members:** 315.

2373 ■ Career Opportunities in Education and Related Services
InfoBase Holdings Inc.
132 W 31st., 17 Fl.
New York, NY 10001-3406
Ph: (212)967-8800
Fax: (800)678-3633
E-mail: info@infobasepublishing.com
URL: http://www.infobasepublishing.com

Frequency: Latest edition 2nd; Published April, 2006. **Price:** $49.50 Individuals Hardcover. **Pages:**

320. **Description:** Susan Echaore-McDavid. Second edition, 2006. 320 pages. **Covers:** 103 job titles in education, including job profiles, duties, salaries, prospects, experience, skills, and more. **Includes:** Appendixes with addresses of colleges and universities offering programs for featured jobs as well as organizations and Internet resources. **Entries include:** Web sites and addresses of professional organizations.

2374 ■ *Careers for Fashion Plates and Other Trendsetters*

The McGraw-Hill Companies Inc.
PO Box 182604
Columbus, OH 43272
Ph: (212)512-2000
Free: 877-833-5524
Fax: (614)759-3749
E-mail: customer.service@mcgraw-hill.com
URL: http://www.mcgraw-hill.com

Description: Lucia Mauro. 2008. $14.95 (paper). 176 pages. Describes career opportunities in fashion, entertainment, retail, and promotion, with advice from fashion professionals. **Includes:** Appendix of U.S. and Canadian organizations and fashion schools that provide information about job opportunities and educational requirements. Also includes bibliographical references. Appendix of U.S. and Canadian organizations and fashion schools that provide information about job opportunities and educational requirements. Also includes bibliographical references. **Entries include:** Name, address, URL.

2375 ■ *Careers for the Stagestruck and Other Dramatic Types*

The McGraw-Hill Companies Inc.
PO Box 182604
Columbus, OH 43272
Ph: (212)512-2000
Free: 877-833-5524
Fax: (614)759-3749
E-mail: customer.service@mcgraw-hill.com
URL: http://www.mcgraw-hill.com

Description: Lucia Mauro. Second edition, 2004. $13.95 (paper). 160 pages. **Includes:** Appendices of arts organizations, colleges and universities, and other job-hunting and arts education resources, as well as bibliographical references. Appendices of arts organizations, colleges and universities, and other job-hunting and arts education resources, as well as bibliographical references. **Entries include:** Name, address.

2376 ■ College Language Association

PO Box 38515
Tallahassee, FL 32315
Ph: (404)364-8382
Fax: (404)228-2562
E-mail: mchandler@oglethorpe.edu
URL: http://www.clascholars.org

Description: Teachers of English and modern foreign languages, primarily in historically black colleges and universities. Maintains placement service.

2377 ■ College Media Association

2301 Vanderbilt Pl.
VU Sta. B 35166
Nashville, TN 37235
Ph: (415)338-3134
Fax: (901)678-4798
E-mail: rsplbrgr@memphis.edu
URL: http://www.collegemedia.org

Description: Professional association serving advisers, directors, and chairmen of boards of college student media (newspapers, yearbooks, magazines, handbooks, directories, and radio and television stations); heads of schools and departments of journalism; and others interested in junior college, college, and university student media. Serves as a clearinghouse for student media; acts as consultant on student theses and dissertations on publications. Encourages high school journalism and examines its relationships to college and professional journalism. Conducts national survey of student media in rotation

each year by type: newspapers, magazines, and yearbooks; radio and television stations. Compiles statistics. Maintains placement service and speakers' bureau.

2378 ■ College Reading and Learning Association

66 George St.
Charleston, SC 29424
E-mail: thomasmm1@cofc.edu
URL: http://www.crla.net

Description: Professionals involved in college/adult reading, learning assistance, developmental education, and tutorial services. Promotes communication for the purpose of professional growth. **Members:** 1,200.

2379 ■ Conference on College Composition and Communication

1111 W Kenyon Rd.
Urbana, IL 61801-1096
Ph: (217)328-3870
Free: 800-369-6283
E-mail: cccc@ncte.org
URL: http://www.ncte.org/cccc

Description: Represents college and university educators involved in teaching composition and communication. **Members:** 7,000.

2380 ■ Decision Sciences Institute

75 Piedmont Ave., Ste. 340
Atlanta, GA 30303
Ph: (404)413-7710
Fax: (404)413-7714
E-mail: dsi@gsu.edu
URL: http://www.decisionsciences.org

Description: Businesspersons and members of business school faculties. Maintains placement service.

2381 ■ Eastern Finance Association

PO Box 244023
Montgomery, AL 36124-4023
E-mail: membershipservices@blackwellpublishers.co.uk
URL: http://etnpconferences.net/efa

Description: College and university professors and financial officers; libraries. Provides a meeting place for persons interested in any aspect of finance, including financial management, investments, and banking. Sponsors research competitions.

2382 ■ Financial Management Association International

University of South Florida
College of Business Administration
4202 E Fowler Ave., BSN 3331
Tampa, FL 33620-5500
Ph: (813)974-2084
Fax: (813)974-3318
E-mail: fma@coba.usf.edu
URL: http://www.fma.org

Description: Professors of financial management; corporate financial officers. Facilitates exchange of ideas among persons involved in financial management or the study thereof. Conducts workshops for comparison of current research projects and development of cooperative ventures in writing and research. Sponsors honorary society for superior students at 300 colleges and universities. Offers placement services.

2383 ■ Friends Council on Education

1507 Cherry St.
Philadelphia, PA 19102
Ph: (215)241-7245
Fax: (215)241-7299
E-mail: info@friendscouncil.org
URL: http://www.friendscouncil.org

Description: Representatives appointed by Friends Yearly Meetings; heads of Quaker secondary and elementary schools and colleges; members-at-large. Acts as a clearinghouse for information on Quaker schools and colleges. Holds meetings and confer-

ences on education and provides in-service training for teachers, administrators and trustees in Friends schools. **Members:** 82.

2384 ■ *Grants, Fellowships, and Prizes of Interest to Historians*

American Historical Association
400 A St. SE
Washington, DC 20003-3889
Ph: (202)544-2422
Fax: (202)544-8307
E-mail: grantguide@theaha.org
URL: http://www.historians.org

Frequency: Annual; latest edition 2006. **Covers:** Over 450 sources of funding (scholarships, fellowships, internships, awards, and book and essay prizes) in the United States and abroad for graduate students, postdoctoral researchers, and institutions in the humanities. **Includes:** Bibliography and list of named fellowships. **Entries include:** Name of source, institution name or contact, address, phone, eligibility and proposal requirements, award or stipend amount, location requirements for research, application deadlines. **Arrangement:** Alphabetical in three categories: support for individual research and teaching; grants for groups and organizations for research and education; and book, article, essay, and manuscript prizes.

2385 ■ International Association of Baptist Colleges and Universities

8120 Sawyer Brown Rd., Ste. 108
Nashville, TN 37221-1410
Ph: (615)673-1896
Fax: (615)662-1396
E-mail: tim_fields@baptistschools.org
URL: http://www.baptistschools.org

Description: Southern Baptist senior colleges, universities, junior colleges, academies, and Bible schools. Promotes Christian education through literature, faculty workshops, student recruitment, teacher placement, trustee orientation, statistical information, and other assistance to members.

2386 ■ International Association for Computer and Information Science

735 Meadowbrook Dr.
Mount Pleasant, MI 48858
Ph: (989)774-1175
Fax: (989)774-1174
E-mail: lee1ry@cmich.edu
URL: http://www.acisinternational.org

Description: Represents individuals in the fields of computer and information science. Disseminates the latest developments in the fields of computer and information science. Provides a forum for researchers in education and computer and information science industries.

2387 ■ International Association of Counselors and Therapists

8852 SR 3001
Laceyville, PA 18623
Ph: (570)869-1021
Free: 800-553-6886
Fax: (570)869-1249
E-mail: staff@iact.org
URL: http://www.iact.org

Description: Mental health professionals, medical professionals, social workers, clergy, educators, hypnotherapists, counselors, and individuals interested in the helping professions. Promotes enhanced professional image and prestige for complementary therapy. Provides a forum for exchange of information and ideas among practitioners of traditional and nontraditional therapies and methodologies; fosters unity among "grassroots" practitioners and those with advanced academic credentials. Facilitates the development of new therapy programs. Conducts educational, research, and charitable programs. Awards credits for continuing education. Maintains speakers' bureau and library; operates referral and placement services; compiles statistics. Assists in the development of local chapters. **Members:** 7,000.

2388 ■ **The International Educator**
PO Box 513
Cummaquid, MA 02637
Ph: (508)790-1990
Free: 877-375-6668
Fax: (508)790-1922
E-mail: tie@tieonline.com
URL: http://www.tieonline.com

Description: Facilitates the placement of teachers and administrators in American, British, and international schools. Seeks to create a network that provides for professional development opportunities and improved financial security of members. Offers advice and information on international school news, recent educational developments, job placement, and investment, consumer, and professional development opportunities. Makes available insurance and travel benefits. Operates International Schools Internship Program. **Members:** 3,500.

2389 ■ **Modern Language Association of America**
26 Broadway, 3rd Fl.
New York, NY 10004-1789
Ph: (646)576-5000
Fax: (646)458-0030
E-mail: execdirector@mla.org
URL: http://www.mla.org

Description: Provides opportunities for the members to share their scholarly findings and teaching experiences with colleagues and to discuss trends in the academy. Works to strengthen the study and teaching of language and literature.

2390 ■ **NAFSA: Association of International Educators**
1307 New York Ave. NW, 8th Fl.
Washington, DC 20005-4701
Ph: (202)737-3699
Free: 800-836-4994
Fax: (202)737-3657
E-mail: inbox@nafsa.org
URL: http://www.nafsa.org

Description: Individuals, organizations, and institutions dealing with international educational exchange, including foreign student advisers, overseas educational advisers, credentials and admissions officers, administrators and teachers of English as a second language, community support personnel, study-abroad administrators, and embassy cultural or educational personnel. Promotes self-regulation standards and responsibilities in international educational exchange; offers professional development opportunities primarily through publications, workshops, grants, and regional and national conferences. Advocates for increased awareness and support of international education and exchange on campuses, in government, and in communities. Offers services including: a job registry for employers and professionals involved with international education; a consultant referral service. Sponsors joint liaison activities with a variety of other educational and government organizations to conduct a census of foreign student enrollment in the U.S.; conducts workshops about specific subjects and countries.

2391 ■ **National Alliance of Black School Educators**
310 Pennsylvania Ave. SE
Washington, DC 20003
Ph: (202)608-6310
Free: 800-221-2654
Fax: (202)608-6319
E-mail: info@nabse.org
URL: http://www.nabse.org

Description: Black educators from all levels; others indirectly involved in the education of black youth. Promotes awareness, professional expertise, and commitment among black educators. Goals are to: eliminate and rectify the results of racism in education; work with state, local, and national leaders to raise the academic achievement level of all black students; increase members' involvement in legislative activities; facilitate the introduction of a curriculum that more completely embraces black America; improve the ability of black educators to promote problem resolution; create a meaningful and effective network of strength, talent, and professional support. Sponsors workshops, commission meetings, and special projects. Encourages research, especially as it relates to blacks, and the presentation of papers during national conferences. Plans to establish a National Black Educators Data Bank and offer placement service. **Members:** 7,000.

2392 ■ **National Art Education Association**
1806 Robert Fulton Dr., Ste. 300
Reston, VA 20191
Ph: (703)860-8000
Free: 800-299-8321
Fax: (703)860-2960
E-mail: info@arteducators.org
URL: http://www.arteducators.org

Description: Teachers of art at elementary, middle, secondary, and college levels; colleges, libraries, museums, and other educational institutions. Studies problems of teaching art; encourages research and experimentation. Serves as a clearinghouse for information on art education programs, materials, and methods of instruction. Sponsors special institutes. Cooperates with other national organizations for the furtherance of creative art experiences for youth.

2393 ■ **National Association for Bilingual Education**
8701 Georgia Ave., Ste. 700
Silver Spring, MD 20910
Ph: (240)450-3700
Fax: (240)450-3799
E-mail: nabe@nabe.org
URL: http://www.nabe.org

Description: Devoted to representing both the interests of language-minority students and the bilingual education professionals who serve them. Works to ensure that "learning is a reality for every student, regardless of his or her mother tongue"; and establishes contact with national organizations.

2394 ■ **National Association of College and University Business Officers**
1110 Vermont Ave. NW, Ste. 800
Washington, DC 20005
Ph: (202)861-2500
Free: 800-462-4916
Fax: (202)861-2583
E-mail: john.walda@nacubo.org
URL: http://www.nacubo.org

Description: Colleges, universities, and companies that are members of a regional association. Develops and maintains national interest in improving the principles and practices of business and financial administration in higher education. Sponsors workshops in fields such as cash management, grant and contract maintenance, accounting, investment, student loan administration, and costing. Conducts research and information exchange programs between college and university personnel; compiles statistics.

2395 ■ **National Association of Deans and Directors of Schools of Social Work**
1701 Duke St., Ste. 200
Alexandria, VA 22314
Ph: (703)683-8080
Fax: (703)683-8099
E-mail: naddssw@cswe.org
URL: http://www.naddssw.org

Description: Represents deans and directors of graduate social work programs that are in candidacy or accredited by CSWE. Works to promote excellence in social work education. Supports deans and directors in their professional development and effectiveness as academic administrators.

2396 ■ **National Association for Developmental Education**
500 N Estrella Pkwy., Ste. B2
PMB 412
Goodyear, AZ 85338
Free: 877-233-9455
Fax: (623)792-5747
E-mail: office@nade.net
URL: http://www.nade.net

Description: Developmental educators. Seeks to improve the theory and practice of developmental education. Serves as a forum for the exchange of information among members; facilitates communication and cooperation between members and individuals and organizations working in related fields. Sponsors research, evaluation, programming, and training programs.

2397 ■ **National Association of Intercollegiate Athletics**
1200 Grand Blvd.
Kansas City, MO 64106
Ph: (816)595-8000
Fax: (816)595-8200
E-mail: info@naia.org
URL: http://www.naia.org

Description: Fully accredited four-year colleges and universities. Works to develop intercollegiate athletic programs as an integral part of the total educational program of the college rather than as a separate commercial or promotional adjunct. Organizes and administers all areas of intercollegiate athletics at the national level including rules and standards, sectional, regional, conference, and national competition. Aims toward uniformity and equity in policies and practices. Sponsors 23 national championships for men and women to provide national competitive opportunities for colleges and universities with a similar philosophy of athletics; football, basketball, baseball, golf, soccer, cross country, swimming, wrestling, outdoor track and field, indoor track and field, tennis, volleyball, and softball. Maintains hall of fame in all sports in which there are championship events in the meritorious service area. Compiles statistics.

2398 ■ **National Association for Sport and Physical Education**
1900 Association Dr.
Reston, VA 20191-1598
Ph: (703)476-3410
Free: 800-213-7193
Fax: (703)476-8316
E-mail: naspe@aahperd.org
URL: http://www.aahperd.org/naspe

Description: Men and women professionally involved with physical activity and sports. Seeks to improve the total sport and physical activity experience in America. Conducts research and education programs in such areas as sport psychology, curriculum development, kinesiology, history, philosophy, sport sociology, and the biological and behavioral basis of human activity. Develops and distributes public information materials which explain the value of physical education programs. Supports councils involved in organizing and supporting elementary, secondary, and college physical education and sport programs; administers the National Council of Athletic Training in conjunction with the National Association for Girls and Women in Sport; serves the professional interests of coaches, trainers, and officials. Maintains hall of fame, placement service, and media resource center for public information and professional preparation. Member benefits include group insurance and discounts. **Members:** 16,000.

2399 ■ **National Communication Association**
1765 N St. NW
Washington, DC 20036
Ph: (202)464-4622
Fax: (202)464-4600
E-mail: nkidd@natcom.org
URL: http://www.natcom.org

Description: Elementary, secondary, college, and university teachers, speech clinicians, media specialists, communication consultants, students, theater directors, and other interested persons; libraries and other institutions. Works to promote study, criticism, research, teaching, and application of the artistic, humanistic, and scientific principles of communication, particularly speech communication. Sponsors the publication of scholarly volumes in speech. Conducts international debate tours in the U.S. and abroad. Maintains placement service. **Members:** 7,700.

2400 ■ National Council for Geographic Education
1145 17th St. NW, Rm. 7620
Washington, DC 20036
Ph: (202)857-7695
Fax: (202)618-6249
E-mail: ncge@ncge.org
URL: http://www.ncge.org

Description: Teachers of geography and social studies in elementary and secondary schools, colleges and universities; geographers in governmental agencies and private businesses. Encourages the training of teachers in geographic concepts, practices, teaching methods and techniques; works to develop effective geographic educational programs in schools and colleges and with adult groups; stimulates the production and use of accurate and understandable geographic teaching aids and materials.

2401 ■ National Council of Teachers of Mathematics
1906 Association Dr.
Reston, VA 20191-1502
Ph: (703)620-9840
Free: 800-235-7566
Fax: (703)476-2970
E-mail: nctm@nctm.org
URL: http://www.nctm.org

Description: Aims to improve teaching and learning of mathematics.

2402 ■ Organization of American Historians
112 N Bryan Ave.
Bloomington, IN 47408-4141
Ph: (812)855-7311
Fax: (812)855-0696
E-mail: oah@oah.org
URL: http://www.oah.org

Description: Professional historians, including college faculty members, secondary school teachers, graduate students, and other individuals in related fields; institutional subscribers are college, university, high school and public libraries, and historical agencies. Promotes historical research and study. Sponsors 12 prize programs for historical writing; maintains speakers' bureau. Conducts educational programs.

2403 ■ *Overseas Employment Opportunities for Educators: Department of Defense Dependents Schools*
DIANE Publishing Co.
PO Box 617
Darby, PA 19023-0617
Ph: (610)461-6200
Free: 800-782-3833
Fax: (610)461-6130
E-mail: dianepublishing@gmail.com
URL: http://www.dianepublishing.net

Description: Barry Leonard, editor. $20.00. 52 pages. An introduction to teachings positions in the Dept. of Defense Dependents Schools (DoDDS), a worldwide school system, operated by the DoD in 14 countries.

2404 ■ U.S.-China Education Foundation
970 W Valley Pkwy., No. 220
Escondido, CA 92025
E-mail: uscef@sage-usa.net
URL: http://www.sage-usa.net

Description: Aims to promote the learning of the Chinese languages (including Mandarin, Cantonese, and minority languages such as Mongolian) by Americans, and the learning of English by Chinese. Conducts short-term travel-study program to prepare Americans and Chinese for stays of four, six, or eight months or one to four years in China or the U.S., respectively. Operates teacher placement service and speakers' bureau. A project of The Society for the Development of Global Education (S.A.G.E. Inc.). **Members:** 3,700.

2405 ■ University Photographers Association of America
Community College
9000 W College Pkwy.
Palos Hills, IL 60465
E-mail: carpenter@morainevalley.edu
URL: http://www.upaa.org

Description: College and university personnel engaged professionally in photography, audiovisual work, or journalism for universities. Seeks to advance applied photography and the profession through the exchange of thoughts and opinions among its members. Awards fellowship for exceptional work in the advancement of photography. Provides a medium for exchange of ideas and technical information on photography, especially university photographic work. Sponsors exhibits. Provides placement service for members. **Members:** 300.

SOURCES OF HELP-WANTED ADS

2406 ■ *ACM Transactions on Internet Technology*
Association for Computing Machinery
2 Penn Plz., Ste. 701
New York, NY 10121-0701
Ph: (212)626-0500
Free: 800-342-6626
Fax: (212)944-1318
E-mail: acmhelp@acm.org
URL: http://toit.acm.org

Frequency: Quarterly; February, May, August and November. **Price:** $190 Nonmembers print only; $152 Nonmembers online only; $228 Nonmembers online and print. **Description:** Publication of the Association for Computing Machinery. Brings together many computing disciplines including computer software engineering, computer programming languages, middleware, database management, security, knowledge discovery and data mining, networking and distributed systems, communications, performance and scalability, and more. Covers the results and roles of the individual disciplines and the relationships among them.

2407 ■ *Communications of the ACM*
Association for Computing Machinery
2 Penn Plz., Ste. 701
New York, NY 10121-0701
Ph: (212)626-0500
Free: 800-342-6626
Fax: (212)944-1318
E-mail: acmhelp@acm.org
URL: http://cacm.acm.org

Frequency: Monthly. **Price:** $99 Members professional. **Description:** Computing news magazine.

2408 ■ *Communications and Network*
Scientific Research Publishing
PO Box 54821
Irvine, CA 92619-4821
E-mail: cn@scirp.org
URL: http://www.scirp.org/journal/cn/

Frequency: Quarterly. **Price:** $236 Individuals. **Description:** Journal publishing articles on the latest advancements in communications and network technologies.

2409 ■ *Computer Economics Report*
Computer Economics Inc.
2082 Business Center Dr., Ste. 240
Irvine, CA 92612-1164
Ph: (949)831-8700
Fax: (949)442-7688
E-mail: info@computereconomics.com
URL: http://www.computereconomics.com

Description: Monthly. $695. 20 pages. Provides analyses of new IBM technologies and acquisitions and financial management strategies from an end-user perspective. Recurring features include cost comparisons, price/performance analyses, new product forecasts, and evaluations of acquisition techniques for medium and large computer systems. Also available in international edition.

2410 ■ *Computers and Composition*
Elsevier Science Inc.
Secondary Publishing Division
650 Ave. of the Americas
New York, NY 10011
Ph: (212)633-3980
Free: 888-437-4636
Fax: (212)633-3975
URL: http://www.elsevier.com/wps/find/journalde-scription.cws_home/620371/description#description

Frequency: 4/yr. **Price:** $454 Individuals and institution; online; $82 Individuals print; $454 Institutions print. **Description:** Journal covering computers in writing classes, programs, and research.

2411 ■ *Computerworld Top 100*
IDG Communications Inc.
492 Old Connecticut Path
Framingham, MA 01701
Ph: (508)872-0080
URLs: http://www.idg.com/www/IDGProducts.nsf/ByKey/Bulgaria_Publication_Computerworld-Top-100; http://computerworld.bg/supplement/top100

Frequency: Annual. **Description:** Magazine for analyzing trends and events of information technology business.

2412 ■ *Cutter IT Journal*
Cutter Information Corp.
37 Broadway, Ste. 1
Arlington, MA 02474
Ph: (781)648-8700
Free: 800-964-5118
Fax: (781)648-1950
E-mail: service@cutter.com
URL: http://www.cutter.com/itjournal.html

Description: Monthly. $485. Provides IT managers with practical and objective views on the latest technology and management trends.

2413 ■ *Eclipse Review*
BZ Media LLC
7 High St. Ste. 407
Huntington, NY 11743
Ph: (631)421-4158
URL: http://www.eclipsesource.com/contact.htm

Description: Magazine for IT professionals.

2414 ■ *Foundations and Trends in Networking*
Now Publishers
PO Box 1024
Hanover, MA 02339-1001
Ph: (781)871-0245
E-mail: zac.rolnik@nowpublishers.com
URL: http://www.nowpublishers.com/journals/NET/latest

Price: $440 Individuals online only; $510 Individuals print and online; €440 Other countries online only; €510 Other countries print and online. **Description:** Academic journal publishing new research in computer networking.

2415 ■ *Government Computer News*
PostNewsweek Tech Media
10 G St. NE, Ste. 500
Washington, DC 20002-4228
Ph: (202)772-2500
Free: 866-447-6864
Fax: (202)772-2511
URL: http://gcn.com/

Frequency: Semimonthly; 30/yr. **Description:** Magazine for professionals interested in government IT.

2416 ■ *HIMSS Insider*
Healthcare Information and Management Systems Society
33 W Monroe St., Ste. 1700
Chicago, IL 60603-5616
Ph: (312)664-4467
Fax: (312)664-6143
E-mail: himss@himss.org
URL: http://www.himss.org/ASP/index.asp

Description: Monthly. Reports the news of the Healthcare Information and Management Systems Society (HIMSS), which provides leadership in healthcare for the management of technology, information, and change through publications, educational opportunities, and member services.

2417 ■ *IEEE Security & Privacy Magazine*
IEEE Computer Society
10662 Los Vaqueros Cir.
Los Alamitos, CA 90720-1314
Ph: (714)821-8380
Free: 800-272-6657
Fax: (714)821-4010
E-mail: help@computer.org
URL: http://www.computer.org/portal/site/security/

Frequency: Bimonthly. **Price:** $19.95 Individuals online; $65 Nonmembers print; $17.50 Students; $35 Individuals professional. **Description:** Journal that aims to explore role and importance of networked infrastructure and developing lasting security solutions.

2418 ■ *Information Executive*
Association of Information Technology Professionals
330 N Wabash Ave., Ste. 2000
Chicago, IL 60611-4267
Ph: (312)245-1070
Free: 800-224-9371
Fax: (312)673-6659
E-mail: aitp_hq@aitp.org
URL: http://www.aitp.org

Description: Ten issues/year. Provides up-to-date information on the changes and developments of the information systems industry.

2419 ■ *Information Technology Adviser*
American Future Systems Inc.
370 Technology Dr.
Malvern, PA 19355-1315
Ph: (610)695-8600
Free: 800-220-5000
Fax: (610)647-8089
E-mail: customer_service@pbp.com
URL: http://www.pbp.com/ITA.asp

Description: Semimonthly. $299/year. Presents information to keep IT/IS managers up-to-date on how technology cuts costs, boosts productivity, and makes companies more successful. Recurring features include interviews, news of research, a calendar of events, news of educational opportunities, and a column titled Sharpen Your Judgment.

2420 ■ *InfoWorld: Defining Technology for Business*
InfoWorld Media Group
501 2nd St.
San Francisco, CA 94107
Free: 800-227-8365
E-mail: letters@infoworld.com
URL: http://www.infoworld.com/

Frequency: Weekly. **Price:** $180 Individuals.
Description: Weekly publication.

2421 ■ *IT Solutions Guide*
SYS-CON Media
577 Chestnut Ridge Rd.
Woodcliff Lake, NJ 07677
Ph: (201)802-3000
Fax: (201)782-9601
E-mail: subscribe@sys-con.com
URL: http://itsolutions.sys-con.com

Frequency: Quarterly. **Description:** Magazine for IT professionals.

2422 ■ *Journal of Computer Networks and Communications*
Hindawi Publishing Corp.
410 Park Ave., 15th Fl.
287 PMB
New York, NY 10022-4407
Fax: (215)893-4392
E-mail: jcnc@hindawi.com
URL: http://www.hindawi.com/journals/jcnc/

Frequency: 2/yr. **Price:** $595 Individuals print & online. **Description:** Journal covering important areas of information technology.

2423 ■ *Journal of Computer Science*
Science Publications
Vails Gate Heights Dr.
Vails Gate, NY 12584-0879
URL: http://thescipub.com/jcs.toc

Frequency: Monthly. **Description:** Scholarly journal covering many areas of computer science, including: concurrent, parallel and distributed processing; artificial intelligence; image and voice processing; quality software and metrics; computer-aided education; wireless communication; real time processing; evaluative computation; and data bases and information recovery and neural networks.

2424 ■ *Monitor: CPCUG's Print Magazine*
Capital PC User Group
19209 Mt. Airey Rd.
Brookeville, MD 20833
Ph: (301)560-6442
Fax: (301)760-3303
E-mail: editor@cpcug.org
URL: http://monitor.cpcug.org/index.html

Frequency: Quarterly. **Description:** Magazine covering computer hardware and software reviews, special interest user group news, advertisers and author/subject index, and calendar of events.

2425 ■ *PC WORLD: The Magazine of Business Computing*
101 Communications
501 2nd St.
San Francisco, CA 94107
Ph: (415)243-0500
Fax: (415)442-1891
E-mail: pcwletters@pcworld.com
URL: http://www.pcworld.com

Frequency: Quarterly. **Price:** $19.97 Individuals; $29.97 Two years. **Description:** Technology or business magazine meeting the informational needs of tech-savvy managers, both at work and at home.

2426 ■ *Queue: Tomorrow's Computing Today*
Association for Computing Machinery
2 Penn Plz., Ste. 701
New York, NY 10121-0701
Ph: (212)626-0500
Free: 800-342-6626
Fax: (212)944-1318
E-mail: queue@acm.org
URL: http://queue.acm.org/

Frequency: Monthly. **Price:** Free. **Description:** Online magazine aimed at the computer professional. Magazine editorial does not provide solutions for the "here-and-now", but instead helps decision-makers plan future projects by examining the challenges and problems they are most likely to face.

2427 ■ *Report on IBM*
DataTrends Publications Inc.
614 Jacobs Ct. SW
Leesburg, VA 20175-5004
Ph: (571)313-9916
Fax: (703)779-2267
E-mail: sarah@datatrendspublications.com
URL: http://www.datatrendspublications.com

Description: Biweekly. $495. Involved with International Business Machines Corporation (IBM) activities and lines of business, with emphasis on information systems in businesses, factories and homes. Contains news and articles on new IBM introductions, new markets and market strategies, and industry trends.

2428 ■ *Revenue*
Montgomery Media International
55 New Montgomery St., Ste. 617
San Francisco, CA 94105
Ph: (415)371-8800
E-mail: info@mthink.com
URL: http://www.revenuetoday.com/

Description: Magazine covering internet marketing strategies.

2429 ■ *SIGMIS Management Information Systems*
Association for Computing Machinery
2 Penn Plz., Ste. 701
New York, NY 10121-0701
Ph: (212)626-0500
Free: 800-342-6626
Fax: (212)944-1318
E-mail: acmhelp@acm.org
URL: http://www.sigmis.org

Description: Quarterly. Covers information systems and technologies for management.

2430 ■ *Systems Management News*
BZ Media LLC
7 High St. Ste. 407
Huntington, NY 11743
Ph: (631)421-4158
URL: http://www.sysmannews.com/

Frequency: Monthly. **Description:** Magazine providing news, analysis and strategic technology articles that help IT managers understand.

2431 ■ *Ubiquity*
Association for Computing Machinery
2 Penn Plz., Ste. 701
New York, NY 10121-0701
Ph: (212)626-0500
Free: 800-342-6626
Fax: (212)944-1318
E-mail: editors@ubiquity.acm.org
URL: http://ubiquity.acm.org

Frequency: Weekly. **Price:** Free. **Description:** Web-based magazine of the Association for Computing Machinery dedicated to fostering critical analysis and in-depth commentary, including book reviews, on issues relating to the nature, constitution, structure, science, engineering, cognition, technology, practices and paradigms of the IT profession.

2432 ■ *WITI FastTrack*
UBM L.L.C.
240 W 35th St.
New York, NY 10001
Ph: (516)562-5000
Free: 800-842-0798
Fax: (516)562-7830
E-mail: contact@ubmtechnology.com
URL: http://www.witi.com/corporate/fasttrack.php

Frequency: Semiannual. **Description:** Semiannual publication featuring in-depth content on the issues facing today's women professionals in technology.

PLACEMENT AND JOB REFERRAL SERVICES

2433 ■ **Randstad Engineering**
225 Scientific Dr.
Norcross, GA 30092
Ph: (770)390-9888
URL: http://engineering.randstadusa.com

Description: Provides staffing solutions for companies that have needs for qualified technical professionals. Serves as a vital link between technical professionals and the companies that need technical personnel.

EMPLOYER DIRECTORIES AND NETWORKING LISTS

2434 ■ *Vault Guide to the Top Tech Employers*
Vault.com Inc.
132 W 31st St., 17th Fl.
New York, NY 10001-3406
Ph: (212)366-4212
Free: 800-535-2074
Fax: (212)366-6117
E-mail: customerservice@vault.com
URL: http://www.vault.com/wps/portal/usa/store/bookdetail?item_no=782

Frequency: Latest edition June, 2009. **Price:** $19.95 Individuals Online; $19.95 Members Gold. **Pages:** 538. **Covers:** Technology industry employers. **Entries include:** Name, address, phone, fax, website, and other branch office location. Also include company overviews, recent company news, information on the hiring process, key competitors, and employment contact.

HANDBOOKS AND MANUALS

2435 ■ *America's Top 100 Computer and Technical Jobs*
JIST Publishing
875 Montreal Way
Saint Paul, MN 55102-4245
Ph: (317)613-4200
Free: 800-648-5478

Fax: (800)328-4564
E-mail: info@jist.com
URL: http://www.jist.com

Description: Michael J. Farr. 2009. $17.95. 400 pages. Job hunting in computer and technical industries.

2436 ■ Expert Resumes for Computer and Web Jobs
JIST Publishing
875 Montreal Way
Saint Paul, MN 55102-4245
Ph: (317)613-4200
Free: 800-648-5478
Fax: (800)328-4564
E-mail: info@jist.com
URL: http://www.jist.com

Description: Wendy Enelow and Louise Kursmark. Third edition, 2011. $17.95 (paper). 304 pages. Contains a collection of sample resumes and resume writing advice including how to create and use an electronic resume. Contains an appendix that includes internet resources for an online job search, writing cover letters, as well as a collection of sample letters.

2437 ■ Expert Resumes for Managers and Executives
Jist Works
875 Montreal Way
Saint Paul, MN 55102
Free: 800-648-5478
E-mail: info@jist.com
URL: http://www.jist.com/shop/product.php?productid =16727

Description: Wendy S. Enelow, Louise M. Kursmark. 2012. $17.95. 274 pages. Contains a collection of sample resumes and resume writing advice including how to create and use an electronic resume. Contains an appendix that includes internet resources for an online job search, writing cover letters, as well as a collection of sample letters.

2438 ■ Manager's Handbook: Everything You Need to Know about How Business and Management Work
Pearson Learning Group
145 S Mount Zion Rd.
Lebanon, IN 46052
Ph: (804)402-6933
Free: 800-526-9907
Fax: (800)393-3156
E-mail: pasley@pearsonlearning.com
URL: http://www.k12pearson.com

Price: $24.95. **Publication includes:** Principal content of publication is reference guide for new and experienced managers. **Indexes:** Alphabetical.

EMPLOYMENT AGENCIES AND SEARCH FIRMS

2439 ■ Michael Anthony Associates Inc.
44 Washington St., Ste. 250
Wellesley, MA 02481-1802
Ph: (781)237-4950
Free: 800-337-4950
Fax: (781)237-6811
E-mail: manthony@maainc.com
URL: http://www.maainc.com

Description: Applications development, systems programming, communications, and database specialists servicing the IBM mainframe, midrange, and PC marketplace. Provides technical expertise of conversions, system software installation and upgrades, performance and tuning, capacity planning, and data communications. In addition to contract services, also provides retained search and contingency placement of computer professionals ranging from senior staff to senior management.

2440 ■ ATR Technology
1230 Oakmead Pkwy., Ste. 110
Sunnyvale, CA 94085
Ph: (408)328-8000
E-mail: corporate@atr1.com
URL: http://www.atr-technology.com

Description: Serves as an executive search firm specializing in the placement of information technology professionals ranging from complex software application development and infrastructure support to enterprise-wide project management.

2441 ■ Aureus Group
C&A Plz., 13609 California St., Ste. 100
Omaha, NE 68154-3503
Ph: (402)891-6900
Free: 888-239-5993
Fax: (402)891-1290
E-mail: omaha@aureusgroup.com
URL: http://www.aureusgroup.com

Description: Executive search and recruiting consultants specializing in accounting and finance, information systems and technology, health care administration, and wealth management.

2442 ■ Busch International
1000 Fremont Ave., Ste. 195
Los Altos, CA 94024
Ph: (650)949-6500
E-mail: jack@buschint.com
URL: http://www.buschint.com

Description: Executive search firm focused solely on high-technology electronics.

2443 ■ Capitol Staffing Inc.
460 Briarwood Dr., Briarwood 1 Bldg., Ste. 110
Jackson, MS 39206
Ph: (601)957-1755
Fax: (601)957-3880
E-mail: info@capitolstaffing.com
URL: http://www.capitolstaffing.com

Description: Personnel consultancy that focuses on office administration, management, sales, accounting, medical, information technology, accounting, and engineering/technical fields. Industries served: insurance, finance, medical, communications, investment, industry, and small businesses.

2444 ■ Career Advocates International
1539 Ave. A
Katy, TX 77493
Ph: (281)371-3917
E-mail: hank@careeradvocates.org
URL: http://www.careeradvocates.org

Description: Provides permanent placement and temporary staffing for executive and staff level positions. Specializes in multiple niches including: sales and marketing, accounting and financial services, banking, communications, human resources, chemicals, oil and gas, medical and dental, legal, information technology, energy, technology, engineering, manufacturing, construction, and light industrial.

2445 ■ Centennial, Inc.
8044 Montgomery Rd., Ste. 260
Cincinnati, OH 45236
Ph: (513)366-3760
Fax: (513)366-3761
URL: http://www.centennialinc.com

Description: Serves as an executive search firm specializing in the areas of executive and general management, accounting and finance, human resources, information technology, manufacturing, engineering, marketing and advertising, not-for-profit, sales and business development, and supply chain and logistics.

2446 ■ cFour Partners
100 Wilshire Blvd., Ste. 1840
Santa Monica, CA 90401
Ph: (310)471-5444

Fax: (310)388-0411
E-mail: info@cfour.com
URL: http://www.cfour.com/web/default.asp

Description: Executive search firm.

2447 ■ Chanko-Ward Ltd.
2 W 45th St., Ste. 1201
New York, NY 10036
Ph: (212)869-4040
Fax: (212)869-0281
E-mail: info@chankoward.com
URL: http://www.chankoward.com

Description: Primarily engaged in executive recruiting for individuals and corporations; where disciplines of accounting; planning, mergers and acquisitions; finance; or management information systems required.

2448 ■ Chaves & Associates
c/o InSite Search
418 Meadow St.
Fairfield, CT 06824
Ph: (203)222-2222
Fax: (203)341-8844
E-mail: info@insitesearch.com
URL: http://www.insitesearch.com

Description: Executive search firm.

2449 ■ Clovis, LLC
10411 Motor City Dr., Ste. 450
Bethesda, MD 20817
Ph: (301)365-8480
Free: 888-925-6847
Fax: (301)576-3579
E-mail: solutions@clovisgroup.com
URL: http://www.clovisgroup.com

Description: Serves as recruitment outsourcing staffing firm for information technology, accounting, and finance professionals.

2450 ■ CNR Search & Services
30752 Via Conquista
San Juan Capistrano, CA 92675
Ph: (949)488-0065
E-mail: cnrkenmiller@juno.com
URL: http://www.cnrsearch.com

Description: A highly respected international boutique search firm with a worldwide client-base. Our clients include both emerging and prominent corporations across a wide range of industries.

2451 ■ Computer Management
7982 Honeygo Blvd., No. 23
Baltimore, MD 21236
Ph: (410)679-7000
E-mail: info@technicaljobs.com
URL: http://www.technicaljobs.com

Description: Search firm focusing on filling jobs for database administration, network administration, web development, and software.

2452 ■ Conselium
14850 Montfort Dr., Ste. 106
Dallas, TX 75254
Ph: (972)934-8444
URL: http://www.conselium.com

Description: Executive search firm with a core expertise in corporate compliance, audit, and information technology security.

2453 ■ Cornell Global
PO Box 7113
Wilton, CT 06897
Ph: (203)762-0730
E-mail: info@cornellglobal.com
URL: http://www.cornellglobal.com

Description: Executive search firm with areas of expertise in the following areas: advertising, public relations, marketing, sales, finance and accounting, risk management, private equity and venture capital, construction, industrial, manufacturing, life sciences, publishing, information technology, engineering, human resources, legal, and logisitics.

2454 ■ CSI Executive Search LLC
9600 Great Hills Trail, Ste. 150W
Austin, TX 78759
Ph: (512)301-1119
Fax: (512)301-5559
E-mail: info@csi-executivesearch.com
URL: http://www.csi-executivesearch.com

Description: Executive search firm that specializes in the following arenas: accounting, engineering, healthcare, information technology, and legal.

2455 ■ Dahl-Morrow International
1821 Michael Faraday Dr., Ste. 202
Reston, VA 20190-5348
Ph: (703)787-8117
Fax: (703)787-8114
E-mail: dmi@dahl-morrowintl.com
URL: http://www.dahl-morrowintl.com

Description: Executive search firm specializing in high technology.

2456 ■ DillonGray
1796 Equestrian Dr.
Pleasanton, CA 94588
Ph: (925)846-9396
E-mail: info@dillongray.com
URL: http://www.dillongray.com

Description: Executive search firm focused on technology related companies.

2457 ■ Doleman Enterprises
11160-F S Lakes Dr., Ste. 326
Reston, VA 22091
Ph: (703)742-5454
Fax: (703)708-6992
E-mail: doleman@patriot.net

Description: Human resources firm specializes in recruiting for the high-tech, data and computer engineering and pharmaceutical industries.

2458 ■ Durakis Executive Search
PO Box 1523
Columbia, MD 21044
Ph: (410)740-7078
URL: http://www.durakis.com

Description: Executive search firm.

2459 ■ Dynamic Search Systems Inc.
220 W Campus Dr., Ste. 201
Arlington Heights, IL 60004-1499
Ph: (847)304-0700
Fax: (847)304-5859
E-mail: candidate@dssjobs.com
URL: http://www.dssjobs.com

Description: Provider of executive and professional search services to the IT community. Firm specializes in the placement of developers, programmers, programmer analysts, systems analysts, project leaders, project managers, systems programmers, data processing consultants, IT directors, and other information technology related candidates. Industries served: All.

2460 ■ EDP Staffing, LLC
PO Box 651
Hebron, CT 06231
Free: 860-781-6064
E-mail: info@edpstaffingllc.com
URL: http://www.edpstaffingllc.com

Description: Serves as an e-commerce and IT management search firm. Provides staffing solutions for contingency, retained, contract or temporary staffing. Specializes in the recruitment and placement of e-commerce applications specialists, core IT staff members or IT management professionals.

2461 ■ Effective Search Inc.
301 N Main St., Ste. 1320
Wichita, KS 67202-4813

Ph: (805)740-1999
E-mail: effsrch@aol.com

Description: Conducts executive professional level searches only. Firm specializes in information technology IT.

2462 ■ Executive Directions Inc.
PO Box 5742
Sarasota, FL 34277
Ph: (941)922-9180
E-mail: info@execdir.com
URL: http://www.execdir.com

Description: Executive search firm.

2463 ■ Focus Learning Corp.
1880 Santa Barbara St., Ste. 120
San Luis Obispo, CA 93401
Ph: (805)543-4895
Free: 800-458-5116
Fax: (805)543-4897
E-mail: info@focuslearning.com
URL: http://www.focuslearning.com

Description: Provider of professional services to corporations for the development and implementation of training programs. Assists clients with needs assessment related to training and professional development, goals definition, and development of training materials. Industries served include: government, utility, aerospace, business, and computer.

2464 ■ Howard Fischer Associates International Inc.
1800 Kennedy Blvd., Ste. 700
Philadelphia, PA 19103
Ph: (215)568-8363
Fax: (215)568-4815
E-mail: search@hfischer.com
URL: http://www.hfischer.com

Description: Executive search firm. Branches in Campbell, CA and Boston, MA.

2465 ■ Integrisource
1689 Mahan Center Blvd., Ste. B
Tallahassee, FL 32308
Ph: (850)575-5454
Free: 877-575-5454
Fax: (850)575-0984
E-mail: recruiting@integrisource.net
URL: http://www.integrisource.net

Description: Provides information technology staffing services to public and private organizations.

2466 ■ JES Search Firm Inc.
1021 Stovall Blvd., Ste. 600
Atlanta, GA 30319
Ph: (404)812-0622
Fax: (404)812-1910
E-mail: admin@jessearch.com
URL: http://www.jessearch.com

Description: Contract and permanent information technology search firm specializing in placing software developers as well as other information systems professionals.

2467 ■ Wendell L. Johnson Associates Inc.
12 Grandview Dr., Ste. 1117
Danbury, CT 06811-4321
Ph: (203)743-4112
Fax: (203)778-5377

Description: Executive search firm specializing in areas of workforce diversity, accounting/finance, human resources, marketing/sales, strategic planning and management information systems.

2468 ■ KLR Executive Search Group L.L.C.
951 N Main St.
Providence, RI 02904
Ph: (401)274-2001
Fax: (401)831-4018
E-mail: email@klrsearchgroup.com
URL: http://www.klrsearchgroup.com

Description: Career recruitment firm specializes in

the placement of accounting and financial and information technology professionals.

2469 ■ Louis Rudzinsky Associates Inc.
7 Mystic St., Ste. 203
Arlington, MA 02474
Ph: (781)862-6727
Fax: (781)862-6868
E-mail: lra@lra.com
URL: http://www.lra.com

Description: Provider of recruitment, placement, and executive search to industry (software, electronics, optics) covering positions in general management, manufacturing, engineering, and marketing. Personnel consulting activities include counsel to small and startup companies. Industries served: electronics, aerospace, optical, laser, computer, software, imaging, electro-optics, biotechnology, advanced materials, and solid-state/semiconductor.

2470 ■ LW Foote Company
PO Box 52762
Bellevue, WA 98004
Ph: (425)451-1660
E-mail: email@lwfoote.com
URL: http://www.lwfoote.com

Description: Executive search firm.

2471 ■ Management Architects
PO Box 350
Sonoma, CA 95476
Ph: (707)945-1340
E-mail: doug@managementarchitects.net
URL: http://www.managementarchitects.net

Description: Executive search firm. Focuses on networking industries.

2472 ■ Houser Martin Morris
110th Ave. NE, 110 Atrium Pl., Ste. 580
Bellevue, WA 98004
Ph: (425)453-2700
Fax: (425)453-8726
E-mail: info@houser.com
URL: http://www.houser.com

Description: Focus is in the areas of retained executive search, professional, and technical recruiting. Areas of specialization include software engineering, sales and marketing, information technology, legal, human resources, accounting and finance, manufacturing, factory automation and engineering.

2473 ■ Phillip's Personnel/Phillip's Temps
1675 Broadway, Ste. 2410
Denver, CO 80204
Ph: (303)893-1850
Fax: (303)893-0639
E-mail: info@phillipspersonnel.com
URL: http://www.phillipspersonnel.com

Description: Personnel recruiting and staffing consultants in: accounting and finance, management information systems, sales and marketing, engineering, administration, and general and executive management. Industries served: telecommunications, distribution, financial services, and general business.

2474 ■ Spectrum Group, LLC
1919 Gallows Rd., Ste. 600
Vienna, VA 22182
Ph: (703)738-1200
Fax: (703)761-9477
E-mail: web@spectrumcareers.com
URL: http://www.spectrumcareers.com

Description: Serves as executive search firm for accounting and finance, information technology, and sales and marketing industries.

2475 ■ TRC Staffing Services Inc.
115 Perimeter Center Pl. NE, Ste. 850
Atlanta, GA 30346
Ph: (770)392-1411
Free: 800-488-8008

Fax: (770)392-7926
E-mail: info@trcstaff.com
URL: http://www.trcstaffing.com

Description: A full-service executive search company with permanent placements encompassing engineering, industrial sales, financial and computer science positions. Screen, interview and verify past employment for all candidates prior to referral. Also assist personnel staffs in the attainment of their EEO/AAP goals with the placement of talented individuals in positions which were underutilized with minorities and/or women. Industries served: all.

ONLINE JOB SOURCES AND SERVICES

2476 ■ Benchfolks.com
URL: http://www.benchfolks.com

Description: Provides a one-stop shop for IT professionals, companies/clients and vendors/suppliers by catering to their employment needs. Caters to individual needs like professional standing in terms of qualification, level of expertise, experience gained and requirement of the industry.

2477 ■ ComputerWork.com
URL: http://www.computerwork.com

Description: Job search and resume submission service for professionals in information technology.

2478 ■ Computerworld Careers
URL: http://www.computerworld.com/careertopics/careers

Description: Offers career opportunities for IT (information technology) professionals. Job seekers may search the jobs database, register at the site, and read about job surveys and employment trends. Employers may post jobs.

2479 ■ Computing Research Association Job Announcements
URL: http://www.cra.org/ads

Description: Contains dated links to national college and university computer technology positions.

2480 ■ Dice.com
URL: http://www.dice.com

Description: Job search database for computer consultants and high-tech professionals, listing thousands of high tech permanent contract and consulting jobs for programmers, software engineers, systems administrators, web developers, and hardware engineers. Also free career advice e-mail newsletter and job posting e-alerts.

2481 ■ Guru.com
URL: http://www.guru.com

Description: Job board specializing in contract jobs for creative and information technology professionals. Also provides online incorporation and educational opportunities for independent contractors along with articles and advice.

2482 ■ InformationTechnologyCrossing.com
URL: http://www.informationtechnologycrossing.com

Description: Provides information on IT jobs.

2483 ■ IT Classifieds
URL: http://www.itclassifieds.com

Description: Serves as career site for information technology professionals.

2484 ■ ItJobs.com
URL: http://www.itjobs.com

Description: Provides information technology employment opportunities for the following categories: internet/intranet/extranet, network systems, open systems, client/server, software engineering and development, software QA and testing, ERP applications and management consulting, and legacy systems.

2485 ■ JustTechJobs.com
URL: http://www.justtechjobs.com

Description: Serves as a jobsite that provides employers with a technology specific focus and provides job seekers with job postings aimed at those specific tech jobs. Offers a community of 15 million tech professionals and also supports several technology websites.

2486 ■ Spherion
URL: http://www.spherion.com

Description: Recruitment firm specializing in accounting and finance, sales and marketing, interim executives, technology, engineering, retail and human resources.

2487 ■ Tech-Engine.com
URL: http://techengine.com

Description: Features employment listings concerning the IT and engineering fields. Features employers and recruiters information, resume posting and career resources.

2488 ■ TechCareers
URL: http://www.techcareers.com

Description: Features career-related resources, news, and job postings for information technology and engineering professionals.

2489 ■ ZDNet Tech Jobs
URL: http://www.zdnet.com

Description: Site houses a listing of national employment opportunities for professionals in high tech fields. Also contains resume building tips and relocation resources.

TRADESHOWS

2490 ■ Information Architecture Summit
American Society for Information Science and Technology
8555 16th St., Ste. 850
Silver Spring, MD 20910
Ph: (301)495-0900
Fax: (301)495-0810
E-mail: asis@asis.org
URL: http://www.asis.org

Annual. Features presentations from research and industry leaders, and opportunities for personal interaction among information architects and other user experience professionals.

2491 ■ Large Installation System Administration Conference
USENIX, the Advanced Computing Systems Association
2560 9th St., Ste. 215
Berkeley, CA 94710
Ph: (510)528-8649
Fax: (510)548-5738
E-mail: webster@usenix.org
URL: http://www.usenix.org

Frequency: Annual. Includes exhibits of books, products, and services that can optimize systems, networks, and internet management. 2013 November 3-8; Washington, DC; 2014 November 9-14; Seattle, WA; 2015 November 8-13; Washington, DC; 2016 December 4-9; Boston, MA. Provides networking opportunities for computing professionals.

2492 ■ Urban and Regional Information Systems Association Annual Conference and Exhibition
Urban and Regional Information Systems Association
701 Lee St., Ste. 680
Des Plaines, IL 60016
Ph: (847)824-6300

Fax: (847)824-6363
E-mail: info@urisa.org
URL: http://www.urisa.org
Frequency: Annual.

2493 ■ USENIX Annual Technical Conference
USENIX, the Advanced Computing Systems Association
2560 9th St., Ste. 215
Berkeley, CA 94710
Ph: (510)528-8649
Fax: (510)548-5738
E-mail: webster@usenix.org
URL: http://www.usenix.org

Frequency: Annual. Includes exhibits of products and services for the advancement of computing systems.

2494 ■ XPLOR International Conference and Vendor Forum
Xplor International
24156 State Rd. 54, Ste. 4
Lutz, FL 33559
Ph: (813)949-6170
Fax: (813)949-9977
E-mail: skip@xplor.org
URL: http://www.xplor.org

Frequency: Annual. **Primary Exhibits:** Equipment, supplies, and services for users and manufacturers of advanced electronic document systems.

ONLINE AND DATABASE SERVICES

2495 ■ Security Administrator Jobs
URL: http://www.securityadministratorjobs.org

Description: Serves as job board for security administrator employment opportunities and candidate recruiting. Provides listings of available security administrator positions.

OTHER SOURCES

2496 ■ AFCOM
9100 Chester Towne Centre Rd.
West Chester, OH 45069
Ph: (714)643-8110
Fax: (714)997-9743
E-mail: membership@afcom.com
URL: http://www.afcom.com

Description: Data center, networking and enterprise systems management professionals from medium and large scale mainframe, midrange and client/server data centers worldwide. Works to meet the professional needs of the enterprise system management community. Provides information and support through educational events, research and assistance hotlines, and surveys.

2497 ■ American Society for Information Science and Technology
8555 16th St., Ste. 850
Silver Spring, MD 20910
Ph: (301)495-0900
Fax: (301)495-0810
E-mail: asis@asis.org
URL: http://www.asis.org

Description: Information specialists, scientists, librarians, administrators, social scientists, and others interested in the use, organization, storage, retrieval, evaluation, and dissemination of recorded specialized information. Seeks to improve the information transfer process through research, development, application, and education. Provides a forum for the discussion, publication, and critical analysis of work dealing with the theory, practice, research, and development of elements involved in communication of information. Members are engaged in a variety of activities and specialties including classification and coding systems, automatic and associative indexing, machine translation of languages, special librarian-ship and library systems analysis, and copyright is-sues. Sponsors National Auxiliary Publications Service, which provides reproduction services and a central depository for all types of information. Maintains placement service. Sponsors numerous special interest groups. Conducts continuing educa-tion programs and professional development workshops.

2498 ■ Association of Information Technology Professionals
330 N Wabash Ave., Ste. 2000
Chicago, IL 60611-4267
Ph: (312)245-1070
Free: 800-224-9371
Fax: (312)673-6659
E-mail: aitp_hq@aitp.org
URL: http://www.aitp.org

Description: Managerial personnel, staff, educators, and individuals interested in the management of information resources. Founder of the Certificate in Data Processing examination program, now administered by an intersociety organization. Maintains Legislative Communications Network. Professional education programs include EDP-oriented business and management principles self-study courses and a series of videotaped manage-ment development seminars. Sponsors student organizations around the country interested in information technology and encourages members to serve as counselors for the Scout computer merit badge. Conducts research projects, including a busi-ness information systems curriculum for two- and four-year colleges.

2499 ■ Association for Women in Computing
PO Box 2768
Oakland, CA 94602
E-mail: info@awc-hq.org
URL: http://www.awc-hq.org

Description: Individuals interested in promoting the education, professional development, and advance-ment of women in computing.

2500 ■ *Career Opportunities in Computers and Cyberspace*
InfoBase Holdings Inc.
132 W 31st., 17 Fl.
New York, NY 10001-3406
Ph: (212)967-8800
Fax: (800)678-3633
E-mail: info@infobasepublishing.com
URLs: http://www.infobasepublishing.com; http://www.infobasepublishing.com/Bookdetail.aspx?ISBN=1438110669&eBooks=1

Frequency: Published March, 2004. **Description:** Harry Henderson. Second edition, 2004. 256 pages. **Covers:** Nearly 200 professions, clustering them by skill, objectives, and work conditions. **Includes:** Ap-pendices of educational institutions, periodicals, directories, and associations. **Entries include:** Education, salaries, employment prospects.

2501 ■ *Career Opportunities in Library and Information Science*
InfoBase Holdings Inc.
132 W 31st., 17 Fl.
New York, NY 10001-3406
Ph: (212)967-8800
Fax: (800)678-3633
E-mail: info@infobasepublishing.com
URLs: http://www.infobasepublishing.com; http://www.infobasepublishing.com/Bookdetail.aspx?ISBN=0816075468

Frequency: Published July, 2009. **Price:** $49.50 Individuals hardcover. **Pages:** 392. **Description:** Linda P. Carvell. 2005. 225 pages. **Covers:** More than 85 different jobs typically held by librarians, including academic, government, K-12, outside the library, public, and special. **Includes:** Appendices of educational institutions, periodicals, directories, and associations.

2502 ■ Computing Technology Industry Association
3500 Lacey Rd., Ste. 100
Downers Grove, IL 60515-5439
Ph: (630)678-8300
Fax: (630)678-8384
E-mail: membership@comptia.org
URL: http://www.comptia.org

Description: Trade association of more than 19,000 companies and professional IT members in the rapidly converging computing and communications market. Has members in more than 89 countries and provides a unified voice for the industry in the areas of e-commerce standards, vendor-neutral certifica-tion, service metrics, public policy and workforce development. Serves as information clearinghouse and resource for the industry; sponsors educational programs.

2503 ■ EC-Council
6330 Riverside Plaza Ln. NW, Ste. 210
Albuquerque, NM 87120
Ph: (505)341-3228
Fax: (505)341-0050
E-mail: info@eccouncil.org
URL: http://www.eccouncil.org

Description: Supports and enhances the role of individuals and organizations who design, create, manage or market security and e-business solutions. Offers Electronic Commerce Consultant certification and educational, technical, placement, and discounted services to its members. Provides a forum where discussion and information exchange can operate freely in the context of mutual trust and benefit.

2504 ■ Healthcare Information and Management Systems Society
33 W Monroe St., Ste. 1700
Chicago, IL 60603-5616
Ph: (312)664-4467
Fax: (312)664-6143
E-mail: himss@himss.org
URL: http://www.himss.org

Description: Represents persons who, by education and/or appropriate experience, are professionally qualified to engage in the analysis, design, and operation of health care information systems, management engineering, telecommunications, and clinical systems professions. Also, corporate members include companies with information technology solutions for health care organizations. Provides leadership in health care for the manage-ment of systems, information, and change, while striving for high quality, efficient and effective patient care through analysis and technology implementa-tion. Maintains speakers' bureau. Offers placement service.

2505 ■ IEEE Computer Society
2001 L St. NW, Ste. 700
Washington, DC 20036
Ph: (202)371-0101
Free: 800-272-6657

Fax: (202)728-9614
E-mail: help@computer.org
URL: http://www.computer.org

Description: Computer professionals. Promotes the development of computer and information sciences and fosters communication within the information processing community. Sponsors conferences, symposia, workshops, tutorials, technical meetings, and seminars. Operates Computer Society Press. Presents scholarships; bestows technical achieve-ment and service awards and certificates. **Members:** 90,000.

2506 ■ International Association for Computer and Information Science
735 Meadowbrook Dr.
Mount Pleasant, MI 48858
Ph: (989)774-1175
Fax: (989)774-1174
E-mail: lee1ry@cmich.edu
URL: http://www.acisinternational.org

Description: Represents individuals in the fields of computer and information science. Disseminates the latest developments in the fields of computer and information science. Provides a forum for research-ers in education and computer and information sci-ence industries.

2507 ■ IT Service Management Forum USA
PO Box 1907
Cypress, TX 77410
Ph: (626)963-1900
Fax: (888)959-0673
E-mail: info@itsmfusa.org
URL: http://www.itsmfusa.org

Description: Promotes IT Service Management best practices through knowledge sharing and educational and networking opportunities. Advances the cred-ibility and professionalism of all its members. Assists with the planning, development and implementation strategies of IT service management best practices.

2508 ■ Urban and Regional Information Systems Association
701 Lee St., Ste. 680
Des Plaines, IL 60016
Ph: (847)824-6300
Fax: (847)824-6363
E-mail: info@urisa.org
URL: http://www.urisa.org

Description: Represents professionals using Geographic Information Systems (GIS) and other information technologies to solve challenges in state and local government agencies. Promotes the effec-tive and ethical use of spatial information and information technologies for the understanding and management of urban and regional systems. Produces a number of educational conferences and publications.

2509 ■ USENIX, the Advanced Computing Systems Association
2560 9th St., Ste. 215
Berkeley, CA 94710
Ph: (510)528-8649
Fax: (510)548-5738
E-mail: webster@usenix.org
URL: http://www.usenix.org

Description: Represents the community of engineers, system administrators, scientists, and technicians working on the cutting edge of the computing world. Aims to foster technical excellence and innovation that pertains to computer systems. Supports and disseminates research with a practical bias. Provides a neutral forum for discussion of technical issues and encourages computing outreach into the community at large.

Sources of Help-Wanted Ads

2510 ■ *ACM Transactions on Internet Technology*
Association for Computing Machinery
2 Penn Plz., Ste. 701
New York, NY 10121-0701
Ph: (212)626-0500
Free: 800-342-6626
Fax: (212)944-1318
E-mail: acmhelp@acm.org
URL: http://toit.acm.org

Frequency: Quarterly; February, May, August and November. **Price:** $190 Nonmembers print only; $152 Nonmembers online only; $228 Nonmembers online and print. **Description:** Publication of the Association for Computing Machinery. Brings together many computing disciplines including computer software engineering, computer programming languages, middleware, database management, security, knowledge discovery and data mining, networking and distributed systems, communications, performance and scalability, and more. Covers the results and roles of the individual disciplines and the relationships among them.

2511 ■ *Communications of the ACM*
Association for Computing Machinery
2 Penn Plz., Ste. 701
New York, NY 10121-0701
Ph: (212)626-0500
Free: 800-342-6626
Fax: (212)944-1318
E-mail: acmhelp@acm.org
URL: http://cacm.acm.org

Frequency: Monthly. **Price:** $99 Members professional. **Description:** Computing news magazine.

2512 ■ *Communications and Network*
Scientific Research Publishing
PO Box 54821
Irvine, CA 92619-4821
E-mail: cn@scirp.org
URL: http://www.scirp.org/journal/cn/

Frequency: Quarterly. **Price:** $236 Individuals. **Description:** Journal publishing articles on the latest advancements in communications and network technologies.

2513 ■ *Computers and Composition*
Elsevier Science Inc.
Secondary Publishing Division
650 Ave. of the Americas
New York, NY 10011
Ph: (212)633-3980
Free: 888-437-4636
Fax: (212)633-3975
URL: http://www.elsevier.com/wps/find/journaldescription.cws_home/620371/description#description

Frequency: 4/yr. **Price:** $454 Individuals and institution; online; $82 Individuals print; $454 Institutions

print. **Description:** Journal covering computers in writing classes, programs, and research.

2514 ■ *Computerworld*
International Data Group Inc.
PO Box 9171
Framingham, MA 01701
Ph: (508)879-0700
E-mail: info@idg.com
URL: http://www.computerworld.com

Frequency: Weekly. **Price:** $129 Individuals; $129 Canada; $295 Other countries; $250 Individuals Mexico/Central/South America; $29 Individuals digital edition. **Description:** Newspaper for information systems executives.

2515 ■ *Computerworld Top 100*
IDG Communications Inc.
492 Old Connecticut Path
Framingham, MA 01701
Ph: (508)872-0080
URLs: http://www.idg.com/www/IDGProducts.nsf/
ByKey/Bulgaria_Publication_Computerworld-Top
-100; http://computerworld.bg/supplement/top100

Frequency: Annual. **Description:** Magazine for analyzing trends and events of information technology business.

2516 ■ *Cutter IT Journal*
Cutter Information Corp.
37 Broadway, Ste. 1
Arlington, MA 02474
Ph: (781)648-8700
Free: 800-964-5118
Fax: (781)648-1950
E-mail: service@cutter.com
URL: http://www.cutter.com/itjournal.html

Description: Monthly. $485. Provides IT managers with practical and objective views on the latest technology and management trends.

2517 ■ *Datamation: The Emerging Technologies Magazine for Today's IS*
Reed Elsevier Group plc - Reed Business Information
360 Park Ave. S
New York, NY 11010
Ph: (212)791-4208
E-mail: corporatecommunications@reedbusiness.com
URL: http://www.datamation.com

Frequency: Semimonthly. **Description:** Magazine on computers and information processing.

2518 ■ *Eclipse Review*
BZ Media LLC
7 High St. Ste. 407
Huntington, NY 11743
Ph: (631)421-4158
URL: http://www.eclipsesource.com/contact.htm

Description: Magazine for IT professionals.

2519 ■ *Foundations and Trends in Networking*
Now Publishers
PO Box 1024
Hanover, MA 02339-1001
Ph: (781)871-0245
E-mail: zac.rolnik@nowpublishers.com
URL: http://www.nowpublishers.com/journals/NET/
latest

Price: $440 Individuals online only; $510 Individuals print and online; €440 Other countries online only; €510 Other countries print and online. **Description:** Academic journal publishing new research in computer networking.

2520 ■ *Government Computer News*
PostNewsweek Tech Media
10 G St. NE, Ste. 500
Washington, DC 20002-4228
Ph: (202)772-2500
Free: 866-447-6864
Fax: (202)772-2511
URL: http://gcn.com/

Frequency: Semimonthly; 30/yr. **Description:** Magazine for professionals interested in government IT.

2521 ■ *IEEE Security & Privacy Magazine*
IEEE Computer Society
10662 Los Vaqueros Cir.
Los Alamitos, CA 90720-1314
Ph: (714)821-8380
Free: 800-272-6657
Fax: (714)821-4010
E-mail: help@computer.org
URL: http://www.computer.org/portal/site/security/

Frequency: Bimonthly. **Price:** $19.95 Individuals online; $65 Nonmembers print; $17.50 Students; $35 Individuals professional. **Description:** Journal that aims to explore role and importance of networked infrastructure and developing lasting security solutions.

2522 ■ *IEEE Software: Building the Community of Leading Software Practitioners*
IEEE Computer Society
10662 Los Vaqueros Cir.
Los Alamitos, CA 90720-1314
Ph: (714)821-8380
Free: 800-272-6657
Fax: (714)821-4010
E-mail: software@computer.org
URL: http://www.computer.org/portal/web/software/
home

Frequency: Bimonthly. **Price:** $990 Individuals online; $1,040 Individuals print; $1,300 Individuals print and online. **Description:** Magazine covering the computer software industry for the community of leading software practitioners.

2523 ■ iSeries News Magazine
Intertec Publishing
5 Penn Plz., 13th Fl.
New York, NY 10001-1810
Ph: (212)613-9700
Free: 800-795-5445
Fax: (212)613-9749
E-mail: service@iseriesnetwork.com
URL: http://www.systeminetwork.com/info/network-pubs/news400/about.html

Frequency: 11/yr. **Price:** $149 U.S. and Canada; $199 Other countries. **Description:** Trade magazine for programmers and data processing managers who use IBM iSeries.

2524 ■ IT Solutions Guide
SYS-CON Media
577 Chestnut Ridge Rd.
Woodcliff Lake, NJ 07677
Ph: (201)802-3000
Fax: (201)782-9601
E-mail: subscribe@sys-con.com
URL: http://itsolutions.sys-con.com

Frequency: Quarterly. **Description:** Magazine for IT professionals.

2525 ■ Journal of Computer Networks and Communications
Hindawi Publishing Corp.
410 Park Ave., 15th Fl.
287 PMB
New York, NY 10022-4407
Fax: (215)893-4392
E-mail: jcnc@hindawi.com
URL: http://www.hindawi.com/journals/jcnc/

Frequency: 2/yr. **Price:** $595 Individuals print & online. **Description:** Journal covering important areas of information technology.

2526 ■ Journal of Computer Science
Science Publications
Vails Gate Heights Dr.
Vails Gate, NY 12584-0879
URL: http://thescipub.com/jcs.toc

Frequency: Monthly. **Description:** Scholarly journal covering many areas of computer science, including: concurrent, parallel and distributed processing; artificial intelligence; image and voice processing; quality software and metrics; computer-aided education; wireless communication; real time processing; evaluative computation; and data bases and information recovery and neural networks.

2527 ■ Monitor: CPCUG's Print Magazine
Capital PC User Group
19209 Mt. Airey Rd.
Brookeville, MD 20833
Ph: (301)560-6442
Fax: (301)760-3303
E-mail: editor@cpcug.org
URL: http://monitor.cpcug.org/index.html

Frequency: Quarterly. **Description:** Magazine covering computer hardware and software reviews, special interest user group news, advertisers and author/subject index, and calendar of events.

2528 ■ Queue: Tomorrow's Computing Today
Association for Computing Machinery
2 Penn Plz., Ste. 701
New York, NY 10121-0701
Ph: (212)626-0500
Free: 800-342-6626
Fax: (212)944-1318
E-mail: queue@acm.org
URL: http://queue.acm.org/

Frequency: Monthly. **Price:** Free. **Description:** Online magazine aimed at the computer professional. Magazine editorial does not provide solutions for the "here-and-now", but instead helps decision-makers plan future projects by examining the challenges and problems they are most likely to face.

2529 ■ Revenue
Montgomery Media International
55 New Montgomery St., Ste. 617
San Francisco, CA 94105
Ph: (415)371-8800
E-mail: info@mthink.com
URL: http://www.revenuetoday.com/

Description: Magazine covering internet marketing strategies.

2530 ■ Ubiquity
Association for Computing Machinery
2 Penn Plz., Ste. 701
New York, NY 10121-0701
Ph: (212)626-0500
Free: 800-342-6626
Fax: (212)944-1318
E-mail: editors@ubiquity.acm.org
URL: http://ubiquity.acm.org

Frequency: Weekly. **Price:** Free. **Description:** Web-based magazine of the Association for Computing Machinery dedicated to fostering critical analysis and in-depth commentary, including book reviews, on issues relating to the nature, constitution, structure, science, engineering, cognition, technology, practices and paradigms of the IT profession.

2531 ■ WITI FastTrack
UBM L.L.C.
240 W 35th St.
New York, NY 10001
Ph: (516)562-5000
Free: 800-842-0798
Fax: (516)562-7830
E-mail: contact@ubmtechnology.com
URL: http://www.witi.com/corporate/fasttrack.php

Frequency: Semiannual. **Description:** Semiannual publication featuring in-depth content on the issues facing today's women professionals in technology.

EMPLOYER DIRECTORIES AND NETWORKING LISTS

2532 ■ Computer Directory
Computer Directories Inc.
23815 Nichols Sawmill Rd.
Hockley, TX 77447
Ph: (281)305-4170
E-mail: admin@compdirinc.com
URL: http://www.compdirinc.com

Frequency: Annual; fall. **Pages:** 500 per volume. **Covers:** Approximately 130,000 computer installations; 19 separate volumes for Alaska/Hawaii, Connecticut/New Jersey, Dallas/Ft. Worth, Eastern Seaboard, Far Midwest, Houston, Illinois, Midatlantic, Midcentral, Mideast, Minnesota/Wisconsin, North Central, New England, New York Metro, Northwest, Ohio, Pennsylvania/West Virginia, Southeast, and Southwest Texas. **Entries include:** Company name, address, phone, fax, email, name and title of contact, hardware used, software application, operating system, programming language, computer graphics, networking system. **Arrangement:** Geographical. **Indexes:** Alphabetical, industry, hardware.

2533 ■ Directory of Top Computer Executives
Applied Computer Research Inc.
PO Box 41730
Phoenix, AZ 85080
Ph: (623)937-4700
Free: 800-234-2227
Fax: (623)937-3115
E-mail: tara@topitexecs.com
URL: http://www.itmarketintelligence.com

Frequency: Semiannual; June and December. **Price:** $345 Individuals single volume, per issue; $520 U.S. and Canada single volume, per year; $620 Individuals two-volume set, per issue; $930 U.S. and Canada two-volume set, per year; $925 Individuals three-volume set, per issue; $1,390 U.S. and Canada

three-volume set, per year. **Pages:** 1,100 3 volumes. **Covers:** In three volumes, over 65,000 U.S. and Canadian executives with major information technology or communications responsibilities in over 35,500 U.S. and Canadian companies. **Includes:** Listings of manufacturer and model numbers of systems that are installed at each company. **Entries include:** Company name, address, phone, subsidiary and/or division names, major systems installed, names and titles of top information system executives, number of IT employees, number of PCs, and web address. **Arrangement:** Geographical within separate eastern, western, and Canadian volumes. **Indexes:** Industry; alphabetical by company name.

2534 ■ Vault Guide to the Top Internet Industry Employers
Vault.com Inc.
132 W 31st St., 17th Fl.
New York, NY 10001-3406
Ph: (212)366-4212
Free: 800-535-2074
Fax: (212)366-6117
E-mail: customerservice@vault.com
URL: http://www.vault.com

Frequency: Latest edition February, 2006. **Price:** $19.95 Individuals Online; $19.95 Members Gold. **Pages:** 256. **Covers:** Top employers in the Internet industry in United States. **Entries include:** Company name, contact person, address, location, phone and fax numbers, statistics and emails.

2535 ■ Vault Guide to the Top Tech Employers
Vault.com Inc.
132 W 31st St., 17th Fl.
New York, NY 10001-3406
Ph: (212)366-4212
Free: 800-535-2074
Fax: (212)366-6117
E-mail: customerservice@vault.com
URL: http://www.vault.com/wps/portal/usa/store/bookdetail?item_no=782

Frequency: Latest edition June, 2009. **Price:** $19.95 Individuals Online; $19.95 Members Gold. **Pages:** 538. **Covers:** Technology industry employers. **Entries include:** Name, address, phone, fax, website, and other branch office location. Also include company overviews, recent company news, information on the hiring process, key competitors, and employment contact.

HANDBOOKS AND MANUALS

2536 ■ America's Top 100 Computer and Technical Jobs
JIST Publishing
875 Montreal Way
Saint Paul, MN 55102-4245
Ph: (317)613-4200
Free: 800-648-5478
Fax: (800)328-4564
E-mail: info@jist.com
URL: http://www.jist.com

Description: Michael J. Farr. 2009. $17.95. 400 pages. Job hunting in computer and technical industries.

2537 ■ Chief Electronic Computer Operator
National Learning Corporation
212 Michael Dr.
Syosset, NY 11791
Ph: (516)921-8888
Free: 800-632-8888
Fax: (516)921-8743
E-mail: info@passbooks.com
URL: http://www.passbooks.com

Description: 2009. $34.95 (paper). Serves as an exam preparation guide for chief electronic computer operators.

2538 ■ *Expert Resumes for Computer and Web Jobs*
JIST Publishing
875 Montreal Way
Saint Paul, MN 55102-4245
Ph: (317)613-4200
Free: 800-648-5478
Fax: (800)328-4564
E-mail: info@jist.com
URL: http://www.jist.com

Description: Wendy Enelow and Louise Kursmark. Third edition, 2011. $17.95 (paper). 304 pages. Contains a collection of sample resumes and resume writing advice including how to create and use an electronic resume. Contains an appendix that includes internet resources for an online job search, writing cover letters, as well as a collection of sample letters.

EMPLOYMENT AGENCIES AND SEARCH FIRMS

2539 ■ **The Aspire Group**
711 Boylston St.
Boston, MA 02116-2616
Free: 800-487-2967
Fax: (617)500-7284
URL: http://www.bmanet.com/Aspire/index.html

Description: Employment agency.

2540 ■ **Worlco Computer Resources, Inc.**
901 Rte. 38
Cherry Hill, NJ 08002
Ph: (610)293-9070
Fax: (856)665-8903
E-mail: recruiter@worlco.com
URL: http://www.worlco.com

Description: Employment agency and executive search firm. Second location in Cherry Hill, New Jersey.

ONLINE JOB SOURCES AND SERVICES

2541 ■ **ComputerJobs.com**
URL: http://www.computerjobs.com

Description: Provides listings of computer-related job opportunities.

2542 ■ **ComputerWork.com**
URL: http://www.computerwork.com

Description: Job search and resume submission service for professionals in information technology.

2543 ■ **Computerworld Careers**
URL: http://www.computerworld.com/careertopics/careers

Description: Offers career opportunities for IT (information technology) professionals. Job seekers may search the jobs database, register at the site, and read about job surveys and employment trends. Employers may post jobs.

2544 ■ **Computing Research Association Job Announcements**
URL: http://www.cra.org/ads

Description: Contains dated links to national college and university computer technology positions.

2545 ■ **Guru.com**
URL: http://www.guru.com

Description: Job board specializing in contract jobs for creative and information technology professionals. Also provides online incorporation and educational opportunities for independent contractors along with articles and advice.

2546 ■ **InformationTechnologyCrossing.com**
URL: http://www.informationtechnologycrossing.com

Description: Provides information on IT jobs.

2547 ■ **ItJobs.com**
URL: http://www.itjobs.com

Description: Provides information technology employment opportunities for the following categories: internet/intranet/extranet, network systems, open systems, client/server, software engineering and development, software QA and testing, ERP applications and management consulting, and legacy systems.

2548 ■ **JustTechJobs.com**
URL: http://www.justtechjobs.com

Description: Serves as a jobsite that provides employers with a technology specific focus and provides job seekers with job postings aimed at those specific tech jobs. Offers a community of 15 million tech professionals and also supports several technology websites.

2549 ■ **Tech-Engine.com**
URL: http://techengine.com

Description: Features employment listings concerning the IT and engineering fields. Features employers and recruiters information, resume posting and career resources.

2550 ■ **ThinkEnergyGroup.com**
URL: http://www.thinkenergygroup.com

Description: Serves as a job board for professionals looking for positions in engineering, power plant, energy, and technical fields. Contains advice and tips on interviews, job searching, resume writing, hiring, and management. Provides choices of work location, pay rates in the field of expertise and contract, temp-to-hire, and direct hiring options.

2551 ■ **ZDNet Tech Jobs**
URL: http://www.zdnet.com

Description: Site houses a listing of national employment opportunities for professionals in high tech fields. Also contains resume building tips and relocation resources.

TRADESHOWS

2552 ■ **XPLOR International Conference and Vendor Forum**
Xplor International
24156 State Rd. 54, Ste. 4
Lutz, FL 33559
Ph: (813)949-6170
Fax: (813)949-9977
E-mail: skip@xplor.org
URL: http://www.xplor.org

Frequency: Annual. **Primary Exhibits:** Equipment, supplies, and services for users and manufacturers of advanced electronic document systems.

OTHER SOURCES

2553 ■ **AFCOM**
9100 Chester Towne Centre Rd.
West Chester, OH 45069
Ph: (714)643-8110
Fax: (714)997-9743
E-mail: membership@afcom.com
URL: http://www.afcom.com

Description: Data center, networking and enterprise systems management professionals from medium and large scale mainframe, midrange and client/server data centers worldwide. Works to meet the professional needs of the enterprise system management community. Provides information and support through educational events, research and assistance hotlines, and surveys.

2554 ■ **Association for Computing Machinery - Special Interest Group on Accessible Computing**
2 Penn Plz., Ste. 701
New York, NY 10121-0701
Ph: (212)626-0500
Free: 800-342-6626
Fax: (212)944-1318
E-mail: chair_sigaccess@acm.org
URL: http://www.sigaccess.org

Description: Promotes the professional interests of computing personnel with physical disabilities and the application of computing and information technology in solving relevant disability problems. Works to educate the public to support careers for the disabled. **Members:** 453.

2555 ■ **Association of Information Technology Professionals**
330 N Wabash Ave., Ste. 2000
Chicago, IL 60611-4267
Ph: (312)245-1070
Free: 800-224-9371
Fax: (312)673-6659
E-mail: aitp_hq@aitp.org
URL: http://www.aitp.org

Description: Managerial personnel, staff, educators, and individuals interested in the management of information resources. Founder of the Certificate in Data Processing examination program, now administered by an intersociety organization. Maintains Legislative Communications Network. Professional education programs include EDP-oriented business and management principles self-study courses and a series of videotaped management development seminars. Sponsors student organizations around the country interested in information technology and encourages members to serve as counselors for the Scout computer merit badge. Conducts research projects, including a business information systems curriculum for two- and four-year colleges.

2556 ■ **Association for Women in Computing**
PO Box 2768
Oakland, CA 94602
E-mail: info@awc-hq.org
URL: http://www.awc-hq.org

Description: Individuals interested in promoting the education, professional development, and advancement of women in computing.

2557 ■ **Black Data Processing Associates**
9500 Arena Dr., Ste. 350
Largo, MD 20774
Ph: (301)584-3135
Fax: (301)560-8300
E-mail: office@bdpa.org
URL: http://www.bdpa.org

Description: Represents persons employed in the information processing industry, including electronic data processing, electronic word processing and data communications; others interested in information processing. Seeks to accumulate and share information processing knowledge and business expertise to increase the career and business potential of minorities in the information processing field. Conducts professional seminars, workshops, tutoring services and community introductions to data processing. Makes annual donation to the United Negro College Fund.

2558 ■ **Computing Research Association**
1828 L St. NW, Ste. 800
Washington, DC 20036-4632
Ph: (202)234-2111
Fax: (202)667-1066
E-mail: info@cra.org
URL: http://www.cra.org

Description: An association of more than 200 North American academic departments of computer science, computer engineering, and related fields; laboratories and centers in industry government, and academia engaging in basic computing research; and affiliated professional societies.

2559 ■ MIT Computer Science and Artificial Intelligence Laboratory
32 Vassar St.
Cambridge, MA 02139
Ph: (617)253-5851
Fax: (617)258-8682
URL: http://www.csail.mit.edu
Description: Active since 1959. interdisciplinary

laboratory of over 200 people that spans several academic departments and has active projects ongoing with members of every academic school at MIT. Offers research, current job listings, and educational outreach.

2560 ■ National Association of Government Webmasters
86 Woodstone Rd.
Rockaway, NJ 07866

Ph: (973)594-6249
E-mail: board@nagw.org
URL: http://www.nagw.org

Description: Provides a way for local and state government webmasters to share knowledge, ideas and resources with others who have similar positions. Coordinates national conferences, monthly webinars, and facilitates the networking of all members with a listserv. Strives to merge the combined efforts of state and local webmasters into one strong voice.

SOURCES OF HELP-WANTED ADS

2561 ■ ACM Transactions on Graphics
Association for Computing Machinery
2 Penn Plz., Ste. 701
New York, NY 10121-0701
Ph: (212)626-0500
Free: 800-342-6626
Fax: (212)944-1318
E-mail: acmhelp@acm.org
URL: http://tog.acm.org/
Frequency: Quarterly. **Price:** $220 Nonmembers;
$176 Nonmembers online; $264 Nonmembers online
& print. **Description:** Computer graphics journal.

2562 ■ ACM Transactions on Internet Technology
Association for Computing Machinery
2 Penn Plz., Ste. 701
New York, NY 10121-0701
Ph: (212)626-0500
Free: 800-342-6626
Fax: (212)944-1318
E-mail: acmhelp@acm.org
URL: http://toit.acm.org
Frequency: Quarterly; February, May, August and
November. **Price:** $190 Nonmembers print only;
$152 Nonmembers online only; $228 Nonmembers
online and print. **Description:** Publication of the Association for Computing Machinery. Brings together
many computing disciplines including computer
software engineering, computer programming
languages, middleware, database management,
security, knowledge discovery and data mining,
networking and distributed systems, communications,
performance and scalability, and more. Covers the
results and roles of the individual disciplines and the
relationships among them.

2563 ■ Communications of the ACM
Association for Computing Machinery
2 Penn Plz., Ste. 701
New York, NY 10121-0701
Ph: (212)626-0500
Free: 800-342-6626
Fax: (212)944-1318
E-mail: acmhelp@acm.org
URL: http://cacm.acm.org
Frequency: Monthly. **Price:** $99 Members professional. **Description:** Computing news magazine.

2564 ■ Communications and Network
Scientific Research Publishing
PO Box 54821
Irvine, CA 92619-4821
E-mail: cn@scirp.org
URL: http://www.scirp.org/journal/cn/
Frequency: Quarterly. **Price:** $236 Individuals.
Description: Journal publishing articles on the latest
advancements in communications and network
technologies.

2565 ■ Computers and Composition
Elsevier Science Inc.
Secondary Publishing Division
650 Ave. of the Americas
New York, NY 10011
Ph: (212)633-3980
Free: 888-437-4636
Fax: (212)633-3975
URL: http://www.elsevier.com/wps/find/journalde-
scription.cws_home/620371/description#description
Frequency: 4/yr. **Price:** $454 Individuals and institution; online; $82 Individuals print; $454 Institutions
print. **Description:** Journal covering computers in
writing classes, programs, and research.

2566 ■ Computerworld
International Data Group Inc.
PO Box 9171
Framingham, MA 01701
Ph: (508)879-0700
E-mail: info@idg.com
URL: http://www.computerworld.com
Frequency: Weekly. **Price:** $129 Individuals; $129
Canada; $295 Other countries; $250 Individuals
Mexico/Central/South America; $29 Individuals digital
edition. **Description:** Newspaper for information
systems executives.

2567 ■ Computerworld Top 100
IDG Communications Inc.
492 Old Connecticut Path
Framingham, MA 01701
Ph: (508)872-0080
URLs: http://www.idg.com/www/IDGProducts.nsf/
ByKey/Bulgaria_Publication_Computerworld-Top
-100; http://computerworld.bg/supplement/top100
Frequency: Annual. **Description:** Magazine for
analyzing trends and events of information technology business.

2568 ■ Computing Surveys
Association for Computing Machinery
c/o Lorenzo Alvisi, Assoc. Ed.
University of Texas at Austin
Department of Computer Science
1 University Sta. C0500
Austin, TX 78712-0233
Ph: (512)471-9792
Fax: (512)232-7886
E-mail: acmhelp@acm.org
URL: http://surveys.acm.org/
Frequency: Quarterly. **Price:** $205 Nonmembers
print only; $164 Nonmembers online only; $246
Nonmembers online & print. **Description:** Journal
presenting surveys and tutorials in computer science.

2569 ■ Cutter IT Journal
Cutter Information Corp.
37 Broadway, Ste. 1
Arlington, MA 02474
Ph: (781)648-8700
Free: 800-964-5118

Fax: (781)648-1950
E-mail: service@cutter.com
URL: http://www.cutter.com/itjournal.html
Description: Monthly. $485. Provides IT managers
with practical and objective views on the latest
technology and management trends.

2570 ■ Datamation: The Emerging Technologies Magazine for Today's IS
Reed Elsevier Group plc - Reed Business Information
360 Park Ave. S
New York, NY 11010
Ph: (212)791-4208
E-mail: corporatecommunications@reedbusiness.
com
URL: http://www.datamation.com
Frequency: Semimonthly. **Description:** Magazine
on computers and information processing.

2571 ■ Eclipse Review
BZ Media LLC
7 High St. Ste. 407
Huntington, NY 11743
Ph: (631)421-4158
URL: http://www.eclipsesource.com/contact.htm
Description: Magazine for IT professionals.

2572 ■ Foundations and Trends in Networking
Now Publishers
PO Box 1024
Hanover, MA 02339-1001
Ph: (781)871-0245
E-mail: zac.rolnik@nowpublishers.com
URL: http://www.nowpublishers.com/journals/NET/
latest
Price: $440 Individuals online only; $510 Individuals
print and online; €440 Other countries online only;
€510 Other countries print and online. **Description:**
Academic journal publishing new research in
computer networking.

2573 ■ Government Computer News
PostNewsweek Tech Media
10 G St. NE, Ste. 500
Washington, DC 20002-4228
Ph: (202)772-2500
Free: 866-447-6864
Fax: (202)772-2511
URL: http://gcn.com/
Frequency: Semimonthly; 30/yr. **Description:**
Magazine for professionals interested in government
IT.

2574 ■ IEEE Computer Graphics and Applications
IEEE Computer Society
10662 Los Vaqueros Cir.
Los Alamitos, CA 90720-1314
Ph: (714)821-8380
Free: 800-272-6657

Fax: (714)821-4010
E-mail: cga-ma@computer.org
URL: http://www.computer.org/portal/web/cga
Frequency: Bimonthly. **Price:** $1,020 Individuals online; $1,065 Individuals print; $1,330 Individuals print and online. **Description:** Magazine addressing the interests and needs of professional designers and users of computer graphics hardware, software, and systems.

2575 ■ IEEE Security & Privacy Magazine
IEEE Computer Society
10662 Los Vaqueros Cir.
Los Alamitos, CA 90720-1314
Ph: (714)821-8380
Free: 800-272-6657
Fax: (714)821-4010
E-mail: help@computer.org
URL: http://www.computer.org/portal/site/security/
Frequency: Bimonthly. **Price:** $19.95 Individuals online; $65 Nonmembers print; $17.50 Students; $35 Individuals professional. **Description:** Journal that aims to explore role and importance of networked infrastructure and developing lasting security solutions.

2576 ■ IEEE Software: Building the Community of Leading Software Practitioners
IEEE Computer Society
10662 Los Vaqueros Cir.
Los Alamitos, CA 90720-1314
Ph: (714)821-8380
Free: 800-272-6657
Fax: (714)821-4010
E-mail: software@computer.org
URL: http://www.computer.org/portal/web/software/home
Frequency: Bimonthly. **Price:** $990 Individuals online; $1,040 Individuals print; $1,300 Individuals print and online. **Description:** Magazine covering the computer software industry for the community of leading software practitioners.

2577 ■ InfoWorld: Defining Technology for Business
InfoWorld Media Group
501 2nd St.
San Francisco, CA 94107
Free: 800-227-8365
E-mail: letters@infoworld.com
URL: http://www.infoworld.com/
Frequency: Weekly. **Price:** $180 Individuals. **Description:** Weekly publication.

2578 ■ International Journal of Computational Bioscience
ACTA Press
Bldg. B6, Ste. 101
Calgary, AB, Canada T3E 7J9
Ph: (403)288-1195
Fax: (403)247-6851
E-mail: journals@actapress.com
URL: http://www.actapress.com/Content_of_Journal.aspx?journalID=148
Frequency: Annual. **Price:** $120 Individuals. **Description:** Journal featuring research articles that combine biological and computational research to enhance the scientific understanding of life.

2579 ■ International Journal for Multiscale Computational Engineering
Begell House Inc.
50 Cross Hwy.
Redding, CT 06896
Ph: (203)938-1300
Fax: (203)938-1304
E-mail: orders@begellhouse.com
URL: http://www.begellhouse.com/journals/61fd1b191cf7e96f
Price: $1,332 Institutions. **Description:** Journal featuring the advancement of multiscale computational science and engineering.

2580 ■ iSeries News Magazine
Intertec Publishing
5 Penn Plz., 13th Fl.
New York, NY 10001-1810
Ph: (212)613-9700
Free: 800-795-5445
Fax: (212)613-9749
E-mail: service@iseriesnetwork.com
URL: http://www.systeminetwork.com/info/network-pubs/news400/about.html
Frequency: 11/yr. **Price:** $149 U.S. and Canada; $199 Other countries. **Description:** Trade magazine for programmers and data processing managers who use IBM iSeries.

2581 ■ IT Solutions Guide
SYS-CON Media
577 Chestnut Ridge Rd.
Woodcliff Lake, NJ 07677
Ph: (201)802-3000
Fax: (201)782-9601
E-mail: subscribe@sys-con.com
URL: http://itsolutions.sys-con.com
Frequency: Quarterly. **Description:** Magazine for IT professionals.

2582 ■ Journal of Computer Networks and Communications
Hindawi Publishing Corp.
410 Park Ave., 15th Fl.
287 PMB
New York, NY 10022-4407
Fax: (215)893-4392
E-mail: jcnc@hindawi.com
URL: http://www.hindawi.com/journals/jcnc/
Frequency: 2/yr. **Price:** $595 Individuals print & online. **Description:** Journal covering important areas of information technology.

2583 ■ Journal of Computer Science
Science Publications
Vails Gate Heights Dr.
Vails Gate, NY 12584-0879
URL: http://thescipub.com/jcs.toc
Frequency: Monthly. **Description:** Scholarly journal covering many areas of computer science, including: concurrent, parallel and distributed processing; artificial intelligence; image and voice processing; quality software and metrics; computer-aided education; wireless communication; real time processing; evaluative computation; and data bases and information recovery and neural networks.

2584 ■ Monitor: CPCUG's Print Magazine
Capital PC User Group
19209 Mt. Airey Rd.
Brookeville, MD 20833
Ph: (301)560-6442
Fax: (301)760-3303
E-mail: editor@cpcug.org
URL: http://monitor.cpcug.org/index.html
Frequency: Quarterly. **Description:** Magazine covering computer hardware and software reviews, special interest user group news, advertisers and author/subject index, and calendar of events.

2585 ■ PC Today: Computing for Small Business
Sandhills Publishing Co.
131 W Grand Dr.
Lincoln, NE 68521
Ph: (402)479-2181
Free: 800-331-1978
Fax: (402)479-2195
E-mail: editor@pctoday.com
URL: http://www.pctoday.com/
Frequency: Monthly. **Price:** $29 Individuals; $37 Canada; $64 Canada 2 years; $2.42 Individuals print; $17 Individuals online only; $69 Other countries; $48 Individuals 2 years; $64 Individuals 3 years; $82 Canada 3 years; $64 Canada 2 years. **Description:** Magazine for personal computer users.

2586 ■ PC WORLD: The Magazine of Business Computing
101 Communications
501 2nd St.
San Francisco, CA 94107
Ph: (415)243-0500
Fax: (415)442-1891
E-mail: pcwletters@pcworld.com
URL: http://www.pcworld.com
Frequency: Quarterly. **Price:** $19.97 Individuals; $29.97 Two years. **Description:** Technology or business magazine meeting the informational needs of tech-savvy managers, both at work and at home.

2587 ■ Queue: Tomorrow's Computing Today
Association for Computing Machinery
2 Penn Plz., Ste. 701
New York, NY 10121-0701
Ph: (212)626-0500
Free: 800-342-6626
Fax: (212)944-1318
E-mail: queue@acm.org
URL: http://queue.acm.org/
Frequency: Monthly. **Price:** Free. **Description:** Online magazine aimed at the computer professional. Magazine editorial does not provide solutions for the "here-and-now", but instead helps decision-makers plan future projects by examining the challenges and problems they are most likely to face.

2588 ■ Revenue
Montgomery Media International
55 New Montgomery St., Ste. 617
San Francisco, CA 94105
Ph: (415)371-8800
E-mail: info@mthink.com
URL: http://www.revenuetoday.com/
Description: Magazine covering internet marketing strategies.

2589 ■ Ubiquity
Association for Computing Machinery
2 Penn Plz., Ste. 701
New York, NY 10121-0701
Ph: (212)626-0500
Free: 800-342-6626
Fax: (212)944-1318
E-mail: editors@ubiquity.acm.org
URL: http://ubiquity.acm.org/
Frequency: Weekly. **Price:** Free. **Description:** Web-based magazine of the Association for Computing Machinery dedicated to fostering critical analysis and in-depth commentary, including book reviews, on issues relating to the nature, constitution, structure, science, engineering, cognition, technology, practices and paradigms of the IT profession.

2590 ■ WITI FastTrack
UBM L.L.C.
240 W 35th St.
New York, NY 10001
Ph: (516)562-5000
Free: 800-842-0798
Fax: (516)562-7830
E-mail: contact@ubmtechnology.com
URL: http://www.witi.com/corporate/fasttrack.php
Frequency: Semiannual. **Description:** Semiannual publication featuring in-depth content on the issues facing today's women professionals in technology.

EMPLOYER DIRECTORIES AND NETWORKING LISTS

2591 ■ Computer Directory
Computer Directories Inc.
23815 Nichols Sawmill Rd.
Hockley, TX 77447
Ph: (281)305-4170
E-mail: admin@compdirinc.com
URL: http://www.compdirinc.com

Frequency: Annual; fall. **Pages:** 500 per volume. **Covers:** Approximately 130,000 computer installations; 19 separate volumes for Alaska/Hawaii, Connecticut/New Jersey, Dallas/Ft. Worth, Eastern Seaboard, Far Midwest, Houston, Illinois, Midatlantic, Midcentral, Mideast, Minnesota/Wisconsin, North Central, New England, New York Metro, Northwest, Ohio, Pennsylvania/West Virginia, Southeast, and Southwest Texas. **Entries include:** Company name, address, phone, fax, email, name and title of contact, hardware used, software application, operating system, programming language, computer graphics, networking system. **Arrangement:** Geographical. **Indexes:** Alphabetical, industry, hardware.

2592 ■ Critical Technologies Sourcebook

Frequency: Annual; February. **Price:** $5,000 payment must accompany order. **Pages:** 400. **Covers:** Over 300 companies involved in the development of artificial intelligence technology such as voice recognition systems, intelligent text systems, computer programming languages, virtual reality, and fuzzy logic. **Includes:** Discussion of trends and sectors of the artificial intelligence industry. **Entries include:** Company name, address, phone, contact person, year established, whether public or private, description of research and technology. **Arrangement:** Company name. **Indexes:** Alphabetical (with phone).

2593 ■ Directory of Top Computer Executives

Applied Computer Research Inc.
PO Box 41730
Phoenix, AZ 85080
Ph: (623)937-4700
Free: 800-234-2227
Fax: (623)937-3115
E-mail: tara@topitexecs.com
URL: http://www.itmarketintelligence.com
Frequency: Semiannual; June and December. **Price:** $345 Individuals single volume, per issue; $520 U.S. and Canada single volume, per year; $620 Individuals two-volume set, per issue; $930 U.S. and Canada two-volume set, per year; $925 Individuals three-volume set, per issue; $1,390 U.S. and Canada three-volume set, per year. **Pages:** 1,100 3 volumes. **Covers:** In three volumes, over 65,000 U.S. and Canadian executives with major information technology or communications responsibilities in over 35,500 U.S. and Canadian companies. **Includes:** Listings of manufacturer and model numbers of systems that are installed at each company. **Entries include:** Company name, address, phone, subsidiary and/or division names, major systems installed, names and titles of top information system executives, number of IT employees, number of PCs, and web address. **Arrangement:** Geographical within separate eastern, western, and Canadian volumes. **Indexes:** Industry; alphabetical by company name.

2594 ■ Vault Guide to the Top Tech Employers

Vault.com Inc.
132 W 31st St., 17th Fl.
New York, NY 10001-3406
Ph: (212)366-4212
Free: 800-535-2074
Fax: (212)366-6117
E-mail: customerservice@vault.com
URL: http://www.vault.com/wps/portal/usa/store/bookdetail?item_no=782
Frequency: Latest edition June, 2009. **Price:** $19.95 Individuals Online; $19.95 Members Gold. **Pages:** 538. **Covers:** Technology industry employers. **Entries include:** Name, address, phone, fax, website, and other branch office location. Also include company overviews, recent company news, information on the hiring process, key competitors, and employment contact.

HANDBOOKS AND MANUALS

2595 ■ America's Top 100 Computer and Technical Jobs

JIST Publishing
875 Montreal Way
Saint Paul, MN 55102-4245

Ph: (317)613-4200
Free: 800-648-5478
Fax: (800)328-4564
E-mail: info@jist.com
URL: http://www.jist.com
Description: Michael J. Farr. 2009. $17.95. 400 pages. Job hunting in computer and technical industries.

2596 ■ Expert Resumes for Computer and Web Jobs

JIST Publishing
875 Montreal Way
Saint Paul, MN 55102-4245
Ph: (317)613-4200
Free: 800-648-5478
Fax: (800)328-4564
E-mail: info@jist.com
URL: http://www.jist.com
Description: Wendy Enelow and Louise Kursmark. Third edition, 2011. $17.95 (paper). 304 pages. Contains a collection of sample resumes and resume writing advice including how to create and use an electronic resume. Contains an appendix that includes internet resources for an online job search, writing cover letters, as well as a collection of sample letters.

2597 ■ New Programmer's Survival Manual

The Pragmatic Bookshelf
c/o Dave Thomas
2831 El Dorado Pkwy., No. 103-381
Frisco, TX 75033
Ph: (214)233-6543
E-mail: dave@pragprog.com
URL: http://pragprog.com
Description: Josh Carter. 2011. $29.00 (paper). 250 pages. Offers an in-depth look at the professional programming industry. Introduces novice programmers to professional practices for working on large-scale programs. Includes tips and tools for navigating the corporate environment, working with teammates, and dealing with other people from other departments.

2598 ■ Practices of an Agile Developer: Working in the Real World

Pragamatic Bookshelf
9650 Strickland Rd., Ste. 103, PMB 255
Raleigh, NC 27615
Ph: (919)847-3884
Free: 800-699-7764
E-mail: sales@pragmaticprogrammer.com
URL: http://pragprog.com/titles/pad/practices-of-an-agile-developer
Description: Venkat Subramaniam and Andy Hunt. 2006. $29.95. 208 pages. Provides expertise in the areas of development processes, coding techniques, developer attitudes, project and team management, and iterative and incremental learning techniques in the field of computer programming.

2599 ■ Principal Computer Programmer

National Learning Corporation
212 Michael Dr.
Syosset, NY 11791
Ph: (516)921-8888
Free: 800-632-8888
Fax: (516)921-8743
E-mail: info@passbooks.com
URL: http://www.passbooks.com
Description: 2009. $34.95 (paper). Serves as an exam preparation guide for principal computer programmers.

EMPLOYMENT AGENCIES AND SEARCH FIRMS

2600 ■ Access Staffing

360 Lexington Ave., 8th Fl.
New York, NY 10017

Ph: (212)687-5440
Fax: (212)557-2544
URL: http://www.accessstaffingco.com
Description: Serves as a staffing firm covering accounting/financial, advertising, bilingual Japanese, creative, event planning, fashion/retail, healthcare/human services, human resources, information technology, insurance, legal, light industrial, and office support.

2601 ■ Michael Anthony Associates Inc.

44 Washington St., Ste. 250
Wellesley, MA 02481-1802
Ph: (781)237-4950
Free: 800-337-4950
Fax: (781)237-6811
E-mail: manthony@maainc.com
URL: http://www.maainc.com
Description: Applications development, systems programming, communications, and database specialists servicing the IBM mainframe, midrange, and PC marketplace. Provides technical expertise of conversions, system software installation and upgrades, performance and tuning, capacity planning, and data communications. In addition to contract services, also provides retained search and contingency placement of computer professionals ranging from senior staff to senior management.

2602 ■ The Aspire Group

711 Boylston St.
Boston, MA 02116-2616
Free: 800-487-2967
Fax: (617)500-7284
URL: http://www.bmanet.com/Aspire/index.html
Description: Employment agency.

2603 ■ ATR Technology

1230 Oakmead Pkwy., Ste. 110
Sunnyvale, CA 94085
Ph: (408)328-8000
E-mail: corporate@atr1.com
URL: http://www.atr-technology.com
Description: Serves as an executive search firm specializing in the placement of information technology professionals ranging from complex software application development and infrastructure support to enterprise-wide project management.

2604 ■ BG & Associates

10112 Langhorne Ct., Ste. B
Bethesda, MD 20817-1250
Ph: (301)365-4046
Fax: (301)365-0435
E-mail: bgajob@erols.com
Description: Firm specializes in the recruitment and placement of consultants on a national basis primarily in the areas of information technology, finance/accounting, and human resources.

2605 ■ Busch International

1000 Fremont Ave., Ste. 195
Los Altos, CA 94024
Ph: (650)949-6500
E-mail: jack@buschint.com
URL: http://www.buschint.com
Description: Executive search firm focused solely on high-technology electronics.

2606 ■ C Associates

1619 G St. SE
Washington, DC 20056-3868
Ph: (202)518-8595
Fax: (202)387-7033
Description: Personnel consultants specialize in the placement of computer professionals, concentrating in UNIX/C++ candidates. Serves private industries as well as government contractors. Also focus on oracle, ASP and visual basic developers, programmers, system administrators and web developers.

2607 ■ Capitol Staffing Inc.
460 Briarwood Dr., Briarwood 1 Bldg., Ste. 110
Jackson, MS 39206
Ph: (601)957-1755
Fax: (601)957-3880
E-mail: info@capitolstaffing.com
URL: http://www.capitolstaffing.com
Description: Personnel consultancy that focuses on office administration, management, sales, accounting, medical, information technology, accounting, and engineering/technical fields. Industries served: insurance, finance, medical, communications, investment, industry, and small businesses.

2608 ■ Career Advocates International
1539 Ave. A
Katy, TX 77493
Ph: (281)371-3917
E-mail: hank@careeradvocates.org
URL: http://www.careeradvocates.org
Description: Provides permanent placement and temporary staffing for executive and staff level positions. Specializes in multiple niches including: sales and marketing, accounting and financial services, banking, communications, human resources, chemicals, oil and gas, medical and dental, legal, information technology, energy, technology, engineering, manufacturing, construction, and light industrial.

2609 ■ Computer Management
7982 Honeygo Blvd., No. 23
Baltimore, MD 21236
Ph: (410)679-7000
E-mail: info@technicaljobs.com
URL: http://www.technicaljobs.com
Description: Search firm focusing on filling jobs for database administration, network administration, web development, and software.

2610 ■ Cornell Global
PO Box 7113
Wilton, CT 06897
Ph: (203)762-0730
E-mail: info@cornellglobal.com
URL: http://www.cornellglobal.com
Description: Executive search firm with areas of expertise in the following areas: advertising, public relations, marketing, sales, finance and accounting, risk management, private equity and venture capital, construction, industrial, manufacturing, life sciences, publishing, information technology, engineering, human resources, legal, and logisitics.

2611 ■ CSI Executive Search LLC
9600 Great Hills Trail, Ste. 150W
Austin, TX 78759
Ph: (512)301-1119
Fax: (512)301-5559
E-mail: info@csi-executivesearch.com
URL: http://www.csi-executivesearch.com
Description: Executive search firm that specializes in the following arenas: accounting, engineering, healthcare, information technology, and legal.

2612 ■ Dahl-Morrow International
1821 Michael Faraday Dr., Ste. 202
Reston, VA 20190-5348
Ph: (703)787-8117
Fax: (703)787-8114
E-mail: dmi@dahl-morrowintl.com
URL: http://www.dahl-morrowintl.com
Description: Executive search firm specializing in high technology.

2613 ■ The Datafinders Group, Inc.
PO Box 1624
Fort Lee, NJ 07024
Ph: (201)845-7700
Fax: (201)969-1065
E-mail: info@datafinders.net
URL: http://www.datafinders.net
Description: Executive search firm.

2614 ■ DillonGray
1796 Equestrian Dr.
Pleasanton, CA 94588
Ph: (925)846-9396
E-mail: info@dillongray.com
URL: http://www.dillongray.com
Description: Executive search firm focused on technology related companies.

2615 ■ Dynamic Search Systems Inc.
220 W Campus Dr., Ste. 201
Arlington Heights, IL 60004-1499
Ph: (847)304-0700
Fax: (847)304-5859
E-mail: candidate@dssjobs.com
URL: http://www.dssjobs.com
Description: Provider of executive and professional search services to the IT community. Firm specializes in the placement of developers, programmers, programmer analysts, systems analysts, project leaders, project managers, systems programmers, data processing consultants, IT directors, and other information technology related candidates. Industries served: All.

2616 ■ KLR Executive Search Group L.L.C.
951 N Main St.
Providence, RI 02904
Ph: (401)274-2001
Fax: (401)831-4018
E-mail: info@klrsearchgroup.com
URL: http://www.klrsearchgroup.com
Description: Career recruitment firm specializes in the placement of accounting and financial and information technology professionals.

2617 ■ Houser Martin Morris
110th Ave. NE, 110 Atrium Pl., Ste. 580
Bellevue, WA 98004
Ph: (425)453-2700
Fax: (425)453-8726
E-mail: info@houser.com
URL: http://www.houser.com
Description: Focus is in the areas of retained executive search, professional, and technical recruiting. Areas of specialization include software engineering, sales and marketing, information technology, legal, human resources, accounting and finance, manufacturing, factory automation and engineering.

2618 ■ Nesco Inc.
6140 Parkland Blvd., Ste. 110
Mayfield Heights, OH 44124-6106
Ph: (440)461-6000
Fax: (440)449-3111
E-mail: corporate@nescoresource.com
URL: http://www.nescoresource.com
Description: Offers staffing and consulting solutions in the fields of engineering, information technology, accounting and finance, manufacturing and distribution, and administrative and customer services.

2619 ■ Q&A Recruiting
J.P. Morgan International Plz., Bldg. III
14241 Dallas Pkwy., Ste. 550
Dallas, TX 75254
Ph: (972)720-1020
Fax: (972)720-1023
E-mail: jobs@qarecruiting.com
URL: http://www.qarecruiting.com
Description: Provides staffing services for accounting, finance, tax, information technology, payroll or accounting support, and human resources.

2620 ■ Recruiting Partners
3494 Camino Tassajara Rd., No. 404
Danville, CA 94506
Ph: (925)964-0249
E-mail: info@recruitingpartners.com
URL: http://www.recruitingpartners.com
Description: Serves as an executive and technical recruiting firm that specializes in accounting, legal, information technology, engineering, executive management and technical writing.

2621 ■ Spectrum Group, LLC
1919 Gallows Rd., Ste. 600
Vienna, VA 22182
Ph: (703)738-1200
Fax: (703)761-9477
E-mail: web@spectrumcareers.com
URL: http://www.spectrumcareers.com
Description: Serves as executive search firm for accounting and finance, information technology, and sales and marketing industries.

2622 ■ Strategic Staffing Solutions L.C.
645 Griswold St., Ste. 2900
Detroit, MI 48226-4206
Free: 888-738-3261
E-mail: s3corporate@strategicstaff.com
URL: http://www.strategicstaff.com
Description: Services: Computer consulting firm.

2623 ■ Technical Talent Locators Ltd.
5570 Sterrett Pl., Ste. 208
Columbia, MD 21044
Ph: (410)740-0091
Fax: (301)621-4227
E-mail: steve@ttlgroup.com
URL: http://www.ttlgroup.com
Description: Permanent employment agency working within the following fields: software and database engineering; computer, communication, and telecommunication system engineering; and other computer-related disciplines.

2624 ■ TRC Staffing Services Inc.
115 Perimeter Center Pl. NE, Ste. 850
Atlanta, GA 30346
Ph: (770)392-1411
Free: 800-488-8008
Fax: (770)392-7926
E-mail: info@trcstaff.com
URL: http://www.trcstaffing.com
Description: A full-service executive search company with permanent placements encompassing engineering, industrial sales, financial and computer science positions. Screen, interview and verify past employment for all candidates prior to referral. Also assist personnel staffs in the attainment of their EEO/AAP goals with the placement of talented individuals in positions which were underutilized with minorities and/or women. Industries served: all.

2625 ■ Wallach Associates Inc.
7811 Montrose Rd., Ste. 505
Potomac, MD 20854
Ph: (301)340-0300
Free: 800-296-2084
Fax: (301)340-8008
URL: http://www.wallach.org
Description: Specialists in recruitment of professional personnel, primarily in information technology and electronic systems and engineering, energy research and development, management consulting, operations research, computers, defense systems, and programmers. Specializes in Internet and software engineer for intelligence community.

2626 ■ Worlco Computer Resources, Inc.
901 Rte. 38
Cherry Hill, NJ 08002
Ph: (610)293-9070
Fax: (856)665-8903
E-mail: recruiter@worlco.com
URL: http://www.worlco.com
Description: Employment agency and executive search firm. Second location in Cherry Hill, New Jersey.

ONLINE JOB SOURCES AND SERVICES

2627 ■ AIJobs.net
URL: http://www.aijobs.net
Description: Features artificial intelligence jobs and careers, resumes search and postings.

2628 ■ ComputerJobs.com
URL: http://www.computerjobs.com
Description: Provides listings of computer-related job opportunities.

2629 ■ ComputerWork.com
URL: http://www.computerwork.com
Description: Job search and resume submission service for professionals in information technology.

2630 ■ Computerworld Careers
URL: http://www.computerworld.com/careertopics/careers
Description: Offers career opportunities for IT (information technology) professionals. Job seekers may search the jobs database, register at the site, and read about job surveys and employment trends. Employers may post jobs.

2631 ■ Computing Research Association Job Announcements
URL: http://www.cra.org/ads
Description: Contains dated links to national college and university computer technology positions.

2632 ■ Dice.com
URL: http://www.dice.com
Description: Job search database for computer consultants and high-tech professionals, listing thousands of high tech permanent contract and consulting jobs for programmers, software engineers, systems administrators, web developers, and hardware engineers. Also free career advice e-mail newsletter and job posting e-alerts.

2633 ■ Guru.com
URL: http://www.guru.com
Description: Job board specializing in contract jobs for creative and information technology professionals. Also provides online incorporation and educational opportunities for independent contractors along with articles and advice.

2634 ■ InformationTechnologyCrossing.com
URL: http://www.informationtechnologycrossing.com
Description: Provides information on IT jobs.

2635 ■ ItJobs.com
URL: http://www.itjobs.com
Description: Provides information technology employment opportunities for the following categories: internet/intranet/extranet, network systems, open systems, client/server, software engineering and development, software QA and testing, ERP applications and management consulting, and legacy systems.

2636 ■ Jobs for Programmers
URL: http://www.prgjobs.com
Description: Job board site for computer programmers that allows them to browse through thousands of programming jobs, even search for special jobs with sign-on bonuses, relocation funding, and 4-day work weeks. Resume posting is free.

2637 ■ Jobs4IT.com
URL: http://www.informationtechnologyjobs.com/
Description: Features information technology job opportunities, job fairs, business opportunities, news, events, continuing education guide, resume database, distribution services and other career resources.

2638 ■ JustTechJobs.com
URL: http://www.justtechjobs.com
Description: Serves as a jobsite that provides employers with a technology specific focus and provides job seekers with job postings aimed at those specific tech jobs. Offers a community of 15 million tech professionals and also supports several technology websites.

2639 ■ PrgJobs.com
URL: http://www.prgjobs.com
Description: Serves as an employment site for programmers.

2640 ■ ProgrammingCareers.com
URL: http://www.programmingcareers.com
Description: Provides programming jobs to computer software developers and programmers. Functions mainly as an advertiser, and is not involved in the hiring process. Connects job seekers in related professions with employers and employment recruiters.

2641 ■ Tech-Engine.com
URL: http://techengine.com
Description: Features employment listings concerning the IT and engineering fields. Features employers and recruiters information, resume posting and career resources.

2642 ■ TechCareers
URL: http://www.techcareers.com
Description: Features career-related resources, news, and job postings for information technology and engineering professionals.

2643 ■ ThinkEnergyGroup.com
URL: http://www.thinkenergygroup.com
Description: Serves as a job board for professionals looking for positions in engineering, power plant, energy, and technical fields. Contains advice and tips on interviews, job searching, resume writing, hiring, and management. Provides choices of work location, pay rates in the field of expertise and contract, temp-to-hire, and direct hiring options.

2644 ■ ZDNet Tech Jobs
URL: http://www.zdnet.com
Description: Site houses a listing of national employment opportunities for professionals in high tech fields. Also contains resume building tips and relocation resources.

TRADESHOWS

2645 ■ Large Installation System Administration Conference
USENIX, the Advanced Computing Systems Association
2560 9th St., Ste. 215
Berkeley, CA 94710
Ph: (510)528-8649
Fax: (510)548-5738
E-mail: webster@usenix.org
URL: http://www.usenix.org
Frequency: Annual. Includes exhibits of books, products, and services that can optimize systems, networks, and internet management. 2013 November 3-8; Washington, DC; 2014 November 9-14; Seattle, WA; 2015 November 8-13; Washington, DC; 2016 December 4-9; Boston, MA. Provides networking opportunities for computing professionals.

2646 ■ USENIX Annual Technical Conference
USENIX, the Advanced Computing Systems Association
2560 9th St., Ste. 215
Berkeley, CA 94710

Ph: (510)528-8649
Fax: (510)548-5738
E-mail: webster@usenix.org
URL: http://www.usenix.org
Frequency: Annual. Includes exhibits of products and services for the advancement of computing systems.

2647 ■ XPLOR International Conference and Vendor Forum
Xplor International
24156 State Rd. 54, Ste. 4
Lutz, FL 33559
Ph: (813)949-6170
Fax: (813)949-9977
E-mail: skip@xplor.org
URL: http://www.xplor.org
Frequency: Annual. **Primary Exhibits:** Equipment, supplies, and services for users and manufacturers of advanced electronic document systems.

OTHER SOURCES

2648 ■ AAAI Press
2275 E Bayshore Rd., Ste. 160
Palo Alto, CA 94303
Ph: (650)328-3123
Fax: (650)321-4457
URL: http://www.aaai.org/Press/press.php
Description: Manufacturing: Publishes edited collections, monographs, proceedings, and technical reports in the field of Artificial Intelligence. Co-publishes with MIT Press. Accepts unsolicited manuscripts. Reaches market through direct mail, trade sales, wholesalers and MIT Press.

2649 ■ American Indian Science and Engineering Society
PO Box 9828
Albuquerque, NM 87119-9828
Ph: (505)765-1052
Fax: (505)765-5608
E-mail: pam@aises.org
URL: http://www.aises.org
Description: Represents American Indian and non-Indian students and professionals in science, technology, and engineering fields; corporations representing energy, mining, aerospace, electronic, and computer fields. Seeks to motivate and encourage students to pursue undergraduate and graduate studies in science, engineering, and technology. Sponsors science fairs in grade schools, teacher training workshops, summer math/science sessions for 8th-12th graders, professional chapters, and student chapters in colleges. Offers scholarships. Adult members serve as role models, advisers, and mentors for students. Operates placement service.

2650 ■ Association for the Advancement of Artificial Intelligence
2275 E Bayshore Blvd., Ste. 160
Palo Alto, CA 94303
Ph: (650)328-3123
Fax: (650)321-4457
URL: http://www.aaai.org/home.html
Description: Artificial Intelligence researchers; students, libraries, corporations, and others interested in the subject. (Artificial Intelligence is a discipline in which an attempt is made to approximate the human thinking process through computers.) Seeks to unite researchers and developers of Artificial Intelligence in order to provide an element of cohesion in the field. Serves as focal point and organizer for conferences; areas of interest include interpretation of visual data, robotics, expert systems, natural language processing, knowledge representation, and Artificial Intelligence programming technologies. Holds tutorials. Also publishes AI Magazine and AI Review.

2651 ■ Association for Computing Machinery
2 Penn Plz., Ste. 701
New York, NY 10121-0701
Ph: (212)626-0500
Free: 800-342-6626
Fax: (212)944-1318
E-mail: acmhelp@acm.org
URL: http://www.acm.org

Description: Biological, medical, behavioral, and computer scientists; hospital administrators; programmers and others interested in application of computer methods to biological, behavioral, and medical problems.

2652 ■ Association for Computing Machinery - Special Interest Group on Accessible Computing
2 Penn Plz., Ste. 701
New York, NY 10121-0701
Ph: (212)626-0500
Free: 800-342-6626
Fax: (212)944-1318
E-mail: chair_sigaccess@acm.org
URL: http://www.sigaccess.org

Description: Promotes the professional interests of computing personnel with physical disabilities and the application of computing and information technology in solving relevant disability problems. Works to educate the public to support careers for the disabled. **Members:** 453.

2653 ■ Association of Information Technology Professionals
330 N Wabash Ave., Ste. 2000
Chicago, IL 60611-4267
Ph: (312)245-1070
Free: 800-224-9371
Fax: (312)673-6659
E-mail: aitp_hq@aitp.org
URL: http://www.aitp.org

Description: Managerial personnel, staff, educators, and individuals interested in the management of information resources. Founder of the Certificate in Data Processing examination program, now administered by an intersociety organization. Maintains Legislative Communications Network. Professional education programs include EDP-oriented business and management principles self-study courses and a series of videotaped management development seminars. Sponsors student organizations around the country interested in information technology and encourages members to serve as counselors for the Scout computer merit badge. Conducts research projects, including a business information systems curriculum for two- and four-year colleges.

2654 ■ Association for Women in Computing
PO Box 2768
Oakland, CA 94602
E-mail: info@awc-hq.org
URL: http://www.awc-hq.org

Description: Individuals interested in promoting the education, professional development, and advancement of women in computing.

2655 ■ Black Data Processing Associates
9500 Arena Dr., Ste. 350
Largo, MD 20774
Ph: (301)584-3135
Fax: (301)560-8300
E-mail: office@bdpa.org
URL: http://www.bdpa.org

Description: Represents persons employed in the information processing industry, including electronic data processing, electronic word processing and data communications; others interested in information processing. Seeks to accumulate and share information processing knowledge and business expertise to increase the career and business potential of minorities in the information processing field. Conducts professional seminars, workshops, tutoring services and community introductions to data processing. Makes annual donation to the United Negro College Fund.

2656 ■ *Career Opportunities in the Internet, Video Games, and Multimedia*
InfoBase Holdings Inc.
132 W 31st., 17 Fl.
New York, NY 10001-3406
Ph: (212)967-8800
Fax: (800)678-3633
E-mail: info@infobasepublishing.com
URL: http://www.ferguson.infobasepublishing.com

Description: Allan Taylor, James Robert Parish and Dan Fiden. 2007. $49.50. 384 pages. **Includes:** Appendices of educational institutions, periodicals, directories, and associations. Appendices of educational institutions, periodicals, directories, and associations.

2657 ■ *Career Opportunities in Science*
InfoBase Holdings Inc.
132 W 31st., 17 Fl.
New York, NY 10001-3406
Ph: (212)967-8800
Fax: (800)678-3633
E-mail: info@infobasepublishing.com
URL: http://factsonfile.infobasepublishing.com

Frequency: Latest edition 2008. **Price:** $49.50 Individuals hardcover. **Pages:** 344. **Description:** Susan Echaore-McDavid. Second edition, 2008. 332 pages. **Covers:** More than 80 jobs, such as biochemist, molecular biologist, bioinformatic specialist, pharmacologist, computer engineer, geographic information systems specialist, science teacher, forensic scientist, patent agent, as well as physicist, astronomer, chemist, zoologist, oceanographer, and geologist. **Includes:** Appendices of educational institutions, periodicals, directories, and associations.

2658 ■ Computing Research Association
1828 L St. NW, Ste. 800
Washington, DC 20036-4632

Ph: (202)234-2111
Fax: (202)667-1066
E-mail: info@cra.org
URL: http://www.cra.org

Description: An association of more than 200 North American academic departments of computer science, computer engineering, and related fields; laboratories and centers in industry government, and academia engaging in basic computing research; and affiliated professional societies.

2659 ■ IEEE Computer Society
2001 L St. NW, Ste. 700
Washington, DC 20036
Ph: (202)371-0101
Free: 800-272-6657
Fax: (202)728-9614
E-mail: help@computer.org
URL: http://www.computer.org

Description: Computer professionals. Promotes the development of computer and information sciences and fosters communication within the information processing community. Sponsors conferences, symposia, workshops, tutorials, technical meetings, and seminars. Operates Computer Society Press. Presents scholarships; bestows technical achievement and service awards and certificates. **Members:** 90,000.

2660 ■ MIT Computer Science and Artificial Intelligence Laboratory
32 Vassar St.
Cambridge, MA 02139
Ph: (617)253-5851
Fax: (617)258-8682
URL: http://www.csail.mit.edu

Description: Active since 1959. Interdisciplinary laboratory of over 200 people that spans several academic departments and has active projects ongoing with members of every academic school at MIT. Offers research, current job listings, and educational outreach.

2661 ■ USENIX, the Advanced Computing Systems Association
2560 9th St., Ste. 215
Berkeley, CA 94710
Ph: (510)528-8649
Fax: (510)548-5738
E-mail: webster@usenix.org
URL: http://www.usenix.org

Description: Represents the community of engineers, system administrators, scientists, and technicians working on the cutting edge of the computing world. Aims to foster technical excellence and innovation that pertains to computer systems. Supports and disseminates research with a practical bias. Provides a neutral forum for discussion of technical issues and encourages computing outreach into the community at large.

SOURCES OF HELP-WANTED ADS

2662 ■ ACM Transactions on Internet Technology
Association for Computing Machinery
2 Penn Plz., Ste. 701
New York, NY 10121-0701
Ph: (212)626-0500
Free: 800-342-6626
Fax: (212)944-1318
E-mail: acmhelp@acm.org
URL: http://toit.acm.org
Frequency: Quarterly; February, May, August and November. **Price:** $190 Nonmembers print only; $152 Nonmembers online only; $228 Nonmembers online and print. **Description:** Publication of the Association for Computing Machinery. Brings together many computing disciplines including computer software engineering, computer programming languages, middleware, database management, security, knowledge discovery and data mining, networking and distributed systems, communications, performance and scalability, and more. Covers the results and roles of the individual disciplines and the relationships among them.

2663 ■ Communications of the ACM
Association for Computing Machinery
2 Penn Plz., Ste. 701
New York, NY 10121-0701
Ph: (212)626-0500
Free: 800-342-6626
Fax: (212)944-1318
E-mail: acmhelp@acm.org
URL: http://cacm.acm.org
Frequency: Monthly. **Price:** $99 Members professional. **Description:** Computing news magazine.

2664 ■ Communications and Network
Scientific Research Publishing
PO Box 54821
Irvine, CA 92619-4821
E-mail: cn@scirp.org
URL: http://www.scirp.org/journal/cn/
Frequency: Quarterly. **Price:** $236 Individuals. **Description:** Journal publishing articles on the latest advancements in communications and network technologies.

2665 ■ Computers and Composition
Elsevier Science Inc.
Secondary Publishing Division
650 Ave. of the Americas
New York, NY 10011
Ph: (212)633-3980
Free: 888-437-4636
Fax: (212)633-3975
URL: http://www.elsevier.com/wps/find/journaldescription.cws_home/620371/description#description
Frequency: 4/yr. **Price:** $454 Individuals and institution; online; $82 Individuals print; $454 Institutions

print. **Description:** Journal covering computers in writing classes, programs, and research.

2666 ■ Computerworld
International Data Group Inc.
PO Box 9171
Framingham, MA 01701
Ph: (508)879-0700
E-mail: info@idg.com
URL: http://www.computerworld.com
Frequency: Weekly. **Price:** $129 Individuals; $129 Canada; $295 Other countries; $250 Individuals Mexico/Central/South America; $29 Individuals digital edition. **Description:** Newspaper for information systems executives.

2667 ■ Computerworld Top 100
IDG Communications Inc.
492 Old Connecticut Path
Framingham, MA 01701
Ph: (508)872-0080
URLs: http://www.idg.com/www/IDGProducts.nsf/ByKey/Bulgaria_Publication_Computerworld-Top-100; http://computerworld.bg/supplement/top100
Frequency: Annual. **Description:** Magazine for analyzing trends and events of information technology business.

2668 ■ Eclipse Review
BZ Media LLC
7 High St. Ste. 407
Huntington, NY 11743
Ph: (631)421-4158
URL: http://www.eclipsesource.com/contact.htm
Description: Magazine for IT professionals.

2669 ■ Foundations and Trends in Networking
Now Publishers
PO Box 1024
Hanover, MA 02339-1001
Ph: (781)871-0245
E-mail: zac.rolnik@nowpublishers.com
URL: http://www.nowpublishers.com/journals/NET/latest
Price: $440 Individuals online only; $510 Individuals print and online; €440 Other countries online only; €510 Other countries print and online. **Description:** Academic journal publishing new research in computer networking.

2670 ■ Government Computer News
PostNewsweek Tech Media
10 G St. NE, Ste. 500
Washington, DC 20002-4228
Ph: (202)772-2500
Free: 866-447-6864
Fax: (202)772-2511
URL: http://gcn.com/
Frequency: Semimonthly; 30/yr. **Description:** Magazine for professionals interested in government IT.

2671 ■ IEEE Security & Privacy Magazine
IEEE Computer Society
10662 Los Vaqueros Cir.
Los Alamitos, CA 90720-1314
Ph: (714)821-8380
Free: 800-272-6657
Fax: (714)821-4010
E-mail: help@computer.org
URL: http://www.computer.org/portal/site/security/
Frequency: Bimonthly. **Price:** $19.95 Individuals online; $65 Nonmembers print; $17.50 Students; $35 Individuals professional. **Description:** Journal that aims to explore role and importance of networked infrastructure and developing lasting security solutions.

2672 ■ IT Solutions Guide
SYS-CON Media
577 Chestnut Ridge Rd.
Woodcliff Lake, NJ 07677
Ph: (201)802-3000
Fax: (201)782-9601
E-mail: subscribe@sys-con.com
URL: http://itsolutions.sys-con.com
Frequency: Quarterly. **Description:** Magazine for IT professionals.

2673 ■ Journal of Computer Networks and Communications
Hindawi Publishing Corp.
410 Park Ave., 15th Fl.
287 PMB
New York, NY 10022-4407
Fax: (215)893-4392
E-mail: jcnc@hindawi.com
URL: http://www.hindawi.com/journals/jcnc/
Frequency: 2/yr. **Price:** $595 Individuals print & online. **Description:** Journal covering important areas of information technology.

2674 ■ Journal of Computer Science
Science Publications
Vails Gate Heights Dr.
Vails Gate, NY 12584-0879
URL: http://thescipub.com/jcs.toc
Frequency: Monthly. **Description:** Scholarly journal covering many areas of computer science, including: concurrent, parallel and distributed processing; artificial intelligence; image and voice processing; quality software and metrics; computer-aided education; wireless communication; real time processing; evaluative computation; and data bases and information recovery and neural networks.

2675 ■ Machine Design: Proven America's Most Useful Design Engineering Magazine
Intertec Publishing
5 Penn Plz., 13th Fl.
New York, NY 10001-1810
Ph: (212)613-9700
Free: 800-795-5445

Fax: (212)613-9749
E-mail: bethany.weaver@penton.com
URL: http://machinedesign.com/
Frequency: 22/yr. **Description:** Magazine on design engineering function.

2676 ■ *Monitor: CPCUG's Print Magazine*
Capital PC User Group
19209 Mt. Airey Rd.
Brookeville, MD 20833
Ph: (301)560-6442
Fax: (301)760-3303
E-mail: editor@cpcug.org
URL: http://monitor.cpcug.org/index.html
Frequency: Quarterly. **Description:** Magazine covering computer hardware and software reviews, special interest user group news, advertisers and author/subject index, and calendar of events.

2677 ■ *PC WORLD: The Magazine of Business Computing*
101 Communications
501 2nd St.
San Francisco, CA 94107
Ph: (415)243-0500
Fax: (415)442-1891
E-mail: pcwletters@pcworld.com
URL: http://www.pcworld.com
Frequency: Quarterly. **Price:** $19.97 Individuals; $29.97 Two years. **Description:** Technology or business magazine meeting the informational needs of tech-savvy managers, both at work and at home.

2678 ■ *Queue: Tomorrow's Computing Today*
Association for Computing Machinery
2 Penn Plz., Ste. 701
New York, NY 10121-0701
Ph: (212)626-0500
Free: 800-342-6626
Fax: (212)944-1318
E-mail: queue@acm.org
URL: http://queue.acm.org/
Frequency: Monthly. **Price:** Free. **Description:** Online magazine aimed at the computer professional. Magazine editorial does not provide solutions for the "here-and-now", but instead helps decision-makers plan future projects by examining the challenges and problems they are most likely to face.

2679 ■ *Revenue*
Montgomery Media International
55 New Montgomery St., Ste. 617
San Francisco, CA 94105
Ph: (415)371-8800
E-mail: info@mthink.com
URL: http://www.revenuetoday.com/
Description: Magazine covering internet marketing strategies.

2680 ■ *Ubiquity*
Association for Computing Machinery
2 Penn Plz., Ste. 701
New York, NY 10121-0701
Ph: (212)626-0500
Free: 800-342-6626
Fax: (212)944-1318
E-mail: editors@ubiquity.acm.org
URL: http://ubiquity.acm.org
Frequency: Weekly. **Price:** Free. **Description:** Web-based magazine of the Association for Computing Machinery dedicated to fostering critical analysis and in-depth commentary, including book reviews, on issues relating to the nature, constitution, structure, science, engineering, cognition, technology, practices and paradigms of the IT profession.

2681 ■ *WITI FastTrack*
UBM L.L.C.
240 W 35th St.
New York, NY 10001
Ph: (516)562-5000
Free: 800-842-0798
Fax: (516)562-7830
E-mail: contact@ubmtechnology.com
URL: http://www.witi.com/corporate/fasttrack.php
Frequency: Semiannual. **Description:** Semiannual publication featuring in-depth content on the issues facing today's women professionals in technology.

Employer Directories and Networking Lists

2682 ■ *Computer Directory*
Computer Directories Inc.
23815 Nichols Sawmill Rd.
Hockley, TX 77447
Ph: (281)305-4170
E-mail: admin@compdirinc.com
URL: http://www.compdirinc.com
Frequency: Annual; fall. **Pages:** 500 per volume. **Covers:** Approximately 130,000 computer installations; 19 separate volumes for Alaska/Hawaii, Connecticut/New Jersey, Dallas/Ft. Worth, Eastern Seaboard, Far Midwest, Houston, Illinois, Midatlantic, Midcentral, Mideast, Minnesota/Wisconsin, North Central, New England, New York Metro, Northwest, Ohio, Pennsylvania/West Virginia, Southeast, and Southwest Texas. **Entries include:** Company name, address, phone, fax, email, name and title of contact, hardware used, software application, operating system, programming language, computer graphics, networking system. **Arrangement:** Geographical. **Indexes:** Alphabetical, industry, hardware.

2683 ■ *Directory of Top Computer Executives*
Applied Computer Research Inc.
PO Box 41730
Phoenix, AZ 85080
Ph: (623)937-4700
Free: 800-234-2227
Fax: (623)937-3115
E-mail: tara@topitexecs.com
URL: http://www.itmarketintelligence.com
Frequency: Semiannual; June and December. **Price:** $345 Individuals single volume, per issue; $520 U.S. and Canada single volume, per year; $620 Individuals two-volume set, per issue; $930 U.S. and Canada two-volume set, per year; $925 Individuals three-volume set, per issue; $1,390 U.S. and Canada three-volume set, per year. **Pages:** 1,100 3 volumes. **Covers:** In three volumes, over 65,000 U.S. and Canadian executives with major information technology or communications responsibilities in over 35,500 U.S. and Canadian companies. **Includes:** Listings of manufacturer and model numbers of systems that are installed at each company. **Entries include:** Company name, address, phone, subsidiary and/or division names, major systems installed, names and titles of top information system executives, number of IT employees, number of PCs, and web address. **Arrangement:** Geographical within separate eastern, western, and Canadian volumes. **Indexes:** Industry; alphabetical by company name.

Handbooks and Manuals

2684 ■ *America's Top 100 Computer and Technical Jobs*
JIST Publishing
875 Montreal Way
Saint Paul, MN 55102-4245
Ph: (317)613-4200
Free: 800-648-5478
Fax: (800)328-4564
E-mail: info@jist.com
URL: http://www.jist.com
Description: Michael J. Farr. 2009. $17.95. 400 pages. Job hunting in computer and technical industries.

2685 ■ *Expert Resumes for Computer and Web Jobs*
JIST Publishing
875 Montreal Way
Saint Paul, MN 55102-4245
Ph: (317)613-4200
Free: 800-648-5478
Fax: (800)328-4564
E-mail: info@jist.com
URL: http://www.jist.com
Description: Wendy Enelow and Louise Kursmark. Third edition, 2011. $17.95 (paper). 304 pages. Contains a collection of sample resumes and resume writing advice including how to create and use an electronic resume. Contains an appendix that includes internet resources for an online job search, writing cover letters, as well as a collection of sample letters.

Employment Agencies and Search Firms

2686 ■ Recruiting Partners
3494 Camino Tassajara Rd., No. 404
Danville, CA 94506
Ph: (925)964-0249
E-mail: info@recruitingpartners.com
URL: http://www.recruitingpartners.com
Description: Serves as an executive and technical recruiting firm that specializes in accounting, legal, information technology, engineering, executive management and technical writing.

Online Job Sources and Services

2687 ■ ComputerJobs.com
URL: http://www.computerjobs.com
Description: Provides listings of computer-related job opportunities.

2688 ■ ComputerWork.com
URL: http://www.computerwork.com
Description: Job search and resume submission service for professionals in information technology.

2689 ■ Computerworld Careers
URL: http://www.computerworld.com/careertopics/careers
Description: Offers career opportunities for IT (information technology) professionals. Job seekers may search the jobs database, register at the site, and read about job surveys and employment trends. Employers may post jobs.

2690 ■ Computing Research Association Job Announcements
URL: http://www.cra.org/ads
Description: Contains dated links to national college and university computer technology positions.

2691 ■ Guru.com
URL: http://www.guru.com
Description: Job board specializing in contract jobs for creative and information technology professionals. Also provides online incorporation and educational opportunities for independent contractors along with articles and advice.

2692 ■ InformationTechnologyCrossing.com
URL: http://www.informationtechnologycrossing.com
Description: Provides information on IT jobs.

2693 ■ Jobs4IT.com
URL: http://www.informationtechnologyjobs.com/
Description: Features information technology job opportunities, job fairs, business opportunities, news, events, continuing education guide, resume

database, distribution services and other career resources.

2694 ■ JustTechJobs.com
URL: http://www.justtechjobs.com

Description: Serves as a jobsite that provides employers with a technology specific focus and provides job seekers with job postings aimed at those specific tech jobs. Offers a community of 15 million tech professionals and also supports several technology websites.

2695 ■ TechniciansNow.com
URL: http://www.techniciansnow.com

Description: Provides an avenue to showcase jobs and products vital to the mechanical and technical trade communities.

2696 ■ ZDNet Tech Jobs
URL: http://www.zdnet.com

Description: Site houses a listing of national employment opportunities for professionals in high tech fields. Also contains resume building tips and relocation resources.

TRADESHOWS

2697 ■ Large Installation System Administration Conference
USENIX, the Advanced Computing Systems Association
2560 9th St., Ste. 215
Berkeley, CA 94710
Ph: (510)528-8649
Fax: (510)548-5738
E-mail: webster@usenix.org
URL: http://www.usenix.org

Frequency: Annual. Includes exhibits of books, products, and services that can optimize systems, networks, and internet management. 2013 November 3-8; Washington, DC; 2014 November 9-14; Seattle, WA; 2015 November 8-13; Washington, DC; 2016 December 4-9; Boston, MA. Provides networking opportunities for computing professionals.

2698 ■ USENIX Annual Technical Conference
USENIX, the Advanced Computing Systems Association
2560 9th St., Ste. 215
Berkeley, CA 94710
Ph: (510)528-8649
Fax: (510)548-5738
E-mail: webster@usenix.org
URL: http://www.usenix.org

Frequency: Annual. Includes exhibits of products and services for the advancement of computing systems.

OTHER SOURCES

2699 ■ Association for Computing Machinery - Special Interest Group on Accessible Computing
2 Penn Plz., Ste. 701
New York, NY 10121-0701
Ph: (212)626-0500
Free: 800-342-6626
Fax: (212)944-1318
E-mail: chair_sigaccess@acm.org
URL: http://www.sigaccess.org

Description: Promotes the professional interests of computing personnel with physical disabilities and the application of computing and information technology in solving relevant disability problems. Works to educate the public to support careers for the disabled. **Members:** 453.

2700 ■ Association of Information Technology Professionals
330 N Wabash Ave., Ste. 2000
Chicago, IL 60611-4267
Ph: (312)245-1070
Free: 800-224-9371
Fax: (312)673-6659
E-mail: aitp_hq@aitp.org
URL: http://www.aitp.org

Description: Managerial personnel, staff, educators, and individuals interested in the management of information resources. Founder of the Certificate in Data Processing examination program, now administered by an intersociety organization. Maintains Legislative Communications Network. Professional education programs include EDP-oriented business and management principles self-study courses and a series of videotaped management development seminars. Sponsors student organizations around the country interested in information technology and encourages members to serve as counselors for the Scout computer merit badge. Conducts research projects, including a business information systems curriculum for two- and four-year colleges.

2701 ■ Association for Women in Computing
PO Box 2768
Oakland, CA 94602
E-mail: info@awc-hq.org
URL: http://www.awc-hq.org

Description: Individuals interested in promoting the education, professional development, and advancement of women in computing.

2702 ■ Computing Research Association
1828 L St. NW, Ste. 800
Washington, DC 20036-4632
Ph: (202)234-2111
Fax: (202)667-1066
E-mail: info@cra.org
URL: http://www.cra.org

Description: An association of more than 200 North American academic departments of computer science, computer engineering, and related fields; laboratories and centers in industry government, and academia engaging in basic computing research; and affiliated professional societies.

2703 ■ Electronics Technicians Association International
5 Depot St.
Greencastle, IN 46135-8024
Ph: (765)653-8262
Free: 800-288-3824
Fax: (765)653-4287
E-mail: eta@eta-i.org
URL: http://www.eta-i.org

Description: Skilled electronics technicians. Provides placement service; offers certification examinations for electronics technicians and satellite, fiber optics, and data cabling installers. Compiles wage and manpower statistics. Administers FCC Commercial License examinations and certification of computer network systems technicians and web and internet specialists.

2704 ■ International Society of Certified Electronics Technicians
3608 Pershing Ave.
Fort Worth, TX 76107-4527
Ph: (817)921-9101
Free: 800-946-0201
Fax: (817)921-3741
E-mail: info@iscet.org
URL: http://www.iscet.org

Description: Technicians in 50 countries who have been certified by the society. Seeks to provide a fraternal bond among certified electronics technicians, raise their public image and improve the effectiveness of industry education programs for technicians. Offers training programs in new electronics information. Maintains library of service literature for consumer electronic equipment, including manuals and schematics for out-of-date equipment. Offers all FCC licenses. Sponsors testing program for certification of electronics technicians in the fields of audio, communications, computer, consumer, industrial, medical electronics, radar, radio-television and video.

2705 ■ MIT Computer Science and Artificial Intelligence Laboratory
32 Vassar St.
Cambridge, MA 02139
Ph: (617)253-5851
Fax: (617)258-8682
URL: http://www.csail.mit.edu

Description: Active since 1959. Interdisciplinary laboratory of over 200 people that spans several academic departments and has active projects ongoing with members of every academic school at MIT. Offers research, current job listings, and educational outreach.

2706 ■ National Electronics Service Dealers Association Inc.
3608 Pershing Ave.
Fort Worth, TX 76107-4527
Ph: (817)921-9061
Free: 800-797-9197
Fax: (817)921-3741
E-mail: mack@nesda.com
URL: http://www.nesda.com

Description: Local and state electronic service associations and companies. Supplies technical service information on business management training to electronic service dealers. Offers certification and training programs through International Society of Certified Electronics Technicians. Conducts technical service and business management seminars.

2707 ■ USENIX, the Advanced Computing Systems Association
2560 9th St., Ste. 215
Berkeley, CA 94710
Ph: (510)528-8649
Fax: (510)548-5738
E-mail: webster@usenix.org
URL: http://www.usenix.org

Description: Represents the community of engineers, system administrators, scientists, and technicians working on the cutting edge of the computing world. Aims to foster technical excellence and innovation that pertains to computer systems. Supports and disseminates research with a practical bias. Provides a neutral forum for discussion of technical issues and encourages computing outreach into the community at large.

Computer Support Specialists

Sources of Help-Wanted Ads

2708 ■ *ACM Transactions on Internet Technology*
Association for Computing Machinery
2 Penn Plz., Ste. 701
New York, NY 10121-0701
Ph: (212)626-0500
Free: 800-342-6626
Fax: (212)944-1318
E-mail: acmhelp@acm.org
URL: http://toit.acm.org
Frequency: Quarterly; February, May, August and November. **Price:** $190 Nonmembers print only; $152 Nonmembers online only; $228 Nonmembers online and print. **Description:** Publication of the Association for Computing Machinery. Brings together many computing disciplines including computer software engineering, computer programming languages, middleware, database management, security, knowledge discovery and data mining, networking and distributed systems, communications, performance and scalability, and more. Covers the results and roles of the individual disciplines and the relationships among them.

2709 ■ *Communications of the ACM*
Association for Computing Machinery
2 Penn Plz., Ste. 701
New York, NY 10121-0701
Ph: (212)626-0500
Free: 800-342-6626
Fax: (212)944-1318
E-mail: acmhelp@acm.org
URL: http://cacm.acm.org
Frequency: Monthly. **Price:** $99 Members professional. **Description:** Computing news magazine.

2710 ■ *Communications and Network*
Scientific Research Publishing
PO Box 54821
Irvine, CA 92619-4821
E-mail: cn@scirp.org
URL: http://www.scirp.org/journal/cn/
Frequency: Quarterly. **Price:** $236 Individuals. **Description:** Journal publishing articles on the latest advancements in communications and network technologies.

2711 ■ *Computers and Composition*
Elsevier Science Inc.
Secondary Publishing Division
650 Ave. of the Americas
New York, NY 10011
Ph: (212)633-3980
Free: 888-437-4636
Fax: (212)633-3975
URL: http://www.elsevier.com/wps/find/journaldescription.cws_home/620371/description#description
Frequency: 4/yr. **Price:** $454 Individuals and institution; online; $82 Individuals print; $454 Institutions

print. **Description:** Journal covering computers in writing classes, programs, and research.

2712 ■ *Computers in Libraries*
Information Today, Inc.
143 Old Marlton Pke.
Medford, NJ 08055-8750
Ph: (609)654-6266
Free: 800-300-9868
Fax: (609)654-4309
E-mail: custserv@infotoday.com
URL: http://www.infotoday.com/cilmag/default.shtml
Frequency: Monthly. **Price:** $99.95 Individuals; $188 Two years; $288 Individuals 3 year; $118 Canada and Mexico; $131 Other countries; $69.95 Individuals K-12; $132 Two years K-12; $88 Canada and Mexico K-12; $101 Other countries K-12. **Description:** Library science magazine that provides complete coverage of the news and issues in the rapidly evolving field of library information technology.

2713 ■ *Computerworld Top 100*
IDG Communications Inc.
492 Old Connecticut Path
Framingham, MA 01701
Ph: (508)872-0080
URLs: http://www.idg.com/www/IDGProducts.nsf/ByKey/Bulgaria_Publication_Computerworld-Top-100; http://computerworld.bg/supplement/top100
Frequency: Annual. **Description:** Magazine for analyzing trends and events of information technology business.

2714 ■ *Eclipse Review*
BZ Media LLC
7 High St. Ste. 407
Huntington, NY 11743
Ph: (631)421-4158
URL: http://www.eclipsesource.com/contact.htm
Description: Magazine for IT professionals.

2715 ■ *Foundations and Trends in Networking*
Now Publishers
PO Box 1024
Hanover, MA 02339-1001
Ph: (781)871-0245
E-mail: zac.rolnik@nowpublishers.com
URL: http://www.nowpublishers.com/journals/NET/latest
Price: $440 Individuals online only; $510 Individuals print and online; €440 Other countries online only; €510 Other countries print and online. **Description:** Academic journal publishing new research in computer networking.

2716 ■ *Government Computer News*
PostNewsweek Tech Media
10 G St. NE, Ste. 500
Washington, DC 20002-4228
Ph: (202)772-2500
Free: 866-447-6864

Fax: (202)772-2511
URL: http://gcn.com/
Frequency: Semimonthly; 30/yr. **Description:** Magazine for professionals interested in government IT.

2717 ■ *IEEE Security & Privacy Magazine*
IEEE Computer Society
10662 Los Vaqueros Cir.
Los Alamitos, CA 90720-1314
Ph: (714)821-8380
Free: 800-272-6657
Fax: (714)821-4010
E-mail: help@computer.org
URL: http://www.computer.org/portal/site/security/
Frequency: Bimonthly. **Price:** $19.95 Individuals online; $65 Nonmembers print; $17.50 Students; $35 Individuals professional. **Description:** Journal that aims to explore role and importance of networked infrastructure and developing lasting security solutions.

2718 ■ *IT Solutions Guide*
SYS-CON Media
577 Chestnut Ridge Rd.
Woodcliff Lake, NJ 07677
Ph: (201)802-3000
Fax: (201)782-9601
E-mail: subscribe@sys-con.com
URL: http://itsolutions.sys-con.com
Frequency: Quarterly. **Description:** Magazine for IT professionals.

2719 ■ *Journal of Computer Networks and Communications*
Hindawi Publishing Corp.
410 Park Ave., 15th Fl.
287 PMB
New York, NY 10022-4407
Fax: (215)893-4392
E-mail: jcnc@hindawi.com
URL: http://www.hindawi.com/journals/jcnc/
Frequency: 2/yr. **Price:** $595 Individuals print & online. **Description:** Journal covering important areas of information technology.

2720 ■ *Journal of Computer Science*
Science Publications
Vails Gate Heights Dr.
Vails Gate, NY 12584-0879
URL: http://thescipub.com/jcs.toc
Frequency: Monthly. **Description:** Scholarly journal covering many areas of computer science, including: concurrent, parallel and distributed processing; artificial intelligence; image and voice processing; quality software and metrics; computer-aided education; wireless communication; real time processing; evaluative computation; and data bases and information recovery and neural networks.

2721 ■ *Monitor: CPCUG's Print Magazine*
Capital PC User Group
19209 Mt. Airey Rd.
Brookeville, MD 20833
Ph: (301)560-6442
Fax: (301)760-3303
E-mail: editor@cpcug.org
URL: http://monitor.cpcug.org/index.html

Frequency: Quarterly. **Description:** Magazine covering computer hardware and software reviews, special interest user group news, advertisers and author/subject index, and calendar of events.

2722 ■ *PC Today: Computing for Small Business*
Sandhills Publishing Co.
131 W Grand Dr.
Lincoln, NE 68521
Ph: (402)479-2181
Free: 800-331-1978
Fax: (402)479-2195
E-mail: editor@pctoday.com
URL: http://www.pctoday.com/

Frequency: Monthly. **Price:** $29 Individuals; $37 Canada; $64 Canada 2 years; $2.42 Individuals print; $17 Individuals online only; $69 Other countries; $48 Individuals 2 years; $64 Individuals 3 years; $82 Canada 3 years; $64 Canada 2 years. **Description:** Magazine for personal computer users.

2723 ■ *PC WORLD: The Magazine of Business Computing*
101 Communications
501 2nd St.
San Francisco, CA 94107
Ph: (415)243-0500
Fax: (415)442-1891
E-mail: pcwletters@pcworld.com
URL: http://www.pcworld.com

Frequency: Quarterly. **Price:** $19.97 Individuals; $29.97 Two years. **Description:** Technology or business magazine meeting the informational needs of tech-savvy managers, both at work and at home.

2724 ■ *Queue: Tomorrow's Computing Today*
Association for Computing Machinery
2 Penn Plz., Ste. 701
New York, NY 10121-0701
Ph: (212)626-0500
Free: 800-342-6626
Fax: (212)944-1318
E-mail: queue@acm.org
URL: http://queue.acm.org/

Frequency: Monthly. **Price:** Free. **Description:** Online magazine aimed at the computer professional. Magazine editorial does not provide solutions for the "here-and-now", but instead helps decision-makers plan future projects by examining the challenges and problems they are most likely to face.

2725 ■ *Revenue*
Montgomery Media International
55 New Montgomery St., Ste. 617
San Francisco, CA 94105
Ph: (415)371-8800
E-mail: info@mthink.com
URL: http://www.revenuetoday.com/

Description: Magazine covering internet marketing strategies.

2726 ■ *Ubiquity*
Association for Computing Machinery
2 Penn Plz., Ste. 701
New York, NY 10121-0701
Ph: (212)626-0500
Free: 800-342-6626
Fax: (212)944-1318
E-mail: editors@ubiquity.acm.org
URL: http://ubiquity.acm.org

Frequency: Weekly. **Price:** Free. **Description:** Web-based magazine of the Association for Computing Machinery dedicated to fostering critical analysis and in-depth commentary, including book reviews, on issues relating to the nature, constitution, structure, science, engineering, cognition, technology, practices and paradigms of the IT profession.

2727 ■ *WITI FastTrack*
UBM L.L.C.
240 W 35th St.
New York, NY 10001
Ph: (516)562-5000
Free: 800-842-0798
Fax: (516)562-7830
E-mail: contact@ubmtechnology.com
URL: http://www.witi.com/corporate/fasttrack.php

Frequency: Semiannual. **Description:** Semiannual publication featuring in-depth content on the issues facing today's women professionals in technology.

EMPLOYER DIRECTORIES AND NETWORKING LISTS

2728 ■ *Computer Directory*
Computer Directories Inc.
23815 Nichols Sawmill Rd.
Hockley, TX 77447
Ph: (281)305-4170
E-mail: admin@compdirinc.com
URL: http://www.compdirinc.com

Frequency: Annual; fall. **Pages:** 500 per volume. **Covers:** Approximately 130,000 computer installations; 19 separate volumes for Alaska/Hawaii, Connecticut/New Jersey, Dallas/Ft. Worth, Eastern Seaboard, Far Midwest, Houston, Illinois, Midatlantic, Midcentral, Mideast, Minnesota/Wisconsin, North Central, New England, New York Metro, Northwest, Ohio, Pennsylvania/West Virginia, Southeast, and Southwest Texas. **Entries include:** Company name, address, phone, fax, email, name and title of contact, hardware used, software application, operating system, programming language, computer graphics, networking system. **Arrangement:** Geographical. **Indexes:** Alphabetical, industry, hardware.

2729 ■ *Vault Guide to the Top Tech Employers*
Vault.com Inc.
132 W 31st St., 17th Fl.
New York, NY 10001-3406
Ph: (212)366-4212
Free: 800-535-2074
Fax: (212)366-6117
E-mail: customerservice@vault.com
URL: http://www.vault.com/wps/portal/usa/store/
bookdetail?item_no=782

Frequency: Latest edition June, 2009. **Price:** $19.95 Individuals Online; $19.95 Members Gold. **Pages:** 538. **Covers:** Technology industry employers. **Entries include:** Name, address, phone, fax, website, and other branch office location. Also include company overviews, recent company news, information on the hiring process, key competitors, and employment contact.

HANDBOOKS AND MANUALS

2730 ■ *America's Top 100 Computer and Technical Jobs*
JIST Publishing
875 Montreal Way
Saint Paul, MN 55102-4245
Ph: (317)613-4200
Free: 800-648-5478
Fax: (800)328-4564
E-mail: info@jist.com
URL: http://www.jist.com

Description: Michael J. Farr. 2009. $17.95. 400 pages. Job hunting in computer and technical industries.

EMPLOYMENT AGENCIES AND SEARCH FIRMS

2731 ■ Michael Anthony Associates Inc.
44 Washington St., Ste. 250
Wellesley, MA 02481-1802
Ph: (781)237-4950
Free: 800-337-4950
Fax: (781)237-6811
E-mail: manthony@maainc.com
URL: http://www.maainc.com

Description: Applications development, systems programming, communications, and database specialists servicing the IBM mainframe, midrange, and PC marketplace. Provides technical expertise of conversions, system software installation and upgrades, performance and tuning, capacity planning, and data communications. In addition to contract services, also provides retained search and contingency placement of computer professionals ranging from senior staff to senior management.

2732 ■ Chaves & Associates
c/o InSite Search
418 Meadow St.
Fairfield, CT 06824
Ph: (203)222-2222
Fax: (203)341-8844
E-mail: info@insitesearch.com
URL: http://www.insitesearch.com

Description: Executive search firm.

2733 ■ CNR Search & Services
30752 Via Conquista
San Juan Capistrano, CA 92675
Ph: (949)488-0065
E-mail: cnrkenmiller@juno.com
URL: http://www.cnrsearch.com

Description: A highly respected international boutique search firm with a worldwide client-base. Our clients include both emerging and prominent corporations across a wide range of industries.

2734 ■ Doleman Enterprises
11160-F S Lakes Dr., Ste. 326
Reston, VA 22091
Ph: (703)742-5454
Fax: (703)708-6992
E-mail: doleman@patriot.net

Description: Human resources firm specializes in recruiting for the high-tech, data and computer engineering and pharmaceutical industries.

2735 ■ EDP Staffing, LLC
PO Box 651
Hebron, CT 06231
Free: 860-781-6064
E-mail: info@edpstaffingllc.com
URL: http://www.edpstaffingllc.com

Description: Serves as an e-commerce and IT management search firm. Provides staffing solutions for contingency, retained, contract or temporary staffing. Specializes in the recruitment and placement of e-commerce applications specialists, core IT staff members or IT management professionals.

2736 ■ Louis Rudzinsky Associates Inc.
7 Mystic St., Ste. 203
Arlington, MA 02474
Ph: (781)862-6727
Fax: (781)862-6868
E-mail: lra@lra.com
URL: http://www.lra.com

Description: Provider of recruitment, placement, and executive search to industry (software, electronics, optics) covering positions in general management, manufacturing, engineering, and marketing. Personnel consulting activities include counsel to small and startup companies. Industries served: electronics, aerospace, optical, laser, computer, software, imaging, electro-optics, biotechnology, advanced materials, and solid-state/semiconductor.

2737 ■ Professional Computer Resources Inc.
1500 S Blvd., No. 201B
Charlotte, NC 28203
Ph: (704)332-7226
Free: 888-727-2458
Fax: (704)332-7288
E-mail: christiaan@pcr.net
URL: http://www.pcr.net
Description: Executive search firm.

2738 ■ Wallach Associates Inc.
7811 Montrose Rd., Ste. 505
Potomac, MD 20854
Ph: (301)340-0300
Free: 800-296-2084
Fax: (301)340-8008
URL: http://www.wallach.org
Description: Specialists in recruitment of professional personnel, primarily in information technology and electronic systems and engineering, energy research and development, management consulting, operations research, computers, defense systems, and programmers. Specializes in Internet and software engineer for intelligence community.

ONLINE JOB SOURCES AND SERVICES

2739 ■ ComputerJobs.com
URL: http://www.computerjobs.com
Description: Provides listings of computer-related job opportunities.

2740 ■ ComputerWork.com
URL: http://www.computerwork.com
Description: Job search and resume submission service for professionals in information technology.

2741 ■ Computerworld Careers
URL: http://www.computerworld.com/careertopics/careers
Description: Offers career opportunities for IT (information technology) professionals. Job seekers may search the jobs database, register at the site, and read about job surveys and employment trends. Employers may post jobs.

2742 ■ Computing Research Association Job Announcements
URL: http://www.cra.org/ads
Description: Contains dated links to national college and university computer technology positions.

2743 ■ Guru.com
URL: http://www.guru.com
Description: Job board specializing in contract jobs for creative and information technology professionals. Also provides online incorporation and educational opportunities for independent contractors along with articles and advice.

2744 ■ InformationTechnologyCrossing.com
URL: http://www.informationtechnologycrossing.com
Description: Provides information on IT jobs.

2745 ■ JustTechJobs.com
URL: http://www.justtechjobs.com
Description: Serves as a jobsite that provides employers with a technology specific focus and provides job seekers with job postings aimed at those specific tech jobs. Offers a community of 15 million tech professionals and also supports several technology websites.

2746 ■ Tech-Engine.com
URL: http://techengine.com
Description: Features employment listings concern-

ing the IT and engineering fields. Features employers and recruiters information, resume posting and career resources.

2747 ■ ZDNet Tech Jobs
URL: http://www.zdnet.com
Description: Site houses a listing of national employment opportunities for professionals in high tech fields. Also contains resume building tips and relocation resources.

TRADESHOWS

2748 ■ Large Installation System Administration Conference
USENIX, the Advanced Computing Systems Association
2560 9th St., Ste. 215
Berkeley, CA 94710
Ph: (510)528-8649
Fax: (510)548-5738
E-mail: webster@usenix.org
URL: http://www.usenix.org
Frequency: Annual. Includes exhibits of books, products, and services that can optimize systems, networks, and internet management. 2013 November 3-8; Washington, DC; 2014 November 9-14; Seattle, WA; 2015 November 8-13; Washington, DC; 2016 December 4-9; Boston, MA. Provides networking opportunities for computing professionals.

2749 ■ USENIX Annual Technical Conference
USENIX, the Advanced Computing Systems Association
2560 9th St., Ste. 215
Berkeley, CA 94710
Ph: (510)528-8649
Fax: (510)548-5738
E-mail: webster@usenix.org
URL: http://www.usenix.org
Frequency: Annual. Includes exhibits of products and services for the advancement of computing systems.

2750 ■ XPLOR International Conference and Vendor Forum
Xplor International
24156 State Rd. 54, Ste. 4
Lutz, FL 33559
Ph: (813)949-6170
Fax: (813)949-9977
E-mail: skip@xplor.org
URL: http://www.xplor.org
Frequency: Annual. **Primary Exhibits:** Equipment, supplies, and services for users and manufacturers of advanced electronic document systems.

OTHER SOURCES

2751 ■ Association of Information Technology Professionals
330 N Wabash Ave., Ste. 2000
Chicago, IL 60611-4267
Ph: (312)245-1070
Free: 800-224-9371
Fax: (312)673-6659
E-mail: aitp_hq@aitp.org
URL: http://www.aitp.org
Description: Managerial personnel, staff, educators, and individuals interested in the management of information resources. Founder of the Certificate in Data Processing examination program, now administered by an intersociety organization. Maintains Legislative Communications Network. Professional education programs include EDP-oriented business and management principles self-study courses and a series of videotaped management development seminars. Sponsors student

organizations around the country interested in information technology and encourages members to serve as counselors for the Scout computer merit badge. Conducts research projects, including a business information systems curriculum for two- and four-year colleges.

2752 ■ Association for Women in Computing
PO Box 2768
Oakland, CA 94602
E-mail: info@awc-hq.org
URL: http://www.awc-hq.org
Description: Individuals interested in promoting the education, professional development, and advancement of women in computing.

2753 ■ *Career Opportunities in Computers and Cyberspace*
InfoBase Holdings Inc.
132 W 31st., 17 Fl.
New York, NY 10001-3406
Ph: (212)967-8800
Fax: (800)678-3633
E-mail: info@infobasepublishing.com
URLs: http://www.infobasepublishing.com; http://www.infobasepublishing.com/Bookdetail.aspx?ISBN=1438110669&eBooks=1
Frequency: Published March, 2004. **Description:** Harry Henderson. Second edition, 2004. 256 pages. **Covers:** Nearly 200 professions, clustering them by skill, objectives, and work conditions. **Includes:** Appendices of educational institutions, periodicals, directories, and associations. **Entries include:** Education, salaries, employment prospects.

2754 ■ *Career Opportunities in Science*
InfoBase Holdings Inc.
132 W 31st., 17 Fl.
New York, NY 10001-3406
Ph: (212)967-8800
Fax: (800)678-3633
E-mail: info@infobasepublishing.com
URL: http://factsonfile.infobasepublishing.com
Frequency: Latest edition 2008. **Price:** $49.50 Individuals hardcover. **Pages:** 344. **Description:** Susan Echaore-McDavid. Second edition, 2008. 332 pages. **Covers:** More than 80 jobs, such as biochemist, molecular biologist, bioinformatic specialist, pharmacologist, computer engineer, geographic information systems specialist, science teacher, forensic scientist, patent agent, as well as physicist, astronomer, chemist, zoologist, oceanographer, and geologist. **Includes:** Appendices of educational institutions, periodicals, directories, and associations.

2755 ■ Computing Research Association
1828 L St. NW, Ste. 800
Washington, DC 20036-4632
Ph: (202)234-2111
Fax: (202)667-1066
E-mail: info@cra.org
URL: http://www.cra.org
Description: An association of more than 200 North American academic departments of computer science, computer engineering, and related fields; laboratories and centers in industry government, and academia engaging in basic computing research; and affiliated professional societies.

2756 ■ MIT Computer Science and Artificial Intelligence Laboratory
32 Vassar St.
Cambridge, MA 02139
Ph: (617)253-5851
Fax: (617)258-8682
URL: http://www.csail.mit.edu
Description: Active since 1959. Interdisciplinary laboratory of over 200 people that spans several academic departments and has active projects ongoing with members of every academic school at MIT. Offers research, current job listings, and educational outreach.

**2757 ■ USENIX, the Advanced Computing
  Systems Association**
2560 9th St., Ste. 215
Berkeley, CA 94710
Ph: (510)528-8649

Fax: (510)548-5738
E-mail: webster@usenix.org
URL: http://www.usenix.org
Description: Represents the community of
engineers, system administrators, scientists, and
technicians working on the cutting edge of the

computing world. Aims to foster technical excellence
and innovation that pertains to computer systems.
Supports and disseminates research with a practical
bias. Provides a neutral forum for discussion of
technical issues and encourages computing outreach
into the community at large.

2758 ■ *ACM Transactions on Internet Technology*
Association for Computing Machinery
2 Penn Plz., Ste. 701
New York, NY 10121-0701
Ph: (212)626-0500
Free: 800-342-6626
Fax: (212)944-1318
E-mail: acmhelp@acm.org
URL: http://toit.acm.org
Frequency: Quarterly; February, May, August and November. **Price:** $190 Nonmembers print only; $152 Nonmembers online only; $228 Nonmembers online and print. **Description:** Publication of the Association for Computing Machinery. Brings together many computing disciplines including computer software engineering, computer programming languages, middleware, database management, security, knowledge discovery and data mining, networking and distributed systems, communications, performance and scalability, and more. Covers the results and roles of the individual disciplines and the relationships among them.

2759 ■ *Communications of the ACM*
Association for Computing Machinery
2 Penn Plz., Ste. 701
New York, NY 10121-0701
Ph: (212)626-0500
Free: 800-342-6626
Fax: (212)944-1318
E-mail: acmhelp@acm.org
URL: http://cacm.acm.org
Frequency: Monthly. **Price:** $99 Members professional. **Description:** Computing news magazine.

2760 ■ *Communications and Network*
Scientific Research Publishing
PO Box 54821
Irvine, CA 92619-4821
E-mail: cn@scirp.org
URL: http://www.scirp.org/journal/cn/
Frequency: Quarterly. **Price:** $236 Individuals. **Description:** Journal publishing articles on the latest advancements in communications and network technologies.

2761 ■ *Computers and Composition*
Elsevier Science Inc.
Secondary Publishing Division
650 Ave. of the Americas
New York, NY 10011
Ph: (212)633-3980
Free: 888-437-4636
Fax: (212)633-3975
URL: http://www.elsevier.com/wps/find/journaldescription.cws_home/620371/description#description
Frequency: 4/yr. **Price:** $454 Individuals and institution; online; $82 Individuals print; $454 Institutions print. **Description:** Journal covering computers in writing classes, programs, and research.

2762 ■ *Computerworld*
International Data Group Inc.
PO Box 9171
Framingham, MA 01701
Ph: (508)879-0700
E-mail: info@idg.com
URL: http://www.computerworld.com
Frequency: Weekly. **Price:** $129 Individuals; $129 Canada; $295 Other countries; $250 Individuals Mexico/Central/South America; $29 Individuals digital edition. **Description:** Newspaper for information systems executives.

2763 ■ *Computerworld Top 100*
IDG Communications Inc.
492 Old Connecticut Path
Framingham, MA 01701
Ph: (508)872-0080
URLs: http://www.idg.com/www/IDGProducts.nsf/ByKey/Bulgaria_Publication_Computerworld-Top-100; http://computerworld.bg/supplement/top100
Frequency: Annual. **Description:** Magazine for analyzing trends and events of information technology business.

2764 ■ *Computing Surveys*
Association for Computing Machinery
c/o Lorenzo Alvisi, Assoc. Ed.
University of Texas at Austin
Department of Computer Science
1 University Sta. C0500
Austin, TX 78712-0233
Ph: (512)471-9792
Fax: (512)232-7886
E-mail: acmhelp@acm.org
URL: http://surveys.acm.org/
Frequency: Quarterly. **Price:** $205 Nonmembers print only; $164 Nonmembers online only; $246 Nonmembers online & print. **Description:** Journal presenting surveys and tutorials in computer science.

2765 ■ *Cutter IT Journal*
Cutter Information Corp.
37 Broadway, Ste. 1
Arlington, MA 02474
Ph: (781)648-8700
Free: 800-964-5118
Fax: (781)648-1950
E-mail: service@cutter.com
URL: http://www.cutter.com/itjournal.html
Description: Monthly. $485. Provides IT managers with practical and objective views on the latest technology and management trends.

2766 ■ *Datamation: The Emerging Technologies Magazine for Today's IS*
Reed Elsevier Group plc - Reed Business Information
360 Park Ave. S
New York, NY 11010
Ph: (212)791-4208
E-mail: corporatecommunications@reedbusiness.com
URL: http://www.datamation.com
Frequency: Semimonthly. **Description:** Magazine on computers and information processing.

2767 ■ *Eclipse Review*
BZ Media LLC
7 High St. Ste. 407
Huntington, NY 11743
Ph: (631)421-4158
URL: http://www.eclipsesource.com/contact.htm
Description: Magazine for IT professionals.

2768 ■ *Foundations and Trends in Networking*
Now Publishers
PO Box 1024
Hanover, MA 02339-1001
Ph: (781)871-0245
E-mail: zac.rolnik@nowpublishers.com
URL: http://www.nowpublishers.com/journals/NET/latest
Price: $440 Individuals online only; $510 Individuals print and online; €440 Other countries online only; €510 Other countries print and online. **Description:** Academic journal publishing new research in computer networking.

2769 ■ *Government Computer News*
PostNewsweek Tech Media
10 G St. NE, Ste. 500
Washington, DC 20002-4228
Ph: (202)772-2500
Free: 866-447-6864
Fax: (202)772-2511
URL: http://gcn.com/
Frequency: Semimonthly; 30/yr. **Description:** Magazine for professionals interested in government IT.

2770 ■ *IEEE Security & Privacy Magazine*
IEEE Computer Society
10662 Los Vaqueros Cir.
Los Alamitos, CA 90720-1314
Ph: (714)821-8380
Free: 800-272-6657
Fax: (714)821-4010
E-mail: help@computer.org
URL: http://www.computer.org/portal/site/security/
Frequency: Bimonthly. **Price:** $19.95 Individuals online; $65 Nonmembers print; $17.50 Students; $35 Individuals professional. **Description:** Journal that aims to explore role and importance of networked infrastructure and developing lasting security solutions.

2771 ■ *IEEE Software: Building the Community of Leading Software Practitioners*
IEEE Computer Society
10662 Los Vaqueros Cir.
Los Alamitos, CA 90720-1314

Ph: (714)821-8380
Free: 800-272-6657
Fax: (714)821-4010
E-mail: software@computer.org
URL: http://www.computer.org/portal/web/software/home

Frequency: Bimonthly. **Price:** $990 Individuals online; $1,040 Individuals print; $1,300 Individuals print and online. **Description:** Magazine covering the computer software industry for the community of leading software practitioners.

2772 ■ *InfoWorld: Defining Technology for Business*
InfoWorld Media Group
501 2nd St.
San Francisco, CA 94107
Free: 800-227-8365
E-mail: letters@infoworld.com
URL: http://www.infoworld.com/

Frequency: Weekly. **Price:** $180 Individuals. **Description:** Weekly publication.

2773 ■ *IT Solutions Guide*
SYS-CON Media
577 Chestnut Ridge Rd.
Woodcliff Lake, NJ 07677
Ph: (201)802-3000
Fax: (201)782-9601
E-mail: subscribe@sys-con.com
URL: http://itsolutions.sys-con.com

Frequency: Quarterly. **Description:** Magazine for IT professionals.

2774 ■ *Journal of Computer Networks and Communications*
Hindawi Publishing Corp.
410 Park Ave., 15th Fl.
287 PMB
New York, NY 10022-4407
Fax: (215)893-4392
E-mail: jcnc@hindawi.com
URL: http://www.hindawi.com/journals/jcnc/

Frequency: 2/yr. **Price:** $595 Individuals print & online. **Description:** Journal covering important areas of information technology.

2775 ■ *Journal of Computer Science*
Science Publications
Vails Gate Heights Dr.
Vails Gate, NY 12584-0879
URL: http://thescipub.com/jcs.toc

Frequency: Monthly. **Description:** Scholarly journal covering many areas of computer science, including: concurrent, parallel and distributed processing; artificial intelligence; image and voice processing; quality software and metrics; computer-aided education; wireless communication; real time processing; evaluative computation; and data bases and information recovery and neural networks.

2776 ■ *Monitor: CPCUG's Print Magazine*
Capital PC User Group
19209 Mt. Airey Rd.
Brookeville, MD 20833
Ph: (301)560-6442
Fax: (301)760-3303
E-mail: editor@cpcug.org
URL: http://monitor.cpcug.org/index.html

Frequency: Quarterly. **Description:** Magazine covering computer hardware and software reviews, special interest user group news, advertisers and author/subject index, and calendar of events.

2777 ■ *PC Today: Computing for Small Business*
Sandhills Publishing Co.
131 W Grand Dr.
Lincoln, NE 68521
Ph: (402)479-2181
Free: 800-331-1978

Fax: (402)479-2195
E-mail: editor@pctoday.com
URL: http://www.pctoday.com/

Frequency: Monthly. **Price:** $29 Individuals; $37 Canada; $64 Canada 2 years; $2.42 Individuals print; $17 Individuals online only; $69 Other countries; $48 Individuals 2 years; $64 Individuals 3 years; $82 Canada 3 years; $64 Canada 2 years. **Description:** Magazine for personal computer users.

2778 ■ *PC WORLD: The Magazine of Business Computing*
101 Communications
501 2nd St.
San Francisco, CA 94107
Ph: (415)243-0500
Fax: (415)442-1891
E-mail: pcwletters@pcworld.com
URL: http://www.pcworld.com

Frequency: Quarterly. **Price:** $19.97 Individuals; $29.97 Two years. **Description:** Technology or business magazine meeting the informational needs of tech-savvy managers, both at work and at home.

2779 ■ *Queue: Tomorrow's Computing Today*
Association for Computing Machinery
2 Penn Plz., Ste. 701
New York, NY 10121-0701
Ph: (212)626-0500
Free: 800-342-6626
Fax: (212)944-1318
E-mail: queue@acm.org
URL: http://queue.acm.org/

Frequency: Monthly. **Price:** Free. **Description:** Online magazine aimed at the computer professional. Magazine editorial does not provide solutions for the "here-and-now", but instead helps decision-makers plan future projects by examining the challenges and problems they are most likely to face.

2780 ■ *Revenue*
Montgomery Media International
55 New Montgomery St., Ste. 617
San Francisco, CA 94105
Ph: (415)371-8800
E-mail: info@mthink.com
URL: http://www.revenuetoday.com/

Description: Magazine covering internet marketing strategies.

2781 ■ *Ubiquity*
Association for Computing Machinery
2 Penn Plz., Ste. 701
New York, NY 10121-0701
Ph: (212)626-0500
Free: 800-342-6626
Fax: (212)944-1318
E-mail: editors@ubiquity.acm.org
URL: http://ubiquity.acm.org

Frequency: Weekly. **Price:** Free. **Description:** Web-based magazine of the Association for Computing Machinery dedicated to fostering critical analysis and in-depth commentary, including book reviews, on issues relating to the nature, constitution, structure, science, engineering, cognition, technology, practices and paradigms of the IT profession.

2782 ■ *WITI FastTrack*
UBM L.L.C.
240 W 35th St.
New York, NY 10001
Ph: (516)562-5000
Free: 800-842-0798
Fax: (516)562-7830
E-mail: contact@ubmtechnology.com
URL: http://www.witi.com/corporate/fasttrack.php

Frequency: Semiannual. **Description:** Semiannual publication featuring in-depth content on the issues facing today's women professionals in technology.

EMPLOYER DIRECTORIES AND NETWORKING LISTS

2783 ■ *Computer Directory*
Computer Directories Inc.
23815 Nichols Sawmill Rd.
Hockley, TX 77447
Ph: (281)305-4170
E-mail: admin@compdirinc.com
URL: http://www.compdirinc.com

Frequency: Annual; fall. **Pages:** 500 per volume. **Covers:** Approximately 130,000 computer installations; 19 separate volumes for Alaska/Hawaii, Connecticut/New Jersey, Dallas/Ft. Worth, Eastern Seaboard, Far Midwest, Houston, Illinois, Midatlantic, Midcentral, Mideast, Minnesota/Wisconsin, North Central, New England, New York Metro, Northwest, Ohio, Pennsylvania/West Virginia, Southeast, and Southwest Texas. **Entries include:** Company name, address, phone, fax, email, name and title of contact, hardware used, software application, operating system, programming language, computer graphics, networking system. **Arrangement:** Geographical. **Indexes:** Alphabetical, industry, hardware.

2784 ■ *Directory of Top Computer Executives*
Applied Computer Research Inc.
PO Box 41730
Phoenix, AZ 85080
Ph: (623)937-4700
Free: 800-234-2227
Fax: (623)937-3115
E-mail: tara@topitexecs.com
URL: http://www.itmarketintelligence.com

Frequency: Semiannual; June and December. **Price:** $345 Individuals single volume, per issue; $520 U.S. and Canada single volume, per year; $620 Individuals two-volume set, per issue; $930 U.S. and Canada two-volume set, per year; $925 Individuals three-volume set, per issue; $1,390 U.S. and Canada three-volume set, per year. **Pages:** 1,100 3 volumes. **Covers:** In three volumes, over 65,000 U.S. and Canadian executives with major information technology or communications responsibilities in over 35,500 U.S. and Canadian companies. **Includes:** Listings of manufacturer and model numbers of systems that are installed at each company. **Entries include:** Company name, address, phone, subsidiary and/or division names, major systems installed, names and titles of top information system executives, number of IT employees, number of PCs, and web address. **Arrangement:** Geographical within separate eastern, western, and Canadian volumes. **Indexes:** Industry; alphabetical by company name.

2785 ■ *Vault Guide to the Top Tech Employers*
Vault.com Inc.
132 W 31st St., 17th Fl.
New York, NY 10001-3406
Ph: (212)366-4212
Free: 800-535-2074
Fax: (212)366-6117
E-mail: customerservice@vault.com
URL: http://www.vault.com/wps/portal/usa/store/bookdetail?item_no=782

Frequency: Latest edition June, 2009. **Price:** $19.95 Individuals Online; $19.95 Members Gold. **Pages:** 538. **Covers:** Technology industry employers. **Entries include:** Name, address, phone, fax, website, and other branch office location. Also include company overviews, recent company news, information on the hiring process, key competitors, and employment contact.

HANDBOOKS AND MANUALS

2786 ■ *America's Top 100 Computer and Technical Jobs*
JIST Publishing
875 Montreal Way
Saint Paul, MN 55102-4245

Ph: (317)613-4200
Free: 800-648-5478
Fax: (800)328-4564
E-mail: info@jist.com
URL: http://www.jist.com

Description: Michael J. Farr. 2009. $17.95. 400 pages. Job hunting in computer and technical industries.

2787 ■ *Computer Systems Analyst*
National Learning Corporation
212 Michael Dr.
Syosset, NY 11791
Ph: (516)921-8888
Free: 800-632-8888
Fax: (516)921-8743
E-mail: info@passbooks.com
URL: http://www.passbooks.com

Description: 2009. $34.95 (paper). Serves as an exam preparation guide for computer systems analysts.

2788 ■ *Expert Resumes for Computer and Web Jobs*
JIST Publishing
875 Montreal Way
Saint Paul, MN 55102-4245
Ph: (317)613-4200
Free: 800-648-5478
Fax: (800)328-4564
E-mail: info@jist.com
URL: http://www.jist.com

Description: Wendy Enelow and Louise Kursmark. Third edition, 2011. $17.95 (paper). 304 pages. Contains a collection of sample resumes and resume writing advice including how to create and use an electronic resume. Contains an appendix that includes internet resources for an online job search, writing cover letters, as well as a collection of sample letters.

EMPLOYMENT AGENCIES AND SEARCH FIRMS

2789 ■ **Michael Anthony Associates Inc.**
44 Washington St., Ste. 250
Wellesley, MA 02481-1802
Ph: (781)237-4950
Free: 800-337-4950
Fax: (781)237-6811
E-mail: manthony@maainc.com
URL: http://www.maainc.com

Description: Applications development, systems programming, communications, and database specialists servicing the IBM mainframe, midrange, and PC marketplace. Provides technical expertise of conversions, system software installation and upgrades, performance and tuning, capacity planning, and data communications. In addition to contract services, also provides retained search and contingency placement of computer professionals ranging from senior staff to senior management.

2790 ■ **The Aspire Group**
711 Boylston St.
Boston, MA 02116-2616
Free: 800-487-2967
Fax: (617)500-7284
URL: http://www.bmanet.com/Aspire/index.html

Description: Employment agency.

2791 ■ **ATR Technology**
1230 Oakmead Pkwy., Ste. 110
Sunnyvale, CA 94085
Ph: (408)328-8000
E-mail: corporate@atr1.com
URL: http://www.atr-technology.com

Description: Serves as an executive search firm specializing in the placement of information technology professionals ranging from complex software ap-

plication development and infrastructure support to enterprise-wide project management.

2792 ■ **BG & Associates**
10112 Langhorne Ct., Ste. B
Bethesda, MD 20817-1250
Ph: (301)365-4046
Fax: (301)365-0435
E-mail: bgajob@erols.com

Description: Firm specializes in the recruitment and placement of consultants on a national basis primarily in the areas of information technology, finance/accounting, and human resources.

2793 ■ **Capitol Staffing Inc.**
460 Briarwood Dr., Briarwood 1 Bldg., Ste. 110
Jackson, MS 39206
Ph: (601)957-1755
Fax: (601)957-3880
E-mail: info@capitolstaffing.com
URL: http://www.capitolstaffing.com

Description: Personnel consultancy that focuses on office administration, management, sales, accounting, medical, information technology, accounting, and engineering/technical fields. Industries served: insurance, finance, medical, communications, investment, industry, and small businesses.

2794 ■ **Career Advocates International**
1539 Ave. A
Katy, TX 77493
Ph: (281)371-3917
E-mail: hank@careeradvocates.org
URL: http://www.careeradvocates.org

Description: Provides permanent placement and temporary staffing for executive and staff level positions. Specializes in multiple niches including: sales and marketing, accounting and financial services, banking, communications, human resources, chemicals, oil and gas, medical and dental, legal, information technology, energy, technology, engineering, manufacturing, construction, and light industrial.

2795 ■ **Cornell Global**
PO Box 7113
Wilton, CT 06897
Ph: (203)762-0730
E-mail: info@cornellglobal.com
URL: http://www.cornellglobal.com

Description: Executive search firm with areas of expertise in the following areas: advertising, public relations, marketing, sales, finance and accounting, risk management, private equity and venture capital, construction, industrial, manufacturing, life sciences, publishing, information technology, engineering, human resources, legal, and logisitics.

2796 ■ **CSI Executive Search LLC**
9600 Great Hills Trail, Ste. 150W
Austin, TX 78759
Ph: (512)301-1119
Fax: (512)301-5559
E-mail: info@csi-executivesearch.com
URL: http://www.csi-executivesearch.com

Description: Executive search firm that specializes in the following arenas: accounting, engineering, healthcare, information technology, and legal.

2797 ■ **The Datafinders Group, Inc.**
PO Box 1624
Fort Lee, NJ 07024
Ph: (201)845-7700
Fax: (201)969-1065
E-mail: info@datafinders.net
URL: http://www.datafinders.net

Description: Executive search firm.

2798 ■ **Dynamic Search Systems Inc.**
220 W Campus Dr., Ste. 201
Arlington Heights, IL 60004-1499
Ph: (847)304-0700

Fax: (847)304-5859
E-mail: candidate@dssjobs.com
URL: http://www.dssjobs.com

Description: Provider of executive and professional search services to the IT community. Firm specializes in the placement of developers, programmers, programmer analysts, systems analysts, project leaders, project managers, systems programmers, data processing consultants, IT directors, and other information technology related candidates. Industries served: All.

2799 ■ **EDP Staffing, LLC**
PO Box 651
Hebron, CT 06231
Free: 860-781-6064
E-mail: info@edpstaffingllc.com
URL: http://www.edpstaffingllc.com

Description: Serves as an e-commerce and IT management search firm. Provides staffing solutions for contingency, retained, contract or temporary staffing. Specializes in the recruitment and placement of e-commerce applications specialists, core IT staff members or IT management professionals.

2800 ■ **JES Search Firm Inc.**
1021 Stovall Blvd., Ste. 600
Atlanta, GA 30319
Ph: (404)812-0622
Fax: (404)812-1910
E-mail: admin@jessearch.com
URL: http://www.jessearch.com

Description: Contract and permanent information technology search firm specializing in placing software developers as well as other information systems professionals.

2801 ■ **KLR Executive Search Group L.L.C.**
951 N Main St.
Providence, RI 02904
Ph: (401)274-2001
Fax: (401)831-4018
E-mail: info@klrsearchgroup.com
URL: http://www.klrsearchgroup.com

Description: Career recruitment firm specializes in the placement of accounting and financial and information technology professionals.

2802 ■ **Houser Martin Morris**
110th Ave. NE, 110 Atrium Pl., Ste. 580
Bellevue, WA 98004
Ph: (425)453-2700
Fax: (425)453-8726
E-mail: info@houser.com
URL: http://www.houser.com

Description: Focus is in the areas of retained executive search, professional, and technical recruiting. Areas of specialization include software engineering, sales and marketing, information technology, legal, human resources, accounting and finance, manufacturing, factory automation and engineering.

2803 ■ **Nesco Inc.**
6140 Parkland Blvd., Ste. 110
Mayfield Heights, OH 44124-6106
Ph: (440)461-6000
Fax: (440)449-3111
E-mail: corporate@nescoresource.com
URL: http://www.nescoresource.com

Description: Offers staffing and consulting solutions in the fields of engineering, information technology, accounting and finance, manufacturing and distribution, and administrative and customer services.

2804 ■ **Q&A Recruiting**
J.P. Morgan International Plz., Bldg. III
14241 Dallas Pkwy., Ste. 550
Dallas, TX 75254
Ph: (972)720-1020
Fax: (972)720-1023
E-mail: jobs@qarecruiting.com
URL: http://www.qarecruiting.com

Description: Provides staffing services for accounting, finance, tax, information technology, payroll or accounting support, and human resources.

2805 ■ **Spectrum Group, LLC**
1919 Gallows Rd., Ste. 600
Vienna, VA 22182
Ph: (703)738-1200
Fax: (703)761-9477
E-mail: web@spectrumcareers.com
URL: http://www.spectrumcareers.com

Description: Serves as executive search firm for accounting and finance, information technology, and sales and marketing industries.

2806 ■ **Sullivan and Cogliano**
230 2nd Ave.
Waltham, MA 02451
Ph: (781)890-7890
Fax: (781)906-7801
E-mail: jobs@sullivancogliano.com
URL: http://www.sullivancogliano.com

Description: Technical staffing firm.

2807 ■ **Technical Talent Locators Ltd.**
5570 Sterrett Pl., Ste. 208
Columbia, MD 21044
Ph: (410)740-0091
Fax: (301)621-4227
E-mail: steve@ttlgroup.com
URL: http://www.ttlgroup.com

Description: Permanent employment agency working within the following fields: software and database engineering; computer, communication, and telecommunication system engineering; and other computer-related disciplines.

2808 ■ **TRC Staffing Services Inc.**
115 Perimeter Center Pl. NE, Ste. 850
Atlanta, GA 30346
Ph: (770)392-1411
Free: 800-488-8008
Fax: (770)392-7926
E-mail: info@trcstaff.com
URL: http://www.trcstaffing.com

Description: A full-service executive search company with permanent placements encompassing engineering, industrial sales, financial and computer science positions. Screen, interview and verify past employment for all candidates prior to referral. Also assist personnel staffs in the attainment of their EEO/AAP goals with the placement of talented individuals in positions which were underutilized with minorities and/or women. Industries served: all.

2809 ■ **Wallach Associates Inc.**
7811 Montrose Rd., Ste. 505
Potomac, MD 20854
Ph: (301)340-0300
Free: 800-296-2084
Fax: (301)340-8008
URL: http://www.wallach.org

Description: Specialists in recruitment of professional personnel, primarily in information technology and electronic systems and engineering, energy research and development, management consulting, operations research, computers, defense systems, and programmers. Specializes in Internet and software engineer for intelligence community.

2810 ■ **Worlco Computer Resources, Inc.**
901 Rte. 38
Cherry Hill, NJ 08002
Ph: (610)293-9070
Fax: (856)665-8903
E-mail: recruiter@worlco.com
URL: http://www.worlco.com

Description: Employment agency and executive search firm. Second location in Cherry Hill, New Jersey.

Online Job Sources and Services

2811 ■ **Computer Systems Analyst Jobs**
URL: http://computer-systems-analyst-jobs.intellego-publishing.com

Description: Contains statistics, informative articles and updated list of current open positions for computer systems analysts. Includes news concerning prospects for a career in computer systems analysis.

2812 ■ **ComputerWork.com**
URL: http://www.computerwork.com

Description: Job search and resume submission service for professionals in information technology.

2813 ■ **Computerworld Careers**
URL: http://www.computerworld.com/careertopics/careers

Description: Offers career opportunities for IT (information technology) professionals. Job seekers may search the jobs database, register at the site, and read about job surveys and employment trends. Employers may post jobs.

2814 ■ **Computing Research Association Job Announcements**
URL: http://www.cra.org/ads

Description: Contains dated links to national college and university computer technology positions.

2815 ■ **Guru.com**
URL: http://www.guru.com

Description: Job board specializing in contract jobs for creative and information technology professionals. Also provides online incorporation and educational opportunities for independent contractors along with articles and advice.

2816 ■ **InformationTechnologyCrossing.com**
URL: http://www.informationtechnologycrossing.com

Description: Provides information on IT jobs.

2817 ■ **ItJobs.com**
URL: http://www.itjobs.com

Description: Provides information technology employment opportunities for the following categories: internet/intranet/extranet, network systems, open systems, client/server, software engineering and development, software QA and testing, ERP applications and management consulting, and legacy systems.

2818 ■ **Jobs for Programmers**
URL: http://www.prgjobs.com

Description: Job board site for computer programmers that allows them to browse through thousands of programming jobs, even search for special jobs with sign-on bonuses, relocation funding, and 4-day work weeks. Resume posting is free.

2819 ■ **Jobs4IT.com**
URL: http://www.informationtechnologyjobs.com/

Description: Features information technology job opportunities, job fairs, business opportunities, news, events, continuing education guide, resume database, distribution services and other career resources.

2820 ■ **JustTechJobs.com**
URL: http://www.justtechjobs.com

Description: Serves as a jobsite that provides employers with a technology specific focus and provides job seekers with job postings aimed at those specific tech jobs. Offers a community of 15 million tech professionals and also supports several technology websites.

2821 ■ **Tech-Engine.com**
URL: http://techengine.com

Description: Features employment listings concerning the IT and engineering fields. Features employers and recruiters information, resume posting and career resources.

2822 ■ **ZDNet Tech Jobs**
URL: http://www.zdnet.com

Description: Site houses a listing of national employment opportunities for professionals in high tech fields. Also contains resume building tips and relocation resources.

Tradeshows

2823 ■ **Large Installation System Administration Conference**
USENIX, the Advanced Computing Systems Association
2560 9th St., Ste. 215
Berkeley, CA 94710
Ph: (510)528-8649
Fax: (510)548-5738
E-mail: webster@usenix.org
URL: http://www.usenix.org

Frequency: Annual. Includes exhibits of books, products, and services that can optimize systems, networks, and internet management. 2013 November 3-8; Washington, DC; 2014 November 9-14; Seattle, WA; 2015 November 8-13; Washington, DC; 2016 December 4-9; Boston, MA. Provides networking opportunities for computing professionals.

2824 ■ **USENIX Annual Technical Conference**
USENIX, the Advanced Computing Systems Association
2560 9th St., Ste. 215
Berkeley, CA 94710
Ph: (510)528-8649
Fax: (510)548-5738
E-mail: webster@usenix.org
URL: http://www.usenix.org

Frequency: Annual. Includes exhibits of products and services for the advancement of computing systems.

2825 ■ **XPLOR International Conference and Vendor Forum**
Xplor International
24156 State Rd. 54, Ste. 4
Lutz, FL 33559
Ph: (813)949-6170
Fax: (813)949-9977
E-mail: skip@xplor.org
URL: http://www.xplor.org

Frequency: Annual. **Primary Exhibits:** Equipment, supplies, and services for users and manufacturers of advanced electronic document systems.

Other Sources

2826 ■ **American Indian Science and Engineering Society**
PO Box 9828
Albuquerque, NM 87119-9828
Ph: (505)765-1052
Fax: (505)765-5608
E-mail: pam@aises.org
URL: http://www.aises.org

Description: Represents American Indian and non-Indian students and professionals in science, technology, and engineering fields; corporations representing energy, mining, aerospace, electronic, and computer fields. Seeks to motivate and encourage students to pursue undergraduate and graduate studies in science, engineering, and technology. Sponsors science fairs in grade schools, teacher training workshops, summer math/science sessions for 8th-12th graders, professional chapters, and student chapters in colleges. Offers scholarships. Adult members serve as role models, advisers, and mentors for students. Operates placement service.

2827 ■ Association for Computing Machinery - Special Interest Group on Accessible Computing
2 Penn Plz., Ste. 701
New York, NY 10121-0701
Ph: (212)626-0500
Free: 800-342-6626
Fax: (212)944-1318
E-mail: chair_sigaccess@acm.org
URL: http://www.sigaccess.org

Description: Promotes the professional interests of computing personnel with physical disabilities and the application of computing and information technology in solving relevant disability problems. Works to educate the public to support careers for the disabled. **Members:** 453.

2828 ■ Association of Information Technology Professionals
330 N Wabash Ave., Ste. 2000
Chicago, IL 60611-4267
Ph: (312)245-1070
Free: 800-224-9371
Fax: (312)673-6659
E-mail: aitp_hq@aitp.org
URL: http://www.aitp.org

Description: Managerial personnel, staff, educators, and individuals interested in the management of information resources. Founder of the Certificate in Data Processing examination program, now administered by an intersociety organization. Maintains Legislative Communications Network. Professional education programs include EDP-oriented business and management principles self-study courses and a series of videotaped management development seminars. Sponsors student organizations around the country interested in information technology and encourages members to

serve as counselors for the Scout computer merit badge. Conducts research projects, including a business information systems curriculum for two- and four-year colleges.

2829 ■ Association for Women in Computing
PO Box 2768
Oakland, CA 94602
E-mail: info@awc-hq.org
URL: http://www.awc-hq.org

Description: Individuals interested in promoting the education, professional development, and advancement of women in computing.

2830 ■ Black Data Processing Associates
9500 Arena Dr., Ste. 350
Largo, MD 20774
Ph: (301)584-3135
Fax: (301)560-8300
E-mail: office@bdpa.org
URL: http://www.bdpa.org

Description: Represents persons employed in the information processing industry, including electronic data processing, electronic word processing and data communications; others interested in information processing. Seeks to accumulate and share information processing knowledge and business expertise to increase the career and business potential of minorities in the information processing field. Conducts professional seminars, workshops, tutoring services and community introductions to data processing. Makes annual donation to the United Negro College Fund.

2831 ■ *Career Opportunities in Computers and Cyberspace*
InfoBase Holdings Inc.
132 W 31st., 17 Fl.
New York, NY 10001-3406
Ph: (212)967-8800
Fax: (800)678-3633
E-mail: info@infobasepublishing.com
URLs: http://www.infobasepublishing.com; http://www
.infobasepublishing.com/Bookdetail.aspx?ISBN
=1438110669&eBooks=1

Frequency: Published March, 2004. **Description:** Harry Henderson. Second edition, 2004. 256 pages. **Covers:** Nearly 200 professions, clustering them by skill, objectives, and work conditions. **Includes:** Appendices of educational institutions, periodicals, directories, and associations. **Entries include:** Education, salaries, employment prospects.

2832 ■ IEEE Computer Society
2001 L St. NW, Ste. 700
Washington, DC 20036
Ph: (202)371-0101
Free: 800-272-6657
Fax: (202)728-9614
E-mail: help@computer.org
URL: http://www.computer.org

Description: Computer professionals. Promotes the development of computer and information sciences and fosters communication within the information processing community. Sponsors conferences, symposia, workshops, tutorials, technical meetings, and seminars. Operates Computer Society Press. Presents scholarships; bestows technical achievement and service awards and certificates. **Members:** 90,000.

2833 ■ USENIX, the Advanced Computing Systems Association
2560 9th St., Ste. 215
Berkeley, CA 94710
Ph: (510)528-8649
Fax: (510)548-5738
E-mail: webster@usenix.org
URL: http://www.usenix.org

Description: Represents the community of engineers, system administrators, scientists, and technicians working on the cutting edge of the computing world. Aims to foster technical excellence and innovation that pertains to computer systems. Supports and disseminates research with a practical bias. Provides a neutral forum for discussion of technical issues and encourages computing outreach into the community at large.

SOURCES OF HELP-WANTED ADS

2834 ■ *American City and County*
Penton
9800 Metcalf Ave.
Overland Park, KS 66212
Ph: (913)341-1300
Free: 866-748-4926
Fax: (913)967-1905
E-mail: corporatecustomerservice@penton.com
URL: http://americancityandcounty.com
Frequency: Monthly. **Description:** Municipal and county administration magazine.

2835 ■ *American Professional Constructor*
American Institute of Constructors
700 N Fairfax St., Ste. 510
Alexandria, VA 22314
Ph: (703)683-4999
Fax: (571)527-3105
E-mail: info@professionalconstructor.org
URL: http://www.professionalconstructor.org/aic/ publications/
Frequency: Biennial. **Price:** $112 Individuals. **Description:** Journal covering general interest and technical articles for construction professionals.

2836 ■ *BIA News*
Brick Industry Association
1850 Centennial Park Dr., Ste. 301
Reston, VA 20191
Ph: (703)620-0010
Fax: (703)620-3928
E-mail: brickinfo@bia.org
URL: http://www.gobrick.com/html/pr.html
Frequency: Monthly. **Price:** $30 Individuals. **Description:** Trade publication covering issues for the brick industry.

2837 ■ *Builder: The Magazine of the National Association of Home Builders*
DoveTale Publishers
1 Thomas Cir. NW
Washington, DC 20005
Ph: (202)339-0744
Free: 877-275-8647
Fax: (202)785-1974
E-mail: builder@omeda.com
URLs: http://www.hanleywood.com/default.aspx ?page=magazines; http://www.builderonline.com
Frequency: 13/yr. **Price:** $29.95 U.S. and Canada; $54.95 U.S. and Canada 2 years; $192 Other countries. **Description:** Magazine covering housing and construction industry.

2838 ■ *Building Systems Magazine*
Active Interest Media
4125 Lafayette Ctr. Dr., Ste. 100
Chantilly, VA 20151
Ph: (703)222-9411
Fax: (703)222-3209
URLs: http://www.buildingsystems.com; http://www .aimmedia.com/article_display_19.html
Frequency: Bimonthly. **Description:** Magazine featuring innovative construction technologies for builders, developers and general contractors.

2839 ■ *Civil Engineering-ASCE*
American Society of Civil Engineers - Architectural Engineering Institute
1801 Alexander Bell Dr.
Reston, VA 20191-4400
Free: 800-548-2723
E-mail: aei@asce.org
URL: http://pubs.asce.org/magazines/CEMag/
Frequency: Monthly. **Price:** $230 Institutions; $275 Institutions, other countries; $230 Individuals; $275 Other countries; $30 Members domestic; $69 Other countries member; $30 Students member; domestic; $69 Students member; international. **Description:** Professional magazine.

2840 ■ *Construction Business Owner: The business management resource for contractors*
Cahaba Media Group
1900 28th Ave. S
Birmingham, AL 35209
Ph: (205)212-9402
URL: http://www.constructionbusinessowner.com/
Frequency: Monthly. **Price:** Free. **Description:** Magazine that provides information for construction management and industry business information.

2841 ■ *Construction Claims Monthly*
Business Publishers Inc.
2222 Sedwick Dr.
Durham, NC 27713
Ph: (301)587-6300
Free: 800-223-8720
Fax: (800)508-2592
E-mail: custserv@bpinews.com
URL: http://www.bpinews.com
Description: Monthly. $402/year. Covers significant legal developments governing contract payment and performance. Features an article on construction claims law; summaries of recent decisions with expert commentary; and highlights of actions by the federal boards of contract appeals and the Comptroller General.

2842 ■ *Constructor: The Construction Management Magazine*
Associated General Contractors of America
2300 Wilson Blvd., Ste. 400
Arlington, VA 22201
Ph: (703)548-3118
Free: 800-242-1767
Fax: (703)548-3119
E-mail: info@agc.org
URL: http://constructor.agc.org/
Frequency: Bimonthly. **Price:** $95 Individuals.

Description: Management magazine for the Construction Industry.

2843 ■ *Consulting-Specifying Engineer*
CFE Media LLC
1111 W 22nd St., Ste. 250
Oak Brook, IL 60523
Ph: (630)571-4070
Fax: (630)214-4504
URLs: http://www.csemag.com; http://mediakit.cfe-media.com/cseimk/csewebcasts.html
Frequency: 13/yr. **Description:** The integrated engineering magazine of the building construction industry.

2844 ■ *Daily Journal of Commerce*
New Orleans Publishing Group Inc.
111 Veterans Blvd., Ste. 1440
Metairie, LA 70005
Ph: (504)834-9292
Fax: (504)832-3550
E-mail: mail@nopg.com
URLs: http://www.djc-gp.com; http://www.djcgulfcoast .com
Frequency: Daily. **Price:** $525 Individuals online; $375 Individuals 6 months; $225 Individuals 3 months. **Description:** Trade newspaper covering construction news in Louisiana and Mississippi.

2845 ■ *ENR: Engineering News-Record: The Construction Weekly*
The McGraw-Hill Companies Inc.
2 Penn Plz., 9th Fl.
New York, NY 10121
Ph: (212)904-3507
Fax: (212)904-2820
E-mail: customer.service@mcgraw-hill.com
URL: http://enr.construction.com/Default.asp
Frequency: Weekly. **Price:** $87 Individuals print and online. **Description:** Magazine focusing on engineering and construction.

2846 ■ *ISHN*
BNP Media
2401 W Big Beaver Rd., Ste. 700
Troy, MI 48084
Ph: (248)362-3700
Free: 800-952-6643
Fax: (248)362-5103
E-mail: privacy@bnpmedia.com
URL: http://www.ishn.com/
Frequency: Monthly. **Price:** Free. **Description:** Business-to-business magazine for safety and health managers at high-hazard worksites in manufacturing, construction, health facilities, and service industries. Content covering OSHA and EPA regulations, howto features, safety and health management topics, and the latest product news.

2847 ■ *Journal of Light Construction*
DoveTale Publishers
1 Thomas Cir. NW
Washington, DC 20005
Ph: (202)339-0744
Free: 877-275-8647
Fax: (202)785-1974
E-mail: hwmicustomerservice@hanleywood.com
URL: http://www.jlconline.com
Description: Monthly. Contains articles, news, and information related to construction. Topics include building science, foundation and framing, heating, ventilation, and air conditioning (HVAC) and plumbing.

2848 ■ *Kitchen and Bath Business*
E-mail: kbb@mediabrains.com
URL: http://www.kbbonline.com/kbb/index.shtml
Frequency: Monthly. **Price:** $79 Individuals; $94 Canada; $139 Other countries. **Description:** Trade magazine on kitchen and bath remodeling and construction.

2849 ■ *Landscape Construction: Large installations and site prep*
Moose River Media
374 Emerson Falls Rd.
Saint Johnsbury, VT 05819
Free: 800-422-7147
Fax: (802)748-1866
URL: http://www.lcmmagazine.com/
Frequency: Monthly. **Description:** Magazine featuring landscaping.

2850 ■ *MetalMag: MetalMag*
DoveTale Publishers
1 Thomas Cir. NW
Washington, DC 20005
Ph: (202)339-0744
Free: 877-275-8647
Fax: (202)785-1974
E-mail: mtm@omeda.com
URL: http://www.metalmag.com/
Frequency: Bimonthly. **Description:** Magazine for industrial construction professionals.

2851 ■ *The Municipality*
League of Wisconsin Municipalities
122 W Washington Ave., Ste. 300
Madison, WI 53703-2715
Ph: (608)267-2380
Free: 800-991-5502
Fax: (608)267-0645
E-mail: jmstaral@lwm-info.org
URL: http://www.lwm-info.org/
Frequency: Monthly. **Price:** $25/year. **Description:** Magazine for officials of Wisconsin's local municipal governments.

2852 ■ *NAHRO Monitor*
National Association of Housing and Redevelopment Officials
630 Eye St. NW
Washington, DC 20001-3736
Ph: (202)289-3500
Free: 877-866-2476
Fax: (202)289-8181
E-mail: nahro@nahro.org
URL: http://www.nahro.org/nahro_monitor
Description: Biweekly. Disseminates news on low-income housing and community development issues. Intended for member professionals and government officials.

2853 ■ *The NAWIC Image*
National Association of Women in Construction
327 S Adams St.
Fort Worth, TX 76104
Ph: (817)877-5551
Free: 800-552-3506
Fax: (817)877-0324
E-mail: nawic@nawic.org
URL: http://www.nawic.org

Description: Bimonthly. Fosters career advancement for women in construction. Features women business owners, training for construction trades and educational programs. Recurring features include columns titled "Issues and Trends," "Road to Success," "Chapter Highlights," "Members on the Move," and "Q&A."

2854 ■ *PE*
National Society of Professional Engineers
1420 King St.
Alexandria, VA 22314-2794
Ph: (703)684-2800
Fax: (703)836-4875
E-mail: memserv@nspe.org
URL: http://www.nspe.org/PEmagazine/index.html
Frequency: Semimonthly; 10/yr. **Price:** included in membership dues; $50 for nonmembers. **Description:** Covers matters of importance to engineering educators and students.

2855 ■ *Professional Builder: The Magazine of the Housing and Light Construction Industry*
SGC Horizon L.L.C.
3030 W Salt Creek Ln., Ste. 201
Arlington Heights, IL 60005
Ph: (847)391-1000
Fax: (847)390-0408
URL: http://www.housingzone.com/
professionalbuilder
Frequency: Monthly. **Price:** Free. **Description:** The integrated engineering magazine of the building construction industry.

2856 ■ *Remodeling*
DoveTale Publishers
1 Thomas Cir. NW
Washington, DC 20005
Ph: (202)339-0744
Free: 877-275-8647
Fax: (202)785-1974
E-mail: rm@omeda.com
URL: http://www.remodeling.hw.net
Frequency: 13/yr. **Price:** $24.95 Individuals; $39.95 Individuals Canadian residents; $192 Individuals international residents. **Description:** Trade magazine for the professional remodeling industry.

2857 ■ *Residential Architect*
DoveTale Publishers
1 Thomas Cir. NW
Washington, DC 20005
Ph: (202)339-0744
Free: 877-275-8647
Fax: (202)785-1974
E-mail: res@omeda.com
URL: http://www.residentialarchitectmediakit.com/r5/home.asp
Frequency: 9/yr. **Price:** $39.95 Individuals; $66 Canada; $132.50 Other countries. **Description:** Magazine for architects, designers, and building professionals.

2858 ■ *Residential Concrete*
DoveTale Publishers
8726 W Higgins Rd.
Chicago, IL 60631
Ph: (773)284-2400
E-mail: hwmicustomerservice@hanleywood.com
URLs: http://www.hanleywood.com/default.aspx?page=b2bresconcrete; http://www.concreteconstruction.net/industry-news.asp?sectionID=716&articleID=540600
Frequency: Bimonthly. **Price:** $30 Individuals; $46 Two years; $39 Canada and Mexico; $64 Two years Canada & Mexico; $93 Other countries; $162 Other countries two years. **Description:** Magazine featuring the use of concrete in residential concrete construction.

2859 ■ *Tools of the Trade*
DoveTale Publishers
1 Thomas Cir. NW
Washington, DC 20005
Ph: (202)339-0744
Free: 877-275-8647
Fax: (202)785-1974
E-mail: hwmicustomerservice@hanleywood.com
URL: http://www.hanleywood.com/?page=toolsofthetrade&section=res_rem
Frequency: Bimonthly. **Price:** $36 Individuals; $66 Canada; $192 Other countries; $70 Two years. **Description:** Magazine featuring tools for commercial and residential construction.

2860 ■ *Western City*
League of California Cities
1400 K St., 4th Fl.
Sacramento, CA 95814
Ph: (916)658-8200
Free: 800-262-1801
Fax: (916)658-8240
E-mail: okabel@cacities.org
URL: http://www.westerncity.com
Frequency: Monthly. **Price:** $39 Individuals; $63 Two years; $52 Other countries; $26.50 Students. **Description:** Municipal interest magazine.

EMPLOYER DIRECTORIES AND NETWORKING LISTS

2861 ■ *ABC Today--Associated Builders and Contractors National Membership Directory Issue*
Associated Builders and Contractors
440 1st St. NW, Ste. 200
Washington, DC 20001
E-mail: gotquestions@abc.org
URL: http://www.abc.org
Frequency: Annual; Latest Edition 2011. **Price:** $150 plus $7.00 shipping. **Publication includes:** List of approximately 19,000 member construction contractors and suppliers. **Entries include:** Company name, address, phone, name of principal executive, code to volume of business, business specialty. **Arrangement:** Classified by chapter, then by work specialty.

2862 ■ *ENR--Top 400 Construction Contractors Issue*
The McGraw-Hill Companies Inc.
PO Box 182604
Columbus, OH 43272
Ph: (212)512-2000
Free: 877-833-5524
Fax: (614)759-3749
E-mail: customer.service@mcgraw-hill.com
URL: http://enr.construction.com/toplists/Contractors/001-100.asp
Frequency: Annual; Latest edition 2011. **Price:** $35 Individuals. **Publication includes:** List of 400 United States contractors receiving largest dollar volumes of contracts in preceding calendar year. Separate lists of 50 largest design/construct management firms; 50 largest program and construction managers; 25 building contractors; 25 heavy contractors. **Entries include:** Company name, headquarters location, total value of contracts received in preceding year, value of foreign contracts, countries in which operated, construction specialties. **Arrangement:** By total value of contracts received.

HANDBOOKS AND MANUALS

2863 ■ *Construction*
InfoBase Holdings Inc.
132 W 31st., 17 Fl.
New York, NY 10001-3406
Ph: (212)967-8800

Fax: (800)678-3633
E-mail: info@infobasepublishing.com
URL: http://www.ferguson.infobasepublishing.com

Price: $30 Hardcover. **Description:** 2010. 128 pages. Contains profiles of 20 careers in the field of construction with emphasis on the nature of work, requirements, salary, and career outlook. Includes full-color photographs, index, glossary, resources, and side bars.

2864 ■ *Construction Careers*
Amicus Publishing
PO Box 1329
Mankato, MN 56002
Ph: (507)388-9357
Fax: (507)388-1779
E-mail: info@amicuspublishing.us
URL: http://www.amicuspublishing.us

Price: $35.65. **Description:** Cath Senker. 2011. 48 pages. Describes jobs in the construction and building trades, such as equipment operators, carpenters, electricians, and inspectors. Includes profiles of workers in the industry.

2865 ■ *Senior Construction Inspector*
National Learning Corporation
212 Michael Dr.
Syosset, NY 11791
Ph: (516)921-8888
Free: 800-632-8888
Fax: (516)921-8743
E-mail: info@passbooks.com
URL: http://www.passbooks.com

Description: 2009. $39.95 (paper). Serves as an exam preparation guide for senior construction inspectors.

EMPLOYMENT AGENCIES AND SEARCH FIRMS

2866 ■ **20-20 Foresight Executive Search Inc.**
150 N Michigan Ave., Ste. 2800
Chicago, IL 60601
Ph: (708)246-2100
E-mail: bcavoto@202-4.com
URL: http://www.2020-4.com

Description: Executive search firm. Affiliate offices in California and Washington DC.

2867 ■ **Cook Associates Inc.**
212 W Kinzie St.
Chicago, IL 60610
Ph: (312)329-0900
Fax: (312)329-1528
URL: http://www.cookassociates.com

Description: Management and executive recruiting specialists offering a commitment to clients to find the candidates and to find those candidates as efficiently as possible. Approach provides a flexible and effective structure that serves the special needs of both large and small companies. Serves the following industries: industrial, equipment manufacturer, food processing, graphic arts, chemical process, retailing, mechanical products, health care services, financial and professional services, legal, consumer products, construction and engineering, packaging, pulp and paper.

2868 ■ **Frank Palma Associates**
17 Beechwood Ln.
Kinnelon, NJ 07405
Ph: (973)838-9490
Fax: (973)492-5639
E-mail: fpalma@fpassocs.com
URL: http://www.fpassocs.com

Description: Executive search firm. Additional location in Duluth, GA.

2869 ■ **Golden Gate Staffing**
1422 Springs Rd., Ste. B
Vallejo, CA 94591
Ph: (707)552-6767
E-mail: info@goldengatestaffing.com
URL: http://www.goldengatestaffing.com

Description: Provides project based, temporary, full-time and permanent placement staffing services.

2870 ■ **Real Estate Executive Search, Inc.**
225 E Dania Beach Blvd., Ste. 200
Dania Beach, FL 33004
Ph: (954)927-6000
Fax: (954)927-6003
E-mail: reesearch954@aol.com
URL: http://reesearchinc.com

Description: Executive search firm for the real estate and finance fields.

2871 ■ **Synergy Professionals**
1029 N Peachtree Pkwy., Ste. 252
Peachtree City, GA 30269
Ph: (770)450-8130
E-mail: contact@synergyprof.com
URL: http://www.synergyprof.com

Description: Serves as a professional recruiting firm devoted exclusively to the construction industry.

ONLINE JOB SOURCES AND SERVICES

2872 ■ **Build Your Future Career Center**
URL: http://www.jobtarget.com/home/home.cfm?site_id=13781

Description: Features construction industry job listings. Includes resume bank that lists profiles voluntarily posted by job seekers.

2873 ■ **Building Inspector Jobs**
URL: http://www.buildinginspectorjobs.org

Description: Serves as a job board for building inspector employment opportunities.

2874 ■ **BuildZ Construction Jobs Network**
URL: http://buildz.net

Description: Provides listings of construction jobs throughout the U.S. Features news related to the construction industry.

2875 ■ **CareerCastConstruction Network**
URL: http://construction.careercast.com

Description: Provides job database that offers opportunities in the field of construction industry. Allows job seekers to build and post their resumes, and employers to post job vacancies as they search for qualified candidates.

2876 ■ **Construction Inspector Jobs**
URL: http://www.constructioninspectorjobs.org

Description: Serves as a job board for construction inspector employment opportunities.

2877 ■ **ConstructionCrossing.com**
URL: http://www.constructioncrossing.com

Description: Lists new employment opportunities specifically related to the construction personnel profession.

2878 ■ **ConstructionEducation.com**
URL: http://www.constructioneducation.com

Description: Includes link page with list of professional resources, employment opportunities listed by company, and construction-related recruiters' pages, as well as general job search websites. Also contains on-site job bank.

2879 ■ **ConstructionGigs.net**
URL: http://www.constructiongigs.net

Description: Provides an up-to-date listings of job

opportunities and career resources for construction workers.

2880 ■ **Construction.jobs**
URL: http://construction.jobs

Description: Connects employers and job seekers in the construction industry. Features a searchable database of available construction employment opportunities in the U.S.

2881 ■ **ConstructMyFuture.com**
URL: http://www.constructmyfuture.com

Description: Offers comprehensive information for students, parents, and educators on varied careers in construction. Includes a searchable database of colleges, universities and trade schools that offer degrees in construction fields.

2882 ■ **ENR Industry Jobs Site**
URL: http://industry-jobs.enr.com/main/default.asp

Description: Provides job searching and recruitment services in the field of architecture, engineering and construction (AEC) industry. Offers comprehensive database of career opportunities for job seekers and resume of top AEC professionals for employers.

2883 ■ **GeneralConstructionJobs.com**
URL: http://www.generalconstructionjobs.com/a/jobs/find-jobs

Description: Serves as a job board for online employment advertising built exclusively for the general construction industry.

2884 ■ **Great Green Careers**
URL: http://www.greatgreencareers.com

Description: Serves as online resource that connects employers and job seekers in the green jobs industries.

2885 ■ **iHireConstruction**
URL: http://www.ihireconstruction.com

Description: Helps recruiters and hiring managers find qualified candidates in different fields and specialties of construction industry. Provides job listings, customizable online profiles, resume writing services, and job alerts to job seekers.

2886 ■ **United States Construction Jobs**
URL: http://us.theconstructionjob.com

Description: Contains construction jobs by location. Allow construction recruiters and employers to advertise their construction jobs openings.

OTHER SOURCES

2887 ■ **American Society of Home Inspectors**
932 Lee St., Ste. 101
Des Plaines, IL 60016
Ph: (847)759-2820
Fax: (847)759-1620
E-mail: frankl@ashi.org
URL: http://www.homeinspector.org

Description: Professional home inspectors whose goals are to: establish home inspector qualifications; set standards of practice for home inspections; adhere to a code of ethics; keep the concept of "objective third party" intact; inform members of the most advanced methods and techniques, and educate consumers on the value of home inspections. Conducts seminars through local chapters.

2888 ■ **Associated Builders and Contractors**
440 1st St. NW, Ste. 200
Washington, DC 20001
E-mail: gotquestions@abc.org
URL: http://www.abc.org

Description: Construction contractors, subcontractors, suppliers and associates. Aims to foster and perpetuate the principles of rewarding construction workers and management on the basis of merit. Sponsors management education programs and craft training; also sponsors apprenticeship and skill training programs. Disseminates technological and labor relations information.

2889 ■ Associated General Contractors of America
2300 Wilson Blvd., Ste. 400
Arlington, VA 22201
Ph: (703)548-3118
Free: 800-242-1767
Fax: (703)548-3119
E-mail: info@agc.org
URL: http://www.agc.org

Description: General construction contractors; subcontractors; industry suppliers; service firms. Provides market services through its divisions. Conducts special conferences and seminars designed specifically for construction firms. Compiles statistics on job accidents reported by member firms. Maintains 65 committees, including joint cooperative committees with other associations and liaison committees with federal agencies.

2890 ■ National Association of Black Women in Construction
1910 NW 105 Ave.
Pembroke Pines, FL 33026
Ph: (954)323-3587
Free: 866-364-4998
Fax: (954)437-4998
E-mail: info@nabwic.org
URL: http://nabwic.org

Description: Promotes the advancement of black women in the construction industry. Supports aspiring construction executives. Provides advocacy, mentorship and professional development for its members.

2891 ■ National Association of Home Builders - Systems Builder Council
1201 15th St. NW
Washington, DC 20005
Ph: (202)266-8200
Free: 800-368-5242
Fax: (202)266-8400
URL: http://www.nahb.org/reference_list.aspx?sectionID=815

Description: Operates under the Building Systems Council of NAHB. Modular building manufacturers. Monitors state and federal housing legislation that impacts the building industry. Provides a forum for communication, networking and recruiting for those involved in manufacturing modular building systems. Addresses and solves problems specific to the council; offers consumer leads service.

2892 ■ National Association of Women in Construction
327 S Adams St.
Fort Worth, TX 76104
Ph: (817)877-5551
Free: 800-552-3506
Fax: (817)877-0324
E-mail: nawic@nawic.org
URL: http://www.nawic.org

Description: Seeks to enhance the success of women in the construction industry.

2893 ■ National Center for Construction Education and Research
13614 Progress Blvd.
Alachua, FL 32615-9407
Ph: (386)518-6500
Free: 888-622-3720
Fax: (386)518-6303
E-mail: marketing@nccer.org
URL: http://www.nccer.org

Description: Education foundation committed to the development and publication of Contren(TM) Learning Series, the source of craft training, management education and safety resources for the construction industry.

2894 ■ Professional Women in Construction
315 E 56th St.
New York, NY 10022-3730
Ph: (212)486-7745
Fax: (212)486-0228
URL: http://www.pwcusa.org

Description: Management-level women and men in construction and allied industries; owners, suppliers, architects, engineers, field personnel, office personnel and bonding/surety personnel. Provides a forum for exchange of ideas and promotion of political and legislative action, education and job opportunities for women in construction and related fields; forms liaisons with other trade and professional groups; develops research programs. Strives to reform abuses and to assure justice and equity within the construction industry. Sponsors mini-workshops. Maintains Action Line, which provides members with current information on pertinent legislation and on the association's activities and job referrals.

SOURCES OF HELP-WANTED ADS

2895 ■ Daily Journal of Commerce
New Orleans Publishing Group Inc.
111 Veterans Blvd., Ste. 1440
Metairie, LA 70005
Ph: (504)834-9292
Fax: (504)832-3550
E-mail: mail@nopg.com
URLs: http://www.djc-gp.com; http://www.djcgulfcoast
  .com
Frequency: Daily. **Price:** $525 Individuals online;
$375 Individuals 6 months; $225 Individuals 3
months. **Description:** Trade newspaper covering
construction news in Louisiana and Mississippi.

2896 ■ The Industrial Projects Report
Industrial Projects Services, Inc.
PO Box 274231
Tampa, FL 33688
Free: 800-849-4821
Fax: (813)265-0331
E-mail: deven.taylor@industrialprojectsreport.com
URL: http://industrialprojectsreport.com
Frequency: Monthly. **Description:** Features up-to-
date information, job board, and construction forum
for skilled crafts people and management personnel.
Contains advertisements from staffing companies
looking for construction management, supervision
professionals and skilled-craft professionals for
projects nationwide. Includes reports on industrial
projects' location, approximate job durations, wages
and other benefits. Helps technical colleges and
trade schools in recruiting students to their trade
programs.

2897 ■ Industrial Tradesman Magazine
106 Cinema Dr., Ste. B
Wilmington, NC 28403
Ph: (910)793-0580
Fax: (910)793-0582
URL: http://www.industrialtradesman.com
Frequency: Monthly. **Price:** $98.95 1 year subscrip-
tion. **Description:** Contains construction project list-
ings including location, pay rate and benefits, dura-
tion, and the crafts being hired.

2898 ■ Journal of Light Construction
DoveTale Publishers
1 Thomas Cir. NW
Washington, DC 20005
Ph: (202)339-0744
Free: 877-275-8647
Fax: (202)785-1974
E-mail: hwmicustomerservice@hanleywood.com
URL: http://www.jlconline.com
Description: Monthly. Contains articles, news, and
information related to construction. Topics include
building science, foundation and framing, heating,
ventilation, and air conditioning (HVAC) and plumb-
ing.

HANDBOOKS AND MANUALS

2899 ■ CAST Exam Secrets Study Guide
Mometrix Media, LLC
3827 Phelan Blvd., No. 179
Beaumont, TX 77707
Free: 800-673-8175
Fax: (866)235-0173
E-mail: css@mometrix.com
URL: http://www.mo-media.com
Price: $43.98 Includes shipping and handling.
Description: 2011. Provides tips and information that
are specially selected to prepare and succeed on the
Construction and Skilled Trades (CAST) Exam.

2900 ■ Cement Mason
National Learning Corporation
212 Michael Dr.
Syosset, NY 11791
Ph: (516)921-8888
Free: 800-632-8888
Fax: (516)921-8743
E-mail: info@passbooks.com
URL: http://www.passbooks.com
Price: $34.95 Paperback; $54.95 Hardcover.
Description: 2012. Serves as exam and career
preparation guide for cement masons.

2901 ■ Concrete Construction
Craftsman Book Co.
6058 Corte Del Cedro
Carlsbad, CA 92011-1514
Ph: (760)438-7828
Free: 800-829-8123
Fax: (760)438-0398
E-mail: support@costbook.com
URL: http://www.craftsman-book.com
Price: $28.75. **Description:** Ken Nolan. 2010. 288
pages. Contains detailed, step-by-step instructions
for the concrete construction worker tasks. Includes
illustrations, charts, estimating data, rules of thumb
and examples.

2902 ■ Concrete Construction Worker
National Learning Corporation
212 Michael Dr.
Syosset, NY 11791
Ph: (516)921-8888
Free: 800-632-8888
Fax: (516)921-8743
E-mail: info@passbooks.com
URL: http://www.passbooks.com
Price: $34.95 Paperback. **Description:** 2012.
Serves as exam and career preparation guide for
concrete construction workers.

2903 ■ Construction
InfoBase Holdings Inc.
132 W 31st., 17 Fl.
New York, NY 10001-3406
Ph: (212)967-8800

Fax: (800)678-3633
E-mail: info@infobasepublishing.com
URL: http://www.ferguson.infobasepublishing.com
Price: $30 Hardcover. **Description:** 2010. 128
pages. Contains profiles of 20 careers in the field of
construction with emphasis on the nature of work,
requirements, salary, and career outlook. Includes
full-color photographs, index, glossary, resources,
and side bars.

2904 ■ Construction Careers
Amicus Publishing
PO Box 1329
Mankato, MN 56002
Ph: (507)388-9357
Fax: (507)388-1779
E-mail: info@amicuspublishing.us
URL: http://www.amicuspublishing.us
Price: $35.65. **Description:** Cath Senker. 2011. 48
pages. Describes jobs in the construction and build-
ing trades, such as equipment operators, carpenters,
electricians, and inspectors. Includes profiles of
workers in the industry.

2905 ■ Construction Chart Book
Center for Construction Research and Training
AFL-CIO
8484 Georgia Ave., Ste. 1000
Silver Spring, MD 20910
Ph: (301)578-8500
Fax: (301)578-8572
E-mail: cpwrwebsite@cpwr.com
URL: http://www.cpwr.com
Description: Fifth Edition. Covers all aspects of the
U.S. construction industry -economics, demograph-
ics, employment and income, education and training,
and safety and health issues.

**2906 ■ The Construction Sector in the U.S.
  Economy: Elements and Employment
  Analyses**
Nova Science Publishers Inc.
400 Oser Ave., Ste. 1600
Hauppauge, NY 11788-3667
Ph: (631)231-7269
Fax: (631)231-8175
E-mail: nova.main@novapublishers.com
URL: http://www.novapublishers.com
Price: $47 Regular; $42.30 Discounted. **Descrip-
tion:** Nelson M. McDonald and Claude A. Marshall.
2012. Outlines the structure of the construction
industry and describes congressional initiatives that
affect the sector.

**2907 ■ Construction & Skilled Trades
  Selection Test (CAST)**
National Learning Corporation
212 Michael Dr.
Syosset, NY 11791
Ph: (516)921-8888
Free: 800-632-8888

Fax: (516)921-8743
E-mail: info@passbooks.com
URL: http://www.passbooks.com
Price: $39.95 Paperback; $59.95 Hardcover.
Description: 2011. Serves as guide for construction and skilled trades workers preparing for vocational licensing exam.

2908 ■ *Construction Technology Trainee Guide*
Prentice Hall
200 Old Tappan Rd.
Old Tappan, NJ 07675
Free: 800-223-1360
Fax: (800)445-6991
URL: http://www.prenticehall.com
Description: Third Edition, 2009. $186.67 (hardcover). 936 pages. Features a highly illustrated design, technical hints and tips from construction industry experts, and review questions.

2909 ■ *Let's Meet a Construction Worker*
Millbrook Press Inc.
c/o Lerner Publishing Group
241 1st Ave. N
Minneapolis, MN 55401
Ph: (612)332-3344
Free: 800-328-4929
Fax: (800)332-1132
E-mail: info@lernerbooks.com
URL: http://www.lernerbooks.com
Price: $6.95 Paperback. **Description:** Bridget Heos. 2013. 24 pages. Contains detailed information about the role of construction workers in communities. Features full-color illustrations, glossary, index, and original artwork.

2910 ■ *Maintenance and Construction Helper*
National Learning Corporation
212 Michael Dr.
Syosset, NY 11791
Ph: (516)921-8888
Free: 800-632-8888
Fax: (516)921-8743
E-mail: info@passbooks.com
URL: http://www.passbooks.com
Price: $34.95 Paperback. **Description:** 2010. Serves as exam and career preparation guide for maintenance and construction helpers.

2911 ■ *Spanish Vocabulary and Grammar for Construction Workers*
Maria Oliveira Language Learning Center
2644 Appian Way, Ste. 102
Pinole, CA 94564
Ph: (510)223-3320
Free: 877-251-8353
Fax: (510)223-3320
E-mail: maria@marialanguages.com
URL: http://www.marialanguages.com
Price: $34.95 includes 2 CDs and workbook. **Description:** 2009. Helps in improving communication at work sites that employ both Spanish- and English-speaking employees. Serves as an effective tool for applicants aspiring to get hired in Spanish-speaking construction companies.

EMPLOYMENT AGENCIES AND SEARCH FIRMS

2912 ■ Tradesmen International Inc.
9760 Shepard Rd.
Macedonia, OH 44056
Ph: (440)349-3432
Free: 800-573-0850
Fax: (440)349-4092
E-mail: gaffolter@tradesmen-international.com
URL: http://www.tradesmen-international.com
Description: Serves as a Construction Labor Support company that provides skilled workers to

contractors and industrial clients to help maximize labor productivity.

ONLINE JOB SOURCES AND SERVICES

2913 ■ A/E/C JobBank
URL: http://www.aecjobbank.com
Description: Helps job seekers find employment opportunities in the construction industry. Allows employers and recruiters to post construction jobs and source top resumes.

2914 ■ Baker Concrete Construction
URL: http://bakerconcrete.jobs
Description: Post job openings in construction industry. Jobs can be search by location and by keywords.

2915 ■ Build Your Future Career Center
URL: http://www.jobtarget.com/home/home.cfm?site_id=13781
Description: Features construction industry job listings. Includes resume bank that lists profiles voluntarily posted by job seekers.

2916 ■ BuildZ Construction Jobs Network
URL: http://buildz.net
Description: Provides listings of construction jobs throughout the U.S. Features news related to the construction industry.

2917 ■ CareerCastConstruction Network
URL: http://construction.careercast.com
Description: Provides job database that offers opportunities in the field of construction industry. Allows job seekers to build and post their resumes, and employers to post job vacancies as they search for qualified candidates.

2918 ■ Careersinconstruction.com
URL: http://www.careersinconstruction.com
Description: Contains job listing for construction industry.

2919 ■ Cement Mason or Concrete Finisher Jobs
URL: http://cement.mason.or.concrete.finisher.jobs.jobsearchsite.com
Description: Provides available cement mason or concrete finisher jobs and career resources.

2920 ■ CommercialConstructionJobs.org
URL: http://commercialconstructionjobs.org
Description: Serves as a job board for applicants looking for a career in construction. Includes job listings from company career pages, other job boards, newspapers and associations.

2921 ■ ConcreteHelper.com
URL: http://concretehelper.com/jobs-2
Description: Features a job board that helps increase education and employment among concrete industry and construction laborers.

2922 ■ Construction Help Wanted
URL: http://www.constructionhelpwanted.net
Description: Serves as an online resource for those seeking jobs in construction. Allows people to look for specified jobs according to location.

2923 ■ Construction Job Board Network
URL: http://www.constructionjobboardnetwork.com/site/constructionjobboardnetwork
Description: Helps job seekers find career opportunities in the construction industry.

2924 ■ Construction Jobs
URL: http://construction.jobs.net
Description: Serves as a resource for various

employment opportunities in the construction industry.

2925 ■ Construction Jobs Directory
URL: http://www.constructionjobsdirectory.net
Description: Serves as a resource for various construction job opportunities.

2926 ■ Construction Jobs Network
URL: http://constructionjobs.net
Description: Provides job seekers access to construction employment opportunities for both construction management, construction professional and construction trade jobs. Features construction jobs, employer, and resume directories.

2927 ■ Construction Labor Source
URL: http://constructionlaborsource.com
Description: Serves as an online business to business network for contractors, builders, staffing companies, and qualified tradespeople. Enables builders and contractors to gain direct access to the labor pool through online profiles and trade specific searches.

2928 ■ Construction Laborer Jobs
URL: http://www.constructionlaborerjobs.com
Description: Serves as niche job board for construction laborer employment opportunities and candidate recruiting. Provides listings of available construction laborer positions.

2929 ■ Construction Skilled Trades Jobs
URL: http://construction.skilled.trades.jobs.jobsearchsite.com
Description: Provides online jobs and career resources related to construction skilled trades.

2930 ■ Construction Worker Job Search
URL: http://construction.worker.jobs.jobsearchsite.com
Description: Provides available construction worker jobs and career resources. Allows employers to post jobs and search resumes to find qualified candidates that match their requirements.

2931 ■ Construction Worker Jobs
URL: http://www.constructionworkerjobs.us
Description: Serves as job board for construction worker employment opportunities and candidate recruiting. Provides listings of available construction worker positions in the U.S.

2932 ■ ConstructionGigs.net
URL: http://www.constructiongigs.net
Description: Provides an up-to-date listings of job opportunities and career resources for construction workers.

2933 ■ Construction.jobs
URL: http://construction.jobs
Description: Connects employers and job seekers in the construction industry. Features a searchable database of available construction employment opportunities in the U.S.

2934 ■ ConstructionJobStore.com
URL: http://www.constructionjobstore.com
Description: Features online job listing in the construction industry. Offers career guide resources and job alert services.

2935 ■ ConstructionLaborer.com
URL: http://www.constructionlaborer.com
Description: Serves as online tool that connects employers and job seekers in the construction industry. Allows construction laborers to find jobs and post and search resumes.

2936 ■ **Constructionworkerjobs.info**
URL: http://www.constructionworkerjobs.info
Description: Serves as a job board for construction worker employment opportunities and candidate recruiting.

2937 ■ **ConstructionWorkforce.net**
URL: http://www.constructionworkforce.net
Description: Offers career opportunities for construction workers.

2938 ■ **ConstructMyFuture.com**
URL: http://www.constructmyfuture.com
Description: Offers comprehensive information for students, parents, and educators on varied careers in construction. Includes a searchable database of colleges, universities and trade schools that offer degrees in construction fields.

2939 ■ **CrewHotSpot.com**
URL: http://crewhotspot.com
Description: Serves as an online tool for job seekers interested in construction industry.

2940 ■ **ENR Industry Jobs Site**
URL: http://industry-jobs.enr.com/main/default.asp
Description: Provides job searching and recruitment services in the field of architecture, engineering and construction (AEC) industry. Offers comprehensive database of career opportunities for job seekers and resume of top AEC professionals for employers.

2941 ■ **GreatPossibilities.com**
URL: http://www.greatpossibilities.com
Description: Serves the construction industry.

Features architecture and design firms, construction trades, industry products and related services through the construction industry directory.

2942 ■ **HeavyCivilJobs.com**
URL: http://heavyciviljobs.com
Description: Serves as an online tool that helps construction workers and civil engineers the opportunity to look for a job in heavy civil disciplines.

2943 ■ **hotConstructionJobs.com**
URL: http://hotconstructionjobs.com
Description: Offers construction workers the opportunity to post their profile and resume to attract employers.

2944 ■ **iHireConstruction**
URL: http://www.ihireconstruction.com
Description: Helps recruiters and hiring managers find qualified candidates in different fields and specialties of construction industry. Provides job listings, customizable online profiles, resume writing services, and job alerts to job seekers.

2945 ■ **Laborer Jobs**
URL: http://laborer.jobs.jobsearchsite.com
Description: Provides available laborer jobs and career resources. Allows employers to post jobs and search resumes to find qualified candidates.

2946 ■ **PavingJobs.com**
URL: http://pavingjobs.com
Description: Serves as a career center specifically

designed for the asphalt and concrete paving community.

2947 ■ **Referwork Jobs**
URL: http://www.referwork-jobs.com
Description: Provides a searchable database of major jobs in construction and related specialties.

2948 ■ **RoadBuildingJobs.com**
URL: http://roadbuildingjobs.com
Description: Serves as an online job source for construction workers and place for employers seeking qualified road builders.

2949 ■ **United States Construction Jobs**
URL: http://us.theconstructionjob.com
Description: Contains construction jobs by location. Allow construction recruiters and employers to advertise their construction jobs openings.

2950 ■ **USA Construction Jobs**
URL: http://www.usaconstructionjobs.com
Description: Features job listings in construction and general labor.

ONLINE AND DATABASE SERVICES

2951 ■ **CareersForBuilders.com**
URL: http://www.careersforbuilders.com
Description: Features a searchable database of employment opportunities for different types of construction work. Includes career resources on job hunting tools and tips.

Construction Managers

SOURCES OF HELP-WANTED ADS

2952 ■ ABC Newsline
Associated Builders and Contractors
440 1st St. NW, Ste. 200
Washington, DC 20001
E-mail: gotquestions@abc.org
URL: http://www.abc.org

Description: Weekly. Designed to keep readers alerted to important changes within ABC and the construction industry. Reports on legislative issues, construction trends, conferences and meetings, and ABC services. Recurring features include news of members and columns titled Labor Relations, Construction Law, Computer Corner, Bottom Line, and Chapter News.

2953 ■ American Institute of Constructors and the Constructor Commission Newsletter
American Institute of Constructors and the Constructor Commission
PO Box 26334
Alexandria, VA 22314
Ph: (703)683-4999
Fax: (571)527-3105
E-mail: dwright@professionalconstructor.org
URL: http://www.professionalconstructor.org

Description: Bimonthly. Concerned with construction practice, design, administration, and teaching. Carries news of members, listings of job opportunities, local chapter reports, notices of new publications, and conferences on construction topics.

2954 ■ American Professional Constructor
American Institute of Constructors
700 N Fairfax St., Ste. 510
Alexandria, VA 22314
Ph: (703)683-4999
Fax: (571)527-3105
E-mail: info@professionalconstructor.org
URL: http://www.professionalconstructor.org/aic/publications/

Frequency: Biennial. **Price:** $112 Individuals.
Description: Journal covering general interest and technical articles for construction professionals.

2955 ■ Asphalt Roofing Manufacturers Association Newsletter
Asphalt Roofing Manufacturers Association
750 National Press Bldg.
529 14th St. NW
Washington, DC 20045
Ph: (202)591-2450
Fax: (202)591-2445
E-mail: rhitchcock@kellencompany.com
URL: http://www.asphaltroofing.org/

Description: Semi-annual. Reports news and information of interest to professionals in the asphalt roofing industry. Highlights Association activities and discusses developments in the industry, including oc-

cupational safety and health measures, changes in industry codes and standards, environmental issues, and legislative and regulatory actions.

2956 ■ BIA News
Brick Industry Association
1850 Centennial Park Dr., Ste. 301
Reston, VA 20191
Ph: (703)620-0010
Fax: (703)620-3928
E-mail: brickinfo@bia.org
URL: http://www.gobrick.com/html/pr.html

Frequency: Monthly. **Price:** $30 Individuals.
Description: Trade publication covering issues for the brick industry.

2957 ■ Builder and Developer
Peninsula Publishing Inc.
1602 Monrovia Ave.
Newport Beach, CA 92663-2808
Ph: (949)631-0308
Fax: (949)631-2475
E-mail: nslevin@penpubinc.com
URL: http://www.bdmag.com

Frequency: 11/yr. **Description:** Magazine for homebuilders.

2958 ■ Building Industry Technology
U.S. Department of Commerce - Technology Administration - National Technical Information Service
5301 Shawnee Rd.
Alexandria, VA 22312
Ph: (703)605-6040
Free: 800-553-NTIS
Fax: (703)605-6900
E-mail: info@ntis.gov
URL: http://www.ntis.gov/products/alerts.aspx

Description: Biweekly. $255. Consists of abstracts of reports on architectural and environmental design, building standards, construction materials and equipment, and structural analyses. Recurring features include a form for ordering reports from NTIS. Also available via e-mail.

2959 ■ Building Systems Magazine
Active Interest Media
4125 Lafayette Ctr. Dr., Ste. 100
Chantilly, VA 20151
Ph: (703)222-9411
Fax: (703)222-3209
URLs: http://www.buildingsystems.com; http://www.aimmedia.com/article_display_19.html

Frequency: Bimonthly. **Description:** Magazine featuring innovative construction technologies for builders, developers and general contractors.

2960 ■ CM Advisor
Construction Management Association of America Inc.
7926 Jones Branch Dr., Ste. 800
Mc Lean, VA 22102

Ph: (703)356-2622
Fax: (703)356-6388
E-mail: info@cmaanet.org
URL: http://www.cmaanet.org

Description: Bimonthly. Provides information on construction management and its technical, legal, and legislative issues. Recurring features include letters to the editor, news of research, a calendar of events, reports of meetings, news of educational opportunities, book reviews, notices of publications available, and columns titled Government Affairs and For Your Information.

2961 ■ Concrete & Masonry Construction Products
DoveTale Publishers
1 Thomas Cir. NW
Washington, DC 20005
Ph: (202)339-0744
Free: 877-275-8647
Fax: (202)785-1974
E-mail: hwmicustomerservice@hanleywood.com
URL: http://www.hanleywoodopportunities.com/Index.asp?Cat=cc&Pub=cmcp&Sect=Intro

Frequency: Bimonthly. **Price:** Free. **Description:** Publication that covers carpenter tips, tools, and up keep.

2962 ■ Construction Business Owner: The business management resource for contractors
Cahaba Media Group
1900 28th Ave. S
Birmingham, AL 35209
Ph: (205)212-9402
URL: http://www.constructionbusinessowner.com/

Frequency: Monthly. **Price:** Free. **Description:** Magazine that provides information for construction management and industry business information.

2963 ■ Construction Claims Monthly
Business Publishers Inc.
2222 Sedwick Dr.
Durham, NC 27713
Ph: (301)587-6300
Free: 800-223-8720
Fax: (800)508-2592
E-mail: custserv@bpinews.com
URL: http://www.bpinews.com

Description: Monthly. $402/year. Covers significant legal developments governing contract payment and performance. Features an article on construction claims law; summaries of recent decisions with expert commentary; and highlights of actions by the federal boards of contract appeals and the Comptroller General.

2964 ■ Construction Superintendent: The Commercial Builder's Source for Current News, technology & Methods
Inform Publishing Group L.L.C.
8040 E Morgan Trl., Ste. 23
Scottsdale, AZ 85258

Ph: (480)361-6300
Fax: (480)361-6394
URL: http://www.consupt.com/

Frequency: Bimonthly. **Description:** Magazine featuring current news, technology, and methods in the construction field.

2965 ■ Daily Journal of Commerce
New Orleans Publishing Group Inc.
111 Veterans Blvd., Ste. 1440
Metairie, LA 70005
Ph: (504)834-9292
Fax: (504)832-3550
E-mail: mail@nopg.com
URLs: http://www.djc-gp.com; http://www.djcgulfcoast
.com

Frequency: Daily. **Price:** $525 Individuals online; $375 Individuals 6 months; $225 Individuals 3 months. **Description:** Trade newspaper covering construction news in Louisiana and Mississippi.

2966 ■ Design Cost Data: Cost Estimating Magazine for Design and Construction
DC & D Technologies Inc.
PO Box 948
Valrico, FL 33595-0948
Ph: (813)662-6830
Free: 800-533-5680
Fax: (813)662-6793
E-mail: webmaster@dcd.com
URL: http://www.dcd.com

Frequency: Bimonthly. **Price:** $94 Individuals silver; $157 Two years silver; $149 Individuals gold; $239 Two years gold. **Description:** Publication providing real cost data case studies of various types completed around the country for design and building professionals.

2967 ■ Environmental Building News
Building Green Inc.
122 Birge St., Ste. 30
Brattleboro, VT 05301-3206
Ph: (802)257-7300
Free: 800-861-0954
Fax: (802)257-7304
E-mail: info@buildinggreen.com
URL: http://www.buildinggreen.com/landing/ebnper-
formance1102.html

Description: Monthly. $99/year. Covers the building trade with an environmental slant. Covers nontoxic materials, better landscaping and water use, and resources for energy conservation in a technical manner.

2968 ■ Equipment World
Randall-Reilly Publishing Company L.L.C.
3200 Rice Mine Rd. NE
Tuscaloosa, AL 35406
Ph: (205)345-0958
Free: 800-633-5953
Fax: (205)345-0958
E-mail: mreilly@randallpub.com
URL: http://www.equipmentworld.com

Frequency: Monthly. **Description:** Magazine featuring construction contractors, equipment manufacturers, and dealers and providers of services and supplies to the construction industry.

2969 ■ EUCA Magazine
Engineering and Utility Contractors Association
17 Crow Canyon Ct., Ste. 100
San Ramon, CA 94583
Ph: (925)855-7900
Fax: (925)855-7909
E-mail: info@unitedcontractors.org
URL: http://www.euca.com

Description: Monthly. Supports the Association in its efforts to "provide innovative ideas and strong leadership" to those in the contracting industry. Focuses on various issues pertinent to members and industry executives, including legislative and regulatory developments, occupational safety concerns, new products and technologies, and industry trends and

developments. Recurring features include interviews, news of research, reports of meetings, news of educational opportunities, notices of publications available, and a calendar of events. Contains member profiles and news of members, Association elections, and administrative decisions.

2970 ■ Green Home Builder: America's Premier Green Homebuilding Resource
Peninsula Publishing Inc.
1602 Monrovia Ave.
Newport Beach, CA 92663-2808
Ph: (949)631-0308
Fax: (949)631-2475
E-mail: nslevin@penpubinc.com
URL: http://www.greenhomebuildermag.com/

Frequency: Quarterly. **Description:** Magazine for home builders and home building industry.

2971 ■ The Industrial Projects Report
Industrial Projects Services, Inc.
PO Box 274231
Tampa, FL 33688
Free: 800-849-4821
Fax: (813)265-0331
E-mail: deven.taylor@industrialprojectsreport.com
URL: http://industrialprojectsreport.com

Frequency: Monthly. **Description:** Features up-to-date information, job board, and construction forum for skilled crafts people and management personnel. Contains advertisements from staffing companies looking for construction management, supervision professionals and skilled-craft professionals for projects nationwide. Includes reports on industrial projects' location, approximate job durations, wages and other benefits. Helps technical colleges and trade schools in recruiting students to their trade programs.

2972 ■ ISHN
BNP Media
2401 W Big Beaver Rd., Ste. 700
Troy, MI 48084
Ph: (248)362-3700
Free: 800-952-6643
Fax: (248)362-5103
E-mail: privacy@bnpmedia.com
URL: http://www.ishn.com/

Frequency: Monthly. **Price:** Free. **Description:** Business-to-business magazine for safety and health managers at high-hazard worksites in manufacturing, construction, health facilities, and service industries. Content covering OSHA and EPA regulations, howto features, safety and health management topics, and the latest product news.

2973 ■ Kitchen and Bath Business
E-mail: kbb@mediabrains.com
URL: http://www.kbbonline.com/kbb/index.shtml

Frequency: Monthly. **Price:** $79 Individuals; $94 Canada; $139 Other countries. **Description:** Trade magazine on kitchen and bath remodeling and construction.

2974 ■ Landscape Construction: Large installations and site prep
Moose River Media
374 Emerson Falls Rd.
Saint Johnsbury, VT 05819
Free: 800-422-7147
Fax: (802)748-1866
URL: http://www.lcmmagazine.com/

Frequency: Monthly. **Description:** Magazine featuring landscaping.

2975 ■ MetalMag: MetalMag
DoveTale Publishers
1 Thomas Cir. NW
Washington, DC 20005
Ph: (202)339-0744
Free: 877-275-8647

Fax: (202)785-1974
E-mail: mtm@omeda.com
URL: http://www.metalmag.com/

Frequency: Bimonthly. **Description:** Magazine for industrial construction professionals.

2976 ■ Offshore Field Development International
ODS-Petrodata Inc.
3200 Wilcrest Dr., Ste. 170
Houston, TX 77042
Ph: (832)463-3000
Fax: (832)463-3100
E-mail: tmarsh@ods-petrodata.com
URL: http://www.ods-petrodata.com

Description: Monthly. Reports on petroleum-related offshore construction projects worldwide, from the planning stage through final installation. Covers platforms, pipelines, subsea completions, and mooring terminals. Recurring features include sections on construction barge locations and possible areas for future development.

2977 ■ Remodeling
DoveTale Publishers
1 Thomas Cir. NW
Washington, DC 20005
Ph: (202)339-0744
Free: 877-275-8647
Fax: (202)785-1974
E-mail: rm@omeda.com
URL: http://www.remodeling.hw.net

Frequency: 13/yr. **Price:** $24.95 Individuals; $39.95 Individuals Canadian residents; $192 Individuals international residents. **Description:** Trade magazine for the professional remodeling industry.

2978 ■ Replacement Contractor
DoveTale Publishers
1 Thomas Cir. NW
Washington, DC 20005
Ph: (202)339-0744
Free: 877-275-8647
Fax: (202)785-1974
E-mail: rcon@omeda.com
URLs: http://www.omeda.com/rcon/; http://www
.replacementcontractoronline.com

Frequency: 4/yr. **Price:** $29.95 Individuals; $39.95 Canada; $49.95 Other countries. **Description:** Magazine for contractors engaged in roofing, siding, decking and window replacement.

2979 ■ Residential Architect
DoveTale Publishers
1 Thomas Cir. NW
Washington, DC 20005
Ph: (202)339-0744
Free: 877-275-8647
Fax: (202)785-1974
E-mail: res@omeda.com
URL: http://www.residentialarchitectmediakit.com/r5/
home.asp

Frequency: 9/yr. **Price:** $39.95 Individuals; $66 Canada; $132.50 Other countries. **Description:** Magazine for architects, designers, and building professionals.

2980 ■ Residential Concrete
DoveTale Publishers
8726 W Higgins Rd.
Chicago, IL 60631
Ph: (773)284-2400
E-mail: hwmicustomerservice@hanleywood.com
URLs: http://www.hanleywood.com/default.aspx
?page=b2bresconcrete; http://www.concretecon-
struction.net/industry-news.asp?sectionID=716&ar-
ticleID=540600

Frequency: Bimonthly. **Price:** $30 Individuals; $46 Two years; $39 Canada and Mexico; $64 Two years Canada & Mexico; $93 Other countries; $162 Other countries two years. **Description:** Magazine featuring the use of concrete in residential concrete construction.

2981 ■ *Residential Contractor: The U.S. Home Construction Industry Source*
Peninsula Publishing Inc.
1602 Monrovia Ave.
Newport Beach, CA 92663-2808
Ph: (949)631-0308
Fax: (949)631-2475
E-mail: nslevin@penpubinc.com
URL: http://www.residentialcontractormag.com/
Frequency: Quarterly. **Description:** Magazine for small volume residential builders, contractors, and specialty trades.

2982 ■ *Residential Design & Build*
Cygnus Business Media Inc.
1233 Janesville Ave.
Fort Atkinson, WI 53538
Ph: (847)454-2700
Fax: (847)454-2759
E-mail: info@cygnus.com
URLs: http://www.rdbmagazine.com; http://www
.cygnusb2b.com/PropertyPub.cfm?PropertyID=177
Frequency: 9/yr. **Description:** Magazine providing advice and insight on the design/build project delivery method, as well as information on the latest design trends, new products and home building professionals.

2983 ■ *Tools of the Trade*
DoveTale Publishers
1 Thomas Cir. NW
Washington, DC 20005
Ph: (202)339-0744
Free: 877-275-8647
Fax: (202)785-1974
E-mail: hwmicustomerservice@hanleywood.com
URL: http://www.hanleywood.com/?page
=toolsofthetrade&section=res_rem
Frequency: Bimonthly. **Price:** $36 Individuals; $66 Canada; $192 Other countries; $70 Two years.
Description: Magazine featuring tools for commercial and residential construction.

EMPLOYER DIRECTORIES AND NETWORKING LISTS

2984 ■ *Athletic Business--Professional Directory Section*
Athletic Business Publications Inc.
4130 Lien Rd.
Madison, WI 53704
Ph: (608)249-0186
Free: 800-722-8764
Fax: (608)249-1153
E-mail: editors@hardwoodfloorsmag.com
URL: http://www.athleticbusiness.com
Frequency: Monthly; Latest edition 2010. **Price:** $8 per issue. **Publication includes:** List of architects, engineers, contractors, and consultants in athletic facility planning and construction; all listings are paid.
Entries include: Company name, address, phone, fax and short description of company. **Arrangement:** Alphabetical.

2985 ■ *Contractor's Directory*
Government Data Publications Inc.
2300 M St. NW
Washington, DC 20037
Ph: (202)416-1761
Free: 800-275-4688
Fax: (718)998-5960
E-mail: gdp@govdata.com
URL: http://www.govdata.com
Frequency: Annual; February. **Price:** $49.50 Diskette edition; $15; $49.50 CD-ROM. **Pages:** 150.
Covers: Contractors who have received government contract under Public Law 95-507, which requires preferential treatment of small business for subcontracts. **Entries include:** Contractor name and address. Supplementary to 'Small Business Preferential Subcontracts Opportunities Monthly,'

which lists companies with government contracts over $500,000 ($1,000,000 for construction) (see separate entry). **Arrangement:** Same information given alphabetically and by ZIP code.

HANDBOOKS AND MANUALS

2986 ■ *Becoming a Construction Manager*
John Wiley & Sons Inc.
111 River St.
Hoboken, NJ 07030-5774
Ph: (201)748-6000
Free: 800-225-5945
Fax: (201)748-6088
E-mail: info@wiley.com
URL: http://www.wiley.com
Description: John J. McKeon. 2012. $39.95 (paper). 224 pages. Serves as a guide for job seekers interested in or beginning a career in construction management. Provides an overview of the profession, educational requirements, and specialties. Includes interviewing tips and resource section on professional organizations and educational opportunities.

2987 ■ *Construction*
InfoBase Holdings Inc.
132 W 31st., 17 Fl.
New York, NY 10001-3406
Ph: (212)967-8800
Fax: (800)678-3633
E-mail: info@infobasepublishing.com
URL: http://www.ferguson.infobasepublishing.com
Price: $30 Hardcover. **Description:** 2010. 128 pages. Contains profiles of 20 careers in the field of construction with emphasis on the nature of work, requirements, salary, and career outlook. Includes full-color photographs, index, glossary, resources, and side bars.

2988 ■ *Expert Resumes for Managers and Executives*
Jist Works
875 Montreal Way
Saint Paul, MN 55102
Free: 800-648-5478
E-mail: info@jist.com
URL: http://www.jist.com/shop/product.php?productid
=16727
Description: Wendy S. Enelow, Louise M. Kursmark. 2012. $17.95. 274 pages. Contains a collection of sample resumes and resume writing advice including how to create and use an electronic resume. Contains an appendix that includes internet resources for an online job search, writing cover letters, as well as a collection of sample letters.

2989 ■ *Information Technologies for Construction Managers, Architects, and Engineers*
Cengage Learning Inc.
200 1st Stamford Pl., Ste. 400
Stamford, CT 06902-6753
Ph: (203)965-8600
Free: 800-354-9706
Fax: (800)487-8488
E-mail: investors@cengage.com
URL: http://www.cengage.com
Description: Trefor Williams. 2007. $102.95. 256 pages. Profiles information technology applications in construction trades, from traditional computer applications to emerging Web-based and mobile technologies.

2990 ■ *Manager's Handbook: Everything You Need to Know about How Business and Management Work*
Pearson Learning Group
145 S Mount Zion Rd.
Lebanon, IN 46052
Ph: (804)402-6933
Free: 800-526-9907

Fax: (800)393-3156
E-mail: pasley@pearsonlearning.com
URL: http://www.k12pearson.com
Price: $24.95. **Publication includes:** Principal content of publication is reference guide for new and experienced managers. **Indexes:** Alphabetical.

2991 ■ *Preparing for Design-Build Projects: A Primer for Owners, Engineers, and Contractors*
American Society of Civil Engineers - Architectural Engineering Institute
1801 Alexander Bell Dr.
Reston, VA 20191-4400
Free: 800-548-2723
E-mail: aei@asce.org
URL: http://www.asce.org/aei
Description: Douglas D. Gransberg, James E. Koch and Keith R. Molenaar. 2006. $64.00. 296 pages.

EMPLOYMENT AGENCIES AND SEARCH FIRMS

2992 ■ *20-20 Foresight Executive Search Inc.*
150 N Michigan Ave., Ste. 2800
Chicago, IL 60601
Ph: (708)246-2100
E-mail: bcavoto@202-4.com
URL: http://www.2020-4.com
Description: Executive search firm. Affiliate offices in California and Washington DC.

2993 ■ *Career Advocates International*
1539 Ave. A
Katy, TX 77493
Ph: (281)371-3917
E-mail: hank@careeradvocates.org
URL: http://www.careeradvocates.org
Description: Provides permanent placement and temporary staffing for executive and staff level positions. Specializes in multiple niches including: sales and marketing, accounting and financial services, banking, communications, human resources, chemicals, oil and gas, medical and dental, legal, information technology, energy, technology, engineering, manufacturing, construction, and light industrial.

2994 ■ *The Cherbonnier Group Inc.*
1 Riverway, Ste. 1700
Houston, TX 77056
Ph: (713)688-4701
E-mail: consult@thecherbonniergroup.com
URL: http://www.thecherbonniergroup.com
Description: Executive search firm.

2995 ■ *The Consulting Group*
420 Lexington Ave.
New York, NY 10017
Ph: (212)751-8484
E-mail: mitchell@consultinggroupny.com
URL: http://www.consultinggroupny.com
Description: Executive search firm.

2996 ■ *Contractor Marketing*
2285 Old Post Rd.
Beavercreek, OH 45434
Ph: (937)776-7170
E-mail: larry@contractormarketing.com
URL: http://www.contractormarketing.com
Description: Executive search firm.

2997 ■ *Contractors & Builders*
8888 Clairemont Mesa Blvd., Ste. J
San Diego, CA 92123
Ph: (858)874-7500
Free: 877-862-2632
E-mail: sandiego@contractorsandbuilders.com
URL: http://www.contractorsandbuilders.com
Description: Specializes in connecting construction

workers and managers with direct-hire and temporary positions.

2998 ■ Cook Associates Inc.
212 W Kinzie St.
Chicago, IL 60610
Ph: (312)329-0900
Fax: (312)329-1528
URL: http://www.cookassociates.com

Description: Management and executive recruiting specialists offering a commitment to clients to find the candidates and to find those candidates as efficiently as possible. Approach provides a flexible and effective structure that serves the special needs of both large and small companies. Serves the following industries: industrial, equipment manufacturer, food processing, graphic arts, chemical process, retailing, mechanical products, health care services, financial and professional services, legal, consumer products, construction and engineering, packaging, pulp and paper.

2999 ■ Crown Advisors Inc.
100 McKnight Park Dr., Ste. 110
Pittsburgh, PA 15237
Ph: (412)348-1540
E-mail: info@crownsearch.com
URL: http://www.crownsearch.com

Description: Executive search firm.

3000 ■ Edward Dellon Associates Inc.
450 N Brand Blvd., Ste. 600
Glendale, CA 91203
Ph: (310)286-0625
URL: http://edwarddellonassociatesinc.com

Description: Executive search firm.

3001 ■ HardHatJobs Inc.
1200 Executive Dr. E, Ste. 127A
Richardson, TX 75081
Ph: (972)808-9200
Fax: (972)808-9203
E-mail: bill@hardhatjobs.com
URL: http://www.hardhatjobs.com

Description: Executive search and consulting for Commercial Construction, Construction Engineering and Construction Management professionals. Presidents, CEO's, COO's, Business Development, Executive Vice Presidents, VP, CFO"s, Program, Project and Construction Managers, Superintendents, Schedulers, Project Accountants, Cost Controllers and Safety Engineers.

3002 ■ Robert Howe and Associates
3331 Bolero Dr.
Atlanta, GA 30341
Ph: (770)270-1211
Fax: (770)270-1209
E-mail: rwhamill@roberthoweassociates.com
URL: http://www.roberthoweassociates.com

Description: Provider of consulting services in the area of executive search and recruitment. Industries served: healthcare, hospitality, chemical, metals, electronics, construction, and food processing.

3003 ■ Kimmel & Associates Inc.
25 Page Ave.
Asheville, NC 28801
Ph: (828)251-9900
Fax: (828)251-9955
E-mail: kimmel@kimmel.com
URL: http://www.kimmel.com

Description: Specializes in the construction, waste, architecture, engineering, logistics and supply chain industries.

3004 ■ McNichol Associates
8419 Germantown Ave.
Philadelphia, PA 19118
Ph: (215)922-4142
Fax: (215)922-0178

Description: Performs executive search for middle and senior-level managers, marketing and techni-

cal personnel for professional design firms; construction, management and general contractors; engineering-construction organizations; environmental firms and others needing technical management personnel.

3005 ■ Oliver & Rozner Associates
598 Madison Ave., Ste. 11
New York, NY 10022
Ph: (212)688-1850

Description: Provider of recruitment solutions. It is engaged in marketing, advertising, data processing, research and development services.

3006 ■ Specialty Consultants Inc.
2710 Gateway Twr.
Pittsburgh, PA 15222-1189
Ph: (412)355-8200
Fax: (412)355-0498
E-mail: info@specialtyconsultants.com
URL: http://www.specon.com

Description: Provider of executive recruiting services for companies in the construction and real estate industry. Identifies candidates through an extensive research database and industry contacts. Services also include compensation surveys, organizational development and executive coaching.

3007 ■ S.R. Clarke
105 Huntercombe
Williamsburg, VA 23188
Ph: (703)344-0256
Fax: (949)608-5052
URL: http://www.srclarke.com/index.html

Description: Serves as an executive search and recruitment firm specializing in commercial construction, commercial real estate development, residential asset management, residential construction and development, subcontractor trades, finance, accounting, administration, heavy construction, architectural design and engineering design.

3008 ■ Synergy Professionals
1029 N Peachtree Pkwy., Ste. 252
Peachtree City, GA 30269
Ph: (770)450-8130
E-mail: contact@synergyprof.com
URL: http://www.synergyprof.com

Description: Serves as a professional recruiting firm devoted exclusively to the construction industry.

ONLINE JOB SOURCES AND SERVICES

3009 ■ A/E/C JobBank
URL: http://www.aecjobbank.com

Description: Helps job seekers find employment opportunities in the construction industry. Allows employers and recruiters to post construction jobs and source top resumes.

3010 ■ AECWorkForce.com
URL: http://aecworkforce.com

Description: Serves as job board for professionals and employers in architecture, engineering and construction.

3011 ■ Builder Jobs
URL: http://builderjobs.pro.adicio.com

Description: Serves as an online career resource for home building professionals. Features career development articles, salary tools, home building and construction job listings, resume postings, and job alerts.

3012 ■ BuildZ Construction Jobs Network
URL: http://buildz.net

Description: Provides listings of construction jobs throughout the U.S. Features news related to the construction industry.

3013 ■ CareerCastConstruction Network
URL: http://construction.careercast.com

Description: Provides job database that offers opportunities in the field of construction industry. Allows job seekers to build and post their resumes, and employers to post job vacancies as they search for qualified candidates.

3014 ■ Construction Executive Online
URL: http://www.constructionexecutive.com

Description: Serves as a career management center for construction executives. Provides members access to a job board of executive construction jobs and to career counseling from top executive coaches.

3015 ■ Construction Jobs
URL: http://construction.jobs.net

Description: Serves as a resource for various employment opportunities in the construction industry.

3016 ■ Construction Jobs Network
URL: http://constructionjobs.net

Description: Provides job seekers access to construction employment opportunities for both construction management, construction professional and construction trade jobs. Features construction jobs, employer, and resume directories.

3017 ■ ConstructionCrossing.com
URL: http://www.constructioncrossing.com

Description: Lists new employment opportunities specifically related to the construction personnel profession.

3018 ■ ConstructionEducation.com
URL: http://www.constructioneducation.com

Description: Includes link page with list of professional resources, employment opportunities listed by company, and construction-related recruiters' pages, as well as general job search websites. Also contains on-site job bank.

3019 ■ ConstructionGigs.net
URL: http://www.constructiongigs.net

Description: Provides an up-to-date listings of job opportunities and career resources for construction workers.

3020 ■ Construction.jobs
URL: http://construction.jobs

Description: Connects employers and job seekers in the construction industry. Features a searchable database of available construction employment opportunities in the U.S.

3021 ■ ConstructionJobs.com
URL: http://www.constructionjobs.com/index_eng.cfm

Description: Serves as an employment job board and resume database built exclusively for the construction, design, and building industries. Provides targeted candidate searches by geographic region, specific industries, job titles, education, and experience.

3022 ■ ConstructionJobStore.com
URL: http://www.constructionjobstore.com

Description: Features online job listing in the construction industry. Offers career guide resources and job alert services.

3023 ■ ConstructMyFuture.com
URL: http://www.constructmyfuture.com

Description: Offers comprehensive information for students, parents, and educators on varied careers in construction. Includes a searchable database of colleges, universities and trade schools that offer degrees in construction fields.

3024 ■ ENR Industry Jobs Site
URL: http://industry-jobs.enr.com/main/default.asp
Description: Provides job searching and recruitment services in the field of architecture, engineering and construction (AEC) industry. Offers comprehensive database of career opportunities for job seekers and resume of top AEC professionals for employers.

3025 ■ GeneralConstructionJobs.com
URL: http://www.generalconstructionjobs.com/a/jobs/ find-jobs
Description: Serves as a job board for online employment advertising built exclusively for the general construction industry.

3026 ■ IHireBuildingTrades
URL: http://www.ihirebuildingtrades.com
Description: Serves as a job posting board that specializes in matching building jobs and construction candidates.

3027 ■ iHireConstruction
URL: http://www.ihireconstruction.com
Description: Helps recruiters and hiring managers find qualified candidates in different fields and specialties of construction industry. Provides job listings, customizable online profiles, resume writing services, and job alerts to job seekers.

3028 ■ Referwork Jobs
URL: http://www.referwork-jobs.com
Description: Provides a searchable database of major jobs in construction and related specialties.

3029 ■ United States Construction Jobs
URL: http://us.theconstructionjob.com
Description: Contains construction jobs by location. Allow construction recruiters and employers to advertise their construction jobs openings.

3030 ■ USA Construction Jobs
URL: http://www.usaconstructionjobs.com
Description: Features job listings in construction and general labor.

TRADESHOWS

3031 ■ American Institute of Constructors Annual Forum
American Institute of Constructors
700 N Fairfax St., Ste. 510
Alexandria, FL 22314
Ph: (703)683-4999
Fax: (571)527-3105
URL: http://www.professionalconstructor.org/
Frequency: Annual. **Primary Exhibits:** Exhibits related to professionals engaged in construction practice, education and research.

3032 ■ The Builders' Show
National Association of Home Builders - Systems Builder Council
1201 15th St. NW
Washington, DC 20005
Ph: (202)266-8200
Free: 800-368-5242
Fax: (202)266-8400
URL: http://www.nahb.org/reference_list.aspx?sec-tionID=815
Frequency: Annual. **Primary Exhibits:** Building products, equipment, and services.

3033 ■ CONEXPO-CON/AGG
International Concrete and Aggregates Group
900 Spring St.
Silver Spring, MD 20910
Ph: (301)587-3140
Free: 800-867-6060
Fax: (301)587-4260
Frequency: Triennial. **Primary Exhibits:** Construc-

tion and construction materials industry equipment, supplies, and services.

3034 ■ Construct and The CSI Annual Convention
Construction Specifications Institute
110 S Union St., Ste. 100
Alexandria, VA 22314-3351
Free: 800-689-2900
Fax: (703)236-4600
E-mail: csi@csinet.org
URL: http://www.csinet.org
Frequency: Annual. **Primary Exhibits:** Products and services used in non-residential construction.

3035 ■ Construction Financial Management Association Annual Conference and Exhibition
Construction Financial Management Association
100 Village Blvd., Ste. 200
Princeton, NJ 08540
Ph: (609)452-8000
Free: 888-421-9996
Fax: (609)452-0474
E-mail: sbinstock@cfma.org
URL: http://www.cfma.org
Frequency: Annual. **Primary Exhibits:** Equipment, supplies, and services for the construction industry.

3036 ■ Constructo - International Exhibition of the Construction Industry
APEX
207 E. Franklin Ave., Ste. B
El Segundo, CA 90245
E-mail: apexcommunity@apex.org
URL: http://www.apex.org
Frequency: Annual. **Primary Exhibits:** Construction equipment, supplies, and services.

3037 ■ International Construction and Utility Equipment Exposition
Association of Equipment Manufacturers
6737 W Washington St., Ste. 2400
Milwaukee, WI 53214
Ph: (414)272-0943
Free: 866-AEM-0442
Fax: (414)272-1170
E-mail: aem@aem.org
URL: http://www.aem.org
Frequency: Biennial. **Primary Exhibits:** Utility and construction equipment, supplies, and services.

3038 ■ JLC LIVE Residential Construction Show - Pacific Northwest
Hanley-Wood Exhibitions
6191 N State Hwy. 161, Ste. 500
Irving, TX 75038
Ph: (972)536-6300
Fax: (972)536-6301
URL: http://www.hanley-wood.com
Frequency: Annual. **Primary Exhibits:** Housing and construction industry equipment, supplies, and services.

3039 ■ Michigan Construction & Design Tradeshow
American Institute of Architects, Michigan Chapter
553 E Jefferson Ave.
Detroit, MI 48226
Ph: (313)965-4100
Fax: (313)965-1501
E-mail: aiami@aiami.com
URL: http://www.aiami.com
Frequency: Annual. **Primary Exhibits:** Construction industry equipment, supplies, and services.

3040 ■ National Association of Demolition Contractors Annual Convention
National Demolition Association
16 N Franklin St., Ste. 203
Doylestown, PA 18901-3536
Ph: (215)348-4949
Free: 800-541-2412

Fax: (215)348-8422
E-mail: info@demolitionassociation.com
URL: http://www.demolitionassociation.com
Frequency: Annual. **Primary Exhibits:** Demolition equipment, supplies, and services.

3041 ■ Power Show Ohio
Ohio-Michigan Equipment Dealers Association
6124 Avery Rd.
Dublin, OH 43016
Ph: (614)889-1309
Fax: (614)889-0463
E-mail: info@amgllcusa.com
URL: http://www.omeda.org
Frequency: Annual. **Primary Exhibits:** Construction equipment, agricultural equipment, and outdoor power equipment. **Dates and Locations:** Columbus, OH; Ohio Exposition Center.

3042 ■ Women Construction Owners and Executives, U.S.A Annual Meeting
Women Construction Owners and Executives U.S.A.
1004 Duke St.
Alexandria, VA 22314
Free: 800-788-3548
Fax: (202)330-5151
E-mail: info@wcoeusa.org
URL: http://www.wcoeusa.org
Frequency: Annual. **Primary Exhibits:** Exhibits relating to women construction owners.

3043 ■ World Congress of the World Federation of Building Service Contractors
World Federation of Building Service Contractors
c/o Andrew Large, Executive Vice President
478-480 Salisbury House, London Wall
London EC2M 5QQ, United Kingdom
Ph: 44 20 79209632
Fax: 44 20 76386990
E-mail: ldock@galiservice.com
URL: http://www.wfbsc.org
Frequency: Biennial. **Primary Exhibits:** Floor care and carpet care equipment, building service contracting equipment, supplies, and services.

3044 ■ World of Masonry
Ecobuild Federal, LCC
1645 Falmouth Rd., Ste. 1A
Centerville, MA 02632
Ph: (508)790-4751
Free: 800-996-3863
Fax: (508)790-4750
E-mail: support@aecst.com
URL: http://www.aececobuild.com/
Frequency: Annual. **Primary Exhibits:** Concrete and masonry construction products and equipment.

ONLINE AND DATABASE SERVICES

3045 ■ CareersForBuilders.com
URL: http://www.careersforbuilders.com
Description: Features a searchable database of employment opportunities for different types of construction work. Includes career resources on job hunting tools and tips.

OTHER SOURCES

3046 ■ American Concrete Institute
38800 Country Club Dr.
Farmington Hills, MI 48331-3439
Ph: (248)848-3700
Fax: (248)848-3701
E-mail: ann.daugherty@acifoundation.org
URL: http://www.concrete.org
Description: Comprised of engineers, architects, contractors, educators, and others interested in improving techniques of design construction and maintenance of concrete products and structures.

Advances engineering and technical education, scientific investigation and research, and development of standards for design and construction incorporating concrete and related materials. Gathers, correlates, and disseminates information for the improvement of the design, construction, manufacture, use and maintenance of concrete products and structures. **Members:** 20,000.

3047 ■ **American Road and Transportation Builders Association**
1219 28th St. NW
Washington, DC 20007-3389
Ph: (202)289-4434
Fax: (202)289-4435
E-mail: general@artba.org
URL: http://www.artba.org

Description: Advances the interests of the transportation construction industry. Promotes the growth and protection of transportation infrastructure investment to meet the public and business demand for safe and efficient travel. Works to ensure its members' views and business concerns are addressed before Congress, the White House, federal agencies and news media.

3048 ■ **American Society of Civil Engineers - Architectural Engineering Institute**
1801 Alexander Bell Dr.
Reston, VA 20191-4400
Free: 800-548-2723
E-mail: aei@asce.org
URL: http://www.asce.org/aei

Description: Seeks to advance the state-of-the-art and state-of-the-practice of the building industry worldwide by facilitating effective and timely technology transfer. Provides a multidisciplinary forum for building industry professionals to examine technical, scientific and professional issues of common interest.

3049 ■ **American Society of Home Inspectors**
932 Lee St., Ste. 101
Des Plaines, IL 60016
Ph: (847)759-2820
Fax: (847)759-1620
E-mail: frankl@ashi.org
URL: http://www.homeinspector.org

Description: Professional home inspectors whose goals are to: establish home inspector qualifications; set standards of practice for home inspections; adhere to a code of ethics; keep the concept of "objective third party" intact; inform members of the most advanced methods and techniques, and educate consumers on the value of home inspections. Conducts seminars through local chapters.

3050 ■ **American Society of Professional Estimators**
2525 Perimeter Place Dr., Ste. 103
Nashville, TN 37214

Ph: (615)316-9200
Free: 888-EST-MATE
Fax: (615)316-9800
E-mail: psmith@aspenational.org
URL: http://www.aspenational.org

Description: Construction cost estimators. Develops professional and ethical standards in construction estimating. Offers continuing education to established professionals; provides certification for estimators.

3051 ■ **Associated Builders and Contractors**
440 1st St. NW, Ste. 200
Washington, DC 20001
E-mail: gotquestions@abc.org
URL: http://www.abc.org

Description: Construction contractors, subcontractors, suppliers and associates. Aims to foster and perpetuate the principles of rewarding construction workers and management on the basis of merit. Sponsors management education programs and craft training; also sponsors apprenticeship and skill training programs. Disseminates technological and labor relations information.

3052 ■ **Associated General Contractors of America**
2300 Wilson Blvd., Ste. 400
Arlington, VA 22201
Ph: (703)548-3118
Free: 800-242-1767
Fax: (703)548-3119
E-mail: info@agc.org
URL: http://www.agc.org

Description: General construction contractors; subcontractors; industry suppliers; service firms. Provides market services through its divisions. Conducts special conferences and seminars designed specifically for construction firms. Compiles statistics on job accidents reported by member firms. Maintains 65 committees, including joint cooperative committees with other associations and liaison committees with federal agencies.

3053 ■ **Construction Industry Round Table**
8115 Old Dominion Dr., Ste. 210
McLean, VA 22102-2324
Ph: (202)466-6777
E-mail: cirt@cirt.org
URL: http://www.cirt.org

Description: Represents the interests of CEOs from architectural, engineering and construction firms doing business in the United States. Enhances and develops strong management approaches through networking and peer interaction. Seeks to improve the industry's image and relationships with public and private clients. **Members:** 100.

3054 ■ **Construction Management Association of America**
7926 Jones Branch Dr., Ste. 800
McLean, VA 22102
Ph: (703)356-2622
Fax: (703)356-6388
E-mail: info@cmaanet.org
URL: http://cmaanet.org

Description: Association website contains a job databank, professional resources books for sale, and career development seminars to attend. Must be a member to fully utilize site, which also includes more project leads, discussion forums, and more.

3055 ■ **National Association of Black Women in Construction**
1910 NW 105 Ave.
Pembroke Pines, FL 33026
Ph: (954)323-3587
Free: 866-364-4998
Fax: (954)437-4998
E-mail: info@nabwic.org
URL: http://nabwic.org

Description: Promotes the advancement of black women in the construction industry. Supports aspiring construction executives. Provides advocacy, mentorship and professional development for its members.

3056 ■ **National Association of Home Builders - Systems Builder Council**
1201 15th St. NW
Washington, DC 20005
Ph: (202)266-8200
Free: 800-368-5242
Fax: (202)266-8400
URL: http://www.nahb.org/reference_list.aspx?sectionID=815

Description: Operates under the Building Systems Council of NAHB. Modular building manufacturers. Monitors state and federal housing legislation that impacts the building industry. Provides a forum for communication, networking and recruiting for those involved in manufacturing modular building systems. Addresses and solves problems specific to the council; offers consumer leads service.

3057 ■ **Residential Construction Workers' Association**
3660D Wheeler Ave.
Alexandria, VA 22304
Ph: (703)212-8294
Fax: (703)212-8295
E-mail: info@astracor.org
URL: http://www.astracor.org

Description: Represents the interests of residential construction workers. Aims to improve the lives of all workers employed in residential construction. Provides job and social service referrals. Informs workers of their rights and benefits and provides training in different construction trades.

3058 ■ *ACJS Today*
Academy of Criminal Justice Sciences
7339 Hanover Pkwy., Ste. A
Greenbelt, MD 20770
Ph: (301)446-6300
Free: 800-757-2257
Fax: (301)446-2819
E-mail: info@acjs.org
URL: http://www.acjs.org/

Description: Four issues/year. Circulation is 2,000. Contains criminal justice information.

3059 ■ *American City and County*
Penton
9800 Metcalf Ave.
Overland Park, KS 66212
Ph: (913)341-1300
Free: 866-748-4926
Fax: (913)967-1905
E-mail: corporatecustomerservice@penton.com
URL: http://americancityandcounty.com

Frequency: Monthly. **Description:** Municipal and county administration magazine.

3060 ■ *Law and Order: The Magazine for Police Management*
Hendon Publishing
130 N Waukegan Rd., Ste. 202
Deerfield, IL 60015-5652
Ph: (847)444-3300
Free: 800-843-9764
Fax: (847)444-3333
E-mail: law&ordermag@halldata.com
URL: http://www.hendonpub.com/publications/lawandorder/

Frequency: Monthly. **Price:** $22 individuals. **Description:** Law enforcement trade magazine.

3061 ■ *The Municipality*
League of Wisconsin Municipalities
122 W Washington Ave., Ste. 300
Madison, WI 53703-2715
Ph: (608)267-2380
Free: 800-991-5502
Fax: (608)267-0645
E-mail: jmstaral@lwm-info.org
URL: http://www.lwm-info.org/

Frequency: Monthly. **Price:** $25/year. **Description:** Magazine for officials of Wisconsin's local municipal governments.

3062 ■ *On the Line*
American Correctional Association
206 N Washington St., Ste. 200
Alexandria, VA 22314
Ph: (703)224-0000
Free: 800-222-5646

Fax: (703)224-0179
URL: http://www.aca.org/

Description: Five issues/year. Provides updates on the Association's efforts to improve correctional standards and to develop adequate physical facilities. Presents national news of the corrections field. Recurring features include job listings, news of research, notices of publications available, reports of meetings, and a calendar of events.

3063 ■ *Western City*
League of California Cities
1400 K St., 4th Fl.
Sacramento, CA 95814
Ph: (916)658-8200
Free: 800-262-1801
Fax: (916)658-8240
E-mail: okabel@cacities.org
URL: http://www.westerncity.com

Frequency: Monthly. **Price:** $39 Individuals; $63 Two years; $52 Other countries; $26.50 Students. **Description:** Municipal interest magazine.

EMPLOYER DIRECTORIES AND NETWORKING LISTS

3064 ■ *National Directory of Law Enforcement Administrators, Correctional Institutions & Related Agencies*
National Public Safety Information Bureau
601 Main St.
Stevens Point, WI 54481
Ph: (715)345-2772
Free: 800-647-7579
Fax: (715)345-7288
E-mail: info@safetysource.com
URL: http://www.safetysource.com

Frequency: Annual; Latest edition 2012. **Price:** $149 Individuals USA; $199 online, complimentary print copy. **Pages:** 969. **Covers:** Police departments, sheriffs, coroners, criminal prosecutors, child support agencies, state law enforcement and criminal investigation agencies; federal criminal investigation and related agencies; state and federal correctional institutions; campus law enforcement departments; County jails, airport and harbor police, Bureau of Indian Affairs officials, plus new homeland security section. **Entries include:** Name, address, phone, fax, names and titles of key personnel, number of officers, population served. **Arrangement:** Separate geographical sections for police chiefs, coroners, sheriffs, prosecutors, prisons and state criminal investigation agencies; also separate sections for federal agencies and miscellaneous law enforcement and related agencies. **Indexes:** Departments.

3065 ■ *Who's Who in Jail Management Jail Directory, 5th Edition*
American Jail Association
1135 Professional Ct.
Hagerstown, MD 21740-5853

Ph: (301)790-3930
Fax: (301)790-2941
E-mail: kim_spadaro@sheriff.org
URL: http://www.aja.org

Description: Provides information on local jails in the United States. $75.00 for members; $85.00 for nonmembers.

HANDBOOKS AND MANUALS

3066 ■ *The Correctional Officer: A Practical Guide*
Carolina Academic Press
700 Kent St.
Durham, NC 27701
Ph: (919)489-7486
Free: 800-489-7486
Fax: (919)493-5668
E-mail: cap@cap-press.com
URL: http://www.cap-press.com

Description: Gary F. Cornelius. 2010. $40.00 (paper). 406 pages. Provides a clear, realistic understanding of a correctional officer's job. Includes information on maintaining positive traits and job skills that can enhance the career of a correctional officer.

3067 ■ *Master the Corrections Officer Exams*
Peterson's Publishing
3 Columbia Cir., Ste. 205
Albany, NY 12203-5158
Ph: (609)896-1800
E-mail: pubmarketing@petersons.com
URL: http://www.petersonspublishing.com

Description: 2010. $18.95. 312 pages. Provides detailed information and review to help aspirants pass the corrections officer exam. Includes latest information on job requirements, application procedure and officer screening process, as well as practice tests and guidelines for the oral interview.

ONLINE JOB SOURCES AND SERVICES

3068 ■ **Corrections.com**
URL: http://www.corrections.com

Description: Serves as an online community for the corrections industry. Features a news site dealing with prison and parole issues, including jobs that are available across the country.

TRADESHOWS

3069 ■ **American Jail Association Training Conference & Jail Expo**
American Jail Association
1135 Professional Ct.
Hagerstown, MD 21740-5853

Ph: (301)790-3930
Fax: (301)790-2941
E-mail: kim_spadaro@sheriff.org
URL: http://www.aja.org

Frequency: Annual. **Primary Exhibits:** Jail supplies & services for correctional facilities; construction design; training; officer equipment and correctional equipment, supplies, and services.

3070 ■ International Community Corrections Association Research Conference
International Community Corrections Association
8701 Georgia Ave., Ste. 402
Silver Spring, MD 20910
Ph: (301)585-6090
Fax: (301)585-6094
E-mail: info@iccaweb.org
URL: http://www.iccaweb.org

Frequency: Annual. Presents research findings of evidence-based best practices in prisoner reentry, juvenile justice, treatment, and organizational management.

OTHER SOURCES

3071 ■ American Correctional Association
206 N Washington St., Ste. 200
Alexandria, VA 22314
Ph: (703)224-0000
Free: 800-222-5646
Fax: (703)224-0179
URL: http://www.aca.org

Description: Correctional administrators, wardens, superintendents, members of prison and parole boards, probation officers, psychologists, educators, sociologists, and other individuals; institutions and associations involved in the correctional field. Promotes improved correctional standards, including selection of personnel, care, supervision, education, training, employment, treatment, and post-release adjustment of inmates. Studies causes of crime and juvenile delinquency and methods of crime control and prevention through grants and contracts.

Compiles statistics. Conducts research programs and training of correctional professionals. Offers accreditation of institutions and certification for correctional executive, manager, supervisor, and officer.

3072 ■ American Probation and Parole Association
2760 Research Park Dr.
Lexington, KY 40511-8482
Ph: (859)244-8203
Fax: (859)244-8001
E-mail: appa@csg.org
URL: http://www.appa-net.org

Description: Comprises of probation/parole executives, line officers, and other interested individuals. Seeks to improve and advance progressive probation/parole practices through the development of knowledge, skills, resources, and legislation. Promotes legislative programs, sponsors research programs, and conducts regional workshops.

3073 ■ American Society of Criminology
1314 Kinnear Rd., Ste. 212
Columbus, OH 43212-1156
Ph: (614)292-9207
Fax: (614)292-6767
E-mail: asc@asc41.com
URL: http://www.asc41.com

Description: Represents professional and academic criminologists, students of criminology in accredited universities, psychiatrists, psychologists, and sociologists. Develops criminology as a science and academic discipline. Aids in the construction of criminological curricula in accredited universities. Upgrades the practitioner in criminological fields (police, prisons, probation, parole, delinquency workers). Conducts research programs and sponsors three student paper competitions. Provides placement service at annual convention.

3074 ■ *Careers for Legal Eagles and Other Law-and-Order Types*
The McGraw-Hill Companies Inc.
PO Box 182604
Columbus, OH 43272

Ph: (212)512-2000
Free: 877-833-5524
Fax: (614)759-3749
E-mail: customer.service@mcgraw-hill.com
URL: http://www.mcgraw-hill.com

Description: Blythe Camenson. Second edition, 2005. $13.95 (paper). 176 pages. **Publication includes:** Appendix of professional associations in the United States and Canada that offer career and job-hunting information. **Entries include:** Association name, address, website address.

3075 ■ International Community Corrections Association
8701 Georgia Ave., Ste. 402
Silver Spring, MD 20910
Ph: (301)585-6090
Fax: (301)585-6094
E-mail: info@iccaweb.org
URL: http://www.iccaweb.org

Description: Represents agencies and individuals working in community-based correctional programs. Promotes the development of community-based correctional programs and treatment. Assists members through the exchange of information regarding management and treatment.

3076 ■ Nine Lives Associates
Executive Protection Institute
16 Penn Pl., Ste. 1130
New York, NY 10001
Ph: (212)268-4555
Fax: (212)563-4783
E-mail: info@personalprotection.com
URL: http://www.personalprotection.com/nla.cfm

Description: Law enforcement, correctional, military, and security professionals who have been granted Personal Protection Specialist Certification through completion of the protective services program offered by the Executive Protection Institute; conducts research; EPI programs emphasize personal survival skills and techniques for the protection of others. Provides professional recognition for qualified individuals engaged in executive protection assignments. Maintains placement service. Operates speakers' bureau; compiles statistics. **Members:** 3,000.

Cosmetologists and Hairdressers

SOURCES OF HELP-WANTED ADS

3077 ■ *Beauty Launchpad: What's Taking Off in the World of Beauty*
Creative Age Publications Inc.
7628 Densmore Ave.
Van Nuys, CA 91406-2042
Ph: (818)782-7328
Free: 800-442-5667
Fax: (818)782-7450
URL: http://www.beautylaunchpad.com/index.php
Description: Fashion magazine.

3078 ■ *Beauty Store Business*
Creative Age Publications Inc.
7628 Densmore Ave.
Van Nuys, CA 91406-2042
Ph: (818)782-7328
Free: 800-442-5667
Fax: (818)782-7450
URL: http://www.beautystorebusiness.com/
Frequency: Monthly. **Description:** Business magazine for beauty industry professionals and beauty store owners.

3079 ■ *Cosmetics & Toiletries: The International Magazine of Cosmetic Technology*
E-mail: lhince@allured.com
URL: http://www.cosmeticsandtoiletries.com
Frequency: Monthly. **Price:** $98 Individuals; $137 Canada; $189 Other countries; $169 Two years; $231 Canada two years; $330 Other countries two years. **Description:** Trade magazine on cosmetic and toiletries manufacturing with an emphasis on product research and development issues.

3080 ■ *Global Cosmetic Industry: The Business Magazine for the Global Beauty Industry*
Allured Business Media
336 Gundersen Dr., Ste. A
Carol Stream, IL 60188-2403
Ph: (630)653-2155
Fax: (630)653-2192
E-mail: customerservice@allured.com
URL: http://www.gcimagazine.com/
Frequency: Monthly. **Price:** Free to qualified subscribers all countries - Digital; Free to qualified subscribers US - print; 45 Other countries print only. **Description:** Trade publication covering the cosmetics industry worldwide.

3081 ■ *Hair Gallery*
Multi-Media International
106 Apple St., Ste. 301
Tinton Falls, NJ 07724
Ph: (732)530-0505
URL: http://mmimags.com/HairGallery.html
Frequency: 8/yr. **Price:** $9.99 Single issue; $12.99

Single issue Canada. **Description:** Magazine featuring gallery of hairstyles.

3082 ■ *Live Design: The Art & Technology of Show Business*
Penton
249 W 17th St.
New York, NY 10011
Ph: (913)341-1300
Free: 866-748-4926
Fax: (913)967-1905
E-mail: corporatecustomerservice@penton.com
URL: http://livedesignonline.com
Frequency: 9/yr. **Description:** The business of entertainment technology and design.

3083 ■ *Modern Salon*
Vance Publishing Corp.
400 Knightsbridge Pkwy.
Lincolnshire, IL 60069-3613
Ph: (847)634-2600
Free: 800-255-5113
Fax: (847)634-4342
E-mail: info@vancepublishing.com
URL: http://www.modernsalon.com/
Frequency: Monthly. **Description:** Magazine focusing on hairstyling salons for men and women.

3084 ■ *Nailpro*
Creative Age Publications Inc.
7628 Densmore Ave.
Van Nuys, CA 91406-2042
Ph: (818)782-7328
Free: 800-442-5667
Fax: (818)782-7450
E-mail: nailpro@creativeage.com
URL: http://www.nailpro.com
Frequency: Monthly. **Description:** Salon owners and nail technicians read Nailpro for continuing education in techniques and services, marketing and management tips, product information and industry news.

3085 ■ *Renew*
Annex Publishing & Printing Inc.
PO Box 530
105 Donly Drive St.
Simcoe, ON, Canada N3Y 4N5
Ph: (519)429-3966
Free: 800-265-2827
Fax: (519)429-3094
E-mail: mfredericks@annexweb.com
URL: http://www.renewprofessional.com/
Frequency: Bimonthly. **Price:** $20 Individuals; $38 Other countries. **Description:** Magazine for salon, spa, and skin care professionals.

3086 ■ *Skin Inc.: Professional Skin Care*
E-mail: customerservice@allured.com
URL: http://www.skininc.com/
Frequency: Monthly. **Price:** $49 Individuals; $57

Canada; $98 Other countries. **Description:** The complete business guide for face and body care.

3087 ■ *Soap and Cosmetics*
Chemical Week Associates
2 Grand Central Tower
140 E 45th St., 40th Fl.
New York, NY 10017
Ph: (212)884-9528
Free: 800-774-5733
Fax: (212)883-9514
E-mail: webmaster@chemweek.com
URL: http://www.chemweek.com/verticals/sc/
Frequency: Monthly. **Price:** $225.97 Individuals print + online; $259.97 Canada print + online; $629 Other countries print + online. **Description:** Trade publication covering the cosmetics industry.

HANDBOOKS AND MANUALS

3088 ■ *Cosmetologist*
National Learning Corporation
212 Michael Dr.
Syosset, NY 11791
Ph: (516)921-8888
Free: 800-632-8888
Fax: (516)921-8743
E-mail: info@passbooks.com
URL: http://www.passbooks.com
Description: 2009. $34.95 (paper). Serves as an exam preparation guide for cosmetologists.

3089 ■ *The Makeup Artist Handbook: Techniques for Film, Television, Photography, and Theatre*
Focal Press
225 Wyman St.
Waltham, MA 02451
Free: 800-545-2522
E-mail: usbkInfo@elsevier.com
URL: http://www.focalpress.com
Description: Gretchen Davis and Mindy Hall. 2012. $44.95 (paperback). 320 pages. 2nd edition. Contains Hollywood-style makeup tips and techniques for aspiring and professional makeup artists. Includes full reference section with relevant websites, business listings and contacts.

TRADESHOWS

3090 ■ American Association of Cosmetology Schools Annual Conference - AACS Annual Convention & Expo
American Association of Cosmetology Schools
9927 E Bell Rd., Ste. 110
Scottsdale, AZ 85260
Ph: (480)281-0431
Free: 800-831-1086

Fax: (480)905-0993
E-mail: jim@beautyschools.org
URL: http://beautyschools.org
Frequency: Annual. **Primary Exhibits:** Beauty supplies and products, and cosmetology services.

3091 ■ Cosmoprof North America
Professional Beauty Association
15825 N 71st St., Ste. 100
Scottsdale, AZ 85254
Ph: (480)281-0424
Free: 800-468-2274
Fax: (480)905-0708
E-mail: info@probeauty.org
URL: http://www.probeauty.org
Annual. Promotes emerging trends from within all segments of the beauty industry. Features guest speakers. Fosters the establishment of new contacts and renewal of old business connections.

3092 ■ International Beauty Show, New York
Advanstar Communications
641 Lexington Ave., 8th Fl.
New York, NY 10022
Ph: (212)951-6600
Free: 800-346-0085
Fax: (212)951-6793
E-mail: info@advanstar.com
URL: http://www.advanstar.com
Frequency: Annual. **Primary Exhibits:** Beauty and health related equipment, supplies, and services.

3093 ■ Midwest Beauty Show
Chicago Cosmetologists Inc.
330 N Wabash Ave., Ste. 2000
Chicago, IL 60611
Ph: (312)321-6809
Free: 800-648-2505
Fax: (312)245-1080
E-mail: info@americasbeautyshow.com
URL: http://www.americasbeautyshow.com
Frequency: Annual. **Primary Exhibits:** Goods and services for the beauty trade.

3094 ■ Premiere Orlando
Premiere Shows, Inc.
1049 Willa Springs Dr., Ste. 1001
Winter Springs, FL 32708
Ph: (407)265-3131
Free: 800-335-7469
Fax: (407)265-3134
E-mail: sales@premiereshows.com
URL: http://www.premiereshows.com
Frequency: Annual. **Primary Exhibits:** Products and services for hair, nail, and skin care professionals and the beauty industry.

OTHER SOURCES

3095 ■ American Association of Cosmetology Schools
9927 E Bell Rd., Ste. 110
Scottsdale, AZ 85260

Ph: (480)281-0431
Free: 800-831-1086
Fax: (480)905-0993
E-mail: jim@beautyschools.org
URL: http://beautyschools.org
Description: Owners and teachers in cosmetology schools.

3096 ■ *Careers for Self-Starters and Other Entrepreneurial Types*
The McGraw-Hill Companies Inc.
PO Box 182604
Columbus, OH 43272
Ph: (212)512-2000
Free: 877-833-5524
Fax: (614)759-3749
E-mail: customer.service@mcgraw-hill.com
URL: http://www.mcgraw-hill.com
Blythe Camenson. **Frequency:** September 2004. **Price:** $9.95 (US).; $13.95 (US). **Description:** Blythe Camenson. Second edition, 2004. $9.95 (paper). 129 pages. **Includes:** Appendix of associations that provide information on education, training, and certification opportunities, as well as advice on starting businesses; recommended reading list. Appendix of associations that provide information on education, training, and certification opportunities, as well as advice on starting businesses; recommended reading list. **Entries include:** Name, address, brief description of information resources.

3097 ■ Intercoiffure America
1507 Belmont Ave.
Seattle, WA 98122
Ph: (206)550-4309
Free: 800-442-3007
Fax: (818)782-2913
E-mail: stacie@bowiesalonandspa.com
URL: http://intercoiffure.com
Description: Owners of beauty salons in the United States and Canada who meet the ethical standards set down by Intercoiffure. Seeks to make the women of America the best in hair fashion. **Members:** 260.

3098 ■ International SalonSpa Business Network
207 E Ohio St., No. 361
Chicago, IL 60611
Free: 866-444-4272
Fax: (866)444-5139
E-mail: margie@salonspanetwork.org
URL: http://salonspanetwork.org
Description: Beauty salon chains. Collects and processes data on industry standards; proactively works to affect the outcome of pending legislation and regulations governing the cosmetology industry; provides continuing education programs on management issues to members; works for free exchange of corporate information, solutions to common problems, advertising ideas, and incentive programs amongst members; takes part in and supports other industry associations. **Members:** 60.

3099 ■ National Beauty Culturists' League
25 Logan Cir. NW
Washington, DC 20005-3725
Ph: (202)332-2695
Fax: (202)332-0940
E-mail: nbcl@bellsouth.net
URL: http://www.nbcl.org
Description: Beauticians, cosmetologists, and beauty products manufacturers. Encourages standardized, scientific, and approved methods of hair, scalp, and skin treatments. Offers scholarships and plans to establish a research center. Sponsors: National Institute of Cosmetology, a training course in operating and designing and business techniques. Maintains hall of fame; conducts research program.

3100 ■ National Coalition of Estheticians, Manufacturers/Distributors and Associations
484 Spring Ave.
Ridgewood, NJ 07450
Ph: (201)670-4100
Fax: (201)670-4265
E-mail: nceaorg@aol.com
URL: http://www.ncea.tv
Description: Establishes standards and practices for skin care industry. Provides political representation for estheticians to state legislators and licensing boards. Provides a forum to discuss issues that affect the skin care industry and individual licensees.

3101 ■ National Latino Cosmetology Association
7925 W Russell Rd. Unit 401285
Las Vegas, NV 89140-8053
Ph: (702)448-5020
Free: 877-658-3801
Fax: (702)448-8993
E-mail: info@nlcamerican.org
URL: http://www.nlcamerican.org
Description: Represents Latino beauty industry professionals and businesses. Enhances professional knowledge, business growth, and career focus in the beauty industry. Offers resources, strategies, and tools to meet the needs of businesses, professionals, and other individuals in the beauty industry.

3102 ■ Professional Beauty Association
15825 N 71st St., Ste. 100
Scottsdale, AZ 85254
Ph: (480)281-0424
Free: 800-468-2274
Fax: (480)905-0708
E-mail: info@probeauty.org
URL: http://www.probeauty.org
Description: Manufacturers and manufacturers' representatives of beauty and barber products, cosmetics, equipment, and supplies used in or resold by beauty salons or barbershops. Promotes the beauty industry; works to ensure product safety; disseminates information. Holds educational seminars; organizes charity events. **Members:** 41.

Cost Estimators

SOURCES OF HELP-WANTED ADS

3103 ■ *Builder: The Magazine of the National Association of Home Builders*
DoveTale Publishers
1 Thomas Cir. NW
Washington, DC 20005
Ph: (202)339-0744
Free: 877-275-8647
Fax: (202)785-1974
E-mail: builder@omeda.com
URLs: http://www.hanleywood.com/default.aspx
?page=magazines; http://www.builderonline.com

Frequency: 13/yr. **Price:** $29.95 U.S. and Canada; $54.95 U.S. and Canada 2 years; $192 Other countries. **Description:** Magazine covering housing and construction industry.

3104 ■ *Constructor: The Construction Management Magazine*
Associated General Contractors of America
2300 Wilson Blvd., Ste. 400
Arlington, VA 22201
Ph: (703)548-3118
Free: 800-242-1767
Fax: (703)548-3119
E-mail: info@agc.org
URL: http://constructor.agc.org/

Frequency: Bimonthly. **Price:** $95 Individuals. **Description:** Management magazine for the Construction Industry.

3105 ■ *Design Cost Data: Cost Estimating Magazine for Design and Construction*
DC & D Technologies Inc.
PO Box 948
Valrico, FL 33595-0948
Ph: (813)662-6830
Free: 800-533-5680
Fax: (813)662-6793
E-mail: webmaster@dcd.com
URL: http://www.dcd.com

Frequency: Bimonthly. **Price:** $94 Individuals silver; $157 Two years silver; $149 Individuals gold; $239 Two years gold. **Description:** Publication providing real cost data case studies of various types completed around the country for design and building professionals.

3106 ■ *ENR: Engineering News-Record: The Construction Weekly*
The McGraw-Hill Companies Inc.
2 Penn Plz., 9th Fl.
New York, NY 10121
Ph: (212)904-3507
Fax: (212)904-2820
E-mail: customer.service@mcgraw-hill.com
URL: http://enr.construction.com/Default.asp

Frequency: Weekly. **Price:** $87 Individuals print and online. **Description:** Magazine focusing on engineering and construction.

3107 ■ *Professional Builder: The Magazine of the Housing and Light Construction Industry*
SGC Horizon L.L.C.
3030 W Salt Creek Ln., Ste. 201
Arlington Heights, IL 60005
Ph: (847)391-1000
Fax: (847)390-0408
URL: http://www.housingzone.com/
professionalbuilder

Frequency: Monthly. **Price:** Free. **Description:** The integrated engineering magazine of the building construction industry.

EMPLOYER DIRECTORIES AND NETWORKING LISTS

3108 ■ *ABC Today--Associated Builders and Contractors National Membership Directory Issue*
Associated Builders and Contractors
440 1st St. NW, Ste. 200
Washington, DC 20001
E-mail: gotquestions@abc.org
URL: http://www.abc.org

Frequency: Annual; Latest Edition 2011. **Price:** $150 plus $7.00 shipping. **Publication includes:** List of approximately 19,000 member construction contractors and suppliers. **Entries include:** Company name, address, phone, name of principal executive, code to volume of business, business specialty. **Arrangement:** Classified by chapter, then by work specialty.

3109 ■ *ENR--Top 400 Construction Contractors Issue*
The McGraw-Hill Companies Inc.
PO Box 182604
Columbus, OH 43272
Ph: (212)512-2000
Free: 877-833-5524
Fax: (614)759-3749
E-mail: customer.service@mcgraw-hill.com
URL: http://enr.construction.com/toplists/Contractors/
001-100.asp

Frequency: Annual; Latest edition 2011. **Price:** $35 Individuals. **Publication includes:** List of 400 United States contractors receiving largest dollar volumes of contracts in preceding calendar year. Separate lists of 50 largest design/construct management firms; 50 largest program and construction managers; 25 building contractors; 25 heavy contractors. **Entries include:** Company name, headquarters location, total value of contracts received in preceding year, value of foreign contracts, countries in which operated, construction specialties. **Arrangement:** By total value of contracts received.

3110 ■ *ENR--Top 500 Design Firms Issue*
The McGraw-Hill Companies Inc.
PO Box 182604
Columbus, OH 43272
Ph: (212)512-2000
Free: 877-833-5524
Fax: (614)759-3749
E-mail: customer.service@mcgraw-hill.com
URL: http://enr.construction.com/toplists/
sourcebooks/2010/designfirms/

Frequency: Annual; latest edition 2010. **Price:** $82 Individuals yearly subscription; $87 Individuals print and online. **Publication includes:** List of 500 leading architectural, engineering, and specialty design firms selected on basis of annual billings. **Entries include:** Company name, headquarters location, type of firm, current and prior year rank in billings, types of services, countries in which operated in preceding year. **Arrangement:** Ranked by billings.

HANDBOOKS AND MANUALS

3111 ■ *Construction*
InfoBase Holdings Inc.
132 W 31st., 17 Fl.
New York, NY 10001-3406
Ph: (212)967-8800
Fax: (800)678-3633
E-mail: info@infobasepublishing.com
URL: http://www.ferguson.infobasepublishing.com

Price: $30 Hardcover. **Description:** 2010. 128 pages. Contains profiles of 20 careers in the field of construction with emphasis on the nature of work, requirements, salary, and career outlook. Includes full-color photographs, index, glossary, resources, and side bars.

3112 ■ *From Product Description to Cost: A Practical Approach for Cost Estimators*
Springer Publishing Co.
11 W 42nd St., 15th Fl.
New York, NY 10036
Ph: (212)431-4370
Free: 877-687-7476
Fax: (212)941-7842
E-mail: cs@springerpub.com
URL: http://www.springerpub.com

Description: Pierre Foussier. 2006. $205.00. Profiles cost estimating, covering data preparation, general cost estimating, the use of cost models, and risk analysis used in cost estimations.

EMPLOYMENT AGENCIES AND SEARCH FIRMS

3113 ■ *Kimmel & Associates Inc.*
25 Page Ave.
Asheville, NC 28801
Ph: (828)251-9900
Fax: (828)251-9955
E-mail: kimmel@kimmel.com
URL: http://www.kimmel.com

Description: Specializes in the construction, waste, architecture, engineering, logistics and supply chain industries.

3114 ■ Real Estate Executive Search, Inc.
225 E Dania Beach Blvd., Ste. 200
Dania Beach, FL 33004
Ph: (954)927-6000
Fax: (954)927-6003
E-mail: reesearch954@aol.com
URL: http://reesearchinc.com

Description: Executive search firm for the real estate and finance fields.

3115 ■ Synergy Professionals
1029 N Peachtree Pkwy., Ste. 252
Peachtree City, GA 30269
Ph: (770)450-8130
E-mail: contact@synergyprof.com
URL: http://www.synergyprof.com

Description: Serves as a professional recruiting firm devoted exclusively to the construction industry.

ONLINE JOB SOURCES AND SERVICES

3116 ■ Construction Executive Online
URL: http://www.constructionexecutive.com

Description: Serves as a career management center for construction executives. Provides members access to a job board of executive construction jobs and to career counseling from top executive coaches.

OTHER SOURCES

3117 ■ AACE International
1265 Suncrest Towne Ctr Dr.
Morgantown, WV 26505-1876
Ph: (304)296-8444
Free: 800-858-2678
Fax: (304)291-5728
E-mail: info@aacei.org
URL: http://www.aacei.org

Description: Professional society of cost managers, cost engineers, estimators, schedulers and planners, project managers, educators, representatives of all branches of engineering, engineering students, and others. Conducts technical and educational programs. Offers placement service. Compiles statistics. Operates certification program for Certified Cost Engineers (CCE); Certified Cost Consultants (CCC); Interim Cost Consultants (ICC); Planning & Scheduling Professionals (PSP); and Earned Value Professionals (EVP).

3118 ■ American Road and Transportation Builders Association
1219 28th St. NW
Washington, DC 20007-3389
Ph: (202)289-4434
Fax: (202)289-4435
E-mail: general@artba.org
URL: http://www.artba.org

Description: Advances the interests of the transportation construction industry. Promotes the growth and protection of transportation infrastructure investment to meet the public and business demand for safe and efficient travel. Works to ensure its members' views and business concerns are addressed before Congress, the White House, federal agencies and news media.

3119 ■ American Society of Professional Estimators
2525 Perimeter Place Dr., Ste. 103
Nashville, TN 37214
Ph: (615)316-9200
Free: 888-EST-MATE
Fax: (615)316-9800
E-mail: psmith@aspenational.org
URL: http://www.aspenational.org

Description: Construction cost estimators. Develops professional and ethical standards in construction estimating. Offers continuing education to established professionals; provides certification for estimators.

3120 ■ Associated Builders and Contractors
440 1st St. NW, Ste. 200
Washington, DC 20001
E-mail: gotquestions@abc.org
URL: http://www.abc.org

Description: Construction contractors, subcontractors, suppliers and associates. Aims to foster and perpetuate the principles of rewarding construction workers and management on the basis of merit. Sponsors management education programs and craft training; also sponsors apprenticeship and skill training programs. Disseminates technological and labor relations information.

3121 ■ Associated General Contractors of America
2300 Wilson Blvd., Ste. 400
Arlington, VA 22201
Ph: (703)548-3118
Free: 800-242-1767
Fax: (703)548-3119
E-mail: info@agc.org
URL: http://www.agc.org

Description: General construction contractors; subcontractors; industry suppliers; service firms. Provides market services through its divisions. Conducts special conferences and seminars designed specifically for construction firms. Compiles statistics on job accidents reported by member firms. Maintains 65 committees, including joint cooperative committees with other associations and liaison committees with federal agencies.

3122 ■ International Society of Parametric Analysts
8221 Old Courthouse Rd., Ste. 106
Vienna, VA 22182
Ph: (703)938-5090
Fax: (703)938-5091
E-mail: ispa@sceaonline.net
URL: http://www.ispa-cost.org

Description: Engineers, designers, statisticians, estimators, and managers in industry, the military, and government who develop and use computerized, parametric cost-estimating models. Conducts educational activities to promote usage of parametric modeling techniques for purposes of cost estimating, risk analysis, and technology forecasting. Sponsors placement service.

3123 ■ National Association of Home Builders - Systems Builder Council
1201 15th St. NW
Washington, DC 20005
Ph: (202)266-8200
Free: 800-368-5242
Fax: (202)266-8400
URL: http://www.nahb.org/reference_list.aspx?sectionID=815

Description: Operates under the Building Systems Council of NAHB. Modular building manufacturers. Monitors state and federal housing legislation that impacts the building industry. Provides a forum for communication, networking and recruiting for those involved in manufacturing modular building systems. Addresses and solves problems specific to the council; offers consumer leads service.

3124 ■ National Association of Women in Construction
327 S Adams St.
Fort Worth, TX 76104
Ph: (817)877-5551
Free: 800-552-3506
Fax: (817)877-0324
E-mail: nawic@nawic.org
URL: http://www.nawic.org

Description: Seeks to enhance the success of women in the construction industry.

3125 ■ National Center for Construction Education and Research
13614 Progress Blvd.
Alachua, FL 32615-9407
Ph: (386)518-6500
Free: 888-622-3720
Fax: (386)518-6303
E-mail: marketing@nccer.org
URL: http://www.nccer.org

Description: Education foundation committed to the development and publication of Contren(TM) Learning Series, the source of craft training, management education and safety resources for the construction industry.

3126 ■ Professional Women in Construction
315 E 56th St.
New York, NY 10022-3730
Ph: (212)486-7745
Fax: (212)486-0228
URL: http://www.pwcusa.org

Description: Management-level women and men in construction and allied industries; owners, suppliers, architects, engineers, field personnel, office personnel and bonding/surety personnel. Provides a forum for exchange of ideas and promotion of political and legislative action, education and job opportunities for women in construction and related fields; forms liaisons with other trade and professional groups; develops research programs. Strives to reform abuses and to assure justice and equity within the construction industry. Sponsors mini-workshops. Maintains Action Line, which provides members with current information on pertinent legislation and on the association's activities and job referrals.

3127 ■ Society of Cost Estimating and Analysis
8221 Old Courthouse Rd., Ste. 106
Vienna, VA 22182
Ph: (703)938-5090
Fax: (703)938-5091
E-mail: scea@sceaonline.org
URL: http://www.sceaonline.org

Description: Works to improve cost estimating and analysis in government and industry and to enhance the professional competence and achievements of its members. Administers a professional certification program leading to the designation of Certified Cost Estimator/Analyst; offers extensive literature in the field through its Professional Development Program. Goals of the Society include enhancing the profession of cost estimating and analysis, fostering the professional growth of its members, enhancing the understanding and application of cost estimating, analysis and related disciplines throughout government and industry and providing forums and media through which current issues of interest to the profession can be addressed and advances in the state-of-the-art can be shared.

SOURCES OF HELP-WANTED ADS

3128 ■ Homeland Response
Intertec Publishing
5 Penn Plz., 13th Fl.
New York, NY 10001-1810
Ph: (212)613-9700
Free: 800-795-5445
Fax: (212)613-9749
E-mail: bethany.weaver@penton.com
URL: http://www.respondersafetyonline.com/
Frequency: Bimonthly. **Description:** Magazine covering homeland security.

3129 ■ International Counterterrorism & Security
Counterterrorism & Security Inc.
PO Box 10265
Arlington, VA 22210
Ph: (703)243-0993
Fax: (703)243-1197
E-mail: iacsp@erols.com
URL: http://www.iacsp.com/publications.php
Frequency: Quarterly. **Description:** Journal covering terrorism and security analysis.

3130 ■ Studies in Conflict and Terrorism
Routledge
c/o Bruce Hoffman, Ed.-in-Ch.
Georgetown University
214 3600 N St. NW
Washington, DC 20057
Ph: (212)216-7800
Free: 800-634-7064
Fax: (212)564-7854
E-mail: book.orders@tandf.co.uk
URL: http://www.tandf.co.uk/journals/titles/1057610x.asp
Frequency: 12/yr. **Price:** $478 Individuals print only; $1,251 Individuals online only; $1,390 Individuals print and online. **Description:** Journal publishing research on all forms of conflict and terrorism.

PLACEMENT AND JOB REFERRAL SERVICES

3131 ■ Security and Investigative Placement
7710 Woodmont Ave., No. 209
Bethesda, MD 20814
Ph: (301)229-6360
E-mail: klavinder@siplacement.com
URL: http://www.siplacement.com
Description: Places professionals in security and investigation positions within corporate, financial, legal, accounting and consulting firms. Candidates possess backgrounds in financial investigation, fraud, anti-money laundering, forensic accounting, investigative research, computer forensics and cyber investigation, security management, threat assessment, and global risk mitigation.

EMPLOYER DIRECTORIES AND NETWORKING LISTS

3132 ■ Counterterrorism: A Reference Handbook
ABC-Clio Inc.
130 Cremona Dr.
Santa Barbara, CA 93117-5516
Ph: (805)968-1911
Free: 800-368-6868
Fax: (805)685-9685
E-mail: crussell@abc-clio.com
URL: http://www.abc-clio.com
Frequency: Latest edition 2004. **Price:** $55 Individuals print. **Pages:** 293 1 volume. **Covers:** The wave of terrorism in the post-Cold War era and the ways in which states and societies are responding.

HANDBOOKS AND MANUALS

3133 ■ Counterterrorism Handbook: Tactics, Procedures, and Techniques, 3rd Ed.
CRC Press
c/o Taylor & Francis Group, LLC
6000 Broken Sound Pkwy., NW
Boca Raton, FL 33487-2713
Ph: (561)994-0555
Free: 800-272-7737
Fax: (800)374-3401
E-mail: orders@taylorandfrancis.com
URL: http://www.crcpress.com
Description: Frank Bolz, Jr., Kenneth J. Dudonis, and David P. Schulz. 2005. $78.36. 432 pages. Experts provide information to assist in understanding tactics, strategies and techniques to counter terrorism; topics include all aspects of terrorism, bomb threats, risk assessment, hostage situations, and weapons of mass destruction. Part of the Practical Aspects of Criminal and Forensic Investigations series, Volume 41.

3134 ■ Democracy and Counterterrorism: Lessons from the Past
United States Institute of Peace Press
1200 17th St. NW
Washington, DC 20036
Ph: (202)457-1700
Free: 800-868-8064
Fax: (202)429-6063
E-mail: usip_requests@usip.org
URL: http://www.usip.org
Description: Robert J. Art and Louise Richardson. January 2007. $65.00 hardcopy, $28 (paper). 481 pages. A comparative study of the policies, strategies, and instruments used by various democratic governments in the fight against terrorism.

3135 ■ First Responder Chem-Bio Handbook
Tempest Publishing
PO Box 22572
Alexandria, VA 22304-9257
Ph: (703)370-2962
Fax: (703)370-1571
E-mail: info@tempestpublishing.com
URL: http://www.chem-bio.com
Description: $49.00 CD-ROM. Provides critical information to help analysts counter chem-bio terrorism threats. Also available in CD-ROM which contains fully searchable and indexed electronic versions of the handbook.

3136 ■ Journal of Transportation Security
Springer Publishing Co.
11 W 42nd St., 15th Fl.
New York, NY 10036
Ph: (212)431-4370
Free: 877-687-7476
Fax: (212)941-7842
E-mail: cs@springerpub.com
URL: http://link.springer.com/journal/12198
Frequency: Quarterly. **Description:** Disseminates transportation security research, thought, and analysis for teachers, researchers, policy makers and practitioners.

3137 ■ Terror on the Internet: The New Arena, the New Challenges
United States Institute of Peace Press
1200 17th St. NW
Washington, DC 20036
Ph: (202)457-1700
Free: 800-868-8064
Fax: (202)429-6063
E-mail: usip_requests@usip.org
URL: http://www.usip.org
Description: Gabriel Weimann. April 2006. $20.00. 320 pages. Examination of the new psychology of terrorists and the ways in which they use the Internet to accomplish their goals.

3138 ■ The War of Ideas: Jihadism against Democracy
Palgrave Macmillan
175 5th Ave.
New York, NY 10010
Ph: (212)982-9300
Free: 800-221-7945
Fax: (212)777-6359
E-mail: customerservice@mpsvirginia.com
URL: http://www.us.macmillan.com
Description: Required reading for senior intelligence managers to help understand the game plan, goals and denial and deception of Jihadism against the U.S.

ONLINE JOB SOURCES AND SERVICES

3139 ■ Airportjobs.Us
URL: http://www.airportjobs.us

Description: Helps job seekers find airport career opportunities with top companies. Allows employers and recruiters to match qualified candidates with open airport postions.

3140 ■ ClearedConnections.com
URL: http://www.clearedconnections.com

Description: Online resource lists jobs for those security-cleared professionals including counterintelligence specialists.

3141 ■ CollegeRecruiter.com
URL: http://www.collegerecruiter.com

Description: Job listings.

3142 ■ IntelligenceCareers.com
URL: http://home.intelligencecareers.com

Description: Provides an online job search for intelligence positions by state, U.S. Forces overseas, and worldwide.

3143 ■ US Army Recruiting Command: GoArmy.com
URL: http://www.goarmy.com

Description: Online resource lists jobs, particularly those in the field of counterintelligence.

3144 ■ USADefenseIndustryJobs.com
URL: http://usadefenseindustryjobs.com

Description: Provides an online job search for intelligence positions with the American defense industry.

TRADESHOWS

3145 ■ AFCEA Intelligence Annual Fall and Spring Classified Symposia
AFCEA Intelligence
4400 Fair Lakes Ct.
Fairfax, VA 22033-3800
Ph: (703)631-6219
Fax: (703)631-6133
URL: http://www.afcea.org/mission/intel
Annual.

3146 ■ International Association of Crime Analysts Annual Training Conference
International Association of Crime Analysts
9218 Metcalf Ave., No. 364
Overland Park, KS 66212
Free: 800-609-3419
E-mail: iaca@iaca.net
URL: http://www.iaca.net
Annual.

OTHER SOURCES

3147 ■ AFCEA Intelligence
4400 Fair Lakes Ct.
Fairfax, VA 22033-3899
Ph: (703)631-6219
Fax: (703)631-6133
URL: http://www.afcea.org/mission/intel

Description: As part of the AFCEA International, the Association was established in 1981 to enhance outreach to the U.S. Intelligence Community and to support intelligence professionals in the government, military and private sector.

3148 ■ Association of Former Intelligence Officers
7700 Leesburg Pike, Ste. 324
Falls Church, VA 22043
Ph: (703)790-0320

Fax: (703)991-1278
E-mail: afio@afio.com
URL: http://www.afio.com

Description: Represents educational association of current and former intelligence professionals, security and counterterrorism practitioners and some U.S. citizens. Enhances public understanding of the role and importance of intelligence for national security, counterterrorism and to deal with threats in the contemporary world. Engages in career guidance for young people who are interested in intelligence or homeland security careers.

3149 ■ Central Intelligence Agency
Office of Public Affairs
Washington, DC 20505
Ph: (703)482-0623
Fax: (571)204-3800
URL: http://www.cia.gov

Description: U.S. government agency providing national security intelligence to senior U.S. policymakers. Separated into four basic components: National Clandestine Service, Directorate of Intelligence, Directorate of Science & Technology, and the Directorate of Support.

3150 ■ Central Valley Crime and Intelligence Analysts Association
PO Box 20756
Bakersfield, CA 93390
Ph: (661)391-7466
E-mail: info@cvciaa.org
URL: http://cvciaa.org

Description: Works to enhance crime and intelligence analysis as a tool in law enforcement.

3151 ■ Centre for Counterintelligence and Security System
PO Box 538
Great Falls, VA 22066
Ph: (703)642-7450
Free: 800-779-4007
Fax: (703)642-7451
URL: http://cicentre.com

Description: Provides advanced counterintelligence, counterterrorism and security training, analysis and consulting.

3152 ■ IntelCenter
PO Box 22572
Alexandria, VA 22304-9257
Ph: (800)719-8750
Fax: (800)217-0610
E-mail: info@intelcenter.com
URL: http://www.intelcenter.com

Description: Assists intelligence, counterterrorism and first responder professionals to prevent every act of terrorism, including the use of biological agents, chemical weapons, dirty devices or hijacked airliners. The firm studies terrorist groups and other threat actors as well as capabilities and intentions, warnings and indicators, operational characteristics and other points to better understand how to interdict terrorist operations and reduce the likelihood of future attacks.

3153 ■ International Association of Crime Analysts
9218 Metcalf Ave., No. 364
Overland Park, KS 66212
Free: 800-609-3419
E-mail: iaca@iaca.net
URL: http://www.iaca.net

Description: Crime analysts, intelligence analysts, police officers of all ranks, educators and students.

3154 ■ International Association of Law Enforcement Intelligence Analysts
PO Box 13857
Richmond, VA 23225
Fax: (804)565-2059
E-mail: admin@ialeia.org
URL: http://www.ialeia.org

Description: Promotes the development and enhancement of law enforcement intelligence analysts.

3155 ■ International Counter-Terrorism Officers Association
PO Box 580009
Flushing, NY 11358
Ph: (212)564-5048
Fax: (718)661-4044
E-mail: info@ictoa.org
URL: http://www.ictoa.org

Description: Promotes unity to combat and understand terrorism. Provides training, education and networking to enhance terrorism awareness. Supports members with advanced counter-terrorism measures. Ensures safety and security through international networking.

3156 ■ Law Enforcement Intelligence Unit
1825 Bell St., Ste. 205
Sacramento, CA 95825
Ph: (916)263-1187
Fax: (916)263-1180
E-mail: leiu@doj.ca.gov
URL: http://leiu.org

Description: Provides leadership and promotes professionalism in the criminal intelligence community.

3157 ■ Memorial Institute for the Prevention of Terrorism
621 N Robinson Ave., Ste. 400
Oklahoma City, OK 73102
Ph: (405)278-6300
Fax: (405)232-5132
E-mail: cid@mipt.org
URL: http://www.mipt.org

Description: Works to provide information about terrorism prevention and responder preparedness to better understand existing and growing terrorist threats.

3158 ■ National Geospatial-Intelligence Agency
Office of Corporate Communications
Public Affairs Branch, MS N73-OCCAE
7500 GEOINT Dr.
Springfield, VA 22150-7500
E-mail: recruitment@nga.mil
URL: http://www.nga.mil

Description: Provides timely, relevant and accurate geospatial intelligence in support of national security.

3159 ■ Student Association on Terrorism and Security Analysis
402 MacNaughton Hall
Syracuse University
Syracuse, NY 13244-1030
E-mail: satsa@maxwell.syr.edu
URL: http://satsa.syr.edu

Description: Dedicated to the critical analysis of terrorism, counterterrorism policy, and national and international security issues.

3160 ■ United States Institute of Peace
2301 Constitution Ave. NW
Washington, DC 20037
Ph: (202)457-1700
Fax: (202)429-6063
E-mail: info@usip.org
URL: http://www.usip.org

Description: Independent, nonpartisan, national institution funded by Congress to help prevent, manage and resolve threats to security and development worldwide, including interstate wars, internal armed conflicts, ethnic and religious strife, extremism, terrorism, and the proliferation of weapons of mass destruction.

Couriers and Messengers

SOURCES OF HELP-WANTED ADS

3161 ■ American Shipper
American Shipper
200 W Forsyth St., Ste. 1000
Jacksonville, FL 32202
Ph: (904)355-2601
Free: 800-874-6422
Fax: (904)791-8836
URL: http://www.americanshipper.com
Frequency: Monthly. **Price:** $36 Individuals.
Description: Transportation and shipping magazine.

3162 ■ OAG Air Cargo Guide
Official Airline Guides
3025 Highland Pkwy., Ste. 200
Downers Grove, IL 60515-5561
Ph: (630)515-5300
Free: 800-342-5624
Fax: (630)515-5301
E-mail: contactus@oag.com
URLs: http://www.oag.com; http://www2.oag.com/tt/
catalog/freight.html
Frequency: Monthly. **Description:** Guide to shipping
freight by air containing current domestic,
international and combination passenger cargo flight
schedules.

EMPLOYER DIRECTORIES AND NETWORKING LISTS

**3163 ■ Air Cargo World--Express Delivery
Guide Issue**
DMG World Media Ltd.
Queensway House
2 Queensway
Red Hill RH1 1QS, United Kingdom
Ph: 44 1737 855527
Fax: (173)7 855470
URL: http://www.aircargoworld.com/Resources/Air
-Express
Frequency: Annual; Latest edition 2009. **Publica-
tion includes:** List of approximately 200 air and
truck express carriers. **Entries include:** Company
name, address, contact person, phone, telex,
services offered, mode of transportation, maximum
size of package, method of payment, areas served.
Arrangement: Alphabetical. **Indexes:** Organization
name.

3164 ■ DACA Directory
Distributors & Consolidators of America
2240 Bernays Dr.
York, PA 17404
Free: 888-519-9195
Fax: (717)764-6531
E-mail: dacacarriers@comcast.net
URL: http://www.dacacarriers.com

Frequency: Latest edition 2008. **Covers:** firms and
individuals active in the shipping, warehousing,
receiving, distribution, or consolidation of freight ship-
ments.

**3165 ■ International Air Cargo Association
Membership Directory**
URL: http://www.tiaca.org
Description: Directory of membership organizations
listed alphabetically by category and industry.

**3166 ■ Messenger Courier Association of
America--Network Guide and Membership
Directory**
Customized Logistics and Delivery Association
750 National Press Bldg.
529 14th St. NW
Washington, DC 20045
Ph: (202)591-2460
Fax: (202)223-9741
E-mail: info@mcaa.com
URL: http://www.mcaa.com
Frequency: Annual; January. **Price:** $235. **Pages:**
100. **Covers:** Approximately 500 member air courier
companies. **Entries include:** Company name, office
personnel, warehouse facilities area served. **Ar-
rangement:** Geographical by airport city.

3167 ■ Smart Mail
Pitney Bowes Inc.
1 Elmcroft Rd.
Stamford, CT 06926
Ph: (203)356-5000
Free: 800-367-5690
Fax: (203)351-6059
E-mail: info@pitneybowes.com
URL: http://www.pitneybowes.com
Frequency: Quarterly. **Pages:** 700. **Covers:** Courier
companies that provide same day, overnight and
second-day delivery service of small packages
throughout the United States. **Entries include:**
Courier name, rates, phone, destinations, delivery
times, types of service, hours of operation, company
profile. **Arrangement:** Geographical.

HANDBOOKS AND MANUALS

3168 ■ Common Support Data Dictionary
Airlines for America
Publications Department
1301 Pennsylvania Ave. NW, Ste. 1100
Washington, DC 20004
Ph: (202)626-4062
Fax: (202)626-4081
E-mail: pubs@airlines.org
Description: CD-ROM single user: $255.00 member,
$365.00 non-member; CD-ROM multi user: $550.00
member, $785 non-member. Catalog of all data ele-
ments, terms, and tags that are used in association
specifications; provides standardized names, defini-

tions, and properties for data used within the air
transport industry.

ONLINE JOB SOURCES AND SERVICES

3169 ■ Messenger Jobs
URL: http://www.messengerjobs.org
Description: Provides a searchable database of
available jobs for messengers, couriers and delivery
personnel.

OTHER SOURCES

3170 ■ Air Cargo Annual Conference
Express Delivery & Logistics Association
400 Admiral Blvd.
Kansas City, MO 64106
Ph: (816)221-0254
Fax: (816)472-7765
E-mail: info@expressassociation.org
URL: http://www.expressassociation.org
Description: Conference held annually in March in
cooperation with the Air and Expedited Motor Carri-
ers Association and the Airforwarders Association.

**3171 ■ Air and Expedited Motor Carriers
Association**
9532 Liberia Ave., No. 705
Manassas, VA 20110
Ph: (703)361-5208
Fax: (703)361-5274
E-mail: fiona@aemca.org
URL: http://aemca.org
Description: Advocates for air and expedited cargo
trucking companies that provide ground transportation services, including airport-to-airport connecting
runs and local air and expedited cargo pickup and
delivery. Members include firms using a variety of
equipment including tractor-trailers and straight
trucks while serving an entire region or group of
states or provinces; firms using mainly straight trucks
and vans, serving metropolitan areas around one
major regional airport; firms working with airports
nationwide, running line hauls day and night providing connecting service; and ancillary providers of
goods and services to the air and expedited freight
trucking industry, such as computer software, communications equipment, roller bed equipment, truck
bodies, insurance, legal counsel, etc.

3172 ■ Airforwarders Association
750 National Press Bldg.
529 14th St. NW, Ste. 750
Washington, DC 20045
Ph: (202)591-2456
Fax: (202)223-9741
E-mail: bfried@airforwarders.org
URL: http://www.airforwarders.org
Description: Works as an alliance for the airforward-

ing industry, including indirect air carriers, cargo airlines, and affiliated businesses located in the U.S.

3173 ■ Airlines for America
1301 Pennsylvania Ave. NW, Ste. 1100
Washington, DC 20004-7017
Ph: (202)626-4000
E-mail: a4a@airlines.org
URL: http://www.airlines.org

Description: Trade organization representing principle U.S. airlines and their affiliates responsible for transporting airline passenger and cargo traffic.

3174 ■ Courier Association of Seattle
756 Garfield St.
Seattle, WA 98109
Ph: (206)969-2267
E-mail: el_gato@speakeasy.org
URL: http://www.scn.org/caos

Description: Promotes the interests of the bicycle messenger industry in Seattle, Washington.

3175 ■ Customized Logistics and Delivery Association
750 National Press Bldg.
529 14th St. NW
Washington, DC 20045
Ph: (202)591-2460
Fax: (202)223-9741
E-mail: info@mcaa.com
URL: http://www.mcaa.com

Description: Trade organization of local and international messenger courier companies. Addresses issues facing the industry, including municipal traffic ordinances that impede industry operations. Works to establish driver pools and to develop centralized core computer service bureaus for smaller courier companies. Provides training, discount purchasing programs, and legislative and regulatory issue monitoring. Conducts educational and research programs; compiles statistics.

3176 ■ Express Delivery and Logistics Association
400 Admiral Blvd.
Kansas City, MO 64106-1508
Ph: (816)221-0254
Free: 888-838-0761
Fax: (816)472-7765
E-mail: jim@expressassociation.org
URL: http://www.expressassociation.org

Description: Represents air couriers, small package express delivery companies, airlines and associated industry members (75); supports companies and facilities such as airlines and airports. Seeks to: provide industry forum for ideas, educate members about new technologies within the industry; represent air couriers before governmental bodies; inform members of legislation affecting the industry; develop and maintain relationships among members. Conducts seminars and workshops. **Members:** 75.

3177 ■ The International Air Cargo Association
PO Box 661510
Miami, FL 33266
Ph: (786)265-7011
Fax: (786)265-7012
E-mail: secgen@tiaca.org
URL: http://www.tiaca.org/tiaca/default.asp

Description: Supports and assists the air cargo industry and works to improve its role in world trade expansion.

3178 ■ New York Bike Messenger Foundation
1945 Pacific St.
Brooklyn, NY 11233
URL: http://www.nybmf.org

Description: Supports bicycle messengers in New York City by providing assistance and financial support to injured messengers and promoting programs that assist in the research and advancement of the messenger workforce.

3179 ■ New York State Messenger and Courier Association
PO Box 106
New York, NY 10024
Ph: (646)789-4472
Fax: (212)721-1620
E-mail: info@nysmca.org
URL: http://www.nysmca.org

Description: Promotes the interests of the messenger and courier industry in New York.

3180 ■ San Francisco Bike Messenger Association
255 9th St.
San Francisco, CA 94103
E-mail: naccc07@nacc07sf.com
URL: http://www.ahalenia.com/sfbma

Description: Promotes unity and solidarity among bicycle messengers in the San Francisco Bay Area and seeks to raise the status of the profession.

SOURCES OF HELP-WANTED ADS

3181 ■ *American Banker: The Financial Services Daily*
SourceMedia Inc. - Banking Group
1 State St. Plz., 27th Fl.
New York, NY 10004
Ph: (212)803-8200
Free: 800-221-1809
Fax: (212)843-9600
E-mail: custserv@AmericanBanker.com
URLs: http://www.americanbanker.com; http://media.americanbanker.com/home.html
Frequency: Daily. **Price:** $995 Individuals. **Description:** Newspaper for senior executives in banking and other financial services industries. Coverage includes trends, analysis, and statistics of the legislative scene in Washington; finance; mortgages; technology; small business; and regional banking.

3182 ■ *Brookings Papers on Economic Activity*
Brookings Institution Press
1775 Massachusetts Ave. NW
Washington, DC 20036
Ph: (202)797-6000
Free: 800-275-1447
Fax: (202)797-6195
E-mail: brookingspapers@brookings.edu
URL: http://www.brookings.edu/about/projects/bpea
Frequency: Semiannual. **Price:** $60 Individuals; $100 Institutions; $74 Other countries; $114 Institutions, other countries. **Description:** Publication covering economics and business.

3183 ■ *Business Credit: The Publication for Credit and Finance Professionals*
National Association of Credit Management
8840 Columbia 100 Pkwy.
Columbia, MD 21045-2158
Ph: (410)740-5560
Fax: (410)740-5574
E-mail: nacm_national@nacm.org
URL: http://www.nacm.org/index.php?option=com_content&view=category&layout=blog&id=77&Itemid=188
Frequency: 10/yr. **Price:** C$60 Canada; $65 Other countries; $54 Individuals; $48 Libraries; $7 Single issue. **Description:** Magazine covering finance, business risk management, providing information for the extension of credit, maintenance of accounts receivable, and cash asset management.

3184 ■ *Commercial Lending Review*
Wolters Kluwer Law & Business - CCH
CCH Inc.
2700 Lake Cook Rd.
Riverwoods, IL 60015
Ph: (847)267-7000

Fax: (978)371-2961
E-mail: cust_serv@cch.com
URL: http://www.commerciallendingreview.com/
Frequency: Bimonthly. **Price:** $445 Individuals. **Description:** Journal covering all aspects of lending for commercial banks, community and regional banks and other financial institutions.

3185 ■ *Northwestern Financial Review*
NFR Communications Inc.
7400 Metro Blvd., Ste. 217
Minneapolis, MN 55439
Ph: (952)835-2275
Fax: (952)835-2295
E-mail: info@northwesternfinancialreview.com
URL: http://www.northwesternfinancialreview.com
Frequency: 24/yr. **Price:** $99 Individuals. **Description:** Trade publication covering commercial banking.

3186 ■ *U.S. Banker: Charting the Future of Financial Services*
SourceMedia Inc.
1 State Street Plz., 27th Fl.
New York, NY 10004
Ph: (212)803-6066
Free: 800-221-1809
Fax: (212)843-9635
E-mail: custserv@sourcemedia.com
URL: http://www.americanbanker.com/usb.html
Frequency: Monthly. **Price:** $109 Individuals; $139 Individuals Canada; $139 Individuals outside North America; $179 Two years; $239 Two years Canada; $239 Two years outside North America. **Description:** Magazine serving the financial services industry.

EMPLOYER DIRECTORIES AND NETWORKING LISTS

3187 ■ *The Bank Directory*
Accuity Inc.
4709 W Golf Rd.
Skokie, IL 60076-1231
Ph: (847)676-9600
Free: 800-321-3373
Fax: (847)933-8101
E-mail: custserv@accuitysolutions.com
URL: http://store.accuitysolutions.com/order.html
Frequency: Semiannual; June and December. **Price:** $1,195 Individuals. **Covers:** In five volumes, about 11,000 banks and 50,000 branches of United States banks, and 60,000 foreign banks and branches engaged in foreign banking; Federal Reserve system and other United States government and state government banking agencies; 500 largest North American and International commercial banks; paper and automated clearinghouses. Volumes 1 and 2 contain North American listings; volumes 3 and 4, international listings (also cited as 'Thomson International Bank Directory; volume 5, Worldwide Correspondents Guide containing key correspondent

data to facilitate funds transfer. **Includes:** Bank operations information, asset ranking in state and country, bank routing numbers in numeric sequence, discontinued or changed bank names in geographical sequence. **Entries include:** For domestic banks--Bank name, address, phone, telex, cable, date established, routing number, charter type, bank holding company affiliation, memberships in Federal Reserve System and other banking organizations, principal officers by function performed, principal correspondent banks, and key financial data (deposits, etc.). For international banks--Bank name, address, phone, fax, telex, cable, SWIFT address, transit or sort codes within home country, ownership, financial data, names and titles of key personnel, branch locations. For branches--Bank name, address, phone, charter type, ownership and other details comparable to domestic bank listings. **Arrangement:** Geographical. **Indexes:** Alphabetical, geographical.

3188 ■ *Corporate Finance Sourcebook: The Guide to Major Capital Investment Sources and Related Financial Services*
LexisNexis
9443 Springboro Pke.
Dayton, OH 45342
Ph: (937)865-6800
Free: 800-227-4908
Fax: (937)865-1211
E-mail: nrpsales@marquiswhoswho.com
URL: http://www.financesourcebook.com
Frequency: Annual; Latest edition 2010. **Price:** $695 Individuals list price; $556 Individuals. **Covers:** Securities research analysts; major private lenders; investment banking firms; commercial banks; United States-based foreign banks; commercial finance firms; leasing companies; foreign investment bankers in the United States; pension managers; banks that offer master trusts; cash managers; business insurance brokers; business real estate specialists; lists about 3,500 firms; 14,500 key financial experts. **Entries include:** All entries include firm name, address, phone, e-mail, and names and titles of officers, contacts, or specialists in corporate finance. Additional details are given as appropriate, including names of major clients, number of companies served, services, total assets, branch locations, years in business. **Arrangement:** Classified by line of business and then alphabetized within that line of business. **Indexes:** Firm name, personnel name, geographical.

3189 ■ *North American Financial Institutions Directory*
Accuity Inc.
4709 W Golf Rd.
Skokie, IL 60076-1231
Ph: (847)676-9600
Free: 800-321-3373
Fax: (847)933-8101
E-mail: custserv@accuitysolutions.com
URL: http://store.accuitysolutions.com/order.html
Frequency: Semiannual; January and July. **Price:**

$955 Individuals. **Covers:** 15,000 banks and their branches; over 2,000 head offices, and 15,500 branches of savings and loan associations; over 5,500 credit unions with assets over $5 million; Federal Reserve System and other U.S. government and state government banking agencies; bank holding, commercial finance, and leasing companies; coverage includes the United States, Canada, Mexico, and Central America. **Includes:** Bank routing numbers in numeric sequence; maps; discontinued banks. **Entries include:** Bank name, address, phone, fax, telex, principal officers and directors, date established, financial data, association memberships, attorney or counsel, correspondent banks, out-of-town branch, holding company affiliation, ABA transit number and routing symbol, MICR number with check digit, credit card(s) issued, trust powers, current par value and dividend of common stock, kind of charter. **Arrangement:** Geographical. **Indexes:** Alphabetical.

3190 ■ *Who's Who in Finance and Industry*
Marquis Who's Who L.L.C.
300 Connell Dr., Ste. 2000
Berkeley Heights, NJ 07922
Ph: (908)673-1000
Free: 800-473-7020
Fax: (908)673-1179
E-mail: finance@marquiswhoswho.com
URL: http://www.marquiswhoswho.com

Frequency: Biennial; latest edition 37th; 2009-2010. **Price:** $349 Individuals. **Pages:** 1,264. **Covers:** Over 24,000 individuals. **Entries include:** Name, home and office addresses, personal, career, and family data; civic and political activities; memberships, publications, awards. **Arrangement:** Alphabetical.

HANDBOOKS AND MANUALS

3191 ■ *The Million-Dollar Financial Services Practice: A Proven System for Becoming a Top Producer*
AMACOM Publishing
c/o American Management Association
1601 Broadway
New York, NY 10019-7434
Ph: (212)586-8100
Free: 800-714-6395
Fax: (518)891-0368
E-mail: pubs_cust_serv@amanet.org
URL: http://www.amacombooks.org

Description: David J. Mullen. 2007. $30.00 (hardback). 352 pages. Features information on how to become a financial advisor using the methods given in the book. Combines marketing, prospecting, sales, and time management techniques into a system that will help readers build a successful and lucrative practice.

3192 ■ *Opportunities in Hospital Administration Careers*
The McGraw-Hill Companies Inc.
PO Box 182604
Columbus, OH 43272
Ph: (212)512-2000
Free: 877-833-5524
Fax: (614)759-3749
E-mail: customer.service@mcgraw-hill.com
URL: http://www.mcgraw-hill.com

Description: I. Donald Snook. 2006. $13.95. 160 pages. Discusses opportunities for administrators in a variety of management settings: hospital, department, clinic, group practice, HMO, mental health, and extended care facilities.

EMPLOYMENT AGENCIES AND SEARCH FIRMS

3193 ■ Adams Inc. Financial Recruiting
17330 Wright St., Ste. 101
Omaha, NE 68130

Ph: (402)333-3009
Free: 800-536-4933
Fax: (402)333-3448
E-mail: info@adams-inc.com
URL: http://www.adams-inc.com

Description: Provides recruitment and candidate placement in the banking/financial, trust/investment, and credit card industries.

3194 ■ Butterfass, Pepe & MacCallan Inc.
PO Box 179
Franklin Lakes, NJ 07417
Ph: (201)560-9500
Fax: (201)560-9506
E-mail: staff@butterfasspepe.com
URL: http://www.bpmi.com

Description: Executive search firm.

3195 ■ Cheryl Alexander & Associates
8588 Shadow Creek Dr.
Maple Grove, MN 55311
Ph: (763)416-4570
E-mail: cheryl@cherylalexander.com
URL: http://www.cherylalexander.com

Description: Executive search firm.

3196 ■ Cross Hill Partners LLC
845 Third Ave., 6th Fl.
New York, NY 10022
Ph: (646)405-7500
Fax: (866)927-4449
E-mail: info@crosshillpartners.com
URL: http://www.crosshillpartners.com

Description: Executive search firm.

3197 ■ Douglas-Allen Inc.
Tower Square, 24th Fl.
Springfield, MA 01115
Ph: (413)739-0900
E-mail: research@douglas-allen.com
URL: http://www.douglas-allen.com

Description: Executive search firm.

3198 ■ Financial Professionals
4100 Spring Valley Rd., Ste. 250
Dallas, TX 75244
Ph: (972)991-8999
Fax: (972)702-0776
E-mail: response@fpstaff.net
URL: http://www.fpstaff.net

Description: Executive search consultants with additional offices in Forth Worth and Houston.

3199 ■ Robert Half Finance & Accounting
2884 Sand Hill Rd.
Menlo Park, CA 94025
Free: 800-474-4253
URL: http://www.roberthalffinance.com

Description: Provides recruitment services in the areas of accounting and finance.

ONLINE JOB SOURCES AND SERVICES

3200 ■ BankingCareers.com
URL: http://www.bankingcareers.com

Description: Provides lists of jobs and products to the banking and finance community.

3201 ■ FinancialServicesCrossing.com
URL: http://www.financialservicescrossing.com

Description: Offers a collection of top financial services job openings carefully researched by analysts. Provides instant access to a comprehensive pool of listings in the industry of financial services.

TRADESHOWS

3202 ■ Pennsylvania Association of Community Bankers Convention
Pennsylvania Association of Community Bankers
2405 N Front St.
Harrisburg, PA 17110
Ph: (717)231-7447
Free: 800-443-5076
Fax: (717)231-7445
E-mail: pacb@pacb.org
URL: http://www.pacb.org

Frequency: Annual. **Primary Exhibits:** Equipment, supplies, and services for community banks, thrifts, and associate firms.

OTHER SOURCES

3203 ■ American Bankers Association
1120 Connecticut Ave. NW
Washington, DC 20036
Ph: (202)663-5268
Free: 800-226-5377
Fax: (202)828-5053
E-mail: custserv@aba.com
URL: http://www.aba.com

Description: Members are principally commercial banks and trust companies; combined assets of members represent approximately 90% of the U.S. banking industry; approximately 94% of members are community banks with less than $500 million in assets. Seeks to enhance the role of commercial bankers as preeminent providers of financial services through communications, research, legal action, lobbying of federal legislative and regulatory bodies, and education and training programs. Serves as spokesperson for the banking industry; facilitates exchange of information among members. Maintains the American Institute of Banking, an industry-sponsored adult education program. Conducts educational and training programs for bank employees and officers through a wide range of banking schools and national conferences. Maintains liaison with federal bank regulators; lobbies Congress on issues affecting commercial banks; testifies before congressional committees; represents members in U.S. postal rate proceedings. Serves as secretariat of the International Monetary Conference and the Financial Institutions Committee for the American National Standards Institute. Files briefs and lawsuits in major court cases affecting the industry. Conducts teleconferences with state banking associations on such issues as regulatory compliance; works to build consensus and coordinate activities of leading bank and financial service trade groups. Provides services to members including: public advocacy; news media contact; insurance program providing directors and officers with liability coverage, financial institution bond, and trust errors and omissions coverage; research service operated through ABA Center for Banking Information; fingerprint set processing in conjunction with the Federal Bureau of Investigation; discounts on operational and income-producing projects through the Corporation for American Banking. Conducts conferences, forums, and workshops covering subjects such as small business, consumer credit, agricultural and community banking, trust management, bank operations, and automation. Sponsors ABA Educational Foundation and the Personal Economics Program, which educates schoolchildren and the community on banking, economics, and personal finance. **Members:** 1,000.

3204 ■ American Credit Union Mortgage Association
PO Box 400955
Las Vegas, NV 89140
Free: 877-442-2862
Fax: (702)823-3950
E-mail: bdorsa@acuma.org
URL: http://www.acuma.org/wp

Description: Credit unions providing real estate lending services. Promotes adherence to high standards of ethics and practice in the issuing of mortgage loans. Represents members' interests before regulatory agencies and industrial associations; conducts research and educational programs; maintains speakers' bureau; compiles statistics. **Members:** 200.

3205 ■ American Financial Services Association
919 18th St. NW, Ste. 300
Washington, DC 20006-5526
E-mail: cstinebert@afsamail.org
URL: http://www.afsaonline.org

Description: Represents companies whose business is primarily direct credit lending to consumers and/or the purchase of sales finance paper on consumer goods. Has members that have insurance and retail subsidiaries; some are themselves subsidiaries of highly diversified parent corporations. Encourages the business of financing individuals and families for necessary and useful purposes at reasonable charges, including interest; promotes consumer understanding of basic money management principles as well as constructive uses of consumer credit. Includes educational services such as films, textbooks and study units for the classroom and budgeting guides for individuals and families. Compiles statistical reports; offers seminars.

3206 ■ Association for Financial Professionals
4520 E West Hwy., Ste. 750
Bethesda, MD 20814
Ph: (301)907-2862
Fax: (301)907-2864
URL: http://www.afponline.org

Description: Seeks to establish a national forum for the exchange of concepts and techniques related to improving the management of treasury and the careers of professionals through research, education, publications and recognition of the treasury management profession through a certification program. Conducts educational programs. Operates career center.

3207 ■ *Career Opportunities in Banking, Finance, and Insurance*
InfoBase Holdings Inc.
132 W 31st., 17 Fl.
New York, NY 10001-3406
Ph: (212)967-8800
Fax: (800)678-3633
E-mail: info@infobasepublishing.com
URL: http://factsonfile.infobasepublishing.com

Frequency: Latest edition 2nd; Published February, 2007. **Price:** $49.50 Individuals hardcover. **Description:** Thomas P. Fitch. Second edition, 2007. 267 pages. Lists of colleges with programs supporting banking, finance, and industry; professional associations; professional certifications; regulatory agencies; and Internet resources for career planning. **Publication includes:** Lists of colleges with programs supporting banking, finance, and industry; professional associations; professional certifications; regulatory agencies; and Internet resources for career planning. Principal content of publication is job descriptions for professions in the banking, finance, and insurance industries. **Indexes:** Alphabetical.

3208 ■ Commercial Finance Association
370 7th Ave., Ste. 1801
New York, NY 10001-3979
Ph: (212)792-9390
Fax: (212)564-6053
URL: http://www.cfa.com

Description: Organizations engaged in asset-based financial services including commercial financing and factoring and lending money on a secured basis to small- and medium-sized business firms. Acts as a forum for information and consideration about ideas, opportunities and legislation concerning asset-based financial services. Seeks to improve the industry's legal and operational procedures. Offers job placement and reference services for members. Sponsors School for Field Examiners and other educational programs. Compiles statistics; conducts seminars and surveys; maintains speakers' bureau and 21 committees.

3209 ■ Consumer Data Industry Association
1090 Vermont Ave. NW, Ste. 200
Washington, DC 20005-4964
Ph: (202)371-0910
Fax: (202)371-0134
E-mail: cdia@cdiaonline.org
URL: http://www.cdiaonline.org

Description: Serves as international association of credit reporting and collection service offices. Maintains hall of fame and biographical archives; conducts specialized educational programs. Offers computerized services and compiles statistics.

3210 ■ Credit Professionals International
10726 Manchester Rd., Ste. 210
Saint Louis, MO 63122
Ph: (314)821-9393
Fax: (314)821-7171
E-mail: creditpro@creditprofessionals.org
URL: http://www.creditprofessionals.org

Description: Represents individuals employed in credit or collection departments of business firms or professional offices. Conducts educational program in credit work. Sponsors Career Club composed of members who have been involved in credit work for at least 25 years. **Members:** 700.

3211 ■ Credit Union Executives Society
5510 Research Park Dr.
Madison, WI 53711-5377
Ph: (608)271-2664
Free: 800-252-2664
Fax: (608)271-2303
E-mail: cues@cues.org
URL: http://www.cues.org

Description: Advances the professional development of credit union CEOs, senior management and directors. Serves as an international membership association dedicated to the professional development of credit union CEOs, senior management and directors.

3212 ■ National Association of Credit Management
8840 Columbia 100 Pkwy.
Columbia, MD 21045-2158
Ph: (410)740-5560
Fax: (410)740-5574
E-mail: nacm_national@nacm.org
URL: http://www.nacm.org

Description: Provides information, products and services for effective business credit and accounts receivable management.

3213 ■ National Association of Credit Union Services Organizations
3419 Via Lido
PMB 135
Newport Beach, CA 92663
Ph: (949)645-5296
Free: 888-462-2870
Fax: (949)645-5297
E-mail: info@nacuso.org
URL: http://www.nacuso.org

Description: Credit union service organizations and their employees. Promotes professional advancement of credit union service organization staff; seeks to insure adherence to high standards of ethics and practice among members. Conducts research and educational programs; formulates and enforces standards of conduct and practice; maintains speakers' bureau; compiles statistics. **Members:** 400.

3214 ■ National Association of Federal Credit Unions
3138 10th St. N
Arlington, VA 22201-2149
Free: 800-336-4644
E-mail: fbecker@nafcu.org
URL: http://www.nafcu.org

Description: Serves as federally-chartered credit unions. Offers legislative and regulatory advocacy, compliance assistance, training and professional development and a range of products. Provides information on the latest industry developments and proposed and final regulations. Represents members' interests before federal regulatory bodies and Congress. Compiles statistics and holds educational conferences.

3215 ■ National Bankers Association
1513 P St. NW
Washington, DC 20005
Ph: (202)588-5432
Fax: (202)588-5443
E-mail: mgrant@nationalbankers.org
URL: http://www.nationalbankers.org

Description: Minority banking institutions owned by minority individuals and institutions. Serves as an advocate for the minority banking industry. Organizes banking services, government relations, marketing, scholarship, and technical assistance programs. Offers placement services; compiles statistics.

3216 ■ Risk Management Association
1801 Market St., Ste. 300
Philadelphia, PA 19103-1613
Ph: (215)446-4000
Fax: (215)446-4101
E-mail: rmaar@rmahq.org
URL: http://www.rmahq.org

Description: Commercial and savings banks, and savings and loan, and other financial services companies. Conducts research and professional development activities in areas of loan administration, asset management, and commercial lending and credit to increase professionalism.

SOURCES OF HELP-WANTED ADS

3217 ■ *AAHPERD UpdatePLUS*
American Alliance for Health, Physical Education, Recreation and Dance
1900 Association Dr.
Reston, VA 20191-1598
Ph: (703)476-3400
Free: 800-213-7193
Fax: (703)476-9527
E-mail: membership@aahperd.org
URL: http://www.aahperd.org
Description: Six issues/year. Provides news and information on the Alliance. Discusses current issues and research in the areas of health, physical education, recreation, dances, fitness, and adapted physical education. Recurring features include a calendar of events, reports of meetings, news of educational opportunities, job listings, notices of publications available, and columns titled President's Message, Membership Corner, and From the EVP's Desk.

3218 ■ *ArtSEARCH*
Theatre Communications Group
520 8th Ave., 24th Fl.
New York, NY 10018-4156
Ph: (212)609-5900
Fax: (212)609-5901
E-mail: tcg@tcg.org
URL: http://www.tcg.org
Description: Biweekly. Publishes classified listings for job opportunities in the arts, especially theatre, dance, music, and educational institutions. Listings include opportunities in administration, artistic, education, production, and career development.

3219 ■ *Daily Variety*
Variety Media Publications
6 Bell Yard
London WC2A 2JR, United Kingdom
Ph: 44 20 75205200
Fax: 44 20 75205237
E-mail: richard.woolley@variety.co.uk
URLs: http://www.reedbusiness.com/index.asp?layout=theListProfile&theListID=535&g roupid=28&industryid=28; http://www.variety.com
Frequency: Daily. **Price:** $329.99 Individuals.
Description: Global entertainment newspaper (tabloid).

3220 ■ *Dance Magazine*
Dance Magazine Inc.
333 7th Ave., 11th Fl.
New York, NY 10001
Ph: (646)459-4800
Free: 800-331-1750
Fax: (646)459-4900
E-mail: dancemag@dancemagazine.com
URL: http://www.dancemagazine.com
Frequency: Monthly. **Price:** $34.95 Individuals; $64.90 Two years; $46.95 Canada; $88.90 Canada 2

years; $66.95 Other countries; $128.90 Other countries 2 years. **Description:** Performing arts magazine featuring all forms of dance with profiles, news, photos, reviews of performances, and information on books, videos, films, schools, health, and technique.

3221 ■ *Ross Reports Television and Film: Agents & Casting Directors-Television Production-Films in Development*
Nielsen Business Media Inc.
770 Broadway
New York, NY 10003-9522
Ph: (646)654-4500
Free: 866-890-8541
Fax: (646)654-5584
E-mail: bmcomm@nielsen.com
URLs: http://www.backstage.com; http://www.penrose-press.com/idd/MAG29876.card
Frequency: Bimonthly. **Price:** $65 Individuals; $10 Individuals. **Description:** Trade publication covering talent agents and casting directors in New York and Los Angeles, as well as television and film production. Special national issue of agents and casting directors is published annually. Sister publication to Back Stage, Back Stage West.

3222 ■ *Variety: The International Entertainment Weekly*
Reed Elsevier Group plc - Reed Business Information
360 Park Ave. S
New York, NY 11010
Ph: (212)791-4208
E-mail: corporatecommunications@reedbusiness.com
URL: http://www.reedbusiness.com/us.html
Frequency: Weekly; 50/yr. **Price:** $259 Individuals; $25 Individuals monthly. **Description:** Newspaper (tabloid) reporting on theatre, television, radio, music, and movies.

EMPLOYER DIRECTORIES AND NETWORKING LISTS

3223 ■ *Contemporary Theatre, Film, and Television*
Cengage Learning Inc.
200 1st Stamford Pl., Ste. 400
Stamford, CT 06902-6753
Ph: (203)965-8600
Free: 800-354-9706
Fax: (800)487-8488
E-mail: investors@cengage.com
URL: http://www.gale.cengage.com
Frequency: Bimonthly; Latest edition Volume 119.
Price: $308 Individuals volume 116. **Covers:** 116 volumes, more than 20,000 leading and up-and-coming performers, directors, writers, producers, designers, managers, choreographers, technicians,

composers, executives, and dancers in the United States, Canada, Great Britain and the world. Each volume includes updated biographies for people listed in previous volumes and in "Who's Who in the Theatre," which this series has superseded. **Entries include:** Name, agent and/or office addresses; personal and career data; stage, film, and television credits; writings, awards, other information. **Arrangement:** Alphabetical. **Indexes:** Cumulative name index also covers entries in "Who's Who in the Theatre" editions 1-17 and in "Who Was Who in the Theatre."

3224 ■ *New England Theatre Conference--Resource Directory*
New England Theatre Conference
215 Knob Hill Dr.
Hamden, CT 06518
Ph: (617)851-8535
E-mail: mail@netconline.org
URLs: http://www.netconline.org; http://www.netconline.org/netc-membership.php
Frequency: Annual; January. **Pages:** 84. **Covers:** 800 individuals and 100 groups. **Entries include:** For individuals--Name, address, telephone, e-mail and tax indicating type or level of theater activity, theater and school affiliation. For groups--Name, address; telephone, box office, fax, e-mail, names and addresses of delegates. **Arrangement:** Alphabetical. **Indexes:** Members by Division.

HANDBOOKS AND MANUALS

3225 ■ *Ballet Dancers in Career Transition: Sixteen Success Stories*
McFarland and Company Incorporated Publishers
960 Nc Hwy. 88 W
Jefferson, NC 28640-8813
Ph: (336)246-4460
Free: 800-253-2187
Fax: (336)246-5018
E-mail: info@mcfarlandpub.com
URL: http://www.mcfarlandpub.com
Description: Nancy Upper. May 2004. $39.95 (paper). Illustrated. 278 Pages.

3226 ■ *Creative Careers: Paths for Aspiring Actors, Artists, Dancers, Musicians and Writers*
SuperCollege
3286 Oak Ct.
Belmont, CA 94002
Ph: (650)618-2221
Fax: (650)618-2221
E-mail: supercollege@supercollege.com
URL: http://www.supercollege.com
Description: Elaina Loveland. 2009. $17.95. 352 pages. Provides tips and advice for job seekers aiming for a career in the field of arts. Includes details on salaries, job descriptions, job outlook, training and education requirements for each artistic career.

3227 ■ *The Dancer's Survival Manual:*
Everything You Need to Know from the
First Class to Career Change
University Press of Florida
15 NW 15th St.
Gainesville, FL 32611
Ph: (352)392-1351
Free: 800-226-3822
Fax: (352)392-0590
E-mail: press@upf.com
URL: http://www.upf.com

Description: Marian Horosko and Judith Kupersmith.
2009. $27.50 (paperback). 224 pages. Covers every
aspect of a career in dance, including the major decisions and challenges dancers face throughout their
careers.

3228 ■ *Resumes for Performing Arts*
Careers
The McGraw-Hill Companies Inc.
PO Box 182604
Columbus, OH 43272
Ph: (212)512-2000
Free: 877-833-5524
Fax: (614)759-3749
E-mail: customer.service@mcgraw-hill.com
URL: http://www.mcgraw-hill.com

Description: 2004. $10.95 (paper). 160 pages.

3229 ■ *Starting Your Career as a Dancer*
Allworth Press
307 W 36th St., 11th Fl.
New York, NY 10018
Ph: (212)643-6816
Free: 800-491-2808
Fax: (212)643-6819
E-mail: pub@allworth.com
URL: http://www.allworth.com

Description: Mande Dagenais. 2012. $19.95
(paper). 256 pages. Serves as a comprehensive and
practical guide for dancers. Offers insider advice and
knowledge on what it really takes to get into the business, be in the business, and survive in the business.

ONLINE JOB SOURCES AND SERVICES

3230 ■ **Answers4Dancers.com**
URL: http://www.answers4dancers.com

Description: Provides resources such as listings of
auditions and jobs, tips and secrets, tools and training, videos, and success stories to job seekers in the
dance and choreography industry.

3231 ■ **Dance.net**
URL: http://www.dance.net

Description: Strives to offer dancers a place on the
internet to learn about all dance forms and meet fellow students, dancers, instructors, coaches,
choreographers, and studio owners. Provides a
database of jobs.

TRADESHOWS

3232 ■ **Texas Association for Health,**
Physical Education, Recreation, and Dance
Annual State Convention
Texas Association for Health, Physical Education,
Recreation and Dance
7910 Cameron Rd.
Austin, TX 78754
Ph: (512)459-1299
Fax: (512)459-1290
E-mail: lynda@tahperd.org
URL: http://www.tahperd.org

Frequency: Annual. **Primary Exhibits:** Publications,
equipment, and supplies for health, physical education, recreation, and dance.

OTHER SOURCES

3233 ■ *100 Careers in the Music Business*
Barron's Educational Series Inc.
250 Wireless Blvd.
Hauppauge, NY 11788
Ph: (631)434-3311
Free: 800-645-3476
Fax: (631)434-3723
E-mail: barrons@barronseduc.com
URL: http://www.barronseduc.com

Description: Tanja L. Crouch. 2008. $15.29 (paper).
320 pages. Provides information on how and where
to find employment opportunities in the music
industry. **Includes:** Includes lists of names, addresses, and websites of music unions, organizations, directories, and periodicals, as well as schools
offering degrees in music business management.
Includes lists of names, addresses, and websites of
music unions, organizations, directories, and
periodicals, as well as schools offering degrees in
music business management.

3234 ■ **American Alliance for Health,**
Physical Education, Recreation and Dance
1900 Association Dr.
Reston, VA 20191-1598
Ph: (703)476-3400
Free: 800-213-7193
Fax: (703)476-9527
E-mail: membership@aahperd.org
URL: http://www.aahperd.org

Description: Students and educators in physical
education, dance, health, athletics, safety education,
recreation, and outdoor education. Sponsors placement service.

3235 ■ **American Dance Guild**
320 W 83rd St., Apt. 7D
New York, NY 10024
Ph: (212)627-9407
E-mail: gloria.mclean@earthlink.net
URL: http://americandanceguild.org

Description: Serves the dance professional by
providing: a networking system between dance artists and dance educators; an informed voice on
behalf of the dance field to governmental,
educational and corporate institutions and the
general public; international dance festivals, conferences and dance film festivals; educational publications and videos; the ADG Fannie Weiss Scholarship; the ADG Harkness Resource for Dance Study.

3236 ■ *Career Opportunities in Theater and*
the Performing Arts
InfoBase Holdings Inc.
132 W 31st., 17 Fl.
New York, NY 10001-3406
Ph: (212)967-8800
Fax: (800)678-3633
E-mail: info@infobasepublishing.com
URL: http://www.infobasepublishing.com

Frequency: Latest edition 3rd; Published April, 2006.
Description: Shelly Field. Third edition, 2006. 304
pages. **Covers:** 80 careers, from acting to designing
to dance therapy. **Includes:** Appendices of major
agencies, unions, associations, periodicals, and
directories.

3237 ■ *Careers for the Stagestruck and*
Other Dramatic Types
The McGraw-Hill Companies Inc.
PO Box 182604
Columbus, OH 43272
Ph: (212)512-2000
Free: 877-833-5524
Fax: (614)759-3749
E-mail: customer.service@mcgraw-hill.com
URL: http://www.mcgraw-hill.com

Description: Lucia Mauro. Second edition, 2004.
$13.95 (paper). 160 pages. **Includes:** Appendices of
arts organizations, colleges and universities, and

other job-hunting and arts education resources, as
well as bibliographical references. Appendices of arts
organizations, colleges and universities, and other
job-hunting and arts education resources, as well as
bibliographical references. **Entries include:** Name,
address.

3238 ■ **Dance Notation Bureau**
111 John St., Ste. 704
New York, NY 10038
Ph: (212)571-7011
Fax: (212)571-7012
E-mail: dnbinfo@dancenotation.org
URL: http://www.dancenotation.org

Description: Documents and preserves dance works
through the use of graphic notation. Conducts
research into movement-related analysis techniques
and programs. Maintains extension at Ohio State
University, Columbus. Maintains placement service;
assists choreographers in copyrighting, licensing,
and restaging of their dance works. Offers service for
dance reconstructors and circulating library materials
to members. Maintains archive of original Labano-
tated dance scores in the world.

3239 ■ **Dance/USA**
1111 16th St. NW, Ste. 300
Washington, DC 20036
Ph: (202)833-1717
Fax: (202)833-2686
E-mail: afitterer@danceusa.org
URL: http://www.danceusa.org

Description: Comprised of dancers, dance
companies, artists, and others involved in non-profit
professional dance. Sustains and advances professional dance by addressing the needs, concerns, and
interests of artists, administrators, and organizations.
Enhances the infrastructure for dance creation and
distribution, education, and dissemination of information.

3240 ■ **Institute of American Indian Arts**
83 Avan Nu Po Rd.
Santa Fe, NM 87508-1300
Ph: (505)424-2300
Fax: (505)424-0050
URL: http://www.iaia.edu

Description: Federally chartered private institution.
Offers 4-year degrees in Creative Writing, New
Media Arts, Museum Studies, Indigenous Studies
and Studio arts primarily to Native American and
Alaska Natives (but school is open enrollment).
Emphasis is placed upon Indian traditions as the
basis for creative expression in fine arts including
painting, sculpture, museum studies, creative writing,
printmaking, photography, communications, design,
and dance, as well as training in metal crafts, jewelry,
ceramics, textiles, and various traditional crafts.
Students are encouraged to identify with their
heritage and to be aware of themselves as members
of a culture rich in architecture, the fine arts, music,
pageantry, and the humanities. All programs are
based on elements of the Native American cultural
heritage that emphasizes differences between Native
American and non-Native American cultures. Sponsors Indian arts-oriented junior college offering Associate of Fine Arts degrees in various fields as well
as seminars, an exhibition program, and traveling
exhibits. Maintains extensive library, museum, and
biographical archives.

3241 ■ **International Tap Association**
PO Box 150574
Austin, TX 78715
Ph: (303)443-7989
E-mail: info@tapdance.org
URL: http://www.tapdance.org

Description: Represents the interests of tap dancers, performers, studios, choreographers, teachers,
scholars, historians, students, and other tap
enthusiasts. Promotes understanding, preservation,
and development of tap dance as an art form.
Encourages the creation of new tap performance
venues and touring circuits. Preserves the history of

tap through archival documentation and research. Establishes support mechanisms and communication networks for tap. **Members:** 1,000.

3242 ■ National Dance Association
1900 Association Dr.
Reston, VA 20191-1502
Ph: (703)476-3400
Free: 800-213-7193
Fax: (703)476-9527
E-mail: nda@aahperd.org
URL: http://www.aahperd.org/nda

Description: Dance educators, choreographers, schools and dance/arts administrators, researchers, performers, dance medicine/science specialists, technologists, therapists and others associated with dance/arts education. Works with 160 federal and state agencies, arts and education associations, foundations, and businesses and corporations to ensure that: (1) quality dance/arts education is available to all Americans regardless of age, sex, ability, interest, or culture; and (2) quality dance/arts educa-

lion becomes a part ot U.S. education for all children.

3243 ■ *National Directory of Arts Internships*
National Network for Artist Placement
935 West Ave. 37
Los Angeles, CA 90065
Ph: (323)222-4035
E-mail: info@artistplacement.com
URL: http://www.artistplacement.com
Frequency: Biennial; odd years; latest edition 11th. **Price:** $95 Individuals softcover, plus $12 shipping and handling. **Covers:** Over 5,000 internship opportunities in dance, music, theater, art, design, film, and video & over 1,250 host organizations. **Entries include:** Name of sponsoring organization, address, name of contact; description of positions available, eligibility requirements, stipend or salary (if any), application procedures. **Arrangement:** Classified by discipline, then geographical.

3244 ■ North American Irish Dance Federation
2317 Peppermill Pointe Ct.
Springfield, IL 62712
E-mail: sharon@naidf.com
URL: http://www.naidf.com

Description: Fosters the growth and development of Irish dance and culture. Encourages the pursuit of excellence among teachers and performers. Offers certification programs for teachers who are interested in furthering their dance education.

3245 ■ *Stage Directors Handbook: Complete Opportunities for Directors and Choreographers*
Theatre Communications Group
520 8th Ave., 24th Fl.
New York, NY 10018-4156
Ph: (212)609-5900
Fax: (212)609-5901
E-mail: tcg@tcg.org
URL: http://www.tcg.org/ecommerce/showbookdetails .cfm?ID=TCG5568

Frequency: Latest edition 2nd. **Price:** $19.95 Individuals paperback. **Pages:** 240. **Covers:** Resources for professional directors and choreographers. **Includes:** Essays by specialists treating selected topics. **Entries include:** Contact information, description.

Database Administrators

SOURCES OF HELP-WANTED ADS

3246 ■ *Communications of the ACM*
Association for Computing Machinery
2 Penn Plz., Ste. 701
New York, NY 10121-0701
Ph: (212)626-0500
Free: 800-342-6626
Fax: (212)944-1318
E-mail: acmhelp@acm.org
URL: http://cacm.acm.org

Frequency: Monthly. **Price:** $99 Members professional. **Description:** Computing news magazine.

3247 ■ *Computerworld*
International Data Group Inc.
PO Box 9171
Framingham, MA 01701
Ph: (508)879-0700
E-mail: info@idg.com
URL: http://www.computerworld.com

Frequency: Weekly. **Price:** $129 Individuals; $129 Canada; $295 Other countries; $250 Individuals Mexico/Central/South America; $29 Individuals digital edition. **Description:** Newspaper for information systems executives.

3248 ■ *Computing Surveys*
Association for Computing Machinery
c/o Lorenzo Alvisi, Assoc. Ed.
University of Texas at Austin
Department of Computer Science
1 University Sta. C0500
Austin, TX 78712-0233
Ph: (512)471-9792
Fax: (512)232-7886
E-mail: acmhelp@acm.org
URL: http://surveys.acm.org/

Frequency: Quarterly. **Price:** $205 Nonmembers print only; $164 Nonmembers online only; $246 Nonmembers online & print. **Description:** Journal presenting surveys and tutorials in computer science.

3249 ■ *Datamation: The Emerging Technologies Magazine for Today's IS*
Reed Elsevier Group plc - Reed Business Information
360 Park Ave. S
New York, NY 11010
Ph: (212)791-4208
E-mail: corporatecommunications@reedbusiness.com
URL: http://www.datamation.com

Frequency: Semimonthly. **Description:** Magazine on computers and information processing.

3250 ■ *InfoWorld: Defining Technology for Business*
InfoWorld Media Group
501 2nd St.
San Francisco, CA 94107
Free: 800-227-8365
E-mail: letters@infoworld.com
URL: http://www.infoworld.com/

Frequency: Weekly. **Price:** $180 Individuals. **Description:** Weekly publication.

3251 ■ *iSeries News Magazine*
Intertec Publishing
5 Penn Plz., 13th Fl.
New York, NY 10001-1810
Ph: (212)613-9700
Free: 800-795-5445
Fax: (212)613-9749
E-mail: service@iseriesnetwork.com
URL: http://www.systeminetwork.com/info/network-pubs/news400/about.html

Frequency: 11/yr. **Price:** $149 U.S. and Canada; $199 Other countries. **Description:** Trade magazine for programmers and data processing managers who use IBM iSeries.

EMPLOYER DIRECTORIES AND NETWORKING LISTS

3252 ■ *Computer Directory*
Computer Directories Inc.
23815 Nichols Sawmill Rd.
Hockley, TX 77447
Ph: (281)305-4170
E-mail: admin@compdirinc.com
URL: http://www.compdirinc.com

Frequency: Annual; fall. **Pages:** 500 per volume. **Covers:** Approximately 130,000 computer installations; 19 separate volumes for Alaska/Hawaii, Connecticut/New Jersey, Dallas/Ft. Worth, Eastern Seaboard, Far Midwest, Houston, Illinois, Midatlantic, Midcentral, Mideast, Minnesota/Wisconsin, North Central, New England, New York Metro, Northwest, Ohio, Pennsylvania/West Virginia, Southeast, and Southwest Texas. **Entries include:** Company name, address, phone, fax, email, name and title of contact, hardware used, software application, operating system, programming language, computer graphics, networking system. **Arrangement:** Geographical. **Indexes:** Alphabetical, industry, hardware.

3253 ■ *Information Sources: The IIA Annual Membership Directory*
Software and Information Industry Association
1090 Vermont Ave. NW, 6th Fl.
Washington, DC 20005-4095
Ph: (202)289-7442
Fax: (202)289-7097
URL: http://www.siia.net

Frequency: Continuous. **Covers:** More than 800 companies involved in the creation, distribution, and use of information products, services, and technology. Entries are prepared by companies described. **Entries include:** Company name, address, phone, names of executives, international partners, regional offices, trade and brand names, and description of products and services. **Arrangement:** Alphabetical. **Indexes:** Product, personal name, trade name, geographical, corporate parents, international and niche markets.

3254 ■ *Signal Magazine--AFCEA Source Book Issue*
E-mail: signal@afcea.org
URL: http://www.afcea.org/sourcebook

Frequency: Annual; Latest edition 2010. **Publication includes:** List of member companies concerned with communications, design, production, maintenance and operation of communications, electronics, command and control, computers, intelligence systems and imagery. **Entries include:** Company name, address, phone, names and titles of key personnel, financial keys, trade and brand names, products or services, affiliations, description of organizational purpose, objectives. **Arrangement:** Alphabetical. **Indexes:** By disciplines.

HANDBOOKS AND MANUALS

3255 ■ *DBA Survivor: Become a Rock Star DBA*
Apress, Inc.
233 Spring St.
New York, NY 10013
Ph: (212)460-1500
Fax: (212)460-1575
E-mail: support@apress.com
URL: http://www.apress.com

Description: Thomas LaRock. 2010. $39.99. 250 pages. Helps new database administrators understand more about the field. Features basics of database administration and different types of database support. Provides tips and advice to get ahead in the profession.

EMPLOYMENT AGENCIES AND SEARCH FIRMS

3256 ■ *ATR Technology*
1230 Oakmead Pkwy., Ste. 110
Sunnyvale, CA 94085
Ph: (408)328-8000
E-mail: corporate@atr1.com
URL: http://www.atr-technology.com

Description: Serves as an executive search firm specializing in the placement of information technology professionals ranging from complex software application development and infrastructure support to enterprise-wide project management.

3257 ■ *Capitol Staffing Inc.*
460 Briarwood Dr., Briarwood 1 Bldg., Ste. 110
Jackson, MS 39206

Ph: (601)957-1755
Fax: (601)957-3880
E-mail: info@capitolstaffing.com
URL: http://www.capitolstaffing.com

Description: Personnel consultancy that focuses on office administration, management, sales, accounting, medical, information technology, accounting, and engineering/technical fields. Industries served: insurance, finance, medical, communications, investment, industry, and small businesses.

3258 ■ **Cardinal Mark Inc.**
17113 Minnetonka Blvd., Ste. 112
Minnetonka, MN 55345
Ph: (952)314-4636
Fax: (610)228-7390
E-mail: jimz@cardinalmark.com
URL: http://www.cardinalmark.com

Description: Executive search firm concentrated on telecommunication industry.

3259 ■ **Computer Management**
7982 Honeygo Blvd., No. 23
Baltimore, MD 21236
Ph: (410)679-7000
E-mail: info@technicaljobs.com
URL: http://www.technicaljobs.com

Description: Search firm focusing on filling jobs for database administration, network administration, web development, and software.

3260 ■ **Integrisource**
1689 Mahan Center Blvd., Ste. B
Tallahassee, FL 32308
Ph: (850)575-5454
Free: 877-575-5454
Fax: (850)575-0984
E-mail: recruiting@integrisource.net
URL: http://www.integrisource.net

Description: Provides information technology staffing services to public and private organizations.

3261 ■ **Recruiting Partners**
3494 Camino Tassajara Rd., No. 404
Danville, CA 94506

Ph: (925)964-0249
E-mail: info@recruitingpartners.com
URL: http://www.recruitingpartners.com

Description: Serves as an executive and technical recruiting firm that specializes in accounting, legal, information technology, engineering, executive management and technical writing.

Online Job Sources and Services

3262 ■ **ComputerWork.com**
URL: http://www.computerwork.com

Description: Job search and resume submission service for professionals in information technology.

3263 ■ **Database Administrator Jobs**
URL: http://www.databaseadministratorjobs.net

Description: Features a searchable database of employment opportunities for database administrators.

3264 ■ **DatabaseAnalyst.com**
URL: http://www.databaseanalyst.com

Description: Features database analyst jobs and products for the software development industry.

3265 ■ **Guru.com**
URL: http://www.guru.com

Description: Job board specializing in contract jobs for creative and information technology professionals. Also provides online incorporation and educational opportunities for independent contractors along with articles and advice.

3266 ■ **ItJobs.com**
URL: http://www.itjobs.com

Description: Provides information technology employment opportunities for the following categories: internet/intranet/extranet, network systems, open systems, client/server, software engineering and development, software QA and testing, ERP applications and management consulting, and legacy systems.

3267 ■ **Jobs4IT.com**
URL: http://www.informationtechnologyjobs.com/

Description: Features information technology job opportunities, job fairs, business opportunities, news, events, continuing education guide, resume database, distribution services and other career resources.

3268 ■ **NetworkEngineer.com**
URL: http://www.networkengineer.com

Description: Provides lists of job and career opportunities for network engineers.

3269 ■ **ThinkEnergyGroup.com**
URL: http://www.thinkenergygroup.com

Description: Serves as a job board for professionals looking for positions in engineering, power plant, energy, and technical fields. Contains advice and tips on interviews, job searching, resume writing, hiring, and management. Provides choices of work location, pay rates in the field of expertise and contract, temp-to-hire, and direct hiring options.

3270 ■ **ZDNet Tech Jobs**
URL: http://www.zdnet.com

Description: Site houses a listing of national employment opportunities for professionals in high tech fields. Also contains resume building tips and relocation resources.

Other Sources

3271 ■ **Metadata Professional Organization**
PO Box 170455
Boston, MA 02117
Ph: (973)379-7212
E-mail: president@metadataprofessional.org
URL: http://www.metadataprofessional.org

Description: Represents business and IT professionals in all areas of meta-data practice including administrators, developers, architects and managers. Brings together individuals with interests, expertise, or hands-on experience in meta-data use from all areas of private and public enterprise throughout the world. Seeks to disseminate technical and professional information to meta-data practitioners of all levels of experience. Provides meta-data professionals with a community that fosters discussion, advancement and increased understanding of meta-data as it is applied in the field.

SOURCES OF HELP-WANTED ADS

3272 ■ *ACD News*
American College of Dentists
839J Quince Orchard Blvd.
Gaithersburg, MD 20878-1614
Ph: (301)977-3223
Fax: (301)977-3330
E-mail: office@acd.org
URLs: http://www.acd.org/publications.htm#ACD-News; http://www.acd.org/publications.htm
Frequency: Triennial. **Description:** Tri-annual. Presents accounts of College meetings, as well as remarks from the College's president. Publishes notices of scheduled events, spotlights individuals recognized or given awards by the College, and profiles convocation speakers, and other dental organizations. Recurring features include reports of meetings.

3273 ■ *ACP Messenger*
American College of Prosthodontists
211 E Chicago Ave., Ste. 1000
Chicago, IL 60611
Ph: (312)573-1260
URL: http://www.prosthodontics.org/products/Messenger.asp
Description: Quarterly newsletter featuring industry news as well as classified advertising.

3274 ■ *AGD Impact Newsletter*
Academy of General Dentistry
560 W Lake St., 6th Fl.
Chicago, IL 60611-6600
Ph: (888)243-3368
Free: 888-243-DENT
Fax: (312)335-3443
E-mail: impact@agd.org
URLs: http://www.agd.org; http://www.agd.org/publications/?publD=4
Frequency: Monthly. **Price:** $65 Institutions; $50 Nonmembers; $70 Institutions, Canada; $55 Nonmembers Canada; $80 Institutions, other countries; $65 Nonmembers other countries. **Description:** Monthly. Covers the issues and trends that impact on general dentists and the profession. Includes CDE course list and fact sheets for patients.

3275 ■ *American Academy of Implant Dentistry Newsletter*
American Academy of Implant Dentistry
211 E Chicago Ave., Ste. 750
Chicago, IL 60611
Ph: (312)335-1550
Free: 877-335-2243
Fax: (312)335-9090
E-mail: info@aaid.com
URL: http://www.aaid-implant.org
Description: Quarterly. Covers current activities in the field of implant dentistry, particularly the educational programs of the Academy.

3276 ■ *American Dental Hygienists' Association Access*
American Dental Hygienists' Association
444 N Michigan Ave., Ste. 3400
Chicago, IL 60611
Ph: (312)440-8900
E-mail: exec.office@adha.net
URL: http://www.adha.org/publications/index.html
Frequency: 10/yr. **Price:** $48 Individuals; $85 Two years; $120 Individuals for 3 years. **Description:** Magazine covering current dental hygiene topics, regulatory and legislative developments, and association news.

3277 ■ *Bulletin of Dental Education*
American Dental Education Association
1400 K St. NW, Ste. 1100
Washington, DC 20005
Ph: (202)289-7201
Fax: (202)289-7204
URL: http://www.adea.org
Description: Monthly. Contains news and information on dental education. Recurring features include a calendar of events, reports of meetings, news of educational opportunities, job listings, and notices of publications available.

3278 ■ *CDS Review*
Chicago Dental Society
401 N Michigan Ave., Ste. 200
Chicago, IL 60611
Ph: (312)836-7300
Fax: (312)836-7337
E-mail: rgrove@cds.org
URL: http://www.cds.org/cds_review/
Frequency: 7/yr. **Price:** $25 Individuals; $30 Institutions and schools in USA & Canada; $45 Other countries; $5 Single issue. **Description:** Dental journal.

3279 ■ *Dental Economics*
PennWell Publishing Co.
1421 S Sheridan Rd.
Tulsa, OK 74112
Ph: (918)835-3161
Free: 800-331-4463
Fax: (918)831-9497
E-mail: Headquarters@PennWell.com
URL: http://www.dentaleconomics.com/index.html
Frequency: Monthly. **Price:** $132 Individuals; $179 Canada and Mexico; $248 Other countries; $211 Two years; $312 Canada and Mexico; $428 Other countries two years; $65 online. **Description:** Magazine featuring business-related articles for dentists.

3280 ■ *Dental Town: Dental Town*
Dental Town
9633 S 48th St., Ste. 200
Phoenix, AZ 85044
Ph: (480)598-0001

Fax: (480)598-3450
E-mail: lorie@towniecentral.com
URL: http://www.dentaltown.com/
Frequency: Monthly. **Description:** Magazine that offers information on the dental industry and latest dental equipment.

3281 ■ *Illinois Dental News*
Illinois State Dental Society
1010 S Second St.
Springfield, IL 62704
Ph: (217)525-1406
Free: 800-475-4737
Fax: (217)525-8872
E-mail: info@isds.org
URL: http://www.isds.org/memberBenefits/publications/IllinoisDentalNews/index.asp
Frequency: Annual. **Price:** $10 Single issue outside United States; $45 Individuals non-members; $90 Nonmembers outside United States; $5 Single issue; $25 for members. **Description:** Dental magazine.

3282 ■ *InterFace*
Special Care Dentistry Association
330 N Wabash Ave., Ste. 2000
Chicago, IL 60611
Ph: (312)527-6764
Fax: (312)673-6663
E-mail: scda@scdaonline.org
URL: http://www.scdonline.org/displaynewsletter.cfm
Description: Quarterly. Publishes news of geriatric dentistry as well as news of the Society, its members and activities. Recurring features include legislative updates, a calendar of events, news of members, book reviews, editorials, a message from the president, bibliographies, and biographies.

3283 ■ *Journal of the American Dental Association*
American Dental Association
211 E Chicago Ave.
Chicago, IL 60611-2678
Ph: (312)440-2500
Free: 800-947-4746
Fax: (312)440-3542
E-mail: berryj@ada.org
URL: http://jada.ada.org/
Frequency: Monthly. **Price:** $128 Individuals U.S. and Mexico; $161 Institutions U.S. and Mexico; $16 Single issue U.S. and Mexico; $141 Canada U.S. and Mexico; $183 Institutions Canada, plus airmail; $24 Single issue Canada, plus airmail; $161 Individuals Canada, plus airmail; $204 Institutions Canada, plus airmail; $24; $22 Single issue Canada, plus airmail. **Description:** Trade journal for the dental profession.

3284 ■ *Journal of Dental Hygiene*
American Dental Hygienists' Association
444 N Michigan Ave., Ste. 3400
Chicago, IL 60611

Ph: (312)440-8900
E-mail: communications@adha.net
URLs: http://www.adha.org/publications/index.html;
http://adha.publisher.ingentaconnect.com/content/adha/jdh
Frequency: Quarterly. **Price:** $45 Individuals; $65 Two years; $90 Individuals 3 years. **Description:** Professional journal on dental hygiene.

3285 ■ Journal of Dental Research
Pine Forge Press
2455 Teller Rd.
Thousand Oaks, CA 91320-2234
Ph: (805)499-4224
Free: 800-818-7243
Fax: (805)499-0871
E-mail: sales@pfp.sagepub.com
URLs: http://www.dentalresearch.org/i4a/pages/index.cfm?pageid=3326; http://www.sagepub.com/journals/Journal201925
Frequency: Monthly. **Price:** $922 Institutions print & online; $440 Individuals print only; $829 Institutions online only; $903 Institutions print only. **Description:** Peer-reviewed dental science journal.

3286 ■ Maryland State Dental Association Newsletter
Maryland State Dental Association
6410F Dobbin Rd.
Columbia, MD 21045
Ph: (410)964-2880
Fax: (410)964-0583
E-mail: mddent@msda.com
URL: http://www.msda.com
Description: Monthly. Reports on health, legislative, economic, and medical issues that are pertinent to dentistry. Recurring features include letters to the editor, interviews, news of research, a calendar of events, reports of meetings, news of educational opportunities, and job listings.

3287 ■ MDS Connection
Massachusetts Dental Society
Two Willow St., No. 200
Southborough, MA 01745-1027
Ph: (508)480-9797
Free: 800-342-8747
Fax: (508)480-0002
E-mail: madental@massdental.org
URL: http://www.massdental.org/
Description: Bimonthly. Provides news on the Society's activities and articles on the dental profession. Recurring features include reports of meetings, news of educational opportunities, job listings, and notices of publications available.

3288 ■ News From The NIDCR
National Institutes of Health - National Institute of Dental and Craniofacial Research
31 Center Dr., Rm. 2C39
MSC 2190
Bethesda, MD 20892-2190
Ph: (301)496-4261
Free: 866-232-4528
Fax: (301)480-4098
E-mail: nidcrinfo@mail.nih.gov
URL: http://www.nidcr.nih.gov
Description: Bimonthly. Includes the latest news about funding opportunities, training and career development opportunities, NIDCR and NIH news, and science advances.

3289 ■ Pediatric Dentistry Today
American Academy of Pediatric Dentistry
211 E Chicago Ave., Ste. 1700
Chicago, IL 60611-2637
Ph: (312)337-2169
Fax: (312)337-6329
URL: http://www.aapd.org
Description: Bimonthly. Reports on the activities of the Academy, which seeks to advance the specialty of pediatric dentistry through practice, education, and research. Recurring features include news of

research, profiles of members, and legislative updates.

3290 ■ RDH: The National Magazine for Dental Hygiene Professionals
PennWell Publishing Co.
1421 S Sheridan Rd.
Tulsa, OK 74112
Ph: (918)835-3161
Free: 800-331-4463
Fax: (918)831-9497
E-mail: Headquarters@PennWell.com
URL: http://www.rdhmag.com/index.html
Frequency: Monthly. **Price:** $79 Individuals; $112 Canada; $141 Other countries; $40 U.S. and other countries digital. **Description:** Magazine for dental hygiene professionals covering practice management, patient motivation, practice options, financial planning, personal development, preventive oral health care and treatment, home care instruction, radiology, anesthesia, nutrition, and new products.

3291 ■ Washington State Dental Laboratory Association Newsletter
URL: http://www.wsdla.com
Description: Association newsletter featuring articles of interest to dental laboratory technicians as well as classified advertising for technical positions available.

3292 ■ Westviews
Western Los Angeles Dental Society
14722 Hawthorne Blvd., No. B
Lawndale, CA 90260-1505
Ph: (310)349-2199
Fax: (310)349-2175
E-mail: wlads@pacbell.net
URL: http://www.westernlads.org
Description: Six issues/year. Carries items relating to organized dentistry and the clinical aspects of dentistry. Covers local community events involving the organization or the profession; provides updates of states agency actions affecting dentistry.

EMPLOYER DIRECTORIES AND NETWORKING LISTS

3293 ■ American Academy of Pediatric Dentistry--Membership Directory
American Academy of Pediatric Dentistry
211 E Chicago Ave., Ste. 1700
Chicago, IL 60611-2637
Ph: (312)337-2169
Fax: (312)337-6329
URL: http://www.aapd.org
Frequency: Annual; November. **Pages:** 80. **Covers:** 5,600 pediatric dentists and several dentists in practice, teaching, and research. **Entries include:** Name, address, phone. **Arrangement:** Alphabetical. **Indexes:** Geographical.

3294 ■ Health Professionals Directory
Sussex Directories Inc.
10 Market St., Ste. 750
Camana Bay
Grand Cayman, Cayman Islands
URL: http://sussexdirectories.com

3295 ■ International Association for Orthodontics--Membership Directory
International Association for Orthodontics
750 N Lincoln Memorial Dr., Ste. 422
Milwaukee, WI 53202
Ph: (414)272-2757
Fax: (414)272-2754
E-mail: worldheadquarters@iaortho.org
URL: http://www.iaortho.org
Frequency: Annual; June. **Covers:** 2,500 general and children's dentists who also work to correct facial and jaw irregularities. **Entries include:** Name, office address and phone, orthodontic techniques

practiced. **Arrangement:** Geographical. **Indexes:** Personal name.

3296 ■ Washington Physicians Directory
The Washington Physicians Directory
13912 Overton Ln.
Silver Spring, MD 20904
Ph: (301)384-1506
Fax: (301)384-6854
E-mail: wpd@wpdnetwork.com
URL: http://www.wpdnetwork.com
Frequency: Annual; Latest edition 50th Anniversary Edition; 2012. **Pages:** 800. **Covers:** 9,800 physicians in private practice or on full-time staff at hospitals in the Washington, D.C., metropolitan area. **Entries include:** Name, medical school and year of graduation; up to four office addresses with phone numbers for each; up to four medical specialties (indicating board certifications), Unique Physician Identification Numbers (UPIN), and e-mail. **Arrangement:** Alphabetical. **Indexes:** Geographical (within medical specialty); foreign language.

3297 ■ Worldwide Online Search Directory
URL: http://www.aacd.com/professional/membership-benefits.asp#4
Description: Provides a worldwide listing of members of the American Academy of Cosmetic Dentistry.

HANDBOOKS AND MANUALS

3298 ■ Clinical Primer: A Pocket Guide for Dental Assistants
Lippincott Williams & Wilkins
16522 Hunters Green Pky.
Hagerstown, MD 21740
Ph: (301)233-2300
Free: 800-638-3030
Fax: (301)233-2398
E-mail: orders@lww.com
URL: http://www.lww.com
Description: Melanie Mitchell. 2006. $41.95. Help you learn and retain important information you need as a dental assistant.

3299 ■ Dental Assisting: A Comprehensive Approach
Cengage Learning Inc.
200 1st Stamford Pl., Ste. 400
Stamford, CT 06902-6753
Ph: (203)965-8600
Free: 800-354-9706
Fax: (800)487-8488
E-mail: investors@cengage.com
URL: http://www.cengage.com
Description: Donna J. Phinney, Judy H. Halstead. Third edition, 2008. $132.95. Designed to help you prepare for and pass the DANB certification exam, as well as to manage the challenges of working in the modern day dental office. Illustrated. 976 pages.

3300 ■ Levison's Textbook for Dental Nurses
Wiley-Blackwell
350 Main St.
Malden, MA 02148
Ph: (781)388-8200
Free: 800-216-2552
Fax: (781)388-8210
URL: http://www.wiley.com
Description: Carole Hollins. Tenth edition, 2008. Illustrated. $41.99. 440 Pages. Educational.

3301 ■ Materials and Procedures for Today's Dental Assistant
Cengage Learning Inc.
200 1st Stamford Pl., Ste. 400
Stamford, CT 06902-6753
Ph: (203)965-8600
Free: 800-354-9706

Fax: (800)487-8488
E-mail: investors@cengage.com
URL: http://www.cengage.com

Description: Ellen Dietz-Bourguignon. 2006. $73.25. 296 pages. Profiles training and skills for individuals interested in a career as a dental assistant.

3302 ■ Opportunities in Dental Care Careers
McGraw-Hill Professional
PO Box 182604
Columbus, OH 43272
Ph: (877)833-5524
Free: 800-262-4729
Fax: (614)759-3749
E-mail: pbg.ecommerce_custserv@mcgraw-hill.com
URL: http://www.mhprofessional.com/product.php
  ?isbn=0071493069

Description: Bonnie Kendall. $12.95 (e-book). 160 pages. Provides a complete overview of the job possibilities in dental industry. Includes the skill and training requirements to current salary figures.

3303 ■ Opportunities in Health and Medical Careers
The McGraw-Hill Companies Inc.
PO Box 182604
Columbus, OH 43272
Ph: (212)512-2000
Free: 877-833-5524
Fax: (614)759-3749
E-mail: customer.service@mcgraw-hill.com
URL: http://www.mcgraw-hill.com

Description: I. Donald Snook, Jr. and Leo D'Orazio. 2004. $14.95 (paper). 157 pages. Covers the full range of medical and health occupations. Illustrated.

3304 ■ Resumes for Health and Medical Careers
The McGraw-Hill Companies Inc.
PO Box 182604
Columbus, OH 43272
Ph: (212)512-2000
Free: 877-833-5524
Fax: (614)759-3749
E-mail: customer.service@mcgraw-hill.com
URL: http://www.mcgraw-hill.com

Description: Third edition, 2008. $12.95 (paper). 144 pages.

EMPLOYMENT AGENCIES AND SEARCH FIRMS

3305 ■ Actuary Resources
115 N Castle Heights Ave., Ste. 202
Lebanon, TN 37087-2768
Ph: (615)360-5171
Fax: (615)360-5173
E-mail: info@actuaryresources.org
URL: http://www.actuaryresources.org

Description: Provides staffing services to several different types of industries. Offers a free screening service to clients.

3306 ■ Capitol Staffing Inc.
460 Briarwood Dr., Briarwood 1 Bldg., Ste. 110
Jackson, MS 39206
Ph: (601)957-1755
Fax: (601)957-3880
E-mail: info@capitolstaffing.com
URL: http://www.capitolstaffing.com

Description: Personnel consultancy that focuses on office administration, management, sales, accounting, medical, information technology, accounting, and engineering/technical fields. Industries served: insurance, finance, medical, communications, investment, industry, and small businesses.

3307 ■ Career Advocates International
1539 Ave. A
Katy, TX 77493

Ph: (281)371-3917
E-mail: hank@careeradvocates.org
URL: http://www.careeradvocates.org

Description: Provides permanent placement and temporary staffing for executive and staff level positions. Specializes in multiple niches including: sales and marketing, accounting and financial services, banking, communications, human resources, chemicals, oil and gas, medical and dental, legal, information technology, energy, technology, engineering, manufacturing, construction, and light industrial.

3308 ■ DDS Staffing Resources Inc.
9755 Dogwood Rd., Ste. 200
Roswell, GA 30075-4663
Ph: (770)998-7779
Free: 888-668-7779
Fax: (770)552-0176
E-mail: ddsstaffing@ddsstaffing.com
URL: http://www.ddsstaffing.com

Description: Dental staffing agency.

3309 ■ Team Placement Service Inc.
1414 Prince St., Ste. 202
Alexandria, VA 22314
Ph: (703)820-8618
Free: 800-495-6767
Fax: (703)820-3368
E-mail: info@teamplace.com
URL: http://www.teamplace.com

Description: Full-service personnel consultants provide placement for healthcare staff, physician and dentist, private practice, and hospitals. Conduct interviews, tests, and reference checks to select the top 20% of applicants. Survey applicants' skill levels, provide backup information on each candidate, select compatible candidates for consideration, and insure the hiring process minimizes potential legal liability. Industries served: healthcare and government agencies providing medical, dental, biotech, laboratory, hospitals, and physician search.

ONLINE JOB SOURCES AND SERVICES

3310 ■ CareersInDental.com
URL: http://www.careersindental.com

Description: Serves as a job board for the dental industry. Features listings of employment opportunities and job openings in the field.

3311 ■ DentalAssistantJobs.com
URL: http://www.dentalassistantjobs.com

Description: Features job opportunities, resume search, postings and employment for dental assistant professionals.

3312 ■ DentalCrossing.com
URL: http://www.dentalcrossing.com

Description: Provides employment opportunities for dentists, dental assistants, dental hygienists, and dental lab technicians.

3313 ■ DentalJobsBoard.net
URL: http://www.dentaljobsboard.net

Description: Features dentist jobs, dental hygiene jobs, dental assistant jobs, and jobs for dental lab technicians.

3314 ■ DentalPortal.com
URL: http://www.dentalportal.com

Description: Search engine for finding dentists, orthodontists, oral surgeons, and other dental professionals.

3315 ■ DentalPost.net
URL: http://www.dentalpost.net

Description: Lists dental jobs including dentist jobs, dental hygienist jobs, dental assistant jobs, dental lab technician jobs, and dental front office jobs.

3316 ■ DentalWorkers.com
URL: http://www.dentalworkers.com/employment

Description: Serves as an online employment resource among dental professionals. Provides classified ads for dental jobs, and free resume posting for workers.

3317 ■ Dentist Job Cafe
URL: http://www.dentistjobcafe.com

Description: Features dental job listings. Provides employment services for dentists, dental hygienists, and dental assistants.

3318 ■ DentistJobsNow.com
URL: http://www.dentist-jobs-now.com

Description: Provides assistance to new and practicing dentists, hygienists, and dental assistants in finding employment.

3319 ■ DentistryJob.com
URL: http://www.dentistryjob.com

Description: Serves as a job board for dentistry professionals.

3320 ■ HEALTHeCAREERS Network
URL: http://www.healthecareers.com

Description: Career search site for jobs in all health care specialties; educational resources; visa and licensing information for relocation; interesting articles; relocation tools; links to professional organizations and general resources.

3321 ■ iHireDental
URL: http://www.ihiredental.com

Description: Features dental jobs in different specialty areas.

3322 ■ ProHealthJobs.com
URL: http://prohealthjobs.com/jobboard

Description: Career resources site for the medical and health care field. Lists professional opportunities, product information, continuing education and open positions.

TRADESHOWS

3323 ■ American Academy of Pediatric Dentistry Annual Session
American Academy of Pediatric Dentistry
211 E Chicago Ave., Ste. 1700
Chicago, IL 60611-2637
Ph: (312)337-2169
Fax: (312)337-6329
URL: http://www.aapd.org

Frequency: Annual. **Primary Exhibits:** Dental products and publications.

3324 ■ Thomas P. Hinman Dental Meeting & Exhibits
Thomas P. Hinman Dental Society of Atlanta
33 Lenox Pte.
Atlanta, GA 30324-3172
Ph: (404)231-1663
Fax: (404)231-9638
URL: http://www.hinman.org

Frequency: Annual. **Primary Exhibits:** Dental equipment, supplies, and services. **Dates and Locations:** Atlanta, GA; Atlanta Market Center.

3325 ■ Star of the North Meeting
Minnesota Dental Association
1335 Industrial Blvd, Ste. 200
Minneapolis, MN 55413-4801
Ph: (612)767-8400
Fax: (612)767-8500
E-mail: info@mndental.org
URL: http://www.mndental.org/

Frequency: Annual. **Primary Exhibits:** Dental equipment and supplies, dental laboratory equipment, office equipment, and service organizations. MN.

3326 ■ Yankee Dental Congress
Maine Dental Association
29 Association Dr.
Manchester, ME 04351-0215
Ph: (207)622-7900
Fax: (207)622-6210
E-mail: info@medental.org
URL: http://www.medental.org

Frequency: Annual. **Primary Exhibits:** Dental products, equipment, and services.

OTHER SOURCES

3327 ■ Academy of General Dentistry
560 W Lake St., 6th Fl.
Chicago, IL 60611-6600
Ph: (888)243-3368
Free: 888-243-DENT
Fax: (312)335-3443
E-mail: membership@agd.org
URL: http://www.agd.org

Description: Seeks to serve the needs and represent the interest of general dentists. Fosters their dentists' continued proficiency through quality continuing dental education to better serves the public.

3328 ■ American Academy of Cosmetic Dentistry
402 W Wilson St.
Madison, WI 53703
Ph: (608)222-8583
Free: 800-543-9220
Fax: (608)222-9540
E-mail: info@aacd.com
URL: http://www.aacd.com

Description: Members include more than 8,000 cosmetic and reconstructive dentists, dental laboratory technicians, dental auxiliaries, dental hygienists, educators, researchers and students. Membership benefits include AACD accreditation, registration to AACD's Annual Scientific Session, publications, online search directory, marketing materials, and more.

3329 ■ American College of Dentists
839J Quince Orchard Blvd.
Gaithersburg, MD 20878-1614
Ph: (301)977-3223
Fax: (301)977-3330
E-mail: office@acd.org
URL: http://acd.org

Description: Dentists and others serving in capacities related to the dental profession. Seeks to advance the standards of the profession of dentistry. Conducts educational and research programs. Maintains speakers' bureau and charitable programs.

3330 ■ American College of Prosthodontists
211 E Chicago Ave., Ste. 1000
Chicago, IL 60611
Ph: (312)573-1260
URL: http://www.prosthodontics.org

Description: Membership includes more than 3,300 prosthodontists, dental technicians, dental students and other dental professionals contributing to the specialty. Committed to the esthetic restoration of teeth, including bridges, crowns/caps, dental implants, dentures, partial dentures, whitening and veneers. Membership includes free subscriptions to the Journal of Prosthodontics, the Messenger, and e-blasts.

3331 ■ American Dental Assistants Association
35 E Wacker Dr., Ste. 1730
Chicago, IL 60601-2211
Ph: (312)541-1550
Free: 877-874-3785
Fax: (312)541-1496
E-mail: lsepin@adaa1.com
URL: http://www.dentalassistant.org

Description: Individuals employed as dental assistants in dental offices, clinics, hospitals, or institutions; instructors of dental assistants; dental students. Sponsors workshops and seminars; maintains governmental liaison. Offers group insurance; maintains scholarship trust fund. Dental Assisting National Board examines members who are candidates for title of Certified Dental Assistant.

3332 ■ American Dental Association
211 E Chicago Ave.
Chicago, IL 60611-2678
Ph: (312)440-2500
Free: 800-947-4746
Fax: (312)440-3542
E-mail: berryj@ada.org
URL: http://www.ada.org

Description: Professional society of dentists. Encourages the improvement of the health of the public and promotes the art and science of dentistry in matters of legislation and regulations. Inspects and accredits dental schools and schools for dental hygienists, assistants, and laboratory technicians. Conducts research programs at ADA Foundation Research Institute. Produces dental health education material used in the U.S. Sponsors National Children's Dental Health Month and Give Kids a Smile Day. Compiles statistics on personnel, practice, and dental care needs and attitudes of patients with regard to dental health.

3333 ■ American Dental Education Association
1400 K St. NW, Ste. 1100
Washington, DC 20005
Ph: (202)289-7201
Fax: (202)289-7204
URL: http://www.adea.org

Description: Individuals interested in dental education; schools of dentistry, advanced dental and allied dental education in the U.S., Canada, and Puerto Rico; affiliated institutions of the federal government and corporations. Works to promote better teaching and education in dentistry and dental research and to facilitate exchange of ideas among dental educators. Sponsors meetings, conferences, and workshops; conducts surveys, studies, and special projects and publishes their results. Maintains 37 sections and 8 special interest groups representing many different aspects of dental education. **Members:** 19,000.

3334 ■ American Medical Technologists
10700 W Higgins Rd., Ste. 150
Rosemont, IL 60018
Ph: (847)823-5169
Free: 800-275-1268
Fax: (847)823-0458
E-mail: membership@amt1.com
URL: http://www.amt1.com

Description: Represents medical technologists, medical laboratory technicians, medical assistants, medical administrative specialists, dental assistants, office laboratory technicians, phlebotomy technicians, laboratory consultants, and allied health instructors. Provides allied health professionals with professional certification services and membership programs to enhance their professional and personal growth. Aims to issue certification credentials to medical and dental assistants, clinical laboratory personnel, laboratory consultants, and allied health instructors.

3335 ■ American Public Health Association
800 I St. NW
Washington, DC 20001-3710
Ph: (202)777-2742
Fax: (202)777-2534
E-mail: comments@apha.org
URL: http://www.apha.org

Description: Professional organization of physicians, nurses, educators, academicians, environmentalists, epidemiologists, new professionals, social workers, health administrators, optometrists, podiatrists, pharmacists, dentists, nutritionists, health planners, other community and mental health specialists, and interested consumers. Seeks to protect and promote personal, mental, and environmental health. Services include: promulgation of standards; establishment of uniform practices and procedures; development of the etiology of communicable diseases; research in public health; exploration of medical care programs and their relationships to public health. Sponsors job placement service.

3336 ■ American School Health Association
1760 Old Meadow Rd., Ste. 500
McLean, VA 22102
Ph: (703)506-7675
Fax: (703)506-3266
E-mail: info@ashaweb.org
URL: http://netforum.avectra.com/eWeb/StartPage .aspx?Site=ASHA1&WebCode=HomePage

Description: School physicians, school nurses, counselors, nutritionists, psychologists, social workers, administrators, school health coordinators, health educators, and physical educators working in schools, professional preparation programs, public health, and community-based organizations. Promotes coordinated school health programs that include health education, health services, a healthful school environment, physical education, nutrition services, and psycho-social health services offered in schools collaboratively with families and other members of the community. Offers professional reference materials and professional development opportunities. Conducts pilot programs that inform materials development, provides technical assistance to school professionals, advocates for school health.

3337 ■ Career Opportunities in Health Care
InfoBase Holdings Inc.
132 W 31st., 17 Fl.
New York, NY 10001-3406
Ph: (212)967-8800
Fax: (800)678-3633
E-mail: info@infobasepublishing.com
URL: http://www.ferguson.infobasepublishing.com

Description: Shelly Field. 2007. Third edition. $49. 50. 304 pages. **Includes:** Appendixes provide lists of educational institutions, periodicals, directories, associations, and unions. Appendixes provide lists of educational institutions, periodicals, directories, associations, and unions.

3338 ■ Crown Council
975 Woodoak Ln., Ste. 200
Salt Lake City, UT 84117
Ph: (801)293-8522
Free: 800-276-9658
Fax: (801)293-8524
E-mail: success@crowncouncil.com
URL: http://www.crowncouncil.com

Description: Seeks to improve independent dental practices. Promotes oral health and the fight against oral cancer. Provides patient care and offers state-of-the-art dental procedure facilities.

3339 ■ Health-Care Careers for the 21st Century
JIST Publishing
875 Montreal Way
Saint Paul, MN 55102-4245
Ph: (317)613-4200
Free: 800-648-5478
Fax: (800)328-4564
E-mail: info@jist.com
URL: http://www.jist.com

Price: $9.95 Individuals Softcover. **Pages:** 448. **Covers:** Jobs for health care professionals and career opportunities for those pursuing a health-related career, organized into 80 careers in five groups. **Publication includes:** Appendixes listing job source resources and Web sites for health organizations.

3340 ■ Holistic Dental Association
1825 Ponce de Leon Blvd., No. 148
Coral Gables, FL 33134
Ph: (305)356-7338
Fax: (305)468-6359
E-mail: director@holisticdental.org
URL: http://www.holisticdental.org

Description: Represents dentists, chiropractors, dental hygienists, physical therapists, and medical doctors. Aims to provide a holistic approach to better dental care for patients, and to expand techniques, medications, and philosophies that pertain to extractions, anesthetics, fillings, crowns, and orthodontics. Encourages the use of homeopathic medications, acupuncture, cranial osteopathy, nutritional techniques, and physical therapy in treating patients in addition to conventional treatments. Sponsors training and educational seminars. **Members:** 200.

3341 ■ National Dental Assistants Association
3517 16th St. NW
Washington, DC 20010

Ph: (202)588-1697
Fax: (202)588-1244
E-mail: grannycml@bellsouth.net

Description: An auxiliary of the National Dental Association. Works to encourage education and certification among dental assistants. Conducts clinics and workshops to further the education of members. Bestows annual Humanitarian Award; offers scholarships. **Members:** 500.

3342 ■ National Rural Health Association
4501 College Blvd., No. 225
Leawood, KS 66211
Ph: (816)756-3140
Fax: (816)756-3144
E-mail: mail@nrharural.org
URL: http://www.ruralhealthweb.org

Description: Administrators, physicians, nurses, physician assistants, health planners, academicians, and others interested or involved in rural health care. Creates a better understanding of health care problems unique to rural areas; utilizes a collective approach in finding positive solutions; articulates and represents the health care needs of rural America; supplies current information to rural health care providers; serves as a liaison between rural health care programs throughout the country. Offers continuing education credits for medical, dental, nursing, and management courses.

3343 ■ Special Care Dentistry Association
330 N Wabash Ave., Ste. 2000
Chicago, IL 60611
Ph: (312)527-6764
Fax: (312)673-6663
E-mail: scda@scdaonline.org
URL: http://www.scdonline.org

Description: Dentists, hygienists, and lay public interested in special care dentistry. Aims to improve oral health and well being of people with special needs. Provides a forum for an exchange of clinical ideas and patient management techniques among members. **Members:** 1,000.

SOURCES OF HELP-WANTED ADS

3344 ■ *ACD News*
American College of Dentists
839J Quince Orchard Blvd.
Gaithersburg, MD 20878-1614
Ph: (301)977-3223
Fax: (301)977-3330
E-mail: office@acd.org
URLs: http://www.acd.org/publications.htm#ACD-News; http://www.acd.org/publications.htm
Frequency: Triennial. **Description:** Tri-annual. Presents accounts of College meetings, as well as remarks from the College's president. Publishes notices of scheduled events, spotlights individuals recognized or given awards by the College, and profiles convocation speakers, and other dental organizations. Recurring features include reports of meetings.

3345 ■ *ACP Messenger*
American College of Prosthodontists
211 E Chicago Ave., Ste. 1000
Chicago, IL 60611
Ph: (312)573-1260
URL: http://www.prosthodontics.org/products/Messenger.asp
Description: Quarterly newsletter featuring industry news as well as classified advertising.

3346 ■ *AGD Impact Newsletter*
Academy of General Dentistry
560 W Lake St., 6th Fl.
Chicago, IL 60611-6600
Ph: (888)243-3368
Free: 888-243-DENT
Fax: (312)335-3443
E-mail: impact@agd.org
URLs: http://www.agd.org; http://www.agd.org/publications/?publD=4
Frequency: Monthly. **Price:** $65 Institutions; $50 Nonmembers; $70 Institutions, Canada; $55 Nonmembers Canada; $80 Institutions, other countries; $65 Nonmembers other countries. **Description:** Monthly. Covers the issues and trends that impact on general dentists and the profession. Includes CDE course list and fact sheets for patients.

3347 ■ *American Dental Hygienists' Association Access*
American Dental Hygienists' Association
444 N Michigan Ave., Ste. 3400
Chicago, IL 60611
Ph: (312)440-8900
E-mail: exec.office@adha.net
URL: http://www.adha.org/publications/index.html
Frequency: 10/yr. **Price:** $48 Individuals; $85 Two years; $120 Individuals for 3 years. **Description:** Magazine covering current dental hygiene topics, regulatory and legislative developments, and association news.

3348 ■ *Bulletin of Dental Education*
American Dental Education Association
1400 K St. NW, Ste. 1100
Washington, DC 20005
Ph: (202)289-7201
Fax: (202)289-7204
URL: http://www.adea.org
Description: Monthly. Contains news and information on dental education. Recurring features include a calendar of events, reports of meetings, news of educational opportunities, job listings, and notices of publications available.

3349 ■ *CDS Review*
Chicago Dental Society
401 N Michigan Ave., Ste. 200
Chicago, IL 60611
Ph: (312)836-7300
Fax: (312)836-7337
E-mail: rgrove@cds.org
URL: http://www.cds.org/cds_review/
Frequency: 7/yr. **Price:** $25 Individuals; $30 Institutions and schools in USA & Canada; $45 Other countries; $5 Single issue. **Description:** Dental Journal.

3350 ■ *Dental Economics*
PennWell Publishing Co.
1421 S Sheridan Rd.
Tulsa, OK 74112
Ph: (918)835-3161
Free: 800-331-4463
Fax: (918)831-9497
E-mail: Headquarters@PennWell.com
URL: http://www.dentaleconomics.com/index.html
Frequency: Monthly. **Price:** $132 Individuals; $179 Canada and Mexico; $248 Other countries; $211 Two years; $312 Canada and Mexico; $428 Other countries two years; $65 online. **Description:** Magazine featuring business-related articles for dentists.

3351 ■ *Dental Town: Dental Town*
Dental Town
9633 S 48th St., Ste. 200
Phoenix, AZ 85044
Ph: (480)598-0001
Fax: (480)598-3450
E-mail: lorie@towniecentral.com
URL: http://www.dentaltown.com/
Frequency: Monthly. **Description:** Magazine that offers information on the dental industry and latest dental equipment.

3352 ■ *Illinois Dental News*
Illinois State Dental Society
1010 S Second St.
Springfield, IL 62704
Ph: (217)525-1406
Free: 800-475-4737

Fax: (217)525-8872
E-mail: info@isds.org
URL: http://www.isds.org/memberBenefits/publications/IllinoisDentalNews/index.asp
Frequency: Annual. **Price:** $10 Single issue outside United States; $45 Individuals non-members; $90 Nonmembers outside United States; $5 Single issue; $25 for members. **Description:** Dental magazine.

3353 ■ *InterFace*
Special Care Dentistry Association
330 N Wabash Ave., Ste. 2000
Chicago, IL 60611
Ph: (312)527-6764
Fax: (312)673-6663
E-mail: scda@scdaonline.org
URL: http://www.scdonline.org/displaynewsletter.cfm
Description: Quarterly. Publishes news of geriatric dentistry as well as news of the Society, its members and activities. Recurring features include legislative updates, a calendar of events, news of members, book reviews, editorials, a message from the president, bibliographies, and biographies.

3354 ■ *Journal of the American Dental Association*
American Dental Association
211 E Chicago Ave.
Chicago, IL 60611-2678
Ph: (312)440-2500
Free: 800-947-4746
Fax: (312)440-3542
E-mail: berryj@ada.org
URL: http://jada.ada.org/
Frequency: Monthly. **Price:** $128 Individuals U.S. and Mexico; $161 Institutions U.S. and Mexico; $16 Single issue U.S. and Mexico; $141 Canada U.S. and Mexico; $183 Institutions Canada; $24 Single issue Canada, plus airmail; $161 Individuals Canada, plus airmail; $204 Institutions Canada, plus airmail; $24; $22 Single issue Canada, plus airmail. **Description:** Trade journal for the dental profession.

3355 ■ *Journal of Dental Hygiene*
American Dental Hygienists' Association
444 N Michigan Ave., Ste. 3400
Chicago, IL 60611
Ph: (312)440-8900
E-mail: communications@adha.net
URLs: http://www.adha.org/publications/index.html; http://adha.publisher.ingentaconnect.com/content/adha/jdh
Frequency: Quarterly. **Price:** $45 Individuals; $65 Two years; $90 Individuals 3 years. **Description:** Professional journal on dental hygiene.

3356 ■ *Journal of Dental Research*
Pine Forge Press
2455 Teller Rd.
Thousand Oaks, CA 91320-2234
Ph: (805)499-4224

Free: 800-818-7243
Fax: (805)499-0871
E-mail: sales@pfp.sagepub.com
URLs: http://www.dentalresearch.org/i4a/pages/index
.cfm?pageid=3326; http://www.sagepub.com/
journals/Journal201925

Frequency: Monthly. **Price:** $922 institutions print & online; $440 Individuals print only; $829 Institutions online only; $903 Institutions print only. **Description:** Peer-reviewed dental science journal.

3357 ■ Maryland State Dental Association Newsletter
Maryland State Dental Association
6410F Dobbin Rd.
Columbia, MD 21045
Ph: (410)964-2880
Fax: (410)964-0583
E-mail: mddent@msda.com
URL: http://www.msda.com

Description: Monthly. Reports on health, legislative, economic, and medical issues that are pertinent to dentistry. Recurring features include letters to the editor, interviews, news of research, a calendar of events, reports of meetings, news of educational opportunities, and job listings.

3358 ■ MDS Connection
Massachusetts Dental Society
Two Willow St., No. 200
Southborough, MA 01745-1027
Ph: (508)480-9797
Free: 800-342-8747
Fax: (508)480-0002
E-mail: madental@massdental.org
URL: http://www.massdental.org/

Description: Bimonthly. Provides news on the Society's activities and articles on the dental profession. Recurring features include reports of meetings, news of educational opportunities, job listings, and notices of publications available.

3359 ■ Pediatric Dentistry Today
American Academy of Pediatric Dentistry
211 E Chicago Ave., Ste. 1700
Chicago, IL 60611-2637
Ph: (312)337-2169
Fax: (312)337-6329
URL: http://www.aapd.org

Description: Bimonthly. Reports on the activities of the Academy, which seeks to advance the specialty of pediatric dentistry through practice, education, and research. Recurring features include news of research, profiles of members, and legislative updates.

3360 ■ RDH: The National Magazine for Dental Hygiene Professionals
PennWell Publishing Co.
1421 S Sheridan Rd.
Tulsa, OK 74112
Ph: (918)835-3161
Free: 800-331-4463
Fax: (918)831-9497
E-mail: Headquarters@PennWell.com
URL: http://www.rdhmag.com/index.html

Frequency: Monthly. **Price:** $79 Individuals; $112 Canada; $141 Other countries; $40 U.S. and other countries digital. **Description:** Magazine for dental hygiene professionals covering practice management, patient motivation, practice options, financial planning, personal development, preventive oral health care and treatment, home care instruction, radiology, anesthesia, nutrition, and new products.

3361 ■ Washington State Dental Laboratory Association Newsletter
URL: http://www.wsdla.com

Description: Association newsletter featuring articles of interest to dental laboratory technicians as well as classified advertising for technical positions available.

3362 ■ Westviews
Western Los Angeles Dental Society
14722 Hawthorne Blvd., No. B
Lawndale, CA 90260-1505
Ph: (310)349-2199
Fax: (310)349-2175
E-mail: wlads@pacbell.net
URL: http://www.westernlads.org

Description: Six issues/year. Carries items relating to organized dentistry and the clinical aspects of dentistry. Covers local community events involving the organization or the profession; provides updates of states agency actions affecting dentistry.

EMPLOYER DIRECTORIES AND NETWORKING LISTS

3363 ■ American Academy of Pediatric Dentistry--Membership Directory
American Academy of Pediatric Dentistry
211 E Chicago Ave., Ste. 1700
Chicago, IL 60611-2637
Ph: (312)337-2169
Fax: (312)337-6329
URL: http://www.aapd.org

Frequency: Annual; November. **Pages:** 80. **Covers:** 5,600 pediatric dentists and several dentists in practice, teaching, and research. **Entries include:** Name, address, phone. **Arrangement:** Alphabetical. **Indexes:** Geographical.

3364 ■ Health Professionals Directory
Sussex Directories Inc.
10 Market St., Ste. 750
Camana Bay
Grand Cayman, Cayman Islands
URL: http://sussexdirectories.com

3365 ■ International Association for Orthodontics--Membership Directory
International Association for Orthodontics
750 N Lincoln Memorial Dr., Ste. 422
Milwaukee, WI 53202
Ph: (414)272-2757
Fax: (414)272-2754
E-mail: worldheadquarters@iaortho.org
URL: http://www.iaortho.org

Frequency: Annual; June. **Covers:** 2,500 general and children's dentists who also work to correct facial and jaw irregularities. **Entries include:** Name, office address and phone, orthodontic techniques practiced. **Arrangement:** Geographical. **Indexes:** Personal name.

3366 ■ Washington Physicians Directory
The Washington Physicians Directory
13912 Overton Ln.
Silver Spring, MD 20904
Ph: (301)384-1506
Fax: (301)384-6854
E-mail: wpd@wpdnetwork.com
URL: http://www.wpdnetwork.com

Frequency: Annual; Latest edition 50th Anniversary Edition; 2012. **Pages:** 800. **Covers:** 9,800 physicians in private practice or on full-time staff at hospitals in the Washington, D.C., metropolitan area. **Entries include:** Name, medical school and year of graduation; up to four office addresses with phone numbers for each; up to four medical specialties (indicating board certifications), Unique Physician Identification Numbers (UPIN), and e-mail. **Arrangement:** Alphabetical. **Indexes:** Geographical (within medical specialty); foreign language.

3367 ■ Worldwide Online Search Directory
URL: http://www.aacd.com/professional/membership-benefits.asp#4

Description: Provides a worldwide listing of members of the American Academy of Cosmetic Dentistry.

HANDBOOKS AND MANUALS

3368 ■ Dental Assisting: A Comprehensive Approach
Cengage Learning Inc.
200 1st Stamford Pl., Ste. 400
Stamford, CT 06902-6753
Ph: (203)965-8600
Free: 800-354-9706
Fax: (800)487-8488
E-mail: investors@cengage.com
URL: http://www.cengage.com

Description: Donna J. Phinney, Judy H. Halstead. Third edition, 2008. $132.95. Designed to help you prepare for and pass the DANB certification exam, as well as to manage the challenges of working in the modern day dental office. Illustrated. 976 pages.

3369 ■ Dental Hygienist
National Learning Corporation
212 Michael Dr.
Syosset, NY 11791
Ph: (516)921-8888
Free: 800-632-8888
Fax: (516)921-8743
E-mail: info@passbooks.com
URL: http://www.passbooks.com

Description: 2009. $39.95 (paper). Serves as an exam preparation guide for dental hygienists.

3370 ■ Kaplan Dental Hygienist Licensure Exam
Kaplan Publishing
1 Liberty Plz., 24th Fl.
New York, NY 10006
Ph: (212)632-4973
Free: 800-223-2336
Fax: (800)943-9831
E-mail: kaplanpubsales@kaplan.com
URL: http://www.kaplanpublishing.com

Description: Paula Tomko. 2007. $59.95. Provides a complete review for individuals taking the National Dental Hygienist Licensure exam, including a full-length simulated test and explanations of answers.

3371 ■ Levison's Textbook for Dental Nurses
Wiley-Blackwell
350 Main St.
Malden, MA 02148
Ph: (781)388-8200
Free: 800-216-2552
Fax: (781)388-8210
URL: http://www.wiley.com

Description: Carole Hollins. Tenth edition, 2008. Illustrated. $41.99. 440 Pages. Educational.

3372 ■ Master the Dental Hygienist Exam
Peterson's Publishing
3 Columbia Cir., Ste. 205
Albany, NY 12203-5158
Ph: (609)896-1800
E-mail: pubmarketing@petersons.com
URL: http://www.petersonspublishing.com

Description: 2011. $18.95. 352 pages. Offers test preparation strategies and skill-building review for test takers seeking career advancement in dental hygiene. Includes practice tests, step-by-step career plan and topics covering the dental hygienist's tasks, duties, necessary education and experience, and ethical and legal requirements.

3373 ■ Opportunities in Dental Care Careers
McGraw-Hill Professional
PO Box 182604
Columbus, OH 43272
Ph: (877)833-5524
Free: 800-262-4729

Fax: (614)759-3749
E-mail: pbg.ecommerce_custserv@mcgraw-hill.com
URL: http://www.mhprofessional.com/product.php
?isbn=0071493069

Description: Bonnie Kendall. $12.95 (e-book). 160 pages. Provides a complete overview of the job possibilities in dental industry. Includes the skill and training requirements to current salary figures.

3374 ■ *Opportunities in Health and Medical Careers*
The McGraw-Hill Companies Inc.
PO Box 182604
Columbus, OH 43272
Ph: (212)512-2000
Free: 877-833-5524
Fax: (614)759-3749
E-mail: customer.service@mcgraw-hill.com
URL: http://www.mcgraw-hill.com

Description: I. Donald Snook, Jr. and Leo D'Orazio. 2004. $14.95 (paper). 157 pages. Covers the full range of medical and health occupations. Illustrated.

3375 ■ *Practice Management for Dental Hygienists*
Lippincott Williams & Wilkins
351 W Camden St.
Baltimore, MD 21201
Ph: (410)528-4000
URL: http://www.lww.com

Description: Esther Andrews. 2006. $54.95. 372 pages. Prepares dental hygiene students and dental hygienists to handle the business and operational aspects of the dental office.

3376 ■ *Resumes for Health and Medical Careers*
The McGraw-Hill Companies Inc.
PO Box 182604
Columbus, OH 43272
Ph: (212)512-2000
Free: 877-833-5524
Fax: (614)759-3749
E-mail: customer.service@mcgraw-hill.com
URL: http://www.mcgraw-hill.com

Description: Third edition, 2008. $12.95 (paper). 144 pages.

EMPLOYMENT AGENCIES AND SEARCH FIRMS

3377 ■ Actuary Resources
115 N Castle Heights Ave., Ste. 202
Lebanon, TN 37087-2768
Ph: (615)360-5171
Fax: (615)360-5173
E-mail: info@actuaryresources.org
URL: http://www.actuaryresources.org

Description: Provides staffing services to several different types of industries. Offers a free screening service to clients.

3378 ■ Capitol Staffing Inc.
460 Briarwood Dr., Briarwood 1 Bldg., Ste. 110
Jackson, MS 39206
Ph: (601)957-1755
Fax: (601)957-3880
E-mail: info@capitolstaffing.com
URL: http://www.capitolstaffing.com

Description: Personnel consultancy that focuses on office administration, management, sales, accounting, medical, information technology, accounting, and engineering/technical fields. Industries served: insurance, finance, medical, communications, investment, industry, and small businesses.

3379 ■ Career Advocates International
1539 Ave. A
Katy, TX 77493

Ph: (281)371-3917
E-mail: hank@careeradvocates.org
URL: http://www.careeradvocates.org

Description: Provides permanent placement and temporary staffing for executive and staff level positions. Specializes in multiple niches including: sales and marketing, accounting and financial services, banking, communications, human resources, chemicals, oil and gas, medical and dental, legal, information technology, energy, technology, engineering, manufacturing, construction, and light industrial.

3380 ■ DDS Resources
16020 Swingley Ridge Rd., Ste. 340
Chesterfield, MO 63017
Ph: (636)536-6656
Free: 877-337-0563
Fax: (636)536-6667
E-mail: info@mdr-inc.com
URL: http://www.mdr-inc.com/dentists.aspx

Description: Serves as a dental recruitment agency in the United States. Specializes in matching qualified dentists with dental employers.

3381 ■ DDS Staffing Resources Inc.
9755 Dogwood Rd., Ste. 200
Roswell, GA 30075-4663
Ph: (770)998-7779
Free: 888-668-7779
Fax: (770)552-0176
E-mail: ddsstaffing@ddsstaffing.com
URL: http://www.ddsstaffing.com

Description: Dental staffing agency.

3382 ■ Team Placement Service Inc.
1414 Prince St., Ste. 202
Alexandria, VA 22314
Ph: (703)820-8618
Free: 800-495-6767
Fax: (703)820-3368
E-mail: info@teamplace.com
URL: http://www.teamplace.com

Description: Full-service personnel consultants provide placement for healthcare staff, physician and dentist, private practice, and hospitals. Conduct interviews, tests, and reference checks to select the top 20% of applicants. Survey applicants' skill levels, provide backup information on each candidate, select compatible candidates for consideration, and insure the hiring process minimizes potential legal liability. Industries served: healthcare and government agencies providing medical, dental, biotech, laboratory, hospitals, and physician search.

ONLINE JOB SOURCES AND SERVICES

3383 ■ CareersInDental.com
URL: http://www.careersindental.com

Description: Serves as a job board for the dental industry. Features listings of employment opportunities and job openings in the field.

3384 ■ DentalCrossing.com
URL: http://www.dentalcrossing.com

Description: Provides employment opportunities for dentists, dental assistants, dental hygienists, and dental lab technicians.

3385 ■ DentalJobsBoard.net
URL: http://www.dentaljobsboard.net

Description: Features dentist jobs, dental hygiene jobs, dental assistant jobs, and jobs for dental lab technicians.

3386 ■ DentalPortal.com
URL: http://www.dentalportal.com

Description: Search engine for finding dentists, orthodontists, oral surgeons, and other dental professionals.

3387 ■ DentalPost.net
URL: http://www.dentalpost.net

Description: Lists dental jobs including dentist jobs, dental hygienist jobs, dental assistant jobs, dental lab technician jobs, and dental front office jobs.

3388 ■ DentalWorkers.com
URL: http://www.dentalworkers.com/employment

Description: Serves as an online employment resource among dental professionals. Provides classified ads for dental jobs, and free resume posting for workers.

3389 ■ Dentist Job Cafe
URL: http://www.dentistjobcafe.com

Description: Features dental job listings. Provides employment services for dentists, dental hygienists, and dental assistants.

3390 ■ DentistJobsNow.com
URL: http://www.dentist-jobs-now.com

Description: Provides assistance to new and practicing dentists, hygienists, and dental assistants in finding employment.

3391 ■ DentistryJob.com
URL: http://www.dentistryjob.com

Description: Serves as a job board for dentistry professionals.

3392 ■ HEALTHeCAREERS Network
URL: http://www.healthecareers.com

Description: Career search site for jobs in all health care specialties; educational resources; visa and licensing information for relocation; interesting articles; relocation tools; links to professional organizations and general resources.

3393 ■ iHireDental
URL: http://www.ihiredental.com

Description: Features dental jobs in different specialty areas.

3394 ■ Medjobsdata.com
URL: http://www.medjobsdata.com

Description: Helps jobseekers find a health profession from clinical to administrative.

3395 ■ ProHealthJobs.com
URL: http://prohealthjobs.com/jobboard

Description: Career resources site for the medical and health care field. Lists professional opportunities, product information, continuing education and open positions.

TRADESHOWS

3396 ■ American Academy of Pediatric Dentistry Annual Session
American Academy of Pediatric Dentistry
211 E Chicago Ave., Ste. 1700
Chicago, IL 60611-2637
Ph: (312)337-2169
Fax: (312)337-6329
URL: http://www.aapd.org

Frequency: Annual. **Primary Exhibits:** Dental products and publications.

3397 ■ Thomas P. Hinman Dental Meeting & Exhibits
Thomas P. Hinman Dental Society of Atlanta
33 Lenox Pte.
Atlanta, GA 30324-3172
Ph: (404)231-1663
Fax: (404)231-9638
URL: http://www.hinman.org

Frequency: Annual. **Primary Exhibits:** Dental equipment, supplies, and services. **Dates and Locations:** Atlanta, GA; Atlanta Market Center.

3398 ■ National Dental Association Annual Convention
National Dental Association
3517 16th St. NW
Washington, DC 20010
Ph: (202)588-1697
Fax: (202)588-1244
URL: http://www.ndaonline.org
Frequency: Annual; always last weekend of July or first week in August. **Primary Exhibits:** Dental and Pharmaceutical equipment, supplies, and services.

3399 ■ Star of the North Meeting
Minnesota Dental Association
1335 Industrial Blvd, Ste. 200
Minneapolis, MN 55413-4801
Ph: (612)767-8400
Fax: (612)767-8500
E-mail: info@mndental.org
URL: http://www.mndental.org/
Frequency: Annual. **Primary Exhibits:** Dental equipment and supplies, dental laboratory equipment, office equipment, and service organizations. MN.

3400 ■ Three Rivers Dental Conference
Dental Society of Western Pennsylvania
900 Cedar Ave.
Pittsburgh, PA 15212
Ph: (412)321-5810
Fax: (412)321-7719
E-mail: threeriversdental@verizon.net
URL: http://www.dswp.org
Frequency: Annual. **Primary Exhibits:** Dental products and equipment, computers, office equipment, and insurance.

3401 ■ Yankee Dental Congress
Maine Dental Association
29 Association Dr.
Manchester, ME 04351-0215
Ph: (207)622-7900
Fax: (207)622-6210
E-mail: info@medental.org
URL: http://www.medental.org
Frequency: Annual. **Primary Exhibits:** Dental products, equipment, and services.

OTHER SOURCES

3402 ■ Academy of General Dentistry
560 W Lake St., 6th Fl.
Chicago, IL 60611-6600
Ph: (888)243-3368
Free: 888-243-DENT
Fax: (312)335-3443
E-mail: membership@agd.org
URL: http://www.agd.org
Description: Seeks to serve the needs and represent the interest of general dentists. Fosters their dentists' continued proficiency through quality continuing dental education to better serves the public.

3403 ■ American Academy of Cosmetic Dentistry
402 W Wilson St.
Madison, WI 53703
Ph: (608)222-8583
Free: 800-543-9220
Fax: (608)222-9540
E-mail: info@aacd.com
URL: http://www.aacd.com
Description: Members include more than 8,000 cosmetic and reconstructive dentists, dental laboratory technicians, dental auxiliaries, dental hygienists, educators, researchers and students. Membership benefits include AACD accreditation, registration to AACD's Annual Scientific Session, publications, online search directory, marketing materials, and more.

3404 ■ American Academy of Dental Group Practice
2525 E Arizona Biltmore Cir., Ste. 127
Phoenix, AZ 85016
Ph: (602)381-1185
Fax: (602)381-1093
E-mail: aadgp@aadgp.org
URL: http://www.aadgp.org
Description: Represents active dentists and dental group practices. Aims to improve the level of dental service provided by members through exchanging and expanding of ideas and techniques for patient treatment and practice administration. Promotes group practice and research; accumulates and disseminates information; seeks to achieve the proper recognition for the aims and goals of group practice. Helps support an accreditation program as a system of voluntary peer review.

3405 ■ American Association of Dental Boards
211 E Chicago Ave., Ste. 760
Chicago, IL 60611
Ph: (312)440-7464
E-mail: jtarrant@dentalboards.org
URL: http://dentalboards.org
Description: Represents present and past members of state dental examining boards and board administrators. Assists member agencies with problems related to state dental board examinations and licensure, and enforcement of the state dental practice act. Conducts research; compiles statistics. **Members:** 850.

3406 ■ American College of Dentists
839J Quince Orchard Blvd.
Gaithersburg, MD 20878-1614
Ph: (301)977-3223
Fax: (301)977-3330
E-mail: office@acd.org
URL: http://acd.org
Description: Dentists and others serving in capacities related to the dental profession. Seeks to advance the standards of the profession of dentistry. Conducts educational and research programs. Maintains speakers' bureau and charitable programs.

3407 ■ American College of Prosthodontists
211 E Chicago Ave., Ste. 1000
Chicago, IL 60611
Ph: (312)573-1260
URL: http://www.prosthodontics.org
Description: Membership includes more than 3,300 prosthodontists, dental technicians, dental students and other dental professionals contributing to the specialty. Committed to the esthetic restoration of teeth, including bridges, crowns/caps, dental implants, dentures, partial dentures, whitening and veneers. Membership includes free subscriptions to the Journal of Prosthodontics, the Messenger, and e-blasts.

3408 ■ American Dental Association
211 E Chicago Ave.
Chicago, IL 60611-2678
Ph: (312)440-2500
Free: 800-947-4746
Fax: (312)440-3542
E-mail: berryj@ada.org
URL: http://www.ada.org
Description: Professional society of dentists. Encourages the improvement of the health of the public and promotes the art and science of dentistry in matters of legislation and regulations. Inspects and accredits dental schools and schools for dental hygienists, assistants, and laboratory technicians. Conducts research programs at ADA Foundation Research Institute. Produces dental health education material used in the U.S. Sponsors National Children's Dental Health Month and Give Kids a Smile Day. Compiles statistics on personnel, practice, and dental care needs and attitudes of patients with regard to dental health.

3409 ■ American Dental Education Association
1400 K St. NW, Ste. 1100
Washington, DC 20005
Ph: (202)289-7201
Fax: (202)289-7204
URL: http://www.adea.org
Description: Individuals interested in dental education; schools of dentistry, advanced dental and allied dental education in the U.S., Canada, and Puerto Rico; affiliated institutions of the federal government and corporations. Works to promote better teaching and education in dentistry and dental research and to facilitate exchange of ideas among dental educators. Sponsors meetings, conferences, and workshops; conducts surveys, studies, and special projects and publishes their results. Maintains 37 sections and 8 special interest groups representing many different aspects of dental education. **Members:** 19,000.

3410 ■ American Dental Hygienists' Association
444 N Michigan Ave., Ste. 3400
Chicago, IL 60611
Ph: (312)440-8900
E-mail: exec.office@adha.net
URL: http://www.adha.org
Description: Professional organization of licensed dental hygienists possessing a degree or certificate in dental hygiene granted by an accredited school of dental hygiene. Makes available scholarships, research grants, and continuing education programs. Maintains accrediting service through the American Dental Association's Commission on Dental Accreditation. Compiles statistics.

3411 ■ American Public Health Association
800 I St. NW
Washington, DC 20001-3710
Ph: (202)777-2742
Fax: (202)777-2534
E-mail: comments@apha.org
URL: http://www.apha.org
Description: Professional organization of physicians, nurses, educators, academicians, environmentalists, epidemiologists, new professionals, social workers, health administrators, optometrists, podiatrists, pharmacists, dentists, nutritionists, health planners, other community and mental health specialists, and interested consumers. Seeks to protect and promote personal, mental, and environmental health. Services include: promulgation of standards; establishment of uniform practices and procedures; development of the etiology of communicable diseases; research in public health; exploration of medical care programs and their relationships to public health. Sponsors job placement service.

3412 ■ American School Health Association
1760 Old Meadow Rd., Ste. 500
McLean, VA 22102
Ph: (703)506-7675
Fax: (703)506-3266
E-mail: info@ashaweb.org
URL: http://netforum.avectra.com/eWeb/StartPage .aspx?Site=ASHA1&WebCode=HomePage
Description: School physicians, school nurses, counselors, nutritionists, psychologists, social workers, administrators, school health coordinators, health educators, and physical educators working in schools, professional preparation programs, public health, and community-based organizations. Promotes coordinated school health programs that include health education, health services, a healthful school environment, physical education, nutrition services, and psycho-social health services offered in schools collaboratively with families and other members of the community. Offers professional reference materials and professional development opportunities. Conducts pilot programs that inform materials development, provides technical assistance to school professionals, advocates for school health.

3413 ■ Career Opportunities in Health Care
InfoBase Holdings Inc.
132 W 31st., 17 Fl.
New York, NY 10001-3406
Ph: (212)967-8800
Fax: (800)678-3633
E-mail: info@infobasepublishing.com
URL: http://www.ferguson.infobasepublishing.com

Description: Shelly Field. 2007. Third edition. $49. 50. 304 pages. **Includes:** Appendices provide lists of educational institutions, periodicals, directories, associations, and unions. Appendices provide lists of educational institutions, periodicals, directories, associations, and unions.

3414 ■ Crown Council
975 Woodoak Ln., Ste. 200
Salt Lake City, UT 84117
Ph: (801)293-8522
Free: 800-276-9658
Fax: (801)293-8524
E-mail: success@crowncouncil.com
URL: http://www.crowncouncil.com

Description: Seeks to improve independent dental practices. Promotes oral health and the fight against oral cancer. Provides patient care and offers state-of-the-art dental procedure facilities.

3415 ■ Health-Care Careers for the 21st Century
JIST Publishing
875 Montreal Way
Saint Paul, MN 55102-4245
Ph: (317)613-4200
Free: 800-648-5478
Fax: (800)328-4564
E-mail: info@jist.com
URL: http://www.jist.com

Price: $9.95 Individuals Softcover. **Pages:** 448. **Covers:** Jobs for health care professionals and career opportunities for those pursuing a health-related career, organized into 80 careers in five groups. **Publication includes:** Appendixes listing job source resources and Web sites for health organizations.

3416 ■ Holistic Dental Association
1825 Ponce de Leon Blvd., No. 148
Coral Gables, FL 33134
Ph: (305)356-7338
Fax: (305)468-6359
E-mail: director@holisticdental.org
URL: http://www.holisticdental.org

Description: Represents dentists, chiropractors, dental hygienists, physical therapists, and medical doctors. Aims to provide a holistic approach to better dental care for patients, and to expand techniques, medications, and philosophies that pertain to extractions, anesthetics, fillings, crowns, and orthodontics. Encourages the use of homeopathic medications, acupuncture, cranial osteopathy, nutritional techniques, and physical therapy in treating patients in addition to conventional treatments. Sponsors training and educational seminars. **Members:** 200.

3417 ■ National Dental Hygienists' Association
32753 Stefano Dr.
Brownstown, MI 48173
Free: 800-234-1096
Fax: (734)379-3608
E-mail: bjbeaty3@sbcglobal.net
URL: http://ndhaonline.org

Description: Minority dental hygienists. Cultivates and promotes the art and science of dental hygiene and enhances the professional image of dental hygienists. Attempts to meet the needs of society through educational, political, and social activities while giving the minority dental hygienist a voice in shaping the profession. Encourages cooperation and mutual support among minority professionals. Seeks to increase opportunities for continuing education and employment in the field of dental hygiene. Works to improve individual and community dental health. Sponsors annual seminar, fundraising events, and scholarship programs; participates in career orientation programs; counsels and assists students applying for or enrolled in dental hygiene programs. Maintains liaison with American Dental Hygienists' Association. **Members:** 100.

3418 ■ National Rural Health Association
4501 College Blvd., No. 225
Leawood, KS 66211
Ph: (816)756-3140
Fax: (816)756-3144
E-mail: mail@nrharural.org
URL: http://www.ruralhealthweb.org

Description: Administrators, physicians, nurses, physician assistants, health planners, academicians, and others interested or involved in rural health care. Creates a better understanding of health care problems unique to rural areas; utilizes a collective approach in finding positive solutions; articulates and represents the health care needs of rural America; supplies current information to rural health care providers; serves as a liaison between rural health care programs throughout the country. Offers continuing education credits for medical, dental, nursing, and management courses.

3419 ■ Special Care Dentistry Association
330 N Wabash Ave., Ste. 2000
Chicago, IL 60611
Ph: (312)527-6764
Fax: (312)673-6663
E-mail: scda@scdaonline.org
URL: http://www.scdonline.org

Description: Dentists, hygienists, and lay public interested in special care dentistry. Aims to improve oral health and well being of people with special needs. Provides a forum for an exchange of clinical ideas and patient management techniques among members. **Members:** 1,000.

Dental Lab Technicians

SOURCES OF HELP-WANTED ADS

3420 ■ AAB Bulletin
American Association of Bioanalysts
906 Olive St., Ste. 1200
Saint Louis, MO 63101-1448
Ph: (314)241-1445
Fax: (314)241-1449
URL: http://www.aab.org

Mark S. Birenbaum, Ph.D., Editor. **Frequency:** Quarterly; Quarterly. **Price:** included in membership dues; Included in membership. **Description:** Recurring features include interviews, news of research, a calendar of events, reports of meetings, news of educational opportunities, and job listings.

3421 ■ ACD News
American College of Dentists
839J Quince Orchard Blvd.
Gaithersburg, MD 20878-1614
Ph: (301)977-3223
Fax: (301)977-3330
E-mail: office@acd.org
URLs: http://www.acd.org/publications.htm#ACD-News; http://www.acd.org/publications.htm

Frequency: Triennial. **Description:** Tri-annual. Presents accounts of College meetings, as well as remarks from the College's president. Publishes notices of scheduled events, spotlights individuals recognized or given awards by the College, and profiles convocation speakers, and other dental organizations. Recurring features include reports of meetings.

3422 ■ ACP Messenger
American College of Prosthodontists
211 E Chicago Ave., Ste. 1000
Chicago, IL 60611
Ph: (312)573-1260
URL: http://www.prosthodontics.org/products/Messenger.asp

Description: Quarterly newsletter featuring industry news as well as classified advertising.

3423 ■ American Academy of Implant Dentistry Newsletter
American Academy of Implant Dentistry
211 E Chicago Ave., Ste. 750
Chicago, IL 60611
Ph: (312)335-1550
Free: 877-335-2243
Fax: (312)335-9090
E-mail: info@aaid.com
URL: http://www.aaid-implant.org

Description: Quarterly. Covers current activities in the field of implant dentistry, particularly the educational programs of the Academy.

3424 ■ American Dental Hygienists' Association Access
American Dental Hygienists' Association
444 N Michigan Ave., Ste. 3400
Chicago, IL 60611
Ph: (312)440-8900
E-mail: exec.office@adha.net
URL: http://www.adha.org/publications/index.html

Frequency: 10/yr. **Price:** $48 Individuals; $85 Two years; $120 Individuals for 3 years. **Description:** Magazine covering current dental hygiene topics, regulatory and legislative developments, and association news.

3425 ■ Bulletin of Dental Education
American Dental Education Association
1400 K St. NW, Ste. 1100
Washington, DC 20005
Ph: (202)289-7201
Fax: (202)289-7204
URL: http://www.adea.org

Description: Monthly. Contains news and information on dental education. Recurring features include a calendar of events, reports of meetings, news of educational opportunities, job listings, and notices of publications available.

3426 ■ CDS Review
Chicago Dental Society
401 N Michigan Ave., Ste. 200
Chicago, IL 60611
Ph: (312)836-7300
Fax: (312)836-7337
E-mail: rgrove@cds.org
URL: http://www.cds.org/cds_review/

Frequency: 7/yr. **Price:** $25 Individuals; $30 Institutions and schools in USA & Canada; $45 Other countries; $5 Single issue. **Description:** Dental journal.

3427 ■ Dental Economics
PennWell Publishing Co.
1421 S Sheridan Rd.
Tulsa, OK 74112
Ph: (918)835-3161
Free: 800-331-4463
Fax: (918)831-9497
E-mail: Headquarters@PennWell.com
URL: http://www.dentaleconomics.com/index.html

Frequency: Monthly. **Price:** $132 Individuals; $179 Canada and Mexico; $248 Other countries; $211 Two years; $312 Canada and Mexico; $428 Other countries two years; $65 online. **Description:** Magazine featuring business-related articles for dentists.

3428 ■ Dental Laboratory Association of Texas
URL: http://www.dlat.org

Description: Allows individuals seeking employment as a dental laboratory technician to submit their service, contact information, and resume.

3429 ■ Dental Town: Dental Town
Dental Town
9633 S 48th St., Ste. 200
Phoenix, AZ 85044
Ph: (480)598-0001
Fax: (480)598-3450
E-mail: lorie@towniecentral.com
URL: http://www.dentaltown.com/

Frequency: Monthly. **Description:** Magazine that offers information on the dental industry and latest dental equipment.

3430 ■ Illinois Dental News
Illinois State Dental Society
1010 S Second St.
Springfield, IL 62704
Ph: (217)525-1406
Free: 800-475-4737
Fax: (217)525-8872
E-mail: info@isds.org
URL: http://www.isds.org/memberBenefits/publications/IllinoisDentalNews/index.asp

Frequency: Annual. **Price:** $10 Single issue outside United States; $45 Individuals non-members; $90 Nonmembers outside United States; $5 Single issue; $25 for members. **Description:** Dental magazine.

3431 ■ InterFace
Special Care Dentistry Association
330 N Wabash Ave., Ste. 2000
Chicago, IL 60611
Ph: (312)527-6764
Fax: (312)673-6663
E-mail: scda@scdaonline.org
URL: http://www.scdonline.org/displaynewsletter.cfm

Description: Quarterly. Publishes news of geriatric dentistry as well as news of the Society, its members and activities. Recurring features include legislative updates, a calendar of events, news of members, book reviews, editorials, a message from the president, bibliographies, and biographies.

3432 ■ Journal of Dental Hygiene
American Dental Hygienists' Association
444 N Michigan Ave., Ste. 3400
Chicago, IL 60611
Ph: (312)440-8900
E-mail: communications@adha.net
URLs: http://www.adha.org/publications/index.html; http://adha.publisher.ingentaconnect.com/content/adha/jdh

Frequency: Quarterly. **Price:** $45 Individuals; $65 Two years; $90 Individuals 3 years. **Description:** Professional journal on dental hygiene.

3433 ■ Journal of Dental Research
Pine Forge Press
2455 Teller Rd.
Thousand Oaks, CA 91320-2234
Ph: (805)499-4224
Free: 800-818-7243

Fax: (805)499-0871
E-mail: sales@pfp.sagepub.com
URLs: http://www.dentalresearch.org/i4a/pages/index
.cfm?pageid=3326; http://www.sagepub.com/
journals/Journal201925

Frequency: Monthly. **Price:** $922 Institutions print &
online; $440 Individuals print only; $829 Institutions
online only; $903 Institutions print only. **Description:**
Peer-reviewed dental science journal.

3434 ■ *Journal of Dental Technology*
URL: http://www.jdtunbound.com

Description: Serves dental laboratory professionals
through articles, industry and product news, classified advertising for laboratory technicians and more
(8 issues/year).

3435 ■ *Maryland State Dental Association Newsletter*
Maryland State Dental Association
6410F Dobbin Rd.
Columbia, MD 21045
Ph: (410)964-2880
Fax: (410)964-0583
E-mail: mddent@msda.com
URL: http://www.msda.com

Description: Monthly. Reports on health, legislative,
economic, and medical issues that are pertinent to
dentistry. Recurring features include letters to the
editor, interviews, news of research, a calendar of
events, reports of meetings, news of educational opportunities, and job listings.

3436 ■ *MDS Connection*
Massachusetts Dental Society
Two Willow St., No. 200
Southborough, MA 01745-1027
Ph: (508)480-9797
Free: 800-342-8747
Fax: (508)480-0002
E-mail: madental@massdental.org
URL: http://www.massdental.org/

Description: Bimonthly. Provides news on the
Society's activities and articles on the dental profession. Recurring features include reports of meetings,
news of educational opportunities, job listings, and
notices of publications available.

3437 ■ *Pediatric Dentistry Today*
American Academy of Pediatric Dentistry
211 E Chicago Ave., Ste. 1700
Chicago, IL 60611-2637
Ph: (312)337-2169
Fax: (312)337-6329
URL: http://www.aapd.org

Description: Bimonthly. Reports on the activities of
the Academy, which seeks to advance the specialty
of pediatric dentistry through practice, education, and
research. Recurring features include news of
research, profiles of members, and legislative
updates.

3438 ■ *Washington State Dental Laboratory Association Newsletter*
URL: http://www.wsdla.com

Description: Association newsletter featuring articles
of interest to dental laboratory technicians as well as
classified advertising for technical positions available.

3439 ■ *Westviews*
Western Los Angeles Dental Society
14722 Hawthorne Blvd., No. B
Lawndale, CA 90260-1505
Ph: (310)349-2199
Fax: (310)349-2175
E-mail: wlads@pacbell.net
URL: http://www.westernlads.org

Description: Six issues/year. Carries items relating
to organized dentistry and the clinical aspects of
dentistry. Covers local community events involving
the organization or the profession; provides updates
of states agency actions affecting dentistry.

EMPLOYER DIRECTORIES AND NETWORKING LISTS

3440 ■ *Who's Who In Dental Technology*
National Association of Dental Laboratories
325 John Knox Rd., No. L103
Tallahassee, FL 32303
Free: 800-950-1150
Fax: (850)222-0053
E-mail: nadl@nadl.org
URL: http://www.nadl.org/scr/dir/index.cfm

Description: Directory includes lab owners, technicians, suppliers, education members and
components.

HANDBOOKS AND MANUALS

3441 ■ *Opportunities in Dental Care Careers*
McGraw-Hill Professional
PO Box 182604
Columbus, OH 43272
Ph: (877)833-5524
Free: 800-262-4729
Fax: (614)759-3749
E-mail: pbg.ecommerce_custserv@mcgraw-hill.com
URL: http://www.mhprofessional.com/product.php
?isbn=0071493069

Description: Bonnie Kendall. $12.95 (e-book). 160
pages. Provides a complete overview of the job possibilities in dental industry. Includes the skill and
training requirements to current salary figures.

3442 ■ *Opportunities in Health and Medical Careers*
The McGraw-Hill Companies Inc.
PO Box 182604
Columbus, OH 43272
Ph: (212)512-2000
Free: 877-833-5524
Fax: (614)759-3749
E-mail: customer.service@mcgraw-hill.com
URL: http://www.mcgraw-hill.com

Description: I. Donald Snook, Jr. and Leo D'Orazio.
2004. $14.95 (paper). 157 pages. Covers the full
range of medical and health occupations. Illustrated.

3443 ■ *Resumes for Health and Medical Careers*
The McGraw-Hill Companies Inc.
PO Box 182604
Columbus, OH 43272
Ph: (212)512-2000
Free: 877-833-5524
Fax: (614)759-3749
E-mail: customer.service@mcgraw-hill.com
URL: http://www.mcgraw-hill.com

Description: Third edition, 2008. $12.95 (paper).
144 pages.

EMPLOYMENT AGENCIES AND SEARCH FIRMS

3444 ■ *DDS Resources*
16020 Swingley Ridge Rd., Ste. 340
Chesterfield, MO 63017
Ph: (636)536-6656
Free: 877-337-0563
Fax: (636)536-6667
E-mail: info@mdr-inc.com
URL: http://www.mdr-inc.com/dentists.aspx

Description: Serves as a dental recruitment agency
in the United States. Specializes in matching qualified dentists with dental employers.

3445 ■ *DDS Staffing Resources Inc.*
9755 Dogwood Rd., Ste. 200
Roswell, GA 30075-4663

Ph: (770)998-7779
Free: 888-668-7779
Fax: (770)552-0176
E-mail: ddsstaffing@ddsstaffing.com
URL: http://www.ddsstaffing.com

Description: Dental staffing agency.

ONLINE JOB SOURCES AND SERVICES

3446 ■ *DentalCrossing.com*
URL: http://www.dentalcrossing.com

Description: Provides employment opportunities for
dentists, dental assistants, dental hygienists, and
dental lab technicians.

3447 ■ *DentalLaboratoryTechnician.com*
URL: http://www.dentallaboratorytechnician.com

Description: Connects job seekers and potential
employers. Facilitates searching and posting of available jobs for dental lab technicians.

3448 ■ *DentalPortal.com*
URL: http://www.dentalportal.com

Description: Search engine for finding dentists,
orthodontists, oral surgeons, and other dental professionals.

3449 ■ *DentalPost.net*
URL: http://www.dentalpost.net

Description: Lists dental jobs including dentist jobs,
dental hygienist jobs, dental assistant jobs, dental lab
technician jobs, and dental front office jobs.

3450 ■ *DentalWorkers.com*
URL: http://www.dentalworkers.com/employment

Description: Serves as an online employment
resource among dental professionals. Provides classified ads for dental jobs, and free resume posting for
workers.

3451 ■ *DentistJobsNow.com*
URL: http://www.dentist-jobs-now.com

Description: Provides assistance to new and
practicing dentists, hygienists, and dental assistants
in finding employment.

3452 ■ *HEALTHeCAREERS Network*
URL: http://www.healthecareers.com

Description: Career search site for jobs in all health
care specialties; educational resources; visa and
licensing information for relocation; interesting
articles; relocation tools; links to professional
organizations and general resources.

3453 ■ *iHireDental*
URL: http://www.ihiredental.com

Description: Features dental jobs in different
specialty areas.

3454 ■ *ProHealthJobs.com*
URL: http://prohealthjobs.com/jobboard

Description: Career resources site for the medical
and health care field. Lists professional opportunities,
product information, continuing education and open
positions.

TRADESHOWS

3455 ■ *Chicago Dental Society Midwinter Meeting*
Chicago Dental Society
401 N Michigan Ave., Ste. 200
Chicago, IL 60611
Ph: (312)836-7300
Fax: (312)836-7337
E-mail: rgrove@cds.org
URL: http://www.cds.org

Frequency: Annual. **Primary Exhibits:** Dental

equipment, services, and related business services. **Dates and Locations:** Chicago, IL; McCormick Place.

3456 ■ Fun 'n Sun Weekend
Louisiana Dental Laboratory Association Inc.
PO Box 206
Elkin, NC 28621
Ph: (336)835-9251
Fax: (336)835-9243
E-mail: contactus@ldla.org
URL: http://www.ldla.org
Frequency: Annual.

3457 ■ NADL Vision 21
National Association of Dental Laboratories
325 John Knox Rd., No. L103
Tallahassee, FL 32303
Free: 800-950-1150
Fax: (850)222-0053
E-mail: nadl@nadl.org
URL: http://www.nadl.org
Annual.

3458 ■ Southeastern Conference of Dental Laboratories
Annual.

3459 ■ Star of the North Meeting
Minnesota Dental Association
1335 Industrial Blvd, Ste. 200
Minneapolis, MN 55413-4801
Ph: (612)767-8400
Fax: (612)767-8500
E-mail: info@mndental.org
URL: http://www.mndental.org/
Frequency: Annual. **Primary Exhibits:** Dental equipment and supplies, dental laboratory equipment, office equipment, and service organizations. MN.

3460 ■ Yankee Dental Congress
Maine Dental Association
29 Association Dr.
Manchester, ME 04351-0215
Ph: (207)622-7900
Fax: (207)622-6210
E-mail: info@medental.org
URL: http://www.medental.org
Frequency: Annual. **Primary Exhibits:** Dental products, equipment, and services.

OTHER SOURCES

3461 ■ American Academy of Cosmetic Dentistry
402 W Wilson St.
Madison, WI 53703
Ph: (608)222-8583
Free: 800-543-9220
Fax: (608)222-9540
E-mail: info@aacd.com
URL: http://www.aacd.com
Description: Members include more than 8,000 cosmetic and reconstructive dentists, dental laboratory technicians, dental auxiliaries, dental hygienists, educators, researchers and students. Membership benefits include AACD accreditation, registration to AACD's Annual Scientific Session, publications, online search directory, marketing materials, and more.

3462 ■ American Academy of Dental Group Practice
2525 E Arizona Biltmore Cir., Ste. 127
Phoenix, AZ 85016
Ph: (602)381-1185
Fax: (602)381-1093
E-mail: aadgp@aadgp.org
URL: http://www.aadgp.org
Description: Represents active dentists and dental group practices. Aims to improve the level of dental

service provided by members through exchanging and expanding of ideas and techniques for patient treatment and practice administration. Promotes group practice and research; accumulates and disseminates information; seeks to achieve the proper recognition for the aims and goals of group practice. Helps support an accreditation program as a system of voluntary peer review.

3463 ■ American Association of Bioanalysts
906 Olive St., Ste. 1200
Saint Louis, MO 63101-1448
Ph: (314)241-1445
Fax: (314)241-1449
URL: http://www.aab.org
Description: Professional organization of directors, owners, managers, supervisors, technologists and technicians of bioanalytical clinical laboratories devoting their efforts to clinical laboratory procedure and testing. Sponsors Proficiency Testing Service open to individuals engaged in the clinical laboratory field. Provides specialized education and representation before federal and state legislatures and regulatory agencies.

3464 ■ American College of Dentists
839J Quince Orchard Blvd.
Gaithersburg, MD 20878-1614
Ph: (301)977-3223
Fax: (301)977-3330
E-mail: office@acd.org
URL: http://acd.org
Description: Dentists and others serving in capacities related to the dental profession. Seeks to advance the standards of the profession of dentistry. Conducts educational and research programs. Maintains speakers' bureau and charitable programs.

3465 ■ American College of Prosthodontists
211 E Chicago Ave., Ste. 1000
Chicago, IL 60611
Ph: (312)573-1260
URL: http://www.prosthodontics.org
Description: Membership includes more than 3,300 prosthodontists, dental technicians, dental students and other dental professionals contributing to the specialty. Committed to the esthetic restoration of teeth, including bridges, crowns/caps, dental implants, dentures, partial dentures, whitening and veneers. Membership includes free subscriptions to the Journal of Prosthodontics, the Messenger, and e-blasts.

3466 ■ American Dental Association
211 E Chicago Ave.
Chicago, IL 60611-2678
Ph: (312)440-2500
Free: 800-947-4746
Fax: (312)440-3542
E-mail: berryj@ada.org
URL: http://www.ada.org
Description: Professional society of dentists. Encourages the improvement of the health of the public and promotes the art and science of dentistry in matters of legislation and regulations. Inspects and accredits dental schools and schools for dental hygienists, assistants, and laboratory technicians. Conducts research programs at ADA Foundation Research Institute. Produces dental health education material used in the U.S. Sponsors National Children's Dental Health Month and Give Kids a Smile Day. Compiles statistics on personnel, practice, and dental care needs and attitudes of patients with regard to dental health.

3467 ■ American Dental Education Association
1400 K St. NW, Ste. 1100
Washington, DC 20005
Ph: (202)289-7201
Fax: (202)289-7204
URL: http://www.adea.org
Description: Individuals interested in dental education; schools of dentistry, advanced dental and allied

dental education in the U.S., Canada, and Puerto Rico; affiliated institutions of the federal government and corporations. Works to promote better teaching and education in dentistry and dental research and to facilitate exchange of ideas among dental educators. Sponsors meetings, conferences, and workshops; conducts surveys, studies, and special projects and publishes their results. Maintains 37 sections and 8 special interest groups representing many different aspects of dental education. **Members:** 19,000.

3468 ■ Crown Council
975 Woodoak Ln., Ste. 200
Salt Lake City, UT 84117
Ph: (801)293-8522
Free: 800-276-9658
Fax: (801)293-8524
E-mail: success@crowncouncil.com
URL: http://www.crowncouncil.com
Description: Seeks to improve independent dental practices. Promotes oral health and the fight against oral cancer. Provides patient care and offers state-of-the-art dental procedure facilities.

3469 ■ Florida Dental Laboratory Association
325 John Knox Rd., No. L103
Tallahassee, FL 32303-4121
Ph: (850)224-0711
Fax: (850)222-3019
E-mail: membership@fdla.net
URL: http://www.fdla.net
Description: Represents operators and technicians of dental laboratories and to advance standards of service to the dental profession.

3470 ■ *Health-Care Careers for the 21st Century*
JIST Publishing
875 Montreal Way
Saint Paul, MN 55102-4245
Ph: (317)613-4200
Free: 800-648-5478
Fax: (800)328-4564
E-mail: info@jist.com
URL: http://www.jist.com
Price: $9.95 Individuals Softcover. **Pages:** 448. **Covers:** Jobs for health care professionals and career opportunities for those pursuing a health-related career, organized into 80 careers in five groups. **Publication includes:** Appendixes listing job source resources and Web sites for health organizations.

3471 ■ Holistic Dental Association
1825 Ponce de Leon Blvd., No. 148
Coral Gables, FL 33134
Ph: (305)356-7338
Fax: (305)468-6359
E-mail: director@holisticdental.org
URL: http://www.holisticdental.org
Description: Represents dentists, chiropractors, dental hygienists, physical therapists, and medical doctors. Aims to provide a holistic approach to better dental care for patients, and to expand techniques, medications, and philosophies that pertain to extractions, anesthetics, fillings, crowns, and orthodontics. Encourages the use of homeopathic medications, acupuncture, cranial osteopathy, nutritional techniques, and physical therapy in treating patients in addition to conventional treatments. Sponsors training and educational seminars. **Members:** 200.

3472 ■ Louisiana Dental Laboratory Association Inc.
PO Box 206
Elkin, NC 28621
Ph: (336)835-9251
Fax: (336)835-9243
E-mail: contactus@ldla.org
URL: http://www.ldla.org
Description: Serves dental laboratory technicians in Louisiana and surrounding areas; sponsors a spring meeting annually.

3473 ■ Michigan Association of Commercial Dental Laboratories
c/o Irene Leidich, Executive Secretary and Program Coordinator
22800 Stair Dr.
Clinton Township, MI 48036-2747
Ph: (586)469-1121
Fax: (586)469-1147
E-mail: irene@macdl.org
URL: http://macdl.org

Description: Serves 800 members; promotes the dental laboratory profession through excellence, education, integrity, ethics and standards.

3474 ■ Minnesota Dental Laboratory Association Inc.
7561 9th St., N
Saint Paul, MN 55128
E-mail: midwestdentallabsoc@gmail.com
URL: http://www.mwdentallab.org

Description: Association website provides a link to online advertising for dental technician positions, both wanted and available.

3475 ■ National Association of Dental Laboratories
325 John Knox Rd., No. L103
Tallahassee, FL 32303
Free: 800-950-1150
Fax: (850)222-0053
E-mail: nadl@nadl.org
URL: http://www.nadl.org

Description: Represents 2,900 commercial dental laboratories, manufacturers/suppliers and educators serving the dental profession. Develops criteria for ethical dental laboratories. Offers business and personal insurance programs, Hazardous Materials Training Program, and an infectious disease prevention training program, business management and technical education programs. Compiles statistics; conducts educational and charitable programs.

3476 ■ National Board for Certification in Dental Laboratory Technology
325 John Knox Rd., No. L103
Tallahassee, FL 32303
Ph: (850)205-5627
Free: 800-684-5310
Fax: (850)222-0053
URL: http://www.nbccert.org

Description: Certification program that represents compliance with industry standards and a personal commitment to quality and professionalism.

3477 ■ North Carolina Dental Laboratory Association Inc.
PO Box 206
Elkin, NC 28621
Ph: (336)835-9251
Fax: (336)835-9243
E-mail: contactus@ncdla.org
URL: http://www.ncdla.org

Description: Represents dental laboratory technicians and offers two meetings per year to promote educational opportunities for members.

3478 ■ Oregon Association of Dental Laboratories
PO Box 355
Rockaway Beach, OR 97136
Ph: (503)842-4100
Free: 800-952-2751
Fax: (503)355-0570
E-mail: debra.oadl@hotmail.com
URL: http://www.oregondentallabs.com

Description: Serves owners of dental laboratories and dental laboratory technicians; seeks to advance the professional status of those engaged in the field of dental laboratory technology.

3479 ■ South Carolina Dental Laboratory Association
PO Box 2721
Spartanburg, SC 29304
Ph: (864)809-5587
Fax: (864)576-1490
E-mail: tulare@charter.net
URL: http://www.scdla.org

Description: Promotes the art and science of dental laboratory operations; seeks to further the interests of dental laboratory owners and technicians.

3480 ■ Special Care Dentistry Association
330 N Wabash Ave., Ste. 2000
Chicago, IL 60611
Ph: (312)527-6764
Fax: (312)673-6663
E-mail: scda@scdaonline.org
URL: http://www.scdonline.org

Description: Dentists, hygienists, and lay public interested in special care dentistry. Aims to improve oral health and well being of people with special needs. Provides a forum for an exchange of clinical ideas and patient management techniques among members. **Members:** 1,000.

Dentists

SOURCES OF HELP-WANTED ADS

3481 ■ *AAOMS Surgical Update*
American Association of Oral and Maxillofacial
Surgeons
9700 W Bryn Mawr Ave.
Rosemont, IL 60018-5701
Ph: (847)678-6200
Free: 800-822-6637
Fax: (847)678-6286
E-mail: inquiries@aaoms.org
URL: http://www.aaoms.org

Description: 2/year. Provides the dental profession
and others with current information on the specialty
of oral and maxillofacial surgery and patient care.

3482 ■ *ACD News*
American College of Dentists
839J Quince Orchard Blvd.
Gaithersburg, MD 20878-1614
Ph: (301)977-3223
Fax: (301)977-3330
E-mail: office@acd.org
URLs: http://www.acd.org/publications.htm#ACD-
News; http://www.acd.org/publications.htm

Frequency: Triennial. **Description:** Tri-annual.
Presents accounts of College meetings, as well as
remarks from the College's president. Publishes
notices of scheduled events, spotlights individuals
recognized or given awards by the College, and
profiles convocation speakers, and other dental
organizations. Recurring features include reports of
meetings.

3483 ■ *ACP Messenger*
American College of Prosthodontists
211 E Chicago Ave., Ste. 1000
Chicago, IL 60611
Ph: (312)573-1260
URL: http://www.prosthodontics.org/products/Mes-
senger.asp

Description: Quarterly newsletter featuring industry
news as well as classified advertising.

3484 ■ *ADSA Pulse*
American Dental Society of Anesthesiology
211 E Chicago Ave.
Chicago, IL 60611
Ph: (312)664-8270
Fax: (312)224-8624
E-mail: adsahome@mac.com
URL: http://www.adsahome.org/

Description: Bimonthly. Features articles on
developments in dental anesthesiology. Includes
news of research, editorials, news of the Society and
its members, and a calendar of events.

3485 ■ *AGD Impact Newsletter*
Academy of General Dentistry
560 W Lake St., 6th Fl.
Chicago, IL 60611-6600

Ph: (888)243-3368
Free: 888-243-DENT
Fax: (312)335-3443
E-mail: impact@agd.org
URLs: http://www.agd.org; http://www.agd.org/publi-
cations/?pubID=4

Frequency: Monthly. **Price:** $65 Institutions; $50
Nonmembers; $70 Institutions, Canada; $55
Nonmembers Canada; $80 Institutions, other
countries; $65 Nonmembers other countries.
Description: Monthly. Covers the issues and trends
that impact on general dentists and the profession.
Includes CDE course list and fact sheets for patients.

3486 ■ *American Academy of Implant
Dentistry Newsletter*
American Academy of Implant Dentistry
211 E Chicago Ave., Ste. 750
Chicago, IL 60611
Ph: (312)335-1550
Free: 877-335-2243
Fax: (312)335-9090
E-mail: info@aaid.com
URL: http://www.aaid-implant.org

Description: Quarterly. Covers current activities in
the field of implant dentistry, particularly the
educational programs of the Academy.

3487 ■ *American Association of Women
Dentists Chronicle*
American Association of Women Dentists
216 W Jackson Blvd., Ste. 625
Chicago, IL 60606
Free: 800-920-2293
Fax: (312)750-1203
E-mail: info@aawd.org
URL: http://www.aawd.org/

Description: Quarterly. Includes articles of interest
on dentistry, nutrition, research, education, and
federal services. Provides information on the association, the practice of dentistry, and women in
dentistry.

3488 ■ *American Dental Hygienists'
Association Access*
American Dental Hygienists' Association
444 N Michigan Ave., Ste. 3400
Chicago, IL 60611
Ph: (312)440-8900
E-mail: exec.office@adha.net
URL: http://www.adha.org/publications/index.html

Frequency: 10/yr. **Price:** $48 Individuals; $85 Two
years; $120 Individuals for 3 years. **Description:**
Magazine covering current dental hygiene topics,
regulatory and legislative developments, and association news.

3489 ■ *ASDA News*
American Student Dental Association
211 E Chicago Ave., Ste. 700
Chicago, IL 60611-2687
Ph: (312)440-2795

Free: 800-621-8099
Fax: (312)440-2820
E-mail: editors@asdanet.org
URLs: http://www.asdanet.org/asdanews.aspx; http://
www.allianceada.org

Frequency: Monthly. **Price:** $55 Nonmembers US;
$65 Nonmembers outside US; included in member-
ship dues. **Description:** Monthly. Covers dentistry
and association news. Recurring features include letters to the editor, news of research, a calendar of
events, columns, Q&As, and reports of meetings.

3490 ■ *Bulletin of Dental Education*
American Dental Education Association
1400 K St. NW, Ste. 1100
Washington, DC 20005
Ph: (202)289-7201
Fax: (202)289-7204
URL: http://www.adea.org

Description: Monthly. Contains news and information on dental education. Recurring features include
a calendar of events, reports of meetings, news of
educational opportunities, job listings, and notices of
publications available.

3491 ■ *CDS Review*
Chicago Dental Society
401 N Michigan Ave., Ste. 200
Chicago, IL 60611
Ph: (312)836-7300
Fax: (312)836-7337
E-mail: rgrove@cds.org
URL: http://www.cds.org/cds_review/

Frequency: 7/yr. **Price:** $25 Individuals; $30 Institutions and schools in USA & Canada; $45 Other
countries; $5 Single issue. **Description:** Dental
journal.

3492 ■ *The Cranial Letter*
The Cranial Academy
8202 Clearvista Pkwy., No. 9-D
Indianapolis, IN 46256
Ph: (317)594-0411
Fax: (317)594-9299
E-mail: info@cranialacademy.org
URL: http://www.cranialacademy.org

Description: Quarterly. Provides information about
osteopathy in the cranio-sacral field for doctors of
osteopathy, dentistry, and medicine. Carries news of
reports, papers, seminars, courses offered by the
Academy, and research projects. Recurring features
include obituaries, a calendar of events, and columns
titled President's Message, The Dental Corner, and
Scientific Section.

3493 ■ *Dental Economics*
PennWell Publishing Co.
1421 S Sheridan Rd.
Tulsa, OK 74112
Ph: (918)835-3161
Free: 800-331-4463

Fax: (918)831-9497
E-mail: Headquarters@PennWell.com
URL: http://www.dentaleconomics.com/index.html
Frequency: Monthly. **Price:** $132 Individuals; $179
Canada and Mexico; $248 Other countries; $211 Two
years; $312 Canada and Mexico; $428 Other
countries two years; $65 online. **Description:**
Magazine featuring business-related articles for
dentists.

3494 ■ Dental Implantology Update
AHC Media
950 E Paces Ferry Rd. NE
Atlanta, GA 30326
Ph: (404)262-5476
Free: 800-688-2421
Fax: (404)262-5560
E-mail: editorial_questions@ahcmedia.com
URL: http://www.ahcmedia.com/public/pages/Dental
-Implantology-Update.html#top
Description: Monthly. $599/year. Monitors clinical
techniques and technologies in dental implants and
treating patients.

3495 ■ Dental Town: Dental Town
Dental Town
9633 S 48th St., Ste. 200
Phoenix, AZ 85044
Ph: (480)598-0001
Fax: (480)598-3450
E-mail: lorie@towniecentral.com
URL: http://www.dentaltown.com/
Frequency: Monthly. **Description:** Magazine that of-
fers information on the dental industry and latest
dental equipment.

3496 ■ Dentistry in South Dakota
South Dakota Dental Association
804 N Euclid Ave., Ste. 103
Pierre, SD 57501
Ph: (605)224-9133
Fax: (605)224-9168
E-mail: paul@sddental.org
URL: http://www.sddental.org/communications_sdda
_newsletter.htm
Description: Quarterly. Provides updates on dental
profession issues, small business, employer/
employee relations, nutrition, and safe workplace
practices. Recurring features include letters to the
editor, a calendar of events, reports of meetings,
news of educational opportunities, and a column
titled President's Corner.

3497 ■ Facets
San Diego County Dental Society
1275 W Morena Blvd., Ste. B
San Diego, CA 92110-3860
Ph: (619)275-0244
Free: 800-201-0244
Fax: (619)275-0646
E-mail: linda@sdcds.org
URL: http://www.sdcds.org
Description: Ten issues/year. Reports inhouse
information on the Society. Recurring features
include a calendar of events and columns titled New
Applicants, New Members, Classified Advertising,
and Continuing Education.

3498 ■ HDA News & Reports
Hispanic Dental Association
1111 14th St. NW, Ste. 1100
Washington, DC 20005
Ph: (202)629-3628
Free: 800-852-7921
Fax: (202)629-3802
E-mail: hispanicdental@hdassoc.org
URL: http://www.hdassoc.org
Description: Quarterly. Provides information on HDA
chapters, scholarship programs, and activities.
Contains a classified advertising section, as well as
previews of the annual meeting and reports of the
immediate past meeting.

3499 ■ Illinois Dental News
Illinois State Dental Society
1010 S Second St.
Springfield, IL 62704
Ph: (217)525-1406
Free: 800-475-4737
Fax: (217)525-8872
E-mail: info@isds.org
URL: http://www.isds.org/memberBenefits/publica-
tions/IllinoisDentalNews/index.asp
Frequency: Annual. **Price:** $10 Single issue outside
United States; $45 Individuals non-members; $90
Nonmembers outside United States; $5 Single issue;
$25 for members. **Description:** Dental magazine.

3500 ■ InterFace
Special Care Dentistry Association
330 N Wabash Ave., Ste. 2000
Chicago, IL 60611
Ph: (312)527-6764
Fax: (312)673-6663
E-mail: scda@scdaonline.org
URL: http://www.scdonline.org/displaynewsletter.cfm
Description: Quarterly. Publishes news of geriatric
dentistry as well as news of the Society, its members
and activities. Recurring features include legislative
updates, a calendar of events, news of members,
book reviews, editorials, a message from the
president, bibliographies, and biographies.

**3501 ■ Journal of the American Dental
Association**
American Dental Association
211 E Chicago Ave.
Chicago, IL 60611-2678
Ph: (312)440-2500
Free: 800-947-4746
Fax: (312)440-3542
E-mail: berryj@ada.org
URL: http://jada.ada.org/
Frequency: Monthly. **Price:** $128 Individuals U.S.
and Mexico; $161 Institutions U.S. and Mexico; $16
Single issue U.S. and Mexico; $141 Canada U.S.
and Mexico; $183 Institutions Canada, plus airmail;
$24 Single issue Canada, plus airmail; $161 Individu-
als Canada, plus airmail; $204 Institutions Canada,
plus airmail; $24; $22 Single issue Canada, plus
airmail. **Description:** Trade journal for the dental
profession.

3502 ■ Journal of Dental Hygiene
American Dental Hygienists' Association
444 N Michigan Ave., Ste. 3400
Chicago, IL 60611
Ph: (312)440-8900
E-mail: communications@adha.net
URLs: http://www.adha.org/publications/index.html;
http://adha.publisher.ingentaconnect.com/content/
adha/jdh
Frequency: Quarterly. **Price:** $45 Individuals; $65
Two years; $90 Individuals 3 years. **Description:**
Professional journal on dental hygiene.

3503 ■ Journal of Dental Research
Pine Forge Press
2455 Teller Rd.
Thousand Oaks, CA 91320-2234
Ph: (805)499-4224
Free: 800-818-7243
Fax: (805)499-0871
E-mail: sales@pfp.sagepub.com
URLs: http://www.dentalresearch.org/i4a/pages/index
.cfm?pageid=3326; http://www.sagepub.com/
journals/Journal201925
Frequency: Monthly. **Price:** $922 Institutions print &
online; $440 Individuals print only; $829 Institutions
online only; $903 Institutions print only. **Description:**
Peer-reviewed dental science journal.

3504 ■ Keynotes
The USA Section of the International College of
Dentists
51 Monroe St., Ste. 1400
Rockville, MD 20850

Ph: (301)251-8861
Fax: (240)499-8975
E-mail: office@icd.org
URL: http://www.usa-icd.org/information/publications
.htm
Description: Semiannual. Contains news of the
activities and projects of the organization, which
provides networking and educational opportunities for
professionals in the dental field. Recurring features
include a calendar of events, reports of meetings,
news of educational opportunities, and a column
titled the History Corner.

**3505 ■ Maryland State Dental Association
Newsletter**
Maryland State Dental Association
6410F Dobbin Rd.
Columbia, MD 21045
Ph: (410)964-2880
Fax: (410)964-0583
E-mail: mddent@msda.com
URL: http://www.msda.com
Description: Monthly. Reports on health, legislative,
economic, and medical issues that are pertinent to
dentistry. Recurring features include letters to the
editor, interviews, news of research, a calendar of
events, reports of meetings, news of educational op-
portunities, and job listings.

3506 ■ MDS Connection
Massachusetts Dental Society
Two Willow St., No. 200
Southborough, MA 01745-1027
Ph: (508)480-9797
Free: 800-342-8747
Fax: (508)480-0002
E-mail: madental@massdental.org
URL: http://www.massdental.org/
Description: Bimonthly. Provides news on the
Society's activities and articles on the dental profes-
sion. Recurring features include reports of meetings,
news of educational opportunities, job listings, and
notices of publications available.

3507 ■ Momentum
Eastman Institute for Oral Health
601 Elmwood Ave.
Rochester, NY 14620
URL: http://www.urmc.rochester.edu/dentistry/news-
letters.cfm
Description: Quarterly. Contains news of interest to
Center alumni and friends. Recurring features
include interviews, news of research, a calendar of
events, and a message from the director.

3508 ■ News From The NIDCR
National Institutes of Health - National Institute of
Dental and Craniofacial Research
31 Center Dr., Rm. 2C39
MSC 2190
Bethesda, MD 20892-2190
Ph: (301)496-4261
Free: 866-232-4528
Fax: (301)480-4098
E-mail: nidcrinfo@mail.nih.gov
URL: http://www.nidcr.nih.gov
Description: Bimonthly. Includes the latest news
about funding opportunities, training and career
development opportunities, NIDCR and NIH news,
and science advances.

**3509 ■ Oral & Craniofacial Tissue
Engineering**
Quintessence Publishing Company Inc.
4350 Chandler Dr.
Hanover Park, IL 60133
Ph: (630)736-3600
Free: 800-621-0387
Fax: (630)736-3633
E-mail: contact@quintbook.com
URL: http://www.quintpub.com/journals/octe/gp.php
?journal_name=OCTE
Frequency: Quarterly. **Price:** $138 Individuals.

Description: Journal covering multiple disciplinary lines involving specialties of both dentistry and medicine.

3510 ■ Pediatric Dentistry Today
American Academy of Pediatric Dentistry
211 E Chicago Ave., Ste. 1700
Chicago, IL 60611-2637
Ph: (312)337-2169
Fax: (312)337-6329
URL: http://www.aapd.org

Description: Bimonthly. Reports on the activities of the Academy, which seeks to advance the specialty of pediatric dentistry through practice, education, and research. Recurring features include news of research, profiles of members, and legislative updates.

3511 ■ RDH: The National Magazine for Dental Hygiene Professionals
PennWell Publishing Co.
1421 S Sheridan Rd.
Tulsa, OK 74112
Ph: (918)835-3161
Free: 800-331-4463
Fax: (918)831-9497
E-mail: Headquarters@PennWell.com
URL: http://www.rdhmag.com/index.html

Frequency: Monthly. **Price:** $79 Individuals; $112 Canada; $141 Other countries; $40 U.S. and other countries digital. **Description:** Magazine for dental hygiene professionals covering practice management, patient motivation, practice options, financial planning, personal development, preventive oral health care and treatment, home care instruction, radiology, anesthesia, nutrition, and new products.

3512 ■ Washington State Dental Laboratory Association Newsletter
URL: http://www.wsdla.com

Description: Association newsletter featuring articles of interest to dental laboratory technicians as well as classified advertising for technical positions available.

3513 ■ Westviews
Western Los Angeles Dental Society
14722 Hawthorne Blvd., No. B
Lawndale, CA 90260-1505
Ph: (310)349-2199
Fax: (310)349-2175
E-mail: wlads@pacbell.net
URL: http://www.westernlads.org

Description: Six issues/year. Carries items relating to organized dentistry and the clinical aspects of dentistry. Covers local community events involving the organization or the profession; provides updates of states agency actions affecting dentistry.

3514 ■ WSDA News
Washington State Dental Association
126 NW Canal St.
Seattle, WA 98107
Ph: (206)448-1914
Free: 800-448-3368
Fax: (206)443-9266
E-mail: info@wsda.org
URL: http://www.wsda.org/news

Frequency: Monthly. **Price:** $67/year. **Description:** Recurring features include practice opportunities, news of educational opportunities, and job listings.

EMPLOYER DIRECTORIES AND NETWORKING LISTS

3515 ■ American Academy of Pediatric Dentistry--Membership Directory
American Academy of Pediatric Dentistry
211 E Chicago Ave., Ste. 1700
Chicago, IL 60611-2637
Ph: (312)337-2169

Fax: (312)337-6329
URL: http://www.aapd.org

Frequency: Annual; November. **Pages:** 80. **Covers:** 5,600 pediatric dentists and several dentists in practice, teaching, and research. **Entries include:** Name, address, phone. **Arrangement:** Alphabetical. **Indexes:** Geographical.

3516 ■ Health Professionals Directory
Sussex Directories Inc.
10 Market St., Ste. 750
Camana Bay
Grand Cayman, Cayman Islands
URL: http://sussexdirectories.com

3517 ■ International Association for Orthodontics--Membership Directory
International Association for Orthodontics
750 N Lincoln Memorial Dr., Ste. 422
Milwaukee, WI 53202
Ph: (414)272-2757
Fax: (414)272-2754
E-mail: worldheadquarters@iaortho.org
URL: http://www.iaortho.org

Frequency: Annual; June. **Covers:** 2,500 general and children's dentists who also work to correct facial and jaw irregularities. **Entries include:** Name, office address and phone, orthodontic techniques practiced. **Arrangement:** Geographical. **Indexes:** Personal name.

3518 ■ Washington Physicians Directory
The Washington Physicians Directory
13912 Overton Ln.
Silver Spring, MD 20904
Ph: (301)384-1506
Fax: (301)384-6854
E-mail: wpd@wpdnetwork.com
URL: http://www.wpdnetwork.com

Frequency: Annual; Latest edition 50th Anniversary Edition; 2012. **Pages:** 800. **Covers:** 9,800 physicians in private practice or on full-time staff at hospitals in the Washington, D.C., metropolitan area. **Entries include:** Name, medical school and year of graduation; up to four office addresses with phone numbers for each; up to four medical specialties (indicating board certifications), Unique Physician Identification Numbers (UPIN), and e-mail. **Arrangement:** Alphabetical. **Indexes:** Geographical (within medical specialty); foreign language.

3519 ■ Worldwide Online Search Directory
URL: http://www.aacd.com/professional/membership-benefits.asp#4

Description: Provides a worldwide listing of members of the American Academy of Cosmetic Dentistry.

HANDBOOKS AND MANUALS

3520 ■ Barron's Guide to Medical and Dental Schools
Barron's Educational Series Inc.
250 Wireless Blvd.
Hauppauge, NY 11788
Ph: (631)434-3311
Free: 800-645-3476
Fax: (631)434-3723
E-mail: barrons@barronseduc.com
URL: http://www.barronseduc.com

Description: Sol Wischnitzer and Edith Wischnitzer. Twelve edition, 2009. $17.09. 768 pages. Updated with the latest facts and figures, this school directory and guidance manual presents profiles of all accredited medical, dental, and osteopathic schools in the United States and Canada.

3521 ■ Opportunities in Dental Care Careers
McGraw-Hill Professional
PO Box 182604
Columbus, OH 43272
Ph: (877)833-5524

Free: 800-262-4729
Fax: (614)759-3749
E-mail: pbg.ecommerce_custserv@mcgraw-hill.com
URL: http://www.mhprofessional.com/product.php?isbn=0071493069

Description: Bonnie Kendall. $12.95 (e-book). 160 pages. Provides a complete overview of the job possibilities in dental industry. Includes the skill and training requirements to current salary figures.

3522 ■ Opportunities in Health and Medical Careers
The McGraw-Hill Companies Inc.
PO Box 182604
Columbus, OH 43272
Ph: (212)512-2000
Free: 877-833-5524
Fax: (614)759-3749
E-mail: customer.service@mcgraw-hill.com
URL: http://www.mcgraw-hill.com

Description: I. Donald Snook, Jr. and Leo D'Orazio. 2004. $14.95 (paper). 157 pages. Covers the full range of medical and health occupations. Illustrated.

3523 ■ Resumes for Health and Medical Careers
The McGraw-Hill Companies Inc.
PO Box 182604
Columbus, OH 43272
Ph: (212)512-2000
Free: 877-833-5524
Fax: (614)759-3749
E-mail: customer.service@mcgraw-hill.com
URL: http://www.mcgraw-hill.com

Description: Third edition, 2008. $12.95 (paper). 144 pages.

3524 ■ Senior Dentist
National Learning Corporation
212 Michael Dr.
Syosset, NY 11791
Ph: (516)921-8888
Free: 800-632-8888
Fax: (516)921-8743
E-mail: info@passbooks.com
URL: http://www.passbooks.com

Description: 2009. $69.95 (paper). Serves as an exam preparation guide for senior dentists.

3525 ■ Veterinary Periodontology
John Wiley & Sons Inc.
111 River St.
Hoboken, NJ 07030-5774
Ph: (201)748-6000
Free: 800-225-5945
Fax: (201)748-6088
E-mail: info@wiley.com
URL: http://www.wiley.com/WileyCDA/WileyTitle/productCd-0813816521.html

Price: $124.99 hardcover. **Pages:** 368. **Description:** Covers etiology, pathogenesis, and clinical features of periodontal disease in dogs and cats, including basic and advanced treatments on therapeutic procedures. Guide for veterinary dentist, including specialists, general practitioners, students, and veterinary technicians.

EMPLOYMENT AGENCIES AND SEARCH FIRMS

3526 ■ Actuary Resources
115 N Castle Heights Ave., Ste. 202
Lebanon, TN 37087-2768
Ph: (615)360-5171
Fax: (615)360-5173
E-mail: info@actuaryresources.org
URL: http://www.actuaryresources.org

Description: Provides staffing services to several different types of industries. Offers a free screening service to clients.

3527 ■ DDS Resources
16020 Swingley Ridge Rd., Ste. 340
Chesterfield, MO 63017
Ph: (636)536-6656
Free: 877-337-0563
Fax: (636)536-6667
E-mail: info@mdr-inc.com
URL: http://www.mdr-inc.com/dentists.aspx

Description: Serves as a dental recruitment agency in the United States. Specializes in matching qualified dentists with dental employers.

3528 ■ DDS Staffing Resources Inc.
9755 Dogwood Rd., Ste. 200
Roswell, GA 30075-4663
Ph: (770)998-7779
Free: 888-668-7779
Fax: (770)552-0176
E-mail: ddsstaffing@ddsstaffing.com
URL: http://www.ddsstaffing.com

Description: Dental staffing agency.

3529 ■ Team Placement Service Inc.
1414 Prince St., Ste. 202
Alexandria, VA 22314
Ph: (703)820-8618
Free: 800-495-6767
Fax: (703)820-3368
E-mail: info@teamplace.com
URL: http://www.teamplace.com

Description: Full-service personnel consultants provide placement for healthcare staff, physician and dentist, private practice, and hospitals. Conduct interviews, tests, and reference checks to select the top 20% of applicants. Survey applicants' skill levels, provide backup information on each candidate, select compatible candidates for consideration, and insure the hiring process minimizes potential legal liability. Industries served: healthcare and government agencies providing medical, dental, biotech, laboratory, hospitals, and physician search.

ONLINE JOB SOURCES AND SERVICES

3530 ■ CareersInDental.com
URL: http://www.careersindental.com

Description: Serves as a job board for the dental industry. Features listings of employment opportunities and job openings in the field.

3531 ■ CareerVitals.com
URL: http://www.careervitals.com

Description: Serves as a job board for healthcare professionals in different specializations.

3532 ■ DentalCrossing.com
URL: http://www.dentalcrossing.com

Description: Provides employment opportunities for dentists, dental assistants, dental hygienists, and dental lab technicians.

3533 ■ DentalJobsBoard.net
URL: http://www.dentaljobsboard.net

Description: Features dentist jobs, dental hygiene jobs, dental assistant jobs, and jobs for dental lab technicians.

3534 ■ DentalPortal.com
URL: http://www.dentalportal.com

Description: Search engine for finding dentists, orthodontists, oral surgeons, and other dental professionals.

3535 ■ DentalPost.net
URL: http://www.dentalpost.net

Description: Lists dental jobs including dentist jobs, dental hygienist jobs, dental assistant jobs, dental lab technician jobs, and dental front office jobs.

3536 ■ DentalWorkers.com
URL: http://www.dentalworkers.com/employment

Description: Serves as an online employment resource among dental professionals. Provides classified ads for dental jobs, and free resume posting for workers.

3537 ■ Dentist Job Cafe
URL: http://www.dentistjobcafe.com

Description: Features dental job listings. Provides employment services for dentists, dental hygienists, and dental assistants.

3538 ■ DentistInfo.com
URL: http://www.dentistinfo.com

Description: Provides information on dental practice sales, dental seminars, dental jobs, and free listings and home page creation service.

3539 ■ DentistJobsNow.com
URL: http://www.dentist-jobs-now.com

Description: Provides assistance to new and practicing dentists, hygienists, and dental assistants in finding employment.

3540 ■ DentistryJob.com
URL: http://www.dentistryjob.com

Description: Serves as a job board for dentistry professionals.

3541 ■ HEALTHeCAREERS Network
URL: http://www.healthecareers.com

Description: Career search site for jobs in all health care specialties; educational resources; visa and licensing information for relocation; interesting articles; relocation tools; links to professional organizations and general resources.

3542 ■ iHireDental
URL: http://www.ihiredental.com

Description: Features dental jobs in different specialty areas.

3543 ■ Medzilla.com
URL: http://www.medzilla.com

Description: General medical website which matches employers and job hunters to their ideal employees and jobs through search capabilities. Main files include: Post Jobs, Search Resumes, Post Resumes, Search Jobs, Head Hunters, Articles, Salary Survey.

3544 ■ Monster Healthcare
URL: http://healthcare.monster.com

Description: Delivers nationwide access to healthcare recruiting. Employers can post job listings or ads. Job seekers can post and code resumes, and search over 150,000 healthcare job listings, healthcare career advice columns, career resources information, and member employer profiles and services.

3545 ■ ProHealthJobs.com
URL: http://prohealthjobs.com/jobboard

Description: Career resources site for the medical and health care field. Lists professional opportunities, product information, continuing education and open positions.

3546 ■ SmileJobs.com
URL: http://www.smilejobs.com

Description: Features job opportunities, resume search and postings for dental professionals.

TRADESHOWS

3547 ■ AACD Annual Scientific Sessions
American Academy of Cosmetic Dentistry
402 W Wilson St.
Madison, WI 53703

Ph: (608)222-8583
Free: 800-543-9220
Fax: (608)222-9540
E-mail: info@aacd.com
URL: http://www.aacd.com
Annual.

3548 ■ Academy of General Dentistry Annual Meeting
Academy of General Dentistry
560 W Lake St., 6th Fl.
Chicago, IL 60611-6600
Ph: (888)243-3368
Free: 888-243-DENT
Fax: (312)335-3443
E-mail: membership@agd.org
URL: http://www.agd.org

Frequency: Annual. **Primary Exhibits:** Dental products and services.

3549 ■ Alabama Dental Association Annual Session
Alabama Dental Association
836 Washington Ave.
Montgomery, AL 36104
Ph: (334)265-1684
Fax: (334)262-6218
E-mail: waren@aldaonline.org
URL: http://www.aldaonline.org

Frequency: Annual. **Primary Exhibits:** Dental equipment, sundry dental supplies, computer software, and pharmaceutical and dental instruments. **Dates and Locations:** Orange Beach, AL; Perdido Beach Resort.

3550 ■ American Academy of Esthetic Dentistry Annual Meeting
Annual.

3551 ■ American Academy of Implant Dentistry Annual Meeting
American Academy of Implant Dentistry
211 E Chicago Ave., Ste. 750
Chicago, IL 60611
Ph: (312)335-1550
Free: 877-335-2243
Fax: (312)335-9090
E-mail: info@aaid.com
URL: http://www.aaid.com/index.html

Frequency: Annual. **Primary Exhibits:** Dental equipment, supplies, and services.

3552 ■ American Academy of Pediatric Dentistry Annual Session
American Academy of Pediatric Dentistry
211 E Chicago Ave., Ste. 1700
Chicago, IL 60611-2637
Ph: (312)337-2169
Fax: (312)337-6329
URL: http://www.aapd.org

Frequency: Annual. **Primary Exhibits:** Dental products and publications.

3553 ■ American Association of Dental Schools Annual Session and Exposition
American Dental Education Association
1400 K St. NW, Ste. 1100
Washington, DC 20005
Ph: (202)289-7201
Fax: (202)289-7204
URL: http://www.adea.org

Frequency: Annual. **Primary Exhibits:** Dental equipment and supplies, publications, video equipment, and computers.

3554 ■ American Association of Endodontists Annual Convention and Trade Show
American Association of Endodontists
211 E Chicago Ave., Ste. 1100
Chicago, IL 60611-2691
Ph: (312)266-7255

Free: 800-872-3636
Fax: (312)266-9867
E-mail: info@aae.org
URL: http://www.aae.org

Frequency: Annual. **Primary Exhibits:** Industry-related equipment, supplies, and services.

3555 ▪ American Association of Orthodontists Trade Show and Scientific Session

American Association of Orthodontists
401 N Lindbergh Blvd.
Saint Louis, MO 63141-7816
Ph: (314)993-1700
Free: 800-424-2841
Fax: (314)997-1745
E-mail: info@aaortho.org
URL: http://www.aaoinfo.org

Frequency: Annual. **Primary Exhibits:** Orthodontic equipment and materials.

3556 ▪ Chicago Dental Society Midwinter Meeting

Chicago Dental Society
401 N Michigan Ave., Ste. 200
Chicago, IL 60611
Ph: (312)836-7300
Fax: (312)836-7337
E-mail: rgrove@cds.org
URL: http://www.cds.org

Frequency: Annual. **Primary Exhibits:** Dental equipment, services, and related business services. **Dates and Locations:** Chicago, IL; McCormick Place.

3557 ▪ Detroit Dental Review

Detroit District Dental Society
6 Parklane Blvd., Ste. 440
Dearborn, MI 48126
Ph: (313)337-4900
Fax: (313)337-4579
E-mail: centraloffice@detroitdentalsociety.com
URL: http://www.detroitdentalsociety.com

Frequency: Annual. **Primary Exhibits:** Dental equipment, supplies, and services, including office systems.

3558 ▪ General Session and Exhibition of the IADR

International Association for Dental Research
1619 Duke St.
Alexandria, VA 22314-3406
Ph: (703)548-0066
Fax: (703)548-1883
URL: http://www.iadr.com

Frequency: Annual. **Primary Exhibits:** Dentistry equipment, supplies, and services.

3559 ▪ Greater New York Dental Meeting

NY County Dental Society of the State of New York
6 E 43rd St.
New York, NY 10017
Ph: (212)573-8500
Fax: (212)573-9501
E-mail: info@nycdentalsociety.org
URL: http://www.nycdentalsociety.org

Frequency: Annual. **Primary Exhibits:** Dental products and services. **Dates and Locations:** New York, NY; Jacob K. Javits Convention Center.

3560 ▪ Thomas P. Hinman Dental Meeting & Exhibits

Thomas P. Hinman Dental Society of Atlanta
33 Lenox Pte.
Atlanta, GA 30324-3172
Ph: (404)231-1663
Fax: (404)231-9638
URL: http://www.hinman.org

Frequency: Annual. **Primary Exhibits:** Dental equipment, supplies, and services. **Dates and Locations:** Atlanta, GA; Atlanta Market Center.

3561 ▪ Hispanic Dental Association Annual Meeting

Hispanic Dental Association
1111 14th St. NW, Ste. 1100
Washington, DC 20005
Ph: (202)629-3628
Free: 800-852-7921
Fax: (202)629-3802
E-mail: hispanicdental@hdassoc.org
URL: http://www.hdassoc.org

Frequency: Annual.

3562 ▪ Jewel of the Great Lakes--Wisconsin Dental Meeting

Wisconsin Dental Association
6737 W Washington St., Ste. 2360
West Allis, WI 53214
Ph: (414)276-4520
Fax: (414)276-8431
E-mail: mpaget@wda.org
URL: http://www.wda.org

Frequency: Annual. **Primary Exhibits:** Dental equipment and supplies, office supplies, publications, and data processing.

3563 ▪ Michigan Dental Association Annual Session

Michigan Dental Association
3657 Okemos Rd., Ste. 200
Okemos, MI 48864
Ph: (517)372-9070
Free: 800-589-2632
Fax: (517)372-0008
URL: http://www.smilemichigan.com/

Frequency: Annual. **Primary Exhibits:** Dental equipment, materials, and instruments; computers; software; uniforms; and estate planners.

3564 ▪ Mid-Continent Dental Congress

Greater St. Louis Dental Society
11457 Olde Cabin Rd., Ste. 300
Saint Louis, MO 63141
Ph: (314)569-0444
Fax: (314)569-0448
E-mail: gslds@gslds.org
URL: http://www.gslds.org

Frequency: Annual. **Primary Exhibits:** Dental equipment, supplies, and services.

3565 ▪ National Dental Association Annual Convention

National Dental Association
3517 16th St. NW
Washington, DC 20010
Ph: (202)588-1697
Fax: (202)588-1244
URL: http://www.ndaonline.org

Frequency: Annual; always last weekend of July or first week in August. **Primary Exhibits:** Dental and Pharmaceutical equipment, supplies, and services.

3566 ▪ Nation's Capital Dental Meeting

District of Columbia Dental Society
502 C St. NE
Washington, DC 20002-5810
Ph: (202)547-7613
Fax: (202)546-1482
E-mail: info@dcdental.org
URL: http://www.dcdental.org

Frequency: Annual. **Primary Exhibits:** Equipment, clothing, dental supplies, office management systems, and publications.

3567 ▪ Ohio Dental Association Annual Session

Ohio Dental Association
1370 Dublin Rd.
Columbus, OH 43215-1098
Ph: (614)486-2700
Free: 800-282-1526
Fax: (614)486-0381
E-mail: dentist@oda.org
URL: http://www.oda.org

Frequency: Annual. **Primary Exhibits:** Dental equipment, supplies, and services, computers, and insurance. **Dates and Locations:** Columbus, OH; Greater Columbus Convention Center.

3568 ▪ Pacific Northwest Dental Conference

Washington State Dental Association
126 NW Canal St.
Seattle, WA 98107
Ph: (206)448-1914
Free: 800-448-3368
Fax: (206)443-9266
E-mail: info@wsda.org
URL: http://www.wsda.org

Frequency: Annual. **Primary Exhibits:** Dental supplies, instruments, and equipment. Bellevue, WA.

3569 ▪ Star of the North Meeting

Minnesota Dental Association
1335 Industrial Blvd., Ste. 200
Minneapolis, MN 55413-4801
Ph: (612)767-8400
Fax: (612)767-8500
E-mail: info@mndental.org
URL: http://www.mndental.org/

Frequency: Annual. **Primary Exhibits:** Dental equipment and supplies, dental laboratory equipment, office equipment, and service organizations. MN.

3570 ▪ Star of the South Dental Meeting

Greater Houston Dental Society
1 Greenway Plz., Ste. 110
Houston, TX 77046
Ph: (713)961-4337
Fax: (713)961-3617
URL: http://www.ghds.org

Frequency: Annual. **Primary Exhibits:** Dental equipment, supplies, and dental office amenities.

3571 ▪ Three Rivers Dental Conference

Dental Society of Western Pennsylvania
900 Cedar Ave.
Pittsburgh, PA 15212
Ph: (412)321-5810
Fax: (412)321-7719
E-mail: threeriversdental@verizon.net
URL: http://www.dswp.org

Frequency: Annual. **Primary Exhibits:** Dental products and equipment, computers, office equipment, and insurance.

3572 ▪ Western Regional Dental Convention

Arizona State Dental Association
3193 N. Drinkwater Blvd.
Scottsdale, AZ 85251-6491
Ph: (480)344-5777
Free: 800-866-2732
Fax: (480)344-1442
URL: http://www.azda.org

Frequency: Annual. **Primary Exhibits:** Dental supplies and services. AZ.

3573 ▪ Yankee Dental Congress

Maine Dental Association
29 Association Dr.
Manchester, ME 04351-0215
Ph: (207)622-7900
Fax: (207)622-6210
E-mail: info@medental.org
URL: http://www.medental.org

Frequency: Annual. **Primary Exhibits:** Dental products, equipment, and services.

OTHER SOURCES

3574 ▪ Academy of General Dentistry

560 W Lake St., 6th Fl.
Chicago, IL 60611-6600
Ph: (888)243-3368
Free: 888-243-DENT

Fax: (312)335-3443
E-mail: membership@agd.org
URL: http://www.agd.org

Description: Seeks to serve the needs and represent the interest of general dentists. Fosters their dentists' continued proficiency through quality continuing dental education to better serves the public.

3575 ■ Academy of Operative Dentistry
PO Box 25637
Los Angeles, CA 90025
Ph: (310)794-4387
Fax: (310)825-2536
E-mail: david.jones@med.navy.mil
URL: http://www.academyofoperativedentistry.com

Description: Dentists and persons in allied industries. Seeks to ensure quality in all of operative dentistry, teaching, service and research. **Members:** 1,200.

3576 ■ American Academy of Cosmetic Dentistry
402 W Wilson St.
Madison, WI 53703
Ph: (608)222-8583
Free: 800-543-9220
Fax: (608)222-9540
E-mail: info@aacd.com
URL: http://www.aacd.com

Description: Members include more than 8,000 cosmetic and reconstructive dentists, dental laboratory technicians, dental auxiliaries, dental hygienists, educators, researchers and students. Membership benefits include AACD accreditation, registration to AACD's Annual Scientific Session, publications, online search directory, marketing materials, and more.

3577 ■ American Academy of Dental Group Practice
2525 E Arizona Biltmore Cir., Ste. 127
Phoenix, AZ 85016
Ph: (602)381-1185
Fax: (602)381-1093
E-mail: aadgp@aadgp.org
URL: http://www.aadgp.org

Description: Represents active dentists and dental group practices. Aims to improve the level of dental service provided by members through exchanging and expanding of ideas and techniques for patient treatment and practice administration. Promotes group practice and research; accumulates and disseminates information; seeks to achieve the proper recognition for the aims and goals of group practice. Helps support an accreditation program as a system of voluntary peer review.

3578 ■ American Association of Dental Boards
211 E Chicago Ave., Ste. 760
Chicago, IL 60611
Ph: (312)440-7464
E-mail: jtarrant@dentalboards.org
URL: http://dentalboards.org

Description: Represents present and past members of state dental examining boards and board administrators. Assists member agencies with problems related to state dental board examinations and licensure, and enforcement of the state dental practice act. Conducts research; compiles statistics. **Members:** 850.

3579 ■ American Association of Public Health Dentistry
3085 Stevenson Dr., Ste. 200
Springfield, IL 62703
Ph: (217)529-6941
Fax: (217)529-9120
E-mail: info@aaphd.org
URL: http://www.aaphd.org

Description: Represents individuals concerned with improving the public's oral health. Seeks to find ways to meet the challenge of improving oral health. Com-

mits to the expansion of the knowledge base of dental public health and to fostering competency in its practice.

3580 ■ American Association of Women Dentists
216 W Jackson Blvd., Ste. 625
Chicago, IL 60606
Free: 800-920-2293
Fax: (312)750-1203
E-mail: info@aawd.org
URL: http://www.aawd.org

Description: Represents dental students or dentists who are interested in dentistry and advancing women in dentistry. Dedicates itself to enhancing and promoting unique participation and leadership for women in organized dentistry.

3581 ■ American College of Dentists
839J Quince Orchard Blvd.
Gaithersburg, MD 20878-1614
Ph: (301)977-3223
Fax: (301)977-3330
E-mail: office@acd.org
URL: http://acd.org

Description: Dentists and others serving in capacities related to the dental profession. Seeks to advance the standards of the profession of dentistry. Conducts educational and research programs. Maintains speakers' bureau and charitable programs.

3582 ■ American College of Prosthodontists
211 E Chicago Ave., Ste. 1000
Chicago, IL 60611
Ph: (312)573-1260
URL: http://www.prosthodontics.org

Description: Membership includes more than 3,300 prosthodontists, dental technicians, dental students and other dental professionals contributing to the specialty. Committed to the esthetic restoration of teeth, including bridges, crowns/caps, dental implants, dentures, partial dentures, whitening and veneers. Membership includes free subscriptions to the Journal of Prosthodontics, the Messenger, and e-blasts.

3583 ■ American Dental Association
211 E Chicago Ave.
Chicago, IL 60611-2678
Ph: (312)440-2500
Free: 800-947-4746
Fax: (312)440-3542
E-mail: berryj@ada.org
URL: http://www.ada.org

Description: Professional society of dentists. Encourages the improvement of the health of the public and promotes the art and science of dentistry in matters of legislation and regulations. Inspects and accredits dental schools and schools for dental hygienists, assistants, and laboratory technicians. Conducts research programs at ADA Foundation Research Institute. Produces dental health education material used in the U.S. Sponsors National Children's Dental Health Month and Give Kids a Smile Day. Compiles statistics on personnel, practice, and dental care needs and attitudes of patients with regard to dental health.

3584 ■ American Dental Education Association
1400 K St. NW, Ste. 1100
Washington, DC 20005
Ph: (202)289-7201
Fax: (202)289-7204
URL: http://www.adea.org

Description: Individuals interested in dental education; schools of dentistry, advanced dental and allied dental education in the U.S., Canada, and Puerto Rico; affiliated institutions of the federal government and corporations. Works to promote better teaching and education in dentistry and dental research and to facilitate exchange of ideas among dental educators. Sponsors meetings, conferences, and workshops; conducts surveys, studies, and special projects and

publishes their results. Maintains 37 sections and 8 special interest groups representing many different aspects of dental education. **Members:** 19,000.

3585 ■ American Public Health Association
800 I St. NW
Washington, DC 20001-3710
Ph: (202)777-2742
Fax: (202)777-2534
E-mail: comments@apha.org
URL: http://www.apha.org

Description: Professional organization of physicians, nurses, educators, academicians, environmentalists, epidemiologists, new professionals, social workers, health administrators, optometrists, podiatrists, pharmacists, dentists, nutritionists, health planners, other community and mental health specialists, and interested consumers. Seeks to protect and promote personal, mental, and environmental health. Services include: promulgation of standards; establishment of uniform practices and procedures; development of the etiology of communicable diseases; research in public health; exploration of medical care programs and their relationships to public health. Sponsors job placement service.

3586 ■ American School Health Association
1760 Old Meadow Rd., Ste. 500
McLean, VA 22102
Ph: (703)506-7675
Fax: (703)506-3266
E-mail: info@ashaweb.org
URL: http://netforum.avectra.com/eWeb/StartPage .aspx?Site=ASHA1&WebCode=HomePage

Description: School physicians, school nurses, counselors, nutritionists, psychologists, social workers, administrators, school health coordinators, health educators, and physical educators working in schools, professional preparation programs, public health, and community-based organizations. Promotes coordinated school health programs that include health education, health services, a healthful school environment, physical education, nutrition services, and psycho-social health services offered in schools collaboratively with families and other members of the community. Offers professional reference materials and professional development opportunities. Conducts pilot programs that inform materials development, provides technical assistance to school professionals, advocates for school health.

3587 ■ American Society of Dentist Anesthesiologists
2103 S Tan Ct., Unit C
Chicago, IL 60616
Ph: (312)624-9591
Fax: (773)304-9894
E-mail: abrown@asdahq.org
URL: http://www.asdahq.org

Description: Represents dentists who have completed a minimum of two years of full-time postdoctoral training in anesthesiology. Provides continuing education for dentist and physician anesthesiologists through annual scientific meetings and review courses.

3588 ■ American Student Dental Association
211 E Chicago Ave., Ste. 700
Chicago, IL 60611-2687
Ph: (312)440-2795
Free: 800-621-8099
Fax: (312)440-2820
E-mail: membership@asdanet.org
URL: http://www.asdanet.org

Description: Predoctoral and postdoctoral dental students organized to improve the quality of dental education and to promote the accessibility of oral health care; additional membership categories include predental, postdoctoral, international and associate. Represents dental students before legislative bodies, organizations, and associations that affect dental students. Disseminates information to dental students. Sponsors advocacy program and "externships" including Washington National Health Policy, Chicago Administrative, State Government Affairs, and Research. **Members:** 15,000.

3589 ■ California Dental Association
1201 K St.
Sacramento, CA 95814
Ph: (916)443-0505
Free: 800-232-7645
Fax: (916)443-2943
E-mail: contactcda@cda.org
URL: http://www.cda.org

Description: California dentists. Promotes the science and art of dentistry. **Members:** 24,000.

3590 ■ *Career Opportunities in Health Care*
InfoBase Holdings Inc.
132 W 31st., 17 Fl.
New York, NY 10001-3406
Ph: (212)967-8800
Fax: (800)678-3633
E-mail: info@infobasepublishing.com
URL: http://www.ferguson.infobasepublishing.com

Description: Shelly Field. 2007. Third edition. $49.50. 304 pages. **Includes:** Appendices provide lists of educational institutions, periodicals, directories, associations, and unions. Appendices provide lists of educational institutions, periodicals, directories, associations, and unions.

3591 ■ Crown Council
975 Woodoak Ln., Ste. 200
Salt Lake City, UT 84117
Ph: (801)293-8522
Free: 800-276-9658
Fax: (801)293-8524
E-mail: success@crowncouncil.com
URL: http://www.crowncouncil.com

Description: Seeks to improve independent dental practices. Promotes oral health and the fight against oral cancer. Provides patient care and offers state-of-the-art dental procedure facilities.

3592 ■ *Health-Care Careers for the 21st Century*
JIST Publishing
875 Montreal Way
Saint Paul, MN 55102-4245
Ph: (317)613-4200
Free: 800-648-5478
Fax: (800)328-4564
E-mail: info@jist.com
URL: http://www.jist.com

Price: $9.95 Individuals Softcover. **Pages:** 448. **Covers:** Jobs for health care professionals and career opportunities for those pursuing a health-related career, organized into 80 careers in five groups. **Publication includes:** Appendixes listing job source resources and Web sites for health organizations.

3593 ■ Hispanic Dental Association
1111 14th St. NW, Ste. 1100
Washington, DC 20005
Ph: (202)629-3628
Free: 800-852-7921
Fax: (202)629-3802
E-mail: hispanicdental@hdassoc.org
URL: http://www.hdassoc.org

Description: Provides leadership and representation for dental professionals and students who share a common commitment to improve the oral health of the Hispanic community.

3594 ■ Holistic Dental Association
1825 Ponce de Leon Blvd., No. 148
Coral Gables, FL 33134
Ph: (305)356-7338

Fax: (305)468-6359
E-mail: director@holisticdental.org
URL: http://www.holisticdental.org

Description: Represents dentists, chiropractors, dental hygienists, physical therapists, and medical doctors. Aims to provide a holistic approach to better dental care for patients, and to expand techniques, medications, and philosophies that pertain to extractions, anesthetics, fillings, crowns, and orthodontics. Encourages the use of homeopathic medications, acupuncture, cranial osteopathy, nutritional techniques, and physical therapy in treating patients in addition to conventional treatments. Sponsors training and educational seminars. **Members:** 200.

3595 ■ International Congress of Oral Implantologists
1700 Rte. 23 N, Ste. 360
Wayne, NJ 07470
Ph: (973)783-6300
Free: 800-442-0525
Fax: (973)783-1175
URL: http://www.icoi.org

Description: Dentists and oral surgeons dedicated to the teaching of and research in oral implantology (branch of dentistry dealing with dental implants placed into or on top of the jaw bone). Offers fellowship, mastership, and diplomate certification programs. Compiles statistics and maintains registry of current research in the field. Sponsors classes, seminars, and workshops at universities, hospitals, and societies worldwide. Provides consultation and patient information/referral services. **Members:** 7,500.

3596 ■ National Dental Association
3517 16th St. NW
Washington, DC 20010
Ph: (202)588-1697
Fax: (202)588-1244
URL: http://www.ndaonline.org

Description: Professional society for dentists. Aims to provide quality dental care to the unserved and underserved public and promote knowledge of the art and science of dentistry. Advocates the inclusion of dental care services in health care programs on local, state, and national levels. Fosters the integration of minority dental health care providers in the profession, and promotes dentistry as a viable career for minorities through support programs. Conducts research programs. Group is distinct from the former name of the American Dental Association.

3597 ■ National Rural Health Association
4501 College Blvd., No. 225
Leawood, KS 66211
Ph: (816)756-3140
Fax: (816)756-3144
E-mail: mail@nrharural.org
URL: http://www.ruralhealthweb.org

Description: Administrators, physicians, nurses, physician assistants, health planners, academicians, and others interested or involved in rural health care. Creates a better understanding of health care problems unique to rural areas; utilizes a collective approach in finding positive solutions; articulates and represents the health care needs of rural America; supplies current information to rural health care providers; serves as a liaison between rural health care programs throughout the country. Offers continuing education credits for medical, dental, nursing, and management courses.

3598 ■ North American Sikh Medical and Dental Association
4104 Old Vestal Rd., Ste. 108
Vestal, NY 13850
Ph: (607)729-0726

Fax: (607)729-1341
E-mail: nasmda@gmail.com
URL: http://nasmda.org

Description: Promotes the interests of Sikh physicians and dentists in the United States, Canada and elsewhere. Supports Sikh physicians, dentists and other Sikh professionals pursuing their careers in those fields or any other fields. Assists Sikh medical and dental graduates to establish practices and help them obtain adequate post-graduate training. Seeks to improve the medical education and delivery of medical care in the parent homeland. Compiles a comprehensive directory of Sikh physicians and dentists residing in North America.

3599 ■ Pennsylvania Dental Association
PO Box 3341
Harrisburg, PA 17105-3341
Ph: (717)234-5941
Fax: (717)234-2186
E-mail: rvn@padental.org
URL: http://www.padental.org

3600 ■ Society for Executive Leadership in Academic Medicine International
100 N 20th St., 4th Fl.
Philadelphia, PA 19103-1443
Ph: (215)564-3484
Fax: (215)564-2175
E-mail: selam@selaminternational.org

Description: Advocates for the advancement and promotion of women to executive positions in academic health professions. Supports programs designed for individuals interested in careers in academic medicine and dentistry. Promotes collaborations and networking among members and other organizations that share common goals.

3601 ■ Special Care Dentistry Association
330 N Wabash Ave., Ste. 2000
Chicago, IL 60611
Ph: (312)527-6764
Fax: (312)673-6663
E-mail: scda@scdaonline.org
URL: http://www.scdonline.org

Description: Dentists, hygienists, and lay public interested in special care dentistry. Aims to improve oral health and well being of people with special needs. Provides a forum for an exchange of clinical ideas and patient management techniques among members. **Members:** 1,000.

3602 ■ Ukrainian Medical Association of North America
2247 W Chicago Ave.
Chicago, IL 60622-8957
Ph: (773)278-6262
Free: 888-RXU-MANA
Fax: (773)278-6962
E-mail: umana@umana.org
URL: http://www.umana.org

Description: Physicians, surgeons, dentists, and persons in related professions who are of Ukrainian descent. Provides assistance to members; sponsors lectures. Maintains placement service, museum, biographical and medical archives.

3603 ■ Washington State Dental Association
126 NW Canal St.
Seattle, WA 98107
Ph: (206)448-1914
Free: 800-448-3368
Fax: (206)443-9266
E-mail: info@wsda.org
URL: http://www.wsda.org

Description: Provides representation, leadership, education, information, and other services for members, their staff, and their patients.

SOURCES OF HELP-WANTED ADS

3604 ■ Appliance DESIGN Magazine
BNP Media
2401 W Big Beaver Rd., Ste. 700
Troy, MI 48084
Ph: (248)362-3700
Free: 800-952-6643
Fax: (248)362-5103
E-mail: privacy@bnpmedia.com
URL: http://www.appliancedesign.com

Description: Monthly. Provides solutions for design and engineering teams in the global, commercial and medical appliance/durable goods industry. Includes current industry news and a variety of technical articles on technologies, components, materials and services used in the design and development of new products.

3605 ■ Architect Magazine
Russell S. Ellis
One Thomas Cir. NW, Ste. 600
Washington, DC 20005
Ph: (202)452-0800
Fax: (202)785-1974
E-mail: rellis@hanleywood.com
URL: http://www.architectmagazine.com

Description: Monthly. Free of charge to those who qualify. Online edition is also available. Provides the practicing architect with vital business tips, design inspiration, plus ideas for skill development and practice management.

3606 ■ Builder: The Magazine of the National Association of Home Builders
DoveTale Publishers
1 Thomas Cir. NW
Washington, DC 20005
Ph: (202)339-0744
Free: 877-275-8647
Fax: (202)785-1974
E-mail: builder@omeda.com
URLs: http://www.hanleywood.com/default.aspx ?page=magazines; http://www.builderonline.com

Frequency: 13/yr. **Price:** $29.95 U.S. and Canada; $54.95 U.S. and Canada 2 years; $192 Other countries. **Description:** Magazine covering housing and construction industry.

3607 ■ Design Line
American Institute of Building Design
529 14th St. NW, Ste. 750
Washington, DC 20045
Free: 800-366-2423
Fax: (866)204-0293
URL: http://www.aibd.org

Description: Quarterly. Focuses on all aspects of building design. Recurring features include letters to the editor, interviews, a collection, reports of meetings, news of educational opportunities, and notices of publications available.

3608 ■ Design News
Reed Elsevier Group plc - Reed Business Information
360 Park Ave. S
New York, NY 11010
Ph: (212)791-4208
E-mail: corporatecommunications@reedbusiness. com
URL: http://www.designnews.com

Frequency: Monthly. **Description:** Magazine covering design engineering.

3609 ■ Design Perspectives
Industrial Designers Society of America
555 Grove St., Ste. 200
Herndon, VA 20170-4728
Ph: (703)707-6000
Fax: (703)787-8501
E-mail: idsa@idsa.org
URL: http://www.idsa.org

Description: Ten issues/year. The largest newsletter examining the news and trends of industrial design. Recurring features include: new and cutting-edge products, news of people and events in industrial design, resource section, reports of chapter and national activities of IDSA, and a calendar of events.

3610 ■ Fabric Architecture: The International Membrane Structure and Design Magazine
Industrial Fabrics Association International
1801 County Rd. B W
Roseville, MN 55113-4061
Ph: (651)222-2508
Free: 800-225-4324
Fax: (651)631-9334
E-mail: generalinfo@ifai.com
URLs: http://fabricarchitecturemag.com/; http://www .ifai.com/Home/magazinesplash.cfm

Frequency: Bimonthly. **Price:** $39 Two years; $49 Two years Canada and Mexico; $69 Two years international. **Description:** Magazine specializing in interior and exterior design ideas and technical information for architectural fabric applications in architecture and the landscape.

3611 ■ HOW Magazine
FW Media, Inc.
10151 Carver Rd., Ste. 200
Blue Ash, OH 45242
Ph: (513)531-2690
E-mail: contact_us@fwmedia.com
URL: http://www.howdesign.com

Description: Bimonthly. Focuses on helping designers, whether they work for a design firm, for an in-house design department or for themselves, run successful, creative, profitable studios.

3612 ■ Human Factors and Ergonomics Society Bulletin
Human Factors and Ergonomics Society
1124 Montana Ave., Ste. B
Santa Monica, CA 90403-1617

Ph: (310)394-1811
Fax: (310)394-2410
E-mail: info@hfes.org
URL: http://www.hfes.org

Frequency: Monthly. **Description:** Recurring features include calendar of events, news of educational opportunities, and job listings.

3613 ■ Hydraulics & Pneumatics: The Magazine of Fluid Power and Motion Control Systems
Intertec Publishing
5 Penn Plz., 13th Fl.
New York, NY 10001-1810
Ph: (212)613-9700
Free: 800-795-5445
Fax: (212)613-9749
E-mail: bethany.weaver@penton.com
URLs: http://www.hydraulicspneumatics.com/default .aspx; http://www.penton.com/

Frequency: Monthly. **Price:** $70 Individuals; $100 Two years. **Description:** Magazine of hydraulic and pneumatic systems and engineering.

3614 ■ Job Contact Bulletin
Southeastern Theatre Conference
1175 Revolution Mill Dr., Ste. 14
Greensboro, NC 27405
Ph: (336)272-3645
Fax: (336)272-8810
E-mail: dslusser@camden.k12.ga.us
URL: http://www.setc.org

Frequency: Monthly. **Price:** included in membership dues. **Description:** Lists jobs available in theatres.

3615 ■ Live Design: The Art & Technology of Show Business
Penton
249 W 17th St.
New York, NY 10011
Ph: (913)341-1300
Free: 866-748-4926
Fax: (913)967-1905
E-mail: corporatecustomerservice@penton.com
URL: http://livedesignonline.com

Frequency: 9/yr. **Description:** The business of entertainment technology and design.

3616 ■ Masonry Magazine
Mason Contractors Association of America
1481 Merchant Dr.
Algonquin, IL 60102
Ph: (224)678-9709
Free: 800-536-2225
Fax: (224)678-9714
E-mail: bennett@lionhrtpub.com
URL: http://www.masoncontractors.org

Description: Monthly. $43.00/2 years; $29.00/year. Covers every aspect of the mason contractor profession, from equipment and techniques to building codes and standards, training the future masonry labor force, business planning, promoting business, job interviewing, negotiation and legal issues.

3617 ■ *Producers Masterguide: The International Film Directory & Guide*
Producers Masterguide
60 E 8th St., 34th Fl.
New York, NY 10003-6514
Ph: (212)777-4002
Fax: (212)777-4101
E-mail: nypc@earthlink.net
URL: http://www.producers.masterguide.com/cover.html

Frequency: Annual. **Price:** $185 U.S.; $175 Canada; $205 Other countries. **Description:** An international film and TV production directory and guide for the professional motion picture, broadcast television, feature film, TV commercial, cable/satellite, digital and videotape industries in the U.S., Canada, the UK, the Caribbean Islands, Mexico, Australia, New Zealand, Europe, Israel, Morocco, the Far East, and South America.

3618 ■ *Professional Builder: The Magazine of the Housing and Light Construction Industry*
SGC Horizon L.L.C.
3030 W Salt Creek Ln., Ste. 201
Arlington Heights, IL 60005
Ph: (847)391-1000
Fax: (847)390-0408
URL: http://www.housingzone.com/professionalbuilder

Frequency: Monthly. **Price:** Free. **Description:** The integrated engineering magazine of the building construction industry.

3619 ■ *Society for Environmental Graphic Design-Messages*
Society for Environmental Graphic Design
1000 Vermont Ave. NW, Ste. 400
Washington, DC 20005
Ph: (202)638-5555
Fax: (202)638-0891
E-mail: segd@segd.org
URL: http://www.segd.org/publications/messages.html

Description: Monthly. Reports on Society program news, member services, resources, and product news.

3620 ■ *Visual Merchandising and Store Design*
ST Media Group International Inc.
11262 Cornell Park Dr.
Cincinnati, OH 45242
Ph: (513)421-2050
Free: 800-421-1321
Fax: (513)421-5144
E-mail: info@stmediagroup.com
URLs: http://www.stmediagroup.com/index.php3?d=pubs&p=vm; http://vmsd.com

Frequency: Monthly. **Price:** $42 Individuals U.S.; $66 Individuals 2 years, U.S.; $62 Individuals Canada (surface); $100 Individuals 2 years, Canada (surface); $65 Individuals Mexico/Foreign (surface); $105 Individuals 2 years, Mexico/Foreign (surface); $100 Individuals Mexico, 1st Class; $175 Individuals 2 years, Mexico 1st Class; $115 Individuals Central/South America; $205 Individuals 2 years, Central/South America. **Description:** The leading magazine of the retail design industry covering the latest trends in retail design, store planning, and merchandise presentation.

3621 ■ *Wire & Cable Technology International*
Initial Publications Inc.
3869 Darrow Rd., Ste. 109
Stow, OH 44224
Ph: (330)686-9544
Fax: (330)686-9563
E-mail: info@wiretech.com
URL: http://www.wiretech.com/

Frequency: Bimonthly. **Description:** Magazine for manufacturers of ferrous, nonferrous, bare, and insulated wire.

EMPLOYER DIRECTORIES AND NETWORKING LISTS

3622 ■ *ArchitectureWeek*
Artifice Inc.
1342 High St.
Eugene, OR 97401
Ph: (541)345-7421
Free: 800-203-8324
Fax: (541)345-7438
E-mail: artifice@artifice.com
URL: http://www.architectureweek.com

Description: Weekly. Provides information and images for architects, builders, designers, planners and other AEC industry professionals. Also caters to home makers, students and teachers of design. Covers buildings as they open worldwide.

3623 ■ *Black Book Photography*
Black Book Marketing Group Inc.
740 Broadway, Ste. 202
New York, NY 10003
Ph: (212)979-6700
Free: 800-841-1246
Fax: (212)673-4321
E-mail: info@blackbook.com
URL: http://www.BlackBook.com

Frequency: Annual; Latest edition 2008. **Price:** $60 Individuals Deluxe Edition - Hardcover. **Publication includes:** Over 19,000 art directors, creative directors, photographers and photographic services, design firms, advertising agencies, and other firms whose products or services are used in advertising. **Entries include:** Company name, address, phone. Principal content of publication is 4-color samples from the leading commercial photographers. **Arrangement:** Classified by product/service.

3624 ■ *The Dramatists Guild Resource Directory*
Dramatists Guild of America
1501 Broadway, Ste. 701
New York, NY 10036
Ph: (212)398-9366
Fax: (212)944-0420
E-mail: rsevush@dramatistsguild.com
URL: http://www.dramatistsguild.com

Frequency: Annual; Latest edition 2009. **Description:** Contains up-to-date information on agents, attorneys, grants, producers, conferences, and workshops. **Publication includes:** Lists of Broadway and off-Broadway producers; theater and producing organizations; agents; regional theaters; sources of grants, fellowships, residencies; conferences and festivals; playwriting contests; and sources of financial assistance. **Entries include:** For producers--Name, address, credits, types of plays accepted for consideration. For groups--Name, address, contact name, type of material accepted for consideration, future commitment, hiring criteria, response time. For agents--Name, address. For theaters--Theater name, address, contact name, submission procedure, types of plays accepted for consideration, maximum cast, limitations, equity contract, opportunities, response time. For grants, fellowships, residencies, financial assistance, conferences, and festivals--Name, address, contact name, description, eligibility and application requirements, deadline. For play contests--Name, address, prize, deadline, description. **Arrangement:** Contests are by deadline; others are classified.

3625 ■ *ENR--Top 500 Design Firms Issue*
The McGraw-Hill Companies Inc.
PO Box 182604
Columbus, OH 43272
Ph: (212)512-2000
Free: 877-833-5524

Fax: (614)759-3749
E-mail: customer.service@mcgraw-hill.com
URL: http://enr.construction.com/toplists/sourcebooks/2010/designfirms/

Frequency: Annual; latest edition 2010. **Price:** $82 Individuals yearly subscription; $87 Individuals print and online. **Publication includes:** List of 500 leading architectural, engineering, and specialty design firms selected on basis of annual billings. **Entries include:** Company name, headquarters location, type of firm, current and prior year rank in billings, types of services, countries in which operated in preceding year. **Arrangement:** Ranked by billings.

3626 ■ *Film & Television Directory: The Production Maker Source*
Peter Glenn Publications
306 NE 2nd St., 2nd Fl.
Delray Beach, FL 33483
Ph: (561)404-4290
Free: 888-332-6700
Fax: (561)892-5786
URL: http://www.pgdirect.com/ftintro.asp

Frequency: Biennial. **Price:** $30 Individuals. **Pages:** 450. **Covers:** More than 11,000 producers/production companies, crews, support services, and film commissions in the film, music, and video industries in the United States and parts of Canada. **Entries include:** Company name, address, phone, fax, E-mail and URL addresses, name and title of contact. **Arrangement:** Classified by line of business. **Indexes:** Product/service; advertisers by name.

3627 ■ *Hispanic Talent Directory of South Florida*
Teatro Avante
235 Alcazar Ave.
Coral Gables, FL 33134
Ph: (305)445-8877
Fax: (305)445-1301
E-mail: teavante@aol.com
URL: http://www.teatroavante.com

Frequency: Biennial; May of odd years. **Pages:** 20. **Covers:** Hispanic actors, directors, designers, writers, and producers in the south Florida area. **Entries include:** Name, address, phone, specialty, languages spoken. **Arrangement:** Alphabetical.

3628 ■ *International Dictionary of Films and Filmmakers*
St. James Press
PO Box 9187
Farmington Hills, MI 48333-9187
Ph: (248)699-4253
Free: 800-877-4253
Fax: (248)699-8035
E-mail: gale.galeord@cengage.com
URL: http://www.gale.cengage.com

Frequency: 64; Latest edition 2004. **Price:** $238 Individuals per set of 4 volumes. **Pages:** 5,000 in four volumes. **Covers:** In an illustrated multi-volume set, approximately 500 directors and filmmakers, 650 actors and actresses, and 520 writers and production artists (in volumes 2, 3, and 4 respectively). Both historical and contemporary artists are listed, chosen on the basis of international importance in film history. **Entries include:** Name; personal, education and career data; address, when available; filmography; bibliography of monographs and articles on and by the subject, critical essay, illustrations. Volume 1 contains entries describing approximately 680 significant films. **Arrangement:** Alphabetical in each volume. **Indexes:** Film title and nationality indexes in volumes 2, 3, and 4; geographic and personal name indexes in volume 1.

3629 ■ *New England Theatre Conference--Resource Directory*
New England Theatre Conference
215 Knob Hill Dr.
Hamden, CT 06518

Ph: (617)851-8535
E-mail: mail@netconline.org
URLs: http://www.netconline.org; http://www.netcon-line.org/netc-membership.php

Frequency: Annual; January. **Pages:** 84. **Covers:** 800 individuals and 100 groups. **Entries include:** For individuals--Name, address, telephone, e-mail and fax indicating type or level of theater activity, theater and school affiliation. For groups--Name, address; telephone, box office, fax, e-mail, names and addresses of delegates. **Arrangement:** Alphabetical. **Indexes:** Members by Division.

3630 ■ *Who's Where in American Theatre: A Directory of Affiliated Theatre Artists in the U.S.A.*
Feedback Theatrebooks & Prospero Press
PO Box 174
Brooklin, ME 04616
Ph: (207)359-2781
URL: http://www.feedbacktheatrebooks.com

Frequency: Irregular; latest edition 1992; new edition expected, date not set. **Price:** $7.50. **Pages:** 208. **Covers:** over 3,300 producers, directors, performers, designers, writers, theater artists and scholars in the U.S. **Entries include:** Name, title or position, name of organization with which affiliated, address, phone. **Arrangement:** Alphabetical. **Indexes:** Field of specialty.

HANDBOOKS AND MANUALS

3631 ■ *50 Designers/50 Costumes: Concept to Character*
University of California Press/Journals
2120 Berkeley Way
Berkeley, CA 94704-1012
Ph: (510)642-4247
Free: 800-777-4726
Fax: (510)643-7127
E-mail: journals@ucpress.com
URL: http://www.ucpress.edu

Description: Jeffrey Kurland, Deborah Nadoolman Landis, and Academy of Motion Picture Arts and Sciences. 2005. $27.95. 124 pages. Costume designers discuss the challenges involved in creating designs for motion pictures.

3632 ■ *100 Habits of Successful Graphic Designers: Insider Secrets from the World's Top Talent*
Rockport Publishers Inc.
100 Cummings Ctr., Ste. 406-L
Beverly, MA 01915-6101
Ph: (978)282-9590
Fax: (978)283-2742

Description: Josh Berger and Sarah Dougher. 2005. $18.75. Illustrated. 192 pages.

3633 ■ *365 Habits of Successful Graphic Designers*
Rockport Publishers Inc.
100 Cummings Ctr., Ste. 406-L
Beverly, MA 01915-6101
Ph: (978)282-9590
Fax: (978)283-2742

Description: Laurel Saville, Joshua Berger, Steve Gordon Jr., and Sarah Dougher. 2011. $40.00 (paper). 496 pages. Offers information from freelance designers whose years of experience have helped them find solutions for their clients' design needs.

3634 ■ *An A-Z of Type Designers*
Yale University Press
PO Box 209040
New Haven, CT 06520-9040
Ph: (203)432-0960
Free: 800-405-1619
Fax: (203)432-0948
E-mail: customer.care@triliteral.org
URL: http://www.yalepress.yale.edu/yupbooks

Description: Neil Macmillan. 2006. $35.00. 208 pages.

3635 ■ *Creating a Successful Fashion Collection: Everything You Need to Develop a Great Line and Portfolio*
Barron's Educational Series Inc.
250 Wireless Blvd.
Hauppauge, NY 11788
Ph: (631)434-3311
Free: 800-645-3476
Fax: (631)434-3723
E-mail: barrons@barronseduc.com
URL: http://www.barronseduc.com

Description: Steven Faerm. 2012. $22.99 (paperback). 160 pages. Shows fashion design beginners how to craft a winning portfolio and stand out from the competition. Includes sections on the job search process, creating resumes and cover letters, making a good impression during job interviews, and seeking out internships.

3636 ■ *The Creative Business Guide to Running a Graphic Design Business*
W. W. Norton & Company, Incorporated
500 Fifth Ave.
New York, NY 10110-0017
Ph: (212)354-5500
Free: 800-233-4830
Fax: (212)869-0856
E-mail: ksilvasy-neale@wwnorton.com
URL: http://books.wwnorton.com/books/detail.aspx?ID=9939

Description: Cameron Foote. 2009. $35.00. 416 pages.

3637 ■ *Design Secrets: Products 2: 50 Real-Life Projects Uncovered*
Rockport Publishers Inc.
100 Cummings Ctr., Ste. 406-L
Beverly, MA 01915-6101
Ph: (978)282-9590
Fax: (978)283-2742

Description: Cheryl Dangel Cullen and Lynn Haller. 2006. $30.00. Fifty design projects are presented from conception to completion.

3638 ■ *The Fashion Careers Guidebook: A Guide to Every Career in the Fashion Industry and How to Get In*
Barron's Educational Series Inc.
250 Wireless Blvd.
Hauppauge, NY 11788
Ph: (631)434-3311
Free: 800-645-3476
Fax: (631)434-3723
E-mail: barrons@barronseduc.com
URL: http://www.barronseduc.com

Description: Julia Yates and Donna Gustavsen. 2011. $18.99 (flexibound). 192 pages. Offers detailed descriptions of a variety of career opportunities in fashion. Provides tips on: preparing resumes and portfolios; dealing with job interviews; finding opportunities and following up on job applications; and networking.

3639 ■ *Fashion Designer Survival Guide: Start and Run Your Own Fashion Business*
Kaplan Publishing
1 Liberty Plz., 24th Fl.
New York, NY 10006
Ph: (212)632-4973
Free: 800-223-2336
Fax: (800)943-9831
E-mail: kaplanpubsales@kaplan.com
URL: http://www.kaplanpublishing.com

Description: Mary Gehlar. 2005. $22.95. Advice is given to help designers create their own fashion line.

3640 ■ *Fashion Now, Volume 2*
Taschen America L.L.C.
6671 W Sunset Blvd., Ste. 1508
Los Angeles, CA 90028-7123

Ph: (323)463-4441
Free: 888-827-2436
Fax: (323)463-4442
E-mail: contact-us@taschen.com
URL: http://www.taschen.com

Description: Terry Jones and Susie Rushton. Encyclopedia of fashion personalities as well as a guide to the contemporary fashion industry.

3641 ■ *Field Guide: How to be a Fashion Designer*
Rockport Publishers Inc.
100 Cummings Ctr., Ste. 406-L
Beverly, MA 01915-6101
Ph: (978)282-9590
Fax: (978)283-2742

Description: Marcarena San Martin. 2009. $30.00 (paper). 192 pages. Serves as a basic guide for aspiring fashion designers. Covers fundamental concepts surrounding the business of fashion design from both a creative and marketing perspective. Includes a listing of major fashion schools around the world.

3642 ■ *Field Guide: How to be a Graphic Designer*
Rockport Publishers Inc.
100 Cummings Ctr., Ste. 406-L
Beverly, MA 01915-6101
Ph: (978)282-9590
Fax: (978)283-2742

Description: Ana Labudovic and Nenad Vukusic. 2009. $30.00 (paper). 192 pages. Provides readers with practical tips on how to make it in the world of graphic design. Includes a complete reference of all the best design schools around the world.

3643 ■ *Freelance Fashion Designer's Handbook*
John Wiley & Sons Inc. - Scientific, Technical, Medical, and Scholarly Div. (Wiley-Blackwell)
111 River St.
Hoboken, NJ 07030-5774
Ph: (201)748-6000
Fax: (201)748-6088
E-mail: info@wiley.com
URL: http://www.wiley.com

Description: Paula Keech. 2012. $46.99 (paper). 192 pages. Serves as an essential guide on how to work as a freelance fashion designer. Covers topics on how to become a freelance fashion designer and the technical aspects of being a designer. Includes case studies.

3644 ■ *Fresh Dialogue 6: Friendly Fire*
Princeton Architectural Press
37 E 7th St.
New York, NY 10003
Ph: (212)995-9620
Free: 800-759-0190
Fax: (212)995-9454
E-mail: sales@papress.com
URL: http://www.papress.com

Description: American Institute of Graphic Arts Staff. 2006. $16.95. 112 pages.

3645 ■ *Great Jobs for Theater Majors*
The McGraw-Hill Companies Inc.
PO Box 182604
Columbus, OH 43272
Ph: (212)512-2000
Free: 877-833-5524
Fax: (614)759-3749
E-mail: customer.service@mcgraw-hill.com
URL: http://www.mcgraw-hill.com

Description: Jan Goldberg and Julie DeGalan. 2005. $15.95 (paper). 192 pages.

3646 ■ *How to Be a Graphic Designer without Losing Your Soul*
Princeton Architectural Press
37 E 7th St.
New York, NY 10003

Ph: (212)995-9620
Free: 800-759-0190
Fax: (212)995-9454
E-mail: sales@papress.com
URL: http://www.papress.com

Description: Adrian Shaughnessy. 2010. $24.95 (paper). 176 pages. Contains practical advice with philosophical guidance to help young professionals embark on their careers. Offers guidance and strategies for setting up, running, and promoting a studio; finding work; and collaborating with clients. Includes interviews with leading designers.

3647 ■ *Opportunities in Arts and Crafts Careers*
The McGraw-Hill Companies Inc.
PO Box 182604
Columbus, OH 43272
Ph: (212)512-2000
Free: 877-833-5524
Fax: (614)759-3749
E-mail: customer.service@mcgraw-hill.com
URL: http://www.mcgraw-hill.com

Description: Elizabeth Gardner. 2005. $13.95 (paper). 211 pages.

3648 ■ *Opportunities in Museum Careers*
The McGraw-Hill Companies Inc.
PO Box 182604
Columbus, OH 43272
Ph: (212)512-2000
Free: 877-833-5524
Fax: (614)759-3749
E-mail: customer.service@mcgraw-hill.com
URL: http://www.mcgraw-hill.com

Description: Blythe Camenson. 2006. $13.95 (paper). 160 pages.

3649 ■ *Opportunities in Visual Arts Careers*
The McGraw-Hill Companies Inc.
PO Box 182604
Columbus, OH 43272
Ph: (212)512-2000
Free: 877-833-5524
Fax: (614)759-3749
E-mail: customer.service@mcgraw-hill.com
URL: http://www.mcgraw-hill.com

Description: Mark Salmon. 2008. $14.95 (paper). 160 pages. Points the way to a career in the visual arts, examining opportunities for designers, painters, sculptors, illustrators, animators, photographers, art therapists, educators, and others. Offers a view of the pros and cons of working for an art or design company or on your own.

3650 ■ *Savvy Designers Guide to Success*
F & W Publications Inc.
4700 E Galbraith Rd.
Cincinnati, OH 45236
Ph: (513)531-2690
Free: 800-289-0963
Fax: (513)531-4082
URL: http://www.fwbookstore.com

Description: Jeff Fisher. December 2004. $22.99. 192 pages.

3651 ■ *Talent Is Not Enough: Business Secrets for Designers*
Peachpit Press
1249 8th St.
Berkeley, CA 94710
Ph: (510)524-2178
Free: 800-624-0023
Fax: (510)524-2221
E-mail: ask@peachpit.com
URL: http://www.peachpit.com

Description: Shel Perkins. 2006. $35.99. 392 pages. Guide for any designer whether working for someone else to becoming an independent design firm.

3652 ■ *What Designers Know*
Architectural Press
30 Corporate Dr., Ste. 400
Burlington, MA 01803
Ph: (781)313-4700
Fax: (781)313-4880
E-mail: usbkinfo@elsevier.com
URL: http://www.elsevier.com

Description: Bryan Lawson. 2004. $40.95. 144 pages. Design skills, knowledge and understanding are explored, with each chapter focusing on a different technique.

3653 ■ *Winning Portfolios for Graphic Designers: Create Your Own Graphic Design Portfolio Online and in Print*
Barron's Educational Series Inc.
250 Wireless Blvd.
Hauppauge, NY 11788
Ph: (631)434-3311
Free: 800-645-3476
Fax: (631)434-3723
E-mail: barrons@barronseduc.com
URL: http://www.barronseduc.com

Description: Cath Cadwell. 2010. $21.99 (paperback). 144 pages. Serves as guidebook for aspiring graphic designers in crafting portfolios online or in print. Features demonstrative color illustrations, lists of dos and don'ts, and design element examples. Includes tips on making the best impression at a job interview, and explains how working professionals in the field make their sales pitch to get commissions.

EMPLOYMENT AGENCIES AND SEARCH FIRMS

3654 ■ Adkins & Associates
PO Box 16062
Greensboro, NC 27416
Ph: (336)378-1261
Fax: (336)274-7433
URL: http://www.adkinsassociates.com

Description: Exists as an executive search firm for the fashion industry.

3655 ■ Aquent.com
711 Boylston St.
Boston, MA 02116
Ph: (617)535-5000
Fax: (617)535-6001
URL: http://aquent.us

Description: Aquent finds contract, project-based, and permanent work for a broad range of creative and information technology professionals. Applicants submit their applications, which are reviewed by an Aquent agent and, if qualifications match job opportunities, they will be called in for an interview and skills assessment. If skills and experience are appropriate, then will then be assigned an Aquent agent who will get to work finding contract or permanent jobs. Also offers free career resources.

3656 ■ Artisan Creative
1830 Stoner Ave., No. 6
Los Angeles, CA 90025
Ph: (310)312-2062
Fax: (310)312-0670
E-mail: lainfo@artisancreative.com
URL: http://www.artisancreative.com

Description: Serves as a network of designers, developers, account managers and production people providing companies with temporary staffing, full-time recruitment and project management solutions. Provides clients with the top creative resources to complete creative projects. Provides creative talent with opportunities to work for a variety of clients, in a number of roles, at locations around the country.

3657 ■ Artisan for Hire, Inc.
216 S Jefferson, Ste. 202
Chicago, IL 60661
Ph: (312)382-0200
Free: 800-216-0600
E-mail: chicago@artisantalent.com
URL: http://www.artisantalent.com

Description: Provides listings for jobs within the creative industry.

3658 ■ The Aspire Group
711 Boylston St.
Boston, MA 02116-2616
Free: 800-487-2967
Fax: (617)500-7284
URL: http://www.bmanet.com/Aspire/index.html

Description: Employment agency.

3659 ■ Claremont-Branan, Inc.
1298 Rockbridge Rd., Ste. B
Stone Mountain, GA 30087
Free: 800-875-1292
URL: http://cbisearch.com

Description: Employment agency. Executive search firm.

3660 ■ Creative Placement
13 N Main St.
Norwalk, CT 06854-2702
Ph: (203)838-7772
E-mail: kheine@creativeplacement.com
URL: http://www.creativeplacement.com

Description: Serves as an executive search firm for the creative industry. Provides placement for web, design, branding, packaging, advertising, and promotion.

3661 ■ FILTER, LLC
1505 5th Ave., Ste. 600
Seattle, WA 98101
Ph: (206)682-6005
URL: http://www.filterdigital.com

Description: Serves as creative resources company that provides talent in web, marketing, and creative professions. Represents virtually every discipline: designers, copywriters, web architects, icon artists, illustrators, animators, and other specialized artistic and technological talents.

3662 ■ Gene Kaufman Associates Ltd.
450 7th Ave., Ste. 913
New York, NY 10123-0101
Ph: (212)643-0625

Description: Personnel consultant specializing in recruiting on all levels for the apparel industry in the areas of design, sales, merchandising, production, operations and administration.

3663 ■ PrintLink
620 Park Ave.
Rochester, NY 14607
Ph: (716)856-5054
Free: 800-867-3463
Fax: (716)856-8500
E-mail: usjobs@printlink.com
URL: http://www.printlink.com

Description: Serves as a professional placement firm specializing in the graphic communications industry. Offers discreet, confidential permanent placement for all printing, publishing, packaging and document management positions.

3664 ■ Profiles
217 N Charles St., 4th Fl.
Baltimore, MD 21201
Ph: (410)244-6400
Fax: (410)244-6406
URL: http://careerprofiles.com

Description: Recruits professionals for freelance, temporary, and direct hire opportunities specializing in marketing, advertising, creative, web design, graphic design and communications.

3665 ■ Randolph Associates, Inc.
950 Massachusetts Ave., Ste. 105
Cambridge, MA 02139-3174
Ph: (617)441-8777
Fax: (617)441-8778
E-mail: jobs@greatjobs.com
URL: http://www.greatjobs.com
Description: Employment agency. Provides regular or temporary placement of staff.

3666 ■ RitaSue Siegel Resources, Inc.
PO Box 845
New York, NY 10150
Ph: (917)725-1603
E-mail: contact@ritasue.com
URL: http://www.ritasue.com
Description: Executive search firm specializing in industrial and product design.

3667 ■ Semper, LLC
607 Bolyston St., 3rd Fl.
Boston, MA 02116
Free: 800-954-4993
E-mail: dhresumes1@semperllc.com
URL: http://www.semperllc.com
Description: Serves as a placement firm in the graphic arts and printing industry. Specializes in the print, copy and digital industries. Offers several staffing options such as flexible, permanent, flex-to-hire and direct. Offers outplacement service that provides professional career management assistance and counseling to employees who are facing a career change.

3668 ■ S.R. Clarke
105 Huntercombe
Williamsburg, VA 23188
Ph: (703)344-0256
Fax: (949)608-5052
URL: http://www.srclarke.com/index.html
Description: Serves as an executive search and recruitment firm specializing in commercial construction, commercial real estate development, residential asset management, residential construction and development, subcontractor trades, finance, accounting, administration, heavy construction, architectural design and engineering design.

3669 ■ Starpoint Solutions
22 Cortlandt St., Fl. 14
New York, NY 10007-3152
Ph: (212)962-1550
Free: 877-947-9983
Fax: (212)962-7175
URL: http://www.starpoint.com
Description: Serves as a staffing agency that places candidates in both freelance and full-time positions at Chicago and New York's advertising agencies, interactive agencies, and design firms.

3670 ■ TECHEAD
111 N 17th St.
Richmond, VA 23219
Ph: (804)782-6971
Free: 877--
Fax: (804)782-2033
E-mail: info@techead.com
URL: http://www.techead.com
Description: Offers creative and IT staffing services for both job seekers and employers. Provides graphics support and desktop publishing services to local clients. Provides creative talent and information technology staffing services, ADOBE product software training, and creative web development solutions to clients.

Online Job Sources and Services

3671 ■ ArtBistro.com
URL: http://artbistro.monster.com
Description: Serves as a social network for artists and designers allowing them to advance their careers, share portfolios, make new connections, and read the latest art and design news.

3672 ■ Bright Green Talent - Green Jobs
URL: http://www.brightgreentalent.com/green-jobs
Description: Serves as online tool that offers green jobs listing and career advice to candidates interested and engaged in environmental career.

3673 ■ CasinoGigs.net
URL: http://www.casinogigs.net
Description: Serves as a career community for the gambling industry. Features job openings for casino workers, research into the arts, entertainment & gaming employment market, and a career articles section written and frequented by industry professionals.

3674 ■ Construction Jobs Network
URL: http://constructionjobs.net
Description: Provides job seekers access to construction employment opportunities for both construction management, construction professional and construction trade jobs. Features construction jobs, employer, and resume directories.

3675 ■ Coroflot.com
URL: http://www.coroflot.com
Description: Provides networking and promotional tools, and an employer directory for the design industry.

3676 ■ CreativePublic.com
URL: http://www.creativepublic.com
Description: Offers graphic designers and web designers resources and information. Shows designers what to do and what not to do in the graphic design business world. Gives graphic designers resources for starting their own business or expanding into a freelance role.

3677 ■ Design Engineer Jobzone
URL: http://designengineerjobzone.com/site/2791/about.htm
Description: Database of job openings for design engineers. Lists the latest jobs from top companies in the field.

3678 ■ Designer Today
URL: http://designertoday.com/Home.aspx
Description: Bimonthly. Online graphic design magazine for graphic designers. Features graphic design and related tutorials, graphic design software and hardware product reviews, resources for graphic design training, graphic design jobs as well as the latest in graphic design news.

3679 ■ FashionCareerCenter.com
URL: http://www.fashioncareercenter.com
Description: Collects and maintains job seeker and company information through voluntary posting of information. Features fashion schools and colleges, fashion jobs, and career advices.

3680 ■ FashionCrossing.com
URL: http://www.fashioncrossing.com
Description: Provides job listings and other resources related to fashion employment opportunities.

3681 ■ Graphic Design Freelance Jobs
URL: http://www.graphicdesignfreelancejobs.com
Description: Features listings for freelance graphic design employment.

3682 ■ GraphicArtistDesigner.com
URL: http://www.graphicartistdesigner.com
Description: Connects business professionals with the information and professional contacts needed to advance a career in graphic design. Provides access to books, magazines, articles and continuing education.

3683 ■ Guru.com
URL: http://www.guru.com
Description: Job board specializing in contract jobs for creative and information technology professionals. Also provides online incorporation and educational opportunities for independent contractors along with articles and advice.

3684 ■ Interior Architect Jobs
URL: http://www.interiorarchitectjobs.com
Description: Serves as a niche job board for employment opportunities in the field of interior architecture.

3685 ■ StyleCareers.com
URL: http://www.stylecareers.com
Description: Provides a job board for people in the fashion industry.

3686 ■ Talent Zoo
URL: http://www.talentzoo.com
Description: Serves as a resource for advertising, marketing, digital and creative jobs.

3687 ■ You the Designer
URL: http://www.youthedesigner.com
Description: Serves as an online career resource that contains a graphic design blog, graphic design tips and graphic design job openings.

Tradeshows

3688 ■ American Textile Machinery Exhibition International
American Textile Machinery Association
201 Park Washington Ct.
Falls Church, VA 22046
Ph: (703)538-1789
E-mail: info@atmanet.org
URL: http://www.atmanet.org
Frequency: Annual. **Primary Exhibits:** Machinery and supplies for yarn, fiber, and nonwoven manufacturing, weaving, knitting and finishing, and plant maintenance.

3689 ■ Society for News Design Annual Workshop & Exhibition
Society for News Design
424 E Central Blvd., Ste. 406
Orlando, FL 32801
Ph: (407)420-7748
Fax: (407)420-7697
E-mail: skomives@snd.org
URL: http://www.snd.org
Frequency: Annual. Gathers visual journalists from around the world for workshops and general sessions.

Other Sources

3690 ■ American Design Drafting Association
105 E Main St.
Newbern, TN 38059
Ph: (731)627-0802
Fax: (731)627-9321
E-mail: corporate@adda.org
URL: http://www.adda.org
Description: Designers, drafters, drafting managers, chief drafters, supervisors, administrators, instructors, and students of design and drafting. Encourages a continued program of education for self-improvement and professionalism in design and drafting and computer-aided design/drafting. Informs members of effective techniques and materials used in drawings and other graphic presentations. Evalu-

ates curriculum of educational institutions through certification program; sponsors drafter certification program.

3691 ■ American Society of Furniture Designers
4136 Coachmans Ct.
High Point, NC 27262-5445
Ph: (336)307-0999
URL: http://www.asfd.com

Description: Represents professional furniture designers, teachers, students, corporate suppliers of products and services; others who supply products and services related to furniture design. Seeks to promote the profession of furniture design. Conducts and cooperates in educational courses and seminars for furniture designers and persons planning to enter the field. Maintains placement service.

3692 ■ Association of AE Business Leaders
948 Capp St.
San Francisco, CA 94110-3911
Ph: (415)713-5379
E-mail: events@aebl.org
URL: http://www.aebl.org

Description: Individuals responsible for any or all aspects of business management in a professional design firm. Aims to improve the effectiveness of professional design firms through the growth and development of business management skills. Seeks to: provide a forum for the exchange of ideas and information and discussion and resolution of common problems and issues; establish guidelines for approaches to common management concerns; initiate and maintain professional relationships among members; improve recognition and practice of management as a science in professional design firms; advance and improve reputable service to clients; offer a variety of comprehensive educational programs and opportunities. Maintains speakers' bureau and placement service. Holds seminars. Conducts surveys and research programs. Compiles statistics. **Members:** 500.

3693 ■ Association of Women Industrial Designers
PO Box 468
Old Chelsea Sta.
New York, NY 10010
E-mail: info@awidweb.com
URL: http://www.awidweb.com

Description: Serves as a resource that facilitates access to design talent, networking and social interaction in the design community. Advocates projects that enrich the growing public awareness of the work of women industrial designers. Provides a forum for publicizing the work of members and for the dissemination of current design news and information.

3694 ■ *A Career Handbook for TV, Radio, Film, Video and Interactive Media*
Bloomsbury Publishing PLC
50 Bedford Sq.
London WC1B 3DP, United Kingdom
Ph: 44 020 7631 5600
Fax: 020 7631 5800
E-mail: uk@bloomsbury.com
URL: http://www.bloomsbury.com/uk/a-career
   -handbook-for-tv-radio-film-video-and-interactive
   -media-9780713663204/

Frequency: Monthly. **Price:** £13.49 Individuals. **Covers:** TV, radio, film, video and interactive media specialists.

3695 ■ *Career Opportunities in the Fashion Industry*
InfoBase Holdings Inc.
132 W 31st., 17 Fl.
New York, NY 10001-3406
Ph: (212)967-8800
Fax: (800)678-3633
E-mail: info@infobasepublishing.com
URL: http://factsonfile.infobasepublishing.com/

Frequency: Latest edition 2nd; Published

September, 2007. **Price:** $49.50 Individuals Hardcover. **Pages:** 272. **Description:** Peter Vogt. Second edition, 2007. 262 pages. **Includes:** Appendices of educational institutions, periodicals, directories, and associations. **Publication includes:** Lists of Internet resources, educational institutions, organizations, and associations related to the fashion industry. Principal content of publication is information on careers in the fashion world. **Indexes:** Alphabetical.

3696 ■ *Career Opportunities in the Film Industry*
InfoBase Holdings Inc.
132 W 31st., 17 Fl.
New York, NY 10001-3406
Ph: (212)967-8800
Fax: (800)678-3633
E-mail: info@infobasepublishing.com
URL: http://factsonfile.infobasepublishing.com

Frequency: Latest edition 2nd, 2009. **Price:** $49.50 Individuals hardcover. **Pages:** 296. **Description:** Fred Yager and Jan Yager. Second edition, 2009. 268 pages. **Covers:** More than 80 jobs in the field, from the high-profile positions of director, producer, screenwriter, and actor to the all-important behind-the-scenes positions such as casting director, gaffer, and production designer. **Includes:** Appendices of educational institutions, periodicals, directories, and associations.

3697 ■ *Career Opportunities in the Internet, Video Games, and Multimedia*
InfoBase Holdings Inc.
132 W 31st., 17 Fl.
New York, NY 10001-3406
Ph: (212)967-8800
Fax: (800)678-3633
E-mail: info@infobasepublishing.com
URL: http://www.ferguson.infobasepublishing.com

Description: Allan Taylor, James Robert Parish and Dan Fiden. 2007. $49.50. 384 pages. **Includes:** Appendices of educational institutions, periodicals, directories, and associations. Appendices of educational institutions, periodicals, directories, and associations.

3698 ■ *Career Opportunities in Journalism*
InfoBase Holdings Inc.
132 W 31st., 17 Fl.
New York, NY 10001-3406
Ph: (212)967-8800
Fax: (800)678-3633
E-mail: info@infobasepublishing.com
URL: http://www.ferguson.infobasepublishing.com

Description: Jennifer Bobrow Burns. 2007. $49.50 (hardcover). 336 pages. **Includes:** Appendices of related educational programs, professional associations and publications, companies, and internship and scholarship resources. Appendices of related educational programs, professional associations and publications, companies, and internship and scholarship resources.

3699 ■ *Career Opportunities in Television and Cable*
InfoBase Holdings Inc.
132 W 31st., 17 Fl.
New York, NY 10001-3406
Ph: (212)967-8800
Fax: (800)678-3633
E-mail: info@infobasepublishing.com
URL: http://www.ferguson.infobasepublishing.com

Description: 2006. $49.50. Covers job profiles in television and cable industry, followed by the descriptions of the nature of the job, earnings, prospects for employment, what kind of training and skills it requires, and sources of other relevant information.

3700 ■ *Career Opportunities in Theater and the Performing Arts*
InfoBase Holdings Inc.
132 W 31st., 17 Fl.
New York, NY 10001-3406

Ph: (212)967-8800
Fax: (800)678-3633
E-mail: info@infobasepublishing.com
URL: http://www.infobasepublishing.com

Frequency: Latest edition 3rd; Published April, 2006. **Description:** Shelly Field. Third edition, 2006. 304 pages. **Covers:** 80 careers, from acting to designing to dance therapy. **Includes:** Appendices of major agencies, unions, associations, periodicals, and directories.

3701 ■ *Careers for Fashion Plates and Other Trendsetters*
The McGraw-Hill Companies Inc.
PO Box 182604
Columbus, OH 43272
Ph: (212)512-2000
Free: 877-833-5524
Fax: (614)759-3749
E-mail: customer.service@mcgraw-hill.com
URL: http://www.mcgraw-hill.com

Description: Lucia Mauro. 2008. $14.95 (paper). 176 pages. Describes career opportunities in fashion, entertainment, retail, and promotion, with advice from fashion professionals. **Includes:** Appendix of U.S. and Canadian organizations and fashion schools that provide information about job opportunities and educational requirements. Also includes bibliographical references. Appendix of U.S. and Canadian organizations and fashion schools that provide information about job opportunities and educational requirements. Also includes bibliographical references. **Entries include:** Name, address, URL.

3702 ■ *Careers for the Stagestruck and Other Dramatic Types*
The McGraw-Hill Companies Inc.
PO Box 182604
Columbus, OH 43272
Ph: (212)512-2000
Free: 877-833-5524
Fax: (614)759-3749
E-mail: customer.service@mcgraw-hill.com
URL: http://www.mcgraw-hill.com

Description: Lucia Mauro. Second edition, 2004. $13.95 (paper). 160 pages. **Includes:** Appendices of arts organizations, colleges and universities, and other job-hunting and arts education resources, as well as bibliographical references. Appendices of arts organizations, colleges and universities, and other job-hunting and arts education resources, as well as bibliographical references. **Entries include:** Name, address.

3703 ■ Fusion Architecture
PO Box 66853
Phoenix, AZ 85082-6853
E-mail: info@fusionarchitecture.org
URL: http://www.fusionarchitecture.org

Description: Represents the interests of architecture, urban design, graphic design, engineering and cultural practitioners. Encourages young designers to create design solutions to socio-cultural issues. Promotes the use of graphic and information design tools to reach out and produce projects that have influence on the economics, politics, cultural and social structure facing urban communities.

3704 ■ Industrial Designers Society of America
555 Grove St., Ste. 200
Herndon, VA 20170-4728
Ph: (703)707-6000
Fax: (703)787-8501
E-mail: idsa@idsa.org
URL: http://www.idsa.org

Description: Professional society of industrial designers. Represents the profession in its relations with business, education, government, and international designers; promotes the industrial design profession. Conducts research, educational, and charitable programs. Compiles statistics.

3705 ■ *National Directory of Arts Internships*
National Network for Artist Placement
935 West Ave. 37
Los Angeles, CA 90065
Ph: (323)222-4035
E-mail: info@artistplacement.com
URL: http://www.artistplacement.com

Frequency: Biennial; odd years; latest edition 11th. **Price:** $95 Individuals softcover, plus $12 shipping and handling. **Covers:** Over 5,000 internship opportunities in dance, music, theater, art, design, film, and video & over 1,250 host organizations. **Entries include:** Name of sponsoring organization, address, name of contact; description of positions available, eligibility requirements, stipend or salary (if any), application procedures. **Arrangement:** Classified by discipline, then geographical.

3706 ■ Organization of Women Architects and Design Professionals
PO Box 10078
Berkeley, CA 94709
E-mail: info@owa-usa.org
URL: http://owa-usa.org

Description: Comprised of architects, interior designers, landscape architects, planners, lighting designers, graphic designers, photographers, artists, writers, educators and students. Strives to improve the professional standing of women in architecture and design-related fields. Advocates young women and students entering design related fields through mentoring, education, and employment opportunities.

3707 ■ Society for Design and Process Science
3824 Cedar Springs Rd., Ste. 368
Dallas, TX 75219
Ph: (214)253-9025
Fax: (214)520-0227
E-mail: admin@sdpsnet.org
URL: http://sdpsnet.org/sdps

Description: Promotes the development of design and process science. Encourages and fosters research to advance the discipline of design and process science. Provides leadership and resources to foster cooperation among organizations in establishing international standards. Supports continuing education activities and develops international cooperation and understanding among members.

3708 ■ Society for News Design
424 E Central Blvd., Ste. 406
Orlando, FL 32801
Ph: (407)420-7748
Fax: (407)420-7697
E-mail: skomives@snd.org
URL: http://www.snd.org

Description: Comprised of editors, designers, graphic artists, publishers, illustrators, art directors, photographers, advertising artists, website designers, students and faculty. Encourages high standards of journalism through design. Serves as a forum and resource for all those interested in news design.

3709 ■ Specialty Graphic Imaging Association
10015 Main St.
Fairfax, VA 22031-3489
Ph: (703)330-5600

Free: 888-385-3588
Fax: (703)273-0456
E-mail: sgia@sgia.org
URL: http://www.sgia.org

Description: Serves as a group of graphic printers and suppliers. Provides primary imaging technologies services in screen printing, digital printing, embroidery, sublimation and pad printing to create products or add value to existing products. Provides a listing of employment opportunities.

3710 ■ University and College Designers Association
199 W Enon Spring Rd., Ste. 300
Smyrna, TN 37167
Ph: (615)459-4559
Fax: (615)459-5229
E-mail: info@ucda.com
URL: http://ucda.com

Description: Represents colleges, universities, junior colleges, or technical institutions that have an interest in visual communication design; individuals who are involved in the active production of such communication design or as teachers or students of these related disciplines. Improves members' skills and techniques in communication and design areas such as graphics, photography, signage, films, and other related fields of communication design. Aids and assists members in their efforts to be professionals in their respective fields through programs of education and information. Maintains placement service.

SOURCES OF HELP-WANTED ADS

3711 ■ *ACM Transactions on Internet Technology*
Association for Computing Machinery
2 Penn Plz., Ste. 701
New York, NY 10121-0701
Ph: (212)626-0500
Free: 800-342-6626
Fax: (212)944-1318
E-mail: acmhelp@acm.org
URL: http://toit.acm.org

Frequency: Quarterly; February, May, August and November. **Price:** $190 Nonmembers print only; $152 Nonmembers online only; $228 Nonmembers online and print. **Description:** Publication of the Association for Computing Machinery. Brings together many computing disciplines including computer software engineering, computer programming languages, middleware, database management, security, knowledge discovery and data mining, networking and distributed systems, communications, performance and scalability, and more. Covers the results and roles of the individual disciplines and the relationships among them.

3712 ■ *Computers and Composition*
Elsevier Science Inc.
Secondary Publishing Division
650 Ave. of the Americas
New York, NY 10011
Ph: (212)633-3980
Free: 888-437-4636
Fax: (212)633-3975
URL: http://www.elsevier.com/wps/find/journalde-scription.cws_home/620371/description#description

Frequency: 4/yr. **Price:** $454 Individuals and institution; online; $82 Individuals print; $454 Institutions print. **Description:** Journal covering computers in writing classes, programs, and research.

3713 ■ *Computerworld Top 100*
IDG Communications Inc.
492 Old Connecticut Path
Framingham, MA 01701
Ph: (508)872-0080
URLs: http://www.idg.com/www/IDGProducts.nsf/
ByKey/Bulgaria_Publication_Computerworld-Top
-100; http://computerworld.bg/supplement/top100

Frequency: Annual. **Description:** Magazine for analyzing trends and events of information technology business.

3714 ■ *Eclipse Review*
BZ Media LLC
7 High St. Ste. 407
Huntington, NY 11743
Ph: (631)421-4158
URL: http://www.eclipsesource.com/contact.htm

Description: Magazine for IT professionals.

3715 ■ *Foundations and Trends in Networking*
Now Publishers
PO Box 1024
Hanover, MA 02339-1001
Ph: (781)871-0245
E-mail: zac.rolnik@nowpublishers.com
URL: http://www.nowpublishers.com/journals/NET/
latest

Price: $440 Individuals online only; $510 Individuals print and online; €440 Other countries online only; €510 Other countries print and online. **Description:** Academic journal publishing new research in computer networking.

3716 ■ *Government Computer News*
PostNewsweek Tech Media
10 G St. NE, Ste. 500
Washington, DC 20002-4228
Ph: (202)772-2500
Free: 866-447-6864
Fax: (202)772-2511
URL: http://gcn.com/

Frequency: Semimonthly; 30/yr. **Description:** Magazine for professionals interested in government IT.

3717 ■ *IBPA Independent*
Independent Book Publishers Association
1020 Manhattan Beach Blvd., Ste. 204
Manhattan Beach, CA 90266
Ph: (310)546-1818
Fax: (310)546-3939
E-mail: info@ibpa-online.org
URL: http://www.ibpa-online.org

Description: Monthly. Informs member entrepreneurial book publishers about upcoming marketing programs and other Association activities aimed at helping independent publishers succeed. Also carries articles on topics such as desktop publishing and typesetting systems. Recurring features include member, committee, and research news, notices of educational and cooperative marketing opportunities, a calendar of events, and columns titled News from the "Net" and From the Director's Desk.

3718 ■ *IEEE Security & Privacy Magazine*
IEEE Computer Society
10662 Los Vaqueros Cir.
Los Alamitos, CA 90720-1314
Ph: (714)821-8380
Free: 800-272-6657
Fax: (714)821-4010
E-mail: help@computer.org
URL: http://www.computer.org/portal/site/security/

Frequency: Bimonthly. **Price:** $19.95 Individuals online; $65 Nonmembers print; $17.50 Students; $35 Individuals professional. **Description:** Journal that aims to explore role and importance of networked infrastructure and developing lasting security solutions.

3719 ■ *Independent Publisher Online: The Voice of The Independent Publishing Industry*
Jenkins Group Inc.
1129 Woodmere Ave., Ste. B
Traverse City, MI 49686
Ph: (231)933-0445
Free: 800-706-4636
Fax: (231)933-0448
E-mail: publish@jenkinsgroupinc.com
URL: http://www.independentpublisher.com/

Frequency: Monthly. **Price:** Free. **Description:** On-line magazine containing book reviews and articles about independent publishing.

3720 ■ *IT Solutions Guide*
SYS-CON Media
577 Chestnut Ridge Rd.
Woodcliff Lake, NJ 07677
Ph: (201)802-3000
Fax: (201)782-9601
E-mail: subscribe@sys-con.com
URL: http://itsolutions.sys-con.com

Frequency: Quarterly. **Description:** Magazine for IT professionals.

3721 ■ *Journal of Computer Science*
Science Publications
Vails Gate Heights Dr.
Vails Gate, NY 12584-0879
URL: http://thescipub.com/jcs.toc

Frequency: Monthly. **Description:** Scholarly journal covering many areas of computer science, including: concurrent, parallel and distributed processing; artificial intelligence; image and voice processing; quality software and metrics; computer-aided education; wireless communication; real time processing; evaluative computation; and data bases and information recovery and neural networks.

3722 ■ *Monitor: CPCUG's Print Magazine*
Capital PC User Group
19209 Mt. Airey Rd.
Brookeville, MD 20833
Ph: (301)560-6442
Fax: (301)760-3303
E-mail: editor@cpcug.org
URL: http://monitor.cpcug.org/index.html

Frequency: Quarterly. **Description:** Magazine covering computer hardware and software reviews, special interest user group news, advertisers and author/subject index, and calendar of events.

3723 ■ *Queue: Tomorrow's Computing Today*
Association for Computing Machinery
2 Penn Plz., Ste. 701
New York, NY 10121-0701
Ph: (212)626-0500
Free: 800-342-6626

Fax: (212)944-1318
E-mail: queue@acm.org
URL: http://queue.acm.org/

Frequency: Monthly. **Price:** Free. **Description:** Online magazine aimed at the computer professional. Magazine editorial does not provide solutions for the "here-and-now", but instead helps decision-makers plan future projects by examining the challenges and problems they are most likely to face.

3724 ■ *Revenue*
Montgomery Media International
55 New Montgomery St., Ste. 617
San Francisco, CA 94105
Ph: (415)371-8800
E-mail: info@mthink.com
URL: http://www.revenuetoday.com/

Description: Magazine covering internet marketing strategies.

3725 ■ *WITI FastTrack*
UBM L.L.C.
240 W 35th St.
New York, NY 10001
Ph: (516)562-5000
Free: 800-842-0798
Fax: (516)562-7830
E-mail: contact@ubmtechnology.com
URL: http://www.witi.com/corporate/fasttrack.php

Frequency: Semiannual. **Description:** Semiannual publication featuring in-depth content on the issues facing today's women professionals in technology.

EMPLOYER DIRECTORIES AND NETWORKING LISTS

3726 ■ *The Information Professional's Guide to Career Development Online*
Information Today, Inc.
143 Old Marlton Pke.
Medford, NJ 08055-8750
Ph: (609)654-6266
Free: 800-300-9868
Fax: (609)654-4309
E-mail: custserv@infotoday.com
URL: http://www.infotoday.com

Price: $29.50 Individuals softbound. **Pages:** 392. **Covers:** Web sites, professional associations, and conferences for the career development of information professionals. **Indexes:** Alphabetical.

HANDBOOKS AND MANUALS

3727 ■ *The Complete Help Book for Authors and Publishers*
Hannacroix Creek Books Inc.
1127 High Ridge Rd., Ste. 110B
Stamford, CT 06905-1203
Ph: (203)968-8098
Fax: (203)968-0193
E-mail: hannacroix@aol.com
URL: http://www.hannacroixcreekbooks.com

Description: Jan Yeager. 2007. $29.95. Explores self-publishing for authors.

ONLINE JOB SOURCES AND SERVICES

3728 ■ GetDesktopPublishingJobs.com
URL: http://www.getdesktoppublishingjobs.com

Description: Provides resources for finding and filling desktop publishing positions. Offers job postings and employment opportunities worldwide.

3729 ■ Graphic Artists Guild
URL: http://www.graphicartistsguild.org

Description: JOBLine News section of Guild Resources page contains weekly e-mail newsletter of job listings. Fee: Must subscribe to e-mail newsletter non-member six-month rates start at $80. Visitors may download a free sample.

3730 ■ Guru.com
URL: http://www.guru.com

Description: Job board specializing in contract jobs for creative and information technology professionals. Also provides online incorporation and educational opportunities for independent contractors along with articles and advice.

3731 ■ Publish.com
URL: http://www.publish.com

Description: Offers a variety of resources for desktop publishers.

3732 ■ PublishingMVP.com
URL: http://www.publishingmvp.com

Description: Provides job opportunities in the publishing arena of the marketing industry.

TRADESHOWS

3733 ■ Association of Alternative Newsmedia Web Publishing Conference
Association of Alternative Newsmedia
1156 15th St. NW, Ste. 905
Washington, DC 20005
Ph: (202)289-8484
Fax: (202)289-2004
E-mail: web@aan.org
URL: http://www.altweeklies.com

Biennial. Provides assistance to AAN publishers and editors in strategizing online presence and adapting new electronic-publishing formats and technologies.

3734 ■ National Federation of Press Women Conference
National Federation of Press Women
200 Little Falls St., Ste.405
Falls Church, VA 22046
Ph: (703)237-9804
Free: 800-780-2715
Fax: (703)237-9808
E-mail: presswomen@aol.com
URL: http://www.nfpw.org

Frequency: Annual. Features speakers as well as other activities, workshops, resources, and networking opportunities.

3735 ■ Online News Association Annual Conference
Online News Association
c/o Jane McDonnell, Executive Director
1111 N Capitol St. NE 6th Fl.
Washington, DC 20002
Ph: (646)290-7900
E-mail: director@journalists.org
URL: http://journalists.org

Frequency: Annual. Includes activities such as pre-conference workshops, job fair, online journalism awards banquet and more.

3736 ■ Society for News Design Annual Workshop & Exhibition
Society for News Design
424 E Central Blvd., Ste. 406
Orlando, FL 32801
Ph: (407)420-7748
Fax: (407)420-7697
E-mail: skomives@snd.org
URL: http://www.snd.org

Frequency: Annual. Gathers visual journalists from around the world for workshops and general sessions.

OTHER SOURCES

3737 ■ Association of Alternative Newsmedia
1156 15th St. NW, Ste. 905
Washington, DC 20005
Ph: (202)289-8484
Fax: (202)289-2004
E-mail: web@aan.org
URL: http://www.altweeklies.com

Description: Serves as a diverse group of alt-weekly news organizations covering every major metropolitan area and other less-populated regions of North America. Encourages high-quality journalism among its members. Brings together publications that offer a valuable alternative to the mainstream media.

3738 ■ Association for Women in Computing
PO Box 2768
Oakland, CA 94602
E-mail: info@awc-hq.org
URL: http://www.awc-hq.org

Description: Individuals interested in promoting the education, professional development, and advancement of women in computing.

3739 ■ National Association of Photoshop Professionals
333 Douglas Rd. E
Oldsmar, FL 34677-2922
Ph: (813)433-5000
Free: 800-2013-7323
Fax: (813)433-5015
E-mail: privacy@kelbymediagroup.com
URL: http://www.photoshopuser.com

Description: Association website includes member job bank where visitors can search for available jobs or post their resumes for employer review, along with other career-related resources. Fee: Must be member of association to access; dues are $99 for a one-year membership. **Members:** 71,000.

3740 ■ National Federation of Press Women
200 Little Falls St., Ste.405
Falls Church, VA 22046
Ph: (703)237-9804
Free: 800-780-2715
Fax: (703)237-9808
E-mail: presswomen@aol.com
URL: http://www.nfpw.org

Description: Serves as a group of professional women and men pursuing careers across the communications spectrum.

3741 ■ Online News Association
c/o Jane McDonnell, Executive Director
1111 N Capitol St. NE 6th Fl.
Washington, DC 20002
Ph: (646)290-7900
E-mail: director@journalists.org
URL: http://journalists.org

Description: Promotes the Internet as powerful communications medium and represents online journalists and professionals associated with producing news for digital presentation.

3742 ■ Society for News Design
424 E Central Blvd., Ste. 406
Orlando, FL 32801
Ph: (407)420-7748
Fax: (407)420-7697
E-mail: skomives@snd.org
URL: http://www.snd.org

Description: Comprised of editors, designers, graphic artists, publishers, illustrators, art directors, photographers, advertising artists, website designers, students and faculty. Encourages high standards of journalism through design. Serves as a forum and resource for all those interested in news design.

Dietetic Technicians

SOURCES OF HELP-WANTED ADS

3743 ■ *Princeton Health*
Nautilus Publishing Company
PO Box 40
Taylor, MS 38673
Ph: (662)513-0159
E-mail: info@nautiluspublishing.com
URLs: http://www.nautiluspublishing.com; http://www
.princetonhcs.org/phcs-home/who-we-serve/com-
munity/princeton-health.aspx
Frequency: Bimonthly. **Description:** Health
magazine featuring the latest health-related news
and information.

3744 ■ *SOBeFit*
MPG Publishing
1201 Brickell Ave., Ste. 320
Miami, FL 33131
Ph: (305)375-9595
Fax: (305)375-9596
E-mail: questions@sobefitmagazine.com
URL: http://www.sobefitmagazine.com
Frequency: Bimonthly. **Description:** Magazine
focusing on fitness, nutrition, health, and sports.

3745 ■ *Today's Dietitian*
URL: http://www.todaysdietitian.com
Description: Monthly. Provides career development
resources for nutrition professionals. Features
articles on nutrition including culinary trends, long-
term care issues, new products and technologies,
clinical concerns, career strategies, and research
updates.

EMPLOYER DIRECTORIES AND NETWORKING LISTS

3746 ■ *Crain's List--Chicago's Largest Hospitals*
Crain Communications Inc.
150 N Michigan Ave.
Chicago, IL 60601-7553
Ph: (312)649-5200
Free: 800-678-9595
Fax: (312)280-3150
E-mail: info@crain.com
URL: http://www.chicagobusiness.com/section/lists
Frequency: Published November, 2012. **Price:** $25
Individuals PDF format; $45 Individuals Excel format.
Covers: 25 hospitals in Chicago area ranked by net
patient revenues. **Entries include:** Name, address,
phone number, fax, web address, corporate e-mail,
hospital administrator, network affiliation, 2011 net
patient revenue, percentage change from 2010, 2011
net profits, percentage change from 2011, inpatient
days, available beds, daily occupancy rate, number
of hospital employees as of December 31, 2011, fis-

cal year end, Chairman, President, CEO, Chief
Financial Officer, Human Resources Manager, Media
Relations/Public Relations Director, and Hospital
Administrator.

HANDBOOKS AND MANUALS

3747 ■ *The Clinical Dietitian's Essential Pocket Guide*
Lippincott Williams & Wilkins
2 Commerce Sq.
2001 Market St.
Philadelphia, PA 19103
Ph: (301)223-2300
Free: 800-638-3030
E-mail: ronna.ekhouse@wolterskluwer.com
URL: http://www.lww.com
Description: Mary Width and Tonia Reinhard. 2008.
$37.95. 512 pages. Covers nutritional assessment,
life stage management, and nutrition support.
Includes chapters on the major nutritionally relevant
cases.

3748 ■ *Counselling Skills for Dietitians, 2nd Edition*
John Wiley & Sons Inc.
111 River St.
Hoboken, NJ 07030-5774
Ph: (201)748-6000
Free: 800-225-5945
Fax: (201)748-6088
E-mail: info@wiley.com
URL: http://www.wiley.com
Description: Judy Gable. 2007. $66.99 (paper). 272
pages. Demonstrates how a practitioner can develop
a counselling approach and employ appropriate
counselling skills to overcome the communication dif-
ficulties encountered by dietitians and those engaged
in helping clients change their eating behavior.

3749 ■ *Dietetic Technician, Registered Exam Secrets Study Guide*
Mometrix Media, LLC
3827 Phelan Blvd., No. 179
Beaumont, TX 77707
Free: 800-673-8175
Fax: (866)235-0173
E-mail: css@mometrix.com
URL: http://www.mo-media.com
Description: 2009. Provides guidance on passing
the dietetic technician examinations.

3750 ■ *International Dietetics and Nutrition Terminology Reference Manual: Standardized Language for the Nutrition Care Process, 3rd Edition*
Academy of Nutrition and Dietetics
120 S Riverside Plaza, Ste. 2000
Chicago, IL 60606-6995
Ph: (312)899-0040

Free: 800-877-1600
E-mail: knowledge@eatright.org
URL: http://www.eatright.org
Description: $45.00 for members; 95.00 for non-
members. Serves as a guide for implementing the
nutrition care process.

ONLINE JOB SOURCES AND SERVICES

3751 ■ *CareerVitals.com*
URL: http://www.careervitals.com
Description: Serves as a job board for healthcare
professionals in different specializations.

3752 ■ *DietaryAideJob.com*
URL: http://www.indeed.com/q-Dietary-Aide-jobs.html
Description: Provides dietary aide job listings and
career opportunities. Features other employment opportunities such as job qualification guides and job
descriptions.

3753 ■ *DietaryJobs.com*
URL: http://www.dietaryjobs.com
Description: Offers dietary employment opportuni-
ties. Features dietary jobs across the United States.

3754 ■ *DietaryJobs.org*
URL: http://dietaryjobs.org
Description: Offers dietary job listings and employment opportunities. Enables job searching in specific
locations and specific areas in the dietary field.

3755 ■ *Dietetics.com*
URL: http://www.dietetics.com
Description: Provides dietetic professionals with
information including internet links on topics that affect careers and the profession in general. Contains
employment opportunities for dietetic professionals.

3756 ■ *DieticianJobs.com*
URL: http://www.dieticianjobs.com
Description: Provides dietician job listings and
career opportunities. Also lists salary information.

3757 ■ *DieticianNutritionist.com*
URL: http://www.dieticiannutritionist.com
Description: Serves as a job board for dieticians,
nutritionists, and dietetic professionals. Provides access to books, magazines, articles, and continuing
education. Provides help in finding new jobs, posting
resumes, and accessing career resources.

3758 ■ *Jobs In Dietetics*
URL: http://www.jobsindietetics.com
Description: Provides nationwide career support for
nutritionists as well as dietetics and food service
professionals. Offers a subscription job listing
service.

3759 ■ RDLink.com
URL: http://www.rdlink.com

Description: Provides links to dietetic technicians, dietitians, and nutritionists on the web. Features job listings.

3760 ■ RegisteredDieticiansJobs.com
URL: http://www.registereddieticianjobs.com

Description: Offers career resources for diet and nutrition professionals. Provides jobs searching, resume posting, and career tools for job seekers.

OTHER SOURCES

3761 ■ *300 Ways to Put Your Talent to Work in the Health Field*
National Health Council
1730 M St. NW, Ste. 500
Washington, DC 20036-4561
Ph: (202)785-3910
Fax: (202)785-5923
URL: http://www.nationalhealthcouncil.org

Frequency: Irregular; Latest edition 2002. **Price:** $15 Members; $18 Nonmembers. **Publication includes:** Professional associations, government agencies, institutions, and other organizations offering information or assistance concerning health career education. Principal content of publication is job descriptions and educational requirements for various health professions. **Entries include:** Organization name, address, whether financial aid is offered. **Arrangement:** Classified by occupation.

3762 ■ Academy of Nutrition and Dietetics
120 S Riverside Plaza, Ste. 2000
Chicago, IL 60606-6995
Ph: (312)899-0040
Free: 800-877-1600
E-mail: knowledge@eatright.org
URL: http://www.eatright.org

Description: Represents food and nutrition professionals. Promotes nutrition, health and well-being.

3763 ■ American Society for Nutrition
9650 Rockville Pike
Bethesda, MD 20814-3998
Ph: (301)634-7050
Fax: (301)634-7892
E-mail: info@nutrition.org
URL: http://www.nutrition.org

Description: Quarterly. $30/year. Contains updates on nutrition legislation, public affairs, and public information policies. Reviews the results of nutritional research conducted by members of the Institute, which is comprised of nutrition scientists from universities, government, and industry. Recurring features include news of members, letters to the editor, job listings, notices of publications available, information on awards and fellowships, and news of scientific meetings.

3764 ■ *Career Opportunities in Health Care*
InfoBase Holdings Inc.
132 W 31st., 17 Fl.
New York, NY 10001-3406
Ph: (212)967-8800
Fax: (800)678-3633
E-mail: info@infobasepublishing.com
URL: http://www.ferguson.infobasepublishing.com

Description: Shelly Field. 2007. Third edition. $49.50. 304 pages. **Includes:** Appendices provide lists of educational institutions, periodicals, directories, associations, and unions. Appendices provide lists of educational institutions, periodicals, directories, associations, and unions.

3765 ■ Genetic Metabolic Dietitians International
PO Box 33985
Fort Worth, TX 76162
E-mail: info@gmdi.org
URL: http://www.gmdi.org

Description: Represents the interests of nutritionists and other health care practitioners. Enhances and supports the practice of genetic metabolic nutrition. Provides leadership in nutrition therapy for genetic metabolic disorders through clinical practice, education, advocacy, and research.

3766 ■ *Health-Care Careers for the 21st Century*
JIST Publishing
875 Montreal Way
Saint Paul, MN 55102-4245
Ph: (317)613-4200
Free: 800-648-5478
Fax: (800)328-4564
E-mail: info@jist.com
URL: http://www.jist.com

Price: $9.95 Individuals Softcover. **Pages:** 448. **Covers:** Jobs for health care professionals and career opportunities for those pursuing a health-related career, organized into 80 careers in five groups. **Publication includes:** Appendixes listing job source resources and Web sites for health organizations.

Dietitians and Nutritionists

SOURCES OF HELP-WANTED ADS

3767 ■ *Chef: The Food Magazine for Professionals*
Talcott Communication Corp.
233 N Michigan Ave., Ste. 1780
Chicago, IL 60601
Ph: (312)849-2220
Free: 800-229-1967
Fax: (312)849-2174
E-mail: chef@talcott.com
URL: http://www.chefmagazine.com
Frequency: 11/yr. **Price:** $32 Individuals; $47 Two years; $64 Individuals 3 years; $43 Canada; $96 Other countries. **Description:** Food information for chefs.

3768 ■ *Dietary Manager Magazine*
Dietary Managers Association
406 Surrey Woods Dr.
Saint Charles, IL 60174
Free: 800-323-1908
Fax: (630)587-6308
E-mail: info@dmaonline.org
URL: http://www.dmaonline.org/Publications/Dietary
_Manager.shtml
Frequency: Monthly; 10/yr. **Price:** $40 Individuals.
Description: Professional magazine focusing on nutrition and management issues encountered by dietary managers in non-commercial food service.

3769 ■ *Field & Feast: The Magazine of Food, Agriculture & Health*
Field & Feast
PO Box 205
Four Lakes, WA 99014
E-mail: fieldandfeast@aol.com
URL: http://www.fieldandfeast.net
Frequency: Quarterly. **Price:** $19 Individuals.
Description: Magazine that offers information on organic food cultivation and its health benefits.

3770 ■ *Food Management: Ideas for Colleges, Healthcare, Schools and Business Dining*
Intertec Publishing
5 Penn Plz., 13th Fl.
New York, NY 10001-1810
Ph: (212)613-9700
Free: 800-795-5445
Fax: (212)613-9749
E-mail: bethany.weaver@penton.com
URL: http://food-management.com/
Frequency: Monthly. **Description:** Magazine for foodservice professionals in the onsite 'noncommercial' market.

3771 ■ *FoodService Director: Your Source for Operational Excellence*
Ideal Media L.L.C.
90 Broad St., Ste. 402
New York, NY 10004

Ph: (646)708-7300
Fax: (646)708-7399
URL: http://www.fsdmag.com
Frequency: Monthly. **Price:** $79 Individuals; $99 Canada; $235 Out of country. **Description:** Tabloid newspaper of the noncommercial foodservice market.

3772 ■ *Foodservice East*
The Newbury Street Group Inc.
93 Massachusetts Ave., Ste. 306
Boston, MA 02115
Ph: (617)267-2224
Fax: (617)267-5554
URL: http://www.foodserviceeast.com/
Frequency: Bimonthly; 6/year. **Price:** $30 Individuals. **Description:** Compact Tabloid covering trends and analysis of the foodservice industry in the Northeast. A business-to-business publication featuring news, analysis and trends for the Northeast food service professional.

3773 ■ *Genes and Nutrition*
New Century Health Publishers L.L.C.
PO Box 175
Coppell, TX 75019
Fax: (940)565-8148
E-mail: nchpjournals@gmail.com
URL: http://www.newcenturyhealthpublishers.com/
genes_and_nutrition/
Frequency: Quarterly. **Price:** $428 Institutions; $228 Individuals. **Description:** International, interdisciplinary peer reviewed scientific journal for critical evaluation of research on the relationship between genetics & nutrition with the goal of improving human health.

3774 ■ *Herbs for Health*
Echo Media
900 Circle 75 Pky., Ste. 1600
Atlanta, GA 30339
Ph: (770)955-3535
Fax: (770)955-3599
E-mail: salesinfo@echo-media.com
URLs: http://www.echo-media.com; http://www.echo
-media.com/mediaDetail.php?ID=4907
Frequency: Bimonthly. **Description:** Magazine covering topics ranging from recent scientific research to consumer guides, medicinal recipes, and legislative updates.

3775 ■ *The IHS Primary Care Provider*
U.S. Department of Health and Human Services - Indian Health Service
Reyes Bldg.
801 Thompson Ave., Ste. 400
Rockville, MD 20852-1627
Ph: (301)443-6394
Fax: (301)443-4794
E-mail: charles.grim@ihs.hhs.gov
URL: http://www.ihs.gov/provider
Frequency: Monthly. **Description:** Journal for health

care professionals, physicians, nurses, pharmacists, dentists, and dietitians.

3776 ■ *Journal of the American College of Nutrition*
American College of Nutrition
300 S Duncan Ave., Ste. 225
Clearwater, FL 33755
Ph: (727)446-6086
Fax: (727)446-6202
E-mail: jacn@wayne.edu
URL: http://www.jacn.org
Frequency: Bimonthly. **Price:** $45 Members; $85 Other countries members; $90 Nonmembers; $130 Other countries; $235 Institutions; $275 Institutions, other countries. **Description:** Journal on nutrition.

3777 ■ *Journal of Parenteral and Enteral Nutrition*
Pine Forge Press
2455 Teller Rd.
Thousand Oaks, CA 91320-2234
Ph: (805)499-4224
Free: 800-818-7243
Fax: (805)499-0871
E-mail: sales@pfp.sagepub.com
URL: http://www.sagepub.com
Description: Bimonthly. $400/year for institutions; $190/year for individuals. Serves as a scientific journal of nutrition and metabolic support. Publishes original, peer-reviewed studies that discuss basic and clinical research in the field. Explores the science of optimizing the care of patients receiving enteral or IV therapies. Includes reviews, techniques, brief reports, case reports, abstracts, and advertising.

3778 ■ *Nutrition Notes*
American Society for Nutrition
9650 Rockville Pike
Bethesda, MD 20814-3998
Ph: (301)634-7050
Fax: (301)634-7892
E-mail: info@nutrition.org
URL: http://www.nutrition.org
Description: Quarterly. $30/year. Contains updates on nutrition legislation, public affairs, and public information policies. Reviews the results of nutritional research conducted by members of the Institute, which is comprised of nutrition scientists from universities, government, and industry. Recurring features include news of members, letters to the editor, job listings, notices of publications available, information on awards and fellowships, and news of scientific meetings.

3779 ■ *Nutritional Outlook*
UBM Canon
2901 28th St., Ste. 100
Santa Monica, CA 90405-2975
Ph: (310)445-4200

Fax: (310)445-4299
E-mail: info@nutritionaloutlook.com
URLs: http://www.nutritionaloutlook.com/; http://www.canonmediakit.com/publications/detail.php?publd=35
Frequency: 9/yr. **Description:** Magazine for manufacturer's resource for dietary supplements and healthy foods and beverages.

3780 ■ Real Food: The magazine for the way we eat today
Greenspring Media Group Inc.
600 US Trust Bldg., 730 2nd Ave. S
Minneapolis, MN 55402-1012
Ph: (612)371-5800
Free: 800-933-4398
Fax: (612)371-5801
E-mail: letters@mnmo.com
URL: http://www.realfoodmag.com/
Frequency: Quarterly. **Price:** $20 Individuals.
Description: Magazine featuring food choices.

3781 ■ Southeast Food Service News
Southeast Publishing Company Inc.
c/o Elliott Fischer, Mktg. Dir.
8805 Tamiami Trail N, No. 301
Naples, FL 34108
Ph: (239)514-1258
URL: http://www.sfsn.com
Frequency: Monthly. **Price:** $36 Individuals; $5 Single issue; $59 Individuals directory issue.
Description: Magazine (tabloid) serving the food industry.

3782 ■ Sunbelt Foodservice
Shelby Publishing Company Inc.
517 Green St. NW
Gainesville, GA 30501
Ph: (770)534-8380
Fax: (678)343-2197
E-mail: editor@shelbypublishing.com
URL: http://www.shelbypublishing.com/index.php?option=com_content&task=view&id=24&Itemid=45
Frequency: Monthly. **Price:** $36 Individuals; $60 Two years. **Description:** Trade newspaper (tabloid) covering the food industry geared toward restaurant operators.

3783 ■ Today's Dietitian
URL: http://www.todaysdietitian.com
Description: Monthly. Provides career development resources for nutrition professionals. Features articles on nutrition including culinary trends, long-term care issues, new products and technologies, clinical concerns, career strategies, and research updates.

3784 ■ Vegetarian Times
Active Interest Media
PO Box 420235
Palm Coast, FL 32142-0235
Free: 877-717-8923
E-mail: editor@vegetariantimes.com
URLs: http://www.vegetariantimes.com/; http://www.airmmedia.com/vt.html
Frequency: 10/yr. **Price:** $14.95 Individuals; $26.95 Canada 9 issues; $47.95 Canada 18 issues; $38.95 Other countries 9 issues; $71.95 Other countries 18 issues. **Description:** Magazine devoted to plant-based foods and related topics such as health, fitness, and the environment.

EMPLOYER DIRECTORIES AND NETWORKING LISTS

3785 ■ Crain's List--Chicago's Largest Hospitals
Crain Communications Inc.
150 N Michigan Ave.
Chicago, IL 60601-7553
Ph: (312)649-5200

Free: 800-678-9595
Fax: (312)280-3150
E-mail: info@crain.com
URL: http://www.chicagobusiness.com/section/lists
Frequency: Published November, 2012. **Price:** $25 Individuals PDF format; $45 Individuals Excel format. **Covers:** 25 hospitals in Chicago area ranked by net patient revenues. **Entries include:** Name, address, phone number, fax, web address, corporate e-mail, hospital administrator, network affiliation, 2011 net patient revenue, percentage change from 2010, 2011 net profits, percentage change from 2011, inpatient days, available beds, daily occupancy rate, number of hospital employees as of December 31, 2011, fiscal year end, Chairman, President, CEO, Chief Financial Officer, Human Resources Manager, Media Relations/Public Relations Director, and Hospital Administrator.

3786 ■ Directory of Hospital Personnel
Grey House Publishing
4919 Rte. 22
Amenia, NY 12501
Ph: (518)789-8700
Free: 800-562-2139
Fax: (518)789-0556
E-mail: books@greyhouse.com
URL: http://www.greyhouse.com/hospital_personnel.htm
Frequency: Annual; Latest edition 2011. **Price:** $325 Individuals Softcover. **Pages:** 2,300. **Covers:** 200,000 executives at 6,000 U.S. Hospitals. **Entries include:** Name of hospital, address, phone, number of beds, type and JCAHO status of hospital, names and titles of key department heads and staff, medical and nursing school affiliations; number of residents, interns, and nursing students. **Arrangement:** Geographical. **Indexes:** Hospital name, personnel, hospital size.

3787 ■ Directory of the National Association of Advisors for the Health Professions
National Association of Advisors for the Health Professions
108 Hessel Blvd., Ste. 101
Champaign, IL 61820-6596
Ph: (217)355-0063
Fax: (217)355-1287
E-mail: naahpja@aol.com
URL: http://www.naahp.org
Frequency: Annual; Latest edition 2011. **Price:** $25; $25/issue. **Description:** Includes health professional school announcements and order forms. **Covers:** College and university faculty who advise and counsel students on health careers.

3788 ■ Health Professionals Directory
Sussex Directories Inc.
10 Market St., Ste. 750
Camana Bay
Grand Cayman, Cayman Islands
URL: http://sussexdirectories.com

3789 ■ Hospital Blue Book
Billian Publishing Inc. and Trans World Publishing Inc.
2100 River Edge Pkwy., Ste. 1200
Atlanta, GA 30328
Ph: (770)955-5656
Free: 800-800-5668
Fax: (770)952-0669
E-mail: info@billian.com
URL: http://www.billianshealthdata.com/Products/HealthDATA_Hospital_Blue_Book
Frequency: Annual; Latest edition 2012. **Price:** $250 Individuals national edition; $575 Individuals subscription. **Covers:** More than 6,500 hospitals; some listings also appear in a separate southern edition of this publication. **Entries include:** Name of hospital, accreditation, mailing address, phone, fax, number of beds, type of facility (nonprofit, general, state, etc.); list of administrative personnel and chiefs of medical services, with specific titles. **Arrangement:** Geographical.

3790 ■ Medical and Health Information Directory: A Guide to Organizations, Agencies, Institutions, Programs, Publications, Services, and Other Resources Concerned with Clinical Medicine
Cengage Learning Inc.
200 1st Stamford Pl., Ste. 400
Stamford, CT 06902-6753
Ph: (203)965-8600
Free: 800-354-9706
Fax: (800)487-8488
E-mail: investors@cengage.com
URL: http://www.gale.cengage.com
Frequency: Annual; Latest edition April 2011. **Price:** $1,190 Individuals set; $501 Individuals per volume. **Covers:** In volume 1, more than 33,000 medical and health oriented associations, organizations, institutions, and government agencies, including health maintenance organizations (HMOs), preferred provider organizations (PPOs), insurance companies, pharmaceutical companies, research centers, and medical and allied health schools. In Volume 2, over 20,000 medical book publishers; medical periodicals, directories, audiovisual producers and services, medical libraries and information centers, electronic resources, and health-related internet search engines. In Volume 3, more than 40,500 clinics, treatment centers, care programs, and counseling/diagnostic services for 34 subject areas. **Entries include:** Institution, service, or firm name, address, phone, fax, email and URL; many include names of key personnel and, when pertinent, descriptive annotation. Volume 3 was formerly listed separately as Health Services Directory. **Arrangement:** Classified by organization activity, service, etc. **Indexes:** Each volume has a complete alphabetical name and keyword index.

HANDBOOKS AND MANUALS

3791 ■ Ask the Nutritionists
AuthorHouse
1663 Liberty Dr., Ste. 200
Bloomington, IN 47403
Ph: (812)339-6000
Free: 888-519-5121
Fax: (813)339-6554
E-mail: authorsupport@authorhouse.com
URL: http://www.authorhouse.com
Description: Kathy Thames and George Rapitis. 2005. $12.95.

3792 ■ Counselling Skills for Dietitians, 2nd Edition
John Wiley & Sons Inc.
111 River St.
Hoboken, NJ 07030-5774
Ph: (201)748-6000
Free: 800-225-5945
Fax: (201)748-6088
E-mail: info@wiley.com
URL: http://www.wiley.com
Description: Judy Gable. 2007. $66.99 (paper). 272 pages. Demonstrates how a practitioner can develop a counselling approach and employ appropriate counselling skills to overcome the communication difficulties encountered by dietitians and those engaged in helping clients change their eating behavior.

3793 ■ Opportunities in Health and Medical Careers
The McGraw-Hill Companies Inc.
PO Box 182604
Columbus, OH 43272
Ph: (212)512-2000
Free: 877-833-5524
Fax: (614)759-3749
E-mail: customer.service@mcgraw-hill.com
URL: http://www.mcgraw-hill.com
Description: I. Donald Snook, Jr. and Leo D'Orazio.

2004. $14.95 (paper). 157 pages. Covers the full range of medical and health occupations. Illustrated.

3794 ■ *Opportunities in Nutrition Careers*
McGraw-Hill Professional
PO Box 182604
Columbus, OH 43272
Ph: (877)833-5524
Free: 800-262-4729
Fax: (614)759-3749
E-mail: pbg.ecommerce_custserv@mcgraw-hill.com
URL: http://www.mhprofessional.com/product.php
 ?isbn=0071493069

Description: Carol Coles Caldwell. 2005. $13.95 (paperback). 160 pages. Offers the latest information on nutrition, training and education requirements needed, salary statistics, up-to-date professional and internet resources, and much more.

3795 ■ *The Profession of Dietetics: A Team Approach*
Jones & Bartlett Learning
5 Wall St.
Burlington, MA 01803
Free: 800-832-0034
E-mail: info@jblearning.com
URL: http://www.jblearning.com

Description: June R. Payne-Palacio and Deborah D. Canter. 2010. $60.95 (paper). 235 pages. Reviews the history of dietetics and contains an overview of the profession. Features a practical and personal approach to successfully maneuvering the often complicated and competitive steps to success in the nutrition profession.

3796 ■ *Resumes for Health and Medical Careers*
The McGraw-Hill Companies Inc.
PO Box 182604
Columbus, OH 43272
Ph: (212)512-2000
Free: 877-833-5524
Fax: (614)759-3749
E-mail: customer.service@mcgraw-hill.com
URL: http://www.mcgraw-hill.com

Description: Third edition, 2008. $12.95 (paper). 144 pages.

EMPLOYMENT AGENCIES AND SEARCH FIRMS

3797 ■ Harper Associates
31000 NW Hwy., Ste. 240
Farmington Hills, MI 48334
Ph: (248)932-1170
Fax: (248)932-1214
E-mail: info@harperjobs.com
URL: http://www.harperjobs.com

Description: Executive search firm and employment agency.

3798 ■ Professional Placement Associates, Inc.
287 Bowman Ave.
Purchase, NY 10577-2517
Ph: (914)251-1000
Fax: (914)251-1055
E-mail: careers@ppasearch.com
URL: http://www.ppasearch.com

Description: Executive search firm specializing in the health and medical field.

ONLINE JOB SOURCES AND SERVICES

3799 ■ CareerVitals.com
URL: http://www.careervitals.com

Description: Serves as a job board for healthcare professionals in different specializations.

3800 ■ CNMJobs.com
URL: http://www.cnmjobs.com

Description: Helps registered dietitians and clinical nutritionists to search for jobs and identify companies that are interested in a diverse workforce.

3801 ■ DietaryJobs.com
URL: http://www.dietaryjobs.com

Description: Offers dietary employment opportunities. Features dietary jobs across the United States.

3802 ■ DietaryJobs.org
URL: http://dietaryjobs.org

Description: Offers dietary job listings and employment opportunities. Enables job searching in specific locations and specific areas in the dietary field.

3803 ■ DieticianJobs.com
URL: http://www.dieticianjobs.com

Description: Provides dietician job listings and career opportunities. Also lists salary information.

3804 ■ DieticianNutritionist.com
URL: http://www.dieticiannutritionist.com

Description: Serves as a job board for dieticians, nutritionists, and dietetic professionals. Provides access to books, magazines, articles, and continuing education. Provides help in finding new jobs, posting resumes, and accessing career resources.

3805 ■ DietitianCentral.com
URL: http://www.dietitiancentral.com

Description: Provides information on nutrition jobs, dietician jobs, dietician directory, and jobs in dietetics. Provides information on becoming a dietitian, current and projected national earning averages, job outlook and nature of work.

3806 ■ ExploreHealthCareers.org
URL: http://explorehealthcareers.org/en/home

Description: Provides employment information in health professions. Includes links to health-related education/training programs, financial aid resources, specialized learning opportunities, and current issues in health care.

3807 ■ Get Dietician Jobs
URL: http://www.getdieticianjobs.com

Description: Offers dietician job postings and employment opportunities.

3808 ■ HEALTHeCAREERS Network
URL: http://www.healthecareers.com

Description: Career search site for jobs in all health care specialties; educational resources; visa and licensing information for relocation; interesting articles; relocation tools; links to professional organizations and general resources.

3809 ■ Institute of Food Technologists - IFT Career Center
URL: http://www.ift.org

Description: Offers job information and resources for those considering the Food Science and Technology field. Employers may post for full- or part-time positions and have the option of receiving a resume file of current job seekers. IFT members may register for a six-month confidential service to have their credentials reviewed by food industry employers. Job seekers who list credentials will receive the monthly Jobs Available bulletin. Main files include: Employment and Salary Information, How to Find Your First Job in the Food Sciences, Resources for Non-US Job Seekers, and more.

3810 ■ Jobs In Dietetics
URL: http://www.jobsindietetics.com

Description: Provides nationwide career support for nutritionists as well as dietetics and food service professionals. Offers a subscription job listing service.

3811 ■ NutritionJobs.com
URL: http://www.nutritionjobs.com

Description: Advances the career opportunities for professionals in the fields of nutrition and dietetics. Allows searching or recruiting for jobs online, including timely access to opportunities.

3812 ■ ProHealthJobs.com
URL: http://prohealthjobs.com/jobboard

Description: Career resources site for the medical and health care field. Lists professional opportunities, product information, continuing education and open positions.

3813 ■ RDLink.com
URL: http://www.rdlink.com

Description: Provides links to dietetic technicians, dietitians, and nutritionists on the web. Features job listings.

3814 ■ RegisteredDieticiansJobs.com
URL: http://www.registereddieticianjobs.com

Description: Offers career resources for diet and nutrition professionals. Provides jobs searching, resume posting, and career tools for job seekers.

TRADESHOWS

3815 ■ Annual ASHA School Health Conference
American School Health Association
1760 Old Meadow Rd., Ste. 500
McLean, VA 22102
Ph: (703)506-7675
Fax: (703)506-3266
E-mail: info@ashaweb.org
URL: http://netforum.avectra.com/eWeb/StartPage
 .aspx?Site=ASHA1&WebCode=HomePage

Annual. Gathers professional health educators, counselors, coordinators, and other health professionals responsible for school health promotion. Includes research and workshops on health education.

3816 ■ California Dietetic Association Meeting
California Dietetic Association
7740 Manchester Ave., Ste. 102
Playa Del Rey, CA 90293-8499
Ph: (310)822-0177
Fax: (310)823-0264
E-mail: patsmith@dietitian.org
URL: http://www.dietitian.org

Frequency: Annual. **Primary Exhibits:** Food and nutrition services.

3817 ■ Dietary Managers Association Meeting and Expo
Dietary Managers Association
406 Surrey Woods Dr.
Saint Charles, IL 60174
Free: 800-323-1908
Fax: (630)587-6308
E-mail: info@dmaonline.org
URL: http://dmaonline.ggnet.net

Frequency: Annual. **Primary Exhibits:** Dietary management equipment, supplies, and services.

3818 ■ IAACN Scientific Symposium
International and American Associations of Clinical Nutritionists
15280 Addison Rd., Ste. 130
Addison, TX 75001
Ph: (972)407-9089
Fax: (972)250-0233
E-mail: ddc@clinicalnutrition.com
URL: http://www.iaacn.org

Frequency: Annual. Provides an opportunity for professional growth, networking, and exchange of ideas.

OTHER SOURCES

3819 ■ Academy of Nutrition and Dietetics
120 S Riverside Plaza, Ste. 2000
Chicago, IL 60606-6995
Ph: (312)899-0040
Free: 800-877-1600
E-mail: knowledge@eatright.org
URL: http://www.eatright.org

Description: Represents food and nutrition professionals. Promotes nutrition, health and well-being.

3820 ■ American Association of Nutritional Consultants
220 Parker St.
Warsaw, IN 46580
Ph: (574)269-6165
Free: 888-828-2262
E-mail: registrar@aanc.net
URL: http://www.aanc.net

Description: Professional nutritional consultants. Seeks to create a forum for exchange of nutritional information. Offers benefits such as car rental and laboratory discounts. **Members:** 5,000.

3821 ■ American Public Health Association
800 I St. NW
Washington, DC 20001-3710
Ph: (202)777-2742
Fax: (202)777-2534
E-mail: comments@apha.org
URL: http://www.apha.org

Description: Professional organization of physicians, nurses, educators, academicians, environmentalists, epidemiologists, new professionals, social workers, health administrators, optometrists, podiatrists, pharmacists, dentists, nutritionists, health planners, other community and mental health specialists, and interested consumers. Seeks to protect and promote personal, mental, and environmental health. Services include: promulgation of standards; establishment of uniform practices and procedures; development of the etiology of communicable diseases; research in public health; exploration of medical care programs and their relationships to public health. Sponsors job placement service.

3822 ■ American School Health Association
1760 Old Meadow Rd., Ste. 500
McLean, VA 22102
Ph: (703)506-7675
Fax: (703)506-3266
E-mail: info@ashaweb.org
URL: http://netforum.avectra.com/eWeb/StartPage
.aspx?Site=ASHA1&WebCode=HomePage

Description: School physicians, school nurses, counselors, nutritionists, psychologists, social workers, administrators, school health coordinators, health educators, and physical educators working in schools, professional preparation programs, public health, and community-based organizations. Promotes coordinated school health programs that include health education, health services, a healthful school environment, physical education, nutrition services, and psycho-social health services offered in schools collaboratively with families and other members of the community. Offers professional reference materials and professional development opportunities. Conducts pilot programs that inform materials development, provides technical assistance to school professionals, advocates for school health.

3823 ■ American Society for Nutrition
9650 Rockville Pike
Bethesda, MD 20814-3998
Ph: (301)634-7050
Fax: (301)634-7892
E-mail: info@nutrition.org
URL: http://www.nutrition.org

Description: Quarterly. $30/year. Contains updates on nutrition legislation, public affairs, and public information policies. Reviews the results of nutritional research conducted by members of the Institute, which is comprised of nutrition scientists from universities, government, and industry. Recurring features include news of members, letters to the editor, job listings, notices of publications available, information on awards and fellowships, and news of scientific meetings.

3824 ■ American Society for Parenteral and Enteral Nutrition
8630 Fenton St., Ste. 412
Silver Spring, MD 20910-3805
Ph: (301)587-6315
Free: 800-727-4567
Fax: (301)587-2365
E-mail: aspen@nutr.org
URL: http://www.nutritioncare.org

Description: Seeks to improve patient care by advancing the science and practice of nutrition support therapy. Works closely with other health care organizations to advance a patient-centered approach to nutrition care and with government agencies to promote the optimal use of nutrition therapies.

3825 ■ Association for Healthcare Foodservice
455 S Fourth St., Ste. 650
Louisville, KY 40202
Ph: (502)574-9930
Free: 888-528-9552
Fax: (502)589-3602
E-mail: info@healthcarefoodservice.org
URL: http://www.healthcarefoodservice.org

Description: Represents professionals and suppliers in the self-operated healthcare foodservice industry. Advances healthcare foodservice professionals by ensuring that food and nutrition is a core competency. Provides education, advocacy, and management tools to support members.

3826 ■ *Career Opportunities in Health Care*
InfoBase Holdings Inc.
132 W 31st., 17 Fl.
New York, NY 10001-3406
Ph: (212)967-8800
Fax: (800)678-3633
E-mail: info@infobasepublishing.com
URL: http://www.ferguson.infobasepublishing.com

Description: Shelly Field. 2007. Third edition. $49.50. 304 pages. **Includes:** Appendices provide lists of educational institutions, periodicals, directories, associations, and unions. Appendices provide lists of educational institutions, periodicals, directories, associations, and unions.

3827 ■ Dietary Managers Association
406 Surrey Woods Dr.
Saint Charles, IL 60174
Free: 800-323-1908
Fax: (630)587-6308
E-mail: info@dmaonline.org
URL: http://dmaonline.ggnet.net

Description: Dietary managers united to maintain a high level of competency and quality in dietary departments through continuing education. Provides educational programs and placement service.

3828 ■ Genetic Metabolic Dietitians International
PO Box 33985
Fort Worth, TX 76162
E-mail: info@gmdi.org
URL: http://www.gmdi.org

Description: Represents the interests of nutritionists and other health care practitioners. Enhances and supports the practice of genetic metabolic nutrition. Provides leadership in nutrition therapy for genetic metabolic disorders through clinical practice, education, advocacy, and research.

3829 ■ *Health-Care Careers for the 21st Century*
JIST Publishing
875 Montreal Way
Saint Paul, MN 55102-4245
Ph: (317)613-4200
Free: 800-648-5478
Fax: (800)328-4564
E-mail: info@jist.com
URL: http://www.jist.com

Price: $9.95 Individuals Softcover. **Pages:** 448. **Covers:** Jobs for health care professionals and career opportunities for those pursuing a health-related career, organized into 80 careers in five groups. **Publication includes:** Appendixes listing job source resources and Web sites for health organizations.

3830 ■ IDEA Health and Fitness Association
10455 Pacific Center Ctr.
San Diego, CA 92121
Ph: (858)535-8979
Free: 800-999-4332
Fax: (858)535-8234
E-mail: contact@ideafit.com
URL: http://www.ideafit.com

Description: Provides continuing education for fitness professionals including; fitness instructors, personal trainers, program directors, and club/studio owners. Offers workshops for continuing education credits.

3831 ■ International and American Associations of Clinical Nutritionists
15280 Addison Rd., Ste. 130
Addison, TX 75001
Ph: (972)407-9089
Fax: (972)250-0233
E-mail: ddc@clinicalnutrition.com
URL: http://www.iaacn.org

Description: Physicians (medical, osteopathic, chiropractic), dentists, veterinarians, clinical nutritionists, pharmacists, nurses and scientists; practitioners hold accredited undergraduate, graduate or professional degrees in science and/or nutrition, or in fields related to nutrition with the addition of required core courses. Sponsors the Certified Clinical Nutritionist (CCN) credential under the responsibility of the Clinical Nutrition Certification Board (CNCB). Members work in the U.S. and other countries to stimulate and encourage research in the nutritional aspects of disease, promote the science and study of nutrition and complementary therapies in medical and dental schools, hospitals, colleges and research institutions. Provides a referral service for people seeking nutrition/preventive health care providers. Holds an annual scientific symposium with world-class faculty.

Disaster Recovery Specialists

SOURCES OF HELP-WANTED ADS

3832 ■ *Continuity Insights Magazine*
Gardner Business Media, Inc.
6915 Valley Ave.
Cincinnati, OH 45244-3029
Ph: (513)527-8800
Free: 800-950-8020
Fax: (513)527-8801
E-mail: orderbooks@gardnerweb.com
URL: http://www.gardnerweb.com
Description: Bimonthly. Free for qualified subscribers within the United States and Canada; $96.00 for international subscriptions. Strives to provide readers with industry information and insights to continually improve their skills as business continuity professionals. Features business continuity resources, conferences and other materials dedicated to assure the integrity of business.

3833 ■ *CSO Career*
CSO - Security and Risk
PO Box 9208
Framingham, MA 01701-9208
Ph: (508)872-0080
E-mail: online@cxo.com
URL: http://www.csoonline.com
Description: Biweekly. Newsletter of career and leadership-oriented news, articles, events and job postings.

3834 ■ *CSO Online - Security and Risk*
URL: http://www.csoonline.com/security/jobs/1
Description: Provides news, analysis and research on a broad range of security and risk management topics. Areas of focus include information security, physical security, business continuity, identity and access management and loss prevention.

3835 ■ *SC Magazine*
Haymarket Media Inc.
114 W 26th St., 4th Fl.
New York, NY 10001
Ph: (646)638-6000
Fax: (646)638-6110
E-mail: custserv@haymarketmedia.com
URL: http://www.haymarket.com/sc_magazine/default.aspx
Description: Monthly. Provides IT security professionals with in-depth and unbiased information through timely news, comprehensive analysis, cutting-edge features, contributions from thought leaders and an extensive collection of product reviews in the business.

PLACEMENT AND JOB REFERRAL SERVICES

3836 ■ **Acumin Consulting Ltd.**
PO Box 114
Stockton, NJ 08559-0114
E-mail: careers@acuminconsulting.com
URL: http://www.acuminconsulting.com/JobSeekers/

Description: Provides both permanent and contract risk management staff at all levels to industries spanning all sectors from tier banks to global consultancies across EMEA and the U.S. Helps develop internal risk management teams within end users.

3837 ■ **Alta Associates**
8 Bartles Corner Rd.
Flemington, NJ 08822
Ph: (908)806-8442
Fax: (908)806-8443
E-mail: info@altaassociates.com
URL: http://www.altaassociates.com

Description: Executive recruitment firm specializing in Information Security, IT Audit, Business Resiliency, Risk Management and Privacy.

3838 ■ **Andersen Steinberg Group**
110 Wall St., 11th Fl.
New York, NY 10005-3817
Ph: (646)688-2375
E-mail: usa@andersensteinberg.com
URL: http://www.andersensteinberg.com

Description: Works with corporations across all industries to provide investment banking and financial services, consultancy and outsourcing. Provides organizations with a global head of business continuity, regional heads, national heads, team leads and members. Focuses on business continuity and resilience.

3839 ■ **Artizen, Inc.**
200 Main St., Ste. 21A
Redwood City, CA 94063
Ph: (650)261-9400
E-mail: info1110@artizen.com
URL: http://www.artizen.com

Description: Provides project based, turnkey solutions. Specializes in business process re-engineering and information technology projects.

3840 ■ **BC Management**
17011 Beach Blvd., Ste. 1270
Huntington Beach, CA 92647
Ph: (714)960-7001
Free: 888-250-7001
Fax: (714)369-8034
E-mail: info@bcmanagement.com
URL: http://www.bcmanagement.com

Description: Serves as an executive search firm that specializes in identifying, recruiting, and placing professionals in business continuity, disaster recovery, crisis management, risk management, and information security careers. Renders placement services as an expert in both business continuity and recruiting. Serves both employers and job seekers through extensive industry knowledge, unmatched candidate contacts, and complete candidate screenings.

3841 ■ **Data Center Assistance Group**
78-17 164th St.
Flushing, NY 11366
Ph: (718)591-5553
Fax: (718)380-7322
E-mail: bronackt@dcag.com
URL: http://www.dcag.com

Description: Serves as a full service data processing consulting and personnel placement firm that specializes in emergency management preparedness training, business resumption planning, systems management and workflow optimization. Provides services to clients that result in improved performance and increased productivity through enhanced operations and a safeguarded environment capable of recovering from a wide range of business interruptions. Develops systems that assist client firms in their efforts to optimize the quality of personnel performance and productivity of their firms.

3842 ■ **Enterprise Solutions Inc.**
14850 Quorum Dr., Ste. 410
Dallas, TX 75254
Ph: (972)732-7275
Free: 800-889-4374
Fax: (972)732-7364
E-mail: info@esius.com
URL: http://www.esius.com

Description: Seeks to service the specific IT requirements of customers in an expeditious manner. Provides clients with network centric consulting, contract based staffing and placement services.

3843 ■ **Millennium Search Associates, LLC**
Livingston, NJ 07039
Ph: (973)758-9200
E-mail: info@msasearch.net
URL: http://www.msasearch.net

Description: Provides career consultation for candidates in the Insurance Risk Management, Safety, Claims, Loss Control, Security Management and Business Continuity Planning professions.

3844 ■ **Monarch Business Resiliency**
125 Town Park Dr., Ste. 300
Kennesaw, GA 30144
Ph: (678)921-2574
URL: http://www.monarchresiliency.com

Description: Staffing company that focuses on delivering value to clients by ensuring a more resilient business. Helps companies bring recovery capability in-house through its IT and BCP consultants.

3845 ■ **Request Technology**
200 E 5th Ave., Ste. 116
Naperville, IL 60563
Ph: (630)717-5865
Fax: (630)717-1109
E-mail: opportunity@requesttechnology.com
URL: http://www.requesttechnology.com

Description: Provides placement services for IT professionals throughout the world.

3846 ■ Robert Half Technology
2884 Sand Hill Rd.
Menlo Park, CA 94025
Free: 800-793-5533
URL: http://www.roberthalftechnology.com
Description: Provides IT professionals on a project and full-time basis. Specializes in initiatives ranging from web development and systems integration to network security and technical support. Offers flexible staffing solutions to premier organizations worldwide that require technical expertise on demand.

3847 ■ RSA Corp.
16969 Texas Ave., Ste. 400
Webster, TX 77598-4085
Ph: (281)488-7961
Free: 800-423-5383
Fax: (281)486-1496
E-mail: info@rsacorp.com
URL: http://www.rsacorp.com
Description: Business technology services firm that solves business pains and helps companies grow through technology. Provides human resource search and staffing services for businesses and individuals.

3848 ■ SecurityRecruiter.com
PO Box 398
Woodland Park, CO 80866
Ph: (719)686-8810
Free: 877-417-6830
E-mail: information@securityrecruiter.com
URL: http://www.securityrecruiter.com
Description: Serves corporate clients, select security vendors and security focused professional services organizations. Placement service includes full-time and contract security jobs in the realm of Corporate Governance, Risk Management, Regulatory Compliance, Audit, Privacy, Information Security and Physical Security.

3849 ■ TekSystems Inc.
7437 Race Rd.
Hanover, MD 21076-1112
Ph: (410)540-7700
Free: 888-519-0776
Fax: (410)540-7556
URL: http://www.teksystems.com
Description: Maintains strong relationships with 82% of the Fortune 500 and multiple government agencies. Deploys technical professionals across the globe and matches the right talent and expertise with the right projects.

EMPLOYER DIRECTORIES AND NETWORKING LISTS

3850 ■ Information Emergency Planning and Disaster Recovery Sourcebook
Edwards Information LLC
PO Box 31
Ashton, MD 20861
Ph: (301)774-5414
Free: 800-990-9936
Fax: (301)774-5416
URL: http://www.edwardsinformation.com
Description: Provides a concise guide to disaster planning teams. Includes sections covering items from professional associations, training and conferences affiliated with DR functions, equipment and facilities vendors, clean-up services and software vendors.

HANDBOOKS AND MANUALS

3851 ■ Business Continuity And Disaster Recovery Planning For IT Professionals
Saunders
c/o Reed Elsevier
360 Park Ave., S
New York, NY 10010

Ph: (212)989-5800
Fax: (212)633-3990
URL: http://www.elsevier.com

Description: $59.95. 456 pages. Contains updated information on risks from cyber attacks, rioting, protests, product tampering, bombs, explosions and terrorism. Provides extensive disaster planning and readiness checklists for IT infrastructure, enterprise applications, servers and desktops.

EMPLOYMENT AGENCIES AND SEARCH FIRMS

3852 ■ Abmax, Inc.
PO Box 35326
Tulsa, OK 74153
Ph: (918)627-8324
Fax: (918)628-1521
E-mail: business@abmax.net
URL: http://www.abmax.net
Description: Provides consulting and staffing services within the information technology arena.

3853 ■ Burke & Associates
1234 Summer St., Ste. 202
Stamford, CT 06905
Ph: (203)406-2300
E-mail: info@burkeandassociates.com
URL: http://burkeandassociates.com
Description: Provides services to clients including executive search, interim staffing and consulting services. Specializes in the areas of finance and accounting, human resources and IT.

3854 ■ DES Recruitment
1023 E Baltimore Pike, Ste. 215
Media, PA 19063
Ph: (484)442-8150
E-mail: info@desrecruitment.com
URL: http://www.desrecruitment.com
Description: Staffing solutions and recruiting firm that focuses on SAP recruiting, sales and marketing, information security and diversity.

3855 ■ A.E. Feldman Associates Inc.
445 Northern Blvd.
Great Neck, NY 11021
Ph: (516)719-7900
Fax: (516)719-7910
URL: http://www.aefeldman.com
Description: Executive search and recruiting firm specializing in the financial, accounting, legal, infrastructure and technology industries.

3856 ■ Kelly & Thomas Associates, Inc.
538 Greenview Ct.
Plymouth Meeting, PA 19462
Ph: (610)825-3800
URL: http://www.kellythomas.net
Description: Provides services to clients including executive search, interim staffing and consulting services. Specializes in the areas of engineering, manufacturing, information technology, pharmaceuticals, finance and accounting, construction and building technology, healthcare, food, sales and marketing.

3857 ■ Premier Staffing Partners
416 Ebenezer Rd.
Knoxville, TN 37923
Ph: (865)531-8588
URL: http://www.premierstaffingpartners.com
Description: Specializes in providing highly accomplished information technology professionals for short and long-term contract, contract to hire and direct placement positions.

ONLINE JOB SOURCES AND SERVICES

3858 ■ BankInfoSecurity.com
URL: http://www.bankinfosecurity.com
Description: Serves as a reference tool that promotes education on security issues. Reinforces the need for maintaining customer data confidentiality and integrity. Provides resources for individuals who want to work in the field such as interview tips, job postings, salary and hiring information and a resume center.

3859 ■ Blue Coat Systems Career Center
URL: http://www.bluecoat.com/company/careers
Description: Helps clients deliver the business-critical applications needed to enhance productivity, ensure a proactive line of defense and align network investments with business requirements.

3860 ■ GobsOfJobs.com
URL: http://www.gobsofjobs.com
Description: Acts as an interactive career site devoted to the hardware, software and information technology industries. Functions as a career management tool for job candidates and employers.

3861 ■ InformationTechnologyCrossing.com
URL: http://www.informationtechnologycrossing.com
Description: Provides information on IT jobs.

3862 ■ ITworld
URL: http://www.itworld.com
Description: Participatory site that acts as a forum for IT professionals and technology vendors to discuss challenges and solutions in the IT world.

3863 ■ JustTechJobs.com
URL: http://www.justtechjobs.com
Description: Serves as a jobsite that provides employers with a technology specific focus and provides job seekers with job postings aimed at those specific tech jobs. Offers a community of 15 million tech professionals and also supports several technology websites.

3864 ■ Tech-Engine.com
URL: http://techengine.com
Description: Features employment listings concerning the IT and engineering fields. Features employers and recruiters information, resume posting and career resources.

TRADESHOWS

3865 ■ Enterprise Disaster Recovery/Business Continuity - Designing the Resilient Framework Conference
CAMP Conferences, Inc.
540 W Frontage Rd., Ste. 2205
Northfield, IL 60093
Ph: (312)527-2800
Fax: (847)881-0747
URL: http://campconferences.com/events/2010/disaster1.htm

Features strategies to help design, implement and manage disaster recovery and business continuity frameworks to protect an organization's core IT assets, people and processes.

3866 ■ InfoSec World Conference & Expo
MIS Training Institute
153 Cordaville Rd., Ste. 200
Southborough, MA 01772
Ph: (508)879-7999
Fax: (508)787-0033
E-mail: mis@misti.com
URL: http://www.misti.com/

Annual. Provides education to all levels of information security professionals. Offers practical sessions that give participants the tools to strengthen their security without restricting their business.

3867 ■ Interop
UBM TechWeb
South Tower, Ste. 900
303 2nd St.
San Francisco, CA 94107
Ph: (415)947-6925
Fax: (415)947-6011
URL: http://www.gdconf.com

Annual. Provides opportunities for business and technology leaders to get the latest information on key technologies, learn about the latest trends and meet with leading vendors.

OTHER SOURCES

3868 ■ Association of Contingency Planners - Alamo Chapter
BC Management
17011 Beach Blvd., Ste. 1270
Huntington Beach, CA 92647
Ph: (714)843-5470
E-mail: zboyles@bcmanagement.com
URL: http://alamo.acp-international.com

Description: Practitioners in the field of business continuity. Promotes the advancement of business continuity professionals. Provides networking opportunities to related risk management groups to gain extensive knowledge base of resources, valuable insights and partnerships, and enhance skills that prepare families, communities and the industry.

3869 ■ Association of Contingency Planners - Capital of Texas Chapter
PO Box 13371
Austin, TX 78711-3371
Ph: (512)438-2863
E-mail: president@capitaloftexas.acp-international.com
URL: http://capitaloftexas.acp-international.com/index.html

Description: Practitioners in the field of business continuity. Promotes the advancement of business continuity professionals. Provides a network for the development of business continuity professionals.

3870 ■ Association of Contingency Planners - Central Maryland Chapter
c/o Ginna Rodriguez, President
Global Payments
10705 Red Run Blvd.
Owings Mills, MD 21117
Ph: (443)394-1079
E-mail: president@centralmd.acp-international.com
URL: http://centralmd.acp-international.com

Description: Practitioners in the field of business continuity. Promotes the advancement of business continuity professionals. Provides a network for the development of business continuity professionals.

3871 ■ Association of Contingency Planners, Northern Ohio Chapter
c/o Brian Zawada, Pres.
1200 W 6th St., Ste. 307
Cleveland, OH 44113
Ph: (330)321-8650
E-mail: brian.zawada@avalution.com
URL: http://www.acp-international.com/northohio

Description: Practitioners in the field of business continuity. Promotes the advancement of business continuity professionals. Provides networking opportunities to related risk management groups to gain extensive knowledge base of resources, valuable insights and partnerships, and enhance skills that prepare families, communities and the industry.

3872 ■ Association of Contingency Planners - Sioux Empire Chapter
PO Box 884
Sioux Falls, SD 57101-0884

Ph: (605)782-1771
E-mail: kdarger@metabank.com
URL: http://sioux.acp-international.com

Description: Practitioners in the field of business continuity. Promotes the advancement of business continuity professionals. Provides networking opportunities to related risk management groups to gain extensive knowledge base of resources, valuable insights and partnerships, and enhance skills that prepare families, communities and the industry.

3873 ■ Association of Contingency Planners - The First State Chapter
801 Silver Lake Rd.
Dover, DE 19904
Ph: (302)746-ACP1
E-mail: firststateacp@gmial.com
URL: http://firststate.acp-international.com

Description: Practitioners in the field of business continuity. Promotes the advancement of business continuity professionals. Aims to foster continued professional growth and development in effective contingency and business resumption planning. Provides members with opportunities to set response and recovery trends while strengthening relationships through public and private partnerships.

3874 ■ Business Continuity Planners Association
PO Box 5003
Saint Paul, MN 55101
Ph: (651)998-9609
URL: http://www.bcpa.org

Description: Serves as a mutual benefit association of business professionals responsible for, or participating in, business recovery, crisis management, emergency management, contingency planning, disaster preparedness planning, or a related professional vocation. Provides a professional and educational environment for the exchange of experience, dissemination of information, professional growth, and for added value of mutual interest to the membership. Conducts meetings and disseminates information on the field of disaster recovery.

3875 ■ Business Recovery Managers Association
PO Box 2184
San Francisco, CA 94126
Ph: (925)355-8660
E-mail: webmaster@brma.com
URL: http://www.brma.com

Description: Business continuity professionals and individuals interested in the fields of business recovery, disaster recovery, contingency and continuity planning, and emergency response management. Advances the theory and practice of business recovery, disaster recovery, contingency and continuity planning, and emergency response management. Provides latest trends and technologies available in the business continuity industry.

3876 ■ California Emergency Services Association
PO Box 630220
Simi Valley, CA 93063
Ph: (805)520-5854
Fax: (805)585-3227
E-mail: cesastate@gmail.com
URL: http://www.cesa.net

Description: Composed of emergency managers and planners from all levels of government, hospital/medical professionals, education representatives, public service organizations, business/industry emergency planners, and other individuals interested in this field. Strives to improve emergency planning, training, and response techniques.

3877 ■ CAMP Conferences, Inc.
540 W Frontage Rd., Ste. 2205
Northfield, IL 60093
Ph: (312)527-2800

Fax: (847)881-0747
URL: http://campconferences.com/events/2010/disaster1.htm

3878 ■ Central Arizona Association of Contingency Planners
PO Box 67434
Phoenix, AZ 85082
URL: http://az.acp-international.com

Description: Contingency planners, business continuity professionals, and emergency managers. Provides and facilitates an open environment for the exchange of experience and information. Identifies common planning needs and potential recovery response solutions as well as strengthens relationships through networking opportunities.

3879 ■ Contingency Planning Association of the Carolinas
PO Box 32492
Charlotte, NC 28232-2492
Ph: (704)427-6827
E-mail: chairman@cpaccarolinas.org
URL: http://www.cpaccarolinas.org

Description: Serves as a peer group of professionals/experts in disaster recovery or business continuity who share information, education, and resources in contingency planning in North and South Carolina. Supports proactive preparation for the resumption of business in the event of an unplanned interruption that adversely affects the operation of the organization. Provides a forum for the interchange of ideas, topics and information in the field of business continuity planning and disaster recovery.

3880 ■ DRI International
1115 Broadway, 12th Fl.
New York, NY 10010
Free: 866-542-3744
Fax: (501)513-8026
E-mail: aberman@drii.org
URL: http://www.drii.org

Description: Serves professionals in the field of Business Continuity Management. Promotes advancement in the study, teaching and practice of disaster recovery and business continuity. Devises public and private infrastructure continuity plans and studies; sponsors professional development and other educational programs; conducts examinations and certifies business continuity professionals.

3881 ■ International Consortium for Organizational Resilience
PO Box 1171
Lombard, IL 60148
Ph: (630)705-0910
Free: 866-765-8321
E-mail: info@theicor.org
URL: http://www.theicor.org

Description: Professionals with a demonstrated expertise in organizational resilience. Empowers professionals with skills that will allow them to embed the culture and systems of resilience within their organizations and communities. Provides thought-leadership, professional development and certification-enabling strategies for embedding the culture and systems of resilience within the organization.

3882 ■ Iowa Contingency Planners
PO Box 1365
Des Moines, IA 50305-1365
Ph: (515)957-3838
Fax: (952)555-1212
E-mail: steve.steenhoek@aieglercat.com
URL: http://www.icp-web.net

Description: Serves as a professional group of individuals, companies, and government agencies in the field of contingency planning and emergency management. Provides contingency planning and disaster recovery educational and networking opportunities for members. Conducts meetings, conferences, and trainings in an attempt to completely cover the field of contingency planning and disaster recovery.

3883 ■ **NCS Group**
1941 Citrona Dr.
Fernandina Beach, FL 32034
Free: 888-795-0050
Fax: (888)321-1504
E-mail: gmills@thencsgroup.com
URL: http://www.ncsjobs.com/home.asp

Description: Utilizes information technology as a tool to drive business results. Specializes in project based work as well as strategic staffing.

3884 ■ **NorthEast Disaster Recovery Information X-Change**
2231 Crystal Dr., Ste. 500
Arlington, VA 22202
E-mail: tpatterson@nedrix.com
URL: http://www.nedrix.com

Description: Professionals in the fields of continuity/disaster planning and emergency management. Offers resources for continuity planning and crisis management professionals. Provides access to industry best practices and opportunities to meet and share ideas and experiences with peers through conferences, symposiums, and public/private sector services.

3885 ■ **Storage Networking Industry Association**
4360 Arrows W Dr.
Colorado Springs, CO 80907-3444
Ph: (978)203-0442
Fax: (719)694-1389
E-mail: admin@snia.org
URL: http://www.snia.org

Description: IT professionals. Focuses on developing and promoting standards, technologies and educational services to empower organizations in the management of information. Enables members to develop solutions for storing and managing the massive volumes of information generated by today's businesses. Works to bring recognition on storage issues to the IT world, making storage less complicated for the end user.

3886 ■ **Technology Executives Club**
1580 S Milwaukee Ave., Ste. 305
Libertyville, IL 60048-3773
Ph: (847)837-3900
Fax: (847)837-3901
E-mail: mtuthill@technologyexecutivesclub.com
URL: http://www.technologyexecutivesclub.com/classifiedads-jobs.php

Description: Provides seminars, webinars, whitepapers, on-demand webcasts and newsletters which help IT and business executives stay current and share best practices on information technology in the enterprise. Provides an IT directory, resource center, announcements, community events, classified ads and other tools pursuing business intelligence and efficiency through effective information management.

3887 ■ *AFTRA Magazine*
American Federation of Television and Radio Artists
260 Madison Ave., 9th Fl.
New York, NY 10016-2401
Ph: (212)532-0800
Free: 866-855-5191
Fax: (212)532-2242
E-mail: membership@aftra.com
URL: http://www.aftra.org/

Frequency: Quarterly. **Price:** $3 Individuals.
Description: Membership magazine covering issues
in television and radio broadcasting.

3888 ■ *Community Radio News*
National Federation of Community Broadcasters
1101 Pennsylvania Ave. NW, Ste. 600
Washington, DC 20004
Ph: (202)756-2268
E-mail: comments@nfcb.org
URL: http://www.nfcb.org

Evona Balcziunas, Editor. **Frequency:** Monthly;
Monthly. **Price:** $75/year; Included in membership;
$75 University Libraries. **Description:** Serves as a
medium of communication for independent,
community-licensed radio stations. Recurring
features include job openings and a calendar of
events/conferences for noncommercial broadcasters.

3889 ■ *Feminist Media Studies*
Routledge Journals - Taylor & Francis Group
270 Madison Ave.
New York, NY 10016-0601
Ph: (212)216-7800
Fax: (212)563-2269
URL: http://www.tandfonline.com/toc/rfms20/current

Frequency: 6/year. **Price:** $1,118 Institutions print +
online; $197 Individuals print only; $979 Institutions
online only. **Description:** Journal covering media and
communication studies.

3890 ■ *Radio and Records*
Nielsen Business Media Inc.
770 Broadway
New York, NY 10003-9522
Ph: (646)654-4500
Free: 866-890-8541
Fax: (646)654-5584
E-mail: nbb@omeda.com
URL: http://www.radioandrecords.com

Frequency: Weekly. **Price:** $24.95 Individuals
monthly, print & online; $299 Individuals print & on-
line; $19.95 Individuals monthly, online. **Description:**
Magazine covering every format of music radio,
regulatory developments, news radio, talk radio, and
satellite radio.

3891 ■ *Burrelle's Black/Hispanic Media
Directory*
BurrellesLuce
75 E Northfield Rd.
Livingston, NJ 07039
Ph: (973)992-6600
Free: 800-631-1160
Fax: (973)992-7675
E-mail: sross@burrelleluce.com
URL: http://www.burrellesluce.com

Frequency: Irregular; previous edition 1989; latest
edition 1992. **Price:** $145 plus $4.00 shipping.
Pages: 295. **Covers:** Newspapers, magazines,
newsletters, radio and television programs, and other
media serving the interests of the Black and Hispanic
population. **Entries include:** Publication or station
name, address, phone, names and titles of key
personnel, description of publication or program. **Arrangement:** Geographical. **Indexes:** Geographical.

3892 ■ *Christian Media Directory*
James Lloyd Group
PO Box 448
Jacksonville, OR 97530
Ph: (541)899-8888
E-mail: james@christianmedianetwork.com
URL: http://www.christianmedianetwork.com

Frequency: Irregular. **Price:** $37.70 Individuals.
Covers: Over 8,000 newspapers, periodicals, radio
and television stations, video and film producers, and
music record labels targeting a Christian audience.
Provides market profiles and overview of television
and music video networks. **Entries include:**
Company or individual name, address, phone, fax,
name of contact, description of service, programming, or product. **Arrangement:** Classified by line of
business. **Indexes:** Product/service.

3893 ■ **The Complete Television, Radio &
Cable Industry Directory**
Grey House Publishing
4919 Rte. 22
Amenia, NY 12501
Ph: (518)789-8700
Free: 800-562-2139
Fax: (518)789-0556
E-mail: books@greyhouse.com
URL: http://gold.greyhouse.com/page/datatype96

3894 ■ *FINDERBINDER--Arizona: Arizona's
Updated Media Directory*
Rita Sanders Advertising Public Relations
432 E Southern Ave.
Tempe, AZ 85282
Ph: (480)967-8714

Fax: (480)894-6216
E-mail: rita@ritasanders.com
URL: http://www.finderbinderaz.com

Frequency: Annual. **Price:** $314.07 Individuals on-
line only; $399.88 Individuals print only; $464.86
Individuals print and online. **Pages:** 600. **Description:** "FINDERBINDER" directories are loose-leaf
directories of broadcast and print media covering
states or smaller areas published by companies, usually advertising and public relations firms, licensed to
use the name and format by Finderbinder. Types of
media covered include cable television systems;
daily and weekly newspapers; religious, ethnic, and
labor papers; business, trade, sports, recreation, and
general interest publications; college papers; and
radio and television stations in Arizona. **Entries
include:** Publication or station name, names of
management, editorial, and advertising personnel,
deadlines, frequency or circulation as appropriate,
and other data; cable TV listings. **Arrangement:**
Classified by type of medium. **Indexes:** Publication
or station name.

3895 ■ *FINDERBINDER--Cleveland*
Morgan & Co. Public Relations
Box 395
Richfield, OH 44286

Frequency: Annual. **Description:** "FINDERBINDER"
directories are loose-leaf directories of broadcast and
print media covering states or smaller areas
published by companies, usually advertising and
public relations firms, licensed to use the name and
format by Finderbinder. Types of media covered
include daily and weekly local and outstate
newspapers; religious, ethnic, and labor papers;
business, trade, sports, recreation, and general interest publications; college papers; and radio and television stations in Cleveland and northeastern Ohio.
Entries include: Publication or station name, names
of management, editorial, and advertising personnel,
deadlines, frequency or circulation as appropriate,
and other data; cable TV listings show homes
served. **Arrangement:** Classified by type of medium.
Indexes: Publication or station name.

3896 ■ *FINDERBINDER--Greater Detroit*
C & E Communications Inc.
PO Box 4952
East Lansing, MI 48826
Ph: (517)339-9160
Free: 877-515-9755
Fax: (517)339-7494
E-mail: info@michiganfinderbinder.com
URL: http://www.michiganfinderbinder.com

Frequency: Annual; September; bimonthly updates.
Price: $250 Individuals set including outside
Michigan. **Pages:** 300. **Description:** "FIND-
ERBINDER" directories are loose-leaf directories of
broadcast and print media covering states or smaller
areas published by companies, usually advertising
and public relations firms, licensed to use the name
and format by Finderbinder. Types of media covered
include cable television systems; daily and weekly

newspapers; religious, ethnic, and labor papers; business, trade, sports, recreation, and general interest publications; college papers; and radio and television stations in the seven-county Detroit metro area. **Entries include:** Publication or station name, names of management, editorial, and advertising personnel, deadlines, frequency or circulation as appropriate, and other data; radio, TV, and cable TV listings give name of public service announcement (PSA) director, interview format programs. **Arrangement:** Classified by type of medium. **Indexes:** Publication or station name, geographical, cable by community.

3897 ■ **FINDERBINDER--Kansas City: Greater Kansas Cities News Media Directory**
E-mail: krisf@twowest.com
URL: http://www.twowest.com

Frequency: Annual; February. **Price:** $130 payment must accompany order. **Pages:** 330. **Description:** "FINDERBINDER" directories are loose-leaf directories of broadcast and print media covering states or smaller areas published by companies, usually advertising and public relations firms, licensed to use the name and format by Finderbinder. Types of media covered include cable television systems; daily and weekly newspapers; religious, ethnic, and labor papers; business, trade, sports, recreation, and general interest publications; college papers; and radio and television stations in the 14 county, Kansas City metropolitan area. **Entries include:** Publication or station name; names of management, editorial, and advertising personnel; deadlines, frequency or circulation as appropriate; advertising rates; public relations contacts, including fax numbers, and email addressess; cable TV listings show homes served. **Arrangement:** Classified by type of medium. **Indexes:** Publication or station name, geographic by county, by interests covered.

3898 ■ **FINDERBINDER--New Mexico**
Gary Beals Advertising and Public Relations
4679 Vista St.
San Diego, CA 92116
Ph: (619)284-1145

Description: "FINDERBINDER" directories are loose-leaf directories of broadcast and print media covering states or smaller areas published by companies, usually advertising and public relations firms, licensed to use the name and format by Finderbinder. Types of media covered include cable television systems; daily and weekly newspapers; religious, ethnic, and labor papers; business, trade, sports, recreation, and general interest publications; college papers; and radio and television stations in New Mexico. **Entries include:** Publication or station name, names of management, editorial, and advertising personnel, deadlines, frequency or circulation as appropriate, advertising rates, and other data; cable TV listings show homes served. **Arrangement:** Classified by type of medium. **Indexes:** Publication or station name.

3899 ■ **FINDERBINDER--Northeast Wisconsin**
Bishea, Meili & Associates Inc.
9141 N Briarwood Ct., Ste. 201
Milwaukee, WI 53217
Ph: (414)540-1407
Fax: (414)540-1417

Description: "FINDERBINDER" directories are loose-leaf directories of broadcast and print media covering states or smaller areas published by companies, usually advertising and public relations firms, licensed to use the name and format by Finderbinder. Types of media covered include cable television systems; daily and weekly newspapers; religious, ethnic, and labor papers; business, trade, sports, recreation, and general interest publications; college papers; and radio and television stations in Northeast Wisconsin. **Entries include:** Publication or station name, names of management, editorial, and advertising personnel, deadlines, frequency or circulation as appropriate, advertising rates, and

other data; cable TV listings show homes served. **Arrangement:** Classified by type of medium. **Indexes:** Publication or station name.

3900 ■ **FINDERBINDER--Oklahoma**
FINDERBINDER of Oklahoma
PO Box 3093
Edmond, OK 73083
Ph: (405)570-3569
E-mail: support@finderbinderok.com
URL: http://www.finderbinderok.com

Frequency: Annual. **Price:** $175 online. **Description:** "FINDERBINDER" directories are loose-leaf directories of broadcast and print media covering states or smaller areas published by companies, usually advertising and public relations firms, licensed to use the name and format by Finderbinder. Types of media covered include cable television systems; daily and weekly newspapers; religious, ethnic, and labor papers; business, trade, sports, recreation, and general interest publications; college papers; and radio and television stations in Oklahoma. **Entries include:** Publication or station name, names of management, editorial, and advertising personnel, deadlines, frequency or circulation as appropriate, and other data; cable TV listings show homes served. **Arrangement:** Classified by type of medium. **Indexes:** Publication or station name.

3901 ■ **FINDERBINDER--Outstate Michigan**
C & E Communications Inc.
PO Box 4952
East Lansing, MI 48826
Ph: (517)339-9160
Free: 877-515-9755
Fax: (517)339-7494
E-mail: info@michiganfinderbinder.com
URL: http://www.michiganfinderbinder.com

Frequency: Annual; Latest edition 16th. **Price:** $225 Individuals package; $180 Individuals binder only. **Pages:** 271. **Description:** "FINDERBINDER" directories are loose-leaf directories of broadcast and print media covering states or smaller areas published by companies, usually advertising and public relations firms, licensed to use the name and format by Finderbinder. Types of media covered include cable television systems; daily and weekly newspapers; religious, ethnic, and labor papers; business, trade, sports, recreation, and general interest publications; college papers; and radio and television stations outside the 7-county metropolitan Detroit area. **Entries include:** Publication title or station name, address, phone, names and titles of key personnel, deadlines, frequency, circulation; radio and TV stations also list name of public service announcement director and interview programs. **Arrangement:** Classified by market, then by medium. **Indexes:** Dailies, community papers, other print, radio, TV, and print by topics.

3902 ■ **FINDERBINDER--Pittsburgh**
Gary Beals Advertising and Public Relations
4679 Vista St.
San Diego, CA 92116
Ph: (619)284-1145

Description: "FINDERBINDER" directories are loose-leaf directories of broadcast and print media covering states or smaller areas published by companies, usually advertising and public relations firms, licensed to use the name and format by Finderbinder. Types of media covered include cable television systems; daily and weekly newspapers; religious, ethnic, and labor papers; business, trade, sports, recreation, and general interest publications; college papers; and radio and television stations in Pittsburgh. **Entries include:** Publication or station name, names of management, editorial, and advertising personnel, deadlines, frequency or circulation as appropriate, advertising rates, and other data; cable TV listings show homes served. **Arrangement:** Classified by type of medium. **Indexes:** Publication or station name.

3903 ■ **FINDERBINDER--Syracuse**
Gary Beals Advertising and Public Relations
4679 Vista St.
San Diego, CA 92116
Ph: (619)284-1145

Description: "FINDERBINDER" directories are loose-leaf directories of broadcast and print media covering states or smaller areas published by companies, usually advertising and public relations firms, licensed to use the name and format by Finderbinder. Types of media covered include cable, advertising companies, cable television systems, billboard companies; daily and weekly newspapers; religious, ethnic, and labor papers; business, trade, sports, recreation, and general interest publications; college papers; and radio and television stations in Syracuse. **Entries include:** Publication or station name, names of management, editorial, and advertising personnel, deadlines, frequency or circulation as appropriate, advertising rates, and other data; cable TV listings show homes served. **Arrangement:** Classified by type of medium. **Indexes:** Publication or station name.

3904 ■ **Gale Directory of Publications and Broadcast Media**
Cengage Learning Inc.
200 1st Stamford Pl., Ste. 400
Stamford, CT 06902-6753
Ph: (203)965-8600
Free: 800-354-9706
Fax: (800)487-8488
E-mail: investors@cengage.com
URL: http://www.gale.cengage.com

Frequency: Annual; Latest edition April 2011. **Price:** $1,297 Individuals. **Covers:** Approximately 57,000 publications and broadcasting stations, including newspapers, magazines, journals, radio stations, television stations, radio/television/cable networks, syndicates and cable systems in the U.S. and Canada. Newsletters and directories are excluded. **Includes:** Appendices with maps and statistical tables, city descriptions, state descriptions with statistics, broadcast and cable networks, news and features syndicates. **Entries include:** For publications--Title, publishing and editorial addresses, phone, fax, description, names of editor, publisher, and advertising manager, base advertising rate, page specifications, subscription rate, circulation, frequency, ISSN, former names, additional contacts. For broadcast media--Call letters or cable system name, address, phone, fax, format, networks, owner, date founded, former call letters, operating hours, names and titles of key personnel, local programming, wattage, ad rates, additional contacts. **Arrangement:** Geographical. **Indexes:** Title; radio station format; publisher; geographic market; lists of agricultural, college, foreign language, Jewish, fraternal, black, women's, Hispanic, religious, general circulation, and trade and technical publications (by subject and/or geographical as needed); daily newspaper; daily periodical; free circulation newspaper; and shopping guides (each geographical); list of feature editors at daily newspapers with 50,000 or more circulation.

3905 ■ **Hudson's Washington News Media Contacts Directory**
Grey House Publishing
4919 Rte. 22
Amenia, NY 12501
Ph: (518)789-8700
Free: 800-562-2139
Fax: (518)789-0556
E-mail: books@greyhouse.com
URL: http://www.greyhouse.com/hudsons.htm

Frequency: Annual; Latest edition 2013. **Price:** $329 Individuals online and print. **Covers:** Nearly 5,000 editors, free-lance writers, and news correspondents, plus 4,624 United States, Canadian, and foreign newspapers, radio-TV networks and stations, magazines, and periodicals based or represented in Washington, D.C. **Entries include:** For publications and companies--Name, address, phone, and name of editor or key personnel. For individuals--Name, assignment. **Arrangement:** Classified by activity (e.g., correspondents), media type, etc; newspapers and radio-TV stations sections are arranged geographically; specialized periodicals section is arranged by subject. **Indexes:** Subject.

3906 ■ *Media Directory San Diego County*
San Diego Chamber of Commerce
402 W Broadway, Ste. 1000
San Diego, CA 92101
Ph: (619)544-1300
E-mail: webinfo@sdchamber.org
URL: http://www.sdchamber.org

Frequency: Annual. **Price:** $5. **Pages:** 6. **Covers:** San Diego county newspapers, magazines, news bureaus, radio and television stations. **Entries include:** For publications--Name of publication, address, phone. For radio and television stations--Call letters, frequency, address, mailing address, phone. **Arrangement:** Classified by type of media.

3907 ■ *Minority Employment Report*
Federal Communications Commission - Wireless
Telecommunications Bureau
445 12th St. SW
Washington, DC 20554
Free: 877-480-3201
E-mail: fccinfo@fcc.gov
URL: http://wireless.fcc.gov

Frequency: Annual; December. **Pages:** 1,480. **Covers:** Television and radio stations with ten or more full-time employees. **Entries include:** Station name (call letters or channel), city and state, class of station; total, female, and minority full-time employment in higher and lower pay occupations, and part-time employment for previous five years. **Arrangement:** By state and community.

3908 ■ *Southern California Media Directory*
Public Communicators of Los Angeles
1910 W Sunset Blvd., Ste. 860
Los Angeles, CA 90026-3247
Fax: (213)413-4026
URL: http://www.pcla.org

Frequency: Annual. **Pages:** 500 loose-leaf. **Covers:** 1,500 newspapers, magazines, radio and TV stations, and other media in eight-county southern California area; also covers suppliers of public relations products and services. **Entries include:** Media entries include publication name, address, phone, fax, e-mail and internet address, personnel (up to 30-40 editors, columnists, producers, etc.), circulation, and dates of publication. Supplier entries include company name, address, phone, fax, contact name, list of products or services. **Arrangement:** Geographical.

3909 ■ *Standalone Casting Directories: Presenters*
The Spotlight
7 Leicester Pl.
London WC2H 7RJ, United Kingdom
Ph: 44 20 7437 7631
Fax: 44 20 7437 5881
E-mail: enquiries@spotlight.com
URL: http://www.spotlight.com/shop/presenters

Frequency: Latest edition 2012. **Price:** Free. **Covers:** 500 radio and television personalities in news, entertainment, comedy, celebrity, documentaries, and sport. **Entries include:** Company and individual names, addresses, telephone and fax numbers, e-mails, and websites.

Handbooks and Manuals

3910 ■ *DJing For Dummies*
John Wiley & Sons Inc.
111 River St.
Hoboken, NJ 07030-5774
Ph: (201)748-6000
Free: 800-225-5945

Fax: (201)748-6088
E-mail: info@wiley.com
URL: http://www.wiley.com

Description: John Steventon. 2010. $19.99 (paperback). 424 pages. 2nd edition. Offers newcomers with technical information on starting a career as a disc jockey. Provides advice on creating a unique DJing style, expanding skills and fan base; plus tips on equipment essentials, mixing, and song structure. Includes updated information on the latest software and techniques, content on digital DJing and DJing over the Internet.

3911 ■ *Great Jobs for Music Majors*
The McGraw-Hill Companies Inc.
PO Box 182604
Columbus, OH 43272
Ph: (212)512-2000
Free: 877-833-5524
Fax: (614)759-3749
E-mail: customer.service@mcgraw-hill.com
URL: http://www.mcgraw-hill.com

Description: Jan Goldberg. Second edition, 2004. $15.95 (paper). 180 pages.

3912 ■ *How to Be a DJ*
Course Technology, Inc.
20 Channel Center St.
Boston, MA 02210
Ph: (617)289-7700
Free: 800-354-9706
Fax: (617)289-7844
URL: http://academic.cengage.com/coursetechnology/?CFID=1051488&CFTOKEN=43747877

Description: Chuck Fresh. 2005. 304 pages. Tips for working as a successful disc jockey in radio, bars and clubs, or private parties. Advice is given for choosing hardware and software equipment.

3913 ■ *Opportunities in Broadcasting Careers*
The McGraw-Hill Companies Inc.
PO Box 182604
Columbus, OH 43272
Ph: (212)512-2000
Free: 877-833-5524
Fax: (614)759-3749
E-mail: customer.service@mcgraw-hill.com
URL: http://www.mcgraw-hill.com

Description: Elmo I. Ellis. 2004. $13.95. 176 pages. Discusses opportunities and job search techniques in broadcasting, television, and radio. Illustrated.

3914 ■ *Starting Your Career in Broadcasting: Working On and Off the Air in Radio and Television*
Allworth Press
307 W 36th St., 11th Fl.
New York, NY 10018
Ph: (212)643-6816
Free: 800-491-2808
Fax: (212)643-6819
E-mail: pub@allworth.com
URL: http://www.allworth.com

Description: Chris Schneider. 2007. $19.95 (paper). 240 pages. Provides information on how to get into the communications business. Includes chapters on specific on-air and behind-the-scenes jobs, academic programs in broadcasting, what news and program directors seek in job candidates, how an aspiring broadcaster can buy time on the air, weathering the ups and downs of a competitive industry, and how professionals of all kinds can host their own talk shows.

3915 ■ *What's Up Dawg: How to Become a Superstar in the Music Business*
Hyperion Books
114 5th Ave.
New York, NY 10011-5604
Ph: (917)661-2000
Free: 800-242-7737

Fax: (917)661-6499
E-mail: cust.service@twbg.com
URL: http://www.hyperionbooks.com

Description: Randy Jackson and K.C. Baker. 2004. $19.95 (paper). 208 pages.

Online Job Sources and Services

3916 ■ *djjobs.us*
URL: http://www.djjobs.us

Description: Helps job seekers find the best disc jockey career opportunities with the best companies. Assists employers and recruiters in their recruitment of qualified candidates to fill available positions.

Other Sources

3917 ■ *American Disc Jockey Association*
20118 N 67th Ave., Ste. 300-605
Glendale, AZ 85308
Free: 888-723-5776
Fax: (866)310-4676
URL: http://www.adja.org

Description: Mobile and night club disc jockeys. Seeks to promote the disc jockey as a professional form of entertainment; improves the industry by establishing standards, procedures, and benefits. Assists and trains members; provides forums for professional disc jockeys; conducts educational, charitable, and research programs. **Members:** 1,500.

3918 ■ *A Career Handbook for TV, Radio, Film, Video and Interactive Media*
Bloomsbury Publishing PLC
50 Bedford Sq.
London WC1B 3DP, United Kingdom
Ph: 44 020 7631 5600
Fax: 020 7631 5800
E-mail: uk@bloomsbury.com
URL: http://www.bloomsbury.com/uk/a-career
-handbook-for-tv-radio-film-video-and-interactive
-media-9780713663204/

Frequency: Monthly. **Price:** £13.49 Individuals. **Covers:** TV, radio, film, video and interactive media specialists.

3919 ■ *Career Opportunities in the Music Industry*
InfoBase Holdings Inc.
132 W 31st., 17 Fl.
New York, NY 10001-3406
Ph: (212)967-8800
Fax: (800)678-3633
E-mail: info@infobasepublishing.com
URL: http://www.ferguson.infobasepublishing.com

Description: Shelly Field. Sixth edition, 2009. $49.50. **Includes:** Appendices of major agencies, unions, associations, periodicals, and directories. Appendices of major agencies, unions, associations, periodicals, and directories.

3920 ■ *Career Opportunities in Radio*
InfoBase Holdings Inc.
132 W 31st., 17 Fl.
New York, NY 10001-3406
Ph: (212)967-8800
Fax: (800)678-3633
E-mail: info@infobasepublishing.com
URL: http://www.infobasepublishing.com

Frequency: Published April, 2004. **Price:** $49.50 Individuals hardcover. **Pages:** 336. **Description:** Shelly Field. 2004. 326 pages. **Covers:** More than 70 jobs, such as on-air personality/disc jockey, business reporter, sportscaster, advertising account representative, billing specialist, publicist, studio engineer, program director, website content producer, and more. **Includes:** Appendices of educational institutions, periodicals, directories, unions, and associations.

3921 ■ *Newsclip's Illinois Media*
Newsclip Inc.
363 W Erie St., Ste. 7E
Chicago, IL 60610
Ph: (312)751-7300
E-mail: customerservice@newsclip.com
URL: http://www.newsclip.com/press.htm

Frequency: Annual; Latest edition 2009. **Pages:** 360. **Covers:** About 1,200 newspapers, magazines, and radio, television, and cable television stations located in or serving Illinois. **Entries include:** For print media--Name of publication, address, phone; names of publisher, editors, and advertising managers; deadlines; photo requirements; publication dates; circulation areas and figures; advertising rates. For stations--Address, phone; names of general manager, news director, and advertising manager; station format; wire services used; newscast times; interview shows offered; names of producers and other contacts; prime time advertising rates; broadcast areas and hours. **Arrangement:** Classified by type of medium, then geographical. **Indexes:** Geographical.

Dispensing Opticians

Sources of Help-Wanted Ads

3922 ■ American Optician
Opticians Association of America
4064 E Fir Hill Dr.
Lakeland, TN 38002
Ph: (901)388-2423
Fax: (901)388-2348
E-mail: oaa@oaa.org
URL: http://www.oaa.org
Frequency: Quarterly. **Price:** included in membership dues. **Description:** Contains calendar of events and research reports.

3923 ■ EyeNet: The Trusted Source for Clinical Insights
American Academy of Ophthalmology
655 Beach St.
San Francisco, CA 94109
Ph: (415)561-8500
Fax: (415)561-8533
E-mail: eyenet@aao.org
URL: http://www.eyenetmagazine.org
Frequency: Monthly. **Price:** $128 Nonmembers within U.S.; $180 Nonmembers outside US; $76 Members international; $20 Individuals inactive member. **Description:** Professional magazine of the American Academy of Ophthalmology covering clinical, socioeconomic and political trends affecting their practice for members.

3924 ■ Investigative Ophthalmology & Visual Science
Association for Research in Vision and Ophthalmology
1801 Rockville Pike, Ste. 400
Rockville, MD 20852-5622
Ph: (240)221-2900
Fax: (240)221-0370
E-mail: iovs@arvo.org
URL: http://www.iovs.org
Frequency: Monthly. **Price:** $880 Institutions online only; $550 Individuals online only; $400 Students online only. **Description:** Peer-reviewed journal dealing with all aspects of vision and ophthalmology.

3925 ■ Journal of Electronic Imaging
SPIE
PO Box 10
Bellingham, WA 98227-0010
Ph: (360)676-3290
Free: 888-504-8171
Fax: (360)647-1445
E-mail: customerservice@spie.org
URL: http://spie.org/x620.xml
Frequency: Quarterly. **Price:** $45 Individuals online; $70 Individuals print; $510 Institutions print and online; $550 Institutions, other countries print & online; $395 Institutions online. **Description:** Journal covering issues in optical engineering.

3926 ■ Journal of Optical Communications and Networking
Optical Society of America
2010 Massachusetts Ave. NW
Washington, DC 20036-1023
Ph: (202)223-8130
Free: 800-766-405A
Fax: (202)223-1096
E-mail: jocn@osa.org
URL: http://www.osa-jon.org/journal/jon/about.cfm
Frequency: Monthly. **Price:** $80 Members print & online; $56 Members online only; $180 Other countries members, print & online; $28 Students online only. **Description:** Online journal covering for the optical networking community.

3927 ■ Review of Optometry
Jobson Professional Publications Group
11 Campus Blvd., Ste. 100
Newtown Square, PA 19073
Ph: (610)492-1000
Fax: (610)492-1039
URL: http://www.revoptom.com/
Frequency: Monthly. **Description:** Journal for the optometric profession and optical industry.

Handbooks and Manuals

3928 ■ Opportunities in Health and Medical Careers
The McGraw-Hill Companies Inc.
PO Box 182604
Columbus, OH 43272
Ph: (212)512-2000
Free: 877-833-5524
Fax: (614)759-3749
E-mail: customer.service@mcgraw-hill.com
URL: http://www.mcgraw-hill.com
Description: I. Donald Snook, Jr. and Leo D'Orazio. 2004. $14.95 (paper). 157 pages. Covers the full range of medical and health occupations. Illustrated.

Employment Agencies and Search Firms

3929 ■ Retail Recruiters
2189 Silas Deane Hwy.
Rocky Hill, CT 06067
Ph: (860)721-9550
Fax: (860)257-8813
E-mail: careers@retailrecruitersusa.com
URL: http://www.retailrecruitersusa.com
Description: Employment agency. Affiliate offices in many locations across the country.

Online Job Sources and Services

3930 ■ HEALTHeCAREERS Network
URL: http://www.healthecareers.com

Description: Career search site for jobs in all health care specialties; educational resources; visa and licensing information for relocation; interesting articles; relocation tools; links to professional organizations and general resources.

3931 ■ ProHealthJobs.com
URL: http://prohealthjobs.com/jobboard
Description: Career resources site for the medical and health care field. Lists professional opportunities, product information, continuing education and open positions.

Tradeshows

3932 ■ American Academy of Optometry
American Academy of Optometry
2909 Fairgreen St.
Orlando, FL 32803
Ph: (321)710-3937
Free: 800-969-4226
Fax: (407)893-9890
E-mail: aaoptom@aaoptom.org
URL: http://www.aaopt.org
Frequency: Annual. **Primary Exhibits:** Exhibits focusing on the latest research and patient treatments relating to clinical practice standards, optometric education, and experimental research in visual problems.

3933 ■ International Vision Expo and Conference/East
Reed Exhibitions Contemporary Forums
6377 Clark Ave., Ste. 200
Dublin, CA 94568
Ph: (925)828-7100
Fax: (800)329-9923
E-mail: info@cforums.com
URL: http://www.contemporaryforums.com
Frequency: Annual. **Primary Exhibits:** Equipment, supplies and services for the vision industry.

Other Sources

3934 ■ American Academy of Optometry
2909 Fairgreen St.
Orlando, FL 32803
Ph: (321)710-3937
Free: 800-969-4226
Fax: (407)893-9890
E-mail: aaoptom@aaoptom.org
URL: http://www.aaopt.org
Description: Represents optometrists, educators, and scientists interested in optometric education, and standards of care in visual problems. Conducts continuing education for optometrists and visual scientists. Sponsors 4-day annual meeting.

3935 ■ American Board of Opticianry
6506 Loisdale Rd., Ste. 209
Springfield, VA 22150
Ph: (703)719-5800
Free: 800-296-1379
Fax: (703)719-9144
E-mail: mail@abo-ncle.org
URL: http://www.abo-ncle.org

Description: Provides uniform standards for dispensing opticians by administering the National Opticianry Competency Examination and by issuing the Certified Optician Certificate to those passing the exam. Administers the Master in Ophthalmic Optics Examination and issues certificates to opticians at the advanced level passing the exam. Maintains records of persons certified for competency in eyeglass dispensing. Adopts and enforces continuing education requirements; assists and encourages state licensing boards in the use of the National Opticianry Competency Examination for licensure purposes. **Members:** 30,000.

3936 ■ American Optometric Association
243 N Lindbergh Blvd., Fl. 1
Saint Louis, MO 63141-7881
Ph: (314)991-4100
Free: 800-365-2219
Fax: (314)991-4101
E-mail: ilamo@aoa.org
URL: http://www.aoa.org

Description: Professional association of optometrists, students of optometry, and paraoptometric assistants and technicians. Purposes are: to improve the quality, availability, and accessibility of eye and vision care; to represent the optometric profession; to help members conduct their practices; to promote the highest standards of patient care. Monitors and promotes legislation concerning the scope of optometric practice, alternate health care delivery systems, health care cost containment, Medicare, and other issues relevant to eye/vision care. Supports the International Library, Archives and Museum of Optometry which includes references on ophthalmic and related sciences with emphasis on the history and socioeconomic aspects of optometry. Operates Vision U.S.A. program, which provides free eye care to the working poor, and the InfantSEE program, which provides free vision assessments for infants between six and twelve months of age. Conducts specialized education programs; operates placement service; compiles statistics. Maintains museum. Conducts Seal of Acceptance Program.

3937 ■ Association of University Professors of Ophthalmology
PO Box 193030
San Francisco, CA 94119
Ph: (415)561-8548
Fax: (415)561-8531
E-mail: aupo@aao.org
URL: http://www.aupo.org

Description: Heads of departments or divisions of ophthalmology in accredited medical schools throughout the U.S. and Canada; directors of ophthalmology residency programs in institutions not connected to medical schools. Promotes medical education, research, and patient care relating to ophthalmology. Operates Ophthalmology Matching Program and faculty placement service, which aids ophthalmologists interested in being associated with university ophthalmology programs to locate such programs. **Members:** 315.

3938 ■ National Academy of Opticianry
8401 Corporate Dr., Ste. 605
Landover, MD 20785
Ph: (301)577-4828
Fax: (301)577-3880
E-mail: info@nao.org
URL: http://www.nao.org

Description: Offers review courses for national certification and state licensure examinations to members. Maintains speakers' bureau and Career Progression Program.

3939 ■ National Contact Lens Examiners
6506 Loisdale Rd., Ste. 209
Springfield, VA 22150
Ph: (703)719-5800
Free: 800-296-1379
Fax: (703)719-9144
E-mail: mail@abo-ncle.org
URL: http://www.abo.org

Description: Serves as National certifying agency promoting continued development of opticians and technicians as contact lens fitters by formulating standards and procedures for determination of entry-level competency. Assists in the continuation, development, administration, and monitoring of a national Contact Lens Registry Examination (CLRE), which verifies entry-level competency of contact lens fitters. Issues certificates. Activities include: maintaining records of those certified in contact lens fitting; encouraging state occupational licensing and credentialing agencies to use the CLRE for licensure purposes; identifying contact lens dispensing education needs as a result of findings of examination programs; disseminating information to sponsors of contact lens continuing education programs. **Members:** 8,000.

3940 ■ Opticians Association of America
4064 E Fir Hill Dr.
Lakeland, TN 38002
Ph: (901)388-2423
Fax: (901)388-2348
E-mail: oaa@oaa.org
URL: http://www.oaa.org

Description: Retail dispensing opticians who fill prescriptions for glasses or contact lenses written by a vision care specialist. Works to advance the science of ophthalmic optics. Conducts research and educational programs. Maintains museum and speakers' bureau. Compiles statistics.

Drafters

Sources of Help-Wanted Ads

3941 ■ Architectural Record
The McGraw-Hill Companies Inc.
Two Penn Plz., 9th Fl.
New York, NY 10121-2298
Ph: (212)904-2594
Fax: (212)904-4256
E-mail: customer.service@mcgraw-hill.com
URL: http://archrecord.construction.com

Frequency: Monthly. **Price:** $49 Individuals; $59 Canada; $129 Other countries. **Description:** Magazine focusing on architecture.

3942 ■ Builder: The Magazine of the National Association of Home Builders
DoveTale Publishers
1 Thomas Cir. NW
Washington, DC 20005
Ph: (202)339-0744
Free: 877-275-8647
Fax: (202)785-1974
E-mail: builder@omeda.com
URLs: http://www.hanleywood.com/default.aspx ?page=magazines; http://www.builderonline.com

Frequency: 13/yr. **Price:** $29.95 U.S. and Canada; $54.95 U.S. and Canada 2 years; $192 Other countries. **Description:** Magazine covering housing and construction industry.

3943 ■ Civil Engineering-ASCE
American Society of Civil Engineers - Architectural Engineering Institute
1801 Alexander Bell Dr.
Reston, VA 20191-4400
Free: 800-548-2723
E-mail: aei@asce.org
URL: http://pubs.asce.org/magazines/CEMag/

Frequency: Monthly. **Price:** $230 Institutions; $275 Institutions, other countries; $230 Individuals; $275 Other countries; $30 Members domestic; $69 Other countries member; $30 Students member; domestic; $69 Students member; international. **Description:** Professional magazine.

3944 ■ Constructor: The Construction Management Magazine
Associated General Contractors of America
2300 Wilson Blvd., Ste. 400
Arlington, VA 22201
Ph: (703)548-3118
Free: 800-242-1767
Fax: (703)548-3119
E-mail: info@agc.org
URL: http://constructor.agc.org/

Frequency: Bimonthly. **Price:** $95 Individuals. **Description:** Management magazine for the Construction Industry.

3945 ■ Design News
Reed Elsevier Group plc - Reed Business Information
360 Park Ave. S
New York, NY 11010
Ph: (212)791-4208
E-mail: corporatecommunications@reedbusiness.com
URL: http://www.designnews.com

Frequency: Monthly. **Description:** Magazine covering design engineering.

3946 ■ ENR: Engineering News-Record: The Construction Weekly
The McGraw-Hill Companies Inc.
2 Penn Plz., 9th Fl.
New York, NY 10121
Ph: (212)904-3507
Fax: (212)904-2820
E-mail: customer.service@mcgraw-hill.com
URL: http://enr.construction.com/Default.asp

Frequency: Weekly. **Price:** $87 Individuals print and online. **Description:** Magazine focusing on engineering and construction.

3947 ■ NSBE Magazine: National Society of Black Engineers
NSBE Publications
205 Daingerfield Rd.
Alexandria, VA 22314
Ph: (703)549-2207
Fax: (703)683-5312
E-mail: info@nsbe.org
URL: http://www.nsbe.org/News-Media/Magazines/About-NSBE-Magazine.aspx

Frequency: 3/yr. **Price:** $20 Individuals; $35 Other countries; $15 Students. **Description:** Journal providing information on engineering careers, self-development, and cultural issues for recent graduates with technical majors.

3948 ■ Professional Builder: The Magazine of the Housing and Light Construction Industry
SGC Horizon L.L.C.
3030 W Salt Creek Ln., Ste. 201
Arlington Heights, IL 60005
Ph: (847)391-1000
Fax: (847)390-0408
URL: http://www.housingzone.com/professionalbuilder

Frequency: Monthly. **Price:** Free. **Description:** The integrated engineering magazine of the building construction industry.

Employer Directories and Networking Lists

3949 ■ Directory of Contract Staffing Firms
C.E. Publications Inc.
PO Box 3006
Bothell, WA 98041-3006
Ph: (425)806-5200
Fax: (425)806-5585
E-mail: staff@cjhunter.com
URL: http://www.cjhunter.com/dcsf/overview.html

Frequency: Annual. **Covers:** Nearly 1,300 contract firms actively engaged in the employment of engineering, IT/IS, and technical personnel for 'temporary' contract assignments throughout the world. **Entries include:** Company name, address, phone, name of contact, email, web address. **Arrangement:** Alphabetical. **Indexes:** Geographical.

3950 ■ ENR--Top 500 Design Firms Issue
The McGraw-Hill Companies Inc.
PO Box 182604
Columbus, OH 43272
Ph: (212)512-2000
Free: 877-833-5524
Fax: (614)759-3749
E-mail: customer.service@mcgraw-hill.com
URL: http://enr.construction.com/toplists/sourcebooks/2010/designfirms/

Frequency: Annual; latest edition 2010. **Price:** $82 Individuals yearly subscription; $87 Individuals print and online. **Publication includes:** List of 500 leading architectural, engineering, and specialty design firms selected on basis of annual billings. **Entries include:** Company name, headquarters location, type of firm, current and prior year rank in billings, types of services, countries in which operated in preceding year. **Arrangement:** Ranked by billings.

3951 ■ ProFile--The Architects Sourcebook
Reed Construction Data Inc.
30 Technology Pky. S, Ste. 100
Norcross, GA 30092
Ph: (770)417-4000
Free: 800-424-3996
Fax: (770)417-4002
E-mail: profile@reedbusiness.com
URL: http://www.reedfirstsource.com

Frequency: Annual. **Pages:** 2,400. **Covers:** more than 27,000 architectural firms. **Entries include:** For firms--Firm name, address, phone, fax, year established, key staff and their primary responsibilities (for design, specification, etc.), number of staff personnel by discipline, types of work, geographical area served, projects. "ProFile" is an expanded version of, and replaces, the "Firm Directory." **Arrangement:** Firms are geographical. **Indexes:** Firm name, key individuals, specialization by category, consultants. Firm name, key individuals, specialization by category, consultants.

Handbooks and Manuals

3952 ■ Construction
InfoBase Holdings Inc.
132 W 31st., 17 Fl.
New York, NY 10001-3406
Ph: (212)967-8800

Fax: (800)678-3633
E-mail: info@infobasepublishing.com
URL: http://www.ferguson.infobasepublishing.com
Price: $30 Hardcover. **Description:** 2010. 128 pages. Contains profiles of 20 careers in the field of construction with emphasis on the nature of work, requirements, salary, and career outlook. Includes full-color photographs, index, glossary, resources, and side bars.

3953 ■ *Engineering, Mechanics, and Architecture*
InfoBase Holdings Inc.
132 W 31st., 17 Fl.
New York, NY 10001-3406
Ph: (212)967-8800
Fax: (800)678-3633
E-mail: info@infobasepublishing.com
URL: http://www.ferguson.infobasepublishing.com
Description: Kelly Wiles. 2010. $39.95. 160 pages (hardcover). Serves as a guide for readers interested in switching jobs. Contains useful advice, career tips, interviews and self-asessment questions.

EMPLOYMENT AGENCIES AND SEARCH FIRMS

3954 ■ **Agra Placements, Ltd.**
8435 University Ave., Ste. 6
Des Moines, IA 50325
Ph: (515)225-6563
Free: 888-696-5624
Fax: (515)225-7733
E-mail: careers@agrapl.com
URL: http://www.agraplacements.com

Description: Executive search firm. Branch offices in Peru, IN, Lincoln, IL, and Andover, KS.

3955 ■ **The Aspire Group**
711 Boylston St.
Boston, MA 02116-2616
Free: 800-487-2967
Fax: (617)500-7284
URL: http://www.bmanet.com/Aspire/index.html
Description: Employment agency.

3956 ■ **ENTEGEE Inc.**
70 Blanchard Rd., Ste. 102
Burlington, MA 01803-5100
Free: 800-368-3433
E-mail: corporate@entegee.com
URL: http://www.entegee.com

Description: Specializes in recruiting experienced professionals in the engineering and technical industries. Features a searchable database of employment opportunities in the engineering and technical fields.

3957 ■ **Global Employment Solutions Inc.**
10375 Park Meadows Dr., Ste. 475
Littleton, CO 80124-6724
Ph: (303)216-9500
Fax: (303)216-9533
URL: http://www.gesnetwork.com

Description: Employment agency.

3958 ■ **International Staffing Consultants Inc.**
31655 2nd Ave.
Laguna Beach, CA 92651
Ph: (949)255-5857

Fax: (949)767-5959
E-mail: iscinc@iscworld.com
URL: http://www.iscworld.com
Description: Employment agency. Provides placement on regular or temporary basis. Affiliate office in London.

ONLINE JOB SOURCES AND SERVICES

3959 ■ **iHireConstruction**
URL: http://www.ihireconstruction.com
Description: Helps recruiters and hiring managers find qualified candidates in different fields and specialties of construction industry. Provides job listings, customizable online profiles, resume writing services, and job alerts to job seekers.

OTHER SOURCES

3960 ■ **American Design Drafting Association**
105 E Main St.
Newbern, TN 38059
Ph: (731)627-0802
Fax: (731)627-9321
E-mail: corporate@adda.org
URL: http://www.adda.org
Description: Designers, drafters, drafting managers, chief drafters, supervisors, administrators, instructors, and students of design and drafting. Encourages a continued program of education for self-improvement and professionalism in design and drafting and computer-aided design/drafting. Informs members of effective techniques and materials used in drawings and other graphic presentations. Evaluates curriculum of educational institutions through certification program; sponsors drafter certification program.

Sources of Help-Wanted Ads

3961 ■ *Brookings Papers on Economic Activity*
Brookings Institution Press
1775 Massashusetts Ave. NW
Washington, DC 20036
Ph: (202)797-6000
Free: 800-275-1447
Fax: (202)797-6195
E-mail: brookingspapers@brookings.edu
URL: http://www.brookings.edu/about/projects/bpea

Frequency: Semiannual. **Price:** $60 Individuals; $100 Institutions; $74 Other countries; $114 Institutions, other countries. **Description:** Publication covering economics and business.

3962 ■ *Bulletin of Economic Research*
Blackwell Publishing Inc.
350 Main St.
Malden, MA 02148
Ph: (781)388-8200
Free: 800-216-2522
Fax: (781)388-8210
E-mail: journaladsusa@bos.blackwellpublishing.com
URL: http://as.wiley.com/WileyCDA/WileyTitle/productCd-BOER.html

Frequency: Quarterly. **Price:** $87 Individuals print & online; $1,153 Institutions print & online; $1,002 Institutions print or online; £449 Institutions print or online; £52 Individuals print & online; £517 Institutions print & online. **Description:** Journal focusing on the entire field of economics, econometrics and economic history.

3963 ■ *Economic Journal*
Blackwell Publishing Inc.
350 Main St.
Malden, MA 02148
Ph: (781)388-8200
Free: 800-216-2522
Fax: (781)388-8210
E-mail: journaladsusa@bos.blackwellpublishing.com
URL: http://as.wiley.com/WileyCDA/WileyTitle/productCd-ECOJ.html

Frequency: 8/yr. **Price:** $799 Institutions print and online; $694 Institutions print or online; £502 Institutions print and online; £436 Institutions print or online; €637 Institutions print and online; €554 Institutions print or online. **Description:** Journal focusing on economic issues.

3964 ■ *Economic Perspectives*
Federal Reserve Bank of Chicago
230 S LaSalle St.
Chicago, IL 60604-1427
Ph: (312)322-5322
Free: 888-372-2446
Fax: (312)322-5515
URL: http://www.chicagofed.org/webpages/publications/economic_perspectives/index

Frequency: Quarterly. **Description:** Publication covering the field of economics.

3965 ■ *Economic Policy*
Blackwell Publishing Inc.
350 Main St.
Malden, MA 02148
Ph: (781)388-8200
Free: 800-216-2522
Fax: (781)388-8210
E-mail: journaladsusa@bos.blackwellpublishing.com
URL: http://as.wiley.com/WileyCDA/WileyTitle/productCd-ECOP.html

Frequency: Quarterly. **Price:** $87 Individuals print and online; $48 Students print and online; $721 Institutions print and online; $627 Institutions print or online; £477 Institutions print and online; £415 Institutions print or online; £57 Individuals print and online; €87 Individuals print and online. **Description:** Journal publishing articles from economists and experts in the policy field all over the world.

3966 ■ *Economica*
Blackwell Publishing Inc.
350 Main St.
Malden, MA 02148
Ph: (781)388-8200
Free: 800-216-2522
Fax: (781)388-8210
E-mail: journaladsusa@bos.blackwellpublishing.com
URL: http://as.wiley.com/WileyCDA/WileyTitle/productCd-ECCA.html

Frequency: Quarterly. **Price:** $70 Individuals print and online; $49 Students print and online; $503 Institutions print and online; $457 Institutions print only; $436 Institutions online only; £291 Institutions print and online; $492 Institutions, other countries online only; £46 Individuals print and online; €58 Individuals print and online. **Description:** Journal publishing research in all branches of economics.

3967 ■ *The Economists' Voice*
Walter de Gruyter Inc.
545 8th Ave., Ste. 1650
New York, NY 10018
Ph: (212)564-9223
Free: 800-208-8144
Fax: (212)564-9224
E-mail: info@degruyterny.com
URL: http://www.degruyter.com/view/j/ev

Frequency: Annual. **Price:** $74 Individuals online; €49 Individuals online. **Description:** Journal focusing on current economic issues. Its readership mainly comprises of economists of various hues, and from other professions such as lawyers, policy makers etc.

3968 ■ *OECD Observer*
Organisation for Economic Co-operation and Development - Publications and Information Center
2001 L St. NW, Ste. 650
Washington, DC 20036-4922
Ph: (202)785-6323
Free: 800-456-6323
Fax: (202)785-0350
E-mail: observer@oecd.org
URLs: http://www.oecdobserver.org; http://www.oecd-bookshop.org/oecd/display.asp?k=sub -01011s1&CID=&LANG=EN&ds= theoecdobserver

Price: $101 Individuals print + online; €73 Individuals print + online; £57 Individuals print + online; ¥9,500 Individuals print + online. **Description:** Magazine on economic affairs, science, and technology.

3969 ■ *The Review of Network Economics*
Charles River Associates
John Hancock Tower, 200 Clarendon St., T-33
Boston, MA 02116-5092
Ph: (617)425-3000
Fax: (617)425-3132
URL: http://www.degruyter.com/view/j/rne

Frequency: Quarterly; Mar., June, Sept., and Dec. **Price:** $75 Individuals. **Description:** Journal covering new research in network economics and related subjects, including topics in the economics of networks, regulation, competition law, industrial organization etc.

Employer Directories and Networking Lists

3970 ■ *The Bank Directory*
Accuity Inc.
4709 W Golf Rd.
Skokie, IL 60076-1231
Ph: (847)676-9600
Free: 800-321-3373
Fax: (847)933-8101
E-mail: custserv@accuitysolutions.com
URL: http://store.accuitysolutions.com/order.html

Frequency: Semiannual; June and December. **Price:** $1,195 Individuals. **Covers:** In five volumes, about 11,000 banks and 50,000 branches of United States banks, and 60,000 foreign banks and branches engaged in foreign banking; Federal Reserve system and other United States government and state government banking agencies; 500 largest North American and International commercial banks; paper and automated clearinghouses. Volumes 1 and 2 contain North American listings; volumes 3 and 4, international listings (also cited as 'Thomson International Bank Directory; volume 5, Worldwide Correspondents Guide containing key correspondent data to facilitate funds transfer. **Includes:** Bank operations information, asset ranking in state and country, bank routing numbers in numeric sequence, discontinued or changed bank names in geographical sequence. **Entries include:** For domestic banks-- Bank name, address, phone, telex, cable, date established, routing number, charter type, bank holding company affiliation, memberships in Federal Reserve System and other banking organizations, principal officers by function performed, principal correspondent banks, and key financial data (deposits, etc.). For international banks--Bank name, address, phone, fax, telex, cable, SWIFT address, transit or sort codes within home country, ownership, financial data, names and titles of key personnel, branch locations. For branches--Bank name, address, phone, charter type, ownership and other details comparable to domestic bank listings. **Arrangement:** Geographical. **Indexes:** Alphabetical, geographical.

3971 ■ Business Economics--Membership Directory Issue
National Association for Business Economics
1920 L St. NW, Ste. 300
Washington, DC 20036
Ph: (202)463-6223
Fax: (202)463-6239
E-mail: nabe@nabe.com
URL: http://www.nabe.com

Frequency: Annual; Latest edition 2008. **Price:** $125 electronic with membership; $150 printed. **Publication includes:** List of about 3,000 members of the association, including students. **Entries include:** Name, address, phone, corporate affiliation, economic specialization, industries of research specialization, NABE activities, educational background, work experience. **Arrangement:** Alphabetical by member name, company, and roundtable affiliation. **Indexes:** Company, roundtable, and students.

3972 ■ National Association for Business Economics--Membership Directory
National Association for Business Economics
1920 L St. NW, Ste. 300
Washington, DC 20036
Ph: (202)463-6223
Fax: (202)463-6239
E-mail: nabe@nabe.com
URL: http://www.nabe.com

Frequency: Annual; Latest edition 2008. **Pages:** 136. **Covers:** About 3,600 members internationally. **Includes:** Co. listing section showing members by organization. **Entries include:** Name, address, phone, company affiliation, educational background, prior employment history, areas of specialization and industries of research specialization, roundtable affiliation, Standard Industrial Classification (SIC) code. **Arrangement:** Alphabetical. **Indexes:** Company name, association roundtable affiliation.

3973 ■ National Economists Club--Membership Directory
National Economists Club
PO Box 19281
Washington, DC 20036-0281
Ph: (703)493-8824
E-mail: info@national-economists.org
URL: http://www.national-economists.org

Frequency: Biennial. **Pages:** 100. **Covers:** Nearly 800 professional economists and others having an interest in economic subjects. **Entries include:** Name, address, phone. **Arrangement:** Alphabetical by organization.

3974 ■ North American Financial Institutions Directory
Accuity Inc.
4709 W Golf Rd.
Skokie, IL 60076-1231
Ph: (847)676-9600
Free: 800-321-3373
Fax: (847)933-8101
E-mail: custserv@accuitysolutions.com
URL: http://store.accuitysolutions.com/order.html

Frequency: Semiannual; January and July. **Price:** $955 Individuals. **Covers:** 15,000 banks and their branches; over 2,000 head offices, and 15,500 branches of savings and loan associations; over 5,500 credit unions with assets over $5 million; Federal Reserve System and other U.S. government and state government banking agencies; bank holding, commercial finance, and leasing companies;

coverage includes the United States, Canada, Mexico, and Central America. **Includes:** Bank routing numbers in numeric sequence; maps; discontinued banks. **Entries include:** Bank name, address, phone, fax, telex, principal officers and directors, date established, financial data, association memberships, attorney or counsel, correspondent banks, out-of-town branch, holding company affiliation, ABA transit number and routing symbol, MICR number with check digit, credit card(s) issued, trust powers, current par value and dividend of common stock, kind of charter. **Arrangement:** Geographical. **Indexes:** Alphabetical.

3975 ■ Roster of Women Economists
Committee on the Status of Women in the Economics Profession
4901 Tower Ct.
Tallahassee, FL 32303
Ph: (850)562-1211
Fax: (850)562-3838
E-mail: jhaworth@ersgroup.com
URLs: http://www.cswep.org; http://www.cswep.org/f97chair.html

Frequency: Biennial; odd years. **Covers:** 6,000 women in economics. **Entries include:** Name, address, phone, title, affiliation, degrees, honors, specialty, number of articles and books published. e-mail, fax. Publisher is a standing committee of the American Economic Association. **Arrangement:** Alphabetical. **Indexes:** Geographical, employer, fields of specialization.

3976 ■ Who's Who in Finance and Industry
Marquis Who's Who L.L.C.
300 Connell Dr., Ste. 2000
Berkeley Heights, NJ 07922
Ph: (908)673-1000
Free: 800-473-7020
Fax: (908)673-1179
E-mail: finance@marquiswhoswho.com
URL: http://www.marquiswhoswho.com

Frequency: Biennial; latest edition 37th; 2009-2010. **Price:** $349 Individuals. **Pages:** 1,264. **Covers:** Over 24,000 individuals. **Entries include:** Name, home and office addresses, personal, career, and family data; civic and political activities; memberships, publications, awards. **Arrangement:** Alphabetical.

HANDBOOKS AND MANUALS

3977 ■ Associate Economist
National Learning Corporation
212 Michael Dr.
Syosset, NY 11791
Ph: (516)921-8888
Free: 800-632-8888
Fax: (516)921-8743
E-mail: info@passbooks.com
URL: http://www.passbooks.com

Description: 2009. $39.95 (paper). Serves as an exam preparation guide for associate economists.

3978 ■ Opportunities in Social Science Careers
The McGraw-Hill Companies Inc.
PO Box 182604
Columbus, OH 43272
Ph: (212)512-2000
Free: 877-833-5524
Fax: (614)759-3749
E-mail: customer.service@mcgraw-hill.com
URL: http://www.mcgraw-hill.com

Description: Rosanne J. Marek. 2004. $13.95. 160 Pages. VGM Opportunities Series.

EMPLOYMENT AGENCIES AND SEARCH FIRMS

3979 ■ Choi & Burns LLC
156 W 56th St., 18th Fl.
New York, NY 10019

Ph: (212)755-7051
Fax: (212)335-2610
E-mail: info@choiburns.com
URL: http://www.choiburns.com

Description: Executive search firm focuses on the financial industry.

3980 ■ Dussick Management Associates
White Birch Rd., Ste. 28
Madison, CT 06443
Ph: (203)245-9311
Fax: (203)245-1648
E-mail: vince@dussick.com
URL: http://www.dussick.com

Description: Executive search firm.

3981 ■ Halbrecht & Co.
10195 Main St., Ste. L
Fairfax, VA 22031
Ph: (703)359-2880
Fax: (703)359-2933
E-mail: halbrechtandco@aol.com

Description: Performs professional recruiting in data processing and operations research, economics, corporate planning, market research, telecommunications, and decision support systems.

3982 ■ International Staffing Consultants Inc.
31655 2nd Ave.
Laguna Beach, CA 92651
Ph: (949)255-5857
Fax: (949)767-5959
E-mail: iscinc@iscworld.com
URL: http://www.iscworld.com

Description: Employment agency. Provides placement on regular or temporary basis. Affiliate office in London.

3983 ■ Sales Executives Inc.
33900 W 8 Mile Rd., Ste. 171
Farmington Hills, MI 48335
Ph: (248)615-0100
E-mail: dale@salesexecutives.com
URL: http://www.salesexecutives.com

Description: Employment agency. Executive search firm.

ONLINE JOB SOURCES AND SERVICES

3984 ■ Econ-Jobs.com
URL: http://www.econ-jobs.com

Description: Serves as a job database for careers in economics, econometrics, and finance.

3985 ■ EconCareers.com
URL: http://www.econcareers.com

Description: Serves job seekers with backgrounds in economics, mathematics quantitative methods and econometrics.

OTHER SOURCES

3986 ■ African Studies Association
Rutgers University
Livingston Campus
54 Joyce Kilmer Ave.
Piscataway, NJ 08854
Ph: (848)445-8173
Fax: (732)445-1366
E-mail: secretariat@africanstudies.org
URL: http://www.africanstudies.org

Description: Persons specializing in teaching, writing, or research on Africa including political scientists, historians, geographers, anthropologists, economists, librarians, linguists, and government officials; persons who are studying African subjects; institutional members are universities, libraries, government agencies, and others interested in receiving information about Africa. Seeks to foster communication and to stimulate research among scholars on Africa. Sponsors placement service; conducts panels and discussion groups; presents exhibits and films.

3987 ■ Agricultural and Applied Economics Association
555 E Wells St., Ste. 1100
Milwaukee, WI 53202-3800
Ph: (414)918-3190
Fax: (414)276-3349
E-mail: info@aaea.org
URL: http://www.aaea.org

Description: Professional society of agricultural economists. Serves to enhance the skills, knowledge and professional contribution of those economists who serve society by solving problems related to agriculture, food, resources and economic development. Offers placement service.

3988 ■ American Economic Association
2014 Broadway, Ste. 305
Nashville, TN 37203
Ph: (615)322-2595
Fax: (615)343-7590
E-mail: aeainfo@vanderbilt.edu
URL: http://www.aeaweb.org

Description: Educators, business executives, government administrators, journalists, lawyers, and others interested in economics and its application to present-day problems. Encourages historical and statistical research into actual conditions of industrial life and provides a nonpartisan forum for economic discussion.

3989 ■ Committee on the Status of Women in the Economics Profession
c/o Marjorie McElroy, Chairperson
Duke University
Durham, NC 27708-0097
Ph: (919)660-1840
Fax: (919)684-8974
E-mail: cswep@econ.duke.edu
URL: http://www.aeaweb.org/committees/cswep

Description: A standing committee of American Economic Association. Women economists in the U.S. Aims to support and facilitate equality of opportunity for women economists. Disseminates information about job opportunities, research funding, and research related to the status of women in economics. Sponsors technical sessions.

3990 ■ Economic Policy Institute
1333 H St. NW, Ste. 300
East Tower
Washington, DC 20005-4707

Ph: (202)775-8810
Free: 800-374-4844
Fax: (202)775-0819
E-mail: epi@epi.org
URL: http://www.epi.org

Description: Conducts research and provides a forum for the exchange of information on economic policy issues. Promotes educational programs to encourage discussion of economic policy and economic issues, particularly the economics of poverty, unemployment, inflation, American industry, international competitiveness, and problems of economic adjustment as they affect the community and the individual. Sponsors seminars for economists and citizens.

3991 ■ Institute for Economic Analysis
c/o John S. Atlee, President-Director
360 Mt. Auburn St., Ste. 001
Cambridge, MA 02138
E-mail: info@iea-macro-economics.org
URL: http://iea-macro-economics.org

Description: Seeks to develop tools for macroeconomic analysis and policy that can maintain stable full employment growth, low inflation, low interest rates and equitable distribution of income and wealth. Integrates GDP and financial accounts for more systematic coordination of monetary and fiscal policy. Focuses on federal monetary policy, federal budget deficit/surplus, social security, consumer credit, and world economic recovery.

3992 ■ International Economic Alliance
1 Mifflin Pl., Ste. 400
Cambridge, MA 02138
Ph: (617)418-1981
Fax: (617)812-0499
E-mail: van.mccormick@iealliance.org
URL: http://www.iealliance.org

Description: Aims to further global trade, economic development and advance business relations. Brings together the world's key players and decision-makers (business and government leaders, investors and leading intellectuals) for practical, open, bi-partisan and solution-oriented exchange of ideas. Serves as a source of knowledge, facilitator of relationships, and catalyst for new business opportunities.

3993 ■ International Studies Association
324 Social Sciences
Tucson, AZ 85721
Ph: (520)621-7754
Fax: (520)621-5780
E-mail: isa@isanet.org
URL: http://www.isanet.org

Description: Social scientists and other scholars from a wide variety of disciplines who are specialists

in international affairs and cross-cultural studies; academicians; government officials; officials in international organizations; business executives; students. Promotes research, improved teaching, and the orderly growth of knowledge in the field of international studies; emphasizes a multidisciplinary approach to problems. Conducts conventions, workshops and discussion groups.

3994 ■ National Association for Business Economics
1920 L St. NW, Ste. 300
Washington, DC 20036
Ph: (202)463-6223
Fax: (202)463-6239
E-mail: nabe@nabe.com
URL: http://www.nabe.com

Description: Professional society of institutions, businesses, and students with an active interest in business economics and individuals who are employed by academic, private, or governmental concerns in the area of business-related economic issues. Maintains placement service for members; conducts several seminars per year. Maintains speakers' bureau.

3995 ■ National Council on Economic Education
122 E 42nd St., Ste. 2600
New York, NY 10168
Ph: (212)730-7007
Fax: (212)730-1793
E-mail: customerservice@councilforeconed.org
URL: http://www.councilforeconed.org

Description: Economists, educators, and representatives from business, labor, and finance dedicated to improving economic education by improving the quality and increasing the quantity of economics being taught in all levels of schools and colleges. Initiates curriculum development and research; experiments with new economics courses and ways to prepare teachers and students; provides updated teacher-pupil materials; coordinates national and local programs in economics education. Provides consulting services to educators; sponsors workshops; tests new methods in practical school situations.

3996 ■ Southern Economic Association
University of Tennessee at Chattanooga
313 Fletcher Hall, Dept. 6106
615 McCallie Ave.
Chattanooga, TN 37403-2598
Ph: (423)425-4118
Fax: (423)425-5218
E-mail: sea@utc.edu
URL: http://www.southerneconomic.org

Description: Professional economists in government, business, and academic institutions. Provides placement service for economists.

SOURCES OF HELP-WANTED ADS

3997 ■ *ABHE Newsletter*
Association for Biblical Higher Education
5850 T.G. Lee Blvd., Ste. 130
Orlando, FL 32822
Ph: (407)207-0808
Fax: (407)207-0840
E-mail: info@abhe.org
URL: http://www.abhe.org

Description: Five issues/year (always January, April, June, September, and November). Provides information on issues, events, and resources for Bible college administrators and others interested in Christian higher education. Recurring features include a calendar of events, reports of meetings, news of educational opportunities, book reviews, and notices of publications available.

3998 ■ *About Campus*
John Wiley & Sons Inc.
111 River St.
Hoboken, NJ 07030-5774
Ph: (201)748-6000
Free: 800-225-5945
Fax: (201)748-6088
E-mail: info@wiley.com
URL: http://onlinelibrary.wiley.com/journal/10.1002/
(ISSN)1536-0687

Frequency: Bimonthly. **Price:** $219 Institutions print only; $279 Institutions, Canada and Mexico print only; $330 Institutions, other countries print only; $60 U.S., Canada, and Mexico print only; $96 Other countries print only. **Description:** Journal focused on the critical issues faced by both student affairs and academic affairs staff as they work on helping students learn.

3999 ■ *American Academic*
American Federation of Teachers
555 New Jersey Ave. NW
Washington, DC 20001
Ph: (202)879-4400
URL: http://www.aft.org/pubs-reports/american_academic/index.htm

Description: Higher education policy journal.

4000 ■ *The American School Board Journal: The source for school leaders*
American School Board Journal
1680 Duke St.
Alexandria, VA 22314
Ph: (703)838-6722
Fax: (703)549-6719
E-mail: letter@asbj.com
URLs: http://www.asbj.com; http://www.nsba.org/

Frequency: Monthly. **Price:** $47 Individuals print and online version; $36 Individuals online; $72 Other countries; $53 Individuals Canada. **Description:** Magazine serving school board members, superintendents, and other administrative officials.

4001 ■ *American School & University: Shaping Facilities & Business Decisions*
Penton
9800 Metcalf Ave.
Overland Park, KS 66212
Ph: (913)341-1300
Free: 866-748-4926
Fax: (913)967-1905
E-mail: corporatecustomerservice@penton.com
URLs: http://asumag.com/; http://www.schooldesigns.com

Frequency: Monthly. **Description:** Trade magazine.

4002 ■ *Annals of Medicine*
Informa Healthcare
52 Vanderbilt Ave., 7th Fl.
New York, NY 10017-3846
Ph: (212)520-2777
E-mail: healthcare.enquiries@informa.com
URL: http://informahealthcare.com/ann

Frequency: 4/yr. **Price:** £961 Institutions; $1,579 Institutions; €1,259 Institutions. **Description:** Journal covering health science and medical education.

4003 ■ *ASBSD-Bulletin*
Associated School Boards of South Dakota
306 E Capitol Ave.
Pierre, SD 57501-1059
Ph: (605)773-2500
Fax: (605)773-2501
E-mail: info@asbsd.org
URL: http://www.asbsd.org

Description: Monthly. Deals with policymaking, financing, and innovation in public education. Seeks to promote reorganization and adequate financing. Recurring features include letters to the editor, news of research, reports of meetings, news of educational opportunities, job listings, notices of publications available, and columns titled On the Line, Check This, and Board Policies.

4004 ■ *Change: The Magazine of Higher Learning*
Heldref Publications
325 Chestnut St., Ste. 800
Philadelphia, PA 19106
Ph: (215)625-8900
Free: 800-354-1420
E-mail: ch@heldref.org
URL: http://www.heldref.org/change.php

Frequency: Bimonthly. **Price:** €52 Individuals print only; £39 Institutions print only; $64 Individuals print and online; $207 Institutions print and online. **Description:** Magazine dealing with contemporary issues in higher learning.

4005 ■ *The Chronicle of Higher Education*
The Chronicle of Higher Education
1255 23rd St. NW, Ste. 700
Washington, DC 20037
Ph: (202)466-1000
Free: 800-728-2803

Fax: (202)452-1033
E-mail: editor@chronicle.com
URL: http://chronicle.com

Frequency: Weekly. **Price:** $82.50 Individuals 43 issues; $45 Individuals 21 issues; $140 Individuals 86 issues. **Description:** Higher education magazine (tabloid).

4006 ■ *Community Colleges Journal*
American Association of Community Colleges
1 Dupont Cir. NW, Ste. 410
Washington, DC 20036-1145
Ph: (202)728-0200
Fax: (202)833-2467
E-mail: aaccpub@pmds.com
URL: http://www.aacc.nche.edu/Publications/CCJ/
Pages/default.aspx

Frequency: 6/yr. **Price:** $36 Nonmembers; $36 Members. **Description:** Educational magazine.

4007 ■ *Dean and Provost*
John Wiley & Sons Inc.
111 River St.
Hoboken, NJ 07030-5774
Ph: (201)748-6000
Free: 800-225-5945
Fax: (201)748-6088
E-mail: info@wiley.com
URL: http://onlinelibrary.wiley.com/journal/10.1002/
(ISSN)1943-7587

Frequency: Monthly. **Price:** $222 U.S., Canada, and Mexico individual (print only); $270 Other countries individual (print only); $3,043 Institutions print and online; $3,091 Institutions, Canada and Mexico print and online; $3,109 Institutions, other countries print and online; $2,645 Institutions print only; $2,693 Institutions, Canada and Mexico print only; $2,711 Institutions, other countries print only. **Description:** Journal featuring innovative ways on how to manage all the challenges of leading an institution.

4008 ■ *The Department Chair*
John Wiley & Sons Inc.
111 River St.
Hoboken, NJ 07030-5774
Ph: (201)748-6000
Free: 800-225-5945
Fax: (201)748-6088
E-mail: info@wiley.com
URL: http://onlinelibrary.wiley.com/journal/10.1002/
(ISSN)1936-4393

Frequency: Quarterly. **Price:** $99 Individuals print only; $1,081 Institutions print only; $1,121 Institutions, Canada and Mexico print only; $1,155 Institutions, other countries print only. **Description:** Journal containing articles for chairs, deans, academic vice presidents, and other administrators.

4009 ■ *Education & Treatment of Children*
West Virginia University Press
139 Stansbury Hall
Morgantown, WV 26506

Ph: (304)293-8400
Fax: (304)293-6585
E-mail: press@wvu.edu
URLs: http://wvupressonline.com/journals; http://www
.educationandtreatmentofchildren.net

Frequency: Quarterly. **Price:** $100 Institutions; $50 Individuals; $115 Institutions elsewhere; $65 Individuals elsewhere. **Description:** Periodical featuring information concerning the development of services for children and youth. Includes reports written for educators and other child care and mental health providers focused on teaching, training, and treatment effectiveness.

4010 ■ *Education Week: American Education's Newspaper of Record*
Editorial Projects in Education
6935 Arlington Rd., Ste. 100
Bethesda, MD 20814
Ph: (301)280-3100
Free: 800-346-1834
Fax: (301)280-3200
E-mail: ew@epe.org
URL: http://www.edweek.org/ew

Frequency: 44/yr. **Price:** $90 Individuals print plus online. **Description:** Professional newspaper for elementary and secondary school educators.

4011 ■ *Educational Researcher*
American Educational Research Association
1430 K St. NW, Ste. 1200
Washington, DC 20005-2504
Ph: (202)238-3200
Fax: (202)238-3250
E-mail: webmaster@aera.net
URL: http://www.aera.net/Publications/Journals/iEdu-cationalResearcheri/tabid/12609/Default.aspx

Frequency: Monthly; 9/year. **Price:** $48 Individuals plus foreign mailing charges; $150 Institutions plus foreign mailing charges; $50/year for individuals; $309/year for institutions. **Description:** Educational research journal.

4012 ■ *Enrollment Management Report*
John Wiley & Sons Inc.
111 River St.
Hoboken, NJ 07030-5774
Ph: (201)748-6000
Free: 800-225-5945
Fax: (201)748-6088
E-mail: info@wiley.com
URL: http://onlinelibrary.wiley.com/journal/10.1002/
(ISSN)1945-6263

Frequency: Monthly. **Price:** $225 U.S., Canada, and Mexico individual (print only); $273 Other countries individual (print only); $3,084 Institutions print and online; $3,132 Institutions, Canada and Mexico print and online; $3,150 Institutions, other countries print and online; $2,677 Institutions print only; $2,725 Institutions, Canada and Mexico print only; $2,743 Institutions, other countries print only. **Description:** Journal featuring practical guidance on all aspects of enrollment management including records, registration, recruitment, orientation, admissions, retention and more.

4013 ■ *Environmental Education Research*
Routledge Journals - Taylor & Francis Group
270 Madison Ave.
New York, NY 10016-0601
Ph: (212)216-7800
Fax: (212)563-2269
URL: http://www.tandfonline.com/toc/ceer20/current

Frequency: 6/year. **Price:** $1,594 Institutions print + online; $1,395 Institutions online only; $424 Individuals print only. **Description:** Journal covering all aspects of environmental education.

4014 ■ *Essays in Education*
University of South Carolina
471 University Pky.
Aiken, SC 29801

Ph: (803)648-6851
E-mail: info@sc.edu
URL: http://www.usca.edu/essays/

Frequency: Monthly. **Description:** Journal covering issues that impact and influence education.

4015 ■ *The International Electronic Journal of Health Education*
American Alliance for Health, Physical Education, Recreation and Dance
1900 Association Dr.
Reston, VA 20191-1598
Ph: (703)476-3400
Free: 800-213-7193
Fax: (703)476-9527
E-mail: membership@aahperd.org
URL: http://www.aahperd.org/aahe/publications/iejhe/

Frequency: Annual. **Price:** Free. **Description:** Journal promoting health through education and other systematic strategies.

4016 ■ *International Journal of Early Years Education*
Routledge Journals - Taylor & Francis Group
270 Madison Ave.
New York, NY 10016-0601
Ph: (212)216-7800
Fax: (212)563-2269
URL: http://www.tandfonline.com/toc/ciey20/current

Frequency: 4/yr. **Price:** $795 Institutions online only; $908 Institutions print + online; $314 Individuals print only. **Description:** Journal focusing on education world-wide.

4017 ■ *International Journal of Inclusive Education*
Routledge Journals - Taylor & Francis Group
270 Madison Ave.
New York, NY 10016-0601
Ph: (212)216-7800
Fax: (212)563-2269
URL: http://www.tandfonline.com/toc/tied20/current

Frequency: 10/yr. **Price:** $722 Individuals print only; $1,353 Institutions online only; $1,546 Individuals print + online. **Description:** Journal providing information on the nature of schools, universities and technical colleges for the educators and educational policy-makers.

4018 ■ *International Journal of Leadership in Education*
Routledge
c/o Duncan Waite, PhD, Ed.
Texas State University
601 University Dr.
San Marcos, TX 78666
Ph: (512)245-8918
E-mail: ijle@txstate.edu
URL: http://www.tandfonline.com/toc/tedl20/current

Frequency: Quarterly. **Price:** $277 Individuals print only; $690 Institutions online only; $788 Institutions print and online; £408 Institutions print and online; £367 Institutions online only; £142 Individuals print only. **Description:** Journal dealing with leadership in education.

4019 ■ *International Journal of Whole Schooling*
Whole Schooling Press
Wayne State University
217 Education
Detroit, MI 48202
Ph: (313)577-1607
E-mail: wholeschooling@twmi.rr.com
URL: http://www.wholeschooling.net/Journal_of
_Whole_Schooling/IJWSIndex.html

Price: Free. **Description:** International, refereed academic journal dedicated to exploring ways to improve learning and schooling for all children.

4020 ■ *Journal of Cases in Educational Leadership*
Pine Forge Press
2455 Teller Rd.
Thousand Oaks, CA 91320-2234
Ph: (805)499-4224
Free: 800-818-7243
Fax: (805)499-0871
E-mail: sales@pfp.sagepub.com
URLs: http://jel.sagepub.com; http://www.sagepub
.com/journals/Journal201765

Frequency: Quarterly. **Price:** $479 Institutions online; $103 Individuals online. **Description:** Journal covering cases appropriate for use in programs that prepare educational leaders.

4021 ■ *Journal of College Teaching & Learning*
The Clute Institute for Academic Research
6901 S Pierce St., Ste. 239
Littleton, CO 80128
Ph: (303)904-4750
Fax: (303)259-2420
E-mail: staff@cluteinstitute.com
URL: http://journals.cluteonline.com/index.php/TLC

Frequency: Monthly. **Price:** $495 Institutions with airmail postage. **Description:** Refereed academic journal covering all areas of college level teaching, learning and administration.

4022 ■ *Journal of Curriculum and Supervision*
Association for Supervision and Curriculum Development
1703 N Beauregard St.
Alexandria, VA 22311-1714
Ph: (703)578-9600
Free: 800-933-2723
Fax: (703)575-5400
URL: http://www.ascd.org/publications/jcs/fall2002/
On_Community.aspx

Frequency: Quarterly. **Price:** $39/year for members; $49/year for nonmembers. **Description:** Includes abstracts of selected doctoral dissertations.

4023 ■ *Journal of Diversity in Higher Education*
American Psychological Association
750 First St. NE
Washington, DC 20002-4242
Ph: (202)336-5500
Free: 800-374-2721
Fax: (202)336-5812
E-mail: journals@apa.org
URL: http://www.apa.org/pubs/journals/dhe/index
.aspx

Frequency: Quarterly. **Price:** $65 Members; $89 Other countries members; $415 Institutions; $464 Institutions, other countries; $65 Students; $105 Nonmembers; $134 Other countries nonmembers. **Description:** Journal publishing research findings, theory and promising practices in higher education.

4024 ■ *Journal of Higher Education Outreach and Engagement*
University of Georgia - Institute of Higher Education
Meigs Hall
Athens, GA 30602
Ph: (706)542-3464
Fax: (706)542-7588
E-mail: ihe@uga.edu
URL: http://openjournals.libs.uga.edu/index.php/
jheoe/

Frequency: Semiannual; Quarterly. **Price:** $60 Individuals; $95 Other countries; $30 Students; $65 Students, other countries; $100 Institutions; $199 Institutions, other countries. **Description:** Journal covering higher education outreach and engagement for scholars, practitioners, and professionals.

4025 ■ Journal of Language, Identity, and Education
Routledge Journals - Taylor & Francis Group
270 Madison Ave.
New York, NY 10016-0601
Ph: (212)216-7800
Fax: (212)563-2269
URL: http://www.tandfonline.com/toc/hlie20/current

Frequency: 5/yr. **Price:** $611 Institutions print + online; $535 Institutions online only; $84 Individuals print + online. **Description:** Scholarly, interdisciplinary journal covering issues in language, identity and education worldwide for academics, educators and policy specialists in a variety of disciplines, and others.

4026 ■ Journal of Latinos and Education
Routledge Journals - Taylor & Francis Group
c/o Enrique G. Murillo, Jr., Editor
California State University
College of Education
Center for Equity in Education, 5500 University Pky.
San Bernardino, CA 92407-2397
Ph: (212)216-7800
Fax: (212)563-2269
URL: http://www.tandf.co.uk/journals/titles/15348431.asp

Frequency: Quarterly. **Price:** $557 Institutions print + online; $487 Institutions online only. **Description:** Scholarly, multidisciplinary journal covering educational issues that impact Latinos for researchers, teaching professionals, academics, scholars, institutions, and others.

4027 ■ Journal of STEM Education: Innovations and Research
Auburn University
9088 Haley Ctr.
Auburn, AL 36849
Ph: (334)844-9088
Fax: (334)844-9027
URL: http://ojs.jstem.org/index.php?journal=JSTEM

Frequency: Semiannual. **Description:** Journal for educators in Science, Technology, Engineering, and Mathematics (STEM) education.

4028 ■ Leadership and Policy in Schools
Routledge Journals - Taylor & Francis Group
270 Madison Ave.
New York, NY 10016-0601
Ph: (212)216-7800
Fax: (212)563-2269
URL: http://www.tandfonline.com/toc/nlps20/current

Frequency: Quarterly. **Price:** $658 Institutions print and online; $304 Individuals print only; $576 Institutions online only. **Description:** Journal providing information about leadership and policy in primary and secondary education.

4029 ■ NACE Journal
National Association of Colleges and Employers
62 Highland Ave.
Bethlehem, PA 18017-9481
Ph: (610)868-1421
Free: 800-544-5272
Fax: (610)868-0208
E-mail: cnader@naceweb.org
URL: http://www.naceweb.org/KnowledgeCenter.aspx

Frequency: Quarterly; (September, November, February, April). **Price:** $70 Individuals print; $20 Single issue; $25 Other countries airmail postage; $12.50 Individuals additional copies. **Description:** Journal on career planning, and recruitment of the college educated work force.

4030 ■ NJEA Review
New Jersey Education Association
180 W State St.
Trenton, NJ 08607-1211
Ph: (609)599-4561
Fax: (609)599-1201
E-mail: njeareview@njea.org
URL: http://www.njea.org/page.aspx?z=1094&pz=8

Frequency: Monthly; September through May. **Price:** $250 Nonmembers. **Description:** Educational journal for public school employees.

4031 ■ Oxford Review of Education
Routledge Journals - Taylor & Francis Group
270 Madison Ave.
New York, NY 10016-0601
Ph: (212)216-7800
Fax: (212)563-2269
URL: http://www.tandfonline.com/toc/core20/current

Frequency: 6/yr. **Price:** $529 Individuals print only; $1,243 Institutions online only; $1,420 Institutions print and online. **Description:** Journal covering advance study of education.

4032 ■ The Physics Teacher
American Association of Physics Teachers
Dept. of Physics & Astronomy
Appalachian State University
Boone, NC 28608-2142
Ph: (301)209-3311
Fax: (301)209-0845
E-mail: webmaster@aapt.org
URLs: http://tpt.aapt.org; http://www.aapt.org/Publications/

Frequency: 9/yr. **Price:** $628 Nonmembers domestic; $688 Nonmembers international. **Description:** Scientific education magazine.

4033 ■ School and Community
Missouri State Teachers Association
407 S Sixth St.
Columbia, MO 65205
Free: 800-392-0532
E-mail: info@msta.org
URL: http://www.msta.org/resources/publications/snc/

Frequency: Quarterly. **Description:** Education magazine.

4034 ■ School Effectiveness and School Improvement: An International Journal of Research, Policy and Practice
Routledge
711 3rd Ave., 8th Fl.
New York, NY 10017
Ph: (212)216-7800
Free: 800-634-7064
Fax: (212)564-7854
E-mail: book.orders@tandf.co.uk
URL: http://www.tandf.co.uk/journals/titles/09243453.asp

Frequency: Quarterly. **Price:** £387 Institutions print and online; £348 Institutions online only; £186 Individuals print only; $660 Institutions print and online; $594 Institutions online only; $312 Individuals print only. **Description:** Journal focusing on educational progress of all students.

4035 ■ Teaching and Learning in Nursing
Elsevier Science Inc.
Secondary Publishing Division
650 Ave. of the Americas
New York, NY 10011
Ph: (212)633-3980
Free: 888-437-4636
Fax: (212)633-3975
URL: http://www.jtln.org

Frequency: Quarterly; Monthly. **Price:** $99 Individuals U.S.; $145 Individuals Mexico, Canada, other countries, print and online. **Description:** Includes articles concerning advancement of Associate Degree Nursing education and practice.

4036 ■ Tech Directions: Linking Education to Careers
Prakken Publications Inc.
2851 Boardwalk Dr.
Ann Arbor, MI 48104
Ph: (734)975-2800
Free: 800-530-9673

Fax: (734)975-2787
E-mail: tdedit@techdirections.com
URL: http://www.techdirections.com

Frequency: Monthly; (Aug. through May). **Price:** $30 Individuals U.S.; $47 Institutions; $50 Other countries; $100 Individuals domestic. **Description:** Magazine covering issues, programs, and projects in industrial education, technology education, trade and industry, and vocational-technical career education. Articles are geared for teacher and administrator use and reference from elementary school through postsecondary levels.

4037 ■ Theory and Research in Education
Pine Forge Press
2455 Teller Rd.
Thousand Oaks, CA 91320-2234
Ph: (805)499-4224
Free: 800-818-7243
Fax: (805)499-0871
E-mail: sales@pfp.sagepub.com
URL: http://www.sagepub.com/journalsProdDesc.nav?prodId=Journal201652

Frequency: 3/year. **Price:** $635 Institutions print and online; $572 Institutions online; $622 Institutions print; $91 Individuals print; $228 Institutions single print issue; $39 Individuals single print issue. **Description:** Interdisciplinary journal covering normative and theoretical issues concerning education including multi-faceted philosophical analysis of moral, social, political and epistemological problems and issues arising from educational practice.

4038 ■ Women in Higher Education
Wenniger Co.
5376 Farmco Dr.
Madison, WI 53704
Ph: (608)251-3232
Fax: (608)284-0601
E-mail: career@wihe.com
URL: http://www.wihe.com/

Description: Monthly. Focuses on leadership, career strategies, gender equity, and harassment of women administrators. Recurring features include interviews, news of research, reports of meetings and presentations, news of educational opportunities, job listings, book reviews, notices of publications available, columns titled Profile, Research Briefs, Newswatch, What Should She Do.

EMPLOYER DIRECTORIES AND NETWORKING LISTS

4039 ■ Accredited Institutions of Postsecondary Education: Programs - Candidates
Greenwood Electronic Media
c/o ABC-CLIO
130 Cremona Dr.
Santa Barbara, CA 93117
Ph: (805)968-1911
Free: 800-368-6868
Fax: (866)270-3856
E-mail: customerservice@abc-clio.com
URL: http://www.abc-clio.com/series.aspx?id=51746

Frequency: Annual; latest edition 2006. **Price:** $89.95 Individuals list price; £49.95 Individuals. **Pages:** 984. **Covers:** More than 7,000 accredited institutions and programs of postsecondary education in the United States and U.S. -chartered schools in 14 countries. **Includes:** Section listing the public systems of higher education in each of the 50 states, featuring central administrative office and all branches. **Entries include:** Institution name, address, phone, whether public or private, any religious affiliation, type of institution and student body, branch campuses or affiliated institutions, date of first accreditation and latest reaffirmation of accrediting body, accredited programs in professional fields, level of degrees offered, name of chief executive officer, size and composition of enrollment, type of academic calendar. **Arrangement:** Geographical. **Indexes:** Institution.

4040 ■ *Boarding Schools Directory*

The Association of Boarding Schools
1 N Pack Square., Ste. 301
Asheville, NC 28801
Ph: (828)258-5354
Fax: (828)258-6428
E-mail: tabs@schools.com
URL: http://www.schools.com

Frequency: Annual; Latest edition 2007-2008. **Covers:** Boarding schools that are members of the Association of Boarding Schools. **Entries include:** School name, address, phone, e-mail and url's, grades for which boarding students are accepted, enrollment, brief description. **Arrangement:** Classified by type of school. **Indexes:** Geographical; program; Alphabetical.

4041 ■ *Career College & Technology School Databook*

Chronicle Guidance Publications Inc.
66 Aurora St.
Moravia, NY 13118-3569
Ph: (315)497-0330
Free: 800-899-0454
Fax: (315)497-0339
E-mail: CustomerService@ChronicleGuidance.com
URL: http://www.chronicleguidance.com

Frequency: Annual; latest edition 2009-2010. **Price:** $26.73 Individuals Softbound. **Pages:** 148. **Covers:** Over 940 programs of study offered by more than 1,580 vocational schools. **Includes:** An appendix lists some additional details, including dates programs begin for some schools. **Entries include:** School name, city and ZIP code, phone, programs offered, admissions requirements, costs, enrollment, financial aid programs, year established, and student services. **Arrangement:** Geographical. **Indexes:** Vocation/course.

4042 ■ *Christian Schools International--Directory*

Christian Schools International
3350 E Paris Ave. SE
Grand Rapids, MI 49512-3054
Ph: (616)957-1070
Free: 800-635-8288
Fax: (616)957-5022
E-mail: info@csionline.org
URLs: http://store.csionline.org/index.php?main
_page=index&cPath=15; http://www.csionline.org/
schools

Frequency: Annual; Latest edition 2007-2008. **Price:** $15 Members. **Pages:** 260. **Covers:** Nearly 450 Reformed Christian elementary and secondary schools; related associations; societies without schools. **Entries include:** For schools--School name, address, phone; name, title, and address of officers; names of faculty members. **Arrangement:** Geographical.

4043 ■ *Chronicle Two-Year College Databook*

Chronicle Guidance Publications Inc.
66 Aurora St.
Moravia, NY 13118-3569
Ph: (315)497-0330
Free: 800-899-0454
Fax: (315)497-0339
E-mail: CustomerService@ChronicleGuidance.com
URL: http://www.chronicleguidance.com

Frequency: Annual; latest edition 2009-2010. **Price:** $26.74 Individuals softbound. **Pages:** 478. **Covers:** Over 954 associate, certificate, occupational, and transfer programs offered by more than 2,509 technical institutes, two-year colleges, and universities in the United States. **Includes:** College admissions information. **Entries include:** College charts section gives college name, address, phone; accreditation, enrollment, admissions, costs, financial aid; accrediting associations' names, addresses, and phone numbers. **Arrangement:** Part I is classified by col-

lege major; part II is geographical. **Indexes:** College name.

4044 ■ *College and University Professional Association--Membership Directory*

College and University Professional Association for Human Resources
1811 Commons Point Dr.
Knoxville, TN 37932-1989
Ph: (865)637-7673
Free: 877-287-2474
Fax: (865)637-7674
E-mail: memberservice@cupahr.org
URL: http://www.cupahr.org

Frequency: Online continually updated; access restricted to members. **Covers:** More than 7,000 members interested in college and university human resource administration; over 1,700 institutions. **Entries include:** For members--Personal name, title, affiliation, address, fax, e-mail, phone. For institutions--Organization name, address, phone, and names/titles of representatives. **Arrangement:** Members are alphabetical; institutions are geographical.

4045 ■ *Directory of Public School Systems in the U.S.*

American Association for Employment in Education
947 E Johnstown Rd., No. 170
Gahanna, OH 43230
Ph: (614)485-1111
Fax: (360)244-7802
E-mail: office@aaee.org
URL: http://www.aaee.org/

Frequency: Annual; Winter; latest edition 2004-2005 edition. **Price:** $55 Members; $80 Nonmembers; $55/copy for members; $80/copy for nonmembers. **Pages:** 220. **Description:** Lists nearly 15,000 public schools with the name of the individual responsible for hiring, grade levels, and size of each district. **Covers:** About 14,000 public school systems in the United States and their administrative personnel. **Entries include:** System name, address, phone, website address, name and title of personnel administrator, levels taught and approx. Student population. **Arrangement:** Geographical by state.

4046 ■ *Ganley's Catholic Schools in America--Elementary/Secondary/College & University*

Fisher Publishing Co.
PO Box 5729
Sun City West, AZ 85376
Ph: (623)328-8326
E-mail: info@ganleyscatholicschools.com
URL: http://www.ganleyscatholicschools.com

Frequency: Annual; Latest edition 40th, 2011. **Price:** $67 Individuals. **Covers:** over 8,400 Catholic K-12 Schools. **Arrangement:** Geographical by state, then alphabetical by Diocese name.

4047 ■ *Handbook of Private Schools*

Porter Sargent Publishers Inc.
2 LAN Dr., Ste. 100
Westford, MA 01886
Ph: (978)842-2812
Fax: (978)692-2304
E-mail: info@portersargent.com
URL: http://www.portersargent.com

Frequency: Annual; latest edition 92nd, 2011-2012. **Price:** $99 Individuals plus $7 shipping; cloth binding. **Pages:** 1,312. **Covers:** More than 1,700 elementary and secondary boarding and day schools in the United States. **Entries include:** School name, address, phone, fax, E-mail, URL, type of school (boarding or day), sex and age range, names and titles of administrators, grades offered, academic orientation, curriculum, new admissions yearly, tests required for admission, enrollment and faculty, graduate record, number of alumni, tuition and scholarship figures, summer session, plant evaluation and endowment, date of establishment, calendar, association membership, description of school's offerings and history, test score averages, uniform

requirements, geographical, and demographic date. **Arrangement:** Geographical. **Indexes:** Alphabetical by school name, cross indexed by state, region, grade range, sexes accepted, school features and enrollment.

4048 ■ *Independent Schools Association of the Southwest--Membership List*

Independent Schools Association of the Southwest
505 N Big Spring St., Ste. 406
Midland, TX 79701
Ph: (432)684-9550
Free: 800-688-5007
Fax: (432)684-9401
E-mail: rdurham@isasw.org
URL: http://www.isasw.org

Frequency: Annual; August. **Pages:** 20. **Covers:** Over 84 schools located in Arizona, Kansas, Louisiana, Mexico, New Mexico, Oklahoma, and Texas enrolling over 38,000 students. **Entries include:** School name, address, phone, chief administrative officer, structure, and enrollment. **Arrangement:** Geographical. **Indexes:** Alphabetical.

4049 ■ *MDR's School Directories: State Name*

Market Data Retrieval
6 Armstrong Rd., Ste. 301
Shelton, CT 06484
Ph: (203)926-4800
Free: 800-333-8802
Fax: (203)926-1826
E-mail: mdrinfo@dnb.com
URL: http://www.schooldata.com/mdrdir.asp

Frequency: Annual; Latest edition 2008-2009. **Pages:** 9,800. **Covers:** Over 90,000 public, 8,000 Catholic, and 15,000 other private schools (grades K-12) in the United States; over 15,000 school district offices, and 76,000 school librarians; and 27,000 media specialists, 33,000 technology coordinators. Includes names of over 165,000 school district administrators and staff members in county and state education administration. **Includes:** State statistics; county statistics, district buying power statistics. **Entries include:** District name and address; telephone and fax number; number of schools; number of teachers in the district; district enrollment; special Ed students; limited-English proficient students; minority percentage by race, college bound students; expenditures per student for instructional materials; poverty level; title 1 dollars; site-based management; district open/close dates; construction indicator; technologies and quantities; district-level administrators, *new superintendents shaded*; school name and address--new public shaded; telephone and fax number; principal new principal shaded; librarian, media specialist and technology coordinator; grade span; special programs and school type; student enrollment; technologies and quantities (instructional computer brand noting predominant brand); Multi-Media Computers; Internet connection or access; Tech Sophistication Index. **Arrangement:** Geographical. **Indexes:** District County; District Personnel; Principal; New Public Schools and Key Personnel; District and School Telephone; District URLs.

4050 ■ *National Association of College and University Business Officers--Membership Directory*

National Association of College and University Business Officers
1110 Vermont Ave. NW, Ste. 800
Washington, DC 20005
Ph: (202)861-2500
Free: 800-462-4916
Fax: (202)861-2583
E-mail: john.walda@nacubo.org
URL: http://www.nacubo.org

Frequency: Annual; latest edition 2006. **Pages:** 435. **No. of Listings:** 2,800 institutions; 22,00 people. **Entries include:** Name of institution, address, names of primary representatives. **Arrangement:** Alphabetical and regional.

4051 ■ National Directory for Employment in Education
American Association for Employment in Education
947 E Johnstown Rd., No. 170
Gahanna, OH 43230
Ph: (614)485-1111
Fax: (360)244-7802
E-mail: execdir@aaee.org
URL: http://www.aaee.org/

Frequency: Annual; winter; latest edition 2008-2009. **Price:** $20 Nonmembers Processing fee $2; $10 Members processing fee $2. **Pages:** 200. **Covers:** about 600 placement offices maintained by teacher-training institutions and 300 school district personnel officers and/or superintendents responsible for hiring profesional staff. **Entries include:** Institution name, address, phone, contact name, email address, and website. **Arrangement:** Geographical. **Indexes:** Personal name, subject-field of teacher training, institutions which provide vacancy bulletins and placement services to non-enrolled students.

4052 ■ National School Public Relations Association--Directory
National School Public Relations Association
15948 Derwood Rd.
Rockville, MD 20855-2123
Ph: (301)519-0496
Fax: (301)519-0494
E-mail: info@nspra.org
URL: http://www.nspra.org

Frequency: Annual; January. **Pages:** 132. **Covers:** Approximately 2,000 school system public relations directors, school administrators, principals, and others who are members of the National School Public Relations Association. **Entries include:** Name, affiliation, address, phone. **Arrangement:** Geographical.

4053 ■ Patterson's American Education
Educational Directories Inc.
PO Box 68097
Schaumburg, IL 60168-0097
Ph: (847)891-1250
Free: 800-357-6183
Fax: (847)891-0945
E-mail: info@ediusa.com
URLs: http://www.ediusa.com; http://www.ediusa.com/American-Education.html

Frequency: Annual; Latest edition 2013, vol. 109. **Price:** $97 Individuals plus $8 shipping charges. **Pages:** 740. **Covers:** Over 11,000 school districts in the United States; more than 34,000 public, private, and Catholic high schools, middle schools, and junior high schools; Approximately 300 parochial superintendents; 400 state department of education personnel. **Entries include:** For school districts and schools--District and superintendent Name, address, phone, fax, grade ranges, enrollment, school names, addresses, phone numbers, grade ranges, enrollment, names of principals. For postsecondary schools--School name, address, phone number, URL, e-mail, names of administrator or director of admissions. For private and Catholic high schools--name, address, phone, fax, enrollment, grades offered, name of principal. Postsecondary institutions are covered in 'Patterson's Schools Classified' (see separate entry). **Arrangement:** Geographical by state, then alphabetical by city.

4054 ■ Patterson's Schools Classified
Educational Directories Inc.
PO Box 68097
Schaumburg, IL 60168-0097
Ph: (847)891-1250
Free: 800-357-6183
Fax: (847)891-0945
E-mail: info@ediusa.com
URL: http://www.ediusa.com

Frequency: Annual; Latest edition 2011. **Price:** $23 Individuals plus $7 shipping charges. **Pages:** 258. **Covers:** Over 6,000 accredited colleges, universities, community colleges, junior colleges, career schools and teaching hospitals. **Entries include:** School name, address, phone, URL, e-mail, name of

administrator or admissions officer, description, professional accreditation (where applicable). Updated from previous year's edition of 'Patterson's American Education' (see separate entry). **Arrangement:** Classified by area of study, then geographical by state. **Indexes:** Alphabetical by name.

4055 ■ Private Independent Schools
Bunting and Lyon Inc.
238 N Main St.
Wallingford, CT 06492
Ph: (203)269-3333
Fax: (203)269-8908
E-mail: buntingandlyon@aol.com
URL: http://www.buntingandlyon.com

Frequency: Annual; Latest edition 2010. **Price:** $115 Individuals. **Pages:** 417. **Covers:** 1,200 English-speaking elementary and secondary private schools and summer programs in North America and abroad. **Includes:** 485 photographs. **Entries include:** School name, address, phone, fax, e-mail, website, enrollment, tuition and other fees, financial aid information, administrator's name and educational background, director of admission, regional accreditation, description of programs, curriculum, activities, learning differences grid. **Arrangement:** Geographical. **Indexes:** School name; geographical. Summer programs, general classification grid, learning differences reference grid.

4056 ■ Requirements for Certification of Teachers, Counselors, Librarians, Administrators for Elementary and Secondary Schools
University of Chicago Press - Journals Division
1427 E 60th St.
Chicago, IL 60637-2954
Ph: (773)702-7600
Fax: (773)702-0694
URL: http://www.press.uchicago.edu/ucp/books/book/chicago/R/bo13620337.html

Frequency: Annual; Latest edition 77th. **Price:** $60 cloth. **Pages:** 320. **Publication includes:** List of state and local departments of education. **Entries include:** Office name, address, phone. Principal content of publication is summaries of each state's teaching and administrative certification requirements. **Arrangement:** Geographical.

4057 ■ School Guide
School Guide Publications
210 North Ave.
New Rochelle, NY 10801
Ph: (914)632-7771
Free: 800-433-7771
E-mail: mridder@schoolguides.com
URL: http://distance.schoolguides.com

Frequency: Annual; Latest edition 2008. **Pages:** 290. **Covers:** Over 3,000 colleges, vocational schools, and nursing schools in the United States. **Entries include:** Institution name, address, phone, courses offered, degrees awarded. **Arrangement:** Classified by type of institution, then geographical. **Indexes:** Subject.

HANDBOOKS AND MANUALS

4058 ■ Ferguson Career Coach: Managing Your Career in Education
InfoBase Holdings Inc.
132 W 31st., 17 Fl.
New York, NY 10001-3406
Ph: (212)967-8800
Fax: (800)678-3633
E-mail: info@infobasepublishing.com
URL: http://www.ferguson.infobasepublishing.com

Description: Shelly Field. 2008. $39.95 (hardcover). 272 pages. Contains tips on achieving career success in the field of education. Provides students with advice on making contacts, interviewing, and career strategies.

4059 ■ From Mandate to Achievement: 5 Steps to a Curriculum System That Works!
Corwin Press, Incorporated
2455 Teller Rd.
Thousand Oaks, CA 91320-2218
Ph: (805)499-9734
Free: 800-417-2466
Fax: (800)499-5323
E-mail: order@corwin.com
URL: http://www.corwinpress.com/booksProdDesc.nav?prodId=Book233107&

Description: Elaine Makas. 2009. $38.95 (paperback); $85.95 (hardcover). 248 pages. Guides principals, district administrators, curriculum facilitators and teachers in establishing a consistent and accurate curriculum process that increases academic achievement and drives continuous school improvement.

4060 ■ Getting Serious About the System
Corwin Press, Incorporated
2455 Teller Rd.
Thousand Oaks, CA 91320-2218
Ph: (805)499-9734
Free: 800-417-2466
Fax: (800)499-5323
E-mail: order@corwin.com
URL: http://www.corwinpress.com/booksProdDesc.nav?prodId=Book233107&

Description: D'Ette Cowan, Stacey Joyner and Shirley Beckwith. 2012. $31.95 (paperback). 120 pages. Provides teachers, administrators and leaders with a comprehensive resource in aligning curriculum, instruction and assessment. Presents a step-by-step, research-based approach to district and school transformation.

4061 ■ Leading Curriculum Improvement
Rowman & Littlefield Education
4501 Forbes Blvd., Ste. 200
Lanham, MD 20706
Ph: (301)459-3366
Free: 800-462-6420
Fax: (301)429-5748
E-mail: custserv@rowman.com
URL: http://www.rowmaneducation.com

Description: Marllyn Iallerico. 2011. $40.00 (hardback); $19.95 (paper). 136 pages. Offers guidance and curriculum leadership fundamentals to teacher leaders, instructional coordinators, central office personnel for facilitating curriculum improvement at the building level.

4062 ■ The Principal's Guide to Curriculum Leadership
Corwin
2455 Teller Rd.
Thousand Oaks, CA 91320
Ph: (805)499-9734
Free: 800-233-9936
Fax: (805)499-5323
E-mail: order@corwin.com
URL: http://www.corwin.com

Description: Richard D. Sorenson, Lloyd Milton Goldsmith, Zulma Y. Mendez, and Karen Taylor Maxwell. 2011. $41.95 (paper). 320 pages. Provides practical guidance for principal and other school administrators in initiating curriculum development and change. Features discussion questions, case studies, activities, specialized curriculum models, resources, and references.

EMPLOYMENT AGENCIES AND SEARCH FIRMS

4063 ■ Auerbach Associates
30 Hillside Terr.
Belmont, MA 02478
Ph: (617)489-4895
Fax: (617)489-9111
E-mail: info@auerbach-assc.com
URL: http://www.auerbach-assc.com

Description: Executive search firm focused on nonprofit and higher education industries.

4064 ■ Hazard, Young, Attea and Associates
5600 N River Rd., Ste. 180
Rosemont, IL 60018
Ph: (847)318-0072
Fax: (847)318-6751
E-mail: questions@ecragroup.com
URL: http://www.hyasupersearches.com

Description: Executive search firm serving public school districts. Provides recruiting for school boards throughout the United States.

4065 ■ Institutional Advantage L.L.C.
60 Lake Shore Ln.
Grosse Pointe Farms, MI 48236
Ph: (313)886-6042
Fax: (313)557-1331
E-mail: kts@ia-llc.com
URL: http://www.ia-llc.com

Description: Retained executive search for higher education and not-for-profit clients.

4066 ■ Perez-Arton Consultants Inc.
23 Spring St., Ste. 304
Ossining, NY 10562
Ph: (914)762-2100

Description: Provides executive searches for major academic and administrative units. Conducts institutional evaluations and executive staff assessments. Firm works for colleges, universities and education-related non-profits only.

4067 ■ The Spelman & Johnson Group
3 Chapman Ave.
Easthampton, MA 01027
Ph: (413)529-2895
Free: 800-827-6208
Fax: (413)527-6881
E-mail: info@spelmanandjohnson.com
URL: http://www.spelmanandjohnson.com

Description: Serves as a search firm specializing in filling positions for administrative positions within higher education.

ONLINE JOB SOURCES AND SERVICES

4068 ■ ABCTeachingJobs.com
URL: http://www.abcteachingjobs.com

Description: Serves as a source of teacher job postings and recruitment. Offers jobs for K-12 teachers and administrators.

4069 ■ Education Administration Jobs
URL: http://www.educationadministrationjobs.com

Description: Serves as an online recruiting resource for education administration employees.

4070 ■ Education America Networks
URL: http://www.educationamerica.net

Description: Education employment network for the United States. Provides information and employment opportunities specifically related to the education industry.

4071 ■ National Educators Employment Review
URL: http://www.thereview.com

Description: Matches qualified educators with employment for teachers, specialists, and administrators from kindergarten through college.

4072 ■ School-Jobs.net
URL: http://www.school-jobs.net/jobs

Description: Matches teachers, administrators, support staff, and other school employees to related jobs across the country. Features jobs by salary, location, and area of expertise.

4073 ■ SchoolSpring.com
URL: http://www.schoolspring.com

Description: Serves as an employment source for educators. Offers teaching jobs and other education job listings including complete archiving of all necessary documents and certifications, as well as access to all education jobs in a specific area.

4074 ■ UniversityJobs.com
URL: http://www.universityjobs.com

Description: Provides an online recruitment solution for colleges and universities to hire new faculty and administrators or staff.

4075 ■ WantToTeach.com
URL: http://www.wanttoteach.com

Description: Serves as an education website to search for administrative, instructional and support openings throughout the United States. Features job openings and job fairs and allows access to various education resources.

TRADESHOWS

4076 ■ American Association of School Personnel Administrators Annual Conference
American Association of School Personnel Administrators
11863 W 112th St., Ste. 100
Overland Park, KS 66210-1375
Ph: (913)327-1222
Fax: (913)327-1223
E-mail: aaspa@aaspa.org
URL: http://www.aaspa.org

Frequency: Annual. Provides school personnel professionals with knowledge and professional development opportunities.

4077 ■ Association for Biblical Higher Education Annual Meeting
Association for Biblical Higher Education
5850 T.G. Lee Blvd., Ste. 130
Orlando, FL 32822
Ph: (407)207-0808
Fax: (407)207-0840
E-mail: info@abhe.org
URL: http://www.abhe.org

Frequency: Annual. **Primary Exhibits:** Publications, office equipment, travel information, educational resources, fundraising services, computers, Bible literature, films, and related material for educational institutions.

4078 ■ Association of International Education Administrators Conference
Association of International Education Administrators
Duke University
2204 Erwin Rd., Rm. 107
Durham, NC 27708-0404
Ph: (919)668-1928
Fax: (919)684-8749
E-mail: aiea@duke.edu
URL: http://www.aieaworld.org

Frequency: Annual. Provides practical strategies and solutions to several issues on campus administration. Offers networking opportunities.

4079 ■ CoSN Annual Conference
Consortium for School Networking
1025 Vermont Ave. NW, Ste. 1010
Washington, DC 20005
Ph: (202)861-2676
Free: 866-267-8747
Fax: (202)393-2011
E-mail: info@cosn.org
URL: http://www.cosn.org

Frequency: Annual. Works to open a worldwide dialogue about the issues of technology and school networking. Brings together key education and policy leaders from the U.S. and other nations to examine

global responses to the effective use of Information and Communication Technology (ICT) in education.

4080 ■ NASFAA National Conference
National Association of Student Financial Aid Administrators
1101 Connecticut Ave. NW, Ste. 1100
Washington, DC 20036-4312
Ph: (202)785-0453
Fax: (202)785-1487
E-mail: web@nasfaa.org
URL: http://www.nasfaa.org

Offers professional advice, expert guidance from policymakers, and networking opportunities.

4081 ■ National Association for Bilingual Education Conference
National Association for Bilingual Education
8701 Georgia Ave., Ste. 700
Silver Spring, MD 20910
Ph: (240)450-3700
Fax: (240)450-3799
E-mail: nabe@nabe.org
URL: http://www.nabe.org

Frequency: Annual. Features speakers, sessions, product exhibits, and job fair.

4082 ■ National Association for Developmental Education Conference
National Association for Developmental Education
500 N Estrella Pkwy., Ste. B2
PMB 412
Goodyear, AZ 85338
Free: 877-233-9455
Fax: (623)792-5747
E-mail: office@nade.net
URL: http://www.nade.net

Frequency: Annual. Annual. Offers an opportunity for personal and professional growth. Includes job fair. 2014 March 5-8; Dallas, TX; Hilton Anatole.

4083 ■ National Association of Independent Schools Conference
National Association of Independent Schools
1129 20th St. NW, Ste. 800
Washington, DC 20036-3425
Ph: (202)973-9700
Fax: (888)316-3862
E-mail: info@nais.org
URL: http://www.nais.org

Frequency: Annual; always late February/March. Annual. Gathering of independent school community, serving school heads and leadership teams. Offers networking opportunities and professional development on critical leadership and educational issues.

4084 ■ Southwestern Federation of Administrative Disciplines Convention
Southwestern Federation of Administrative Disciplines
2700 Bay Area Blvd.
Houston, TX 77058

Frequency: Annual. **Primary Exhibits:** Educational materials and services.

4085 ■ UCEA Convention
University Council for Educational Administration
University of Virginia
Curry School of Education
405 Emmet St.
Charlottesville, VA 22904-0265
Ph: (434)243-1041
Fax: (434)924-1384
E-mail: ucea@virginia.edu
URL: http://ucea.org

Frequency: Annual. **Primary Exhibits:** Publications related to educational administration in universities.

REFERENCE WORKS

4086 ■ Expert Resumes for Teachers and Educators
JIST Publishing
875 Montreal Way
Saint Paul, MN 55102-4245
Ph: (317)613-4200
Free: 800-648-5478
Fax: (800)328-4564
E-mail: info@jist.com
URL: http://www.jist.com

Description: Louise M. Kursmark and Wendy Enelow. 2011. $17.95 (softcover). 336 pages. Gives job seekers strategies and ideas needed to craft outstanding resumes and cover letters. Includes samples of cover letters and resumes, an appendix of online career and job search resources, and tips on winning interviews.

OTHER SOURCES

4087 ■ American Association of Christian Schools
602 Belvoir Ave.
East Ridge, TN 37412
Ph: (423)629-4280
Fax: (423)622-7461
E-mail: info@aacs.org
URL: http://www.aacs.org

Description: Maintains teacher/administrator certification program and placement service. Participates in school accreditation program. Sponsors National Academic Tournament. Maintains American Christian Honor Society. Compiles statistics; maintains speakers' bureau and placement service.

4088 ■ American Association of Collegiate Registrars and Admissions Officers
One Dupont Cir. NW, Ste. 520
Washington, DC 20036-1135
Ph: (202)293-9161
Fax: (202)872-8857
E-mail: meetings@aacrao.org
URL: http://www.aacrao.org

Description: Degree-granting postsecondary institutions, government agencies, and higher education coordinating boards, private educational organizations, and education-oriented businesses. Promotes higher education and furthers the professional development of members working in admissions, enrollment management, institutional research, records, and registration.

4089 ■ American Association of School Administrators
1615 Duke St.
Alexandria, VA 22314
Ph: (703)528-0700
Fax: (703)841-1543
E-mail: info@aasa.org
URL: http://www.aasa.org

Description: Professional association of administrators and executives of school systems and educational service agencies; school district superintendents; central, building, and service unit administrators; presidents of colleges, deans, and professors of educational administration; placement officers; executive directors and administrators of education associations. Sponsors numerous professional development conferences annually.

4090 ■ American Association of School Personnel Administrators
11863 W 112th St., Ste. 100
Overland Park, KS 66210-1375
Ph: (913)327-1222
Fax: (913)327-1223
E-mail: aaspa@aaspa.org
URL: http://www.aaspa.org

Description: Represents persons employed in school personnel administration in the U.S., Canada, and beyond. Establishes acceptable school personnel standards, techniques, and practices. Conducts research.

4091 ■ American Association for Women in Community Colleges
PO Box 3098
Gaithersburg, MD 20885
Ph: (301)442-3374
E-mail: info@aawccnatl.org
URL: http://www.aawccnatl.org

Description: Women faculty members, administrators, staff members, students, and trustees of community colleges. Objectives are to: develop communication and disseminate information among women in community, junior, and technical colleges; encourage educational program development; obtain grants for educational projects for community college women. Disseminates information on women's issues and programs. Conducts regional and state professional development workshops and forums. Recognizes model programs that assist women in community colleges. An affiliate council of the American Association of Community Colleges.

4092 ■ American College Personnel Association
1 Dupont Cir. NW, Ste. 300
Washington, DC 20036-1188
Ph: (202)835-2272
Fax: (202)296-3286
E-mail: info@acpa.nche.edu
URL: http://www2.myacpa.org/

Description: Represents individuals employed in higher education and involved in student personnel work, including administration, counseling, research, and teaching. Fosters student development in higher education in areas of service, advocacy, and standards by offering professional programs for educators committed to the overall development of post-secondary students. Sponsors professional and educational activities in cooperation with other organizations. Offers placement services.

4093 ■ American Council on Education, Fellows Program
1 Dupont Cir. NW
Washington, DC 20036-1193
Ph: (202)939-9420
URL: http://www.acenet.edu/AM/Template.cfm?Section=Fellows_Program1

Description: Service arm of the American Council on Education to strengthen leadership in American postsecondary education by identifying and preparing individuals who have shown promise for responsible positions in higher education administration. Objectives are: to encourage and prepare individuals making higher education administration their professional career; to provide opportunities for planned observation and experience in decision-making; to identify and develop potential leaders. Arranges internships whereby senior faculty and administrators are given the opportunity to study higher education leadership as an intern at a host institution. The stipulations are that the fellow will do certain assigned reading in higher education administration, focus on a strategic learning project and serve at the home institution for the academic year following the internship. Provides services for alumni of the program. **Members:** 1,400.

4094 ■ American Federation of School Administrators
1101 17th St. NW, Ste. 408
Washington, DC 20036
Ph: (202)986-4209
Fax: (202)986-4211
E-mail: afsa@afsaadmin.org
URL: http://afsaadmin.org

Description: Principals, vice-principals, directors, supervisors, and administrators involved in pedagogical education. Purposes are to: achieve the highest goals in education; maintain and improve standards, benefits, and conditions for personnel without regard to color, race, sex, background, or national origin; obtain job security; protect seniority and merit; cooperate with all responsible organizations in education; promote understanding, participation, and support of the public, communities, and agencies; be alert to resist attacks and campaigns that would create or entrench a spoils system; promote democratic society by supporting full educational opportunities for every child and student in the nation.

4095 ■ Association of Christian Schools International
PO Box 65130
Colorado Springs, CO 80962-5130
Free: 800-367-0798
Fax: (719)531-0631
E-mail: member_services@acsi.org
URL: http://www.acsi.org

Description: Seeks to enable Christian educators and schools worldwide to effectively prepare students for life. **Members:** 5,400.

4096 ■ Association of College and University Housing Officers International
1445 Summit St.
Columbus, OH 43201-2105
Ph: (614)292-0099
Fax: (614)292-3205
E-mail: office@acuho-i.org
URL: http://www.acuho-i.org

Description: Officials of educational institutions in 13 countries concerned with all aspects of student housing and food service operation. Supports and conducts research. Organizes seminars and workshops. Offers internships. Maintains biographical archives; offers placement service. Compiles statistics.

4097 ■ Association of Departments of English
26 Broadway, 3rd Fl.
New York, NY 10004-1789
Ph: (646)576-5137
Fax: (646)835-4056
E-mail: dlaurence@mla.org
URL: http://www.ade.org

Description: Administrators of college and university departments of English, humanities, rhetoric, and communications. Works to improve the teaching of English and the administration of English departments. Conducts studies and surveys of literature and writing courses. Sponsors sessions at major English conventions and conferences nationwide. Sponsored by Modern Language Association of America.

4098 ■ Association for Education Finance and Policy
6703 Madison Creek Dr.
Columbia, MO 65203
Ph: (573)814-9878
Fax: (314)256-2831
E-mail: info@aefpweb.org
URL: http://www.aefpweb.org

Description: State and national teacher organizations, university personnel, school administrators, state educational agency personnel, legislators and legislative staff, federal agency personnel, and interested foundations and students. Facilitates communication among groups and individuals in the field of educational finance including academicians, researchers, and policymakers. Main interests include traditional school finance concepts, public policy issues, and the review and debate of emerging issues of educational finance. Conducts workshop. Compiles statistics. Maintains placement service. **Members:** 600.

4099 ■ Association for Humanistic Counseling
5999 Stevenson Ave.
Alexandria, VA 22304
Ph: (703)823-9800

Free: 800-347-6647
Fax: (800)473-2329
E-mail: humanisticcounseling@gmail.com
URL: http://afhc.camp9.org

Description: A division of the American Counseling Association. Teachers, educational administrators, community agency workers, counselors, school social workers, and psychologists; others interested in the area of human development. Aims to assist individuals in improving their quality of life. Provides forum for the exchange of information about humanistically-oriented administrative and instructional practices. Supports humanistic practices and research on instructional and organizational methods for facilitating humanistic education; encourages cooperation among related professional groups.

4100 ■ Association of Independent School Admission Professionals
PO Box 709
Madison, CT 06443
Ph: (203)421-7051
E-mail: info@aisap.org
URL: http://www.aisap.org

Description: Supports the advancement of independent school professionals involved in all aspects of admission and enrollment management. Promotes the value of independent school education. Facilitates training and collaborative dialogue among professionals involved and responsible for enrollment management.

4101 ■ Association of International Education Administrators
Duke University
2204 Erwin Rd., Rm. 107
Durham, NC 27708-0404
Ph: (919)668-1928
Fax: (919)684-8749
E-mail: aiea@duke.edu
URL: http://www.aieaworld.org

Description: Senior-level institutional leaders engaged in advancing the international dimensions of higher education.

4102 ■ Association of Latino Administrators and Superintendents
PO Box 65204
Washington, DC 20035
Ph: (202)466-0808
E-mail: contact@alasedu.org
URL: http://www.alasedu.net

Description: Represents the interests of Latino superintendents and administrators. Provides professional development programs to strengthen the skills of superintendents, principals and other administrators. Advocates for policies to ensure the quality of the public education system.

4103 ■ Association for the Study of Higher Education
4505 S Maryland Pkwy.
Las Vegas, NV 89154
Ph: (702)895-2737
Fax: (702)895-4269
E-mail: ashe@unlv.edu
URL: http://www.ashe.ws

Description: Professors, researchers, administrators, policy analysts, graduate students, and others concerned with the study of higher education. Aims to advance the study of higher education and facilitate and encourage discussion of priority issues for research in the study of higher education.

4104 ■ *Career Opportunities in Education and Related Services*
InfoBase Holdings Inc.
132 W 31st., 17 Fl.
New York, NY 10001-3406
Ph: (212)967-8800
Fax: (800)678-3633
E-mail: info@infobasepublishing.com
URL: http://www.infobasepublishing.com

Frequency: Latest edition 2nd; Published April, 2006. **Price:** $49.50 Individuals Hardcover. **Pages:** 320. **Description:** Susan Echaore-McDavid. Second edition, 2006. 320 pages. **Covers:** 103 job titles in education, including job profiles, duties, salaries, prospects, experience, skills, and more. **Includes:** Appendixes with addresses of colleges and universities offering programs for featured jobs as well as organizations and Internet resources. **Entries include:** Web sites and addresses of professional organizations.

4105 ■ College Media Association
2301 Vanderbilt Pl,
VU Sta. B 35166
Nashville, TN 37235
Ph: (415)338-3134
Fax: (901)678-4798
E-mail: rsplbrgr@memphis.edu
URL: http://www.collegemedia.org

Description: Professional association serving advisers, directors, and chairmen of boards of college student media (newspapers, yearbooks, magazines, handbooks, directories, and radio and television stations); heads of schools and departments of journalism; and others interested in junior college, college, and university student media. Serves as a clearinghouse for student media; acts as consultant on student theses and dissertations on publications. Encourages high school journalism and examines its relationships to college and professional journalism. Conducts national survey of student media in rotation each year by type: newspapers, magazines, and yearbooks; radio and television stations. Compiles statistics. Maintains placement service and speakers' bureau.

4106 ■ Consortium for School Networking
1025 Vermont Ave. NW, Ste. 1010
Washington, DC 20005
Ph: (202)861-2676
Free: 866-267-8747
Fax: (202)393-2011
E-mail: info@cosn.org
URL: http://www.cosn.org

Description: Promotes the use of telecommunications in K-12 classrooms to improve learning. Members represent state and local education agencies, non-profits, companies and individuals who share the organization's vision.

4107 ■ Council of Educational Facility Planners International
11445 E Via Linda, Ste. 2-440
Scottsdale, AZ 85259
Ph: (480)391-0840
E-mail: dwaggone@heery.com
URL: http://www.cefpi.org

Description: Individuals and firms who are responsible for planning, designing, creating, maintaining, and equipping the physical environment of education. Sponsors an exchange of information, professional experiences, best practices research results, and other investigative techniques concerning educational facility planning. Activities include publication and review of current and emerging practices in educational facility planning; identification and execution of needed research; development of professional training programs; strengthening of planning services on various levels of government and in institutions of higher learning; leadership in the development of higher standards for facility design and the physical environment of education. Operates speakers' bureau; sponsors placement service; compiles statistics.

4108 ■ Friends Council on Education
1507 Cherry St.
Philadelphia, PA 19102
Ph: (215)241-7245
Fax: (215)241-7299
E-mail: info@friendscouncil.org
URL: http://www.friendscouncil.org

Description: Representatives appointed by Friends

Yearly Meetings; heads of Quaker secondary and elementary schools and colleges; members-at-large. Acts as a clearinghouse for information on Quaker schools and colleges. Holds meetings and conferences on education and provides in-service training for teachers, administrators and trustees in Friends schools. **Members:** 82.

4109 ■ International Association of Baptist Colleges and Universities
8120 Sawyer Brown Rd., Ste. 108
Nashville, TN 37221-1410
Ph: (615)673-1896
Fax: (615)662-1396
E-mail: tim_fields@baptistschools.org
URL: http://www.baptistschools.org

Description: Southern Baptist senior colleges, universities, junior colleges, academies, and Bible schools. Promotes Christian education through literature, faculty workshops, student recruitment, teacher placement, trustee orientation, statistical information, and other assistance to members.

4110 ■ The International Educator
PO Box 513
Cummaquid, MA 02637
Ph: (508)790-1990
Free: 877-375-6668
Fax: (508)790-1922
E-mail: tie@tieonline.com
URL: http://www.tieonline.com

Description: Facilitates the placement of teachers and administrators in American, British, and international schools. Seeks to create a network that provides for professional development opportunities and improved financial security of members. Offers advice and information on international school news, recent educational developments, job placement, and investment, consumer, and professional development opportunities. Makes available insurance and travel benefits. Operates International Schools Internship Program. **Members:** 3,500.

4111 ■ Jesuit Association of Student Personnel Administrators
2500 California Plz.
Omaha, NE 68178
Ph: (402)280-2717
Fax: (402)280-1275
E-mail: mlpetty@loyno.edu
URL: http://jaspa.creighton.edu

Description: Represents administrators of student personnel programs in 28 Jesuit colleges and universities in the United States. Sponsors institutes and seminars for personnel in Jesuit colleges. Cooperates with Catholic and non-Catholic educational associations in various projects. Maintains placement service and conducts workshops. Operates organizational archives and compiles statistics. **Members:** 750.

4112 ■ Jewish Educators Assembly
PO Box 413
Cedarhurst, NY 11516
Ph: (516)569-2537
Fax: (516)295-9039
E-mail: jewisheducators@aol.com
URL: http://www.jewisheducators.org

Description: Educational and supervisory personnel serving Jewish educational institutions. Seeks to: advance the development of Jewish education in the congregation on all levels in consonance with the philosophy of the Conservative Movement; cooperate with the United Synagogue of America Commission on Jewish Education as the policy-making body of the educational enterprise; join in cooperative effort with other Jewish educational institutions and organizations; establish and maintain professional standards for Jewish educators; serve as a forum for the exchange of ideas; promote the values of Jewish education as a basis for the creative continuity of the Jewish people. Maintains placement service and speaker's bureau.

4113 ■ NAFSA: Association of International Educators

1307 New York Ave. NW, 8th Fl.
Washington, DC 20005-4701
Ph: (202)737-3699
Free: 800-836-4994
Fax: (202)737-3657
E-mail: inbox@nafsa.org
URL: http://www.nafsa.org

Description: Individuals, organizations, and institutions dealing with international educational exchange, including foreign student advisers, overseas educational advisers, credentials and admissions officers, administrators and teachers of English as a second language, community support personnel, study-abroad administrators, and embassy cultural or educational personnel. Promotes self-regulation standards and responsibilities in international educational exchange; offers professional development opportunities primarily through publications, workshops, grants, and regional and national conferences. Advocates for increased awareness and support of international education and exchange on campuses, in government, and in communities. Offers services including: a job registry for employers and professionals involved with international education; a consultant referral service. Sponsors joint liaison activities with a variety of other educational and government organizations to conduct a census of foreign student enrollment in the U.S.; conducts workshops about specific subjects and countries.

4114 ■ NASPA - Student Affairs Administrators in Higher Education

111 K St. NE, 10th Fl.
Washington, DC 20002
Ph: (202)265-7500
Fax: (202)898-5737
E-mail: office@naspa.org
URL: http://www.naspa.org

Description: Representatives of degree-granting institutions of higher education which have been fully accredited. Works to enrich the educational experience of all students. Serves colleges and universities by providing leadership and professional growth opportunities for the senior student affairs officer and other professionals who consider higher education and student affairs issues from an institutional perspective. Provides professional development; improves information and research; acts as an advocate for students in higher education. Maintains career service and conducts the Richard F. Stevens Institute. Supports minority undergraduate fellows program.

4115 ■ National Academic Advising Association

Kansas State University
2323 Anderson Ave., Ste. 225
Manhattan, KS 66502-2912
Ph: (785)532-5717
Fax: (785)532-7732
E-mail: nacada@ksu.edu
URL: http://www.nacada.ksu.edu

Description: Academic program advisors, faculty, administrators, counselors, and others concerned with the intellectual, personal, and career development of students in all types of postsecondary educational institutions. Works to support and promotes professional growth of academic advising and academic advisers. Provides a forum for discussion, debate, and exchange of ideas regarding academic advising. Serves as advocate for standards and quality programs in academic advising. Operates consultants' bureau to assist advising services on college campuses. Maintains placement service, speakers' bureau, and information clearinghouse.

4116 ■ National Alliance of Black School Educators

310 Pennsylvania Ave. SE
Washington, DC 20003
Ph: (202)608-6310

Free: 800-221-2654
Fax: (202)608-6319
E-mail: info@nabse.org
URL: http://www.nabse.org

Description: Black educators from all levels; others indirectly involved in the education of black youth. Promotes awareness, professional expertise, and commitment among black educators. Goals are to: eliminate and rectify the results of racism in education; work with state, local, and national leaders to raise the academic achievement level of all black students; increase members' involvement in legislative activities; facilitate the introduction of a curriculum that more completely embraces black America; improve the ability of black educators to promote problem resolution; create a meaningful and effective network of strength, talent, and professional support. Sponsors workshops, commission meetings, and special projects. Encourages research, especially as it relates to blacks, and the presentation of papers during national conferences. Plans to establish a National Black Educators Data Bank and offer placement service. **Members:** 7,000.

4117 ■ National Association for Bilingual Education

8701 Georgia Ave., Ste. 700
Silver Spring, MD 20910
Ph: (240)450-3700
Fax: (240)450-3799
E-mail: nabe@nabe.org
URL: http://www.nabe.org

Description: Devoted to representing both the interests of language-minority students and the bilingual education professionals who serve them. Works to ensure that "learning is a reality for every student, regardless of his or her mother tongue"; and establishes contact with national organizations.

4118 ■ National Association of College and University Business Officers

1110 Vermont Ave. NW, Ste. 800
Washington, DC 20005
Ph: (202)861-2500
Free: 800-462-4916
Fax: (202)861-2583
E-mail: john.walda@nacubo.org
URL: http://www.nacubo.org

Description: Colleges, universities, and companies that are members of a regional association. Develops and maintains national interest in improving the principles and practices of business and financial administration in higher education. Sponsors workshops in fields such as cash management, grant and contract maintenance, accounting, investment, student loan administration, and costing. Conducts research and information exchange programs between college and university personnel; compiles statistics.

4119 ■ National Association for Developmental Education

500 N Estrella Pkwy., Ste. B2
PMB 412
Goodyear, AZ 85338
Free: 877-233-9455
Fax: (623)792-5747
E-mail: office@nade.net
URL: http://www.nade.net

Description: Developmental educators. Seeks to improve the theory and practice of developmental education. Serves as a forum for the exchange of information among members; facilitates communication and cooperation between members and individuals and organizations working in related fields. Sponsors research, evaluation, programming, and training programs.

4120 ■ National Association of Elementary School Principals

1615 Duke St.
Alexandria, VA 22314
Ph: (703)684-3345
Free: 800-386-2377

Fax: (703)549-5568
E-mail: naesp@naesp.org
URL: http://www.naesp.org

Description: Professional association of principals, assistant or vice principals, and aspiring principals; persons engaged in educational research and in the professional education of elementary and middle school administrators. Sponsors National Distinguished Principals Program, President's Award for Educational Excellence, American Student Council Association. Offers annual national convention and exhibition, on-site and internet professional development workshops throughout the year. Recently expanded professional publications offered through the National Principals' Resource Center.

4121 ■ National Association of Episcopal Schools

815 2nd Ave., 3 Fl.
New York, NY 10017
Ph: (212)716-6134
Free: 800-334-7626
Fax: (212)286-9366
E-mail: info@episcopalschools.org
URL: http://www.episcopalschools.org

Description: Represents Episcopal day and boarding schools and preschools. Promotes the educational ministry of the Episcopal Church. Provides publications, consultation services and conference focusing on Episcopal identity of schools, worship, religious education, spirituality, leadership development and governance for heads/directors, administrators, chaplains and teachers of religion, trustees, rectors and other church and school leaders. **Members:** 509.

4122 ■ National Association of Independent Schools

1129 20th St. NW, Ste. 800
Washington, DC 20036-3425
Ph: (202)973-9700
Fax: (888)316-3862
E-mail: info@nais.org
URL: http://www.nais.org

Description: Independent elementary and secondary school members; regional associations of independent schools and related associations. Provides curricular and administrative research and services. Conducts educational programs; compiles statistics.

4123 ■ National Association of Secondary School Principals

1904 Association Dr.
Reston, VA 20191-1537
Ph: (703)860-0200
Free: 800-253-1746
Fax: (703)476-5432
E-mail: bartolettij@nassp.org
URL: http://www.nassp.org

Description: Middle level and high school principals, assistant principals, and aspiring school leaders, others engaged in secondary school administration and/or supervision; college professors teaching courses in secondary education. Administers the National Association of Student Councils (NASC), National Honor Society (NHS), National Junior Honor Society (NJHS), and the National Elementary Honor Society (NEHS).

4124 ■ National Association of Student Affairs Professionals

Fort Valley State University
1005 State University
Fort Valley, GA 31030
Ph: (478)825-6291
URL: http://www.nasap.net

Description: Promotes excellence in the area of student affairs. Provides programs and events to address the issues and needs of student affairs professionals.

4125 ■ National Association of Student Financial Aid Administrators
1101 Connecticut Ave. NW, Ste. 1100
Washington, DC 20036-4312
Ph: (202)785-0453
Fax: (202)785-1487
E-mail: web@nasfaa.org
URL: http://www.nasfaa.org

Description: Postsecondary institutions, agencies, financial aid administrators, students, and other interested individuals. Seeks to promote the professionalism of student financial aid administrators; serves as the national forum for matters related to student aid; represents the interests and needs of students, faculties, and other persons involved in student financial aid.

4126 ■ National Association of Temple Educators
633 3rd Ave.
New York, NY 10017-6778
Ph: (212)452-6510
Fax: (212)452-6512
E-mail: sschickler@natenet.org
URL: http://www.natenet.org

Description: Directors of education in Reform Jewish religious schools, principals, heads of departments, supervisors, educational consultants, students, and authors. Purposes are to: assist in the growth and development of Jewish religious education consistent with the aims of Reform Judaism; stimulate communal interest in Jewish religious education; represent and encourage the profession of temple educator. Conducts surveys on personnel practices, confirmation practices, religious school organization and administration, curricular practices, and other aspects of religious education. Sponsors institutes for principals and educational directors; maintains placement service.

4127 ■ National Community Education Association
3929 Old Lee Hwy., No. 91-A
Fairfax, VA 22030-2401
Ph: (703)359-8973
Fax: (703)359-0972
E-mail: ncea@ncea.com
URL: http://www.ncea.com

Description: Community school directors, principals, superintendents, professors, teachers, students, and laypeople. Promotes and establishes community schools as an integral part of the educational plan of every community. Emphasizes community and parent involvement in the schools, lifelong learning, and enrichment of K-12 and adult education. Serves as a clearinghouse for the exchange of ideas and information, and the sharing of efforts. Offers leadership training.

4128 ■ National Council for Accreditation of Teacher Education
2010 Massachusetts Ave. NW, Ste. 500
Washington, DC 20036
Ph: (202)466-7496
Fax: (202)296-6620
E-mail: ncate@ncate.org
URL: http://www.ncate.org

Description: Representatives from constituent colleges and universities, state departments of education, school boards, teacher, and other professional groups. Voluntary accrediting body devoted exclusively to: evaluation and accreditation of institutions for preparation of elementary and secondary school teachers; preparation of school service personnel, including school principals, supervisors, superintendents, school psychologists, instructional technologists, and other specialists for school-oriented positions.

4129 ■ *Overseas Employment Opportunities for Educators: Department of Defense Dependents Schools*
DIANE Publishing Co.
PO Box 617
Darby, PA 19023-0617
Ph: (610)461-6200
Free: 800-782-3833
Fax: (610)461-6130
E-mail: dianepublishing@gmail.com
URL: http://www.dianepublishing.net

Description: Barry Leonard, editor. $20.00. 52 pages. An introduction to teachings positions in the Dept. of Defense Dependents Schools (DoDDS), a worldwide school system, operated by the DoD in 14 countries.

4130 ■ *Recruiter's Guide: Job Fairs for Educators*
American Association for Employment in Education
947 E Johnstown Rd., No. 170
Gahanna, OH 43230
Ph: (614)485-1111
Fax: (360)244-7802
E-mail: office@aaee.org
URL: http://www.aaee.org

Frequency: Latest edition 2008. **Pages:** 30. **Covers:** Lists of job and career fairs and the institutions which sponsor the programs or participate in programs sponsored by consortia. **Entries include:** Contact information, date and title of event, location, number of expected employers and candidates, percentage of minority candidates expected, employers fees, registration deadlines, e-mail and website addresses.

4131 ■ Schechter Day School Network
820 2nd Ave.
New York, NY 10017
Ph: (212)533-7800
Fax: (212)353-9439
E-mail: cohen@uscj.org
URL: http://schechternetwork.org

Description: A division of the United Synagogue of Conservative Judaism Commission on Jewish Education. Jewish elementary day schools and high schools with a total of over 21,500 students. Named for Solomon Schecher (1850-1915), scholar of Talmud and rabbinical literature at Cambridge and founder of the United Synagogue of America and the Jewish Theological Seminary. Provides visitations and consultations regarding education, governance and administration; publication of advisories and position papers, biennial conferences for lay leaders, annual conferences of the principals council, Shibboley Schechter newsletter, listserves for presidents, School heads, Business managers, and development directors. Also provides dissemination of demographics and statistics, chartering and accreditation of schools, seminars and board training for lay leaders, Schechter website, SHAR"R, 7th and 8th grade trips to Israel, placement service, MaToK-TaNaKH curriculum development project for Solomon Schecher Day schools, residency fellowship program to prepare professional leadership (SREL) and a listing of consultants.

4132 ■ University Council for Educational Administration
University of Virginia
Curry School of Education
405 Emmet St.
Charlottesville, VA 22904-0265
Ph: (434)243-1041
Fax: (434)924-1384
E-mail: ucea@virginia.edu
URL: http://ucea.org

Description: Consortium of universities with educational leadership and policy programs. Develops, promotes and disseminates information on the improvement of preparation, professional development and practice of school and higher education leaders. Conducts research, policy work and program development in educational leadership through inter-university cooperation. Operates placement service.

EMPLOYER DIRECTORIES AND NETWORKING LISTS

4133 ■ *Crain's List--Chicago's Largest Hospitals*
Crain Communications Inc.
150 N Michigan Ave.
Chicago, IL 60601-7553
Ph: (312)649-5200
Free: 800-678-9595
Fax: (312)280-3150
E-mail: info@crain.com
URL: http://www.chicagobusiness.com/section/lists

Frequency: Published November, 2012. **Price:** $25 Individuals PDF format; $45 Individuals Excel format. **Covers:** 25 hospitals in Chicago area ranked by net patient revenues. **Entries include:** Name, address, phone number, fax, web address, corporate e-mail, hospital administrator, network affiliation, 2011 net patient revenue, percentage change from 2010, 2011 net profits, percentage change from 2011, inpatient days, available beds, daily occupancy rate, number of hospital employees as of December 31, 2011, fiscal year end, Chairman, President, CEO, Chief Financial Officer, Human Resources Manager, Media Relations/Public Relations Director, and Hospital Administrator.

4134 ■ *Directory of Hospital Personnel*
Grey House Publishing
4919 Rte. 22
Amenia, NY 12501
Ph: (518)789-8700
Free: 800-562-2139
Fax: (518)789-0556
E-mail: books@greyhouse.com
URL: http://www.greyhouse.com/hospital_personnel
.htm

Frequency: Annual; Latest edition 2011. **Price:** $325 Individuals Softcover. **Pages:** 2,300. **Covers:** 200,000 executives at 6,000 U.S. Hospitals. **Entries include:** Name of hospital, address, phone, number of beds, type and JCAHO status of hospital, names and titles of key department heads and staff, medical and nursing school affiliations; number of residents, interns, and nursing students. **Arrangement:** Geographical. **Indexes:** Hospital name, personnel, hospital size.

4135 ■ *Hospital Blue Book*
Billian Publishing Inc. and Trans World Publishing Inc.
2100 River Edge Pkwy., Ste. 1200
Atlanta, GA 30328
Ph: (770)955-5656
Free: 800-800-5668
Fax: (770)952-0669
E-mail: info@billian.com
URL: http://www.billianshealthdata.com/Products/
HealthDATA_Hospital_Blue_Book

Frequency: Annual; Latest edition 2012. **Price:** $250 Individuals national edition; $575 Individuals subscription. **Covers:** More than 6,500 hospitals; some listings also appear in a separate southern edition of this publication. **Entries include:** Name of hospital, accreditation, mailing address, phone, fax, number of beds, type of facility (nonprofit, general, state, etc.); list of administrative personnel and chiefs of medical services, with specific titles. **Arrangement:** Geographical.

4136 ■ *Medical and Health Information Directory: A Guide to Organizations, Agencies, Institutions, Programs, Publications, Services, and Other Resources Concerned with Clinical Medicine*
Cengage Learning Inc.
200 1st Stamford Pl., Ste. 400
Stamford, CT 06902-6753
Ph: (203)965-8600
Free: 800-354-9706
Fax: (800)487-8488
E-mail: investors@cengage.com
URL: http://www.gale.cengage.com

Frequency: Annual; Latest edition April 2011. **Price:** $1,190 Individuals set; $501 Individuals per volume. **Covers:** In volume 1, more than 33,000 medical and health oriented associations, organizations, institutions, and government agencies, including health maintenance organizations (HMOs), preferred provider organizations (PPOs), insurance companies, pharmaceutical companies, research centers, and medical and allied health schools. In Volume 2, over 20,000 medical book publishers; medical periodicals, directories, audiovisual producers and services, medical libraries and information centers, electronic resources, and health-related internet search engines. In Volume 3, more than 40,500 clinics, treatment centers, care programs, and counseling/diagnostic services for 34 subject areas. **Entries include:** Institution, service, or firm name, address, phone, fax, email and URL; many include names of key personnel and, when pertinent, descriptive annotation. Volume 3 was formerly listed separately as Health Services Directory. **Arrangement:** Classified by organization activity, service, etc. **Indexes:** Each volume has a complete alphabetical name and keyword index.

HANDBOOKS AND MANUALS

4137 ■ *Exploring Health Care Careers, Second Edition*
JIST Publishing
875 Montreal Way
Saint Paul, MN 55102-4245
Ph: (317)613-4200
Free: 800-648-5478
Fax: (800)328-4564
E-mail: info@jist.com
URL: http://www.jist.com

Description: 2006. $125.00. 992 pages. Information about careers in the health industry, including education and certification requirements, earnings, and job outlook.

4138 ■ *Opportunities in Health and Medical Careers*
The McGraw-Hill Companies Inc.
PO Box 182604
Columbus, OH 43272
Ph: (212)512-2000
Free: 877-833-5524
Fax: (614)759-3749
E-mail: customer.service@mcgraw-hill.com
URL: http://www.mcgraw-hill.com

Description: I. Donald Snook, Jr. and Leo D'Orazio. 2004. $14.95 (paper). 157 pages. Covers the full range of medical and health occupations. Illustrated.

4139 ■ *Opportunities in Medical Imaging Careers*
The McGraw-Hill Companies Inc.
PO Box 182604
Columbus, OH 43272
Ph: (212)512-2000
Free: 877-833-5524
Fax: (614)759-3749
E-mail: customer.service@mcgraw-hill.com
URL: http://www.mcgraw-hill.com

Description: Clifford J. Sherry. 2006. $13.95. 160 pages.

4140 ■ *Resumes for Health and Medical Careers*
The McGraw-Hill Companies Inc.
PO Box 182604
Columbus, OH 43272
Ph: (212)512-2000
Free: 877-833-5524
Fax: (614)759-3749
E-mail: customer.service@mcgraw-hill.com
URL: http://www.mcgraw-hill.com

Description: Third edition, 2008. $12.95 (paper). 144 pages.

ONLINE JOB SOURCES AND SERVICES

4141 ■ *HEALTHeCAREERS Network*
URL: http://www.healthecareers.com

Description: Career search site for jobs in all health care specialties; educational resources; visa and licensing information for relocation; interesting articles; relocation tools; links to professional organizations and general resources.

4142 ■ *ProHealthJobs.com*
URL: http://prohealthjobs.com/jobboard

Description: Career resources site for the medical and health care field. Lists professional opportunities, product information, continuing education and open positions.

TRADESHOWS

4143 ■ American Association of Neuromuscular and Electrodiagnostic Medicine Annual Scientific Meeting

American Association of Neuromuscular and Electrodiagnostic Medicine
2621 Superior Dr. NW
Rochester, MN 55901
Ph: (507)288-0100
E-mail: aanem@aanem.org
URL: http://www.aanem.org

Frequency: Annual. **Primary Exhibits:** Electromyographic and electrodiagnostic equipment and accessories, pharmaceutical companies, and publishers.

4144 ■ American Clinical Neurophysiology Society Annual Meeting

American Clinical Neurophysiology Society
555 E Wells St., Ste. 1100
Milwaukee, WI 53202-3800
Ph: (414)918-9803
Fax: (414)276-3349
E-mail: info@acns.org
URL: http://www.acns.org

Frequency: Annual. **Primary Exhibits:** Electroen-

cephalographic and neurophysiology equipment, supplies, and services.

OTHER SOURCES

4145 ■ American Board of Registration of EEG and EP Technologists

2508 Greenbriar Dr., Ste. A
Springfield, IL 62704
Ph: (217)726-7980
Fax: (217)726-7989
E-mail: abreteo@att.net
URL: http://www.abret.org

Description: Serves the electroneurodiagnostic community and patients. Offers credentialing exams to evaluate the skills and knowledge of technologists.

4146 ■ American Society of Electroneurodiagnostic Technologists

402 E Bannister Rd., Ste. A
Kansas City, MO 64131-3019
Ph: (816)931-1120
Fax: (816)931-1145
E-mail: info@aset.org
URL: http://www.aset.org/i4a/pages/index.cfm
   ?pageid=1

Description: Persons engaged in clinical electroencephalographic (EEG) technology, evoked potential responses, nerve conduction studies, and polysomnography (sleep studies). Works for the advance-

ment of electroneurodiagnostic technology education and practice standards.

4147 ■ *Career Opportunities in Health Care*

InfoBase Holdings Inc.
132 W 31st., 17 Fl.
New York, NY 10001-3406
Ph: (212)967-8800
Fax: (800)678-3633
E-mail: info@infobasepublishing.com
URL: http://www.ferguson.infobasepublishing.com

Description: Shelly Field. 2007. Third edition. $49.50. 304 pages. **Includes:** Appendices provide lists of educational institutions, periodicals, directories, associations, and unions. Appendices provide lists of educational institutions, periodicals, directories, associations, and unions.

4148 ■ *Health-Care Careers for the 21st Century*

JIST Publishing
875 Montreal Way
Saint Paul, MN 55102-4245
Ph: (317)613-4200
Free: 800-648-5478
Fax: (800)328-4564
E-mail: info@jist.com
URL: http://www.jist.com

Price: $9.95 Individuals Softcover. **Pages:** 448. **Covers:** Jobs for health care professionals and career opportunities for those pursuing a health-related career, organized into 80 careers in five groups. **Publication includes:** Appendixes listing job source resources and Web sites for health organizations.

SOURCES OF HELP-WANTED ADS

4149 ■ American Heart Journal
Mosby - An Imprint of Elsevier Science Inc. -
Elsevier Inc. Health Sciences
1600 John F. Kennedy Blvd., Ste. 1800
Philadelphia, PA 19103-2899
Ph: (215)239-3275
Fax: (215)239-3286
E-mail: h.licensing@elsevier.com
URL: http://www.ahjonline.com/

Frequency: Monthly. **Price:** $317 Individuals; $151 Students; $421 Other countries; $200 Students, other countries. **Description:** Medical journal serving practicing cardiologists, university-affiliated clinicians, and physicians keeping abreast of developments in the diagnosis and management of cardiovascular disease.

4150 ■ Journal of Cardiopulmonary Rehabilitation: Featuring Research and Advances in Prevention
Lippincott Williams & Wilkins
2 Commerce Sq.
2001 Market St.
Philadelphia, PA 19103
Ph: (301)223-2300
Free: 800-638-3030
E-mail: jcr@sba.com
URL: http://journals.lww.com/jcrjournal/pages/default.aspx

Frequency: 6/yr. **Price:** $148 Individuals; $454 Institutions; $247 Other countries; $615 Institutions, other countries; $76 Individuals in-training. **Description:** Medical journal.

EMPLOYER DIRECTORIES AND NETWORKING LISTS

4151 ■ Crain's List--Chicago's Largest Hospitals
Crain Communications Inc.
150 N Michigan Ave.
Chicago, IL 60601-7553
Ph: (312)649-5200
Free: 800-678-9595
Fax: (312)280-3150
E-mail: info@crain.com
URL: http://www.chicagobusiness.com/section/lists

Frequency: Published November, 2012. **Price:** $25 Individuals PDF format; $45 Individuals Excel format. **Covers:** 25 hospitals in Chicago area ranked by net patient revenues. **Entries include:** Name, address, phone number, fax, web address, corporate e-mail, hospital administrator, network affiliation, 2011 net patient revenue, percentage change from 2010, 2011 net profits, percentage change from 2011, inpatient days, available beds, daily occupancy rate, number of hospital employees as of December 31, 2011, fis-

cal year end, Chairman, President, CEO, Chief Financial Officer, Human Resources Manager, Media Relations/Public Relations Director, and Hospital Administrator.

4152 ■ Directory of Hospital Personnel
Grey House Publishing
4919 Rte. 22
Amenia, NY 12501
Ph: (518)789-8700
Free: 800-562-2139
Fax: (518)789-0556
E-mail: books@greyhouse.com
URL: http://www.greyhouse.com/hospital_personnel.htm

Frequency: Annual; Latest edition 2011. **Price:** $325 Individuals Softcover. **Pages:** 2,300. **Covers:** 200,000 executives at 6,000 U.S. Hospitals. **Entries include:** Name of hospital, address, phone, number of beds, type and JCAHO status of hospital, names and titles of key department heads and staff, medical and nursing school affiliations; number of residents, interns, and nursing students. **Arrangement:** Geographical. **Indexes:** Hospital name, personnel, hospital size.

4153 ■ Hospital Blue Book
Billian Publishing Inc. and Trans World Publishing Inc.
2100 River Edge Pkwy., Ste. 1200
Atlanta, GA 30328
Ph: (770)955-5656
Free: 800-800-5668
Fax: (770)952-0669
E-mail: info@billian.com
URL: http://www.billianshealthdata.com/Products/HealthDATA_Hospital_Blue_Book

Frequency: Annual; Latest edition 2012. **Price:** $250 Individuals national edition; $575 Individuals subscription. **Covers:** More than 6,500 hospitals; some listings also appear in a separate southern edition of this publication. **Entries include:** Name of hospital, accreditation, mailing address, phone, fax, number of beds, type of facility (nonprofit, general, state, etc.); list of administrative personnel and chiefs of medical services, with specific titles. **Arrangement:** Geographical.

4154 ■ Medical and Health Information Directory: A Guide to Organizations, Agencies, Institutions, Programs, Publications, Services, and Other Resources Concerned with Clinical Medicine
Cengage Learning Inc.
200 1st Stamford Pl., Ste. 400
Stamford, CT 06902-6753
Ph: (203)965-8600
Free: 800-354-9706
Fax: (800)487-8488
E-mail: investors@cengage.com
URL: http://www.gale.cengage.com

Frequency: Annual; Latest edition April 2011. **Price:** $1,190 Individuals set; $501 Individuals per volume. **Covers:** In volume 1, more than 33,000 medical and health oriented associations, organizations, institutions, and government agencies, including health maintenance organizations (HMOs), preferred provider organizations (PPOs), insurance companies, pharmaceutical companies, research centers, and medical and allied health schools. In Volume 2, over 20,000 medical book publishers; medical periodicals, directories, audiovisual producers and services, medical libraries and information centers, electronic resources, and health-related internet search engines. In Volume 3, more than 40,500 clinics, treatment centers, care programs, and counseling/diagnostic services for 34 subject areas. **Entries include:** Institution, service, or firm name, address, phone, fax, email and URL; many include names of key personnel and, when pertinent, descriptive annotation. Volume 3 was formerly listed separately as Health Services Directory. **Arrangement:** Classified by organization activity, service, etc. **Indexes:** Each volume has a complete alphabetical name and keyword index.

HANDBOOKS AND MANUALS

4155 ■ Exploring Health Care Careers, Second Edition
JIST Publishing
875 Montreal Way
Saint Paul, MN 55102-4245
Ph: (317)613-4200
Free: 800-648-5478
Fax: (800)328-4564
E-mail: info@jist.com
URL: http://www.jist.com

Description: 2006. $125.00. 992 pages. Information about careers in the health industry, including education and certification requirements, earnings, and job outlook.

4156 ■ The Only EKG Book You'll Ever Need
Lippincott Williams & Wilkins
2 Commerce Sq.
2001 Market St.
Philadelphia, PA 19103
Ph: (301)223-2300
Free: 800-638-3030
E-mail: ronna.ekhouse@wolterskluwer.com
URL: http://www.lww.com

Description: Malcolm S Thaler. Sixth edition, 2009. $61.95. 336 pages.

4157 ■ Opportunities in Health and Medical Careers
The McGraw-Hill Companies Inc.
PO Box 182604
Columbus, OH 43272
Ph: (212)512-2000

Free: 877-833-5524
Fax: (614)759-3749
E-mail: customer.service@mcgraw-hill.com
URL: http://www.mcgraw-hill.com

Description: I. Donald Snook, Jr. and Leo D'Orazio. 2004. $14.95 (paper). 157 pages. Covers the full range of medical and health occupations. Illustrated.

4158 ■ *Opportunities in Medical Imaging Careers*
The McGraw-Hill Companies Inc.
PO Box 182604
Columbus, OH 43272
Ph: (212)512-2000
Free: 877-833-5524
Fax: (614)759-3749
E-mail: customer.service@mcgraw-hill.com
URL: http://www.mcgraw-hill.com

Description: Clifford J. Sherry. 2006. $13.95. 160 pages.

4159 ■ *Resumes for Health and Medical Careers*
The McGraw-Hill Companies Inc.
PO Box 182604
Columbus, OH 43272
Ph: (212)512-2000
Free: 877-833-5524
Fax: (614)759-3749
E-mail: customer.service@mcgraw-hill.com
URL: http://www.mcgraw-hill.com

Description: Third edition, 2008. $12.95 (paper). 144 pages.

EMPLOYMENT AGENCIES AND SEARCH FIRMS

4160 ■ Team Placement Service Inc.
1414 Prince St., Ste. 202
Alexandria, VA 22314
Ph: (703)820-8618
Free: 800-495-6767
Fax: (703)820-3368
E-mail: info@teamplace.com
URL: http://www.teamplace.com

Description: Full-service personnel consultants provide placement for healthcare staff, physician and dentist, private practice, and hospitals. Conduct interviews, tests, and reference checks to select the top 20% of applicants. Survey applicants' skill levels, provide backup information on each candidate, select compatible candidates for consideration, and insure the hiring process minimizes potential legal liability. Industries served: healthcare and government agencies providing medical, dental, biotech, laboratory, hospitals, and physician search.

ONLINE JOB SOURCES AND SERVICES

4161 ■ HEALTHeCAREERS Network
URL: http://www.healthecareers.com

Description: Career search site for jobs in all health care specialties; educational resources; visa and licensing information for relocation; interesting articles; relocation tools; links to professional organizations and general resources.

4162 ■ Hospital Jobs OnLine
URL: http://www.hospitaljobsonline.com

Description: Serves as a niche healthcare job board designed exclusively for hospitals, healthcare companies, and healthcare job seekers.

4163 ■ ProHealthJobs.com
URL: http://prohealthjobs.com/jobboard

Description: Career resources site for the medical and health care field. Lists professional opportunities, product information, continuing education and open positions.

TRADESHOWS

4164 ■ American Association of Neuromuscular and Electrodiagnostic Medicine Annual Scientific Meeting
American Association of Neuromuscular and Electrodiagnostic Medicine
2621 Superior Dr. NW
Rochester, MN 55901
Ph: (507)288-0100
E-mail: aanem@aanem.org
URL: http://www.aanem.org

Frequency: Annual. **Primary Exhibits:** Electromyographic and electrodiagnostic equipment and accessories, pharmaceutical companies, and publishers.

4165 ■ American Clinical Neurophysiology Society Annual Meeting
American Clinical Neurophysiology Society
555 E Wells St., Ste. 1100
Milwaukee, WI 53202-3800
Ph: (414)918-9803
Fax: (414)276-3349
E-mail: info@acns.org
URL: http://www.acns.org

Frequency: Annual. **Primary Exhibits:** Electroencephalographic and neurophysiology equipment, supplies, and services.

4166 ■ American College of Cardiology Annual Scientific Session
American College of Cardiology
2400 N St. NW
Washington, DC 20037
Ph: (202)375-6000

Free: 800-253-4636
Fax: (202)375-7000
E-mail: resource@acc.org
URL: http://www.cardiosource.org/acc
Frequency: Annual. **Primary Exhibits:** Products and services related to cardiovascular medicine.

OTHER SOURCES

4167 ■ Alliance of Cardiovascular Professionals
PO Box 2007
Midlothian, VA 23113
Ph: (804)632-0078
Fax: (804)639-9212
E-mail: peggymcelgunn@comcast.net
URL: http://www.acp-online.org

Description: Strives to meet educational needs. Develops programs to meet those needs. Provides a structure to offer the cardiovascular and pulmonary technology professional a key to the future as a valuable member of the medical team. Seeks advancement for members through communication and education. Provides coordinated programs to orient the newer professional to his field and continuing educational opportunities for technologist personnel; has established guidelines for educational programs in the hospital and university setting. Works with educators and physicians to provide basic, advanced, and in-service programs for technologists. Sponsors registration and certification programs which provide technology professionals with further opportunity to clarify their level of expertise. Compiles statistics.

4168 ■ *Career Opportunities in Health Care*
InfoBase Holdings Inc.
132 W 31st., 17 Fl.
New York, NY 10001-3406
Ph: (212)967-8800
Fax: (800)678-3633
E-mail: info@infobasepublishing.com
URL: http://www.ferguson.infobasepublishing.com

Description: Shelly Field. 2007. Third edition. $49.50. 304 pages. **Includes:** Appendices provide lists of educational institutions, periodicals, directories, associations, and unions. Appendices provide lists of educational institutions, periodicals, directories, associations, and unions.

4169 ■ *Health-Care Careers for the 21st Century*
JIST Publishing
875 Montreal Way
Saint Paul, MN 55102-4245
Ph: (317)613-4200
Free: 800-648-5478
Fax: (800)328-4564
E-mail: info@jist.com
URL: http://www.jist.com

Price: $9.95 Individuals Softcover. **Pages:** 448. **Covers:** Jobs for health care professionals and career opportunities for those pursuing a health-related career, organized into 80 careers in five groups. **Publication includes:** Appendixes listing job source resources and Web sites for health organizations.

SOURCES OF HELP-WANTED ADS

4170 ■ *Appliance Service News*
Gamit Enterprises Inc.
PO Box 809
Saint Charles, IL 60174
Ph: (630)845-9481
Free: 877-747-1625
Fax: (630)845-9483
E-mail: asnews@cin.net
URL: http://asnews.com

Frequency: Monthly. **Price:** $79.95 Individuals domestic; $96.95 Individuals domestic, first class delivery; $101.95 Canada first class delivery; $125.95 Other countries first class delivery; $39.95 Individuals online. **Description:** Magazine for appliance technicians.

4171 ■ *Electric Light & Power*
PennWell Publishing Co.
1421 S Sheridan Rd.
Tulsa, OK 74112
Ph: (918)835-3161
Free: 800-331-4463
Fax: (918)831-9497
E-mail: Headquarters@PennWell.com
URL: http://www.elp.com/index.html

Frequency: Bimonthly. **Price:** $85 Canada; $145 Canada two years; $94 Individuals Mexico; $160 Individuals 2 years, Mexico; $225 Other countries; $403 Other countries 2 years. **Description:** Provides broad view of electric utility industry with in-depth analysis of key business issues for executives and management.

4172 ■ *Electronic Markets*
Springer-Verlag New York Inc.
233 Spring St.
New York, NY 10013
Ph: (212)460-1500
Free: 800-777-4643
Fax: (212)460-1575
E-mail: service-ny@springer.com
URL: http://www.springer.com/
  business+%26+management/
  business+information+systems/journal/12525

Frequency: 4/yr. **Price:** €648 Institutions print or online; €778 Institutions print & enchanced access. **Description:** Journal covering all system concepts of electronic commerce.

4173 ■ *Engineering Economist*
Taylor & Francis
711 3rd Ave., 8th Fl.
New York, NY 10017
Ph: (212)216-7800
Free: 800-634-7064
Fax: (212)563-2269
E-mail: info@taylorandfrancis.com
URL: http://www.tandfonline.com/toc/utee20/current

Frequency: Quarterly. **Price:** $93 Individuals print

only; $159 Institutions online only; $177 Institutions print & online. **Description:** Publication covering business issues in the energy, petroleum and mining industries.

4174 ■ *The High-Tech News*
ETA International
5 Depot St.
Greencastle, IN 46135
Ph: (765)653-8262
Free: 800-288-3824
Fax: (765)653-4287
E-mail: eta@eta-i.org
URL: http://www.eta-i.org

Description: Bimonthly. Serves member technicians with news of the Association and the electronics industry, including items on service, education, employment, management, and events. Contains information on membership, management, telecommunications, and business and technical training programs. Recurring features include editorials, news of research, letters to the editor, book reviews, and a calendar of events.

4175 ■ *Journal of Active and Passive Electronic Devices*
Old City Publishing
c/o Robert Castellano, Ed.-in-Ch.
The Information Network
8740 Lyon Valley Rd.
New Tripoli, PA 18066
Ph: (215)925-4390
Fax: (215)925-4371
E-mail: info@oldcitypublishing.com
URL: http://www.oldcitypublishing.com/JAPED/
  JAPED.html

Frequency: Quarterly. **Price:** $766 Institutions print and online; $157 Individuals print only; €635 Institutions print and online; €148 Individuals print only; ¥76,372 Institutions print and online; ¥19,859 Individuals print only. **Description:** International journal devoted to the science and technology of all types of electronic components.

4176 ■ *Journal of Vacuum Science and Technology A & B: Vacuum, Surfaces and Films*
American Institute of Physics
1 Physics Ellipse
College Park, MD 20740-3843
Ph: (301)209-3100
Fax: (301)209-0843
E-mail: jvst@mcnc.org
URLs: http://www.virtualjournals.org/; http://
  avspublications.org/jvsta; http://avspublications.org/
  jvstb

Frequency: Monthly. **Price:** $1,840 Individuals print & online; $1,980 Other countries print & online (surface); $2,040 Individuals print & online (air). **Description:** Journal containing research review articles in all areas of vacuum science.

4177 ■ *Machine Design: Proven America's Most Useful Design Engineering Magazine*
Intertec Publishing
5 Penn Plz., 13th Fl.
New York, NY 10001-1810
Ph: (212)613-9700
Free: 800-795-5445
Fax: (212)613-9749
E-mail: bethany.weaver@penton.com
URL: http://machinedesign.com/

Frequency: 22/yr. **Description:** Magazine on design engineering function.

4178 ■ *Security Sales & Integration*
Bobit Business Media
3520 Challenger St.
Torrance, CA 90503
Ph: (310)533-2400
Fax: (310)533-2500
E-mail: secsales@bobit.com
URL: http://www.securitysales.com

Frequency: Monthly. **Price:** Free. **Description:** Magazine covering the security industry.

EMPLOYER DIRECTORIES AND NETWORKING LISTS

4179 ■ *American Electronics Association--Member Directory*
American Electronics Association
601 Pennsylvania Ave., South Bldg., Ste. 900
Washington, DC 20004
Ph: (202)589-1144
Free: 800-284-4232
Fax: (202)639-8238
E-mail: info@aea.net
URL: http://www.aea.net/memberdirectory.asp

Covers: Over 3,000 member electronics and high-technology companies and 500 associate member firms including financial institutions, law firms, and accounting firms. **Entries include:** Company name, address, phone, World Wide Web addresses, cable address, fax, names of executives, number of employees, list of products or services, date founded, whether a public or private company, stock market where traded, ticker symbol. **Arrangement:** Alphabetical. **Indexes:** Geographical, product.

4180 ■ *Appliance Design--Buyers Guide*
BNP Media
2401 W Big Beaver Rd., Ste. 700
Troy, MI 48084
Ph: (248)362-3700
Free: 800-952-6643
Fax: (248)362-5103
E-mail: directories@bnpmedia.com
URL: http://buyersguide.appliancedesign.com/
  buyersguide

Frequency: Annual. **Publication includes:** Directory of manufacturers and suppliers of equipment, material, and components to the appliance industry; trade associations. **Entries include:** Company name, address, phone, fax, website, and e-mail. **Arrangement:** Classified by product or service, and by company name. **Indexes:** Product/service, company.

HANDBOOKS AND MANUALS

4181 ■ *Opportunities in Electronics Careers*
The McGraw-Hill Companies Inc.
PO Box 182604
Columbus, OH 43272
Ph: (212)512-2000
Free: 877-833-5524
Fax: (614)759-3749
E-mail: customer.service@mcgraw-hill.com
URL: http://www.mcgraw-hill.com

Description: Mark Rowh. 2007. $13.95 (paper). 221 pages. Discusses career opportunities in commercial and industrial electronics equipment repair, electronics home entertainment repair, electronics engineering, and engineering technology. Includes job outlook and how to get off to a good start on the job.

4182 ■ *Troubleshooting Electrical/Electronic Systems*
American Technical Publishers, Inc.
1155 W 175th St.
Homewood, IL 60430
Ph: (708)957-1100
Free: 800-323-3471
Fax: (708)957-1101
E-mail: service@americantech.net
URL: http://www.go2atp.com/Troubleshooting_Electrical_P14.cfm

Description: Glen A. Mazur and Thomas E. Proctor. Third edition. $78.00. 631 pages. Step-by-step applications show how to troubleshoot electrical and electronic systems.

4183 ■ *Troubleshooting and Repairing Major Appliances*
The McGraw-Hill Companies Inc.
PO Box 182604
Columbus, OH 43272
Ph: (212)512-2000
Free: 877-833-5524
Fax: (614)759-3749
E-mail: customer.service@mcgraw-hill.com
URL: http://www.mcgraw-hill.com

Description: Eric Kleinert. 2007. $59.95. 744 pages.

EMPLOYMENT AGENCIES AND SEARCH FIRMS

4184 ■ **Electronic Search, Inc.**
5105 Tollview Dr., Ste. 245
Rolling Meadows, IL 60008
Ph: (847)506-0700

Fax: (847)506-9999
E-mail: email@electronicsearch.com
URL: http://www.electronicsearch.com

Description: Staffing solutions firm, specializing in filling highly technical requirements in the wireless, telecommunications, and public safety technology industries; includes job listings with contact person, location, job description, qualifications, and compensation.

4185 ■ **Omni Recruiting Group, Inc.**
227 Sandy Springs Pl., Ste. D-370
Atlanta, GA 30328
Ph: (404)256-1575
Fax: (404)256-1585
E-mail: info@omnirecruiting.com
URL: http://www.omnirecruiting.com

Description: Executive search firm specializing in sales.

4186 ■ **S.D. Kelly and Associates, Inc.**
130 S Washington St.
North Attleboro, MA 02760
Ph: (508)809-6496
Fax: (508)809-6495
E-mail: info@sdkelly.com
URL: http://www.sdkelly.com

Description: Employment agency.

TRADESHOWS

4187 ■ **International CES**
Consumer Electronics Association
1919 S Eads St.
Arlington, VA 22202
Ph: (703)907-7600
Free: 866-858-1555
Fax: (703)907-7675
E-mail: info@ce.org
URL: http://www.ce.org

Frequency: Annual. **Primary Exhibits:** Electronic equipment, supplies, and services.

4188 ■ **National Utility Contractors Association Convention**
National Utility Contractor Association
3925 Chain Bridge Rd., Ste. 300
Fairfax, VA 22030
Ph: (703)358-9300
Fax: (703)358-9307
E-mail: vanessa@nuca.com
URL: http://www.nuca.com

Frequency: Annual. **Primary Exhibits:** Equipment, supplies, and services for the construction of utility lines (pipes for storm and sanitary sewers and drainage, water lines, cables, ducts, conduits, and other utility work).

4189 ■ **POWER-GEN International**
Power Engineering
PennWell Publishing
1421 S Sheridan Rd.
Tulsa, OK 74112

Ph: (918)832-9339
Free: 800-331-4463
Fax: (918)831-9834
URL: http://www.power-eng.com
Frequency: Annual. **Primary Exhibits:** Equipment and services for power generation industries.

OTHER SOURCES

4190 ■ **Electronics Technicians Association International**
5 Depot St.
Greencastle, IN 46135-8024
Ph: (765)653-8262
Free: 800-288-3824
Fax: (765)653-4287
E-mail: eta@eta-i.org
URL: http://www.eta-i.org
Description: Skilled electronics technicians. Provides placement service; offers certification examinations for electronics technicians and satellite, fiber optics, and data cabling installers. Compiles wage and manpower statistics. Administers FCC Commercial License examinations and certification of computer network systems technicians and web and internet specialists.

4191 ■ **International Society of Certified Electronics Technicians**
3608 Pershing Ave.
Fort Worth, TX 76107-4527
Ph: (817)921-9101
Free: 800-946-0201
Fax: (817)921-3741
E-mail: info@iscet.org
URL: http://www.iscet.org
Description: Technicians in 50 countries who have been certified by the society. Seeks to provide a fraternal bond among certified electronics technicians, raise their public image and improve the effectiveness of industry education programs for technicians. Offers training programs in new electronics information. Maintains library of service literature for consumer electronic equipment, including manuals and schematics for out-of-date equipment. Offers all FCC licenses. Sponsors testing program for certification of electronics technicians in the fields of audio, communications, computer, consumer, industrial, medical electronics, radar, radio-television and video.

4192 ■ **National Electronics Service Dealers Association Inc.**
3608 Pershing Ave.
Fort Worth, TX 76107-4527
Ph: (817)921-9061
Free: 800-797-9197
Fax: (817)921-3741
E-mail: mack@nesda.com
URL: http://www.nesda.com
Description: Local and state electronic service associations and companies. Supplies technical service information on business management training to electronic service dealers. Offers certification and training programs through International Society of Certified Electronics Technicians. Conducts technical service and business management seminars.

Sources of Help-Wanted Ads

4193 ■ *Aerospace America Magazine*
American Institute of Aeronautics and Astronautics
1801 Alexander Bell Dr., Ste. 500
Reston, VA 20191-4344
Ph: (703)264-7500
Free: 800-639-2422
Fax: (703)264-7551
E-mail: custserv@aiaa.org
URL: http://www.aerospaceamerica.org/Pages/Table-OfContents.aspx

Frequency: Monthly. **Price:** $200 Institutions non member, domestic; $163 for nonmembers in U.S. **Description:** Monthly. Free to members; non-members, $140.00 per year. Covers aeronautics and space technology with special attention to aerospace defense, design, and electronics.

4194 ■ AIE Perspectives Newsmagazine
American Institute of Engineers
4630 Appian Way, Ste. 206
El Sobrante, CA 94803-1875
Ph: (510)758-6240
Fax: (510)758-6240
E-mail: aie@aieonline.org
URL: http://www.members-aie.org

Frequency: Monthly. **Price:** included in membership dues. **Description:** Professional magazine covering engineering.

4195 ■ *Communications of the ACM*
Association for Computing Machinery
2 Penn Plz., Ste. 701
New York, NY 10121-0701
Ph: (212)626-0500
Free: 800-342-6626
Fax: (212)944-1318
E-mail: acmhelp@acm.org
URL: http://cacm.acm.org

Frequency: Monthly. **Price:** $99 Members professional. **Description:** Computing news magazine.

4196 ■ Community Radio News
National Federation of Community Broadcasters
1101 Pennsylvania Ave. NW, Ste. 600
Washington, DC 20004
Ph: (202)756-2268
E-mail: comments@nfcb.org
URL: http://www.nfcb.org

Evona Balcziunas, Editor. **Frequency:** Monthly; Monthly. **Price:** $75/year; Included in membership; $75 University Libraries. **Description:** Serves as a medium of communication for independent, community-licensed radio stations. Recurring features include job openings and a calendar of events/conferences for noncommercial broadcasters.

4197 ■ *Consulting-Specifying Engineer*
CFE Media LLC
1111 W 22nd St., Ste. 250
Oak Brook, IL 60523
Ph: (630)571-4070
Fax: (630)214-4504
URLs: http://www.csemag.com; http://mediakit.cfe-media.com/cseimk/csewebcasts.html

Frequency: 13/yr. **Description:** The integrated engineering magazine of the building construction industry.

4198 ■ *EE Evaluation Engineering: The Magazine of Electronic Evaluation & Test*
Nelson Publishing Inc.
2500 Tamiami Trl. N
Nokomis, FL 34275
Ph: (941)966-9521
Fax: (941)966-2590
E-mail: webteam@nelsonpub.com
URL: http://www.evaluationengineering.com/

Frequency: Monthly. **Price:** Free. **Description:** Trade magazine covering electronic engineering, evaluation and test.

4199 ■ *Electric Light & Power*
PennWell Publishing Co.
1421 S Sheridan Rd.
Tulsa, OK 74112
Ph: (918)835-3161
Free: 800-331-4463
Fax: (918)831-9497
E-mail: Headquarters@PennWell.com
URL: http://www.elp.com/index.html

Frequency: Bimonthly. **Price:** $85 Canada; $145 Canada two years; $94 Individuals Mexico; $160 Individuals 2 years, Mexico; $225 Other countries; $403 Other countries 2 years. **Description:** Provides broad view of electric utility industry with in-depth analysis of key business issues for executives and management.

4200 ■ *The Electrochemical Society Interface*
Electrochemical Society
c/o Krishan Rajeshwar, Ed.
University of Texas at Arlington
Department of Chemistry & Biochemistry
502 Yates St.
Arlington, TX 76019
Ph: (817)272-3810
Fax: (817)272-3808
E-mail: interface@electrochem.org
URL: http://www.electrochem.org/dl/interface/

Frequency: Quarterly. **Price:** $69 Individuals tier 1, print & online; $84 Canada tier 1, print & online; $92 Other countries tier 1, print & online. **Description:** Publication featuring news and articles of interest to members of the Electrochemical Society.

4201 ■ *Electronic Component News: The Information Center for Design Engineers*
Advantage Business Media L.L.C.
100 Enterprise Dr., Ste. 600
Rockaway, NJ 07866-0912
Ph: (973)920-7000
E-mail: advantagecommunications@advantagemedia.com
URL: http://www.ecnmag.com/

Frequency: 15/yr. **Price:** Free; $93 Individuals; C$112 Individuals; $175 Other countries. **Description:** Magazine (tabloid) for electronics design engineers and engineering management.

4202 ■ *Electronic Markets*
Springer-Verlag New York Inc.
233 Spring St.
New York, NY 10013
Ph: (212)460-1500
Free: 800-777-4643
Fax: (212)460-1575
E-mail: service-ny@springer.com
URL: http://www.springer.com/business+%26+management/business+information+systems/journal/12525

Frequency: 4/yr. **Price:** €648 Institutions print or on-line; €778 Institutions print & enchanced access. **Description:** Journal covering all system concepts of electronic commerce.

4203 ■ *Electronic Products*
E-mail: lens@electronicproducts.com
URL: http://www.electronicproducts.com

Frequency: Monthly. **Price:** $12 Individuals. **Description:** Magazine for electronic design engineers and management.

4204 ■ *Energy and Power Engineering*
Scientific Research Publishing
PO Box 54821
Irvine, CA 92619-4821
E-mail: epe@scirp.org
URL: http://www.scirp.org/journal/epe/

Price: $354 Individuals. **Description:** Journal publishing information on all important aspects of electric power engineering.

4205 ■ *Engineering*
Scientific Research Publishing
PO Box 54821
Irvine, CA 92619-4821
E-mail: eng@scirp.org
URL: http://www.scirp.org/journal/eng/

Frequency: Monthly. **Price:** $468 Individuals. **Description:** Peer-reviewed journal publishing articles on the latest advancements in engineering.

4206 ■ *Engineering Economist*
Taylor & Francis
711 3rd Ave., 8th Fl.
New York, NY 10017
Ph: (212)216-7800

Free: 800-634-7064
Fax: (212)563-2269
E-mail: info@taylorandfrancis.com
URL: http://www.tandfonline.com/toc/utee20/current
Frequency: Quarterly. **Price:** $93 Individuals print only; $159 Institutions online only; $177 Institutions print & online. **Description:** Publication covering business issues in the energy, petroleum and mining industries.

4207 ■ *Graduating Engineer & Computer Careers*
Career Recruitment Media
2 LAN Dr., Ste. 100
Westford, MA 01886
Ph: (978)692-5092
Fax: (978)692-4174
E-mail: hshulick@alloyeducation.com
URL: http://www.graduatingengineer.com
Frequency: Quarterly. **Price:** $16.95 Individuals. **Description:** Magazine focusing on employment, education, and career development for entry-level engineers and computer scientists.

4208 ■ *The High-Tech News*
ETA International
5 Depot St.
Greencastle, IN 46135
Ph: (765)653-8262
Free: 800-288-3824
Fax: (765)653-4287
E-mail: eta@eta-i.org
URL: http://www.eta-i.org
Description: Bimonthly. Serves member technicians with news of the Association and the electronics industry, including items on service, education, employment, management, and events. Contains information on membership, management, telecommunications, and business and technical training programs. Recurring features include editorials, news of research, letters to the editor, book reviews, and a calendar of events.

4209 ■ *IEEE Spectrum*
Institute of Electrical and Electronics Engineers USA
2001 L St. NW, Ste. 700
Washington, DC 20036-4910
Ph: (202)785-0017
Fax: (202)785-0835
E-mail: ieeeusa@ieee.org
URL: http://www.spectrum.ieee.org/mc_online
Frequency: Monthly. **Price:** $29.95 U.S. and Canada; $99.95 Other countries. **Description:** Features trends in engineering, science, and technology.

4210 ■ *IEEE Transactions on Electron Devices*
IEEE Electron Devices Society
c/o John D. Cressler, Ed.-in-Ch.
Georgia Institute of Technology
School of Electrical and Computer Engineering
777 Atlantic Dr. NW
Atlanta, GA 30332-0250
Ph: (404)894-5161
Fax: (404)894-4641
E-mail: eds@ieee.org
URL: http://ieeexplore.ieee.org/xpl/RecentIssue.jsp ?punumber=16
Frequency: Monthly. **Description:** Journal covering theory, design, performance and reliability of electron devices.

4211 ■ *The Industrial Projects Report*
Industrial Projects Services, Inc.
PO Box 274231
Tampa, FL 33688
Free: 800-849-4821
Fax: (813)265-0331
E-mail: deven.taylor@industrialprojectsreport.com
URL: http://industrialprojectsreport.com
Frequency: Monthly. **Description:** Features up-to-date information, job board, and construction forum

for skilled crafts people and management personnel. Contains advertisements from staffing companies looking for construction management, supervision professionals and skilled-craft professionals for projects nationwide. Includes reports on industrial projects' location, approximate job durations, wages and other benefits. Helps technical colleges and trade schools in recruiting students to their trade programs.

4212 ■ *Journal of Active and Passive Electronic Devices*
Old City Publishing
c/o Robert Castellano, Ed.-in-Ch.
The Information Network
8740 Lyon Valley Rd.
New Tripoli, PA 18066
Ph: (215)925-4390
Fax: (215)925-4371
E-mail: info@oldcitypublishing.com
URL: http://www.oldcitypublishing.com/JAPED/ JAPED.html
Frequency: Quarterly. **Price:** $766 Institutions print and online; $157 Individuals print only; €635 Institutions print and online; €148 Individuals print only; ¥76,372 Institutions print and online; ¥19,859 Individuals print only. **Description:** International journal devoted to the science and technology of all types of electronic components.

4213 ■ *Machine Design: Proven America's Most Useful Design Engineering Magazine*
Intertec Publishing
5 Penn Plz., 13th Fl.
New York, NY 10001-1810
Ph: (212)613-9700
Free: 800-795-5445
Fax: (212)613-9749
E-mail: bethany.weaver@penton.com
URL: http://machinedesign.com/
Frequency: 22/yr. **Description:** Magazine on design engineering function.

4214 ■ *Microwave Journal: Microwave - RF & Lightwave Technology*
Horizon House Publications Inc.
685 Canton St.
Norwood, MA 02062
Ph: (781)769-9750
Free: 800-966-8526
Fax: (781)769-5037
E-mail: mwj@mwjournal.com
URL: http://www.mwjournal.com
Frequency: Monthly. **Description:** Electronic engineering magazine.

4215 ■ *NSBE Magazine: National Society of Black Engineers*
NSBE Publications
205 Daingerfield Rd.
Alexandria, VA 22314
Ph: (703)549-2207
Fax: (703)683-5312
E-mail: info@nsbe.org
URL: http://www.nsbe.org/News-Media/Magazines/ About-NSBE-Magazine.aspx
Frequency: 3/yr. **Price:** $20 Individuals; $35 Other countries; $15 Students. **Description:** Journal providing information on engineering careers, self-development, and cultural issues for recent graduates with technical majors.

4216 ■ *PE*
National Society of Professional Engineers
1420 King St.
Alexandria, VA 22314-2794
Ph: (703)684-2800
Fax: (703)836-4875
E-mail: memserv@nspe.org
URL: http://www.nspe.org/PEmagazine/index.html
Frequency: Semimonthly; 10/yr. **Price:** included in membership dues; $50 for nonmembers. **Description:** Covers matters of importance to engineering educators and students.

4217 ■ *Power Engineering*
PennWell Publishing Co.
1421 S Sheridan Rd.
Tulsa, OK 74112
Ph: (918)835-3161
Free: 800-331-4463
Fax: (918)831-9497
E-mail: pe@pennwell.com
URLs: http://www.power-eng.com; http://pepei .pennnet.com
Frequency: Monthly; Latest edition November, 2008. **Price:** $88 U.S.; $98 Canada and Mexico; $242 Other countries. **Description:** Magazine focusing on power generation. **Publication includes:** List of manufacturers and suppliers of products and services to the power plant and utility engineering industries. **Entries include:** Company name, location, phone, fax, contact name, e-mail and Web site. **Arrangement:** Classified by product/service, then alphabetical.

4218 ■ *Printed Circuit Design & Manufacture*
UP Media Group Inc.
PO Box 470
Canton, GA 30169
Ph: (404)661-0349
URLs: http://pcdandf.com/cms/; http://www.up-media-group.com
Frequency: Monthly. **Description:** Magazine for engineers and designers of PCBs and related technologies.

4219 ■ *Radio Physics and Radio Astronomy*
Begell House Inc.
50 Cross Hwy.
Redding, CT 06896
Ph: (203)938-1300
Fax: (203)938-1304
E-mail: orders@begellhouse.com
URL: http://www.begellhouse.com/journals/ 6fd1549c0e2c05da
Price: $757 Institutions. **Description:** Journal publishing articles on investigations in present-day radio physics and electronic engineering, radio astronomy and astrophysics.

4220 ■ *RF Design: Engineering Principles and Practice*
Penton
9800 Metcalf Ave.
Overland Park, KS 66212
Ph: (913)341-1300
Free: 866-748-4926
Fax: (913)967-1905
E-mail: corporatecustomerservice@penton.com
URL: http://www.rfdesign.com/
Frequency: Monthly. **Price:** Free. **Description:** Magazine covering the R.F. engineering field.

4221 ■ *SMT*
PennWell Publishing Co.
1421 S Sheridan Rd.
Tulsa, OK 74112
Ph: (918)835-3161
Free: 800-331-4463
Fax: (918)831-9497
E-mail: Headquarters@PennWell.com
URL: http://www.ems007.com/pages/ems007.cgi
Frequency: Monthly. **Price:** $115 U.S. and Canada; $215 Other countries. **Description:** Trade magazine for professional engineers involved in surface mount technology circuit design and board assembly.

4222 ■ *Solid State Technology*
PennWell Publishing Co.
1421 S Sheridan Rd.
Tulsa, OK 74112
Ph: (918)835-3161
Free: 800-331-4463
Fax: (918)831-9497
E-mail: Headquarters@PennWell.com
URL: http://www.electroiq.com/index/Semiconductors .html

Frequency: Monthly. **Price:** $258 Individuals; $360 Canada print; $434 Other countries print. **Description:** Magazine containing electronic and semiconductor engineering news and information.

4223 ■ *SWE, Magazine of the Society of Women Engineers*
Society of Women Engineers
203 N La Salle St., Ste. 1675
Chicago, IL 60601
Ph: (312)596-5223
Free: 877-SWE-INFO
Fax: (312)596-5252
E-mail: hq@swe.org
URL: http://societyofwomenengineers.swe.org/index.php

Frequency: Quarterly. **Price:** $30 Nonmembers. **Description:** Magazine for engineering students and for women and men working in the engineering and technology fields. Covers career guidance, continuing development and topical issues.

4224 ■ *Telecommunications and Radio Engineering*
Begell House Inc.
50 Cross Hwy.
Redding, CT 06896
Ph: (203)938-1300
Fax: (203)938-1304
E-mail: orders@begellhouse.com
URL: http://www.begellhouse.com/journals/0632a9d54950b268

Price: $4,518 Institutions. **Description:** Journal covering telecommunications and radio engineering.

4225 ■ *Test & Measurement World*
UBM Canon
2901 28th St., Ste. 100
Santa Monica, CA 90405-2975
Ph: (310)445-4200
Fax: (310)445-4299
E-mail: tmw@reedbusiness.com
URL: http://www.tmworld.com

Frequency: Monthly. **Price:** Free. **Description:** Electronic engineering magazine specializing in test, measurement and inspection of electronic products.

4226 ■ *Transmission and Distribution World*
Penton
9800 Metcalf Ave.
Overland Park, KS 66212
Ph: (913)341-1300
Free: 866-748-4926
Fax: (913)967-1905
E-mail: corporatecustomerservice@penton.com
URL: http://www.tdworld.com

Frequency: Monthly. **Description:** Magazine about powerline construction, transmission, and distribution.

4227 ■ *Woman Engineer*
Equal Opportunity Publications Inc.
445 Broad Hollow Rd., Ste. 425
Melville, NY 11747
Ph: (631)421-9421
Fax: (631)421-1352
E-mail: info@eop.com
URL: http://www.eop.com

Description: Annual. Magazine that is offered at no charge to qualified female engineering, computer-science, and information-technology students and professionals seeking to find employment and advancement in their careers.

EMPLOYER DIRECTORIES AND NETWORKING LISTS

4228 ■ *American Electronics Association--Member Directory*
American Electronics Association
601 Pennsylvania Ave., South Bldg., Ste. 900
Washington, DC 20004
Ph: (202)589-1144
Free: 800-284-4232
Fax: (202)639-8238
E-mail: info@aea.net
URL: http://www.aea.net/memberdirectory.asp

Covers: Over 3,000 member electronics and high-technology companies and 500 associate member firms including financial institutions, law firms, and accounting firms. **Entries include:** Company name, address, phone, World Wide Web addresses, cable address, fax, names of executives, number of employees, list of products or services, date founded, whether a public or private company, stock market where traded, ticker symbol. **Arrangement:** Alphabetical. **Indexes:** Geographical, product.

4229 ■ *Design News OEM Directory: A Joint Publication of Design News and Product Design and Development*
Reed Elsevier Group plc - Reed Business Information
360 Park Ave. S
New York, NY 11010
Ph: (212)791-4208
E-mail: dn@cahners.com
URL: http://www.reedbusiness.com

Frequency: Annual; November. **Covers:** About 5,000 manufacturers and suppliers of power transmission products, fluid power products, and electrical/electronic components to the OEM (original equipment manufacturer) market in SIC groups 34-39. **Entries include:** Company name, address, phone, fax, URL, e-mail. **Arrangement:** Alphabetical. **Indexes:** Product locator, Trade Name, supplier locator.

4230 ■ *Directory of Contract Staffing Firms*
C.E. Publications Inc.
PO Box 3006
Bothell, WA 98041-3006
Ph: (425)806-5200
Fax: (425)806-5585
E-mail: staff@cjhunter.com
URL: http://www.cjhunter.com/dcsf/overview.html

Frequency: Annual. **Covers:** Nearly 1,300 contract firms actively engaged in the employment of engineering, IT/IS, and technical personnel for 'temporary' contract assignments throughout the world. **Entries include:** Company name, address, phone, name of contact, email, web address. **Arrangement:** Alphabetical. **Indexes:** Geographical.

4231 ■ *Indiana Society of Professional Engineers--Directory*
Indiana Society of Professional Engineers
c/o Lauraine M. Howe, Executive Director
PO Box 20806
Indianapolis, IN 46220
Ph: (317)255-2267
Fax: (317)255-2530
E-mail: indspe@gmail.com
URL: http://www.indspe.org

Frequency: Annual; fall. **Pages:** 150. **Covers:** Member registered engineers, land surveyors, engineering students, and engineers in training. **Entries include:** Member name, address, phone, type of membership, business information, specialty. **Arrangement:** Alpha by chapter area.

4232 ■ *International Association of Electrical Inspectors--Membership Directory*
International Association of Electrical Inspectors
901 Waterfall Way, Ste. 602
Richardson, TX 75080
Ph: (972)235-1455
Free: 800-786-4234
Fax: (972)235-6858
E-mail: iaei@iaei.org
URL: http://www.iaei.org

Frequency: Annual; April. **Covers:** 26,000 state and federal government, industrial, utility, and insurance electrical inspectors, and, as associate members, electricians, manufacturers, engineers, architects, and wiremen. **Entries include:** Name, title, type of member, address, company affiliation. **Arrangement:** Geographical, then by division, chapter, or section, and type of membership, then alphabetical. **Indexes:** Committees; personal name.

4233 ■ *Plunkett's Engineering and Research Industry Almanac: The Only Complete Guide to the Business of Research, Development, and Engineering*
Plunkett Research Ltd.
4102 Bellaire Blvd.
Houston, TX 77025-1004
Ph: (713)932-0000
Fax: (713)932-7080
E-mail: customersupport@plunkettresearch.com
URL: http://www.plunkettresearch.com

Frequency: Annual; Latest edition 2013; New edition expected June 2014. **Price:** $349.99 Individuals eBook, print and CD-ROM. **Pages:** 690. **Covers:** 500 of the largest companies involved in research, engineering and development in the biotech, electronics, aerospace and infotech industries. **Entries include:** Name, address, phone, fax, names and titles of key personnel, subsidiary and branch names and locations, financial data, salaries and benefits, description of products/services, overview of company culture/activities. **Indexes:** Industry, location, sales rank, profit rank.

4234 ■ *Who's Who in Engineering*
American Association of Engineering Societies
1801 Alexander Bell Dr.
Reston, VA 20191
Ph: (202)296-2237
Free: 888-400-2237
Fax: (202)296-1151
E-mail: dbateson@aaes.org
URL: http://www.aaes.org

Frequency: Triennial; Latest edition 9th. **Covers:** About 15,000 engineers who have received professional recognition for outstanding achievement. **Entries include:** Name, address; education and employment history; awards and achievements. **Arrangement:** Alphabetical. **Indexes:** Geographical, field of specialization.

HANDBOOKS AND MANUALS

4235 ■ *Expert Resumes for Engineers*
JIST Publishing
875 Montreal Way
Saint Paul, MN 55102-4245
Ph: (317)613-4200
Free: 800-648-5478
Fax: (800)328-4564
E-mail: info@jist.com
URL: http://www.jist.com

Description: Louise M. Kursmark and Wendy S. Enelow. 2009. $16.95 (softcover). 272 pages. Features a collection of written resume samples for all types of engineers including civil, mechanical, industrial, electrical, electronics, computer, and more. Contains tips and strategies for writing engineering resumes and finding the best jobs.

4236 ■ *Great Jobs for Engineering Majors*
The McGraw-Hill Companies Inc.
PO Box 182604
Columbus, OH 43272
Ph: (212)512-2000
Free: 877-833-5524
Fax: (614)759-3749
E-mail: customer.service@mcgraw-hill.com
URL: http://www.mcgraw-hill.com

Description: Geraldine O. Garner. Second edition, 2008. $16.95. 192 pages. Covers all the career options open to students majoring in engineering.

4237 ■ *Opportunities in Electronics Careers*
The McGraw-Hill Companies Inc.
PO Box 182604
Columbus, OH 43272

Ph: (212)512-2000
Free: 877-833-5524
Fax: (614)759-3749
E-mail: customer.service@mcgraw-hill.com
URL: http://www.mcgraw-hill.com

Description: Mark Rowh. 2007. $13.95 (paper). 221 pages. Discusses career opportunities in commercial and industrial electronics equipment repair, electronics home entertainment repair, electronics engineering, and engineering technology. Includes job outlook and how to get off to a good start on the job.

EMPLOYMENT AGENCIES AND SEARCH FIRMS

4238 ■ The Aspire Group
711 Boylston St.
Boston, MA 02116-2616
Free: 800-487-2967
Fax: (617)500-7284
URL: http://www.bmanet.com/Aspire/index.html

Description: Employment agency.

4239 ■ ATR Engineering
1230 Oakmead Pkwy., Ste. 110
Sunnyvale, CA 94085
Ph: (408)328-8000
E-mail: corporate@atr1.com
URL: http://www.atr-engineering.com

Description: Serves as an executive search firm specializing in the placement of engineering professionals in contract, contract-to-hire and full-time basis across all disciplines including design engineering, manufacturing engineering, hardware engineering, design engineering, electrical engineering and mechanical engineering.

4240 ■ The Bedford Group
3343 Peachtree Rd. NE, Ste. 333
Atlanta, GA 30326
Ph: (404)237-7471
URL: http://www.bedfordgroupconsulting.com

Description: Executive search firm.

4241 ■ Bell Oaks Co.
115 Perimeter Center Pl., Ste. 400
Atlanta, GA 30346
Ph: (678)287-2000
Fax: (678)287-2002
E-mail: info@belloaks.com
URL: http://www.belloaks.com

Description: Personnel service firm.

4242 ■ Career Advocates International
1539 Ave. A
Katy, TX 77493
Ph: (281)371-3917
E-mail: hank@careeradvocates.org
URL: http://www.careeradvocates.org

Description: Provides permanent placement and temporary staffing for executive and staff level positions. Specializes in multiple niches including: sales and marketing, accounting and financial services, banking, communications, human resources, chemicals, oil and gas, medical and dental, legal, information technology, energy, technology, engineering, manufacturing, construction, and light industrial.

4243 ■ Centennial, Inc.
8044 Montgomery Rd., Ste. 260
Cincinnati, OH 45236
Ph: (513)366-3760
Fax: (513)366-3761
URL: http://www.centennialinc.com

Description: Serves as an executive search firm specializing in the areas of executive and general management, accounting and finance, human resources, information technology, manufacturing, engineering, marketing and advertising, not-for-profit, sales and business development, and supply chain and logistics.

4244 ■ Claremont-Branan, Inc.
1298 Rockbridge Rd., Ste. B
Stone Mountain, GA 30087
Free: 800-875-1292
URL: http://cbisearch.com

Description: Employment agency. Executive search firm.

4245 ■ Electronic Careers
21355 Pacific Coast Hwy., Ste. 100
Malibu, CA 90265
Ph: (310)317-6113
E-mail: e-careers@electroniccareers.com
URL: http://www.electroniccareers.com

Description: Executive search firm.

4246 ■ Electronic Search, Inc.
5105 Tollview Dr., Ste. 245
Rolling Meadows, IL 60008
Ph: (847)506-0700
Fax: (847)506-9999
E-mail: email@electronicsearch.com
URL: http://www.electronicsearch.com

Description: Staffing solutions firm, specializing in filling highly technical requirements in the wireless, telecommunications, and public safety technology industries; includes job listings with contact person, location, job description, qualifications, and compensation.

4247 ■ Engineer One Inc.
2315 Laurel Lake Rd.
Knoxville, TN 37932
Ph: (865)692-0404
Fax: (865)691-0110
E-mail: engineerone@engineerone.com
URL: http://www.engineerone.com

Description: Engineering employment service specializing in engineering and management in the chemical process, power utilities, manufacturing, mechanical, electrical, and electronic industries. Maintains an Information Technology Division that works nationwide across all industries. Also provides systems analysis consulting services specializing in VAX based systems.

4248 ■ ENTEGEE Inc.
70 Blanchard Rd., Ste. 102
Burlington, MA 01803-5100
Free: 800-368-3433
E-mail: corporate@entegee.com
URL: http://www.entegee.com

Description: Specializes in recruiting experienced professionals in the engineering and technical industries. Features a searchable database of employment opportunities in the engineering and technical fields.

4249 ■ Essential Solutions
20380 Town Center Ln., Ste. 165
Cupertino, CA 95014
Ph: (408)850-2500
Fax: (408)985-1700
E-mail: info@esiweb.com
URL: http://www.esiweb.com

Description: Serves as an executive search firm specializing in the placement of leaders for venture capital firms and companies focused on wireless, communications/networking, semiconductor, web, software, cleantech, or related technologies.

4250 ■ Executive Recruiters Agency
PO Box 21810
Little Rock, AR 72211
Ph: (501)224-7000
Fax: (501)224-8534
E-mail: jobs@execrecruit.com
URL: http://www.execrecruit.com

Description: Personnel service firm.

4251 ■ Global Employment Solutions Inc.
10375 Park Meadows Dr., Ste. 475
Littleton, CO 80124-6724

Ph: (303)216-9500
Fax: (303)216-9533
URL: http://www.gesnetwork.com

Description: Employment agency.

4252 ■ International Search
9717 E 42nd St.
Tulsa, OK 74147-0898
Ph: (918)627-9070
Fax: (918)524-8604

Description: Personnel consulting group provides placement expertise in engineering, accounting, and data processing. Industries served: Energy, manufacturing, oil and gas, and services.

4253 ■ Kimmel & Associates Inc.
25 Page Ave.
Asheville, NC 28801
Ph: (828)251-9900
Fax: (828)251-9955
E-mail: kimmel@kimmel.com
URL: http://www.kimmel.com

Description: Specializes in the construction, waste, architecture, engineering, logistics and supply chain industries.

4254 ■ Houser Martin Morris
110th Ave. NE, 110 Atrium Pl., Ste. 580
Bellevue, WA 98004
Ph: (425)453-2700
Fax: (425)453-8726
E-mail: info@houser.com
URL: http://www.houser.com

Description: Focus is in the areas of retained executive search, professional, and technical recruiting. Areas of specialization include software engineering, sales and marketing, information technology, legal, human resources, accounting and finance, manufacturing, factory automation and engineering.

4255 ■ Nesco Inc.
6140 Parkland Blvd., Ste. 110
Mayfield Heights, OH 44124-6106
Ph: (440)461-6000
Fax: (440)449-3111
E-mail: corporate@nescoresource.com
URL: http://www.nescoresource.com

Description: Offers staffing and consulting solutions in the fields of engineering, information technology, accounting and finance, manufacturing and distribution, and administrative and customer services.

4256 ■ Pate Resources Group Inc.
505 Orleans St., Ste. 300
Beaumont, TX 77701-3224
Ph: (409)833-4514
Fax: (409)833-4646

Description: Offers executive search and recruiting services to professionals who include physicians, health care administrators, accountants, financial managers; chemical, mechanical, industrial, and electrical engineers; sales and marketing managers, human resources administrators, and general managers and top executives in numerous disciplines. Industries served: health care, petrochemicals, accounting, utility, legal and municipalities.

4257 ■ Phillip's Personnel/Phillip's Temps
1675 Broadway, Ste. 2410
Denver, CO 80204
Ph: (303)893-1850
Fax: (303)893-0639
E-mail: info@phillipspersonnel.com
URL: http://www.phillipspersonnel.com

Description: Personnel recruiting and staffing consultants in: accounting and finance, management information systems, sales and marketing, engineering, administration, and general and executive management. Industries served: telecommunications, distribution, financial services, and general business.

4258 ■ SHS of Cherry Hill
207 Barclay Pavilion W
Cherry Hill, NJ 08034
Ph: (856)216-9030
Fax: (856)219-2011
E-mail: shs@shsofcherryhill.com
URL: http://www.shsofcherryhill.com
Description: Personnel recruiters operating in the disciplines of accounting, sales, insurance, engineering and administration. Industries served: insurance, distribution, manufacturing and service.

4259 ■ SPECTRA Associates
PO Box 688
Stevensville, MT 59870
Ph: (406)369-1188
E-mail: engineering@spectra-assoc.com
URL: http://www.spectra-assoc.com
Description: Serves as an executive search firm specializing in recruitment for engineering markets including companies involved with manufacturing, production and engineering.

4260 ■ Technical Talent Locators Ltd.
5570 Sterrett Pl., Ste. 208
Columbia, MD 21044
Ph: (410)740-0091
Fax: (301)621-4227
E-mail: steve@ttlgroup.com
URL: http://www.ttlgroup.com
Description: Permanent employment agency working within the following fields: software and database engineering; computer, communication, and telecommunication system engineering; and other computer-related disciplines.

4261 ■ Trambley The Recruiter
5325 Wyoming Blvd. NE, Ste. 200
Albuquerque, NM 87109-3132
Ph: (505)821-5440
Fax: (505)821-8509
Description: Personnel consultancy firm recruits and places engineering professionals in specific areas of off-road equipment design and manufacturing. Industries served: Construction, agricultural, lawn and garden, oil exploration and mining equipment manufacturing.

4262 ■ TRS Staffing Solutions USA
3 Polaris Way
Aliso Viejo, CA 92656
Ph: (949)349-3630
Free: 800-248-8774
Fax: (949)349-7196
E-mail: info-av@trsstaffing.com
URL: http://www.trsstaffing.com/us
Description: Specializes in engineering recruitment. Maintains a pool of experienced technical, engineering and professional services personnel.

4263 ■ TSS Consulting Ltd.
2415 E Camelback Rd., Ste. 1090
2525 E Arizona Biltmore Ctr., Ste. A114
Phoenix, AZ 85016
Free: 800-489-2425
Fax: (602)470-8099
URL: http://www.tss-consulting.com
Description: A technical executive search and consulting firm as a boutique executive search firm, specializes in technical contributor or management or executive level electrical engineer searches for venture-backed start-ups. A requirement-driven search organization specializing in critical-need response.

Online Job Sources and Services

4264 ■ ConstructionJobs.com
URL: http://www.constructionjobs.com/index_eng.cfm
Description: Serves as an employment job board and resume database built exclusively for the construction, design, and building industries. Provides targeted candidate searches by geographic region, specific industries, job titles, education, and experience.

4265 ■ ConstructMyFuture.com
URL: http://www.constructmyfuture.com
Description: Offers comprehensive information for students, parents, and educators on varied careers in construction. Includes a searchable database of colleges, universities and trade schools that offer degrees in construction fields.

4266 ■ ElectricalEngineer.com
URL: http://www.electricalengineer.com
Description: Provides job listings, employment information and products for civil engineers.

4267 ■ ElectricalEngineerJobs.com
URL: http://www.electricalengineerjobs.com
Description: Lists electrical engineer jobs from all over the U.S. Allows users to post resumes and career profiles and search jobs by location. Provides information about degree programs, resume writing, interview tips and salaries.

4268 ■ ElectronicsEngineer.com
URL: http://www.electronicsengineer.com
Description: Serves as job board for electronics engineering employers showcasing open jobs and products to electronics engineers and to the EE community.

4269 ■ EnergyAuditorJobs.com
URL: http://www.energyauditorjobs.com
Description: Serves as a clearinghouse for energy auditor jobs. Contains salary information and surveys, resume postings, educational programs, and other related career resources.

4270 ■ Engineering Classifieds
URL: http://www.engineeringclassifieds.com
Description: Serves as a career site for engineering professionals. Provides services including job search agents, resume creation and posting.

4271 ■ EngineerJobs.com
URL: http://www.engineerjobs.com
Description: Provides job opportunities for engineering professionals in the following disciplines: aerospace, agricultural, biomedical, chemical, civil, electrical, environmental, industrial, manufacturing, marine, materials, mechanical, mining, nuclear, petroleum, process, project, quality, sales, software, solar, systems, and structural.

4272 ■ Engineer.net
URL: http://www.engineer.net
Description: Provides engineering employment tools such as job search, job posting, and engineering resumes.

4273 ■ MEP Jobs
URL: http://www.mepjobs.com
Description: Serves as a job board and resume bank for professionals in the mechanical, electrical, and plumbing industries.

4274 ■ Power Engineering
PennWell Publishing Co.
1421 S Sheridan Rd.
Tulsa, OK 74112
Ph: (918)835-3161
Free: 800-331-4463
Fax: (918)831-9497
E-mail: pe@pennwell.com
URLs: http://www.power-eng.com; http://pepei
.pennnet.com
Frequency: Monthly; Latest edition November, 2008.
Price: $88 U.S.; $98 Canada and Mexico; $242 Other countries. **Description:** Magazine focusing on power generation. **Publication includes:** List of manufacturers and suppliers of products and services to the power plant and utility engineering industries. **Entries include:** Company name, location, phone, fax, contact name, e-mail and Web site. **Arrangement:** Classified by product/service, then alphabetical.

4275 ■ PowerPlantPro.com
URL: http://www.powerplantpro.com/main/sendform/
4/18/3472
Description: Dedicated to professionals in the power and energy industry. Features career advice and employer listings.

4276 ■ Spherion
URL: http://www.spherion.com
Description: Recruitment firm specializing in accounting and finance, sales and marketing, interim executives, technology, engineering, retail and human resources.

4277 ■ ThinkEnergyGroup.com
URL: http://www.thinkenergygroup.com
Description: Serves as a job board for professionals looking for positions in engineering, power plant, energy, and technical fields. Contains advice and tips on interviews, job searching, resume writing, hiring, and management. Provides choices of work location, pay rates in the field of expertise and contract, temp-to-hire, and direct hiring options.

Tradeshows

4278 ■ American Society for Engineering Education Annual Conference and Exposition
American Society for Engineering Education
1818 N St. NW, Ste. 600
Washington, DC 20036-2479
Ph: (202)331-3500
Fax: (202)265-8504
E-mail: board@asee.org
URL: http://www.asee.org
Frequency: Annual. **Primary Exhibits:** Publications, engineering supplies and equipment, computers, software, and research companies all products and services related to engineering education.

4279 ■ PCB Design Conference West
UBM L.L.C.
240 W 35th St.
New York, NY 10001
Ph: (516)562-5000
Free: 800-842-0798
Fax: (516)562-7830
E-mail: contact@ubmtechnology.com
URL: http://www.ubm.com
Frequency: Annual. **Primary Exhibits:** To provide circuit board designers education and information about the industry, including tools and techniques.

Other Sources

4280 ■ Acoustical Society of America
2 Huntington Quadrangle, Ste. 1N01
Melville, NY 11747-4505
Ph: (516)576-2360
Fax: (516)576-2377
E-mail: asa@aip.org
URL: http://acousticalsociety.org
Description: Represents members from various fields related to sound including physics, electrical, mechanical and aeronautical engineering, oceanography, biology, physiology, psychology, architecture, speech, noise and noise control, and music. Aims to increase and diffuse the knowledge of acoustics and its practical applications. Organizes meetings, provides reprints of out-of-print classic texts in acoustics, and translation books.

4281 ■ Aircraft Electronics Association
3570 NE Ralph Powell Rd.
Lee's Summit, MO 64064
Ph: (816)347-8400
Fax: (816)347-8405
E-mail: info@aea.net
URL: http://www.aea.net

Description: Companies engaged in the sales, engineering, installation, and service of electronic aviation equipment and systems. Seeks to: advance the science of aircraft electronics; promote uniform and stable regulations and uniform standards of performance; establish and maintain a code of ethics; gather and disseminate technical data; advance the education of members and the public in the science of aircraft electronics. Offers supplement type certificates, test equipment licensing, temporary FCC licensing for new installations, spare parts availability and pricing, audiovisual technician training, equipment and spare parts loan, profitable installation, and service facility operation. Provides employment information, equipment exchange information and service assistance on member installations anywhere in the world.

4282 ■ American Association of Engineering Societies
1801 Alexander Bell Dr.
Reston, VA 20191
Ph: (202)296-2237
Free: 888-400-2237
Fax: (202)296-1151
E-mail: dbateson@aaes.org
URL: http://www.aaes.org

Description: Coordinates the efforts of the member societies in the provision of reliable and objective information to the general public concerning issues which affect the engineering profession and the field of engineering as a whole; collects, analyzes, documents, and disseminates data which will inform the general public of the relationship between engineering and the national welfare; provides a forum for the engineering societies to exchange and discuss their views on matters of common interest; and represents the U.S. engineering community abroad through representation in WFEO and UPADI.

4283 ■ American Indian Science and Engineering Society
PO Box 9828
Albuquerque, NM 87119-9828
Ph: (505)765-1052
Fax: (505)765-5608
E-mail: pam@aises.org
URL: http://www.aises.org

Description: Represents American Indian and non-Indian students and professionals in science, technology, and engineering fields; corporations representing energy, mining, aerospace, electronic, and computer fields. Seeks to motivate and encourage students to pursue undergraduate and graduate studies in science, engineering, and technology. Sponsors science fairs in grade schools, teacher training workshops, summer math/science sessions for 8th-12th graders, professional chapters, and student chapters in colleges. Offers scholarships. Adult members serve as role models, advisers, and mentors for students. Operates placement service.

4284 ■ American Institute of Engineers
4630 Appian Way, Ste. 206
El Sobrante, CA 94803-1875
Ph: (510)758-6240
Fax: (510)758-6240
E-mail: aie@aieonline.org
URL: http://www.aieonline.org

Description: Professional association for engineers, scientists, and mathematicians. Multi-disciplined, non-technical association who aims to improve the stature and image of engineers, scientists, and mathematicians. Provides endorsements, awards and opportunities for small business start-ups within the AIE Councils. Sponsors "LA Engineer", a comedy-drama television series; produces annual "Academy Hall of FAME (TV)".

4285 ■ American Society of Test Engineers
PO Box 389
Nutting Lake, MA 01865-0389
E-mail: aste@earthlink.net
URL: http://www.astetest.org

Description: Companies involved in the electronic testing industry and instrumentation are corporate members; engineers who work in test engineering related fields are regular members. Seeks to foster improved communication among individuals and companies in the testing industry. Offers job referral service. **Members:** 500.

4286 ■ ASPRS, The Imaging and Geospatial Information Society
5410 Grosvenor Ln., Ste. 210
Bethesda, MD 20814-2160
Ph: (301)493-0290
Fax: (301)493-0208
E-mail: asprs@asprs.org
URL: http://www.asprs.org

Description: Firms, individuals, government employees and academicians engaged in photogrammetry, photointerpretation, remote sensing, and geographic information systems and their application to such fields as archaeology, geographic information systems, military reconnaissance, urban planning, engineering, traffic surveys, meteorological observations, medicine, geology, forestry, agriculture, construction and topographic mapping. Seeks to advance knowledge and improve understanding of these sciences and promote responsible applications. Offers voluntary certification program open to persons associated with one or more functional area of photogrammetry, remote sensing and GIS. Surveys the profession of private firms in photogrammetry and remote sensing in the areas of products and services.

4287 ■ Association for the Advancement of Medical Instrumentation
4301 N Fairfax Dr., Ste. 301
Arlington, VA 22203-1633
Ph: (703)525-4890
Free: 800-332-2264
Fax: (703)276-0793
E-mail: mlogan@aami.org
URL: http://www.aami.org

Description: Clinical engineers, biomedical equipment technicians, physicians, hospital administrators, consultants, engineers, manufacturers of medical devices, nurses, researchers and others interested in medical instrumentation. Works to improve the quality of medical care through the application, development, and management of technology. Maintains placement service. Offers certification programs for biomedical equipment technicians and clinical engineers. Produces numerous standards and recommended practices on medical devices and procedures. Offers educational programs.

4288 ■ *Career Opportunities in Engineering*
InfoBase Holdings Inc.
132 W 31st., 17 Fl.
New York, NY 10001-3406
Ph: (212)967-8800
Fax: (800)678-3633
E-mail: info@infobasepublishing.com
URL: http://www.ferguson.infobasepublishing.com

Description: 2006. $49.50. 336 pages. Provides an overview of engineering, followed by a selection of jobs profiled in detail, including the nature of the job, earnings, prospects for employment, what kind of training and skills it requires and sources for further information. **Includes:** Appendices of educational institutions, periodicals, directories, and associations. Appendices of educational institutions, periodicals, directories, and associations.

4289 ■ Cultural Vistas
440 Park Ave. S, 2nd Fl.
New York, NY 10016
Ph: (212)497-3500
Fax: (212)497-3535
E-mail: info@culturalvistas.org
URL: http://culturalvistas.org

Description: Providers worldwide of on-the-job training programs for students and professionals seeking international career development and life-changing experiences. Arranges workplace exchanges in hundreds of professional fields, bringing employers and trainees together from around the world. Client list ranges from small farming communities to Fortune 500 companies.

4290 ■ Engineering Society of Detroit
20700 Civic Center Dr., Ste. 450
Southfield, MI 48076
Ph: (248)353-0735
Fax: (248)353-0736
E-mail: esd@esd.org
URL: http://ww2.esd.org/home.htm

Description: Engineers from all disciplines; scientists and technologists. Conducts technical programs and engineering refresher courses; sponsors conferences and expositions. Maintains speakers' bureau; offers placement services; although based in Detroit, MI, society membership is international. **Members:** 6,000.

4291 ■ Global Semiconductor Alliance
12400 Coit Rd., Ste. 650
Dallas, TX 75251
Ph: (972)866-7579
Free: 888-322-5195
Fax: (972)239-2292
URL: http://www.gsaglobal.org

Description: Represents semiconductor companies including fabless, fab-lite, and integrated device manufacturers. Aims to accelerate the growth and increase of return on invested capital in the global semiconductor industry by fostering a more effective fabless ecosystem through collaboration, integration, and innovation.

4292 ■ International Association for Computer and Information Science
735 Meadowbrook Dr.
Mount Pleasant, MI 48858
Ph: (989)774-1175
Fax: (989)774-1174
E-mail: lee1ry@cmich.edu
URL: http://www.acisinternational.org

Description: Represents individuals in the fields of computer and information science. Disseminates the latest developments in the fields of computer and information science. Provides a forum for researchers in education and computer and information science industries.

4293 ■ International Microelectronic and Packaging Society
611 2nd St. NE
Washington, DC 20002-4909
Ph: (202)548-4001
Free: 888-464-1066
Fax: (202)548-6115
E-mail: modonoghue@imaps.org
URL: http://www.imaps.org

Description: Electronics engineers and specialists in industry, business, and education. Encourages the exchange of information across boundaries of fields of specialization; supports close interactions between the complementary technologies of ceramics, thick and thin films, semiconductor packaging, discrete semiconductor devices, and monolithic circuits. Promotes and assists in the development and expansion of microelectronics instruction in schools and departments of electrical and electronic engineering. Conducts seminars at international, national, regional, and chapter levels.

4294 ■ International Society for Quality Electronic Design
PO Box 607
Los Altos, CA 94023-0607
Ph: (408)573-0100
Fax: (408)573-0200
E-mail: info@isqed.com
URL: http://www.isqed.com
Description: Promotes quality in the design of micro-electronic, nano-electronic and bio-electronic circuits and systems. Fosters research, development and application of design methods and processes. Provides a forum and educational program on quality electronic design.

4295 ■ ISA -The International Society of Automation
67 Alexander Dr.
Research Triangle Park, NC 27709
Ph: (919)549-8411
Fax: (919)549-8288
E-mail: info@isa.org
URL: http://www.isa.org
Description: Sets the standard for automation by helping over 30,000 worldwide members and other professionals solve difficult technical problems, while enhancing their leadership and personal career capabilities. Develops standards; certifies industry professionals; provides education and training; publishes books and technical articles; and hosts the largest conference and exhibition for automation professionals in the Western Hemisphere. Is the founding sponsor of The Automation Federation.

4296 ■ Korean-American Scientists and Engineers Association
1952 Gallows Rd., Ste. 300
Vienna, VA 22182
Ph: (703)748-1221
Fax: (703)748-1331
E-mail: sejong@ksea.org
URL: http://www.ksea.org
Description: Represents scientists and engineers holding single or advanced degrees. Promotes friendship and mutuality among Korean and American scientists and engineers; contributes to Korea's scientific, technological, industrial, and economic developments; strengthens the scientific, technological, and cultural bonds between Korea and

the U.S. Sponsors symposium. Maintains speakers' bureau, placement service, and biographical archives. Compiles statistics. **Members:** 10,000.

4297 ■ National Action Council for Minorities in Engineering
440 Hamilton Ave., Ste. 302
White Plains, NY 10601-1813
Ph: (914)539-4010
Free: 800-888-9929
Fax: (914)539-4032
E-mail: ajohnson@nacme.org
URL: http://www.nacme.org
Description: Leads the national effort to increase access to careers in engineering and other science-based disciplines. Conducts research and public policy analysis, develops and operates national demonstration programs at precollege and university levels, and disseminates information through publications, conferences and electronic media. Serves as a privately funded source of scholarships for minority students in engineering.

4298 ■ National Society of Professional Engineers
1420 King St.
Alexandria, VA 22314-2794
Ph: (703)684-2800
Fax: (703)836-4875
E-mail: memserv@nspe.org
URL: http://www.nspe.org
Description: Represents professional engineers and engineers-in-training in all fields registered in accordance with the laws of states or territories of the U.S. or provinces of Canada; qualified graduate engineers, student members, and registered land surveyors. Is concerned with social, professional, ethical, and economic considerations of engineering as a profession; encompasses programs in public relations, employment practices, ethical considerations, education, and career guidance. Monitors legislative and regulatory actions of interest to the engineering profession.

4299 ■ Society of Hispanic Professional Engineers
13181 Crossroads Pkwy. N, Ste. 450
City of Industry, CA 91746-3496

Ph: (323)725-3970
E-mail: shpenational@shpe.org
URL: http://national.shpe.org
Description: Represents engineers, student engineers, and scientists. Aims to increase the number of Hispanic engineers by providing motivation and support to students. Sponsors competitions and educational programs. Maintains placement service and speakers' bureau; compiles statistics. **Members:** 8,000.

4300 ■ Society of Women Engineers
203 N La Salle St., Ste. 1675
Chicago, IL 60601
Ph: (312)596-5223
Free: 877-SWE-INFO
Fax: (312)596-5252
E-mail: hq@swe.org
URL: http://societyofwomenengineers.swe.org
Description: Educational and service organization representing both students and professional women in engineering and technical fields.

4301 ■ SPIE
PO Box 10
Bellingham, WA 98227-0010
Ph: (360)676-3290
Free: 888-504-8171
Fax: (360)647-1445
E-mail: customerservice@spie.org
URL: http://spie.org
Description: Advances scientific research and engineering applications of optical, photonic, imaging and optoelectronic technologies through meetings, education programs and publications.

4302 ■ Women in Engineering ProActive Network
1901 E Asbury Ave., Ste. 220
Denver, CO 80208
Ph: (303)871-4643
Fax: (303)871-4628
URL: http://www.wepan.org
Description: Women in engineering professions. Includes key strategies such as education and training, research, collaboration, leadership, diversity, advocacy, networking, sustainability, accountability, and volunteerism in order to be a catalyst for change that enhances the success of women in the engineering professions.

SOURCES OF HELP-WANTED ADS

4303 ■ *Builder: The Magazine of the National Association of Home Builders*
DoveTale Publishers
1 Thomas Cir. NW
Washington, DC 20005
Ph: (202)339-0744
Free: 877-275-8647
Fax: (202)785-1974
E-mail: builder@omeda.com
URLs: http://www.hanleywood.com/default.aspx
?page=magazines; http://www.builderonline.com
Frequency: 13/yr. **Price:** $29.95 U.S. and Canada; $54.95 U.S. and Canada 2 years; $192 Other countries. **Description:** Magazine covering housing and construction industry.

4304 ■ *Constructor: The Construction Management Magazine*
Associated General Contractors of America
2300 Wilson Blvd., Ste. 400
Arlington, VA 22201
Ph: (703)548-3118
Free: 800-242-1767
Fax: (703)548-3119
E-mail: info@agc.org
URL: http://constructor.agc.org/
Frequency: Bimonthly. **Price:** $95 Individuals. **Description:** Management magazine for the Construction Industry.

4305 ■ *Daily Journal of Commerce*
New Orleans Publishing Group Inc.
111 Veterans Blvd., Ste. 1440
Metairie, LA 70005
Ph: (504)834-9292
Fax: (504)832-3550
E-mail: mail@nopg.com
URLs: http://www.djc-gp.com; http://www.djcgulfcoast
.com
Frequency: Daily. **Price:** $525 Individuals online; $375 Individuals 6 months; $225 Individuals 3 months. **Description:** Trade newspaper covering construction news in Louisiana and Mississippi.

4306 ■ *Electric Light & Power*
PennWell Publishing Co.
1421 S Sheridan Rd.
Tulsa, OK 74112
Ph: (918)835-3161
Free: 800-331-4463
Fax: (918)831-9497
E-mail: Headquarters@PennWell.com
URL: http://www.elp.com/index.html
Frequency: Bimonthly. **Price:** $85 Canada; $145 Canada two years; $94 Individuals Mexico; $160 Individuals 2 years, Mexico; $225 Other countries; $403 Other countries 2 years. **Description:** Provides broad view of electric utility industry with in-depth analysis of key business issues for executives and management.

4307 ■ *Engineering Economist*
Taylor & Francis
711 3rd Ave., 8th Fl.
New York, NY 10017
Ph: (212)216-7800
Free: 800-634-7064
Fax: (212)563-2269
E-mail: info@taylorandfrancis.com
URL: http://www.tandfonline.com/toc/utee20/current
Frequency: Quarterly. **Price:** $93 Individuals print only; $159 Institutions online only; $177 Institutions print & online. **Description:** Publication covering business issues in the energy, petroleum and mining industries.

4308 ■ *The High-Tech News*
ETA International
5 Depot St.
Greencastle, IN 46135
Ph: (765)653-8262
Free: 800-288-3824
Fax: (765)653-4287
E-mail: eta@eta-i.org
URL: http://www.eta-i.org
Description: Bimonthly. Serves member technicians with news of the Association and the electronics industry, including items on service, education, employment, management, and events. Contains information on membership, management, telecommunications, and business and technical training programs. Recurring features include editorials, news of research, letters to the editor, book reviews, and a calendar of events.

4309 ■ *Professional Builder: The Magazine of the Housing and Light Construction Industry*
SGC Horizon L.L.C.
3030 W Salt Creek Ln., Ste. 201
Arlington Heights, IL 60005
Ph: (847)391-1000
Fax: (847)390-0408
URL: http://www.housingzone.com/
professionalbuilder
Frequency: Monthly. **Price:** Free. **Description:** The integrated engineering magazine of the building construction industry.

EMPLOYER DIRECTORIES AND NETWORKING LISTS

4310 ■ *ABC Today--Associated Builders and Contractors National Membership Directory Issue*
Associated Builders and Contractors
440 1st St. NW, Ste. 200
Washington, DC 20001
E-mail: gotquestions@abc.org
URL: http://www.abc.org
Frequency: Annual; Latest Edition 2011. **Price:** $150 plus $7.00 shipping. **Publication includes:** List of approximately 19,000 member construction contractors and suppliers. **Entries include:** Company name, address, phone, name of principal executive, code to volume of business, business specialty. **Arrangement:** Classified by chapter, then by work specialty.

4311 ■ *Buyer's Guide & Membership Directory*
Independent Electrical Contractors Association
4401 Ford Ave., Ste. 1100
Alexandria, VA 22302
Ph: (703)549-7351
Free: 800-456-4324
Fax: (703)549-7448
E-mail: communications@ieci.org
URL: http://www.ieci.org
Frequency: Annual. **Pages:** 100. **Covers:** Member electrical contracting firms, electrical manufacturers, and distributors. **Entries include:** Name of company, address, names of principals. **Arrangement:** Geographical.

4312 ■ *ENR--Top 400 Construction Contractors Issue*
The McGraw-Hill Companies Inc.
PO Box 182604
Columbus, OH 43272
Ph: (212)512-2000
Free: 877-833-5524
Fax: (614)759-3749
E-mail: customer.service@mcgraw-hill.com
URL: http://enr.construction.com/toplists/Contractors/
001-100.asp
Frequency: Annual; Latest edition 2011. **Price:** $35 Individuals. **Publication includes:** List of 400 United States contractors receiving largest dollar volumes of contracts in preceding calendar year. Separate lists of 50 largest design/construct management firms; 50 largest program and construction managers; 25 building contractors; 25 heavy contractors. **Entries include:** Company name, headquarters location, total value of contracts received in preceding year, value of foreign contracts, countries in which operated, construction specialties. **Arrangement:** By total value of contracts received.

4313 ■ *International Association of Electrical Inspectors--Membership Directory*
International Association of Electrical Inspectors
901 Waterfall Way, Ste. 602
Richardson, TX 75080
Ph: (972)235-1455
Free: 800-786-4234
Fax: (972)235-6858
E-mail: iaei@iaei.org
URL: http://www.iaei.org
Frequency: Annual; April. **Covers:** 26,000 state and federal government, industrial, utility, and insurance electrical inspectors, and, as associate members, electricians, manufacturers, engineers, architects,

and wiremen. **Entries include:** Name, title, type of member, address, company affiliation. **Arrangement:** Geographical, then by division, chapter, or section, and type of membership, then alphabetical. **Indexes:** Committees; personal name.

HANDBOOKS AND MANUALS

4314 ■ *Construction*
InfoBase Holdings Inc.
132 W 31st., 17 Fl.
New York, NY 10001-3406
Ph: (212)967-8800
Fax: (800)678-3633
E-mail: info@infobasepublishing.com
URL: http://www.ferguson.infobasepublishing.com

Price: $30 Hardcover. **Description:** 2010. 128 pages. Contains profiles of 20 careers in the field of construction with emphasis on the nature of work, requirements, salary, and career outlook. Includes full-color photographs, index, glossary, resources, and side bars.

4315 ■ *Construction Technology Trainee Guide*
Prentice Hall
200 Old Tappan Rd.
Old Tappan, NJ 07675
Free: 800-223-1360
Fax: (800)445-6991
URL: http://www.prenticehall.com

Description: Third Edition, 2009. $186.67 (hardcover). 936 pages. Features a highly illustrated design, technical hints and tips from construction industry experts, and review questions.

4316 ■ *Electrician's Exam Preparation Guide*
Craftsman Book Co.
6058 Corte Del Cedro
Carlsbad, CA 92011-1514
Ph: (760)438-7828
Free: 800-829-8123
Fax: (760)438-0398
E-mail: support@costbook.com
URL: http://www.craftsman-book.com

Description: John E. Traister, updated by Dale Brickner. 2008. $49.50 (paper). 352 pages. Covers every area of electrical installation: electrical drawings, services and systems, transformers, capacitors, distribution equipment, branch circuits, feeders, calculations, measuring and testing, and more. Updated to the 2008 NEC.

4317 ■ *Electricity for the Trades*
The McGraw-Hill Companies Inc.
PO Box 182604
Columbus, OH 43272
Ph: (212)512-2000
Free: 877-833-5524
Fax: (614)759-3749
E-mail: customer.service@mcgraw-hill.com
URL: http://www.mcgraw-hill.com

Description: Frank D. Petruzella. 2006. $127. Resource for students in basic electricity trades.

EMPLOYMENT AGENCIES AND SEARCH FIRMS

4318 ■ American Man Power Services
3032 Fleetbrook Dr.
Memphis, TN 38116
Ph: (901)396-5998
Fax: (901)396-5984
URL: http://www.amps-electricians.com

Description: Specializes in providing recruitment and staffing solutions to the electrical service industry. Offers career opportunities to qualified personnel.

4319 ■ Capitol Staffing Inc.
460 Briarwood Dr., Briarwood 1 Bldg., Ste. 110
Jackson, MS 39206
Ph: (601)957-1755
Fax: (601)957-3880
E-mail: info@capitolstaffing.com
URL: http://www.capitolstaffing.com

Description: Personnel consultancy that focuses on office administration, management, sales, accounting, medical, information technology, accounting, and engineering/technical fields. Industries served: insurance, finance, medical, communications, investment, industry, and small businesses.

ONLINE JOB SOURCES AND SERVICES

4320 ■ Build Your Future Career Center
URL: http://www.jobtarget.com/home/home.cfm?site_id=13781

Description: Features construction industry job listings. Includes resume bank that lists profiles voluntarily posted by job seekers.

4321 ■ BuildZ Construction Jobs Network
URL: http://buildz.net

Description: Provides listings of construction jobs throughout the U.S. Features news related to the construction industry.

4322 ■ Construction Help Wanted
URL: http://www.constructionhelpwanted.net

Description: Serves as an online resource for those seeking jobs in construction. Allows people to look for specified jobs according to location.

4323 ■ Construction Jobs Network
URL: http://constructionjobs.net

Description: Provides job seekers access to construction employment opportunities for both construction management, construction professional and construction trade jobs. Features construction jobs, employer, and resume directories.

4324 ■ ConstructionGigs.net
URL: http://www.constructiongigs.net

Description: Provides an up-to-date listings of job opportunities and career resources for construction workers.

4325 ■ Construction.jobs
URL: http://construction.jobs

Description: Connects employers and job seekers in the construction industry. Features a searchable database of available construction employment opportunities in the U.S.

4326 ■ ConstructionJobStore.com
URL: http://www.constructionjobstore.com

Description: Features online job listing in the construction industry. Offers career guide resources and job alert services.

4327 ■ ConstructMyFuture.com
URL: http://www.constructmyfuture.com

Description: Offers comprehensive information for students, parents, and educators on varied careers in construction. Includes a searchable database of colleges, universities and trade schools that offer degrees in construction fields.

4328 ■ ElectricalAgent.com
URL: http://www.electricalagent.com

Description: Lists job opportunities for electricians such as electrical jobs, apartment maintenance jobs, facilities maintenance jobs and other industry related positions.

4329 ■ GetElectricianJobs.com
URL: http://www.getelectricianjobs.com

Description: Offers electrician job postings and employment opportunities.

4330 ■ OffStageJobs.com
URL: http://www.offstagejobs.com

Description: Lists behind-the-scenes jobs in the live entertainment industry. Also features backstage related news and information.

4331 ■ USA Construction Jobs
URL: http://www.usaconstructionjobs.com

Description: Features job listings in construction and general labor.

TRADESHOWS

4332 ■ Edison Electric Institute Convention and Expo
Edison Electric Institute
701 Pennsylvania Ave. NW
Washington, DC 20004-2696
Ph: (202)508-5000
Free: 800-334-5453
Fax: (800)525-5562
E-mail: eblume@eei.org
URL: http://www.eei.org/Pages/default.aspx

Frequency: Annual. **Primary Exhibits:** Exhibits directed to investor-owned electric utility companies operating in the U.S. and abroad.

4333 ■ Electric Expo
Electrical Association of Philadelphia
527 Plymouth Rd., Ste. 408
Plymouth Meeting, PA 19462-1641
Ph: (610)825-1600
Fax: (610)825-1603
E-mail: electric@eap.org
URL: http://www.eap.org

Frequency: Biennial. **Primary Exhibits:** Electrical equipment, supplies, and services.

4334 ■ Electri..FYI - Upstate Electrical Show
Electrical Association of Rochester
PO Box 20219
Rochester, NY 14602-0219
Ph: (585)538-6350
Fax: (585)538-6166
E-mail: info@earoch.com
URL: http://www.eawny.com

Frequency: Triennial. **Primary Exhibits:** Electrical supplies and services.

4335 ■ Independent Electrical Contractors Annual Convention and Expo
Independent Electrical Contractors Association
4401 Ford Ave., Ste. 1100
Alexandria, VA 22302
Ph: (703)549-7351
Free: 800-456-4324
Fax: (703)549-7448
E-mail: info@ieci.org
URL: http://www.ieci.org

Frequency: Annual. **Primary Exhibits:** Equipment, supplies, and services for independent electrical contractors.

4336 ■ Upper Midwest Electrical Expo
North Central Electrical League
2901 Metro Dr., Ste. 203
Bloomington, MN 55425-1556
Ph: (952)854-4405
Free: 800-925-4985
URL: http://www.ncel.org

Frequency: Biennial. **Primary Exhibits:** Electrical equipment, supplies, and services. **Dates and Locations:** Minneapolis, MN; Minneapolis Convention Center & Hilton Hotel.

ONLINE AND DATABASE SERVICES

4337 ■ CareersForBuilders.com
URL: http://www.careersforbuilders.com
Description: Features a searchable database of employment opportunities for different types of construction work. Includes career resources on job hunting tools and tips.

OTHER SOURCES

4338 ■ Associated Builders and Contractors
440 1st St. NW, Ste. 200
Washington, DC 20001
E-mail: gotquestions@abc.org
URL: http://www.abc.org
Description: Construction contractors, subcontractors, suppliers and associates. Aims to foster and perpetuate the principles of rewarding construction workers and management on the basis of merit. Sponsors management education programs and craft training; also sponsors apprenticeship and skill training programs. Disseminates technological and labor relations information.

4339 ■ Associated General Contractors of America
2300 Wilson Blvd., Ste. 400
Arlington, VA 22201
Ph: (703)548-3118
Free: 800-242-1767
Fax: (703)548-3119
E-mail: info@agc.org
URL: http://www.agc.org
Description: General construction contractors; subcontractors; industry suppliers; service firms. Provides market services through its divisions. Conducts special conferences and seminars designed specifically for construction firms. Compiles statistics on job accidents reported by member firms. Maintains 65 committees, including joint cooperative committees with other associations and liaison committees with federal agencies.

4340 ■ Associated Specialty Contractors
3 Bethesda Metro Ctr., Ste. 1100
Bethesda, MD 20814
E-mail: dgw@necanet.org
URL: http://www.assoc-spec-con.org

Description: Works to promote efficient management and productivity. Coordinates the work of specialized branches of the industry in management information, research, public information, government relations and construction relations. Serves as a liaison among specialty trade associations in the areas of public relations, government relations, and with other organizations. Seeks to avoid unnecessary duplication of effort and expense or conflicting programs among affiliates. Identifies areas of interest and problems shared by members, and develops positions and approaches on such problems. **Members:** 9.

4341 ■ Electrical Rebuilder's Association
PO Box 906
Union, MO 63084
Ph: (636)584-7400
Fax: (636)584-7401
E-mail: office@electricalrebuilders.org
URL: http://www.electricalrebuilders.org

Description: Represents rebuilders, suppliers, and individuals involved in the automotive electrical parts rebuilding industry. Promotes the well-being and professionalism of the electrical rebuilding industry in North America through education and training. Serves as a forum for members to exchange information on all aspects of the industry.

4342 ■ Independent Electrical Contractors Association
4401 Ford Ave., Ste. 1100
Alexandria, VA 22302
Ph: (703)549-7351
Free: 800-456-4324
Fax: (703)549-7448
E-mail: info@ieci.org
URL: http://www.ieci.org

Description: Independent electrical contractors, small and large, primarily open shop. Promotes the interests of members; works to eliminate "unwise and unfair business practices" and to protect its members against "unfair or unjust taxes and legislative enactments." Sponsors electrical apprenticeship programs; conducts educational programs on cost control and personnel motivation. Represents independent electrical contractors to the National Electrical Code panel. Conducts surveys on volume of sales and purchases and on type of products used. Has

formulated National Pattern Standards for Apprentice Training for Electricians. **Members:** 3,000.

4343 ■ National Association of Home Builders - Systems Builder Council
1201 15th St. NW
Washington, DC 20005
Ph: (202)266-8200
Free: 800-368-5242
Fax: (202)266-8400
URL: http://www.nahb.org/reference_list.aspx?sectionID=815

Description: Operates under the Building Systems Council of NAHB. Modular building manufacturers. Monitors state and federal housing legislation that impacts the building industry. Provides a forum for communication, networking and recruiting for those involved in manufacturing modular building systems. Addresses and solves problems specific to the council; offers consumer leads service.

4344 ■ National Association of Women in Construction
327 S Adams St.
Fort Worth, TX 76104
Ph: (817)877-5551
Free: 800-552-3506
Fax: (817)877-0324
E-mail: nawic@nawic.org
URL: http://www.nawic.org

Description: Seeks to enhance the success of women in the construction industry.

4345 ■ National Electrical Contractors Association
3 Bethesda Metro Ctr., Ste. 1100
Bethesda, MD 20814
Ph: (301)657-3110
Fax: (301)215-4500
URL: http://www.necanet.org

Description: Contractors erecting, installing, repairing, servicing, and maintaining electric wiring, equipment, and appliances. Provides management services and labor relations programs for electrical contractors; conducts seminars for contractor sales and training. Conducts research and educational programs; compiles statistics. Sponsors honorary society, the Academy of Electrical Contracting.

Sources of Help-Wanted Ads

4346 ■ *Annals of Medicine*
Informa Healthcare
52 Vanderbilt Ave., 7th Fl.
New York, NY 10017-3846
Ph: (212)520-2777
E-mail: healthcare.enquiries@informa.com
URL: http://informahealthcare.com/ann
Frequency: 4/yr. **Price:** £961 Institutions; $1,579 Institutions; €1,259 Institutions. **Description:** Journal covering health science and medical education.

4347 ■ *CME Supplement to Emergency Medicine Clinics of North America*
Elsevier Science Inc.
Secondary Publishing Division
650 Ave. of the Americas
New York, NY 10011
Ph: (212)633-3980
Free: 888-437-4636
Fax: (212)633-3975
URL: http://www.elsevier.com/wps/find/journalde-scription.cws_home/709343/description#description
Frequency: 4/yr. **Price:** $212 Individuals. **Description:** Journal covering emergency medicine clinics.

4348 ■ *Discovery Medicine*
Discovery Medicine
10 Gerard Ave., Ste. 201
Timonium, MD 21093
Ph: (410)252-6229
Fax: (888)833-0526
E-mail: service@discoverymedicine.com
URL: http://www.discoverymedicine.com
Frequency: Bimonthly. **Price:** $599 Institutions digital edition; $99.95 Individuals digital edition. **Description:** Online journal that publishes articles on diseases, biology, new diagnostics, and treatments for medical professionals.

4349 ■ *Emergency Medical Services: The Journal of Emergency Care, Rescue and Transportation*
Cygnus Business Media Inc.
1233 Janesville Ave.
Fort Atkinson, WI 53538
Free: 800-547-7377
E-mail: info@cygnus.com
URL: http://www.emsworld.com
Frequency: Monthly. **Description:** Magazine covering emergency care, rescue and transportation.

4350 ■ *Hospitals & Health Networks*
Health Forum L.L.C.
155 N Wacker Dr., Ste. 400
Chicago, IL 60606
Ph: (312)893-6800
Free: 800-821-2039

Fax: (312)422-4500
URL: http://www.hhnmag.com
Frequency: Weekly. **Price:** Free. **Description:** Publication covering the health care industry.

4351 ■ *The IHS Primary Care Provider*
U.S. Department of Health and Human Services - Indian Health Service
Reyes Bldg.
801 Thompson Ave., Ste. 400
Rockville, MD 20852-1627
Ph: (301)443-6394
Fax: (301)443-4794
E-mail: charles.grim@ihs.hhs.gov
URL: http://www.ihs.gov/provider
Frequency: Monthly. **Description:** Journal for health care professionals, physicians, nurses, pharmacists, dentists, and dietitians.

4352 ■ *Injury*
Mosby Inc.
11830 Westline Industrial Dr.
Saint Louis, MO 63146-3326
Ph: (314)872-8370
Free: 800-325-4177
Fax: (314)432-1380
URL: http://www.journals.elsevier.com/injury/
Frequency: Monthly. **Price:** $255 Individuals print; $1,549.33 Institutions online; $1,859 Institutions print. **Description:** Journal publishing articles and research related to the treatment of injuries such as trauma systems and management; surgical procedures; epidemiological studies; surgery (of all tissues); resuscitation; biomechanics; rehabilitation; anaesthesia; radiology and wound management.

4353 ■ *Intensive and Critical Care Nursing*
Elsevier Inc. - Health Sciences Division - Churchill Livingstone
1600 John F. Kennedy Blvd., Ste. 1800
Philadelphia, PA 19103
Ph: (215)239-3900
Free: 800-523-1649
Fax: (215)238-3990
E-mail: usinfo@sciencedirect.com
URL: http://www.journals.elsevier.com/intensive-and-critical-care-nursing/#description
Frequency: Bimonthly. **Price:** $126 Individuals for all countries except Europe, Japan & Iran; $578 Institutions for all countries except Europe, Japan & Iran; €137 Individuals for European countries and Iran; €651 Institutions for European countries and Iran; ¥14,800 Individuals; ¥70,300 Institutions. **Description:** Journal for nurses in intensive and critical care nursing.

4354 ■ *The Internet Journal of Emergency Medicine*
Internet Scientific Publications L.L.C.
23 Rippling Creek Dr.
Sugar Land, TX 77479
E-mail: wenker@ispub.com
URL: http://www.ispub.com/journal/the-internet-journal-of-emergency-medicine/

Price: Free. **Description:** Electronic journal for medical professionals focusing on the field of emergency medicine.

4355 ■ *Journal of the American Society of Podiatric Medical Assistants*
American Society of Podiatric Medical Assistants
620 Sedgley Dr.
Knoxville, TN 37922
Ph: (812)326-2046
Free: 888-882-7762
Fax: (812)326-2659
E-mail: suehpmac@gmail.com
URL: http://www.aspma.org
Frequency: Quarterly. **Price:** free for members. **Description:** Professional journal covering issues in podiatry.

4356 ■ *Journal of Hospital Medicine*
John Wiley & Sons Inc.
111 River St.
Hoboken, NJ 07030-5774
Ph: (201)748-6000
Free: 800-225-5945
Fax: (201)748-6088
E-mail: info@wiley.com
URL: http://onlinelibrary.wiley.com/journal/10.1002/(ISSN)1553-5606
Frequency: 10/yr. **Price:** $827 U.S., Canada, and Mexico print only; $827 Institutions, other countries print only. **Description:** Journal on hospital medicine.

4357 ■ *The Municipality*
League of Wisconsin Municipalities
122 W Washington Ave., Ste. 300
Madison, WI 53703-2715
Ph: (608)267-2380
Free: 800-991-5502
Fax: (608)267-0645
E-mail: jmstaral@lwm-info.org
URL: http://www.lwm-info.org/
Frequency: Monthly. **Price:** $25/year. **Description:** Magazine for officials of Wisconsin's local municipal governments.

4358 ■ *NAFAC News*
National Association for Ambulatory Urgent Care
18870 Rutledge Rd.
Wayzata, MN 55391
Ph: (612)476-0015
Free: 866-793-1396
Fax: (612)476-0646
E-mail: health1@aol.com
URL: http://www.urgentcare.org
Description: Reports on issues current to the ambulatory urgent care industry, including government activity, national developments, and trends in health care. Recurring features include editorials, news of research, letters to the editor, and Association news. Available online only.

4359 ■ *Same-Day Surgery*
AHC Media
950 E Paces Ferry Rd. NE
Atlanta, GA 30326
Ph: (404)262-5476
Free: 800-688-2421
Fax: (404)262-5560
E-mail: editorial_questions@ahcmedia.com
URL: http://www.ahcmedia.com/public

Description: Monthly. $499. Focuses on the management, structure, and legal and medical aspects of ambulatory surgery. Carries expert opinions and recommendations on policies and procedures.

Employer Directories and Networking Lists

4360 ■ *Crain's List--Chicago's Largest Hospitals*
Crain Communications Inc.
150 N Michigan Ave.
Chicago, IL 60601-7553
Ph: (312)649-5200
Free: 800-678-9595
Fax: (312)280-3150
E-mail: info@crain.com
URL: http://www.chicagobusiness.com/section/lists

Frequency: Published November, 2012. **Price:** $25 Individuals PDF format; $45 Individuals Excel format. **Covers:** 25 hospitals in Chicago area ranked by net patient revenues. **Entries include:** Name, address, phone number, fax, web address, corporate e-mail, hospital administrator, network affiliation, 2011 net patient revenue, percentage change from 2010, 2011 net profits, percentage change from 2011, inpatient days, available beds, daily occupancy rate, number of hospital employees as of December 31, 2011, fiscal year end, Chairman, President, CEO, Chief Financial Officer, Human Resources Manager, Media Relations/Public Relations Director, and Hospital Administrator.

4361 ■ *Directory of Hospital Personnel*
Grey House Publishing
4919 Rte. 22
Amenia, NY 12501
Ph: (518)789-8700
Free: 800-562-2139
Fax: (518)789-0556
E-mail: books@greyhouse.com
URL: http://www.greyhouse.com/hospital_personnel.htm

Frequency: Annual; Latest edition 2011. **Price:** $325 Individuals Softcover. **Pages:** 2,300. **Covers:** 200,000 executives at 6,000 U.S. Hospitals. **Entries include:** Name of hospital, address, phone, number of beds, type and JCAHO status of hospital, names and titles of key department heads and staff, medical and nursing school affiliations; number of residents, interns, and nursing students. **Arrangement:** Geographical. **Indexes:** Hospital name, personnel, hospital size.

4362 ■ *Hospital Blue Book*
Billian Publishing Inc. and Trans World Publishing Inc.
2100 River Edge Pkwy., Ste. 1200
Atlanta, GA 30328
Ph: (770)955-5656
Free: 800-800-5668
Fax: (770)952-0669
E-mail: info@billian.com
URL: http://www.billianshealthdata.com/Products/HealthDATA_Hospital_Blue_Book

Frequency: Annual; Latest edition 2012. **Price:** $250 Individuals national edition; $575 Individuals subscription. **Covers:** More than 6,500 hospitals; some listings also appear in a separate southern edition of this publication. **Entries include:** Name of hospital, accreditation, mailing address, phone, fax, number of beds, type of facility (nonprofit, general,

state, etc.); list of administrative personnel and chiefs of medical services, with specific titles. **Arrangement:** Geographical.

4363 ■ *Medical and Health Information Directory: A Guide to Organizations, Agencies, Institutions, Programs, Publications, Services, and Other Resources Concerned with Clinical Medicine*
Cengage Learning Inc.
200 1st Stamford Pl., Ste. 400
Stamford, CT 06902-6753
Ph: (203)965-8600
Free: 800-354-9706
Fax: (800)487-8488
E-mail: investors@cengage.com
URL: http://www.gale.cengage.com

Frequency: Annual; Latest edition April 2011. **Price:** $1,190 Individuals set; $501 Individuals per volume. **Covers:** In volume 1, more than 33,000 medical and health oriented associations, organizations, institutions, and government agencies, including health maintenance organizations (HMOs), preferred provider organizations (PPOs), insurance companies, pharmaceutical companies, research centers, and medical and allied health schools. In Volume 2, over 20,000 medical book publishers; medical periodicals, directories, audiovisual producers and services, medical libraries and information centers, electronic resources, and health-related internet search engines. In Volume 3, more than 40,500 clinics, treatment centers, care programs, and counseling/diagnostic services for 34 subject areas. **Entries include:** Institution, service, or firm name, address, phone, fax, email and URL; many include names of key personnel and, when pertinent, descriptive annotation. Volume 3 was formerly listed separately as Health Services Directory. **Arrangement:** Classified by organization activity, service, etc. **Indexes:** Each volume has a complete alphabetical name and keyword index.

4364 ■ *National Directory of Fire Chiefs & EMS Administrators*
National Public Safety Information Bureau
601 Main St.
Stevens Point, WI 54481
Ph: (715)345-2772
Free: 800-647-7579
Fax: (715)345-7288
E-mail: info@safetysource.com
URL: http://www.safetysource.com

Frequency: Annual; Latest edition 2013. **Price:** $169 Individuals USA; $199 online (one complimentary print copy). **Covers:** Over 37,000 fire and emergency departments in the U.S. **Entries include:** Department name, address, phone, fax, county, name of chief, type of department, financial structure. **Arrangement:** Geographical.

Handbooks and Manuals

4365 ■ *Exploring Health Care Careers, Second Edition*
JIST Publishing
875 Montreal Way
Saint Paul, MN 55102-4245
Ph: (317)613-4200
Free: 800-648-5478
Fax: (800)328-4564
E-mail: info@jist.com
URL: http://www.jist.com

Description: 2006. $125.00. 992 pages. Information about careers in the health industry, including education and certification requirements, earnings, and job outlook.

4366 ■ *Introduction to the Health Professions*
Jones & Bartlett Learning, LLC
PO Box 417289
Boston, MA 02241-7289

Ph: (978)443-5000
Free: 800-832-0034
Fax: (978)443-8000
E-mail: info@jblearning.com
URL: http://www.jblearning.com

Description: Peggy S. Stanfield, Y. H. Hui and Nanna Cross. 2012. $93.95. 502 pages. Sixth edition. Provides current coverage of all major health professions. Outlines health-related careers, a review of the U.S. healthcare delivery system, managed care, and impact of new technology on healthcare services.

4367 ■ *Master the EMT-Basic Certification Exam*
Peterson's Publishing
3 Columbia Cir., Ste. 205
Albany, NY 12203-5158
Ph: (609)896-1800
E-mail: pubmarketing@petersons.com
URL: http://www.petersonspublishing.com

Description: 2010. $18.95. 240 pages. Prepares test takers for the emergency medical technician qualifying exam. Includes customized study plans, tips on mental and physical preparation, test-taking strategies, advice on managing time and test anxiety. Features an up-to-date list of state EMT agencies, latest training methods and tips for a successful job search.

4368 ■ *Opportunities in Health and Medical Careers*
The McGraw-Hill Companies Inc.
PO Box 182604
Columbus, OH 43272
Ph: (212)512-2000
Free: 877-833-5524
Fax: (614)759-3749
E-mail: customer.service@mcgraw-hill.com
URL: http://www.mcgraw-hill.com

Description: I. Donald Snook, Jr. and Leo D'Orazio. 2004. $14.95 (paper). 157 pages. Covers the full range of medical and health occupations. Illustrated.

4369 ■ *The Paramedic Exam Review*
Cengage Learning Inc.
200 1st Stamford Pl., Ste. 400
Stamford, CT 06902-6753
Ph: (203)965-8600
Free: 800-354-9706
Fax: (800)487-8488
E-mail: investors@cengage.com
URL: http://www.cengage.com

Description: Bob Elling and Kirsten Elling. 2012. $56.95. 464 pages.

4370 ■ *Paramedic Survival Guide*
McGraw-Hill Professional
2 Penn Plz., 12th Fl.
New York, NY 10121-2298
Ph: (212)904-2000
Free: 800-722-4726
Fax: (212)904-6030
E-mail: customer.service@mcgraw-hill.com
URL: http://www.mhprofessional.com

Description: Peter DiPrima Jr. 2012. $25.00. 208 pages. Offers both novice and experienced paramedics case studies, testimonials and advice to help them succeed and advance in their careers. Includes tips on picking the correct EMT job, recruitment and interview process, and various career paths and options open to paramedics.

4371 ■ *Plunkett's Health Care Industry Almanac 2012*
Plunkett Research Ltd.
4102 Bellaire Blvd.
Houston, TX 77025-1004
Ph: (713)932-0000
Fax: (713)932-7080
E-mail: customersupport@plunkettresearch.com
URL: http://www.plunkettresearch.com

Description: Jack W. Plunkett. 2011. $299.99. 717

pages. Features in-depth profiles of leading companies, associations and professional societies in the healthcare field. Covers major issues and trends, market forecasts and industry statistics.

4372 ■ *Resumes for Health and Medical Careers*
The McGraw-Hill Companies Inc.
PO Box 182604
Columbus, OH 43272
Ph: (212)512-2000
Free: 877-833-5524
Fax: (614)759-3749
E-mail: customer.service@mcgraw-hill.com
URL: http://www.mcgraw-hill.com
Description: Third edition, 2008. $12.95 (paper). 144 pages.

EMPLOYMENT AGENCIES AND SEARCH FIRMS

4373 ■ JPM International
26034 Acero
Mission Viejo, CA 92691
Ph: (949)699-4300
Free: 800-685-7856
Fax: (949)699-4333
E-mail: trish@jpmintl.com
URL: http://www.jpmintl.com
Description: Executive search firm and employment agency.

4374 ■ Keystone Healthcare Management
6075 Poplar Ave., Ste. 727
Memphis, TN 38119
Ph: (901)795-3600
Free: 866-291-8600
Fax: (901)795-6060
E-mail: scross@keystonehealthcare.com
URL: http://www.keystonehealthcare.com
Description: Specializes in the organization and management of emergency physician groups, offering support services in emergency department management, emergency medicine and physician placement.

4375 ■ B. E. Smith Inc.
9777 Ridge Dr., Ste. 300
Lenexa, KS 66219
Ph: (913)341-9116
Free: 800-467-9117
E-mail: cricci@besmith.com
URL: http://www.besmith.com
Description: Serves as an executive search to healthcare organizations across the nation. Offers permanent and interim placements.

ONLINE JOB SOURCES AND SERVICES

4376 ■ HEALTHeCAREERS Network
URL: http://www.healthecareers.com
Description: Career search site for jobs in all health care specialties; educational resources; visa and licensing information for relocation; interesting articles; relocation tools; links to professional organizations and general resources.

4377 ■ Hospital Jobs OnLine
URL: http://www.hospitaljobsonline.com
Description: Serves as a niche healthcare job board designed exclusively for hospitals, healthcare companies, and healthcare job seekers.

4378 ■ ProHealthJobs.com
URL: http://prohealthjobs.com/jobboard
Description: Career resources site for the medical and health care field. Lists professional opportunities, product information, continuing education and open positions.

TRADESHOWS

4379 ■ Ambulatory Surgery Center Association - Annual Meeting
Ambulatory Surgery Center Association
1012 Cameron St.
Alexandria, VA 22314
Ph: (703)836-8808
Fax: (703)549-0976
E-mail: asc@ascassociation.org
URL: http://www.ascassociation.org/Home
Frequency: Annual. **Primary Exhibits:** Ambulatory equipment, supplies, and services.

4380 ■ EMS World Expo
Cygnus Business Media
801 Cliff Rd., Ste. 201
Burnsville, MN 55337
Ph: (952)894-8007
Free: 800-827-8009
Fax: (952)894-8252
E-mail: info@farmshows.com
URL: http://www.cygnus.com
Frequency: Annual. Brings all elements of the emergency medical services community together at one time and place. Offers an opportunity to update skills, learn about new developments and techniques, and network with thousands of fellow EMS providers from across the United States and around the world.

4381 ■ Society for Academic Emergency Medicine Annual Meeting
Society for Academic Emergency Medicine
2340 S River Rd., Ste. 208
Des Plaines, IL 60018
Ph: (847)813-9823
Fax: (847)813-5450
E-mail: saem@saem.org
URL: http://www.saem.org
Frequency: Annual. **Primary Exhibits:** Emergency medicine equipment, supplies, and services.

OTHER SOURCES

4382 ■ *300 Ways to Put Your Talent to Work in the Health Field*
National Health Council
1730 M St. NW, Ste. 500
Washington, DC 20036-4561
Ph: (202)785-3910
Fax: (202)785-5923
URL: http://www.nationalhealthcouncil.org
Frequency: Irregular; Latest edition 2002. **Price:** $15 Members; $18 Nonmembers. **Publication includes:** Professional associations, government agencies, institutions, and other organizations offering information or assistance concerning health career education. Principal content of publication is job descriptions and educational requirements for various health professions. **Entries include:** Organization name, address, whether financial aid is offered. **Arrangement:** Classified by occupation.

4383 ■ *Career Opportunities in Health Care*
InfoBase Holdings Inc.
132 W 31st., 17 Fl.
New York, NY 10001-3406
Ph: (212)967-8800
Fax: (800)678-3633
E-mail: info@infobasepublishing.com
URL: http://www.ferguson.infobasepublishing.com
Description: Shelly Field. 2007. Third edition. $49.50. 304 pages. **Includes:** Appendices provide lists of educational institutions, periodicals, directories, associations, and unions. Appendices provide lists of educational institutions, periodicals, directories, associations, and unions.

4384 ■ Commission on Accreditation of Allied Health Education Programs
1361 Park St.
Clearwater, FL 33756
Ph: (727)210-2350
Fax: (727)210-2354
E-mail: megivern@caahep.org
URL: http://www.caahep.org
Description: Serves as a nationally recognized accrediting agency for allied health programs in 23 occupational areas. **Members:** 80.

4385 ■ *Health-Care Careers for the 21st Century*
JIST Publishing
875 Montreal Way
Saint Paul, MN 55102-4245
Ph: (317)613-4200
Free: 800-648-5478
Fax: (800)328-4564
E-mail: info@jist.com
URL: http://www.jist.com
Price: $9.95 Individuals Softcover. **Pages:** 448. **Covers:** Jobs for health care professionals and career opportunities for those pursuing a health-related career, organized into 80 careers in five groups. **Publication includes:** Appendixes listing job source resources and Web sites for health organizations.

4386 ■ National Association of Emergency Medical Technicians
PO Box 1400
Clinton, MS 39060-1400
Ph: (601)924-7744
Free: 800-34-NAEMT
Fax: (601)924-7325
E-mail: info@naemt.org
URL: http://www.naemt.org
Description: Represents and supports EMTS, paramedics and other professionals working in pre-hospital emergency medicine working in all sectors of EMS, including government third-service agencies, fire departments, hospital-based ambulance services, private companies, industrial, special operations settings, and in the military. Acts as a voice for EMS personnel in Washington, DC regarding decisions affecting EMS; speaks on behalf of all EMS providers; representatives sit on boards, associations, expert panels, and commissions to ensure that EMS is represented in decisions affecting health care and public safety; works on behalf of members in the areas of compensation and recognition, recruitment and retention, safety, and education and training.

4387 ■ National Association of EMS Physicians
18000 W 105th St.
Olathe, KS 66061
Ph: (913)895-4611
Free: 800-228-3677
Fax: (913)895-4652
E-mail: info-naemsp@goamp.com
URL: http://www.naemsp.org
Description: Medical directors responsible for emergency medical services and other physicians and nonphysicians dedicated to out-of-hospital emergency care. Promotes career development, communication and cooperation among EMS professionals.

4388 ■ National Association of Female Paramedics
PO Box 1133
Orlando, FL 32802
Ph: (407)932-2839
E-mail: national-director@nafp.org
URL: http://www.nafp.org
Description: Represents women dedicated to providing Emergency Medical Services (EMS). Provides financial assistance through grants, loans, and other funding options to women who are in the field of EMS.

4389 ■ **National Registry of Emergency Medical Technicians**
PO Box 29233
Columbus, OH 43229
Ph: (614)888-4484
Fax: (614)888-8920

E-mail: webmaster@nremt.org
URL: http://www.nremt.org
Description: Promotes the improved delivery of emergency medical services. Assists in the development and evaluation of educational programs to train emergency medical technicians; establishes qualifications for eligibility to apply for registration; prepares and conducts examinations designed to assure the competency of emergency medical technicians and paramedics; establishes a system for biennial registration; establishes procedures for revocation of certificates of registration for cause; maintains a directory of registered emergency medical technicians. **Members:** 170,000.

SOURCES OF HELP-WANTED ADS

4390 ■ *Advances in Developing Human Resources*
Pine Forge Press
2455 Teller Rd.
Thousand Oaks, CA 91320-2234
Ph: (805)499-4224
Free: 800-818-7243
Fax: (805)499-0871
E-mail: sales@pfp.sagepub.com
URL: http://www.sagepub.com/journalsProdDesc.nav?prodId=Journal201475
Frequency: Bimonthly. **Price:** $637 Institutions print & e-access; $573 Institutions e-access; $624 Institutions print only; $110 Individuals print only; $172 Institutions single print issue; $36 Individuals single print issue. **Description:** Journal for professionals working in the field of human resource development.

4391 ■ *Consultants News*
Kennedy Information Inc.
1 Phoenix Mill Ln., 3rd Fl.
Peterborough, NH 03458
Ph: (603)924-1006
Free: 800-531-0007
Fax: (603)924-4460
E-mail: customerservice@kennedyinfo.com
URL: http://www.kennedyinfo.com/rt/rectrends.html
Description: Bimonthly. Provides strategies and tactics for creating and maintaining a competitive work force.

4392 ■ *International Journal of Selection and Assessment*
Blackwell Publishing Inc.
350 Main St.
Malden, MA 02148
Ph: (781)388-8200
Free: 800-216-2522
Fax: (781)388-8210
E-mail: journaladsusa@bos.blackwellpublishing.com
URL: http://www.wiley.com/bw/journal.asp?ref=0965-075X
Frequency: Quarterly. **Price:** $122 Individuals print and online; $95 Students print and online; $1,003 Institutions print and online; $872 Institutions print or online; £597 Institutions, other countries print and online; £519 Institutions, other countries print or online; €111 Individuals print and online, Europe; £74 Individuals print and online. **Description:** Journal publishing articles related to all aspects of personnel selection, staffing, and assessment in organizations.

4393 ■ *SI Review*
Staffing Industry Analysts Inc. - Internet Publishing System
1080 W County Rd. E, St. Paul
Shoreview, MN 55126

Ph: (651)717-4300
URL: http://www.staffingindustry.com/site/Research-Publications/Publications/Staffing-Industry-Review
Frequency: Monthly; 10/yr. **Price:** $99 Individuals; $129 Canada; $149 Other countries. **Description:** Online news publication covering news and developments in employment and staffing.

4394 ■ *Staffing Industry Employment Bulletin*
Staffing Industry Analysts Inc. - Internet Publishing System
1080 W County Rd. E, St. Paul
Shoreview, MN 55126
Ph: (651)717-4300
URL: http://www.staffingindustry.com/
Frequency: Irregular. **Description:** Online news publication covering key events in employment and staffing.

4395 ■ *Staffing Industry News Bulletin*
Staffing Industry Analysts Inc. - Internet Publishing System
1975 W El Camino Real, Ste. 304
Mountain View, CA 94040
Ph: (650)390-6200
Free: 800-950-9496
Fax: (650)390-6210
URL: http://www.staffingindustry.com/
Frequency: Daily. **Price:** $10 Single issue. **Description:** Online publication covering key events in all sectors of the staffing industry.

4396 ■ *Workforce Management: HR Trends and Tools for Business Results*
Crain Communications Inc.
1155 Gratiot Ave.
Detroit, MI 48207-2732
Ph: (313)446-6000
E-mail: info@crain.com
URL: http://www.workforceonline.com
Frequency: Biweekly. **Price:** $79 Individuals; $129 Canada and Mexico; $199 Other countries. **Description:** A Business magazine for human resources management leaders.

EMPLOYER DIRECTORIES AND NETWORKING LISTS

4397 ■ *National Directory of Personnel Service Firms*
National Association of Personnel Services
6625 Hwy. 53 E, Ste. 410-201
Dawsonville, GA 30534
Ph: (706)531-0060
Fax: (866)739-4750
E-mail: president@recruitinglife.com
URL: http://www.recruitinglife.com
Frequency: Annual; spring. **Pages:** 200. **Covers:**

Over 1,100 member private (for-profit) personnel service firms and temporary service firms. **Entries include:** Firm name, address, phone, fax, contact, area of specialization. **Arrangement:** Same information given geographically by employment specialty.

HANDBOOKS AND MANUALS

4398 ■ *The Human Resource Professional's Career Guide: Building a Position of Strength*
John Wiley & Sons, Inc.
1 Wiley Dr.
Somerset, NJ 08873
Free: 877-762-2974
Fax: (800)597-3299
E-mail: custserv@wiley.com
URL: http://www.wiley.com
Description: Jeanne Palmer, Martha I. Finney. June 2004. $44.95. 264 pages.

4399 ■ *Senior Employment Interviewer*
National Learning Corporation
212 Michael Dr.
Syosset, NY 11791
Ph: (516)921-8888
Free: 800-632-8888
Fax: (516)921-8743
E-mail: info@passbooks.com
URL: http://www.passbooks.com
Description: 2009. $34.95 (paper). Serves as an exam preparation guide for senior employment interviewers.

EMPLOYMENT AGENCIES AND SEARCH FIRMS

4400 ■ **The Aspire Group**
711 Boylston St.
Boston, MA 02116-2616
Free: 800-487-2967
Fax: (617)500-7284
URL: http://www.bmanet.com/Aspire/index.html
Description: Employment agency.

4401 ■ **Campbell/Carlson LLC**
PO Box 34323
Charlotte, NC 28234
Ph: (704)373-0234
E-mail: recruiting@campbellcarlson.com
URL: http://www.campbellcarlson.com
Description: Executive search firm.

4402 ■ **Dankowski and Associates, Inc.**
13089 Root Rd.
The Woods, Ste. 200 SE
Columbia Station, OH 44028

Ph: (216)973-0556
E-mail: info@dankowskiassocites.com
URL: http://www.dankowskiassociates.com
Description: Executive search firm.

4403 ■ The Enfield Company
3005 S Lamar Blvd., Ste. D109-172
Austin, TX 78704
Ph: (512)585-0876
URL: http://silverdevelopment.com
Description: Executive search firm.

4404 ■ John J. Davis & Associates Inc.
30 Chatham Rd.
Short Hills, NJ 07078
Ph: (973)467-8339
Fax: (973)467-3706
E-mail: john.davis@jdavisassoc.com
URL: http://www.johnjdavisandassoc.com
Description: Executive search firm.

4405 ■ Protocol Agency Inc.
27001 Agoura Rd., Ste. 210
Calabasas, CA 91301
Free: 877-371-0069
E-mail: corp@protocolexec.com
URL: http://www.protocolagency.com
Description: Executive search firm focusing on a variety of placements.

4406 ■ Williams Executive Search Inc.
8500 Normandale Lake Blvd., Ste. 610
Minneapolis, MN 55437
Ph: (952)767-7900
Fax: (952)767-7905
URL: http://www.williams-exec.com
Description: Executive search firm.

4407 ■ Willmott and Associates, Inc.
922 Waltham St., Ste. 103
Lexington, MA 02421
Ph: (781)863-5400
Fax: (781)863-8000
E-mail: info@willmott.com
URL: http://www.willmott.com
Description: Executive search firm and permanent employment agency. Also fills some temporary placements.

OTHER SOURCES

4408 ■ American Staffing Association
277 S Washington St., Ste. 200
Alexandria, VA 22314-3675
Ph: (703)253-2020
Fax: (703)253-2053
E-mail: asa@americanstaffing.net
URL: http://www.americanstaffing.net/index.cfm
Description: Promotes and represents the staffing industry through legal and legislative advocacy, public relations, education, and the establishment of high standards of ethical conduct.

4409 ■ Association of Career Firms North America
8509 Crown Crescent Ct., Ste. ACF
Charlotte, NC 28227
Ph: (704)849-2500
Fax: (704)845-2420
E-mail: bcrigger@oipartners.net
URL: http://www.acf-northamerica.com
Description: Represents firms providing displaced employees, who are sponsored by their organization, with counsel and assistance in job searching and the techniques and practices of choosing a career. Develops, improves and encourages the art and science of outplacement consulting and the professional standards of competence, objectivity, and integrity in the service of clients. Cooperates with other industrial, technical, educational, professional, and governmental bodies in areas of mutual interest and concern. **Members:** 125.

4410 ■ Employment Support Center
1556 Wisconsin Ave. NW
Washington, DC 20007
Ph: (202)628-2919
Fax: (202)628-2919
E-mail: escjobclubs@gmail.com
URL: http://escjobclubs.angelfire.com
Description: Trains individuals to facilitate support groups for job-seekers. Operates a job bank for employment assistance; helps people learn to network for job contacts; provides technical assistance to employment support self help groups. Maintains speakers' bureau. Provides job-search skills training.

4411 ■ HR Policy Association
1100 13th St. NW, Ste. 850
Washington, DC 20005
Ph: (202)789-8670
Fax: (202)789-0064
E-mail: info@hrpolicy.org
URL: http://www.hrpolicy.org
Description: Senior human resource executives of Fortune 500 companies. Conducts research and publishes findings on matters relating to federal human resources policy and its application and effects. Maintains task forces to study pending employment issues; conducts seminars, and offers a suite of labor relations and HR effectiveness training courses.

4412 ■ International Association of Workforce Professionals
1801 Louisville Rd.
Frankfort, KY 40601
Ph: (502)223-4459
Free: 888-898-9960
Fax: (502)223-4127
E-mail: iawp@iawponline.org
URL: http://www.iawponline.org
Description: Officials and others engaged in job placement, unemployment compensation, and labor market information administration through municipal, state, provincial, and federal government employment agencies and unemployment compensation agencies. Conducts workshops and research. Offers professional development program of study guides and tests.

4413 ■ National Association of Personnel Services
6625 Hwy. 53 E, Ste. 410-201
Dawsonville, GA 30534
Ph: (706)531-0060
Fax: (866)739-4750
E-mail: president@recruitinglife.com
URL: http://www.recruitinglife.com
Description: Private employment and temporary service firms. Compiles statistics on professional agency growth and development; conducts certification program and educational programs. Association is distinct from former name of National Association of Personnel Consultants.

SOURCES OF HELP-WANTED ADS

4414 ■ *Alternative Energy*
ACTA Press
Bldg. B6, Ste. 101
Calgary, AB, Canada T3E 7J9
Ph: (403)288-1195
Fax: (403)247-6851
E-mail: journals@actapress.com
URL: http://www.actapress.com/Content_of_Journal
.aspx?journalid=170
Frequency: Annual. **Price:** $320 Individuals.
Description: Journal covering all areas of alternative energy and its related fields.

ONLINE JOB SOURCES AND SERVICES

4415 ■ **Energy Auditor Jobs**
URL: http://www.energyauditorjobs.com
Description: Connects employers with potential candidates who are seeking energy auditor jobs.

4416 ■ **Justmeans - CSR JOBS**
URL: http://www.justmeans.com
Description: Serves as online resource that provides available career opportunities for the sustainable business industry.

SOURCES OF HELP-WANTED ADS

4417 ■ Aerospace America Magazine
American Institute of Aeronautics and Astronautics
1801 Alexander Bell Dr., Ste. 500
Reston, VA 20191-4344
Ph: (703)264-7500
Free: 800-639-2422
Fax: (703)264-7551
E-mail: custserv@aiaa.org
URL: http://www.aerospaceamerica.org/Pages/Table-OfContents.aspx
Frequency: Monthly. **Price:** $200 Institutions non member, domestic; $163 for nonmembers in U.S. **Description:** Monthly. Free to members; non-members, $140.00 per year. Covers aeronautics and space technology with special attention to aerospace defense, design, and electronics.

4418 ■ AIE Perspectives Newsmagazine
American Institute of Engineers
4630 Appian Way, Ste. 206
El Sobrante, CA 94803-1875
Ph: (510)758-6240
Fax: (510)758-6240
E-mail: aie@aieonline.org
URL: http://www.members-aie.org
Frequency: Monthly. **Price:** included in membership dues. **Description:** Professional magazine covering engineering.

4419 ■ Chemical & Engineering News
American Chemical Society
1155 16th St. NW
Washington, DC 20036
Ph: (202)872-4600
Free: 800-227-5558
E-mail: help@acs.org
URLs: http://pubs.acs.org/cen/about.html; http://pubs.acs.org/cen
Frequency: Weekly; Annual; Latest edition 2011. **Price:** included in membership dues; $120/year for nonmembers. **Description:** Describes policies and activities of the ACS. **Includes:** Statistical data on the chemical industry, including employment totals and foreign firms. **Publication includes:** List of 100 largest chemical producers chosen by total chemical sales. **Entries include:** Company name, current and previous year's rank, industry classification, chemical sales, chemical sales as percentage of total sales, other financial data.

4420 ■ EE Evaluation Engineering: The Magazine of Electronic Evaluation & Test
Nelson Publishing Inc.
2500 Tamiami Trl. N
Nokomis, FL 34275
Ph: (941)966-9521
Fax: (941)966-2590
E-mail: webteam@nelsonpub.com
URL: http://www.evaluationengineering.com/

Frequency: Monthly. **Price:** Free. **Description:** Trade magazine covering electronic engineering, evaluation and test.

4421 ■ Electronic Products
E-mail: lens@electronicproducts.com
URL: http://www.electronicproducts.com
Frequency: Monthly. **Price:** $12 Individuals. **Description:** Magazine for electronic design engineers and management.

4422 ■ Engineering
Scientific Research Publishing
PO Box 54821
Irvine, CA 92619-4821
E-mail: eng@scirp.org
URL: http://www.scirp.org/journal/eng/
Frequency: Monthly. **Price:** $468 Individuals. **Description:** Peer-reviewed journal publishing articles on the latest advancements in engineering.

4423 ■ ENR: Engineering News-Record: The Construction Weekly
The McGraw-Hill Companies Inc.
2 Penn Plz., 9th Fl.
New York, NY 10121
Ph: (212)904-3507
Fax: (212)904-2820
E-mail: customer.service@mcgraw-hill.com
URL: http://enr.construction.com/Default.asp
Frequency: Weekly. **Price:** $87 Individuals print and online. **Description:** Magazine focusing on engineering and construction.

4424 ■ Graduating Engineer & Computer Careers
Career Recruitment Media
2 LAN Dr., Ste. 100
Westford, MA 01886
Ph: (978)692-5092
Fax: (978)692-4174
E-mail: hshulick@alloyeducation.com
URL: http://www.graduatingengineer.com
Frequency: Quarterly. **Price:** $16.95 Individuals. **Description:** Magazine focusing on employment, education, and career development for entry-level engineers and computer scientists.

4425 ■ Mechanical Engineering
ASME International
2 Park Ave.
New York, NY 10016-5990
Ph: (973)882-1170
Free: 800-843-2763
Fax: (973)882-1717
E-mail: memag@asme.org
URL: http://www.memagazine.org
Frequency: Monthly. **Price:** $25 Single issue; $3.50 Single issue international surface. **Description:** Mechanical Engineering featuring technical and industry related technological advancements and news.

4426 ■ Microwave Journal: Microwave - RF & Lightwave Technology
Horizon House Publications Inc.
685 Canton St.
Norwood, MA 02062
Ph: (781)769-9750
Free: 800-966-8526
Fax: (781)769-5037
E-mail: mwj@mwjournal.com
URL: http://www.mwjournal.com
Frequency: Monthly. **Description:** Electronic engineering magazine.

4427 ■ Modern Metals
Trend Publishing Inc.
625 N Michigan Ave., Ste. 1100
Chicago, IL 60611-3118
Ph: (312)654-2300
Free: 800-278-7363
Fax: (312)654-2323
URL: http://www.modernmetals.com
Frequency: Monthly. **Price:** $180 Individuals; $270 Two years; $260 Individuals airmail; $430 Two years airmail. **Description:** Metals fabrication magazine.

4428 ■ NSBE Magazine: National Society of Black Engineers
NSBE Publications
205 Daingerfield Rd.
Alexandria, VA 22314
Ph: (703)549-2207
Fax: (703)683-5312
E-mail: info@nsbe.org
URL: http://www.nsbe.org/News-Media/Magazines/About-NSBE-Magazine.aspx
Frequency: 3/yr. **Price:** $20 Individuals; $35 Other countries; $15 Students. **Description:** Journal providing information on engineering careers, self-development, and cultural issues for recent graduates with technical majors.

4429 ■ PE
National Society of Professional Engineers
1420 King St.
Alexandria, VA 22314-2794
Ph: (703)684-2800
Fax: (703)836-4875
E-mail: memserv@nspe.org
URL: http://www.nspe.org/PEmagazine/index.html
Frequency: Semimonthly; 10/yr. **Price:** included in membership dues; $50 for nonmembers. **Description:** Covers matters of importance to engineering educators and students.

4430 ■ Printed Circuit Design & Manufacture
UP Media Group Inc.
PO Box 470
Canton, GA 30169
Ph: (404)661-0349
URLs: http://pcdandf.com/cms/; http://www.up-media-group.com

Frequency: Monthly. **Description:** Magazine for engineers and designers of PCBs and related technologies.

4431 ■ SMT
PennWell Publishing Co.
1421 S Sheridan Rd.
Tulsa, OK 74112
Ph: (918)835-3161
Free: 800-331-4463
Fax: (918)831-9497
E-mail: Headquarters@PennWell.com
URL: http://www.ems007.com/pages/ems007.cgi

Frequency: Monthly. **Price:** $115 U.S. and Canada; $215 Other countries. **Description:** Trade magazine for professional engineers involved in surface mount technology circuit design and board assembly.

4432 ■ Structure Magazine
American Consulting Engineers Council
1015 15th St. NW, 8th Fl.
Washington, DC 20005-2605
Ph: (202)347-7474
Fax: (202)898-0068
E-mail: acec@acec.org
URL: http://structuremag.org

Frequency: Annual. **Price:** $75 Nonmembers for U.S residents; $40 Students; $90 Canada individual; $135 Other countries; $60 Canada students; $90 Other countries students. **Description:** Magazine focused on providing tips, tools, techniques, and innovative concepts for structural engineers.

4433 ■ SWE, Magazine of the Society of Women Engineers
Society of Women Engineers
203 N La Salle St., Ste. 1675
Chicago, IL 60601
Ph: (312)596-5223
Free: 877-SWE-INFO
Fax: (312)596-5252
E-mail: hq@swe.org
URL: http://societyofwomenengineers.swe.org/index.php

Frequency: Quarterly. **Price:** $30 Nonmembers. **Description:** Magazine for engineering students and for women and men working in the engineering and technology fields. Covers career guidance, continuing development and topical issues.

4434 ■ Technology Interface: The electronic journal for engineering technology
Ball State University
2000 W University Ave.
Muncie, IN 47306
Ph: (765)289-1241
Free: 800-382-8540
Fax: (765)285-2374
E-mail: askus@bsu.edu
URLs: http://web.bsu.edu/tti/Subscribe.htm; http://et.nmsu.edu/~etti/

Description: Journal for the engineering technology profession serving education and industry.

4435 ■ Test & Measurement World
UBM Canon
2901 28th St., Ste. 100
Santa Monica, CA 90405-2975
Ph: (310)445-4200
Fax: (310)445-4299
E-mail: tmw@reedbusiness.com
URL: http://www.tmworld.com

Frequency: Monthly. **Price:** Free. **Description:** Electronic engineering magazine specializing in test, measurement and inspection of electronic products.

4436 ■ Tooling & Production: Providing Solutions for Metalworking Manufacturers
Nelson Publishing Inc.
2500 Tamiami Trl. N
Nokomis, FL 34275
Ph: (941)966-9521

Fax: (941)966-2590
E-mail: webteam@nelsonpub.com
URLs: http://www.manufacturingcenter.com; http://www.toolingandproduction.com
Frequency: Monthly. **Price:** Free. **Description:** Magazine concerning metalworking.

4437 ■ Woman Engineer
Equal Opportunity Publications Inc.
445 Broad Hollow Rd., Ste. 425
Melville, NY 11747
Ph: (631)421-9421
Fax: (631)421-1352
E-mail: info@eop.com
URL: http://www.eop.com

Description: Annual. Magazine that is offered at no charge to qualified female engineering, computer-science, and information-technology students and professionals seeking to find employment and advancement in their careers.

EMPLOYER DIRECTORIES AND NETWORKING LISTS

4438 ■ Directory of Contract Staffing Firms
C.E. Publications Inc.
PO Box 3006
Bothell, WA 98041-3006
Ph: (425)806-5200
Fax: (425)806-5585
E-mail: staff@cjhunter.com
URL: http://www.cjhunter.com/dcsf/overview.html

Frequency: Annual. **Covers:** Nearly 1,300 contract firms actively engaged in the employment of engineering, IT/IS, and technical personnel for 'temporary' contract assignments throughout the world. **Entries include:** Company name, address, phone, name of contact, email, web address. **Arrangement:** Alphabetical. **Indexes:** Geographical.

4439 ■ ENR--Top 500 Design Firms Issue
The McGraw-Hill Companies Inc.
PO Box 182604
Columbus, OH 43272
Ph: (212)512-2000
Free: 877 833-5524
Fax: (614)759-3749
E-mail: customer.service@mcgraw-hill.com
URL: http://enr.construction.com/toplists/sourcebooks/2010/designfirms.html

Frequency: Annual; latest edition 2010. **Price:** $82 Individuals yearly subscription; $87 Individuals print and online. **Publication includes:** List of 500 leading architectural, engineering, and specialty design firms selected on basis of annual billings. **Entries include:** Company name, headquarters location, type of firm, current and prior year rank in billings, types of services, countries in which operated in preceding year. **Arrangement:** Ranked by billings.

4440 ■ Indiana Society of Professional Engineers--Directory
Indiana Society of Professional Engineers
c/o Lauraine M. Howe, Executive Director
PO Box 20806
Indianapolis, IN 46220
Ph: (317)255-2267
Fax: (317)255-2530
E-mail: indspe@gmail.com
URL: http://www.indspe.org

Frequency: Annual; fall. **Pages:** 150. **Covers:** Member registered engineers, land surveyors, engineering students, and engineers in training. **Entries include:** Member name, address, phone, type of membership, business information, specialty. **Arrangement:** Alpha by chapter area.

4441 ■ Plunkett's Engineering and Research Industry Almanac: The Only Complete Guide to the Business of Research, Development, and Engineering
Plunkett Research Ltd.
4102 Bellaire Blvd.
Houston, TX 77025-1004

Ph: (713)932-0000
Fax: (713)932-7080
E-mail: customersupport@plunkettresearch.com
URL: http://www.plunkettresearch.com

Frequency: Annual; Latest edition 2013; New edition expected June 2014. **Price:** $349.99 Individuals eBook, print and CD-ROM. **Pages:** 690. **Covers:** 500 of the largest companies involved in research, engineering and development in the biotech, electronics, aerospace and infotech industries. **Entries include:** Name, address, phone, fax, names and titles of key personnel, subsidiary and branch names and locations, financial data, salaries and benefits, description of products/services, overview of company culture/activities. **Indexes:** Industry, location, sales rank, profit rank.

4442 ■ Profiles of Engineering and Engineering Technology Colleges
American Society for Engineering Education
1818 N St. NW, Ste. 600
Washington, DC 20036-2479
Ph: (202)331-3500
Fax: (202)265-8504
E-mail: board@asee.org
URL: http://www.asee.org

Frequency: Latest edition 2011. **Price:** $75 Nonmembers; $50 Members; $25 Students. **Pages:** 531. **Covers:** U.S. and Canadian schools offering undergraduate and graduate engineering and engineering technology programs. **Entries include:** Name, address, phone, fax.

HANDBOOKS AND MANUALS

4443 ■ Associate Engineering Technician
National Learning Corporation
212 Michael Dr.
Syosset, NY 11791
Ph: (516)921-8888
Free: 800-632-8888
Fax: (516)921-8743
E-mail: info@passbooks.com
URL: http://www.passbooks.com

Description: 2009. $34.95 (paper). Serves as an exam preparation guide for associate engineering technicians.

4444 ■ Engineering, Mechanics, and Architecture
InfoBase Holdings Inc.
132 W 31st., 17 Fl.
New York, NY 10001-3406
Ph: (212)967-8800
Fax: (800)678-3633
E-mail: info@infobasepublishing.com
URL: http://www.ferguson.infobasepublishing.com

Description: Kelly Wiles. 2010. $39.95. 160 pages (hardcover). Serves as a guide for readers interested in switching jobs. Contains useful advice, career tips, interviews and self-asessment questions.

4445 ■ Engineering Technician
National Learning Corporation
212 Michael Dr.
Syosset, NY 11791
Ph: (516)921-8888
Free: 800-632-8888
Fax: (516)921-8743
E-mail: info@passbooks.com
URL: http://www.passbooks.com

Description: 2009. $29.95 (paper). Serves as an exam preparation guide for engineering technicians.

4446 ■ Expert Resumes for Engineers
JIST Publishing
875 Montreal Way
Saint Paul, MN 55102-4245
Ph: (317)613-4200
Free: 800-648-5478

Fax: (800)328-4564
E-mail: info@jist.com
URL: http://www.jist.com

Description: Louise M. Kursmark and Wendy S. Enelow. 2009. $16.95 (softcover). 272 pages. Features a collection of written resume samples for all types of engineers including civil, mechanical, industrial, electrical, electronics, computer, and more. Contains tips and strategies for writing engineering resumes and finding the best jobs.

4447 ■ *Great Jobs for Engineering Majors*
The McGraw-Hill Companies Inc.
PO Box 182604
Columbus, OH 43272
Ph: (212)512-2000
Free: 877-833-5524
Fax: (614)759-3749
E-mail: customer.service@mcgraw-hill.com
URL: http://www.mcgraw-hill.com

Description: Geraldine O. Garner. Second edition, 2008. $16.95. 192 pages. Covers all the career options open to students majoring in engineering.

4448 ■ *Opportunities in Electronics Careers*
The McGraw-Hill Companies Inc.
PO Box 182604
Columbus, OH 43272
Ph: (212)512-2000
Free: 877-833-5524
Fax: (614)759-3749
E-mail: customer.service@mcgraw-hill.com
URL: http://www.mcgraw-hill.com

Description: Mark Rowh. 2007. $13.95 (paper). 221 pages. Discusses career opportunities in commercial and industrial electronics equipment repair, electronics home entertainment repair, electronics engineering, and engineering technology. Includes job outlook and how to get off to a good start on the job.

EMPLOYMENT AGENCIES AND SEARCH FIRMS

4449 ■ Andrew Associates Executive Search Inc.
4800 Meadows Rd., Ste. 300
Lake Oswego, OR 97035
Ph: (503)620-5222
E-mail: aaes@andysrch.com
URL: http://www.andysrch.com

Description: Executive search firm.

4450 ■ Apple and Associates
PO Box 996
Chapin, SC 29036
Ph: (803)932-2000
E-mail: info@appleassoc.com
URL: http://www.appleassoc.com

Description: Provides staffing services to medical device, plastics, pharmaceutical and performance materials industries.

4451 ■ The Aspire Group
711 Boylston St.
Boston, MA 02116-2616
Free: 800-487-2967
Fax: (617)500-7284
URL: http://www.bmanet.com/Aspire/index.html

Description: Employment agency.

4452 ■ Ethos Consulting L.L.C.
3219 E Camelback Rd., Ste. 515
Phoenix, AZ 85018
Ph: (480)296-3801
Fax: (480)664-7270
E-mail: conrad@ethosconsulting.com
URL: http://www.ethosconsulting.com

Description: Executive search firm. Second branch in Scottsdale, AZ.

4453 ■ Global Employment Solutions Inc.
10375 Park Meadows Dr., Ste. 475
Littleton, CO 80124-6724
Ph: (303)216-9500
Fax: (303)216-9533
URL: http://www.gesnetwork.com

Description: Employment agency.

ONLINE JOB SOURCES AND SERVICES

4454 ■ Engineering Classifieds
URL: http://www.engineeringclassifieds.com

Description: Serves as a career site for engineering professionals. Provides services including job search agents, resume creation and posting.

4455 ■ EngineerJobs.com
URL: http://www.engineerjobs.com

Description: Provides job opportunities for engineering professionals in the following disciplines: aerospace, agricultural, biomedical, chemical, civil, electrical, environmental, industrial, manufacturing, marine, materials, mechanical, mining, nuclear, petroleum, process, project, quality, sales, software, solar, systems, and structural.

4456 ■ Engineer.net
URL: http://www.engineer.net

Description: Provides engineering employment tools such as job search, job posting, and engineering resumes.

4457 ■ PowerPlantPro.com
URL: http://www.powerplantpro.com/main/sendform/4/18/3472

Description: Dedicated to professionals in the power and energy industry. Features career advice and employer listings.

4458 ■ Spherion
URL: http://www.spherion.com

Description: Recruitment firm specializing in accounting and finance, sales and marketing, interim executives, technology, engineering, retail and human resources.

4459 ■ TechniciansNow.com
URL: http://www.techniciansnow.com

Description: Provides an avenue to showcase jobs and products vital to the mechanical and technical trade communities.

4460 ■ ThinkEnergyGroup.com
URL: http://www.thinkenergygroup.com

Description: Serves as a job board for professionals looking for positions in engineering, power plant, energy, and technical fields. Contains advice and tips on interviews, job searching, resume writing, hiring, and management. Provides choices of work location, pay rates in the field of expertise and contract, temp-to-hire, and direct hiring options.

OTHER SOURCES

4461 ■ Aircraft Electronics Association
3570 NE Ralph Powell Rd.
Lee's Summit, MO 64064
Ph: (816)347-8400
Fax: (816)347-8405
E-mail: info@aea.net
URL: http://www.aea.net

Description: Companies engaged in the sales, engineering, installation, and service of electronic aviation equipment and systems. Seeks to: advance the science of aircraft electronics; promote uniform and stable regulations and uniform standards of performance; establish and maintain a code of ethics; gather and disseminate technical data; advance the education of members and the public in the sci-

ence of aircraft electronics. Offers supplement type certificates, test equipment licensing, temporary FCC licensing for new installations, spare parts availability and pricing, audiovisual technician training, equipment and spare parts loan, profitable installation, and service facility operation. Provides employment information, equipment exchange information and service assistance on member installations anywhere in the world.

4462 ■ American Association of Engineering Societies
1801 Alexander Bell Dr.
Reston, VA 20191
Ph: (202)296-2237
Free: 888-400-2237
Fax: (202)296-1151
E-mail: dbateson@aaes.org
URL: http://www.aaes.org

Description: Coordinates the efforts of the member societies in the provision of reliable and objective information to the general public concerning issues which affect the engineering profession and the field of engineering as a whole; collects, analyzes, documents, and disseminates data which will inform the general public of the relationship between engineering and the national welfare; provides a forum for the engineering societies to exchange and discuss their views on matters of common interest; and represents the U.S. engineering community abroad through representation in WFEO and UPADI.

4463 ■ American Engineering Association
c/o Harold Ruchelman
533 Waterside Blvd.
Monroe Township, NJ 08831
Ph: (201)664-6954
E-mail: aea@aea.org
URL: http://www.aea.org

Description: Members consist of Engineers and engineering professionals. Purpose to advance the engineering profession and U.S. engineering capabilities. Issues of concern include age discrimination, immigration laws, displacement of U.S. Engineers by foreign workers, trade agreements, off shoring of U.S. Engineering and manufacturing jobs, loss of U.S. manufacturing and engineering capability, and recruitment of foreign students. Testifies before Congress. Holds local Chapter meetings.

4464 ■ American Indian Science and Engineering Society
PO Box 9828
Albuquerque, NM 87119-9828
Ph: (505)765-1052
Fax: (505)765-5608
E-mail: pam@aises.org
URL: http://www.aises.org

Description: Represents American Indian and non-Indian students and professionals in science, technology, and engineering fields; corporations representing energy, mining, aerospace, electronic, and computer fields. Seeks to motivate and encourage students to pursue undergraduate and graduate studies in science, engineering, and technology. Sponsors science fairs in grade schools, teacher training workshops, summer math/science sessions for 8th-12th graders, professional chapters, and student chapters in colleges. Offers scholarships. Adult members serve as role models, advisers, and mentors for students. Operates placement service.

4465 ■ American Institute of Engineers
4630 Appian Way, Ste. 206
El Sobrante, CA 94803-1875
Ph: (510)758-6240
Fax: (510)758-6240
E-mail: aie@aieonline.org
URL: http://www.aieonline.org

Description: Professional association for engineers, scientists, and mathematicians. Multi-disciplined, non-technical association who aims to improve the stature and image of engineers, scientists, and mathematicians. Provides endorsements, awards and opportunities for small business start-ups within the AIE Councils. Sponsors "LA Engineer", a comedy-drama television series; produces annual "Academy Hall of FAME (TV)".

4466 ■ American Society of Certified Engineering Technicians
PO Box 1536
Brandon, MS 39043
Ph: (601)824-8991
E-mail: ascet.freier@gmail.com
URL: http://www.ascet.org

Description: Represents certified and non-certified engineering technicians and technologists. Works to obtain recognition of the contribution of engineering technicians and engineering technologists as an essential part of the engineering-scientific team. Cooperates with engineering and scientific societies. Improves the utilization of the engineering technician and technologist. Assists the educational, social, economic, and ethical development of the engineering technician and technologist. Conducts triennial survey among members to determine employer support, pay scales, and fringe benefits. Offers referral service.

4467 ■ Career Opportunities in Engineering
InfoBase Holdings Inc.
132 W 31st., 17 Fl.
New York, NY 10001-3406
Ph: (212)967-8800
Fax: (800)678-3633
E-mail: info@infobasepublishing.com
URL: http://www.ferguson.infobasepublishing.com

Description: 2006. $49.50. 336 pages. Provides an overview of engineering, followed by a selection of jobs profiled in detail, including the nature of the job, earnings, prospects for employment, what kind of training and skills it requires and sources for further information. **Includes:** Appendices of educational institutions, periodicals, directories, and associations. Appendices of educational institutions, periodicals, directories, and associations.

4468 ■ Cultural Vistas
440 Park Ave. S, 2nd Fl.
New York, NY 10016
Ph: (212)497-3500
Fax: (212)497-3535
E-mail: info@culturalvistas.org
URL: http://culturalvistas.org

Description: Providers worldwide of on-the-job training programs for students and professionals seeking international career development and life-changing experiences. Arranges workplace exchanges in hundreds of professional fields, bringing employers and trainees together from around the world. Client list ranges from small farming communities to Fortune 500 companies.

4469 ■ Electronics Technicians Association International
5 Depot St.
Greencastle, IN 46135-8024
Ph: (765)653-8262
Free: 800-288-3824
Fax: (765)653-4287
E-mail: eta@eta-i.org
URL: http://www.eta-i.org

Description: Skilled electronics technicians. Provides placement service; offers certification examinations for electronics technicians and satellite, fiber optics, and data cabling installers. Compiles wage and manpower statistics. Administers FCC Commercial License examinations and certification of computer network systems technicians and web and internet specialists.

4470 ■ Engineering Society of Detroit
20700 Civic Center Dr., Ste. 450
Southfield, MI 48076
Ph: (248)353-0735
Fax: (248)353-0736
E-mail: esd@esd.org
URL: http://ww2.esd.org/home.htm

Description: Engineers from all disciplines; scientists and technologists. Conducts technical programs and engineering refresher courses; sponsors conferences and expositions. Maintains speakers' bureau; offers placement services; although based in Detroit, MI, society membership is international. **Members:** 6,000.

4471 ■ International Society of Certified Electronics Technicians
3608 Pershing Ave.
Fort Worth, TX 76107-4527
Ph: (817)921-9101
Free: 800-946-0201
Fax: (817)921-3741
E-mail: info@iscet.org
URL: http://www.iscet.org

Description: Technicians in 50 countries who have been certified by the society. Seeks to provide a fraternal bond among certified electronics technicians, raise their public image and improve the effectiveness of industry education programs for technicians. Offers training programs in new electronics information. Maintains library of service literature for consumer electronic equipment, including manuals and schematics for out-of-date equipment. Offers all FCC licenses. Sponsors testing program for certification of electronics technicians in the fields of audio, communications, computer, consumer, industrial, medical electronics, radar, radio-television and video.

4472 ■ ISA -The International Society of Automation
67 Alexander Dr.
Research Triangle Park, NC 27709
Ph: (919)549-8411
Fax: (919)549-8288
E-mail: info@isa.org
URL: http://www.isa.org

Description: Sets the standard for automation by helping over 30,000 worldwide members and other professionals solve difficult technical problems, while enhancing their leadership and personal career capabilities. Develops standards; certifies industry professionals; provides education and training; publishes books and technical articles; and hosts the largest conference and exhibition for automation professionals in the Western Hemisphere. Is the founding sponsor of The Automation Federation.

4473 ■ National Institute for Certification in Engineering Technologies
1420 King St.
Alexandria, VA 22314-2794
Ph: (703)548-1518
Free: 888-476-4238
Fax: (703)836-4875
E-mail: test@nicet.org
URL: http://www.nicet.org

Description: Grants and issues certificates to engineering technicians and technologists who voluntarily apply for certification and satisfy competency criteria through examinations and verification of work experience. Requirements for certification involve work experience in terms of job task proficiency and length of progressively more responsible experience. Levels of certification are Technician Trainee, Associate Engineering Technician, Engineering Technician, Senior Engineering Technician, Associate Engineering Technologist, and Certified Engineering Technologist.

4474 ■ Society of Hispanic Professional Engineers
13181 Crossroads Pkwy. N, Ste. 450
City of Industry, CA 91746-3496
Ph: (323)725-3970
E-mail: shpenational@shpe.org
URL: http://national.shpe.org

Description: Represents engineers, student engineers, and scientists. Aims to increase the number of Hispanic engineers by providing motivation and support to students. Sponsors competitions and educational programs. Maintains placement service and speakers' bureau; compiles statistics. **Members:** 8,000.

4475 ■ Society for Mining, Metallurgy, and Exploration
12999 E Adam Aircraft Cir.
Englewood, CO 80112
Ph: (303)948-4200
Free: 800-763-3132
Fax: (303)973-3845
E-mail: cs@smenet.org
URL: http://www.smenet.org

Description: A member society of the American Institute of Mining, Metallurgical and Petroleum Engineers. Persons engaged in the finding, exploitation, treatment, and marketing of all classes of minerals (metal ores, industrial minerals, and solid fuels) except petroleum. Promotes the arts and sciences connected with the production of useful minerals and metals. Offers specialized education programs; compiles enrollment and graduation statistics from schools offering engineering degrees in mining, mineral, mineral processing/metallurgical, geological, geophysical, and mining technology. Provides placement service and sponsors charitable programs.

4476 ■ Society of Women Engineers
203 N La Salle St., Ste. 1675
Chicago, IL 60601
Ph: (312)596-5223
Free: 877-SWE-INFO
Fax: (312)596-5252
E-mail: hq@swe.org
URL: http://societyofwomenengineers.swe.org

Description: Educational and service organization representing both students and professional women in engineering and technical fields.

4477 ■ Women in Engineering ProActive Network
1901 E Asbury Ave., Ste. 220
Denver, CO 80208
Ph: (303)871-4643
Fax: (303)871-4628
URL: http://www.wepan.org

Description: Women in engineering professions. Includes key strategies such as education and training, research, collaboration, leadership, diversity, advocacy, networking, sustainability, accountability, and volunteerism in order to be a catalyst for change that enhances the success of women in the engineering professions.

HANDBOOKS AND MANUALS

4478 ■ 97 Things Every Software Architect Should Know
O'Reilly and Associates Inc.
1005 Gravenstein Hwy. N
Sebastopol, CA 95472
Ph: (707)827-7019
Free: 800-889-8969
Fax: (707)829-0104
E-mail: orders@oreilly.com
URL: http://www.oreilly.com

Description: Richard Monson-Haefel. 2009. $34.99 (paper). 224 pages. Presents principles on key development issues that go beyond technology. Offers advice for communicating with stakeholders, eliminating complexity, empowering developers, and other practical lessons.

4479 ■ Enterprise Architecture: A Pocket Guide
IT Governance Publishing
25 N Philippi St.
Boise, ID 83706
Free: 877-317-2454
E-mail: servicecentre@itgovernanceusa.com
URL: http://www.itgovernanceusa.com

Description: Tom Graves. 2009. $14.95 (paper). 62 pages. Describes the purpose, role, and value of architecture in the enterprise, and the makeup and skillsets of the architecture team in different business contexts.

4480 ■ Enterprise Architecture: Creating Value by Informed Governance
Springer
233 Spring St.
New York, NY 10013
Ph: (212)460-1500
Fax: (212)460-1575
URL: http://www.springer.com

Description: Martin Op't Land, Erik Proper, Maarten Waage, Jeroen Cloo, and Claudia Steghuis. 2009. $59.95. 146 pages. Provides an overview of enterprise architecture including the process of creating, applying and maintaining it, and taking into account the perspectives of CxOs, business managers, enterprise architects, solution architects, designers, and engineers.

4481 ■ Enterprise Architecture Good Practices Guide
Trafford Publishing
1663 Liberty Dr.
Bloomington, IN 47403
Ph: (250)383-6864
Free: 888-232-4444
Fax: (250)383-6804
E-mail: info@trafford.com
URL: http://www.trafford.com

Description: Jaap Schekkerman. 2008. $73.12

(softcover). 388 pages. Provides guidance to organizations in initiating, developing, using, and maintaining their enterprise architecture practice.

4482 ■ Handbook of Enterprise Systems Architecture in Practice
Information Science Reference
701 E Chocolate Ave.
Hershey, PA 17033
Ph: (717)533-8845
Free: 866-342-6657
Fax: (717)533-8661
E-mail: cust@igi-global.com
URL: http://www.igi-global.com

Description: Pallab Saha. 2007. $165.00. 500 pages. Provides an overview of the practical aspects of enterprise architecture. Includes EA theory, concepts, strategies, implementation challenges, and case studies.

4483 ■ Handbook for Interns and Architects
National Council of Architectural Registration Boards
1801 K St. NW, Ste. 700-K
Washington, DC 20006-1301
Ph: (202)783-6500
Fax: (202)783-0290
E-mail: customerservice@ncarb.org
URL: http://www.ncarb.org

Description: 2012. Free. Provides information on how to become a registered architect and after initial registration, how to seek NCARB certification and registration in other jurisdictions. Provides services to interns and architects such as educational development, developing training requirements, compilation and evaluation of an individual's record on internship activities, transmitting an intern's record to a jurisdiction in support of the intern's application for examination, and/or registration.

4484 ■ Handbook of Research on Enterprise Systems Volume 1
Information Science Reference
701 E Chocolate Ave.
Hershey, PA 17033
Ph: (717)533-8845
Free: 866-342-6657
Fax: (717)533-8661
E-mail: cust@igi-global.com
URL: http://www.igi-global.com

Description: Jatinder N. D. Gupta, Sushil K. Sharma, and Mohammad Abdur Rashid. 2009. $265.00. 460 pages. Addresses the field of enterprise systems and covers progressive technologies, leading theories, and advanced applications.

ONLINE JOB SOURCES AND SERVICES

4485 ■ Enterprise Architecture Center
URL: http://www.enterprisearchitecturecenter.com

Description: Builds enterprise architecture aware-

ness and evangelizes enterprise architecture culture and thought leadership to business and technology professionals. Provides strategic enterprise architecture advisory services and assists in finding enterprise architecture careers and IT architect jobs.

4486 ■ Enterprise Architecture Forum
URL: http://enterprisearchitectureforum.com

Description: Serves as forum that connects architects allows them to share, discuss, and study enterprise architecture. Enables professionals to share their views on the use of EA ROI calculators, the workings of different EA tools, the value of service oriented architecture, and the concept of enterprise applications integration.

4487 ■ IT Architect Jobs
URL: http://itarchitectjobs.com

Description: Dedicated to enterprise and information technology architecture. Covers industry domains such as enterprise architecture, business architecture, applications architecture, information architecture, technology architecture, solution architecture, software architecture, hardware architecture, and process architecture.

4488 ■ SOA Hub
URL: http://www.xwebservices.com/SOA_Services

Description: Serves as a portal for the advancement of service oriented architecture. Features enterprise architecture guides, white papers, tutorials, message boards, job listings, and employment opportunities.

TRADESHOWS

4489 ■ Enterprise Search Summit
Information Today, Inc.
143 Old Marlton Pke.
Medford, NJ 08055-8750
Ph: (609)654-6266
Free: 800-300-9868
Fax: (609)654-4309
E-mail: custserv@infotoday.com
URL: http://www.infotoday.com

Covers how to develop, implement, and enhance internal search capabilities in an organization. Presents and examines the different ways to leverage search tools, information architecture, classification, and other strategies and technologies to deliver meaningful results.

4490 ■ Object Management Group Technical Meeting
Object Management Group
109 Highland Ave.
Needham, MA 02494
Ph: (781)444-0404
Fax: (781)444-0320
E-mail: info@omg.org
URL: http://www.omg.org

Frequency: Periodic. Provides IT architects, business analysts, government experts, vendors, and end-users with a neutral forum to discuss, develop, and adopt standards that enable software interoperability for a wide range of industries.

OTHER SOURCES

4491 ■ Association for Enterprise Information
2111 Wilson Blvd., Ste. 400
Arlington, VA 22201
Ph: (703)247-9474
Fax: (703)522-3192
E-mail: dchesebrough@afei.org
URL: http://www.afei.org/Pages/default.aspx

Description: Represents corporate, government agencies, academic institutions, non-profit organizations, government employees, and individuals. Establishes opportunities for collaboration on enterprise information issues among government, business, and academia.

4492 ■ Business Architects Association
727 S Dearborn St., Ste. 710
Chicago, IL 60605
E-mail: info@businessarchitects.org
URL: http://www.businessarchitectsassociation.org

Description: Promotes and advances the business architect field through education, research, community involvement, and application of methodologies for the benefit of the business community at large. Partners with universities to train practitioners for the field. Facilitates the creation of business architecture groups.

4493 ■ DAMA International
PO Box 7362
Town and Country, MO 63006
Ph: (813)778-5495
Fax: (813)464-7864
E-mail: info@dama.org
URL: http://www.dama.org

Description: Represents the interests of technical and business professionals dedicated to advancing the concepts and practices of information resource management and data resource management. Defines and clarifies the roles of information and data resource management. Educates corporate management by demonstrating how information and data asset management affects corporate performance. Conducts regional and international conferences and symposia. Establishes academic and professional certification programs for the DRM/IRM professional.

4494 ■ Enterprise Architecture Center of Excellence
10895 Lake Point Dr.
Pinckney, MI 48169
Ph: (810)231-6356
Fax: (810)231-6631
E-mail: info@eacoe.org
URL: http://www.eacoe.org

Description: Advances implementation and understanding of enterprise architecture. Provides information and promotes professional and career development among members. Offers practice-based certification, professional networking, and knowledge development opportunities.

4495 ■ Information Architecture Institute
800 Cummings Ctr., Ste. 357W
Beverly, MA 01915
E-mail: info@iainstitute.org
URL: http://iainstitute.org

Description: Supports individuals and organizations specializing in the design and construction of shared information environments. Advances the information architecture profession through education, advocacy, services, and social networking. Provides a framework for members to improve their skills and enhance their professional standing.

Environmental Engineers

SOURCES OF HELP-WANTED ADS

4496 ■ **AIE Perspectives Newsmagazine**
American Institute of Engineers
4630 Appian Way, Ste. 206
El Sobrante, CA 94803-1875
Ph: (510)758-6240
Fax: (510)758-6240
E-mail: aie@aieonline.org
URL: http://www.members-aie.org
Frequency: Monthly. **Price:** included in membership
dues. **Description:** Professional magazine covering
engineering.

4497 ■ **AWWA Streamlines**
American Water Works Association
6666 W Quincy Ave.
Denver, CO 80235-3098
Ph: (303)794-7711
Free: 800-926-7337
Fax: (303)347-0804
URL: http://www.awwa.org/publications/streamlines-
current.cfm
Description: Biweekly, online; print issue is
quarterly. Carries news of the Association and
features about the drinking water industry, including
regulations, legislation, conservation, treatment, quality, distribution, management, and utility operations.
Recurring features include letters to the editor, a
calendar of events, reports of meetings, news of
educational opportunities, notices of publications
available, education and job opportunities in the
industry and legislative news.

4498 ■ **Building Industry Technology**
U.S. Department of Commerce - Technology
Administration - National Technical Information
Service
5301 Shawnee Rd.
Alexandria, VA 22312
Ph: (703)605-6040
Free: 800-553-NTIS
Fax: (703)605-6900
E-mail: info@ntis.gov
URL: http://www.ntis.gov/products/alerts.aspx
Description: Biweekly. $255. Consists of abstracts
of reports on architectural and environmental design,
building standards, construction materials and equip-
ment, and structural analyses. Recurring features
include a form for ordering reports from NTIS. Also
available via e-mail.

4499 ■ **City Trees**
Society of Municipal Arborists
PO Box 641
Watkinsville, GA 30677
Ph: (706)769-7412
Fax: (706)769-7307
E-mail: urbanforestry@prodigy.net
URL: http://www.urban-forestry.com
Description: Bimonthly. Addresses all aspects of

municipal (urban) forestry. Contains technical articles
on species of trees, pest control, conservation, planning, design, and equipment. Recurring features
include lists of new publications, statistics, news of
research, letters to the editor, announcements of
meetings, and columns titled President's Column,
Professor's Column, City of the Month, Park of the
Month, Tree of the Month, and Editor's Column.

4500 ■ **Climate Alert**
Climate Institute
900 17th St. NW, Ste. 700
Washington, DC 20006
Ph: (202)552-4723
Fax: (202)737-6410
E-mail: info@climate.org
URL: http://www.climate.org/publications/climate-alert
.html
Description: Quarterly. Addresses global climate is-
sues in terms of science and policy.

4501 ■ **Drinking Water & Backflow**
Prevention
International Association of Plumbing and Mechani-
cal Officials
4755 E Philadelphia St.
Ontario, CA 91761
Ph: (909)472-4100
Fax: (909)472-4150
E-mail: iapmo@iapmo.org
URLs: http://www.dwbp-online.com.; http://www.iap-
modwbp.org
Krystal Renea Garza, Editor. **Frequency:** Monthly.
Price: $45, U.S. year; $53 Canada and Mexico.;
$59, elsewhere year. **Description:** Monthly. $45.00/
year. Recurring features include news of educational
opportunities, job listings, and a calendar of events.

4502 ■ **Engineering**
Scientific Research Publishing
PO Box 54821
Irvine, CA 92619-4821
E-mail: eng@scirp.org
URL: http://www.scirp.org/journal/eng/
Frequency: Monthly. **Price:** $468 Individuals.
Description: Peer-reviewed journal publishing
articles on the latest advancements in engineering.

4503 ■ **Environmental Building News**
Building Green Inc.
122 Birge St., Ste. 30
Brattleboro, VT 05301-3206
Ph: (802)257-7300
Free: 800-861-0954
Fax: (802)257-7304
E-mail: info@buildinggreen.com
URL: http://www.buildinggreen.com/landing/ebnper-
formance1102.html
Description: Monthly. $99/year. Covers the building
trade with an environmental slant. Covers nontoxic
materials, better landscaping and water use, and

resources for energy conservation in a technical
manner.

4504 ■ **Environmental Business Journal**
Environmental Business International Inc.
4452 Park Blvd., Ste. 306
San Diego, CA 92116
Ph: (619)295-7685
Fax: (619)295-5743
E-mail: ebi@ebiusa.com
URL: http://www.ebiusa.com
Description: Twelve issues/year. $995/year.
Provides research and articles on various segments
of the environmental business industry. Recurring
features include news of research.

4505 ■ **Environmental Education Research**
Routledge Journals - Taylor & Francis Group
270 Madison Ave.
New York, NY 10016-0601
Ph: (212)216-7800
Fax: (212)563-2269
URL: http://www.tandfonline.com/toc/ceer20/current
Frequency: 6/year. **Price:** $1,594 Institutions print +
online; $1,395 Institutions online only; $424 Individu-
als print only. **Description:** Journal covering all
aspects of environmental education.

4506 ■ **Environmental Pollution**
Elsevier Science Inc.
Secondary Publishing Division
650 Ave. of the Americas
New York, NY 10011
Ph: (212)633-3980
Free: 888-437-4636
Fax: (212)633-3975
E-mail: environmentalpollution@mindspring.com
URL: http://www.journals.elsevier.com/environmental
-pollution/
Frequency: Monthly. **Price:** $169 Individuals print;
$5,442 Institutions online; $6,530 Institutions print.
Description: Journal covering issues relevant to
chemical pollutants in air, soil and water.

4507 ■ **Environmental Progress &**
Sustainable Energy
John Wiley & Sons Inc.
c/o Dr. Martin Abraham
College of Science, Technology, Engineering, &
Mathematics
Youngstown State University
Youngstown, OH 44555
Ph: (201)748-6000
Free: 800-225-5945
Fax: (201)748-6088
E-mail: info@wiley.com
URL: http://onlinelibrary.wiley.com/journal/10.1002/
(ISSN)1944-7450/issues
Frequency: Quarterly. **Price:** $843 Institutions print
only; $899 Institutions, Canada and Mexico print
only; $927 Institutions, other countries print only;
$970 Institutions print with online; $1,026 Institutions,

Canada and Mexico print with online; $1,054 Institutions, other countries print with online. **Description:** Journal reporting technological advances vital to engineering professionals whose responsibility includes or is related to environmental issues.

4508 ■ Graduating Engineer & Computer Careers
Career Recruitment Media
2 LAN Dr., Ste. 100
Westford, MA 01886
Ph: (978)692-5092
Fax: (978)692-4174
E-mail: hshulick@alloyeducation.com
URL: http://www.graduatingengineer.com
Frequency: Quarterly. **Price:** $16.95 Individuals. **Description:** Magazine focusing on employment, education, and career development for entry-level engineers and computer scientists.

4509 ■ Green Career Journal
Environmental Career Center
601 N Mechanic St., Ste. 306
Franklin, VA 23851
Ph: (757)727-7895
URL: http://environmentalcareer.com
Description: Monthly. Provides information, articles and insight on the environmental businesses and organizations and their current job openings.

4510 ■ Hardwood Research Bulletin
National Hardwood Lumber Association
6830 Raleigh La Grange Rd.
Memphis, TN 38134-0518
Ph: (901)377-1818
Free: 800-933-0318
Fax: (901)382-6419
E-mail: info@nhla.com
URL: http://www.nhla.com
Description: Monthly. Provides abstracts and digests of current research information concerning hardwood forest management, silviculture, insects, diseases, resource utilization, product development, manufacturing technology, and economics. Lists upcoming events, workshops, short courses, and seminars of interest to members.

4511 ■ The Job Seeker
URL: http://www.thejobseeker.net
Description: Semimonthly. Specializes in environmental and natural resource vacancies nationwide. Lists current vacancies from federal, state, local, private, and non-profit employers. Also available via e-mail.

4512 ■ Journal of Environmental Health: Dedicated to the Advancement of the Environmental Health Professional
National Environmental Health Association
720 S Colorado Blvd., Ste. 1000-N
Denver, CO 80246-1926
Ph: (303)756-9090
Free: 866-956-2258
Fax: (303)691-9490
E-mail: staff@neha.org
URL: http://www.neha.org/JEH/
Frequency: 10/yr. **Price:** $135 Individuals 1 year; $160 Other countries 1 year; $250 Two years U.S.; $300 Two years international. **Description:** Journal presenting environmental health and protection issues.

4513 ■ Minority Engineer Magazine
Employment Opportunity Publications
445 Broad Hollow Rd., Ste. 425
Melville, NY 11747
Ph: (631)421-9421
Fax: (631)421-1352
E-mail: info@eop.com
URL: http://www.eop.com/mags-ME.php
Description: $18.00/year for non-minority engineering student or professional; $34.00/2 years for non-minority engineering student or professional; $49.

00/3 years for non-minority engineering student or professional. Provides job listings, company profiles, and articles geared toward the engineering student and professional.

4514 ■ Natural Resources
Scientific Research Publishing
PO Box 54821
Irvine, CA 92619-4821
E-mail: nr@scirp.org
URL: http://www.scirp.org/journal/nr/
Frequency: Quarterly. **Price:** $156 Individuals. **Description:** Peer-reviewed journal publishing articles on the latest advancements in natural resources.

4515 ■ NSBE Magazine: National Society of Black Engineers
NSBE Publications
205 Daingerfield Rd.
Alexandria, VA 22314
Ph: (703)549-2207
Fax: (703)683-5312
E-mail: info@nsbe.org
URL: http://www.nsbe.org/News-Media/Magazines/About-NSBE-Magazine.aspx
Frequency: 3/yr. **Price:** $20 Individuals; $35 Other countries; $15 Students. **Description:** Journal providing information on engineering careers, self-development, and cultural issues for recent graduates with technical majors.

4516 ■ Structure Magazine
American Consulting Engineers Council
1015 15th St. NW, 8th Fl.
Washington, DC 20005-2605
Ph: (202)347-7474
Fax: (202)898-0068
E-mail: acec@acec.org
URL: http://structuremag.org
Frequency: Annual. **Price:** $75 Nonmembers for U.S residents; $40 Students; $90 Canada individual; $135 Other countries; $60 Canada students; $90 Other countries students. **Description:** Magazine focused on providing tips, tools, techniques, and innovative concepts for structural engineers.

4517 ■ SWE, Magazine of the Society of Women Engineers
Society of Women Engineers
203 N La Salle St., Ste. 1675
Chicago, IL 60601
Ph: (312)596-5223
Free: 877-SWE-INFO
Fax: (312)596-5252
E-mail: hq@swe.org
URL: http://societyofwomenengineers.swe.org/index.php
Frequency: Quarterly. **Price:** $30 Nonmembers. **Description:** Magazine for engineering students and for women and men working in the engineering and technology fields. Covers career guidance, continuing development and topical issues.

4518 ■ The Wildlifer
The Wildlife Society
5410 Grosvenor Ln., Ste. 200
Bethesda, MD 20814-2144
Ph: (301)897-9770
Fax: (301)530-2471
E-mail: tws@wildlife.org
URL: http://joomla.wildlife.org
Description: Monthly. Serves as the Society's official publication of record. Contains items on section and chapter activities, meetings of interest, career notes, job opportunities, and timely articles on significant developments in conservation issues. Recurring features include editorials, news of members, letters to the editor, a calendar of events, and a column titled Call for Papers.

4519 ■ Woman Engineer
Equal Opportunity Publications Inc.
445 Broad Hollow Rd., Ste. 425
Melville, NY 11747
Ph: (631)421-9421
Fax: (631)421-1352
E-mail: info@eop.com
URL: http://www.eop.com
Description: Annual. Magazine that is offered at no charge to qualified female engineering, computer-science, and information-technology students and professionals seeking to find employment and advancement in their careers.

PLACEMENT AND JOB REFERRAL SERVICES

4520 ■ ASA-CSSA-SSSA Career Placement Center
5585 Guilford Rd.
Madison, WI 53711
Ph: (608)273-8080
Fax: (608)273-2021
URL: http://www.careerplacement.org
Description: Serves as a clearinghouse for resumes and personnel listings. Promotes and encourages career opportunities in the agronomic, crop, soil, and environmental sciences.

EMPLOYER DIRECTORIES AND NETWORKING LISTS

4521 ■ Association of Conservation Engineers--Membership Directory
Association of Conservation Engineers
Missouri Dept. of Conservation
Jefferson City, MO 65102-0180
Ph: (573)522-4115
Fax: (573)522-2324
E-mail: greg.mihalevich@mdc.mo.gov
URL: http://conservationengineers.org
Frequency: Annual; June. **Covers:** 280 persons with administrative or engineering background in conservation. **Entries include:** Member name, address, phone, company or institution name. **Arrangement:** Alphabetical.

4522 ■ Conservation Directory
National Wildlife Federation
11100 Wildlife Center Dr.
Reston, VA 20190
Ph: (703)438-6000
Free: 800-822-9919
E-mail: admin@nwf.org
URL: http://www.nwf.org
Frequency: Annual; latest edition 2010. **Covers:** Over 4,258 organizations, agencies, colleges and universities with conservation programs and more than 18,000 officials concerned with environmental conservation, education, and natural resource use and management. **Includes:** List of Nat'l Wildlife Refuges, Nat'l Forests, Nat'l Marine Sanctuaries, Nat'l Parks, Bureau of Land Management districts, Nat'l Seashores, foreign international organizations, and environmental online databases. **Entries include:** Agency name, address, branch or subsidiary office name and address, names and titles of key personnel, descriptions of program areas, size of membership (where appropriate), telephone, fax, e-mail and URL addresses. **Arrangement:** Classified by type of organization. **Indexes:** Personal name, keyword, geographic, organization.

4523 ■ Directory of Contract Staffing Firms
C.E. Publications Inc.
PO Box 3006
Bothell, WA 98041-3006
Ph: (425)806-5200

Fax: (425)806-5585
E-mail: staff@cjhunter.com
URL: http://www.cjhunter.com/dcsf/overview.html
Frequency: Annual. **Covers:** Nearly 1,300 contract firms actively engaged in the employment of engineering, IT/IS, and technical personnel for 'temporary' contract assignments throughout the world. **Entries include:** Company name, address, phone, name of contact, email, web address. **Arrangement:** Alphabetical. **Indexes:** Geographical.

4524 ■ Indiana Society of Professional Engineers--Directory
Indiana Society of Professional Engineers
c/o Lauraine M. Howe, Executive Director
PO Box 20806
Indianapolis, IN 46220
Ph: (317)255-2267
Fax: (317)255-2530
E-mail: indspe@gmail.com
URL: http://www.indspe.org
Frequency: Annual; fall. **Pages:** 150. **Covers:** Member registered engineers, land surveyors, engineering students, and engineers in training. **Entries include:** Member name, address, phone, type of membership, business information, specialty. **Arrangement:** Alpha by chapter area.

4525 ■ Who's Who in Engineering
American Association of Engineering Societies
1801 Alexander Bell Dr.
Reston, VA 20191
Ph: (202)296-2237
Free: 888-400-2237
Fax: (202)296-1151
E-mail: dbateson@aaes.org
URL: http://www.aaes.org
Frequency: Triennial; Latest edition 9th. **Covers:** About 15,000 engineers who have received professional recognition for outstanding achievement. **Entries include:** Name, address; education and employment history; awards and achievements. **Arrangement:** Alphabetical. **Indexes:** Geographical, field of specialization.

4526 ■ Who's Who in Environmental Engineering
American Academy of Environmental Engineers and Scientists
130 Holiday Ct., Ste. 100
Annapolis, MD 21401
Ph: (410)266-3311
Fax: (410)266-7653
E-mail: info@aaees.org
URL: http://www.aaee.net/Website/WhosWho.htm
Frequency: Annual; Latest edition 2011. **Price:** $75 Individuals plus $5.75 shipping and handling payment with order. **Covers:** About 2,400 licensed professional environmental engineers that have been certified by examination in one or more of seven specialties: air pollution control, general environmental engineering, industrial hygiene, hazardous waste management, radiation protection, solid waste management, water supply and wastewater. **Entries include:** Name, affiliation, address, phone, area of specialization, biographical data. **Arrangement:** Alphabetical, geographical, area of specialization.

HANDBOOKS AND MANUALS

4527 ■ Expert Resumes for Engineers
JIST Publishing
875 Montreal Way
Saint Paul, MN 55102-4245
Ph: (317)613-4200
Free: 800-648-5478
Fax: (800)328-4564
E-mail: info@jist.com
URL: http://www.jist.com
Description: Louise M. Kursmark and Wendy S. Enelow. 2009. $16.95 (softcover). 272 pages.

Features a collection of written resume samples for all types of engineers including civil, mechanical, industrial, electrical, electronics, computer, and more. Contains tips and strategies for writing engineering resumes and finding the best jobs.

4528 ■ Great Jobs for Engineering Majors
The McGraw-Hill Companies Inc.
PO Box 182604
Columbus, OH 43272
Ph: (212)512-2000
Free: 877-833-5524
Fax: (614)759-3749
E-mail: customer.service@mcgraw-hill.com
URL: http://www.mcgraw-hill.com
Description: Geraldine O. Garner. Second edition, 2008. $16.95. 192 pages. Covers all the career options open to students majoring in engineering.

4529 ■ Jobs in Environmental Cleanup and Emergency Hazmat Response
The Rosen Publishing Group Inc.
29 E 21st St. Fl. 2
New York, NY 10010-6256
Ph: (212)777-3017
URL: http://www.rosenpublishing.com
Description: Daniel E. Harmon. 2010. $31.95 (library bound). 80 pages. Features jobs in environmental cleanup and emergency hazmat response. Explores numerous career paths for different environmental jobs that require special training or four-year and/or postgraduate degrees. Includes job profiles for professionals such as environmental engineers, geologists, microbiologists, science technicians, conservationists, foresters, park rangers, soil scientists, air control technicians, toxicologists, dredge operators, ecologists, hazardous waste managers, and zoologists.

4530 ■ Sustainable Development in Practice: Case Studies for Engineers and Scientists
John Wiley & Sons Inc.
111 River St.
Hoboken, NJ 07030-5774
Ph: (201)748-6000
Free: 800-225-5945
Fax: (201)748-6088
E-mail: info@wiley.com
URL: http://www.wiley.com
Description: Adisa Azapagic and Slobodan Perdan. 2011. $139.95 (hardcover). 536 pages. 2nd edition. Covers a wide range of sustainability issues in both developed and developing countries. Includes case studies. Serves as reading guide for engineers and scientists concerned with sustainable development.

4531 ■ Transport Modeling for Environmental Engineers and Scientists
John Wiley & Sons Inc.
111 River St.
Hoboken, NJ 07030-5774
Ph: (201)748-6000
Free: 800-225-5945
Fax: (201)748-6088
E-mail: info@wiley.com
URL: http://www.wiley.com
Description: Mark M. Clark. 2009. $132.00 (hardcover). 664 pages. 2nd edition. Covers fundamentals of mass and momentum transport process emphasizing on aerosol and colloidal systems. Presents environmental focus on sedimentation, coagulation, adsorption and other key topics. Includes worked examples and end-of-chapter exercises.

EMPLOYMENT AGENCIES AND SEARCH FIRMS

4532 ■ Amtec Human Capital
2749 Saturn St.
Brea, CA 92821

Ph: (714)993-1900
Fax: (714)993-2419
E-mail: info@amtechc.com
URL: http://www.amtechc.com
Description: Employment agency.

4533 ■ The Angus Group Ltd.
5080 Wooster Rd., Ste. 300
Cincinnati, OH 45226
Ph: (513)961-5575
Fax: (513)961-5616
URL: http://www.angusgroup.com
Description: Executive search firm.

4534 ■ Bell Oaks Co.
115 Perimeter Center Pl., Ste. 400
Atlanta, GA 30346
Ph: (678)287-2000
Fax: (678)287-2002
E-mail: info@belloaks.com
URL: http://www.belloaks.com
Description: Personnel service firm.

4535 ■ Bright Blue Alliance, LLC
4032 N Farwell Ave.
Milwaukee, WI 53211-2109
Ph: (414)377-4677
E-mail: connect@brightbluealliance.com
URL: http://brightbluealliance.com
Description: Serves as executive search and recruitment firm for qualified candidates who are looking for a career in any significant water industry.

4536 ■ Capitol Staffing Inc.
460 Briarwood Dr., Briarwood 1 Bldg., Ste. 110
Jackson, MS 39206
Ph: (601)957-1755
Fax: (601)957-3880
E-mail: info@capitolstaffing.com
URL: http://www.capitolstaffing.com
Description: Personnel consultancy that focuses on office administration, management, sales, accounting, medical, information technology, accounting, and engineering/technical fields. Industries served: insurance, finance, medical, communications, investment, industry, and small businesses.

4537 ■ Career Center, Inc.
2184 Morris Ave.
Union, NJ 07083
Ph: (908)687-1812
Free: 800-227-3379
E-mail: career@careercenterinc.com
URL: http://www.careercenterinc.com
Description: Employment agency.

4538 ■ Centennial, Inc.
8044 Montgomery Rd., Ste. 260
Cincinnati, OH 45236
Ph: (513)366-3760
Fax: (513)366-3761
URL: http://www.centennialinc.com
Description: Serves as an executive search firm specializing in the areas of executive and general management, accounting and finance, human resources, information technology, manufacturing, engineering, marketing and advertising, not-for-profit, sales and business development, and supply chain and logistics.

4539 ■ The Elliott Co.
439 Church St.
Mount Pleasant, SC 29464
Ph: (843)388-0900
E-mail: suppt.staff@elliottco.net
URL: http://www.elliottco.net
Description: Executive search firm.

4540 ■ Executive Recruiters Agency
PO Box 21810
Little Rock, AR 72211
Ph: (501)224-7000

Fax: (501)224-8534
E-mail: jobs@execrecruit.com
URL: http://www.execrecruit.com
Description: Personnel service firm.

4541 ■ JPM International
26034 Acero
Mission Viejo, CA 92691
Ph: (949)699-4300
Free: 800-685-7856
Fax: (949)699-4333
E-mail: trish@jpmintl.com
URL: http://www.jpmintl.com
Description: Executive search firm and employment agency.

4542 ■ McNichol Associates
8419 Germantown Ave.
Philadelphia, PA 19118
Ph: (215)922-4142
Fax: (215)922-0178
Description: Performs executive search for middle and senior-level management, marketing and technical personnel for professional design firms; construction, management and general contractors; engineering-construction organizations; environmental firms and others needing technical management personnel.

4543 ■ Metzner Group
10130 Harmony Rd.
Myersville, MD 21773
Ph: (301)293-4206
Fax: (301)293-4207
E-mail: carol@themetznergroup.com
URL: http://www.themetznergroup.com
Description: Specializes in the recruitment of architects, civil engineers, environmental engineers and planners for the A/E/P communities.

4544 ■ Randolph Associates, Inc.
950 Massachusetts Ave., Ste. 105
Cambridge, MA 02139-3174
Ph: (617)441-8777
Fax: (617)441-8778
E-mail: jobs@greatjobs.com
URL: http://www.greatjobs.com
Description: Employment agency. Provides regular or temporary placement of staff.

4545 ■ Roberson & Co.
10751 Parfet St.
Broomfield, CO 80021
Ph: (303)410-6510
E-mail: roberson@recruiterpro.com
URL: http://www.recruiterpro.com
Description: Professional and executive recruiting firm working the national and international marketplace. Specializes in accounting, finance, data processing and information services, health care, environmental and mining engineering, manufacturing, human resources, and sales and marketing.

4546 ■ Search North America Inc.
PO Box 3577
Sunriver, OR 97707
E-mail: mylinda@searchna.com
URL: http://www.searchna.com
Description: An executive search and recruiting firm whose focus is placing engineers, operations and maintenance managers, sales and marketing management, financial and general management executives (both domestic and international). Industries served: forest products, pulp and paper, waste to energy, environmental services, consulting and equipment suppliers for above related industries.

ONLINE JOB SOURCES AND SERVICES

4547 ■ AEJob.com
URL: http://aejob.com
Description: Provides lists of architectural jobs, engineering jobs and environmental consulting jobs nationwide.

4548 ■ Bright Green Talent - Green Jobs
URL: http://www.brightgreentalent.com/green-jobs
Description: Serves as online tool that offers green jobs listing and career advice to candidates interested and engaged in environmental career.

4549 ■ Conservation Job Board
URL: http://www.conservationjobboard.com
Description: Provides job seekers with a one-stop place for finding the latest job openings related to conservation. Assists employers to find the ideal candidates for their job openings, internships, graduate assistantships, and other volunteer opportunities.

4550 ■ Cyber-Sierra.com
URL: http://www.cyber-sierra.com
Description: Offers employment listings in natural resource occupations, ecology and environmental disciples.

4551 ■ Diversity Environmental Jobs
URL: http://www.diversityenvironmentaljobs.com
Description: Serves as a niche job board that provides diverse environmental career opportunities.

4552 ■ EnergyCentralJobs.com
URL: http://www.energycentraljobs.com
Description: Serves as an on-line job resource for candidates and power companies worldwide. Maintains a job search database dedicated to the power, nuclear, oil and gas career fields.

4553 ■ Engineering Classifieds
URL: http://www.engineeringclassifieds.com
Description: Serves as a career site for engineering professionals. Provides services including job search agents, resume creation and posting.

4554 ■ EngineerJobs.com
URL: http://www.engineerjobs.com
Description: Provides job opportunities for engineering professionals in the following disciplines: aerospace, agricultural, biomedical, chemical, civil, electrical, environmental, industrial, manufacturing, marine, materials, mechanical, mining, nuclear, petroleum, process, project, quality, sales, software, solar, systems, and structural.

4555 ■ Engineer.net
URL: http://www.engineer.net
Description: Provides engineering employment tools such as job search, job posting, and engineering resumes.

4556 ■ Environmental Career Opportunities
URL: http://www.ecojobs.com
Description: Lists environmental jobs in conservation, education, policy, science and engineering.

4557 ■ Environmental Engineering Jobs
URL: http://www.jobsenvironmentalengineering.com
Description: Serves as a job site network that lists environmental engineering jobs from job postings, internet job boards, newspapers and classified ads.

4558 ■ Environmental Expert
URL: http://www.environmental-expert.com
Description: Connects environmental industry professionals from around the globe to companies that provide the products, services and information they need to do their job successfully.

4559 ■ Environmental Jobs
URL: http://environmental.jobs4.org
Description: Offers a searchable database of environmental job opportunities available throughout the United States.

4560 ■ EnvironmentalCrossing.com
URL: http://www.environmentalcrossing.com
Description: Provides a collection of environmental job listings. Includes lists of employer career pages, job websites, association websites, newspaper classifieds and recruitment sites.

4561 ■ EnvironmentalEngineer.com
URL: http://www.environmentalengineer.com
Description: Provides environmental engineering job listings and products to environmental engineers.

4562 ■ EnvironmentalJobs.com
URL: http://environmentaljobs.com
Description: Serves as online tool that provides current listings of environmental jobs.

4563 ■ Great Green Careers
URL: http://www.greatgreencareers.com
Description: Serves as online resource that connects employers and job seekers in the green jobs industries.

4564 ■ Greenopolis Green Job Listings
URL: http://jobs.greenopolis.com/a/jobs/find-jobs
Description: Provides an online searchable listing of diverse green jobs across the United States.

4565 ■ iHireEnvironmental
URL: http://www.ihireenvironmental.com
Description: Provides listings and services pertaining to environmental employment opportunities.

4566 ■ Justmeans - CSR JOBS
URL: http://www.justmeans.com
Description: Serves as online resource that provides available career opportunities for the sustainable business industry.

4567 ■ Rigzone.com
URL: http://www.rigzone.com/jobs/?wwkr=t
Description: Features energy jobs for engineers and professionals covering all types of energy sectors, including oil and gas, renewables, mining, nuclear, power, marine, and railway. Provides any individual, engineer or professional, graduate or with an extensive experience list of jobs that can be browsed by location, job category, or company name, or can be directly found with search functionality.

4568 ■ Spherion
URL: http://www.spherion.com
Description: Recruitment firm specializing in accounting and finance, sales and marketing, interim executives, technology, engineering, retail and human resources.

4569 ■ ThinkEnergyGroup.com
URL: http://www.thinkenergygroup.com
Description: Serves as a job board for professionals looking for positions in engineering, power plant, energy, and technical fields. Contains advice and tips on interviews, job searching, resume writing, hiring, and management. Provides choices of work location, pay rates in the field of expertise and contract, temp-to-hire, and direct hiring options.

TRADESHOWS

4570 ■ Air and Waste Management Association Annual Conference and Exhibition
Air and Waste Management Association
1 Gateway Ctr., 3rd Fl.
420 Fort Duquesne Blvd.
Pittsburgh, PA 15222-1435
Ph: (412)232-3444
Free: 800-270-3444

Fax: (412)232-3450
E-mail: info@awma.org
URL: http://www.awma.org
Frequency: Annual. **Primary Exhibits:** Instrumentation, environmental control products, and services.

4571 ■ American Society for Engineering Education Annual Conference and Exposition
American Society for Engineering Education
1818 N St. NW, Ste. 600
Washington, DC 20036-2479
Ph: (202)331-3500
Fax: (202)265-8504
E-mail: board@asee.org
URL: http://www.asee.org
Frequency: Annual. **Primary Exhibits:** Publications, engineering supplies and equipment, computers, software, and research companies all products and services related to engineering education.

4572 ■ NGWA Annual Convention/Exposition
National Ground Water Association
601 Dempsey Rd.
Westerville, OH 43081
Ph: (614)898-7791
Free: 800-551-7379
Fax: (614)898-7786
E-mail: ngwa@ngwa.org
URL: http://www.ngwa.org
Frequency: Annual. **Primary Exhibits:** Equipment, products and technology for the ground water industry. **Dates and Locations:** Las Vegas, NV; Convention Center.

4573 ■ Texas Ground Water Association Trade Show and Convention
Texas Ground Water Association
221 E 9th St., Ste. 206
San Jacinto Bldg.
Austin, TX 78701-2510
Ph: (512)472-7437
Fax: (512)472-0537
E-mail: lgoodson@twca.org
URL: http://www.tgwa.org
Frequency: Annual. **Primary Exhibits:** Water well equipment, including drills.

4574 ■ WEFTEC
Water Environment Federation
601 Wythe St.
Alexandria, VA 22314-1994
Free: 800-666-0206
Fax: (703)684-2492
E-mail: inquiry@wef.org
URL: http://www.wef.org
Frequency: Annual. **Primary Exhibits:** Water treatment equipment, supplies, and services.

OTHER SOURCES

4575 ■ Air and Waste Management Association
1 Gateway Ctr., 3rd Fl.
420 Fort Duquesne Blvd.
Pittsburgh, PA 15222-1435
Ph: (412)232-3444
Free: 800-270-3444
Fax: (412)232-3450
E-mail: info@awma.org
URL: http://www.awma.org
Description: Serves as environmental, educational, and technical organization. Seeks to provide a neutral forum for the exchange of technical information on a wide variety of environmental topics.

4576 ■ American Academy of Environmental Engineers and Scientists
130 Holiday Ct., Ste. 100
Annapolis, MD 21401

Ph: (410)266-3311
Fax: (410)266-7653
E-mail: info@aaees.org
URL: http://www.aaees.org
Description: Environmentally oriented registered professional engineers certified by examination as Diplomates of the Academy. Seeks to improve the standards of environmental engineering. Certifies those with special knowledge of environmental engineering. Furnishes lists of those certified to the public. Maintains speakers' bureau. Recognizes areas of specialization: Air Pollution Control; General Environmental; Hazardous Waste Management; Industrial Hygiene; Radiation Protection; Solid Waste Management; Water Supply and Wastewater. Requires written and oral examinations for certification. Works with other professional organizations on environmentally oriented activities. Identifies potential employment candidates through Talent Search Service.

4577 ■ American Association of Engineering Societies
1801 Alexander Bell Dr.
Reston, VA 20191
Ph: (202)296-2237
Free: 888-400-2237
Fax: (202)296-1151
E-mail: dbateson@aaes.org
URL: http://www.aaes.org
Description: Coordinates the efforts of the member societies in the provision of reliable and objective information to the general public concerning issues which affect the engineering profession and the field of engineering as a whole; collects, analyzes, documents, and disseminates data which will inform the general public of the relationship between engineering and the national welfare; provides a forum for the engineering societies to exchange and discuss their views on matters of common interest; and represents the U.S. engineering community abroad through representation in WFEO and UPADI.

4578 ■ American Association of Environmental Technicians
2249 Balsan Way
Wellington, FL 33414
Ph: (561)644-1208
Fax: (561)753-6651
E-mail: mahmood7438@bellsouth.net
URL: http://carbonlovers.org
Description: Promotes ethical practices, technical competency and professional standards in the environmental fields. Fosters teamwork and cooperation in understanding of environmental techniques. Provides a forum for the environmental technicians and other environmental professionals.

4579 ■ American Engineering Association
c/o Harold Ruchelman
533 Waterside Blvd.
Monroe Township, NJ 08831
Ph: (201)664-6954
E-mail: aea@aea.org
URL: http://www.aea.org
Description: Members consist of Engineers and engineering professionals. Purpose to advance the engineering profession and U.S. engineering capabilities. Issues of concern include age discrimination, immigration laws, displacement of U.S. Engineers by foreign workers, trade agreements, off shoring of U.S. Engineering and manufacturing jobs, loss of U.S. manufacturing and engineering capability, and recruitment of foreign students. Testifies before Congress. Holds local Chapter meetings.

4580 ■ American Indian Science and Engineering Society
PO Box 9828
Albuquerque, NM 87119-9828
Ph: (505)765-1052

Fax: (505)765-5608
E-mail: pam@aises.org
URL: http://www.aises.org
Description: Represents American Indian and non-Indian students and professionals in science, technology, and engineering fields; corporations representing energy, mining, aerospace, electronic, and computer fields. Seeks to motivate and encourage students to pursue undergraduate and graduate studies in science, engineering, and technology. Sponsors science fairs in grade schools, teacher training workshops, summer math/science sessions for 8th-12th graders, professional chapters, and student chapters in colleges. Offers scholarships. Adult members serve as role models, advisers, and mentors for students. Operates placement service.

4581 ■ American Institute of Engineers
4630 Appian Way, Ste. 206
El Sobrante, CA 94803-1875
Ph: (510)758-6240
Fax: (510)758-6240
E-mail: aie@aieonline.org
URL: http://www.aieonline.org
Description: Professional association for engineers, scientists, and mathematicians. Multi-disciplined, non-technical association who aims to improve the stature and image of engineers, scientists, and mathematicians. Provides endorsements, awards and opportunities for small business start-ups within the AIE Councils. Sponsors "LA Engineer", a comedy-drama television series; produces annual "Academy Hall of FAME (TV)".

4582 ■ *Career Opportunities in Conservation and the Environment*
InfoBase Holdings Inc.
132 W 31st., 17 Fl.
New York, NY 10001-3406
Ph: (212)967-8800
Fax: (800)678-3633
E-mail: info@infobasepublishing.com
URL: http://www.ferguson.infobasepublishing.com
Description: 2007. $49.50. 304 pages. Covers job profiles on conservation and the environment, followed by the descriptions of certification, education, special skills, and training required. **Includes:** Appendices of educational institutions, periodicals, directories, and associations. Appendices of educational institutions, periodicals, directories, and associations.

4583 ■ *Career Opportunities in Engineering*
InfoBase Holdings Inc.
132 W 31st., 17 Fl.
New York, NY 10001-3406
Ph: (212)967-8800
Fax: (800)678-3633
E-mail: info@infobasepublishing.com
URL: http://www.ferguson.infobasepublishing.com
Description: 2006. $49.50. 336 pages. Provides an overview of engineering, followed by a selection of jobs profiled in detail, including the nature of the job, earnings, prospects for employment, what kind of training and skills it requires and sources for further information. **Includes:** Appendices of educational institutions, periodicals, directories, and associations. Appendices of educational institutions, periodicals, directories, and associations.

4584 ■ Defense of Place
c/o Resource Renewal Institute
187 E Blithedale Ave.
Mill Valley, CA 94941
Ph: (415)928-3774
E-mail: hdj@rri.org
URL: http://www.rri.org/defenseofplace.php
Description: Aims to preserve the world's natural resources. Works to create awareness on wildlife conservation. Promotes environmental protection.

4585 ■ Engineering Society of Detroit
20700 Civic Center Dr., Ste. 450
Southfield, MI 48076

Ph: (248)353-0735
Fax: (248)353-0736
E-mail: esd@esd.org
URL: http://ww2.esd.org/home.htm

Description: Engineers from all disciplines; scientists and technologists. Conducts technical programs and engineering refresher courses; sponsors conferences and expositions. Maintains speakers' bureau; offers placement services; although based in Detroit, MI, society membership is international. **Members:** 6,000.

4586 ■ Friends of the Osa
1822 R St. NW, 4th Fl.
Washington, DC 20009
Ph: (202)234-2356
Fax: (202)234-2358
E-mail: info@osaconservation.org
URL: http://osaconservation.org/tag/friends-of-the
-osa

Description: Aims to maintain a largely forested landscape surrounded by an intact coastal zone that protects the Osa's biodiversity while supporting sustainable human livelihoods. Works with local, regional and international partners to protect the region's globally significant biodiversity. Encourages regional and local participation in conservation efforts. Facilitates the exchange of scientific and research expertise.

4587 ■ Indo-Pacific Conservation Alliance
1525 Bernice St.
Honolulu, HI 96817
Ph: (808)848-4124
Fax: (808)847-8252
E-mail: info@indopacific.org
URL: http://www.indopacific.org

Description: Focuses on the study and conservation of the native ecosystems of the tropical Indo-Pacific region. Supports traditional peoples in the stewardship of globally significant natural resources. Works as facilitators to local communities who request help in conserving their natural resources. Provides information, training, equipment and other support to local stakeholders to help conserve and manage natural resources.

4588 ■ Instream Flow Council
c/o Todd Richards, President
Massachusetts Division Fish and Wildlife
1 Rabbit Hill Rd., North Dr.
Westborough, MA 01581
Ph: (508)389-6300
E-mail: todd.richards@state.ma.us
URL: http://www.instreamflowcouncil.org

Description: Represents the interests of state and provincial fish and wildlife management agencies. Increases public awareness and understanding of instream flow issues and stewardship responsibilities. Helps to establish, maintain and administer programs for the quantification, protection and restoration of instream flows for aquatic resources.

4589 ■ Intelligent Transportation Society of America
1100 17th St. NW, Ste. 1200
Washington, DC 20036
Ph: (202)484-4847
Free: 800-374-8472
Fax: (202)484-3483
E-mail: info@itsa.org
URL: http://www.itsa.org

Description: Includes private corporations, public agencies, and academic institutions involved in the research, development, and design of intelligent transportation systems technologies that enhance safety, increase mobility, and sustain the environment.

4590 ■ National Action Council for Minorities in Engineering
440 Hamilton Ave., Ste. 302
White Plains, NY 10601-1813
Ph: (914)539-4010

Free: 800-888-9929
Fax: (914)539-4032
E-mail: ajohnson@nacme.org
URL: http://www.nacme.org

Description: Leads the national effort to increase access to careers in engineering and other science-based disciplines. Conducts research and public policy analysis, develops and operates national demonstration programs at precollege and university levels, and disseminates information through publications, conferences and electronic media. Serves as a privately funded source of scholarships for minority students in engineering.

4591 ■ National Hardwood Lumber Association
6830 Raleigh La Grange Rd.
Memphis, TN 38134-0518
Ph: (901)377-1818
Free: 800-933-0318
Fax: (901)382-6419
E-mail: info@nhla.com
URL: http://www.nhla.com

Description: United States, Canadian and International hardwood lumber and veneer manufacturers, distributors and consumers. Inspects hardwood lumber. Maintains inspection training school. Conducts management and marketing seminars for the hardwood industry. Promotes research in hardwood timber management and utilization. Promotes public awareness of the industry.

4592 ■ National Society of Professional Engineers
1420 King St.
Alexandria, VA 22314-2794
Ph: (703)684-2800
Fax: (703)836-4875
E-mail: memserv@nspe.org
URL: http://www.nspe.org

Description: Represents professional engineers and engineers-in-training in all fields registered in accordance with the laws of states or territories of the U.S. or provinces of Canada; qualified graduate engineers, student members, and registered land surveyors. Is concerned with social, professional, ethical, and economic considerations of engineering as a profession; encompasses programs in public relations, employment practices, ethical considerations, education, and career guidance. Monitors legislative and regulatory actions of interest to the engineering profession.

4593 ■ National Waste and Recycling Association
4301 Connecticut Ave. NW, Ste. 300
Washington, DC 20008-2304
Ph: (202)244-4700
Free: 800-424-2869
Fax: (202)966-4818
E-mail: skneiss@envasns.org
URL: http://www.environmentalisteveryday.org

Description: Manufacturers, designers, and distributors of waste collection, treatment, and storage equipment; waste handling consultants. Promotes effective processing of solid and hazardous wastes and more extensive use of recycling. Represents members' interests; conducts research and educational programs; maintains hall of fame; compiles statistics.

4594 ■ National Wildlife Federation
11100 Wildlife Center Dr.
Reston, VA 20190
Ph: (703)438-6000
Free: 800-822-9919
URL: http://www.nwf.org

Description: Serves as a member-supported conservation group, with over four million members and supporters. Federation of state and territorial affiliates, associate members and individual conservationist-contributors. Seeks to educate, inspire and assist individuals and organizations of

diverse cultures to conserve wildlife and other natural resources and to protect the earth's environment in order to achieve a peaceful, equitable and sustainable future. Encourages the intelligent management of the life-sustaining resources of the earth and promotes greater appreciation of wild places, wildlife and the natural resources shared by all. Publishes educational materials and conservation periodicals.

4595 ■ Ocean Conservation Research
PO Box 559
Lagunitas, CA 94938
Ph: (415)488-0553
E-mail: info@ocr.org
URL: http://ocr.org

Description: Represents scientists, engineers and ocean advocates devoted to improve the environmental health of the sea. Seeks to understand and explore solutions to the growing problem of human generated noise pollution and its impact on marine animals. Promotes the recovery and long term viability of the sea through research focusing on conservation priorities and practices.

4596 ■ Orion Grassroots Network
187 Main St.
Great Barrington, MA 01230
Ph: (413)528-4422
URL: http://www.oriongrassroots.org

Description: Consists of grassroots organizations across the United States. Provides job listing for future green leaders. Offers job posting service on a fee basis.

4597 ■ OurEarth.org
PO Box 62133
Durham, NC 27715
Ph: (410)878-6485
URL: http://www.ourearth.org

Description: Represents graduate and medical students as well as environmental experts and leaders from around the country. Promotes the importance of natural resources energy savings and pollutant reductions. Conducts environmental programs, activities, initiatives, ideas and grassroots efforts across the country.

4598 ■ Rising Tide North America
268 Bush St.
San Francisco, CA 94101
Ph: (503)438-4697
E-mail: contact@risingtidenorthamerica.org
URL: http://www.risingtidenorthamerica.org

Description: Fosters community-based solutions to the climate crisis. Aims to prevent catastrophic global warming by determining the root causes of climate change. Works to support direct action and encourages individuals and organizations to carry out autonomous actions that are in line with these principles.

4599 ■ Rivers Without Borders
PO Box 154
Clinton, WA 98236
Ph: (360)341-1976
E-mail: admin@riverswithoutborders.org
URL: http://riverswithoutborders.org

Description: Represents individuals and groups coordinating to protect the diversity of the river. Aims to maintain the abundance of fish and wildlife species in transboundary watersheds. Provides information on how to conserve the river system.

4600 ■ Save Yemen's Flora and Fauna
1523 River Terrace Dr.
East Lansing, MI 48823
E-mail: jzindani@syff.org
URL: http://www.syff.org

Description: Represents individuals with an interest in environmental protection and wildlife conservation. Works to protect natural resources and wildlife habitats through efforts directed against pollution and violation of environmental laws. Conducts research and educational programs.

4601 ■ Society of Hispanic Professional Engineers
13181 Crossroads Pkwy. N, Ste. 450
City of Industry, CA 91746-3496
Ph: (323)725-3970
E-mail: shpenational@shpe.org
URL: http://national.shpe.org

Description: Represents engineers, student engineers, and scientists. Aims to increase the number of Hispanic engineers by providing motivation and support to students. Sponsors competitions

and educational programs. Maintains placement service and speakers' bureau; compiles statistics. **Members:** 8,000.

4602 ■ Society of Women Engineers
203 N La Salle St., Ste. 1675
Chicago, IL 60601
Ph: (312)596-5223
Free: 877-SWE-INFO
Fax: (312)596-5252
E-mail: hq@swe.org
URL: http://societyofwomenengineers.swe.org
Description: Educational and service organization representing both students and professional women in engineering and technical fields.

4603 ■ Women in Engineering ProActive Network
1901 E Asbury Ave., Ste. 220
Denver, CO 80208
Ph: (303)871-4643
Fax: (303)871-4628
URL: http://www.wepan.org

Description: Women in engineering professions. Includes key strategies such as education and training, research, collaboration, leadership, diversity, advocacy, networking, sustainability, accountability, and volunteerism in order to be a catalyst for change that enhances the success of women in the engineering professions.

SOURCES OF HELP-WANTED ADS

4604 ■ *Green Career Journal*
Environmental Career Center
601 N Mechanic St., Ste. 306
Franklin, VA 23851
Ph: (757)727-7895
URL: http://environmentalcareer.com

Description: Monthly. Provides information, articles and insight on the environmental businesses and organizations and their current job openings.

4605 ■ *MainStream / Streamline*
American Water Works Association
6666 W Quincy Ave.
Denver, CO 80235-3098
Ph: (303)794-7711
Free: 800-926-7337
Fax: (303)347-0804
URL: http://www.awwa.org

Mary A. Parmelee, Editor, mparmele@awwa.org.
Frequency: Biweekly, online; print issue is published quarterly. **Price:** Included in membership; $16, nonmembers U.S. and Canada; $22, nonmembers.
Description: Recurring features include a calendar of events, news of educational opportunities, and education and job opportunities in the industry.

4606 ■ *Natural Resources*
Scientific Research Publishing
PO Box 54821
Irvine, CA 92619-4821
E-mail: nr@scirp.org
URL: http://www.scirp.org/journal/nr/

Frequency: Quarterly. **Price:** $156 Individuals. **Description:** Peer-reviewed journal publishing articles on the latest advancements in natural resources.

EMPLOYER DIRECTORIES AND NETWORKING LISTS

4607 ■ *Conservation Directory*
National Wildlife Federation
11100 Wildlife Center Dr.
Reston, VA 20190
Ph: (703)438-6000
Free: 800-822-9919
E-mail: admin@nwf.org
URL: http://www.nwf.org

Frequency: Annual; latest edition 2010. **Covers:** Over 4,258 organizations, agencies, colleges and universities with conservation programs and more than 18,000 officials concerned with environmental conservation, education, and natural resource use and management. **Includes:** List of Nat'l Wildlife Refuges, Nat'l Forests, Nat'l Marine Sancturies, Nat'l Parks, Bureau of Land Management districts, Nat'l

Seashores, foreign international organizations, and environmental online databases. **Entries include:** Agency name, address, branch or subsidiary office name and address, names and titles of key personnel, descriptions of program areas, size of membership (where appropriate), telephone, fax, e-mail and URL addresses. **Arrangement:** Classified by type of organization. **Indexes:** Personal name, keyword, geographic, organization.

4608 ■ *Physical and Earth Sciences Graduate Program Directories*
EducationDynamics LLC - Prospecting Services Div. - GradSchools.com
1350 Edgmont Ave., Ste. 1100
Chester, PA 19013
Ph: (484)766-2910
Free: 866-GRAD-COM
Fax: (610)499-9205
E-mail: info@edudirectories.com
URL: http://www.gradschools.com

HANDBOOKS AND MANUALS

4609 ■ *Associate Environmental Analyst*
National Learning Corporation
212 Michael Dr.
Syosset, NY 11791
Ph: (516)921-8888
Free: 800-632-8888
Fax: (516)921-8743
E-mail: info@passbooks.com
URL: http://www.passbooks.com

Description: 2009. $34.95 (paper). Serves as a study guide to assist candidates in preparing for the associate environmental analyst examination.

4610 ■ *Environmental Control Specialist*
National Learning Corporation
212 Michael Dr.
Syosset, NY 11791
Ph: (516)921-8888
Free: 800-632-8888
Fax: (516)921-8743
E-mail: info@passbooks.com
URL: http://www.passbooks.com

Description: 2009. $29.95 (paper). Serves as a study guide to assist candidates in preparing for the environmental control specialist examination.

4611 ■ *Environmental Enforcement Specialist*
National Learning Corporation
212 Michael Dr.
Syosset, NY 11791
Ph: (516)921-8888
Free: 800-632-8888
Fax: (516)921-8743
E-mail: info@passbooks.com
URL: http://www.passbooks.com

Description: 2009. $29.95 (paper). Serves as a

study guide to assist candidates in preparing for the environmental enforcement specialist examination.

4612 ■ *Environmental Impact Assessment: A Guide to Best Professional Practices*
CRC Press
c/o Taylor & Francis Group, LLC
6000 Broken Sound Pkwy., NW
Boca Raton, FL 33487-2713
Ph: (561)994-0555
Free: 800-272-7737
Fax: (800)374-3401
E-mail: orders@taylorandfrancis.com
URL: http://www.crcpress.com

Description: Charles H. Eccleston. 2011. $119.95 (hardback). 290 pages. Covers all aspects of environmental impact assessment (EIA). Helps practitioners apply best professional practices in the development of EIAs.

4613 ■ *Environmental Science Experiments*
Chelsea House Publications
c/o Infobase Publishing
132 W 31st St., 17th Fl.
New York, NY 10001
Free: 800-322-8755
Fax: (800)678-3633
E-mail: custserv@factsonfile.com
URL: http://www.infobasepublishing.com

Description: Aviva Ebner. 2011. $35.00 (hardcover). 160 pages. Raises awareness on the challenges in balancing the use of resources with maintaining a healthy environment. Inspires students to pursue an education and career related to environmental studies.

4614 ■ *Green Jobs for a New Economy: The Career Guide to Emerging Opportunities*
Peterson's Publishing
3 Columbia Cir., Ste. 205
Albany, NY 12203-5158
Ph: (609)896-1800
E-mail: pubmarketing@petersons.com
URL: http://www.petersonspublishing.com

Description: 2009. $21.95 (softcover). 400 pages. Provides a blueprint for students and career changers, and includes information about career trends, earning potentials, training and licensure requirements, and job search resources in the green economy.

4615 ■ *Jobs in Environmental Cleanup and Emergency Hazmat Response*
The Rosen Publishing Group Inc.
29 E 21st St. Fl. 2
New York, NY 10010-6256
Ph: (212)777-3017
URL: http://www.rosenpublishing.com

Description: Daniel E. Harmon. 2010. $31.95 (library bound). 80 pages. Features jobs in environmental cleanup and emergency hazmat response. Explores numerous career paths for different environmental jobs that require special training or four-year and/or postgraduate degrees. Includes job profiles for professionals such as environmental engineers, geologists, microbiologists, science technicians, conservationists, foresters, park rangers, soil scientists, air control technicians, toxicologists, dredge operators, ecologists, hazardous waste managers, and zoologists.

4616 ■ Principal Environmental Analyst
National Learning Corporation
212 Michael Dr.
Syosset, NY 11791
Ph: (516)921-8888
Free: 800-632-8888
Fax: (516)921-8743
E-mail: info@passbooks.com
URL: http://www.passbooks.com

Description: 2009. $39.95 (paper). Serves as a study guide to assist candidates in preparing for the principal environmental analyst examination.

4617 ■ Routledge International Handbook of Green Criminology
Routledge
711 3rd Ave., 8th Fl.
New York, NY 10017
Ph: (212)216-7800
Free: 800-634-7064
Fax: (212)564-7854
E-mail: book.orders@tandf.co.uk
URL: http://www.routledge.com

Description: Nigel South and Avi Brisman. 2012. $199.00 (hardcover). 496 pages. Examines a wide range of issues in environmental crimes, harms and threats, including environmental legislation and regulation.

4618 ■ Statistics for Earth and Environmental Scientists
John Wiley & Sons Inc.
111 River St.
Hoboken, NJ 07030-5774
Ph: (201)748-6000
Free: 800-225-5945
Fax: (201)748-6088
E-mail: info@wiley.com
URL: http://www.wiley.com

Description: John Schuenemeyer and Larry Drew. 2011. $110.00 (hardcover). 407 pages. Serves as reference for earth scientists, geologists, hydrologists, and environmental statisticians. Provides treatment of statistical applications for solving real-world environmental problems.

4619 ■ Sustainable Development in Practice: Case Studies for Engineers and Scientists
John Wiley & Sons Inc.
111 River St.
Hoboken, NJ 07030-5774
Ph: (201)748-6000
Free: 800-225-5945
Fax: (201)748-6088
E-mail: info@wiley.com
URL: http://www.wiley.com

Description: Adisa Azapagic and Slobodan Perdan. 2011. $139.95 (hardcover). 536 pages. 2nd edition. Covers a wide range of sustainability issues in both developed and developing countries. Includes case studies. Serves as reading guide for engineers and scientists concerned with sustainable development.

4620 ■ Transport Modeling for Environmental Engineers and Scientists
John Wiley & Sons Inc.
111 River St.
Hoboken, NJ 07030-5774
Ph: (201)748-6000
Free: 800-225-5945
Fax: (201)748-6088
E-mail: info@wiley.com
URL: http://www.wiley.com

Description: Mark M. Clark. 2009. $132.00 (hardcover). 664 pages. 2nd edition. Covers fundamentals of mass and momentum transport process emphasizing on aerosol and colloidal systems. Presents environmental focus on sedimentation, coagulation, adsorption and other key topics. Includes worked examples and end-of-chapter exercises.

EMPLOYMENT AGENCIES AND SEARCH FIRMS

4621 ■ Bright Blue Alliance, LLC
4032 N Farwell Ave.
Milwaukee, WI 53211-2109
Ph: (414)377-4677
E-mail: connect@brightbluealliance.com
URL: http://brightbluealliance.com

Description: Serves as executive search and recruitment firm for qualified candidates who are looking for a career in any significant water industry.

4622 ■ Meticulum, LLC
PO Box 451
Vinalhaven, ME 04863-0451
Ph: (207)470-0447
Fax: (877)773-0447
E-mail: meticulum@meticulum.com
URL: http://www.meticulum.com

Description: Specializes in the identification, recruitment and strategic placement of professionals within the environmental health, biotechnology and pharmaceutical industries.

4623 ■ On Demand Environmental
12770 Merit Dr., Ste. 900
Dallas, TX 75251
Free: 866-862-1399
Fax: (972)934-2344
E-mail: cprice@ondemandenv.com
URL: http://www.ondemandenv.com

Description: Specializes in matching high quality environmental, health and safety (EH&S) and corporate social responsibility (CSR) professionals with career advancement opportunities.

ONLINE JOB SOURCES AND SERVICES

4624 ■ Bright Green Talent - Green Jobs
URL: http://www.brightgreentalent.com/green-jobs

Description: Serves as online tool that offers green jobs listing and career advice to candidates interested and engaged in environmental career.

4625 ■ Conservation Job Board
URL: http://www.conservationjobboard.com

Description: Provides job seekers with a one-stop place for finding the latest job openings related to conservation. Assists employers to find the ideal candidates for their job openings, internships, graduate assistantships, and other volunteer opportunities.

4626 ■ Diversity Environmental Jobs
URL: http://www.diversityenvironmentaljobs.com

Description: Serves as a niche job board that provides diverse environmental career opportunities.

4627 ■ EHSJobs.org
URL: http://ehsjobs.org

Description: Assists Environmental Health and Safety (EHS) professionals and specialists to find jobs and explore related occupations.

4628 ■ Environmental Health Specialist Jobs
URL: http://www.environmentalhealthspecialistjobs.com

Description: Serves as a niche job board that focuses entirely on environmental health specialist employment opportunities and candidate recruiting.

4629 ■ Environmental Jobs
URL: http://environmental.jobs4.org

Description: Offers a searchable database of environmental job opportunities available throughout the United States.

4630 ■ Environmental Jobsite.com
URL: http://www.environmentaljobsite.com

Description: Provides job openings for environmental specialists.

4631 ■ Environmental Scientist Jobs
URL: http://www.environmentalscientistjobs.org

Description: Provides a niche job board that focuses entirely on environmental scientist employment opportunities and candidate recruiting.

4632 ■ EnvironmentalJobResource.com
URL: http://www.environmentaljobresource.com

Description: Provides job listings and other resources for students and professionals engaged in environmental field work.

4633 ■ EnvironmentalJobs.com
URL: http://environmentaljobs.com

Description: Serves as online tool that provides current listings of environmental jobs.

4634

■ EnvironmentalSafetyHealthCrossing.com
URL: http://www.environmentalsafetyhealthcrossing.com

Description: Provides job consolidation service in the employment industry for safety health jobs from every safety health employer, website, company, and organization.

4635 ■ EnvironmentalSpecialistJobs.com
URL: http://www.environmentalspecialistjobs.com

Description: Features environmental specialist jobs, environmental jobs, energy jobs, green jobs, green job seekers and green employers.

4636 ■ Get Environmental Scientist Jobs
URL: http://www.getenvironmentalscientistjobs.com

Description: Offers a one-stop resource for finding and filling environmental scientist positions. Features free environmental scientist job postings and career opportunities.

4637 ■ Great Green Careers
URL: http://www.greatgreencareers.com

Description: Serves as online resource that connects employers and job seekers in the green jobs industries.

4638 ■ Greenopolis Green Job Listings
URL: http://jobs.greenopolis.com/a/jobs/find-jobs

Description: Provides an online searchable listing of diverse green jobs across the United States.

4639 ■ iHireEnvironmental
URL: http://www.ihireenvironmental.com

Description: Provides listings and services pertaining to environmental employment opportunities.

4640 ■ Justmeans - CSR JOBS
URL: http://www.justmeans.com

Description: Serves as online resource that provides available career opportunities for the sustainable business industry.

4641 ■ ScientistCrossing.com
URL: http://www.scientistcrossing.com

Description: Provides job listings and other

resources related to scientist employment opportunities.

OTHER SOURCES

4642 ■ American Water Works Association
6666 W Quincy Ave.
Denver, CO 80235-3098
Ph: (303)794-7711
Free: 800-926-7337
Fax: (303)347-0804
URL: http://www.awwa.org

Description: Water utility managers, superintendents, engineers, chemists, bacteriologists, and other individuals interested in public water supply; municipal- and investor-owned water departments; boards of health; manufacturers of waterworks equipment; government officials and consultants interested in water supply. Offers placement service via member newsletter.

4643 ■ Association of Environmental Health Academic Programs
8620 Roosevelt Way NE, Ste. A
Seattle, WA 98115
Ph: (206)522-5272
Fax: (206)985-9805
E-mail: info@aehap.org
URL: http://www.aehap.org/students/ehinternships .html

Description: Provides useful information for students interested in exploring career options in environmental health. Seeks to increase trained professionals in the field of environmental health.

4644 ■ Campus Safety, Health, and Environmental Management Association - Career Center
c/o Jack Voorhees
One City Centre, Ste. 204
120 W Seventh St.
Bloomington, IN 47404-3839
Ph: (812)245-8084
Fax: (812)245-0588
E-mail: info@cshema.org
URL: http://www.cshema.org

Description: Provides information and career opportunities available to people who are interested or enagaged in environmental health and safety.

4645 ■ Career Opportunities in Conservation and the Environment
InfoBase Holdings Inc.
132 W 31st., 17 Fl.
New York, NY 10001-3406
Ph: (212)967-8800
Fax: (800)678-3633
E-mail: info@infobasepublishing.com
URL: http://www.ferguson.infobasepublishing.com

Description: 2007. $49.50. 304 pages. Covers job profiles on conservation and the environment, followed by the descriptions of certification, education, special skills, and training required. **Includes:** Appendices of educational institutions, periodicals, directories, and associations. Appendices of educational institutions, periodicals, directories, and associations.

4646 ■ Career Opportunities in Science
InfoBase Holdings Inc.
132 W 31st., 17 Fl.
New York, NY 10001-3406
Ph: (212)967-8800
Fax: (800)678-3633
E-mail: info@infobasepublishing.com
URL: http://factsonfile.infobasepublishing.com

Frequency: Latest edition 2008. **Price:** $49.50 Individuals hardcover. **Pages:** 344. **Description:** Susan Echaore-McDavid. Second edition, 2008. 332 pages. **Covers:** More than 80 jobs, such as biochemist, molecular biologist, bioinformatic specialist, pharmacologist, computer engineer, geographic information systems specialist, science teacher, forensic scientist, patent agent, as well as physicist, astronomer, chemist, zoologist, oceanographer, and geologist. **Includes:** Appendices of educational institutions, periodicals, directories, and associations.

4647 ■ Careers for Plant Lovers and Other Green Thumb Types
The McGraw-Hill Companies Inc.
PO Box 182604
Columbus, OH 43272
Ph: (212)512-2000
Free: 877-833-5524
Fax: (614)759-3749
E-mail: customer.service@mcgraw-hill.com
URL: http://www.mcgraw-hill.com

Description: Blythe Camenson. Second edition, 2004. $13.95. 160 pages. **Includes:** Appendices of selected list botancial gardens and arboreta for internships, summer employment, and volunteer opportunities, as well as a list of U.S. National Park Service regional offices. Appendices of selected list botancial gardens and arboreta for internships, summer employment, and volunteer opportunities, as well as a list of U.S. National Park Service regional offices. **Entries include:** Organization name, address.

4648 ■ Climate, Community and Biodiversity Alliance
2011 Crystal Dr., Ste. 500
Arlington, VA 22202
Ph: (703)341-2748
E-mail: info@climate-standards.org
URL: http://www.climate-standards.org

Description: Represents international non-governmental organizations (NGOs) and research institutes that promote integrated solutions to land management. Promotes responsible land management activities that will benefit local communities, minimize climate change and conserve biodiversity.

4649 ■ MarineBio Conservation Society
1995 Fairlee Dr.
Encinitas, CA 92023
Ph: (713)248-2576
E-mail: info@marinebio.org
URL: http://marinebio.org

Description: Works to protect marine life and the ocean for future generations. Creates an awareness of marine conservation issues and their solutions. Supports marine conservation scientists and students involved in the marine life sciences.

4650 ■ National Wildlife Federation
11100 Wildlife Center Dr.
Reston, VA 20190
Ph: (703)438-6000

Free: 800-822-9919
URL: http://www.nwf.org

Description: Serves as a member-supported conservation group, with over four million members and supporters. Federation of state and territorial affiliates, associate members and individual conservationist-contributors. Seeks to educate, inspire and assist individuals and organizations of diverse cultures to conserve wildlife and other natural resources and to protect the earth's environment in order to achieve a peaceful, equitable and sustainable future. Encourages the intelligent management of the life-sustaining resources of the earth and promotes greater appreciation of wild places, wildlife and the natural resources shared by all. Publishes educational materials and conservation periodicals.

4651 ■ Network of Conservation Educators and Practitioners
American Museum of Natural History
Center for Biodiversity and Conservation
Central Park West, 79th St.
New York, NY 10024
Ph: (212)769-5742
Fax: (212)769-5292
E-mail: ncep@amnh.org
URL: http://ncep.amnh.org

Description: Aims to improve the practice of biodiversity conservation. Promotes educational resources on managing and sustaining biological and cultural diversity. Provides opportunities for communication and interaction among conservation educators and practitioners.

4652 ■ Ocean Conservation Research
PO Box 559
Lagunitas, CA 94938
Ph: (415)488-0553
E-mail: info@ocr.org
URL: http://ocr.org

Description: Represents scientists, engineers and ocean advocates devoted to improve the environmental health of the sea. Seeks to understand and explore solutions to the growing problem of human generated noise pollution and its impact on marine animals. Promotes the recovery and long term viability of the sea through research focusing on conservation priorities and practices.

4653 ■ Orion Grassroots Network
187 Main St.
Great Barrington, MA 01230
Ph: (413)528-4422
URL: http://www.oriongrassroots.org

Description: Consists of grassroots organizations across the United States. Provides job listing for future green leaders. Offers job posting service on a fee basis.

4654 ■ Tropical Forest Group
519 Fig Ave.
Santa Barbara, CA 93101
E-mail: info@tropicalforestgroup.org
URL: http://tropicalforestgroup.org

Description: Promotes the conservation and restoration of the planet's remaining tropical forests. Supports research and development of policies that help maintain the planet's most vital biome. Provides assistance to projects that restore and conserve tropical forests.

4655 ■ *Annals of Medicine*
Informa Healthcare
52 Vanderbilt Ave., 7th Fl.
New York, NY 10017-3846
Ph: (212)520-2777
E-mail: healthcare.enquiries@informa.com
URL: http://informahealthcare.com/ann
Frequency: 4/yr. **Price:** £961 Institutions; $1,579
Institutions; €1,259 Institutions. **Description:** Journal
covering health science and medical education.

4656 ■ *Atmospheric and Climate Sciences*
Scientific Research Publishing
PO Box 54821
Irvine, CA 92619-4821
E-mail: acs@scirp.org
URL: http://www.scirp.org/journal/acs/
Frequency: Quarterly. **Price:** $156 Individuals.
Description: Journal publishing articles on climate
atmospheric science.

4657 ■ *CME Supplement to Emergency
Medicine Clinics of North America*
Elsevier Science Inc.
Secondary Publishing Division
650 Ave. of the Americas
New York, NY 10011
Ph: (212)633-3980
Free: 888-437-4636
Fax: (212)633-3975
URL: http://www.elsevier.com/wps/find/journalde-
scription.cws_home/709343/description#description
Frequency: 4/yr. **Price:** $212 Individuals. **Descrip-
tion:** Journal covering emergency medicine clinics.

4658 ■ *Discovery Medicine*
Discovery Medicine
10 Gerard Ave., Ste. 201
Timonium, MD 21093
Ph: (410)252-6229
Fax: (888)833-0526
E-mail: service@discoverymedicine.com
URL: http://www.discoverymedicine.com
Frequency: Bimonthly. **Price:** $599 Institutions
digital edition; $99.95 Individuals digital edition.
Description: Online journal that publishes articles on
diseases, biology, new diagnostics, and treatments
for medical professionals.

4659 ■ *Education & Treatment of Children*
West Virginia University Press
139 Stansbury Hall
Morgantown, WV 26506
Ph: (304)293-8400
Fax: (304)293-6585
E-mail: press@wvu.edu
URLs: http://wvupressonline.com/journals; http://www
.educationandtreatmentofchildren.net

Frequency: Quarterly. **Price:** $100 Institutions; $50
Individuals; $115 Institutions elsewhere; $65 Individuals elsewhere. **Description:** Periodical featuring
information concerning the development of services
for children and youth. Includes reports written for
educators and other child care and mental health
providers focused on teaching, training, and treatment effectiveness.

4660 ■ *Epidemiology*
Lippincott Williams & Wilkins
c/o Allen J. Wilcox, Ed.-in-Ch.
Snow Bldg., Ste. 606
331 W Main St.
Durham, NC 27701
Ph: (919)667-1688
Fax: (919)680-4599
E-mail: ronna.ekhouse@wolterskluwer.com
URL: http://journals.lww.com/epidem/pages/default
.aspx
Frequency: Bimonthly. **Price:** $360 Individuals; $914
Institutions; $189 Individuals in-training; $453 Other
countries; $955 Institutions, other countries; $202
Other countries in-training. **Description:** Professional
medical journal for epidemiologists and related
disciplines.

4661 ■ *Global Change, Peace & Security:
Peace, Security & Global change*
Routledge
711 3rd Ave., 8th Fl.
New York, NY 10017
Ph: (212)216-7800
Free: 800-634-7064
Fax: (212)564-7854
E-mail: book.orders@tandf.co.uk
URL: http://www.tandfonline.com/toc/cpar20/current
Frequency: 3/yr. **Price:** $188 Individuals print; $602
Individuals online only; $669 Individuals print & on-
line. **Description:** Journal promoting physical
therapy and integration.

4662 ■ *The IHS Primary Care Provider*
U.S. Department of Health and Human Services -
Indian Health Service
Reyes Bldg.
801 Thompson Ave., Ste. 400
Rockville, MD 20852-1627
Ph: (301)443-6394
Fax: (301)443-4794
E-mail: charles.grim@ihs.hhs.gov
URL: http://www.ihs.gov/provider
Frequency: Monthly. **Description:** Journal for health
care professionals, physicians, nurses, pharmacists,
dentists, and dietitians.

4663 ■ *Infection Control Today*
Virgo Publishing L.L.C.
3300 N Central Ave. Ste. 300
Phoenix, AZ 85012-2501
Ph: (480)990-1101

Fax: (480)990-0819
E-mail: mikes@vpico.com
URL: http://www.infectioncontroltoday.com
Description: Monthly. Online publication listing job
opportunities in the field of epidemiology.

4664 ■ *Infectious Diseases in Children: The
Pediatrician's No.1 Source*
SLACK Inc.
6900 Grove Rd.
Thorofare, NJ 08086-9447
Ph: (856)848-1000
Free: 877-307-5225
Fax: (856)848-6091
E-mail: idc@slackinc.com
URL: http://www.healio.com/pediatrics/news/print/
infectious-diseases-in-children
Frequency: Monthly. **Price:** $328 Individuals; $656
Individuals two years; $984 Individuals three years;
$525 Institutions; $1,050 Institutions two years;
$1,575 Institutions three years; $44 Single issue.
Description: Newspapers for physician.

4665 ■ *Injury*
Mosby Inc.
11830 Westline Industrial Dr.
Saint Louis, MO 63146-3326
Ph: (314)872-8370
Free: 800-325-4177
Fax: (314)432-1380
URL: http://www.journals.elsevier.com/injury/
Frequency: Monthly. **Price:** $255 Individuals print;
$1,549.33 Institutions online; $1,859 Institutions print.
Description: Journal publishing articles and
research related to the treatment of injuries such as
trauma systems and management; surgical
procedures; epidemiological studies; surgery (of all
tissues); resuscitation; biomechanics; rehabilitation;
anaesthesia; radiology and wound management.

4666 ■ *Journal of Environmental Pathology,
Toxicology and Oncology*
Begell House Inc.
50 Cross Hwy.
Redding, CT 06896
Ph: (203)938-1300
Fax: (203)938-1304
E-mail: orders@begellhouse.com
URL: http://www.begellhouse.com/journals/
0ff459a57a4c08d0
Price: $1,005 Institutions. **Description:** Journal
covering research and reviews of factors and condi-
tions that affect human and animal carcinogenesis.

4667 ■ *Journal of Hospital Medicine*
John Wiley & Sons Inc.
111 River St.
Hoboken, NJ 07030-5774
Ph: (201)748-6000
Free: 800-225-5945

Fax: (201)748-6088
E-mail: info@wiley.com
URL: http://onlinelibrary.wiley.com/journal/10.1002/
(ISSN)1553-5606
Frequency: 10/yr. **Price:** $827 U.S., Canada, and Mexico print only; $827 Institutions, other countries print only. **Description:** Journal on hospital medicine.

4668 ■ *Psychology of Violence*
American Psychological Association
750 First St. NE
Washington, DC 20002-4242
Ph: (202)336-5500
Free: 800-374-2721
Fax: (202)336-5812
E-mail: journals@apa.org
URL: http://www.apa.org/pubs/journals/vio/index.aspx
Frequency: Quarterly. **Price:** $65 Members; $89 Other countries members; $65 Students; $110 Nonmembers; $139 Other countries nonmembers; $441 Institutions; $490 Institutions, other countries. **Description:** Multidisciplinary research journal concerning topics on the psychology of violence and extreme aggression.

4669 ■ *Public Health Jobs Worldwide*
Carlyle Corp.
PO Box 6729
Charlottesville, VA 22906-6729
Ph: (434)985-6444
Free: 800-291-4618
Fax: (434)985-6828
E-mail: info@ineoa.org
URL: http://www.jobspublichealth.com

Description: Weekly. Electronic newspaper with current public health job openings in the United States and worldwide.

4670 ■ *PublicHealthJobs.net*
Association of Schools and Programs of Public Health
1900 M St. NW, Ste. 710
Washington, DC 20036
Ph: (202)296-1099
Fax: (202)296-1252
E-mail: info@asph.org
URL: http://www.publichealthjobs.net

Description: Online service that provides links to epidemiology job postings in the private sector, not-for-profit sector, and the federal government.

HANDBOOKS AND MANUALS

4671 ■ *Managerial Epidemiology and Theory and Practice*
Jones & Bartlett Learning
5 Wall St.
Burlington, MA 01803
Free: 800-832-0034
E-mail: info@jblearning.com
URL: http://www.jblearning.com

Description: G.E. Alan Dever. 2006. $128.95. 598 pages.

ONLINE JOB SOURCES AND SERVICES

4672 ■ Epidemiologist.com
URL: http://www.epidemiologist.com

Description: Serves as an online source of information for professional epidemiologists, including job listings in the field.

4673 ■ EpidemiologistJobs.org
URL: http://epidemiologistjobs.org

Description: Features job sites, company career pages and associations for epidemiologist jobs.

4674 ■ EpidemiologyCareers.com
URL: http://epidemiologycareers.com

Description: Provides a database of epidemiology jobs and resources for job seekers. Includes job title, company, location, job type, salaries, employer and recruiters.

4675 ■ GetEpidemiologistJobs.com
URL: http://www.getepidemiologistjobs.com

Description: Provides a resource for finding and filling epidemiologist positions.

TRADESHOWS

4676 ■ Society for Epidemiologic Research Conference
Society for Epidemiologic Research
PO Box 990
Clearfield, UT 84089
Ph: (801)525-0231
Fax: (801)525-6549
E-mail: membership@epiresearch.org
URL: http://www.epiresearch.org
Frequency: Annual. Primary Exhibits: Epidemiology equipment, supplies, and services.

OTHER SOURCES

4677 ■ American College of Epidemiology
1500 Sunday Dr., Ste. 102
Raleigh, NC 27607
Ph: (919)861-5573
Fax: (919)787-4916
E-mail: info@acepidemiology.org
URL: http://acepidemiology.org

Description: Medical professionals involved in the field of epidemiology. Promotes education in the practice of epidemiology and maintains professional standards in the field. Relates epidemiological issues to public policy. **Members:** Professional epidemiologists. **Purpose:** Promotes the professional development of epidemiologists through educational initiatives; advocates for policies and actions that enhance the science and practice of epidemiology; recognizes excellence in epidemiology; and develops and maintains an active membership representing all aspects of epidemiology. **Activities:** Provides job-listing services for epidemiologists.

4678 ■ Association for Professionals in Infection Control and Epidemiology
1275 K St. NW, Ste. 1000
Washington, DC 20005-4006
Ph: (202)789-1890
Free: 800-650-9570
Fax: (202)789-1899
E-mail: apicinfo@apic.org
URL: http://www.apic.org

Description: Physicians, microbiologists, nurses, epidemiologists, medical technicians, sanitarians, and pharmacists. Aims to improve patient care by improving the profession of infection control through the development of educational programs and standards. Promotes quality research and standardization of practices and procedures. Develops communications among members, and assesses and influences legislation related to the field. Conducts seminars at local level. **Members:** Professionals working in the field of infection control and epidemiology. **Purpose:** Promotes excellence in the prevention and control of infections and related adverse outcomes. **Activities:** Provides a forum for members to network, offers educational opportunities, produces publications, and serves as an advocate in governmental policymaking.

4679 ■ *Career Opportunities in Science*
InfoBase Holdings Inc.
132 W 31st., 17 Fl.
New York, NY 10001-3406

Ph: (212)967-8800
Fax: (800)678-3633
E-mail: info@infobasepublishing.com
URL: http://factsonfile.infobasepublishing.com
Frequency: Latest edition 2008. **Price:** $49.50 Individuals hardcover. **Pages:** 344. **Description:** Susan Echaore-McDavid. Second edition, 2008. 332 pages. **Covers:** More than 80 jobs, such as biochemist, molecular biologist, bioinformatic specialist, pharmacologist, computer engineer, geographic information systems specialist, science teacher, forensic scientist, patent agent, as well as physicist, astronomer, chemist, zoologist, oceanographer, and geologist. **Includes:** Appendices of educational institutions, periodicals, directories, and associations.

4680 ■ Council of State and Territorial Epidemiologists
2872 Woodcock Blvd., Ste. 303
Atlanta, GA 30341
Ph: (770)458-3811
Fax: (770)458-8516
E-mail: lmascola@ph.lacounty.gov
URL: http://www.cste.org/dnn

Description: State epidemiologists. Works to establish closer working relationships among members; consults with and advises appropriate disciplines in other health agencies; provides technical advice and assistance to the Association of State and Territorial Health Officials; works closely with Centers for Disease Control on epidemiology, surveillance, and prevention activities. **Members:** 1,050.

4681 ■ Emergency Management Institute
16825 S Seton Ave.
Emmitsburg, MD 21727
Ph: (301)447-1000
Fax: (301)447-1658
URL: http://training.fema.gov

Description: Offers access to listed employment opportunities in emergency management, including epidemiology, via the website.

4682 ■ *Health-Care Careers for the 21st Century*
JIST Publishing
875 Montreal Way
Saint Paul, MN 55102-4245
Ph: (317)613-4200
Free: 800-648-5478
Fax: (800)328-4564
E-mail: info@jist.com
URL: http://www.jist.com

Price: $9.95 Individuals Softcover. **Pages:** 448. **Covers:** Jobs for health care professionals and career opportunities for those pursuing a health-related career, organized into 80 careers in five groups. **Publication includes:** Appendixes listing job source resources and Web sites for health organizations.

4683 ■ International Society for Environmental Epidemiology
44 Farnsworth St.
Boston, MA 02210
Ph: (617)482-9485
Fax: (617)482-0617
E-mail: peters@helmholtz-muenchen.de
URL: http://www.iseepi.org

Members: Environmental epidemiologists and scientists worldwide. **Purpose:** Provides a forum for the discussion of problems unique to the study of health and the environment. **Activities:** Holds meetings and workshops, publishes newsletter, acts as liaison with academic, governmental, intergovernmental, non-profit, and business institutions. Serves as a forum for networking among its members.

4684 ■ Society for Epidemiologic Research
PO Box 990
Clearfield, UT 84089
Ph: (801)525-0231

Fax: (801)525-6549
E-mail: membership@epiresearch.org
URL: http://www.epiresearch.org

Description: Epidemiologists, researchers, public health administrators, educators, mathematicians, statisticians, and others interested in epidemiological research. Stimulates scientific interest in and promotes the exchange of information about epidemiological research.

4685 ■ Society for Healthcare Epidemiology of America
1300 Wilson Blvd., Ste. 300
Arlington, VA 22209
Ph: (703)684-1006

Fax: (703)684-1009
E-mail: info@shea-online.org
URL: http://www.shea-online.org

Description: Fosters the development and application of the science of healthcare epidemiology (broadly defined as any activity designed to study and/or improve outcomes in any type of healthcare institution or setting). **Members:** Professionals in all branches of medicine, public health, and healthcare epidemiology. **Purpose:** Advances the application of the science of healthcare epidemiology and works to maintain the quality of patient care and healthcare worker safety in all healthcare settings. **Activities:** Hosts meetings and provides a forum for networking among its members.

4686 ■ Society for Pediatric and Perinatal Epidemiologic Research
c/o Sonia Hernandez-Diaz, President-Elect
Harvard University
Kresge Bldg., Rm. 816B
677 Huntington Ave.
Boston, MA 02115
Ph: (617)432-3942
E-mail: shernan@haph.harvard.edu
URL: http://www.sper.org

Members: Professionals interested in the epidemiology of pregnancy, infancy, and childhood. **Purpose:** Fosters pediatric and perinatal epidemiologic research. **Activities:** Produces a newsletter and offers opportunities for networking among its members.

SOURCES OF HELP-WANTED ADS

4687 ■ Association News: America's Most-Read Magazine for State and Regional Associations
Schneider Publishing Company Inc.
11835 W Olympic Blvd., 12th Fl.
Los Angeles, CA 90064
Ph: (310)577-3700
Free: 877-577-3700
Fax: (310)577-3715
E-mail: info@schneiderpublishing.com
URL: http://www.associationnews.com/
Frequency: Monthly. **Price:** Free. **Description:** Magazine containing management and meeting plan information for association executives and meeting planners.

4688 ■ Special Events: The National Magazine for Special Events Professionals
Intertec Publishing
5 Penn Plz., 13th Fl.
New York, NY 10001-1810
Ph: (212)613-9700
Free: 800-795-5445
Fax: (212)613-9749
E-mail: bethany.weaver@penton.com
URLs: http://specialevents.com; http://www.penton
.com/OurMarkets/MarketingandMeetings.aspx
Frequency: Monthly. **Price:** $59 Free to qualified subscribers; $110 Canada; $106 Other countries; $200 Canada two years; $200 Other countries two years. **Description:** Magazine for special event professionals.

EMPLOYER DIRECTORIES AND NETWORKING LISTS

4689 ■ Meeting Professionals International Membership Directory
Meeting Professionals International
3030 Lyndon B. Johnson Fwy., Ste. 1700
Dallas, TX 75234-2759
Ph: (972)702-3000
Fax: (972)702-3070
E-mail: feedback@mpiweb.org
URL: http://www.mpiweb.org/Membership/directory
Frequency: Annual. **Price:** Free. **Covers:** Profiles of the members of Meeting Professionals International.

HANDBOOKS AND MANUALS

4690 ■ Association Meeting and Event Planners
Communication Publications & Resources
2807 N Parham Rd., Ste. 200
Richmond, VA 23294

Free: 800-780-4066
E-mail: customerservice@briefings.com
URL: http://www.briefingsmediagroup.com
Description: Patrick Snyder. 2010. $649.

4691 ■ FabJob Guide to Become an Event Planner
FabJob Inc.
4616-25th Ave. NE, No. 224
Seattle, WA 98105
Ph: (403)873-1018
Free: 888-322-5621
URL: http://www.fabjob.com
Description: Jan Riddell et al. $29.97 (e-book). 273 pages. Offers information on how to plan events, how to get an event planning job, how to start an event planning business, and more. Covers information on where to get creative ideas for events, how to develop the skills needed as an event planner, how to be certified as a professional event planner and more.

4692 ■ How to Start a Home-Based Event Planning Business
Globe Pequot Press Inc.
246 Goose Ln.
Guilford, CT 06437
Ph: (203)458-4500
Free: 888-249-7586
Fax: (800)820-2329
E-mail: gpp.info@globepequot.com
URL: http://www.globepequot.com
Description: Jill Moran. 2010. $18.95. 240 pages. This insider's handbook reveals how to start a successful business planning a wide variety of events from home.

4693 ■ Time Management for Event Planners
John Wiley & Sons Inc.
111 River St.
Hoboken, NJ 07030-5774
Ph: (201)748-6000
Free: 800-225-5945
Fax: (201)748-6088
E-mail: info@wiley.com
URL: http://www.wiley.com
Description: Judy Allen. 2005. $39.95. 256 pages. Time management skills to help event planners balance personal and professional lives.

EMPLOYMENT AGENCIES AND SEARCH FIRMS

4694 ■ Access Staffing
360 Lexington Ave., 8th Fl.
New York, NY 10017
Ph: (212)687-5440
Fax: (212)557-2544
URL: http://www.accessstaffingco.com

Description: Serves as a staffing firm covering accounting/financial, advertising, bilingual Japanese, creative, event planning, fashion/retail, healthcare/human services, human resources, information technology, insurance, legal, light industrial, and office support.

ONLINE JOB SOURCES AND SERVICES

4695 ■ Event-jobs.net
URL: http://www.event-jobs.net
Description: Serves as a job site dedicated to the event industry. Offers job openings and careers from the event industry including event planning jobs.

4696 ■ Event Planner Directory 123
URL: http://www.eventplannerdirectory123.com
Description: Directory of various vendor resources.

4697 ■ ProductionHub.com
URL: http://www.productionhub.com
Description: Serves as an online resource and industry directory for film, television, video, live event and digital media production. Features job opportunities, events, directory and other resources for the production industry.

TRADESHOWS

4698 ■ IAVM Annual Conference and Trade Show
International Association of Venue Managers
635 Fritz Dr., Ste. 100
Coppell, TX 75019-4442
Ph: (972)906-7441
Free: 800-935-4226
Fax: (972)906-7418
E-mail: vicki.hawarden@iavm.org
URL: http://www.iavm.org
Frequency: Annual. Presents exhibits to leaders who represent the entertainment, sports, conventions, trade, hospitality and tourism, movie theatres, and park and recreation departments.

OTHER SOURCES

4699 ■ Association of Collegiate Conference and Events Directors International
2900 S College Ave., Ste. 3B
Fort Collins, CO 80525
Ph: (970)449-4960
Free: 877-502-2233
Fax: (970)449-4965
E-mail: info@acced-i.org
URL: http://acced-i.org

Description: University conference and special events directors; professionals who design, coordinate, and market conferences and special events on college and university campuses. Dedicated to the professional development of the members; promotes the growth and distinction of the profession by uniting personnel and encouraging camaraderie. Promotes high standards of business and ethical conduct; works to foster communication, cooperation, and information sharing. Conducts research programs; collaborates with sister associations. Provides leadership opportunities through committee and board participation. Acts as an information clearinghouse; compiles statistics.

4700 ■ Career Opportunities in Advertising and Public Relations
InfoBase Holdings Inc.
132 W 31st., 17 Fl.
New York, NY 10001-3406
Ph: (212)967-8800
Fax: (800)678-3633
E-mail: info@infobasepublishing.com
URL: http://www.ferguson.infobasepublishing.com

Description: Field, Shelly. 2005. $49.50. 336 pages. **Includes:** Appendices of educational institutions, periodicals, directories, and associations. Appendices of educational institutions, periodicals, directories, and associations.

4701 ■ Career Opportunities in the Retail and Wholesale Industry
InfoBase Holdings Inc.
132 W 31st., 17 Fl.
New York, NY 10001-3406
Ph: (212)967-8800
Fax: (800)678-3633
E-mail: info@infobasepublishing.com
URL: http://www.ferguson.infobasepublishing.com

Description: Field, Shelly. Second edition, 2009. $49.50. 352 pages. **Includes:** Appendices of educational institutions, periodicals, directories, unions, and associations. Appendices of educational institutions, periodicals, directories, unions, and associations.

4702 ■ Careers for Fashion Plates and Other Trendsetters
The McGraw-Hill Companies Inc.
PO Box 182604
Columbus, OH 43272
Ph: (212)512-2000
Free: 877-833-5524
Fax: (614)759-3749
E-mail: customer.service@mcgraw-hill.com
URL: http://www.mcgraw-hill.com

Description: Lucia Mauro. 2008. $14.95 (paper). 176 pages. Describes career opportunities in fashion, entertainment, retail, and promotion, with advice from fashion professionals. **Includes:** Appendix of U.S. and Canadian organizations and fashion schools that provide information about job opportunities and educational requirements. Also includes bibliographical references. Appendix of U.S. and Canadian organizations and fashion schools that provide information about job opportunities and educational requirements. Also includes bibliographical references. **Entries include:** Name, address, URL.

4703 ■ Connected International Meeting Professionals Association
8803 Queen Elizabeth Blvd
Annandale, VA 22003
Ph: (512)684-0889
Fax: (267)390-5193
E-mail: cimpa@cimpa.org
URL: http://www.cimpa.org

Description: Meeting planners, incentive organizers, travel agents, tour operators, and seminar organizers in 42 countries. Works to improve the skills of professional conference and convention planners. Serves as a clearinghouse of information on new travel destinations and planning technologies, techniques, and strategies. Facilitates exchange of information

among Internet professionals. Produces a television program on travel and meetings. Conducts educational courses and awards Certified Internet Meeting Professional designation. Conducts research programs and placement service. Sponsors training courses on the Internet.

4704 ■ Event Service Professionals Association
191 Clarksville Rd.
Princeton Junction, NJ 08550
Ph: (609)799-3712
Fax: (609)799-7032
E-mail: info@acomonline.org
URL: http://www.acomonline.org

Description: Convention service directors and managers of hotels, convention centers, and convention bureaus. Works to increase the effectiveness, productivity and quality of meetings, conventions and exhibitions. Works to establish high ethical standards, improve professional management techniques and increase awareness of client, employer and provider needs. Maintains speakers' bureau, resource center, and placement services; compiles statistics. Conducts research and educational programs. **Members:** Convention service directors and managers of hotels, convention centers, and convention bureaus; suppliers of services and products to the convention bureaus; suppliers of services and products to the convention and meetings industry are affiliate members. **Purpose:** Works to increase the effectiveness, productivity, and quality of meetings, conventions, and exhibitions. Works to establish high ethical standards, improve professional management techniques, and increase awareness of client, employer, and provider needs. Holds summer conference. Maintains speakers' bureau, resource center, and placement services; bestows awards; compiles statistics. Conducts research programs.

4705 ■ Exposition Service Contractors Association
5068 W Plano Pkwy., Ste. 300
Plano, TX 75093
Ph: (972)447-8212
Free: 877-792-3722
Fax: (972)447-8209
E-mail: info@esca.org
URL: http://www.esca.org

Description: Works for the advancement of the exhibition, meeting and special events industries. Serves as a clearinghouse for the exchange of information between members and all other entities of the meetings, exhibition, and convention industries.

4706 ■ GCG Event Partners
125 Main St., Ste. H
Stoneham, MA 02180-1600
Ph: (781)279-9887
Free: 866-424-3836
E-mail: info@gcgeventpartners.com
URL: http://www.gcgeventpartners.com

Description: Network of event planning professionals.

4707 ■ Golf Tournament Association of America
PO Box 47405
Phoenix, AZ 85068
Ph: (602)524-7034
Free: 888-810-4822
Fax: (602)569-0680
E-mail: info@gtaaweb.org
URL: http://www.gtaaweb.org

Description: Represents the interests of golf tournament planners and coordinators. Provides golf tournament planning tips, education and resources to golf tournament planners and coordinators. Conducts golf tournament planning seminars across the country.

4708 ■ International Association of Corporate Entertainment Producers
PO Box 9826
Wilmington, DE 19809-9826
Ph: (312)285-0227
E-mail: info@iacep.com
URL: http://sites.google.com/site/iacepsite

Description: Aims to improve the lives and careers of professionals involved in the corporate entertainment industry. Strives to uphold the professional and ethical standards of the corporate entertainment industry. Provides education, networking, and leadership opportunities for its members.

4709 ■ International Association of Fairs and Expositions
3043 E Cairo St.
Springfield, MO 65802
Ph: (417)862-5771
Free: 800-516-0313
Fax: (417)862-0156
E-mail: iafe@fairsandexpos.com
URL: http://www.fairsandexpos.com

Description: Individuals, corporations, and organizations involved with the planning and management of fairs, expositions. **Members:** State associations of fairs representing 3200 state, district, and county agricultural fairs. Membership also includes 1300 individual fairs. Maintains library.

4710 ■ International Association of Venue Managers
635 Fritz Dr., Ste. 100
Coppell, TX 75019-4442
Ph: (972)906-7441
Free: 800-935-4226
Fax: (972)906-7418
E-mail: vicki.hawarden@iavm.org
URL: http://www.iavm.org

Description: Represents auditorium, arena, stadium, convention center, theatre, amphitheatre, and exhibit hall managers. Conducts seminars in auditorium, arena, and performing arts facility management. Maintains databank of documents pertaining to the industry. Sponsors 23 committees. **Members:** Auditorium, arena, stadium, convention center, theatre, amphitheatre, and exhibit hall managers. **Purpose:** Conducts seminars in auditorium, arena, and stadium management. Presents service awards to members. Maintains data bank of documents pertaining to the industry.

4711 ■ International Festivals and Events Association
2603 Eastover Terr.
Boise, ID 83706
Ph: (208)433-0950
Fax: (208)433-9812
E-mail: nia@ifea.com
URL: http://www.ifea.com/joomla1_5/index.php

Description: Provides professional development opportunities and fundraising ideas for individuals involved in the special events industry.

4712 ■ International Society of Meeting Planners
810 N Farrell Dr.
Palm Springs, CA 92262
Ph: (760)327-5284
Free: 877-743-6802
Fax: (760)327-5631
E-mail: support@assoc-hdqts.org
URL: http://ismp-assoc.org

Description: Meeting planners and related industries. Works to improve professionalism and competency in the industry as well as create new business opportunities for members. Provides networking opportunities. Offers professional designations: the RMP - Registered Meeting Planner, CDS Certified Destination Specialist, ITS - Incentive Travel Specialist, and CEP - Certified Event Planner.

4713 ■ International Special Events Society
330 N Wabash Ave.
Chicago, IL 60611
Ph: (312)321-6853
Free: 800-688-4737
Fax: (312)673-6953
E-mail: info@ises.com
URL: http://www.ises.com

Description: Fosters performance through education. Represents special event producers.

4714 ■ Meeting Professionals International
3030 Lyndon B. Johnson Fwy., Ste. 1700
Dallas, TX 75234-2759
Ph: (972)702-3000
Fax: (972)702-3070
E-mail: feedback@mpiweb.org
URL: http://www.mpiweb.org

Description: Meeting planners, full meeting consultants, and suppliers of goods and services. Works to: improve meeting method education; create an open platform for research and experimentation. Provides survey results, statistics, supply sources, and technical information; offers members assistance with specific problems; encourages information and idea exchange. Maintains professional code; standardizes terminology; monitors legislation affecting the industry. Maintains resource center. Conducts educational, charitable, and research programs. **Members:** More than 19,000, Meeting planners, full meeting consultants, and suppliers of goods and services; Works to: improve meeting method education; create an 'open platform' for research and experimentation; establish a B.S. degree in Meeting Planning at universities throughout the world. **Purpose:** Provides survey results, statistics, supply sources, and technical information; offers members assistance with specific problems; encourages information and idea exchange. Maintains professional code; standardizes terminology; monitors legislation affecting the industry. Organizes seminars and workshops. Maintains resource center.

4715 ■ National Coalition of Black Meeting Planners
4401 Huntchase Dr.
Bowie, MD 20720
Ph: (301)860-0200

Fax: (301)860-0500
E-mail: ncbmp.hq@verizon.net
URL: http://www.ncbmp.com

Members: Black meeting planners. **Purpose:** Purposes are to act as liaison with hotels, airlines, convention centers, and bureaus in an effort to assess the impact of minorities in these fields; assess the needs of the convention industry and how best to meet these needs; enhance members' sophistication in planning meetings; maximize employment of minorities in the convention industry. Maintains speakers' bureau. Conducts educational and research programs and compiles statistics on demographic employment of minorities in the convention industry. Maintains placement service. Bestows awards.

4716 ■ Professional Convention Management Association
35 E Wacker Dr., Ste. 500
Chicago, IL 60601-2105
Ph: (312)423-7262
Free: 877-827-7262
Fax: (312)423-7222
E-mail: deborah.sexton@pcma.org
URL: http://www.pcma.org

Description: Represents the interests of meeting management executives from associations, non-profit organizations, corporations, independent meeting planning companies, and multi-management firms who recognize the importance of meetings to their organization. Provides education, research and advocacy to advance the meetings and hospitality industry. Empowers members with the tools they need to succeed as meeting professionals and to promote the value of the industry to their organizations and the general public. **Members:** Convention coordinators, managers, and CEOs of non-profit organizations. **Purpose:** Works to increase the effectiveness of meetings and conventions through education and promotion of the meetings industry to the industry and the public. Conducts research and educational programs; offers placement service; maintains library; compiles statistics; bestows awards.

4717 ■ Religious Conference Management Association
7702 Woodland Dr., Ste. 120
Indianapolis, IN 46278

Ph: (317)632-1888
Fax: (317)632-7909
E-mail: rcma@rcmaweb.org
URL: http://www.rcmaweb.org

Members: Persons responsible for planning and/or managing major national-international religious conventions, meetings, and assemblies; associate members are individuals who directly support the logistics of religious meetings. **Purpose:** Promotes professional excellence through exchange of ideas, techniques, and methods of management.

4718 ■ Society of Government Meeting Professionals
908 King St., Ste. 200
Alexandria, VA 22314
Ph: (703)549-0892
Fax: (703)549-0708
E-mail: headquarters@sgmp.org
URL: http://www.sgmp.org

Description: Individuals involved in planning government meetings on a full- or part-time basis; suppliers of services to government planners. Provides education in basic and advanced areas of meeting planning and facilitates professional contact with other government planners and suppliers knowledgeable in government contracting. Maintains referral network of planning resources, information on latest techniques, and opportunities to inspect conference facilities. **Members:** 4,000.

4719 ■ Society of Independent Show Organizers
2601 Ocean Park Blvd., Ste. 200
Santa Monica, CA 90405
Ph: (310)450-8831
Free: 877-937-7476
Fax: (310)450-9305
E-mail: info@siso.org
URL: http://www.siso.org

Description: Represents independent show producers. Aims to meet the needs of CEOs and senior management of for-profit show producers in an environment where strategic and tactical decisions can be implemented to maximize profit potential. Provides peer networking opportunities, education, research, white papers, industry trends, and best practices in the events industry. Produces events globally including trade and consumer shows, industry and targeted conferences, and other face-to-face events.

4720 ■ *Beauty Launchpad: What's Taking Off in the World of Beauty*
Creative Age Publications Inc.
7628 Densmore Ave.
Van Nuys, CA 91406-2042
Ph: (818)782-7328
Free: 800-442-5667
Fax: (818)782-7450
URL: http://www.beautylaunchpad.com/index.php
Description: Fashion magazine.

4721 ■ *Clear*
Aekyung Industrial Company Ltd.
83 Guro 2-dong, Guro-gu
Seoul 152 840, South Korea
Ph: 82 02 818 1700
Fax: 82 02 818 1800
URL: http://www.clearmag.com
Frequency: Bimonthly. **Price:** $25 Individuals; $55 Canada; $105 Other countries. **Description:** Contemporary fashion and design journal.

4722 ■ *Daily Variety*
Variety Media Publications
6 Bell Yard
London WC2A 2JR, United Kingdom
Ph: 44 20 75205200
Fax: 44 20 75205237
E-mail: richard.woolley@variety.co.uk
URLs: http://www.reedbusiness.com/index.asp?layout=theListProfile&theListID=535&g roupid=28&industryid=28; http://www.variety.com
Frequency: Daily. **Price:** $329.99 Individuals. **Description:** Global entertainment newspaper (tabloid).

4723 ■ *JQ*
Adams Business Media
5 3rd St., Ste. 820
San Francisco, CA 94103
Ph: (415)839-5060
URL: http://www.jqintl.com/ME2/Default.asp
Frequency: Bimonthly. **Price:** $30 Individuals; $50 Two years; $45 Canada; $90 Canada two years; $110 Other countries USA. **Description:** Trade publication covering the fashion and retail industries.

4724 ■ *New York Moves*
New York Moves Magazine
4097 Lexington Ave.
New York, NY 10163
Ph: (212)396-2394
Fax: (212)202-7615
E-mail: info@newyorkmoves.com
URL: http://www.newyorkmoves.com
Frequency: 8/yr. **Price:** $16 Individuals. **Description:** Fashion and lifestyle magazine for professional women in and around New York City.

4725 ■ *Black Book Photography*
Black Book Marketing Group Inc.
740 Broadway, Ste. 202
New York, NY 10003
Ph: (212)979-6700
Free: 800-841-1246
Fax: (212)673-4321
E-mail: info@blackbook.com
URL: http://www.BlackBook.com
Frequency: Annual; Latest edition 2008. **Price:** $60 Individuals Deluxe Edition - Hardcover. **Publication includes:** Over 19,000 art directors, creative directors, photographers and photographic services, design firms, advertising agencies, and other firms whose products or services are used in advertising. **Entries include:** Company name, address, phone. Principal content of publication is 4-color samples from the leading commercial photographers. **Arrangement:** Classified by product/service.

4726 ■ *Fashion & Print Directory*
Peter Glenn Publications
306 NE 2nd St., 2nd Fl.
Delray Beach, FL 33483
Ph: (561)404-4290
Free: 888-332-6700
Fax: (561)892-5786
URL: http://www.pgdirect.com/fpintro.asp
Frequency: Annual; November; latest edition 47th. **Price:** $39.95 Individuals. **Pages:** 400. **Covers:** Advertising agencies, PR firms, marketing companies, 1,000 client brand companies and related services in the U.S. and Canada. Includes photographers, marketing agency, suppliers, sources of props and rentals, fashion houses, beauty services, locations. **Entries include:** Company name, address, phone; paid listings numbering 5,000 include description of products or services, key personnel. **Arrangement:** Classified by line of business.

4727 ■ *Model & Talent Directory*
Peter Glenn Publications
306 NE 2nd St., 2nd Fl.
Delray Beach, FL 33483
Ph: (561)404-4290
Free: 888-332-6700
Fax: (561)892-5786
URL: http://www.pgdirect.com
Frequency: Annual; Latest edition 26th. **Price:** $22.95 Individuals. **Covers:** Over 1,954 listings of model and talent agencies worldwide. **Arrangement:** Geographical.

4728 ■ *Break into Modeling for Under $20*
St. Martin's Griffin
175 5th Ave.
New York, NY 10010
Ph: (646)307-5151
E-mail: customerservice@mpsvirginia.com
URL: http://us.macmillan.com/breakintomodelingforunder20/JudyGoss
Description: Judy Goss. 2008. $14.95. 224 pages. Focuses on dispelling the misconception that breaking into the modeling business requires expensive head shots and other costly investments. Discusses how one can actually launch a modeling career for $20 or less and gives tips on determining type of model, taking pictures at home in the right poses and clothes, preparing what to say and do at casting calls, avoiding costly scams, and much more.

4729 ■ *Opportunities in Beauty and Modeling Careers*
The McGraw-Hill Companies Inc.
PO Box 182604
Columbus, OH 43272
Ph: (212)512-2000
Free: 877-833-5524
Fax: (614)759-3749
E-mail: customer.service@mcgraw-hill.com
URL: http://www.mcgraw-hill.com
Description: Susan Wood Gearhart. 2004. $13.95. 163 pages.

4730 ■ *Your Modeling Career: You Don't Have to Be a Superstar to Succeed*
Allworth Press
307 W 36th St., 11th Fl.
New York, NY 10018
Ph: (212)643-6816
Free: 800-491-2808
Fax: (212)643-6819
E-mail: pub@allworth.com
URL: http://www.allworth.com
Description: Debbie Press and Skip Press. Second edition, 2004. $24.95 (paper). 272 pages.

4731 ■ *Forte Models*
1231 Stationside Dr.
Oakland, FL 34787
Ph: (407)347-3810
E-mail: info@orlandomodelagent.com
URL: http://www.orlandomodelagent.com
Description: Specializes in providing models to convention and trade show clients.

4732 ■ *FashionCrossing.com*
URL: http://www.fashioncrossing.com
Description: Provides job listings and other

resources related to fashion employment opportunities.

4733 ■ **GetGigs.com**
URL: http://www.getgigs.com

Description: Seeks to provide an on-line experience for creative types, performing artists, and musicians around the world by integrating internet technologies into a one-stop information resource. Also functions as a creative directory and talent network.

4734 ■ **TalentNetworks.com**
URL: http://www.talentnetworks.com/index.html

Description: A business-to-business portal for the fashion, arts, and entertainment industries. Online site contains industry listings, portfolios and news items.

OTHER SOURCES

4735 ■ *Careers for Fashion Plates and Other Trendsetters*
The McGraw-Hill Companies Inc.
PO Box 182604
Columbus, OH 43272
Ph: (212)512-2000
Free: 877-833-5524
Fax: (614)759-3749
E-mail: customer.service@mcgraw-hill.com
URL: http://www.mcgraw-hill.com

Description: Lucia Mauro. 2008. $14.95 (paper). 176 pages. Describes career opportunities in fashion, entertainment, retail, and promotion, with advice from fashion professionals. **Includes:** Appendix of U.S. and Canadian organizations and fashion schools that provide information about job opportunities and educational requirements. Also includes bibliographical references. Appendix of U.S. and Canadian organizations and fashion schools that provide information about job opportunities and educational requirements. Also includes bibliographical references. **Entries include:** Name, address, URL.

Sources of Help-Wanted Ads

4736 ■ *American Banker: The Financial Services Daily*
SourceMedia Inc. - Banking Group
1 State St. Plz., 27th Fl.
New York, NY 10004
Ph: (212)803-8200
Free: 800-221-1809
Fax: (212)843-9600
E-mail: custserv@AmericanBanker.com
URLs: http://www.americanbanker.com; http://media.americanbanker.com/home.html
Frequency: Daily. **Price:** $995 Individuals. **Description:** Newspaper for senior executives in banking and other financial services industries. Coverage includes trends, analysis, and statistics of the legislative scene in Washington; finance; mortgages; technology; small business; and regional banking.

4737 ■ *Bank Advisor*
WiesnerMedia Financial Group
6160 S Syracuse, Ste. 300
Greenwood Village, CO 80111
Ph: (303)662-5200
URL: http://www.producersweb.com/r/baMag/d/main/
Frequency: Bimonthly. **Price:** Free. **Description:** Magazine for advisors, consultants, and managers working with consumers in a sales capacity within the banking industry.

4738 ■ *Bank Investment Consultant*
Bank Investment Consultant
One State Street Plz., 27th Fl.
New York, NY 10004
Ph: (212)803-8200
URL: http://www.bankinvestmentconsultant.com/
Description: Magazine featuring news and analysis for financial advisers and senior sales management in bank investment programs.

4739 ■ *Barron's: The Dow Jones Business and Financial Weekly*
Dow Jones & Company Inc.
1211 Ave, of the Americas
New York, NY 10036-8701
Ph: (212)416-2000
Free: 800-544-0422
Fax: (212)416-4348
E-mail: editors@barrons.com
URLs: http://online.barrons.com/public/main; http://www.dowjones.com
Frequency: Weekly (Mon.). **Price:** $149 Individuals print & online; $99 Individuals print only; $79 Individuals online only. **Description:** Business and finance magazine.

4740 ■ *The Bond Buyer*
SourceMedia Inc.
1 State Street Plz., 27th Fl.
New York, NY 10004

Ph: (212)803-6066
Free: 800-221-1809
Fax: (212)843-9635
E-mail: custserv@sourcemedia.com
URL: http://www.bondbuyer.com/
Frequency: Daily. **Description:** Newspaper focusing on municipal finance.

4741 ■ *Boomer Market Advisor*
Summit Business Media
5081 Olympic Blvd.
Erlanger, KY 41018
Ph: (859)692-2100
Free: 800-543-0874
Fax: (859)692-2000
URLs: http://www.advisorone.com; http://https://highline-sub.halldata.com/site/HLM000747XEnew/init.do
Frequency: Monthly. **Price:** $120 Canada; $160 Other countries. **Description:** Magazine for financial planners who work with variable products.

4742 ■ *Bulletin of Economic Research*
Blackwell Publishing Inc.
350 Main St.
Malden, MA 02148
Ph: (781)388-8200
Free: 800-216-2522
Fax: (781)388-8210
E-mail: journaladsusa@bos.blackwellpublishing.com
URL: http://as.wiley.com/WileyCDA/WileyTitle/productCd-BOER.html
Frequency: Quarterly. **Price:** $87 Individuals print & online; $1,153 Institutions print & online; $1,002 Institutions print or online; £449 Institutions print or online; £52 Individuals print & online; £517 Institutions print & online. **Description:** Journal focusing on the entire field of economics, econometrics and economic history.

4743 ■ *Business Credit: The Publication for Credit and Finance Professionals*
National Association of Credit Management
8840 Columbia 100 Pkwy.
Columbia, MD 21045-2158
Ph: (410)740-5560
Fax: (410)740-5574
E-mail: nacm_national@nacm.org
URL: http://www.nacm.org/index.php?option=com_content&view=category&layout=blog&id=77&Itemid=188
Frequency: 10/yr. **Price:** C$60 Canada; $65 Other countries; $54 Individuals; $48 Libraries; $7 Single issue. **Description:** Magazine covering finance, business risk management, providing information for the extension of credit, maintenance of accounts receivable, and cash asset management.

4744 ■ *CFMA Building Profits*
Construction Financial Management Association
100 Village Blvd., Ste. 200
Princeton, NJ 08540

Ph: (609)452-8000
Free: 888-421-9996
Fax: (609)452-0474
E-mail: sbinstock@cfma.org
URL: http://www.cfma.org
Frequency: Bimonthly. **Price:** Included in membership dues. **Description:** Features tax and accounting alerts, risk management updates, employment and career opportunities and technical articles.

4745 ■ *CFO Magazine*
CFO Publishing
111 W 57th St., 12th Fl.
New York, NY 10019
Ph: (212)698-9787
Fax: (212)459-3007
URL: http://www3.cfo.com
Description: Monthly. Free for U.S. residents; $120.00/year for subscribers outside U.S. Includes a job board for finance executives and employers.

4746 ■ *CFO: Magazine for Senior Financial Executives*
CFO Publishing
111 W 57th St., 12th Fl.
New York, NY 10019
Ph: (212)698-9787
Fax: (212)459-3007
URL: http://www.cfo.com/magazine/index.cfm/about?f=aboutus_nav
Frequency: Monthly. **Price:** $120 Other countries; Free. **Description:** Business magazine for small to mid-sized companies.

4747 ■ *Financial Week: The Newspaper of Corporate Finance*
Crain Communications Inc.
711 3rd Ave.
New York, NY 10017
Ph: (212)210-0100
E-mail: fw_editor@financialweek.com
URL: http://www.financialweek.com/apps/pbcs.dll/frontpage
Price: $79 Individuals; $149 Canada; $199 Other countries. **Description:** Newspaper focusing on the key decision-level financial officers within the 17,000 largest U.S.-based corporations regardless of business and industry.

4748 ■ *Forbes*
Forbes Inc.
60 5th Ave.
New York, NY 10011-8868
Ph: (212)366-8900
Free: 800-295-0893
Fax: (212)620-1863
E-mail: ekutner@forbes.net
URL: http://www.forbes.com
Frequency: Biweekly. **Price:** $19.99 Individuals; $22.25 Canada. **Description:** Magazine reporting on industry, business and finance management.

4749 ■ Government Finance Officers Association Newsletter
Government Finance Officers Association
203 N LaSalle St., Ste. 2700
Chicago, IL 60601-1210
Ph: (312)977-9700
Fax: (312)977-4806
E-mail: inquiry@gfoa.org
URL: http://www.gfoa.org/

Description: Semimonthly. Provides updates on current events, innovations, and federal legislation affecting public finance management for state and local government finance officers. Covers cash management, budgeting, accounting, auditing, and financial reporting, public employee retirement administration, and related issues. Recurring features include news of research, news of members, a calendar of events, and columns titled Career Notes and Employment Opportunities. Subscription includes the bimonthly magazine Government Finance Review.

4750 ■ Government Financial Management Topics
Association of Government Accountants
2208 Mt. Vernon Ave.
Alexandria, VA 22301-1314
Ph: (703)684-6931
Free: 800-AGA-7211
Fax: (703)548-9367
E-mail: agamembers@agacgfm.org
URL: http://www.agacgfm.org/publications/topics

Description: Weekly, Monday. Recurring feature includes job listings.

4751 ■ Healthcare Finance News
HIMSS Media
71 Pineland Dr., Ste. 203
New Gloucester, ME 04260
Ph: (207)688-6270
Fax: (207)688-6273
URL: http://www.healthcarefinancenews.com/

Frequency: Monthly. **Description:** Newspaper delivering essential information, market data, and industry news.

4752 ■ HFM Magazine
Healthcare Financial Management Association
3 Westbrook Corporate Ctr., Ste. 600
Westchester, IL 60154
Ph: (708)531-9600
Free: 800-252-4362
Fax: (708)531-0032
E-mail: memberservices@hfma.org
URL: http://www.hfma.org

Description: Monthly. $250/year for individuals; $151/year for institutions; $240/year for non-US subscribers. Magazine whose primary audience is senior and mid-level healthcare financial managers including CFOs, VPs of finance, controllers, revenue cycle directors, patient financial services managers, business office managers, and others responsible for healthcare financial management.

4753 ■ Journal of Financial and Quantitative Analysis
Journal of Financial & Quantitative Analysis
University of Washington
Foster School of Business
115 Lewis Hall
Seattle, WA 98195-3200
Ph: (206)543-4598
Fax: (206)616-1894
E-mail: jfqa@u.washington.edu
URL: http://www.jfqa.org/

Frequency: Bimonthly. **Price:** $105 Individuals print + online; $89 Individuals print only; $424 Institutions online only; $570 Institutions print + online. **Description:** Journal on research in finance.

4754 ■ The Journal of Taxation
RIA Group
395 Hudson St.
New York, NY 10014
Ph: (212)367-6300

Fax: (212)367-6314
URL: http://ria.thomson.com/estore/detail.aspx?ID =JTAX
Frequency: Monthly. **Price:** $410 Individuals print; $595 Individuals online/print bundle; $465 Individuals online. **Description:** Journal for sophisticated tax practitioners.

4755 ■ Mortgage Banking Magazine: The Magazine of Real Estate Finance
Mortgage Bankers Association
1919 M St. NW, 5th Fl.
Washington, DC 20036
Ph: (202)557-2700
Free: 800-793-6222
E-mail: membership@mba.org
URL: http://www.mortgagebankingmagazine.com

Frequency: Monthly. **Price:** $65 Members; $75 Nonmembers; $90 Other countries. **Description:** Magazine of the real estate finance industry.

4756 ■ National Association of Black Accountants--News Plus
National Association of Black Accountants
7474 Greenway Center Dr., Ste. 1120
Greenbelt, MD 20770
Ph: (301)474-6222
Free: 888-571-2939
Fax: (301)474-3114
E-mail: membership@nabainc.org
URL: http://www.nabainc.org

Frequency: Quarterly. **Price:** Included in membership. **Description:** Addresses concerns of black business professionals, especially in the accounting profession. Reports on accounting education issues, developments affecting the profession, and the Association's activities on the behalf of minorities in the accounting profession. Recurring features include member profiles, job listings, reports of meetings, news of research, and a calendar of events.

4757 ■ National Mortgage News
SourceMedia Inc.
1 State Street Plz., 27th Fl.
New York, NY 10004
Ph: (212)803-6066
Free: 800-221-1809
Fax: (212)843-9635
E-mail: custserv@sourcemedia.com
URL: http://www.nationalmortgagenews.com

Frequency: Weekly. **Description:** Newspaper for mortgage lenders and investment bankers.

4758 ■ Northwestern Financial Revlew
NFR Communications Inc.
7400 Metro Blvd., Ste. 217
Minneapolis, MN 55439
Ph: (952)835-2275
Fax: (952)835-2295
E-mail: info@northwesternfinancialreview.com
URL: http://www.northwesternfinancialreview.com

Frequency: 24/yr. **Price:** $99 Individuals. **Description:** Trade publication covering commercial banking.

4759 ■ Pensions & Investments
Crain Communications Inc.
711 3rd Ave.
New York, NY 10017
Ph: (212)210-0100
E-mail: info@crain.com
URL: http://www.pionline.com

Frequency: Biweekly; Daily. **Price:** $325 Individuals print; $1,495 Individuals daily email; $1,650 Individuals combo. **Description:** Magazine containing news and features on investment management, pension management, corporate finance, and cash management.

4760 ■ The Review of Asset Pricing Studies
Oxford University Press
2001 Evans Rd.
Cary, NC 27513
Free: 800-445-9714

Fax: (919)677-1303
URLs: http://raps.oxfordjournals.org/; http://sfsraps .org/

Price: $28 Single issue. **Description:** Journal publishing articles on the study of financial institutions related to asset prices.

4761 ■ The Review of Network Economics
Charles River Associates
John Hancock Tower, 200 Clarendon St., T-33
Boston, MA 02116-5092
Ph: (617)425-3000
Fax: (617)425-3132
URL: http://www.degruyter.com/view/j/rne

Frequency: Quarterly; Mar., June, Sept., and Dec. **Price:** $75 Individuals. **Description:** Journal covering new research in network economics and related subjects, including topics in the economics of networks, regulation, competition law, industrial organization etc.

4762 ■ Servicing Management: The Magazine for Loan Servicing Administrators
Zackin Publications Inc.
PO Box 2180
Waterbury, CT 06722
Ph: (203)262-4670
Free: 800-325-6745
Fax: (203)262-4680
E-mail: info@zackin.com
URL: http://www.sm-online.com/sm

Frequency: Monthly. **Price:** $48 Individuals; $72 Two years. **Description:** Trade magazine for mortgage professionals involved with mortgage loan servicing .

4763 ■ Strategic Finance: Leadership Strategies in Accounting, Finance, and Information Management
Institute of Management Accountants
10 Paragon Dr., Ste. 1
Montvale, NJ 07645-1774
Ph: (201)573-9000
Free: 800-638-4427
Fax: (201)474-1600
E-mail: ima@imanet.org
URL: http://www.imanet.org/publications.asp

Frequency: Monthly. **Price:** $210 Nonmembers; $48 Members; $25 Students; $18 Single issue back issue. **Description:** Magazine reporting on corporate finance, accounting, cash management, and budgeting.

4764 ■ U.S. Banker: Charting the Future of Financial Services
SourceMedia Inc.
1 State Street Plz., 27th Fl.
New York, NY 10004
Ph: (212)803-6066
Free: 800-221-1809
Fax: (212)843-9635
E-mail: custserv@sourcemedia.com
URL: http://www.americanbanker.com/usb.html

Frequency: Monthly. **Price:** $109 Individuals; $139 Individuals Canada; $139 Individuals outside North America; $179 Two years; $239 Two years Canada; $239 Two years outside North America. **Description:** Magazine serving the financial services industry.

EMPLOYER DIRECTORIES AND NETWORKING LISTS

4765 ■ America's Corporate Finance Directory
LexisNexis
9443 Springboro Pke.
Dayton, OH 45342
Ph: (937)865-6800
Free: 800-227-4908

Fax: (937)865-1211
E-mail: legalnotices@lexisnexis.com
URL: http://www.lexisnexis.com/corpfinancedir

Frequency: Annual; September. **Price:** $1,399
Individuals print. **Pages:** 1,452. **Covers:** Financial
personnel and outside financial services relationships
of 5,000 leading United States corporations and their
wholly-owned United States subsidiaries. **Entries
include:** Company name, address, phone, fax, telex,
e-mail addresses, stock exchange information, earnings, total assets, size of pension/profit-sharing fund
portfolio, number of employees, description of business, wholly-owned U.S. Subsidiaries of parent
company; name and title of key executives; outside
suppliers of financial services. **Arrangement:**
Alphabetical. **Indexes:** Financial responsibilities,
Standard Industrial Classification (SIC) code,
geographical, Personnel, private companies,
company name.

4766 ■ *The Bank Directory*
Accuity Inc.
4709 W Golf Rd.
Skokie, IL 60076-1231
Ph: (847)676-9600
Free: 800-321-3373
Fax: (847)933-8101
E-mail: custserv@accuitysolutions.com
URL: http://store.accuitysolutions.com/order.html

Frequency: Semiannual; June and December.
Price: $1,195 Individuals. **Covers:** In five volumes,
about 11,000 banks and 50,000 branches of United
States banks, and 60,000 foreign banks and
branches engaged in foreign banking; Federal
Reserve system and other United States government
and state government banking agencies; 500 largest
North American and International commercial banks;
paper and automated clearinghouses. Volumes 1
and 2 contain North American listings; volumes 3 and
4, international listings (also cited as 'Thomson
International Bank Directory; volume 5, Worldwide
Correspondents Guide containing key correspondent
data to facilitate funds transfer. **Includes:** Bank
operations information, asset ranking in state and
country, bank routing numbers in numeric sequence,
discontinued or changed bank names in geographical sequence. **Entries include:** For domestic banks--
Bank name, address, phone, telex, cable, date
established, routing number, charter type, bank holding company affiliation, memberships in Federal
Reserve System and other banking organizations,
principal officers by function performed, principal correspondent banks, and key financial data (deposits,
etc.). For international banks--Bank name, address,
phone, fax, telex, cable, SWIFT address, transit or
sort codes within home country, ownership, financial
data, names and titles of key personnel, branch locations. For branches--Bank name, address, phone,
charter type, ownership and other details comparable
to domestic bank listings. **Arrangement:** Geographical. **Indexes:** Alphabetical, geographical.

4767 ■ *CFA Institute--Membership Directory*
CFA Institute
560 Ray C. Hunt Dr.
Charlottesville, VA 22903-2981
Ph: (434)951-5499
Free: 800-247-8132
Fax: (434)951-5262
E-mail: info@cfainstitute.org
URL: http://www.cfainstitute.org

Frequency: Annual; January. **Price:** $150 per year.
Pages: 792. **Covers:** 38,000 security and financial
analysts who are practicing investment analysis.
Entries include: Name, firm affiliation and address,
phone, fax, e-mail. **Arrangement:** Alphabetical.

**4768 ■ *Corporate Finance Sourcebook: The
Guide to Major Capital Investment Sources
and Related Financial Services***
LexisNexis
9443 Springboro Pke.
Dayton, OH 45342
Ph: (937)865-6800

Free: 800-227-4908
Fax: (937)865-1211
E-mail: nrpsales@marquiswhoswho.com
URL: http://www.financesourcebook.com

Frequency: Annual; Latest edition 2010. **Price:** $695
Individuals list price; $556 Individuals. **Covers:**
Securities research analysts; major private lenders;
investment banking firms; commercial banks; United
States-based foreign banks; commercial finance
firms; leasing companies; foreign investment bankers
in the United States; pension managers; banks that
offer master trusts; cash managers; business insurance brokers; business real estate specialists; lists
about 3,500 firms; 14,500 key financial experts.
Entries include: All entries include firm name, address, phone, e-mail, and names and titles of officers, contacts, or specialists in corporate finance. Additional details are given as appropriate, including
names of major clients, number of companies
served, services, total assets, branch locations,
years in business. **Arrangement:** Classified by line
of business and then alphabetized within that line of
business. **Indexes:** Firm name, personnel name,
geographical.

4769 ■ *Directory of Trust Banking*
F1RSTMARK Inc.
25 Vintinner Rd.
Campton, NH 03223
Ph: (603)726-4800
Free: 800-729-2600
Fax: (603)726-4840
E-mail: info@firstmark.com
URL: http://www.firstmark.com/fmkdirs/acc_trust.htm

Price: $575 Individuals. **Covers:** 4,000 U.S. banks
and trust companies. **Entries include:** Contact
information, charter type, officer names and
responsibilities, holding company and owners, and
types of collective investment funds.

**4770 ■ *Directory of Venture Capital and
Private Equity Firms***
Grey House Publishing
4919 Rte. 22
Amenia, NY 12501
Ph: (518)789-8700
Free: 800-562-2139
Fax: (518)789-0556
E-mail: books@greyhouse.com
URL: http://www.greyhouse.com/venture.htm

Description: 2011. $685.00/regular; $450.00/library.
1,200 pages. Gives librarians, entrepreneurs and
others interested in the venture capital and private
equity fields information on the venture capital
industry. Features up-to-date, comprehensive data
on each firm including address, phone and fax
numbers, e-mail and web site addresses for both the
primary and branch locations. Contains details on the
firm's mission statement, industry group preferences,
geographic preferences, average and minimum
investments, and investment criteria. Offers five
indexes: the Geographic Index, Executive Name
Index, Portfolio Company Index, Industry Preference
Index, and College and University Index.

**4771 ■ *North American Financial
Institutions Directory***
Accuity Inc.
4709 W Golf Rd.
Skokie, IL 60076-1231
Ph: (847)676-9600
Free: 800-321-3373
Fax: (847)933-8101
E-mail: custserv@accuitysolutions.com
URL: http://store.accuitysolutions.com/order.html

Frequency: Semiannual; January and July. **Price:**
$955 Individuals. **Covers:** 15,000 banks and their
branches; over 2,000 head offices, and 15,500
branches of savings and loan associations; over
5,500 credit unions with assets over $5 million;
Federal Reserve System and other U.S. government
and state government banking agencies; bank holding, commercial finance, and leasing companies;
coverage includes the United States, Canada,

Mexico, and Central America. **Includes:** Bank routing
numbers in numeric sequence; maps; discontinued
banks. **Entries include:** Bank name, address,
phone, fax, telex, principal officers and directors,
date established, financial data, association memberships, attorney or counsel, correspondent banks, out-
of-town branch, holding company affiliation, ABA
transit number and routing symbol, MICR number
with check digit, credit card(s) issued, trust powers,
current par value and dividend of common stock,
kind of charter. **Arrangement:** Geographical.
Indexes: Alphabetical.

4772 ■ *Who's Who in Finance and Industry*
Marquis Who's Who L.L.C.
300 Connell Dr., Ste. 2000
Berkeley Heights, NJ 07922
Ph: (908)673-1000
Free: 800-473-7020
Fax: (908)673-1179
E-mail: finance@marquiswhoswho.com
URL: http://www.marquiswhoswho.com

Frequency: Biennial; latest edition 37th; 2009-2010.
Price: $349 Individuals. **Pages:** 1,264. **Covers:** Over
24,000 individuals. **Entries include:** Name, home
and office addresses, personal, career, and family
data; civic and political activities; memberships,
publications, awards. **Arrangement:** Alphabetical.

**4773 ■ *Women in Insurance and Financial
Services--Membership Directory***
Women in Insurance and Financial Services
136 Everett Rd.
Albany, NY 12205
Ph: (518)694-5506
Free: 866-264-9437
Fax: (518)935-9232
E-mail: office@wifsnational.org
URL: http://www.wifsnational.org

Covers: list of contact information of WIFS' members
who are devoted to helping women succeed in both
insurance and financial services.

HANDBOOKS AND MANUALS

4774 ■ *Accountants' Handbook*
John Wiley & Sons Inc.
111 River St.
Hoboken, NJ 07030-5774
Ph: (201)748-6000
Free: 800-225-5945
Fax: (201)748-6088
E-mail: info@wiley.com
URL: http://www.wiley.com

Description: D.R. Carmichael and Lynford Graham.
2012. $119.95. 1056 pages. Series covering ac-
counting and financial reporting of interest to accountants, auditors, financial analysts, and users of
accounting information.

**4775 ■ *Expert Resumes for Managers and
Executives***
Jist Works
875 Montreal Way
Saint Paul, MN 55102
Free: 800-648-5478
E-mail: info@jist.com
URL: http://www.jist.com/shop/product.php?productid
=16727

Description: Wendy S. Enelow, Louise M. Kursmark. 2012. $17.95. 274 pages. Contains a collection
of sample resumes and resume writing advice including how to create and use an electronic resume.
Contains an appendix that includes internet
resources for an online job search, writing cover letters, as well as a collection of sample letters.

4776 ■ *Great Jobs for Business Majors*
The McGraw-Hill Companies Inc.
PO Box 182604
Columbus, OH 43272
Ph: (212)512-2000

Free: 877-833-5524
Fax: (614)759-3749
E-mail: customer.service@mcgraw-hill.com
URL: http://www.mcgraw-hill.com

Description: Stephen Lambert. Third edition, 2008. $16.95 (paper). 240 pages.

4777 ■ Manager's Handbook: Everything You Need to Know about How Business and Management Work
Pearson Learning Group
145 S Mount Zion Rd.
Lebanon, IN 46052
Ph: (804)402-6933
Free: 800-526-9907
Fax: (800)393-3156
E-mail: pasley@pearsonlearning.com
URL: http://www.k12pearson.com

Price: $24.95. **Publication includes:** Principal content of publication is reference guide for new and experienced managers. **Indexes:** Alphabetical.

4778 ■ The Million-Dollar Financial Services Practice: A Proven System for Becoming a Top Producer
AMACOM Publishing
c/o American Management Association
1601 Broadway
New York, NY 10019-7434
Ph: (212)586-8100
Free: 800-714-6395
Fax: (518)891-0368
E-mail: pubs_cust_serv@amanet.org
URL: http://www.amacombooks.org

Description: David J. Mullen. 2007. $30.00 (hardback). 352 pages. Features information on how to become a financial advisor using the methods given in the book. Combines marketing, prospecting, sales, and time management techniques into a system that will help readers build a successful and lucrative practice.

4779 ■ Opportunities in Financial Careers
The McGraw-Hill Companies Inc.
PO Box 182604
Columbus, OH 43272
Ph: (212)512-2000
Free: 877-833-5524
Fax: (614)759-3749
E-mail: customer.service@mcgraw-hill.com
URL: http://www.mcgraw-hill.com

Description: Michael Sumichrast and Martin A. Sumichrast. 2004. $13.95 (paper). 160 pages. A guide to planning for and seeking opportunities in this challenging field.

4780 ■ Opportunities in Hospital Administration Careers
The McGraw-Hill Companies Inc.
PO Box 182604
Columbus, OH 43272
Ph: (212)512-2000
Free: 877-833-5524
Fax: (614)759-3749
E-mail: customer.service@mcgraw-hill.com
URL: http://www.mcgraw-hill.com

Description: I. Donald Snook. 2006. $13.95. 160 pages. Discusses opportunities for administrators in a variety of management settings: hospital, department, clinic, group practice, HMO, mental health, and extended care facilities.

4781 ■ Reinventing the CFO: How Financial Managers Can Reinvent Their Roles and Add Greater Value
Harvard Business Review Press
60 Harvard Way
Boston, MA 02163
Ph: (617)783-7400
Free: 800-795-5200
E-mail: custserv@hbsp.harvard.edu
URL: http://hbr.org/books

Description: Jeremy Hope. 2006. $29.95. Outlines

seven critical roles for CFOs to follow in order to streamline processes and regulate risk.

4782 ■ Your Successful Career as a Mortgage Broker
AMACOM Publishing
c/o American Management Association
1601 Broadway
New York, NY 10019-7434
Ph: (212)586-8100
Free: 800-714-6395
Fax: (518)891-0368
E-mail: pubs_cust_serv@amanet.org
URL: http://www.amacombooks.org

Description: David Reed. 2007. $18.95 (paper/ softback). 240 pages. Offers advice on licensing and educational requirements as well as guidance on the different career options available as a mortgage broker, mortgage banker, correspondent mortgage banker, and more. Provides tips on how to quote interest rates; get approved by wholesale lenders; negotiate the steps of the loan process; and market and prospect successfully.

EMPLOYMENT AGENCIES AND SEARCH FIRMS

4783 ■ 20-20 Foresight Executive Search Inc.
150 N Michigan Ave., Ste. 2800
Chicago, IL 60601
Ph: (708)246-2100
E-mail: bcavoto@202-4.com
URL: http://www.2020-4.com

Description: Executive search firm. Affiliate offices in California and Washington DC.

4784 ■ A-L Associates Inc.
60 E 42nd St., Ste. 1534
New York, NY 10036
Ph: (212)878-9000
URL: http://www.alassociatesltd.com

Description: Executive search firm.

4785 ■ A-lign Careers
2202 N Westshore Blvd., Ste. 200
Tampa, FL 33607
Ph: (940)648-5045
Free: 888-702-5446
URL: http://www.aligncareers.com

Description: Specializes in the recruitment of auditing, accounting, and finance personnel.

4786 ■ AC Lordi Search
235 Montgomery St., Ste. 630
San Francisco, CA 94104
Ph: (415)781-8644
E-mail: info@aclordi.com
URL: http://www.aclordi.com

Description: Executive search firm for finance and accounting. Uses referral-based outsourcing, affinity networking, and cold-calling to identify talented accounting professionals.

4787 ■ AccountSource
130 Milestone Way
Greenville, SC 29615
Ph: (864)213-8004
Fax: (864)213-9867
E-mail: recruiters@asijobs.com
URL: http://www.asijobs.com

Description: Acts as a premier placement service for accounting and finance professionals. Offers a wide variety of services including permanent placement, contract, and contract-to-hire staffing solutions.

4788 ■ Adams Inc. Financial Recruiting
17330 Wright St., Ste. 101
Omaha, NE 68130
Ph: (402)333-3009
Free: 800-536-4933

Fax: (402)333-3448
E-mail: info@adams-inc.com
URL: http://www.adams-inc.com

Description: Provides recruitment and candidate placement in the banking/financial, trust/investment, and credit card industries.

4789 ■ Advantage Group
350 N Old Woodward Ave., Ste. 218
Birmingham, MI 48009
Ph: (248)540-0400
Fax: (248)540-0401
E-mail: info@advantage-grp.com
URL: http://advantage-grp.com

Description: Specializes in the placement of accounting and financial executives.

4790 ■ AKS Associates Ltd.
PO Box 2863
Duxbury, MA 02331
Ph: (781)934-5333
Fax: (781)934-6333
E-mail: sandy@akssearch.com
URL: http://www.akssearch.com

Description: Senior search firm. Concentrates on the financial industry.

4791 ■ Allen Evans Klein International
305 Madison Ave.
New York, NY 10165
Ph: (212)983-9300
Fax: (212)983-9272
E-mail: info@allenevans.com
URL: http://www.allenevans.com

Description: Global Executive search firm.

4792 ■ Allerton Heneghan and O'Neill
1415 W 22nd St., Tower Fl.
Oak Brook, IL 60523
Ph: (630)645-2294
Fax: (630)645-2298
E-mail: info@ahosearch.com
URL: http://www.ahosearch.com

Description: Executive search firm.

4793 ■ American Executive Management Inc.
30 Federal St.
Salem, MA 01970
Ph: (978)744-5923
E-mail: execsearch@americanexecutive.us
URL: http://www.americanexecutive.us

Description: Executive search firm. Second location in Boston.

4794 ■ American Human Resources Associates Ltd.
PO Box 18269
Cleveland, OH 44118-0269
Ph: (440)317-0981
E-mail: ahra@ahrsearch.com
URL: http://www.ahrsearch.com

Description: Executive search firm. Focused on real estate, banking and credit & collection.

4795 ■ The Angus Group Ltd.
5080 Wooster Rd., Ste. 300
Cincinnati, OH 45226
Ph: (513)961-5575
Fax: (513)961-5616
URL: http://www.angusgroup.com

Description: Executive search firm.

4796 ■ Arlene Clapp Ltd.
4250 Park Glen Rd.
Minneapolis, MN 55416
Ph: (952)928-7474
E-mail: arlene@arleneclapp.com
URL: http://www.arleneclapp.com

Description: Executive search firm.

4797 ■ Ashton Lane Group
51 John F. Kennedy Pkwy., 1st Fl. W
Short Hills, NJ 07078
Ph: (212)372-9795
E-mail: info@ashtonlanegroup.com
URL: http://www.ashtonlanegroup.com
Description: Specializes in the recruitment of professionals in banking, insurance, and alternative investment industries.

4798 ■ ATR Finance
1230 Oakmead Pkwy., Ste. 110
Sunnyvale, CA 94085
Ph: (408)328-8000
E-mail: corporate@atr1.com
URL: http://www.atr-finance.com
Description: Serves as an executive placement firm for accounting and finance professionals. Offers career opportunities for finance and accounting professionals interested in either consulting or full-time positions.

4799 ■ Aureus Group
C&A Plz., 13609 California St., Ste. 100
Omaha, NE 68154-3503
Ph: (402)891-6900
Free: 888-239-5993
Fax: (402)891-1290
E-mail: omaha@aureusgroup.com
URL: http://www.aureusgroup.com
Description: Executive search and recruiting consultants specializing in accounting and finance, information systems and technology, health care administration, and wealth management.

4800 ■ The Bankers Register
1140 Ave. of the Americas, 14th Fl.
New York, NY 10036
Ph: (212)840-0800
Fax: (212)840-7039
Description: Specialists in the recruitment and placement of men and women in the banking community. Committed exclusively to: commercial banking, international banking, trust/investments, and thrift/mortgage banking.

4801 ■ Bartholdi Partners
PO Box 930
Gainesville, VA 20156-0930
Ph: (703)476-5519
E-mail: info@bartholdisearch.com
URL: http://www.bartholdisearch.com
Description: Executive search firm. Affiliates in San Francisco; San Jose; Phoenix; Scottsdale; Parker, CO; and Framingham, MA.

4802 ■ Bialecki Inc.
780 3rd Ave., Ste. 4203
New York, NY 10017
Ph: (212)755-1090
Fax: (212)755-1130
E-mail: linda@bialecki.com
URL: http://www.bialecki.com
Description: Senior executive search firm focused on the financial industry.

4803 ■ Bolton Group
3500 Piedmont Rd., Ste. 340
Atlanta, GA 30305
Ph: (404)228-4280
Fax: (404)228-2060
URL: http://www.boltongroup.com
Description: Serves as a specialty niche search firm focusing solely in the areas of accounting and finance. Partners with progressive organizations throughout the country, providing accounting and finance specialists in a variety of areas including accounting, finance, tax, treasury, audit/SOX, and financial systems.

4804 ■ Brandjes & Associates
721 Cliveden Rd.
Pikesville, MD 21208-4715

Ph: (410)484-5423
Free: 877-485-8193
Fax: (410)484-6140
Description: Executive Recruiting for the Financial Services Industry.

4805 ■ The Burling Group Ltd.
600 N Kingsbury St., Ste. 1507
Chicago, IL 60654
Ph: (312)397-0888
E-mail: web@burlinggroup.com
URL: http://www.burlinggroup.com
Description: Executive search firm.

4806 ■ Butterfass, Pepe & MacCallan Inc.
PO Box 179
Franklin Lakes, NJ 07417
Ph: (201)560-9500
Fax: (201)560-9506
E-mail: staff@butterfasspepe.com
URL: http://www.bpmi.com
Description: Executive search firm.

4807 ■ Buxbaum Rink Consulting L.L.C.
1 Bradley Rd., Ste. 901
Woodbridge, CT 06525-2296
Ph: (203)389-5949
Fax: (203)397-0615
Description: Personnel consulting firms offer contingency search, recruitment, and placement of accounting and finance, as well as other business management positions. In addition to serving these two major career areas, also provides similar services to operations, marketing and human resources executives. Industries served: manufacturing, financial services, and service.

4808 ■ Canny, Bowen Inc.
400 Madison Ave., Ste. 11D
New York, NY 10017-1925
Ph: (212)949-6611
Fax: (212)949-5191
E-mail: main@cannybowen.com
URL: http://www.cannybowen.com
Description: Executive search firm.

4809 ■ Career Advocates International
1539 Ave. A
Katy, TX 77493
Ph: (281)371-3917
E-mail: hank@careeradvocates.org
URL: http://www.careeradvocates.org
Description: Provides permanent placement and temporary staffing for executive and staff level positions. Specializes in multiple niches including: sales and marketing, accounting and financial services, banking, communications, human resources, chemicals, oil and gas, medical and dental, legal, information technology, energy, technology, engineering, manufacturing, construction, and light industrial.

4810 ■ Carrington & Carrington Ltd.
39 S LaSalle St., Ste. 400
Chicago, IL 60603-1557
Ph: (312)606-0015
Fax: (312)606-0501
E-mail: mcarrington@cclltd.com
URL: http://www.carringtonandcarrington.com
Description: Executive search firm.

4811 ■ CarterBaldwin
200 Mansell Ct. E, Ste. 450
Roswell, GA 30076
Ph: (678)448-0000
Free: 866-781-6844
E-mail: jdelikat@carterbaldwin.com
URL: http://www.carterbaldwin.com
Description: Executive search firm.

4812 ■ Casey Accounting and Finance Resources
4902 Tollview Dr.
Rolling Meadows, IL 60008
Ph: (224)232-5925
E-mail: info@caseyresources.com
URL: http://www.caseyresources.com
Description: Specializes in the placement of accounting and finance professionals for direct hire, temp-to-hire, project staffing and temporary services.

4813 ■ Catalyst Resource Group, LLC
2050 Marconi Dr., Ste. 300
Alpharetta, GA 30005
Ph: (678)366-3500
Free: 877-746-3400
Fax: (678)366-9710
E-mail: info@catalystresourcegroup.com
URL: http://www.catalystresourcegroup.com
Description: Serves as an executive search firm specializing in the placement of accounting and finance professionals.

4814 ■ Centennial, Inc.
8044 Montgomery Rd., Ste. 260
Cincinnati, OH 45236
Ph: (513)366-3760
Fax: (513)366-3761
URL: http://www.centennialinc.com
Description: Serves as an executive search firm specializing in the areas of executive and general management, accounting and finance, human resources, information technology, manufacturing, engineering, marketing and advertising, not-for-profit, sales and business development, and supply chain and logistics.

4815 ■ Chanko-Ward Ltd.
2 W 45th St., Ste. 1201
New York, NY 10036
Ph: (212)869-4040
Fax: (212)869-0281
E-mail: info@chankoward.com
URL: http://www.chankoward.com
Description: Primarily engaged in executive recruiting for individuals and corporations; where disciplines of accounting; planning, mergers and acquisitions; finance; or management information systems required.

4816 ■ Charles Aris, Inc.
300 N Greene St., Ste. 1800
Greensboro, NC 27401
Ph: (336)378-1818
Fax: (336)378-0129
E-mail: info@charlesaris.com
URL: http://www.charlesaris.com
Description: Provides executive search and placement services in the areas of consumer packaged goods, retail, strategy/business development, global life sciences, healthcare, chemicals, textiles/apparel, private equity, and business services.

4817 ■ Choi & Burns LLC
156 W 56th St., 18th Fl.
New York, NY 10019
Ph: (212)755-7051
Fax: (212)335-2610
E-mail: info@choiburns.com
URL: http://www.choiburns.com
Description: Executive search firm focuses on the financial industry.

4818 ■ Clovis, LLC
10411 Motor City Dr., Ste. 450
Bethesda, MD 20817
Ph: (301)365-8480
Free: 888-925-6847
Fax: (301)576-3579
E-mail: solutions@clovisgroup.com
URL: http://www.clovisgroup.com
Description: Serves as recruitment outsourcing

staffing firm for information technology, accounting, and finance professionals.

4819 ■ Coffou Partners Inc.
880 N Lake Shore Dr., No. 13CD
Chicago, IL 60611
Ph: (312)867-1781
E-mail: info@coffou.com
URL: http://www.coffou.com
Description: Executive search firm.

4820 ■ Consultants to Executive Management Company Ltd.
20 S Clark St., Ste. 610
Chicago, IL 60603
Ph: (312)855-1500
Free: 800-800-2362
Fax: (312)855-1510
Description: National personnel consultancy specializes in executive search with focus on accounting and finance, management information systems, professional medical and real estate fields. Industries served: All.

4821 ■ The Consulting Group
420 Lexington Ave.
New York, NY 10017
Ph: (212)751-8484
E-mail: mitchell@consultinggroupny.com
URL: http://www.consultinggroupny.com
Description: Executive search firm.

4822 ■ Cornell Global
PO Box 7113
Wilton, CT 06897
Ph: (203)762-0730
E-mail: info@cornellglobal.com
URL: http://www.cornellglobal.com
Description: Executive search firm with areas of expertise in the following areas: advertising, public relations, marketing, sales, finance and accounting, risk management, private equity and venture capital, construction, industrial, manufacturing, life sciences, publishing, information technology, engineering, human resources, legal, and logisitics.

4823 ■ The Corporate Source Group Inc.
5420 Bay Center Dr., Ste. 105
Tampa, FL 33609
Ph: (813)286-4422
Fax: (978)475-6800
E-mail: inquiry@csg-search.com
URL: http://www.csg-search.com
Description: Executive search firm branches in Boston, MA; Chicago, IL; Los Angeles, CA; New York, NY; Tampa, FL; Washington, DC.

4824 ■ Crowe Horwath L.L.P.
330 E Jefferson Blvd.
South Bend, IN 46624-0007
Ph: (574)232-3992
Fax: (574)236-8692
URL: http://www.crowehorwath.com
Description: Offers accounting and consulting services for the automotive, agricultural, commercial, construction, financial institutions, government, health care, manufacturing, and transportation industries.

4825 ■ CTPartners
28601 Chagrin Blvd., Ste. 600
Cleveland, OH 44122
Ph: (216)682-3200
Free: 800-380-9444
Fax: (216)464-6160
E-mail: comments@ctnet.com
URL: http://www.ctnet.com
Description: Executive search firm. Eight branches spanning the USA.

4826 ■ CyberCoders, Inc.
6591 Irvine Center Dr., Ste. 200
Irvine, CA 92618

Ph: (949)885-5151
Fax: (949)885-5150
E-mail: info@cybercoders.com
URL: http://www.cybercoders.com
Description: Recruitment and job search firm specializing in engineering, executive, financial, accounting, and sales.

4827 ■ Darwin Rhodes
48 Wall St., 11th Fl.
New York, NY 10005
Ph: (212)918-4770
Fax: (212)918-4801
E-mail: newyork@darwinrhodes.com
URL: http://www.darwinrhodes.com
Description: Specializes in the placement of actuarial, employee benefits, insurance and financial planning professionals. Provides clients with a local recruitment and executive search service that are tailored to their particular goals and focus.

4828 ■ Deerfield Associates
572 Washington St., Ste. 15
Wellesley, MA 02482
Ph: (781)237-2800
E-mail: doug@deerfieldassociates.com
URL: http://www.deerfieldassociates.com
Description: Executive search firm.

4829 ■ Karen Dexter & Associates Inc.
2012 Chestnut Ave. N, Ste. 29
Wilmette, IL 60091-1512
Ph: (847)853-9500
Fax: (847)256-7108
Description: Training and development consultant offering interpersonal skills training and one on one performance counseling for employees of large organizations. Industries served: Advertising, banking and finance, consumer products, entertainment, food and beverage, health care, legal profession, manufacturing, government agencies, publishing and broadcasting.

4830 ■ DGL Consultants
3492 Hill Cir.
Colorado Springs, CO 80904
Ph: (719)634-7041
E-mail: info@dglconsultants.com
URL: http://www.dglconsultants.com
Description: Executive search firm with primary expertise in the financial services industry.

4831 ■ DLG Associates Inc.
2210 Roswell Ave., No. 103
Charlotte, NC 28207
Ph: (704)372-2155
Fax: (704)372-2188
E-mail: dguilford@dlgassociates.com
URL: http://www.dlgassociates.com
Description: Executive search firm.

4832 ■ Douglas-Allen Inc.
Tower Square, 24th Fl.
Springfield, MA 01115
Ph: (413)739-0900
E-mail: research@douglas-allen.com
URL: http://www.douglas-allen.com
Description: Executive search firm.

4833 ■ Dowd Associates Inc.
777 Westchester Ave., Ste. 120
White Plains, NY 10604
Ph: (914)251-1515
E-mail: mail@dowdassociates.com
URL: http://www.dowdassociates.com
Description: Specializes in the recruitment of senior level financial professionals.

4834 ■ Eileen Finn & Associates Inc.
230 Park Ave., Fl. 10
New York, NY 10169
Ph: (212)687-1260

Fax: (212)551-1473
E-mail: eileen@eileenfinn.com
URL: http://www.eileenfinn.com
Description: Executive search firm.

4835 ■ Elinvar
1804 Hillsborough St.
Raleigh, NC 27605
URL: http://www.elinvar.com
Description: Accounting, finance, and human resources executive search firm.

4836 ■ Epsen, Fuller & Associates LLC
Two Tempe Wick Rd., Ste. 327
Mendham, NJ 07945
Free: 888-800-9931
URL: http://www.epsenfuller.com
Description: Executive search firm.

4837 ■ Essex Consulting Group Inc.
PO Box 550
Essex, MA 01929
Ph: (978)337-6633
E-mail: brad@essexsearch.com
URL: http://www.essexsearch.com
Description: Executive search firm.

4838 ■ Ethos Consulting L.L.C.
3219 E Camelback Rd., Ste. 515
Phoenix, AZ 85018
Ph: (480)296-3801
Fax: (480)664-7270
E-mail: conrad@ethosconsulting.com
URL: http://www.ethosconsulting.com
Description: Executive search firm. Second branch in Scottsdale, AZ.

4839 ■ Executive Dimensions
5820 Main St., Ste. 403
Williamsville, NY 14221
Ph: (716)632-9034
Fax: (716)632-2889
E-mail: execsearch@executivedimensions.com
URL: http://www.executivedimensions.com
Description: Executive search firm.

4840 ■ Executive Search Consultants Ltd.
3030 N Josey Ln., Ste. 101
Carrollton, TX 75007-5339
Ph: (972)394-4131
Fax: (972)394-2111
Description: Firm offers executive recruitment to the transportation, computer manufacturing, health and beauty aids, consumer package goods and financial service industries.

4841 ■ The Executive Source Inc.
55 5th Ave., 19th Fl.
New York, NY 10003
Ph: (212)691-5505
Fax: (212)691-9839
E-mail: tes1@executivesource.com
URL: http://www.executivesource.com
Description: Executive search firm.

4842 ■ Ferrari Search Group
200 E End Ave., Ste. 5N
New York, NY 10128
Ph: (212)289-5099
Fax: (716)386-2398
E-mail: contactus@ferrarisearchgroup.com
URL: http://www.ferrarisearchgroup.com
Description: Executive search firm.

4843 ■ Financial Professionals
4100 Spring Valley Rd., Ste. 250
Dallas, TX 75244
Ph: (972)991-8999
Fax: (972)702-0776
E-mail: response@fpstaff.net
URL: http://www.fpstaff.net

Description: Executive search consultants with additional offices in Forth Worth and Houston.

4844 ■ Financial Search Group, Ltd.
307 Fourth Ave., Ste. 810
Pittsburgh, PA 15222
Ph: (412)288-0505
Fax: (412)288-0699
E-mail: fsgltd@fsgltd.com
URL: http://www.fsgltd.com

Description: Provides accounting and financial staffing services on a wide variety of companies from contingency or retainer basis.

4845 ■ Foster McKay Group
30 Vreeland Rd.
Florham Park, NJ 07932
Ph: (973)966-0909
Fax: (973)966-6925
E-mail: careers@fostermckaynj.com
URL: http://www.fostermckay.com

Description: Executive search firm that specializes in placing financial, accounting, and tax professionals.

4846 ■ Frank Palma Associates
17 Beechwood Ln.
Kinnelon, NJ 07405
Ph: (973)838-9490
Fax: (973)492-5639
E-mail: fpalma@fpassocs.com
URL: http://www.fpassocs.com

Description: Executive search firm. Additional location in Duluth, GA.

4847 ■ Gans, Gans and Associates
7445 Quail Meadow Rd.
Plant City, FL 33565-3314
Ph: (813)986-4441
Fax: (813)986-4775
E-mail: simone@gansgans.com
URL: http://www.gansgans.com

Description: A human resources firm that specializes in executive search, human resources, management consulting, diversity consulting and resume assessment. Takes a personal approach in the development of tailored programs that consider the corporate culture, history and objectives of client. Industries served: consulting, financial services, legal, insurance, engineering, healthcare, manufacturing, utilities and the public sector.

4848 ■ General Ledger Resources
13280 Evening Creek Dr. S, Ste. 225
San Diego, CA 92128
Ph: (858)391-1017
E-mail: atheodore@gl-resources.com
URL: http://www.gl-resources.com

Description: Serves as a finance and accounting professional services firm with practice areas in consulting services and search and placement.

4849 ■ GK Finance
7242 Metro Blvd., Ste. 100
Edina, MN 55439
Ph: (952)835-5550
Fax: (952)835-7294
E-mail: info@georgekonik.com
URL: http://www.gkastaffing.com/index_financial.php

Description: Specializes in placing qualified candidates in finance and accounting positions. Offers three staffing options: contract (temporary) staffing, contract-to-direct, and direct hire opportunities from entry to senior or management level candidates.

4850 ■ The Hanover Consulting Group
11707 Hunters Run Dr.
Hunt Valley, MD 21030
Ph: (410)785-1912
Fax: (410)785-1913
E-mail: info@thehanovergroup.net
URL: http://www.thehanovergroup.net

Description: Specializes in finding, evaluating, and selecting top talent for the banking and trust industries.

4851 ■ Harder Consulting Inc.
3429 Executive Center Dr., Ste. 101
Austin, TX 78731
Ph: (512)479-0000
Fax: (512)372-9900
E-mail: projects@harderconsulting.com
URL: http://www.harderconsulting.com

Description: A professional employment solutions firm specializing in the areas of accounting, finance, banking and human resources.

4852 ■ International Insurance Consultants Inc.
645 SE 10th St.
Deerfield Beach, FL 33441
Ph: (954)421-0122
Fax: (954)449-0497
E-mail: rc@iicuri.com
URL: http://www.insurancerecruitersusa.com

Description: Offers executive search to the insurance industry. Clients include insurance companies, brokers, consultants and investment banks. Industries served: insurance and financial services industries.

4853 ■ International Search
9717 E 42nd St.
Tulsa, OK 74147-0898
Ph: (918)627-9070
Fax: (918)524-8604

Description: Personnel consulting group provides placement expertise in engineering, accounting, and data processing. Industries served: Energy, manufacturing, oil and gas, and services.

4854 ■ Kforce Inc.
1001 E Palm Ave.
Tampa, FL 33605-3551
Ph: (813)552-5000
Free: 877-453-6723
Fax: (813)552-2493
URL: http://www.kforce.com

Description: Executive search firm specializing in the financial services, insurance, health care, and pharmaceuticals industries.

4855 ■ KLR Executive Search Group L.L.C.
951 N Main St.
Providence, RI 02904
Ph: (401)274-2001
Fax: (401)831-4018
E-mail: info@klrsearchgroup.com
URL: http://www.klrsearchgroup.com

Description: Career recruitment firm specializes in the placement of accounting and financial and information technology professionals.

4856 ■ Kramer Executive Resources, Inc.
17 W 67th St., No. 8A
New York, NY 10023
Ph: (917)923-0160
E-mail: info@kramerexec.com
URL: http://www.kramerexec.com

Description: Specializes in the recruitment of accounting, tax, and financial professionals in the New York metropolitan tri-state region.

4857 ■ Milo Research
305 Madison Ave., Ste. 1762
New York, NY 10165-6227
Ph: (212)972-2780
Fax: (212)983-5854
E-mail: miloresearch@compuserve.com

Description: Human resources firm helps executives find work in the publishing, finance, telecommunications, direct mail and consumer products fields.

4858 ■ Houser Martin Morris
110th Ave. NE, 110 Atrium Pl., Ste. 580
Bellevue, WA 98004
Ph: (425)453-2700
Fax: (425)453-8726
E-mail: info@houser.com
URL: http://www.houser.com

Description: Focus is in the areas of retained executive search, professional, and technical recruiting. Areas of specialization include software engineering, sales and marketing, information technology, legal, human resources, accounting and finance, manufacturing, factory automation and engineering.

4859 ■ Neal Management Inc.
450 7th Ave., Ste. 923
New York, NY 10123-0101
Ph: (212)686-1686
Fax: (212)686-1590

Description: An executive search firm dedicated to the placement of financial professionals.

4860 ■ Oliver & Rozner Associates
598 Madison Ave., Ste. 11
New York, NY 10022
Ph: (212)688-1850

Description: Provider of recruitment solutions. It is engaged in marketing, advertising, data processing, research and development services.

4861 ■ L.J. Parrish & Associates Inc.
PO Box 874
Charles Town, WV 25414
Ph: (304)725-3834
Fax: (301)733-5155

Description: Executive search and human resource consulting firm specializing in financial, general management, and operations management positions. Industries served: All private industry, public accounting firms, and government.

4862 ■ Pate Resources Group Inc.
505 Orleans St., Ste. 300
Beaumont, TX 77701-3224
Ph: (409)833-4514
Fax: (409)833-4646

Description: Offers executive search and recruiting services to professionals who include physicians, health care administrators, accountants, financial managers; chemical, mechanical, industrial, and electrical engineers; sales and marketing managers; human resources administrators, and general managers and top executives in numerous disciplines. Industries served: health care, petrochemicals, accounting, utility, legal and municipalities.

4863 ■ Penn Hill Associates Inc.
14323 Ocean Hwy., Ste. 4131
Pawleys Island, SC 29585-4817
Ph: (843)237-8988
Fax: (843)237-9220
E-mail: janette@pennhillassociates.com

Description: Offers executive search services for consumer finance companies. Industries served: consumer finance, home equity and auto financing.

4864 ■ Penn Search Inc.
1045 1st Ave., Ste. 110
King of Prussia, PA 19406
Ph: (610)964-8820
Fax: (610)964-8916
E-mail: charlied@pennsearch.com
URL: http://www.pennsearch.com

Description: Assists in recruiting and hiring accounting and financial professionals from staff accountant to chief financial officer. Industries served: All.

4865 ■ Phillip's Personnel/Phillip's Temps
1675 Broadway, Ste. 2410
Denver, CO 80204
Ph: (303)893-1850
Fax: (303)893-0639
E-mail: info@phillipspersonnel.com
URL: http://www.phillipspersonnel.com

Description: Personnel recruiting and staffing consultants in: accounting and finance, management information systems, sales and marketing, engineering, administration, and general and executive management. Industries served: telecommunications, distribution, financial services, and general business.

4866 ■ Princeton Executive Search
2667 Nottingham Way
Trenton, NJ 08619
Ph: (609)584-1100

Description: Provider of search and placement for management level professions. Specializes in accounting, banking, engineering and human resources. Industries served: Financial, research and development, insurance, manufacturing, banking and government agencies.

4867 ■ Pro Advantage Executive Search
295 Madison Ave., 12th Fl.
New York, NY 10017
Ph: (212)944-0222
Fax: (212)944-2666
E-mail: info@proadvantagejobs.com
URL: http://www.proadvantagejobs.com

Description: Executive recruiting and research firm specializes in financial services industries. Offers career opportunities in the field of accounting, internal auditing, finance, compliance, tax, operations, and marketing.

4868 ■ Quirk-Corporon and Associates Inc.
1229 N Jackson St., Ste. 205
Milwaukee, WI 53202-2655
Ph: (414)224-9399
Fax: (414)224-9472
E-mail: quirkrecruiters@sbcglobal.net
URL: http://www.quirkinsrecruiters.com

Description: Employment agency specializing in all disciplines of the insurance and financial industries; insurance recruiters, is a contingency and retained recruiting and consulting firm specializing in the placement of permanent candidates; provides talented professional and technical employees, locally and nationally, who are skilled in property or casualty, life or health, employee benefits and managed care; provides a highly respected dimension of counseling skill to both clients and candidates in all areas of staffing and employee relations.

4869 ■ Raines International Inc.
75 Rockefeller Plz., 27th Fl.
New York, NY 10019
Ph: (212)997-1100
Fax: (212)997-0196
E-mail: contact@rainesinternational.com
URL: http://www.rainesinternational.com

Description: International generalist firm specializing in middle to upper management executives. Concentrations include general management, finance and accounting, information technology, operations or procurement, strategic planning, investment banking, real estate or finance, human resources, insurance, and legal.

4870 ■ Raymond Alexander Associates
97 Lackawanna Ave., Ste. 102
Totowa, NJ 07512-2332
Ph: (973)256-1000
Fax: (973)256-5871
E-mail: raa@raymondalexander.com
URL: http://www.raymondalexander.com

Description: Personnel consulting firm conducts executive search services in the specific areas of accounting, tax and finance. Industries served: manufacturing, financial services, and public accounting.

4871 ■ Real Estate Executive Search, Inc.
225 E Dania Beach Blvd., Ste. 200
Dania Beach, FL 33004
Ph: (954)927-6000

Fax: (954)927-6003
E-mail: reesearch954@aol.com
URL: http://reesearchinc.com

Description: Executive search firm for the real estate and finance fields.

4872 ■ Roberson & Co.
10751 Parfet St.
Broomfield, CO 80021
Ph: (303)410-6510
E-mail: roberson@recruiterpro.com
URL: http://www.recruiterpro.com

Description: Professional and executive recruiting firm working the national and international marketplace. Specializes in accounting, finance, data processing and information services, health care, environmental and mining engineering, manufacturing, human resources, and sales and marketing.

4873 ■ Robert Half Management Resources
2884 Sand Hill Rd.
Menlo Park, CA 94025
Free: 888-400-7474
URL: http://www.roberthalfmr.com

Description: Serves as a provider of senior-level accounting and finance professionals on a project and interim basis.

4874 ■ Rocky Mountain Recruiters, Inc.
1776 S Jackson St., Ste. 320
Denver, CO 80210
Ph: (303)296-2000
E-mail: resumes@rmrecruiters.com
URL: http://www.rmrecruiters.com

Description: Accounting and financial executive search firm.

4875 ■ Search North America Inc.
PO Box 3577
Sunriver, OR 97707
E-mail: mylinda@searchna.com
URL: http://www.searchna.com

Description: An executive search and recruiting firm whose focus is placing engineers, operations and maintenance managers, sales and marketing management, financial and general management executives (both domestic and international). Industries served: forest products, pulp and paper, waste to energy, environmental services, consulting and equipment suppliers for above related industries.

4876 ■ Sherpa LLC
1001 Morehead Square Dr., Ste. 600
Charlotte, NC 28203
Ph: (704)374-0001
URL: http://www.sherpallc.com

Description: Specializes in recruiting, staffing, and consulting services for accounting/finance, information technology, and project management in direct hire, temporary and project-based consulting positions.

4877 ■ SHS of Cherry Hill
207 Barclay Pavilion W
Cherry Hill, NJ 08034
Ph: (856)216-9030
Fax: (856)219-2011
E-mail: shs@shsofcherryhill.com
URL: http://www.shsofcherryhill.com

Description: Personnel recruiters operating in the disciplines of accounting, sales, insurance, engineering and administration. Industries served: insurance, distribution, manufacturing and service.

4878 ■ Spectrum Group, LLC
1919 Gallows Rd., Ste. 600
Vienna, VA 22182
Ph: (703)738-1200
Fax: (703)761-9477
E-mail: web@spectrumcareers.com
URL: http://www.spectrumcareers.com

Description: Serves as executive search firm for ac-

counting and finance, information technology, and sales and marketing industries.

4879 ■ S.R. Clarke
105 Huntercombe
Williamsburg, VA 23188
Ph: (703)344-0256
Fax: (949)608-5052
URL: http://www.srclarke.com/index.html

Description: Serves as an executive search and recruitment firm specializing in commercial construction, commercial real estate development, residential asset management, residential construction and development, subcontractor trades, finance, accounting, administration, heavy construction, architectural design and engineering design.

4880 ■ Terry Taylor & Associates
459 Bechman St.
Springdale, PA 15144-1170
Ph: (724)274-5627

Description: An executive search consulting firm specializing in financial, litigation support, performance improvement and management information systems recruitment.

4881 ■ Techtronix Technical Search
5401 N 76th St.
Milwaukee, WI 53217-0173
Ph: (414)466-3100
Fax: (414)466-3598

Description: Firm specializes in recruiting executives for the engineering, information systems, manufacturing, marketing, finance and human resources industries. Industries include electronic, manufacturing and finance.

4882 ■ TRC Staffing Services Inc.
115 Perimeter Center Pl. NE, Ste. 850
Atlanta, GA 30346
Ph: (770)392-1411
Free: 800-488-8008
Fax: (770)392-7926
E-mail: info@trcstaff.com
URL: http://www.trcstaffing.com

Description: A full-service executive search company with permanent placements encompassing engineering, industrial sales, financial and computer science positions. Screen, interview and verify past employment for all candidates prior to referral. Also assist personnel staffs in the attainment of their EEO/AAP goals with the placement of talented individuals in positions which were underutilized with minorities and/or women. Industries served: all.

4883 ■ Val Executive Resources Group
100 Merrick Rd., East Twr., Ste. 302
Rockville Centre, NY 11570-4801
Ph: (516)764-9000
Fax: (516)764-9122
E-mail: info@val-group.com
URL: http://www.val-group.com

Description: Personnel consultants recruiting on contingency and retained search basis specializing in Banking and Finance, to include: Corporate, Commercial and Consumer Banking, Private Banking, Trust, Investments, Human Resources, Marketing, focusing on lower, middle and senior management positions. Industries served: Banking, finance, brokerage, insurance.

4884 ■ Whitney & Associates Inc.
920 2nd Ave. S, Ste. 625
Minneapolis, MN 55402-4103
Ph: (612)338-5600
Fax: (612)349-6129

Description: Accounting and financial personnel recruiting consultants providing full time placement and temporary staffing service with specialized expertise and emphasis in the accounting discipline.

ONLINE JOB SOURCES AND SERVICES

4885 ■ **AccountingCrossing.com**
URL: http://www.accountingcrossing.com

Description: Offers collection of accounting jobs, including CPA, finance manager, corporate accountant, and forensic accounting positions. Features industry-specific articles relating to job searches and developments in the accounting industry.

4886 ■ **American Association of Finance and Accounting**
URL: http://www.aafa.com

Description: Alliance of executive search firms specializing in the recruitment and placement of finance and accounting professionals. Contains career opportunities site with job board for both job seekers and hiring employers. One does not have to be a member to search for jobs.

4887 ■ **BankingCareers.com**
URL: http://www.bankingcareers.com

Description: Provides lists of jobs and products to the banking and finance community.

4888 ■ **BankJobs.com**
URL: http://www.bankjobs.com

Description: Posts jobs and resumes for the banking and finance industry. Allows users to post, preview and search jobs for free.

4889 ■ **CareerBank**
URL: http://www.careerbank.com/home/index.cfm ?site_id=8162

Description: Provides jobs in finance, banking, mortgage, insurance, and accounting. Specializes in online job posting and job search, resume upload and resume database search, and career advice services.

4890 ■ **Careers-In-Business**
Careers-In-Business, LLC
4101 N.W. Urbandale Dr.
Urbandale, IA 50322
E-mail: bizjobs09l@gmail.com
URL: http://www.careers-in-business.com

Description: Careers-In-Business contains information on employment in the business sector, primarily in accounting, finance and consulting. Links to many corporations who hire extensively in this area are included for those wishing to make contacts and/or mail out resumes. Detailed information on job search aids and employer profiles provided. Links to many other career sites also available, as well as links to career-related books for sale through Amazon.

4891 ■ **The Digital Financier**
URL: http://www.dfin.com

Description: Job postings from financial companies. Offers links to major job search websites. Has leads for further training and allows companies to post its own job links.

4892 ■ **Financial Management Jobs**
URL: http://www.financialmanagementjobs.org

Description: Serves as a job board for financial management employment opportunities.

4893 ■ **FinancialJobBank.com**
URL: http://www.financialjobbank.com

Description: Works as a job engine that helps individual to find job openings in the areas of accounting, finance, taxation, banking, and mortgage.

4894 ■ **FinancialJobs.com**
URL: http://www.financialjobs.com

Description: Lists accounting and finance jobs for professionals at all levels of their careers. Features resume writing tips, relocation assistance, networking techniques, salary calculator, and other related links.

4895 ■ **FinancialServicesCrossing.com**
URL: http://www.financialservicescrossing.com

Description: Offers a collection of top financial services job openings carefully researched by analysts. Provides instant access to a comprehensive pool of listings in the industry of financial services.

4896 ■ **InsuranceAgencyCareers.com**
URL: http://www.insuranceagencycareers.com

Description: Online job search provides employment opportunities in the insurance industry.

4897 ■ **Spherion**
URL: http://www.spherion.com

Description: Recruitment firm specializing in accounting and finance, sales and marketing, interim executives, technology, engineering, retail and human resources.

4898 ■ **Transearch.com**
URL: http://www.transearch.com

Description: International executive search firm concentrating in searches for executives in retail, real estate, information technology, industry, life sciences and financial services. Seekers may search job board and submit their resume for recruiter review.

4899 ■ **Vault.com**
URL: http://www.vault.com

Description: Job board website with searches emphasizing jobs in legal, business, consulting and finance fields of practice. Contains online profile posting, resume review, company research, salary calculators and relocation tools.

TRADESHOWS

4900 ■ **Bankers' Association for Finance and Trade Annual Meeting**
Bankers' Association for Finance and Trade
1120 Connecticut Ave. NW
Washington, DC 20036
Ph: (202)663-7575
Fax: (202)663-5538
E-mail: info@baft-ifsa.com
URL: http://www.baft-ifsa.com/eweb

Frequency: Annual. **Primary Exhibits:** Exhibits relating to finance, trade, economic issues, enterprise risk management, supply chain finance, payments and remittances, regulatory compliance, and service.

4901 ■ **Media Financial Management Association Conference**
Media Financial Management Association
550 W Frontage Rd., Ste. 3600
Northfield, IL 60093
Ph: (847)716-7000
Fax: (847)716-7004
E-mail: info@mediafinance.org
URL: http://www.mediafinance.org

Frequency: Annual. **Primary Exhibits:** Exhibits relating to the financial management of radio, television, and cable television operations, including issues such as industry - specific software, collection agencies, insurance, investments, banking, accounting firms and music licensing.

4902 ■ **National Association of Personal Financial Advisors National Conference**
National Association of Personal Financial Advisors
3250 N Arlington Heights Rd., Ste. 109
Arlington Heights, IL 60004
Ph: (847)483-5400
Free: 888-333-6659
Fax: (847)483-5415
E-mail: info@napfa.org
URL: http://www.napfa.org

Frequency: Semiannual. Offers sessions in all areas of financial planning.

4903 ■ **Pennsylvania Association of Community Bankers Convention**
Pennsylvania Association of Community Bankers
2405 N Front St.
Harrisburg, PA 17110
Ph: (717)231-7447
Free: 800-443-5076
Fax: (717)231-7445
E-mail: pacb@pacb.org
URL: http://www.pacb.org

Frequency: Annual. **Primary Exhibits:** Equipment, supplies, and services for community banks, thrifts, and associate firms.

OTHER SOURCES

4904 ■ **American Bankers Association**
1120 Connecticut Ave. NW
Washington, DC 20036
Ph: (202)663-5268
Free: 800-226-5377
Fax: (202)828-5053
E-mail: custserv@aba.com
URL: http://www.aba.com

Description: Members are principally commercial banks and trust companies; combined assets of members represent approximately 90% of the U.S. banking industry; approximately 94% of members are community banks with less than $500 million in assets. Seeks to enhance the role of commercial bankers as preeminent providers of financial services through communications, research, legal action, lobbying of federal legislative and regulatory bodies, and education and training programs. Serves as spokesperson for the banking industry; facilitates exchange of information among members. Maintains the American Institute of Banking, an industry-sponsored adult education program. Conducts educational and training programs for bank employees and officers through a wide range of banking schools and national conferences. Maintains liaison with federal bank regulators; lobbies Congress on issues affecting commercial banks; testifies before congressional committees; represents members in U.S. postal rate proceedings. Serves as secretariat of the International Monetary Conference and the Financial Institutions Committee for the American National Standards Institute. Files briefs and lawsuits in major court cases affecting the industry. Conducts teleconferences with state banking associations on such issues as regulatory compliance; works to build consensus and coordinate activities of leading bank and financial service trade groups. Provides services to members including: public advocacy; news media contact; insurance program providing directors and officers with liability coverage, financial institution bond, and trust errors and omissions coverage; research service operated through ABA Center for Banking Information; fingerprint set processing in conjunction with the Federal Bureau of Investigation; discounts on operational and income-producing projects through the Corporation for American Banking. Conducts conferences, forums, and workshops covering subjects such as small business, consumer credit, agricultural and community banking, trust management, bank operations, and automation. Sponsors ABA Educational Foundation and the Personal Economics Program, which educates schoolchildren and the community on banking, economics, and personal finance. **Members:** 1,000.

4905 ■ **American Financial Services Association**
919 18th St. NW, Ste. 300
Washington, DC 20006-5526
E-mail: cstinebert@afsamail.org
URL: http://www.afsaonline.org

Description: Represents companies whose business is primarily direct credit lending to consumers and/or the purchase of sales finance paper on consumer goods. Has members that have insurance and retail subsidiaries; some are themselves subsidiaries of highly diversified parent corporations. Encourages the business of financing individuals and families for necessary and useful purposes at reasonable charges, including interest; promotes consumer understanding of basic money management principles as well as constructive uses of consumer credit. Includes educational services such as films, textbooks and study units for the classroom and budgeting guides for individuals and families. Compiles statistical reports; offers seminars.

4906 ■ Association of African American Financial Advisors
PO Box 4853
Capitol Heights, MD 20791
Ph: (240)396-2530
Fax: (888)392-5702
E-mail: info@aaafainc.cm
URL: http://aaafainc.com

Description: Seeks to develop and foster professional relationships among African American professionals working in the financial advisory industry. Provides assistance and nurturing for those families that seek to improve their opportunities for participating and prospering financially in an economically progressive society. Strives to create support networks for minority financial professionals. Provides a forum for further education, training and visibility of its members.

4907 ■ Association of Divorce Financial Planners
514 Fourth St.
East Northport, NY 11731
Free: 888-838-7773
E-mail: adfp@divorceandfinance.org
URL: http://www.divorceandfinance.org

Description: Aims to create awareness of the benefits of divorce financial planning. Provides members with continuing education. Promotes communication, networking and peer review.

4908 ■ Association for Financial Professionals
4520 E West Hwy., Ste. 750
Bethesda, MD 20814
Ph: (301)907-2862
Fax: (301)907-2864
URL: http://www.afponline.org

Description: Seeks to establish a national forum for the exchange of concepts and techniques related to improving the management of treasury and the careers of professionals through research, education, publications and recognition of the treasury management profession through a certification program. Conducts educational programs. Operates career center.

4909 ■ Bank Administration Institute
115 S La Salle St., Ste. 3300
Chicago, IL 60603-3900
Free: 800-375-5543
Fax: (312)683-2373
E-mail: info@bai.org
URL: http://www.bai.org

Description: Works to improve the competitive position of banking companies through strategic research and educational offerings.

4910 ■ *Business Job Finder*
Ohio State University - Department of Finance
Max M. Fisher College of Business
700 Fisher Hall
2100 Neil Ave.
Columbus, OH 43210
Ph: (614)292-5026
Fax: (614)292-2418
E-mail: scholl_2@cob.osu.edu
URL: http://www.cob.ohio-state.edu/fin

Description: Internet site containing information on jobs in the business sector, primarily in accounting, finance, and consulting. Links to many corporations who hire extensively in this area are included for those wishing to make contacts and/or mail out

resumes. Detailed information on job search aids and employer profiles are provided with job areas broken down into subject.

4911 ■ *Career Opportunities in Banking, Finance, and Insurance*
InfoBase Holdings Inc.
132 W 31st., 17 Fl.
New York, NY 10001-3406
Ph: (212)967-8800
Fax: (800)678-3633
E-mail: info@infobasepublishing.com
URL: http://factsonfile.infobasepublishing.com

Frequency: Latest edition 2nd; Published February, 2007. **Price:** $49.50 Individuals hardcover. **Description:** Thomas P. Fitch. Second edition, 2007. 267 pages. Lists of colleges with programs supporting banking, finance, and industry; professional associations; professional certifications; regulatory agencies; and Internet resources for career planning. **Publication includes:** Lists of colleges with programs supporting banking, finance, and industry; professional associations; professional certifications; regulatory agencies; and Internet resources for career planning. Principal content of publication is job descriptions for professions in the banking, finance, and insurance industries. **Indexes:** Alphabetical.

4912 ■ Commercial Finance Association
370 7th Ave., Ste. 1801
New York, NY 10001-3979
Ph: (212)792-9390
Fax: (212)564-6053
URL: http://www.cfa.com

Description: Organizations engaged in asset-based financial services including commercial financing and factoring and lending money on a secured basis to small- and medium-sized business firms. Acts as a forum for information and consideration about ideas, opportunities and legislation concerning asset-based financial services. Seeks to improve the industry's legal and operational procedures. Offers job placement and reference services for members. Sponsors School for Field Examiners and other educational programs. Compiles statistics; conducts seminars and surveys; maintains speakers' bureau and 21 committees.

4913 ■ Eastern Finance Association
PO Box 244023
Montgomery, AL 36124-4023
E-mail: membershipservices@blackwellpublishers.co.uk
URL: http://etnpconferences.net/efa

Description: College and university professors and financial officers; libraries. Provides a meeting place for persons interested in any aspect of finance, including financial management, investments, and banking. Sponsors research competitions.

4914 ■ Financial Executives International
1250 Headquarters Plz., West Tower, 7th Fl.
Morristown, NJ 07960
Ph: (973)765-1000
Free: 877-359-1070
Fax: (973)765-1018
E-mail: mhollein@financialexecutives.org
URL: http://www.financialexecutives.org

Description: Professional organization of corporate financial executives performing duties of chief financial officer, controller, treasurer, or vice-president-finance. Sponsors research activities through its affiliated Financial Executives Research Foundation. Maintains offices in Toronto, Canada, and Washington, DC.

4915 ■ Financial Management Association International
University of South Florida
College of Business Administration
4202 E Fowler Ave., BSN 3331
Tampa, FL 33620-5500
Ph: (813)974-2084

Fax: (813)974-3318
E-mail: fma@coba.usf.edu
URL: http://www.fma.org

Description: Professors of financial management; corporate financial officers. Facilitates exchange of ideas among persons involved in financial management or the study thereof. Conducts workshops for comparison of current research projects and development of cooperative ventures in writing and research. Sponsors honorary society for superior students at 300 colleges and universities. Offers placement services.

4916 ■ Financial Managers Society
1 N La Salle St., Ste. 3100
Chicago, IL 60602-4003
Ph: (312)578-1300
Free: 800-275-4367
Fax: (312)578-1308
E-mail: info@fmsinc.org
URL: http://www.fmsinc.org

Description: Works for the needs of finance and accounting professionals from banks, thrifts and credit unions. Offers career-enhancing education, specialized publications, national leadership opportunities and worldwide connections with other industry professionals.

4917 ■ Financial Planning Association
7535 E Hampden Ave., Ste. 600
Denver, CO 80231
Ph: (303)759-4900
Free: 800-322-4237
Fax: (303)759-0749
E-mail: webfeedback@fpanet.org
URL: http://www.fpanet.org

Description: Provides educational opportunities and industry specific resources. Includes information and tools connecting those who provide, support and benefit from professional financial planning.

4918 ■ Financial Women's Association of New York
355 Lexington Ave., 15th Fl.
New York, NY 10017
Ph: (212)297-2133
Fax: (212)370-9047
E-mail: fwaoffice@fwa.org
URL: http://www.nywici.org/links/link_fwa.html

Description: Persons of professional status in the field of finance in the New York metropolitan area. Works to promote and maintain high professional standards in the financial and business communities; provide an opportunity for members to enhance one another's professional contacts; achieve recognition of the contribution of women to the financial and business communities; encourage other women to seek professional positions within the financial and business communities. Activities include educational trips to foreign countries; college internship program including foreign student exchange; high school mentorship program; Washington and international briefings; placement service for members. Maintains speakers' bureau.

4919 ■ International Association of Credit Portfolio Managers
360 Madison Ave., 17th Fl.
New York, NY 10017-7111
Ph: (646)289-5430
Fax: (646)289-5429
E-mail: dara@iacpm.org
URL: http://www.iacpm.org

Description: Represents financial institutions that manage portfolios of corporate loans, bonds, or similar credit sensitive financial instruments. Aims to advance the practice of credit exposure management. Conducts research on the credit portfolio management field. Works with other organizations in addressing issues of mutual interest relating to the measurement and management of portfolio risk. **Members:** 87.

4920 ■ International Association of Qualified Financial Planners
PO Box 7007
Beverly Hills, CA 90212-7007
Free: 877-346-3037
E-mail: info@iaqfp.org
URL: http://www.iaqfp.org

Description: Aims to unite the financial planning profession. Encourages research to advance the discipline, theory and practice of financial planning. Provides a medium for professional interchange and forum.

4921 ■ Media Financial Management Association
550 W Frontage Rd., Ste. 3600
Northfield, IL 60093
Ph: (847)716-7000
Fax: (847)716-7004
E-mail: info@mediafinance.org
URL: http://www.mediafinance.org

Description: Controllers, chief accountants, auditors, business managers, treasurers, secretaries and related newspaper executives, educators, and public accountants. Conducts research projects on accounting methods and procedures for newspapers. Offers placement service; maintains speakers' bureau. Produces conferences and seminars.

4922 ■ National Association of Black Accountants
7474 Greenway Center Dr., Ste. 1120
Greenbelt, MD 20770
Ph: (301)474-6222
Free: 888-571-2939
Fax: (301)474-3114
E-mail: membership@nabainc.org
URL: http://www.nabainc.org

Description: Represents minority students and professionals currently working, or interested in the fields of accounting, finance, technology, consulting or general business. Seeks, promotes, develops, and represents the interests of current and future minority business professionals.

4923 ■ National Association of Corporate Treasurers
12100 Sunset Hills Rd., Ste. 130
Reston, VA 20190
Ph: (703)437-4377
Fax: (703)435-4390
E-mail: nact@nact.org
URL: http://www.nact.org

Description: Serves as a forum for high-level finance executives who perform all or a substantial part of the duties of corporate treasurership. Seeks to produce and facilitate the exchange of information relevant to the management of corporate treasury operations. Sponsors general sessions on such topics as Cash Management Issues for the 90's, Corporate Finance, Data Processing/Electronic Services, International Liquidity Management. Offers job clearinghouse services.

4924 ■ National Association of Personal Financial Advisors
3250 N Arlington Heights Rd., Ste. 109
Arlington Heights, IL 60004
Ph: (847)483-5400
Free: 888-333-6659
Fax: (847)483-5415
E-mail: info@napfa.org
URL: http://www.napfa.org

Description: Full-time, fee-only financial planners.

Serves as a network for fee-only planners to discuss issues relating to practice management, client services, and investments selection. Works to encourage and advance the practice of fee-only financial planning by developing the skills of members and increasing the awareness of fee-only financial planning of consumers.

4925 ■ National Bankers Association
1513 P St. NW
Washington, DC 20005
Ph: (202)588-5432
Fax: (202)588-5443
E-mail: mgrant@nationalbankers.org
URL: http://www.nationalbankers.org

Description: Minority banking institutions owned by minority individuals and institutions. Serves as an advocate for the minority banking industry. Organizes banking services, government relations, marketing, scholarship, and technical assistance programs. Offers placement services; compiles statistics.

4926 ■ National Investment Banking Association
422 Chesterfield Rd.
Bogart, GA 30622
Ph: (706)208-9620
Fax: (706)993-3342
E-mail: emily@nibanet.org
URL: http://www.nibanet.org

Description: Represents regional and independent brokerages, investment banking firms, and related capital market service providers. Provides a forum for small companies seeking access and exposure to underwriters and brokers/dealers in connection with their capital formation. Supports an enhanced capital formation environment for small companies.

4927 ■ National Money Transmitters Association
12 Welwyn Rd., Ste. C
Great Neck, NY 11021
Ph: (516)829-2742
Fax: (516)706-0203
E-mail: david@nmta.us
URL: http://nmta.us/site

Description: Represents the interests, upholds the image, and voices the concerns of U.S. licensed money transmitters, in all public and governmental matters. Aims to advance a regulatory landscape under which money transmitters can operate without biased impediments. Fosters good industry compliance with all state and federal laws. Addresses all issues concerning the money transmission industry.

4928 ■ National Society of Accountants for Cooperatives - Texas Chapter
c/o Gail Faries, Dir.
D. Williams and Company, PC
Lubbock, TX 79490
Ph: (806)785-5982
Fax: (806)785-9381
E-mail: gailf@dwilliams.net

Description: Represents employees of cooperatives, certified public accountants, auditors, chief financial officers, attorneys, and bankers. Unites persons performing accounting, auditing, financial, and legal services for cooperative and nonprofit associations.

4929 ■ Northern New Jersey Chapter of the National Association of Black Accountants
PO Box 1091
Newark, NJ 07101
E-mail: nabannj@nabannj.com
URL: http://www.nabannj.org

Description: Works to develop, encourage and serve as a resource for greater participation by African Americans and other minorities in the accounting, finance, auditing, business, consulting, information technology, and other related professions. Seeks to address the professional needs which enable members and minorities to maximize career potential and build leaders.

4930 ■ Risk and Insurance Management Society
1065 Ave. of the Americas, 13th Fl.
New York, NY 10018
Ph: (212)286-9292
Free: 800-713-7467
Fax: (212)986-9716
E-mail: lists@rims.org
URL: http://www.rims.org

Description: Business association serving corporate risk and insurance managers. Dedicated to advancing the practice of risk management, a discipline that protects physical, financial, and human resources.

4931 ■ Risk Management Association
1801 Market St., Ste. 300
Philadelphia, PA 19103-1613
Ph: (215)446-4000
Fax: (215)446-4101
E-mail: rmaar@rmahq.org
URL: http://www.rmahq.org

Description: Commercial and savings banks, and savings and loan, and other financial services companies. Conducts research and professional development activities in areas of loan administration, asset management, and commercial lending and credit to increase professionalism.

4932 ■ Society of Cost Estimating and Analysis
8221 Old Courthouse Rd., Ste. 106
Vienna, VA 22182
Ph: (703)938-5090
Fax: (703)938-5091
E-mail: scea@sceaonline.org
URL: http://www.sceaonline.org

Description: Works to improve cost estimating and analysis in government and industry and to enhance the professional competence and achievements of its members. Administers a professional certification program leading to the designation of Certified Cost Estimator/Analyst; offers extensive literature in the field through its Professional Development Program. Goals of the Society include enhancing the profession of cost estimating and analysis, fostering the professional growth of its members, enhancing the understanding and application of cost estimating, analysis and related disciplines throughout government and industry and providing forums and media through which current issues of interest to the profession can be addressed and advances in the state-of-the-art can be shared.

4933 ■ Society for Financial Education and Professional Development
2120 Washington Blvd., Ste. 400
Arlington, VA 22204
Ph: (703)920-3807
Fax: (703)920-3809
E-mail: tdaniels@sfepd.org
URL: http://www.sfepd.org

Description: Aims to enhance the level of financial and economic literacy of individuals and households in the United States. Develops and presents customized financial education and professional development seminars and workshops. Works with organizations that support financial education and professional development programs.

SOURCES OF HELP-WANTED ADS

4934 ■ American City and County
Penton
9800 Metcalf Ave.
Overland Park, KS 66212
Ph: (913)341-1300
Free: 866-748-4926
Fax: (913)967-1905
E-mail: corporatecustomerservice@penton.com
URL: http://americancityandcounty.com
Frequency: Monthly. **Description:** Municipal and county administration magazine.

4935 ■ Fire Chief
Penton Media, Inc.
249 W 17th St.
New York, NY 10011
Ph: (212)204-4200
Fax: (212)835-1605
URL: http://firechief.com
Description: Features articles by fire officers from across the country and overseas covering a wide variety of areas that are important to today's fire chief.

4936 ■ Firehouse Magazine
Cygnus Business Media Inc.
1233 Janesville Ave.
Fort Atkinson, WI 53538
Free: 800-547-7377
E-mail: info@cygnus.com
URLs: http://www.firehouse.com; http://www.cygnusb2b.com/PropertyPub.cfm?PropertyID=47
Frequency: Monthly. **Price:** $24.95 Individuals; $44.95 Two years. **Description:** Magazine focusing on fire protection.

4937 ■ IAFC On Scene
International Association of Fire Chiefs
4025 Fair Ridge Dr., Ste. 300
Fairfax, VA 22033-2868
Ph: (703)273-0911
Fax: (703)273-9363
URL: http://www.iafc.org/MemberCenter/OnScenelssueList.cfm?navItemNumber=685
Description: Semimonthly. Covers management, technical, and legislative issues that affect fire fighting professionals, including volunteers. Recurring features include letters to the editor, interviews, news of research, reports of meetings, news of educational opportunities, job listings, notices of publications available, and columns titled Executive Director's Column, Comm Center, Announcements, Section News, President's Column, and Staying Out of Trouble-A Case Study.

4938 ■ International Fire Fighter
International Association of Fire Fighters
1750 New York Ave. NW, Ste. 300
Washington, DC 20006

Ph: (202)737-8484
Fax: (202)737-8418
E-mail: bglanz@iaff.org
URL: http://www.iaff.org/comm/magazine/
Frequency: Bimonthly. **Price:** $18 Individuals.
Description: Union tabloid.

4939 ■ The Municipality
League of Wisconsin Municipalities
122 W Washington Ave., Ste. 300
Madison, WI 53703-2715
Ph: (608)267-2380
Free: 800-991-5502
Fax: (608)267-0645
E-mail: jmstaral@lwm-info.org
URL: http://www.lwm-info.org/
Frequency: Monthly. **Price:** $25/year. **Description:** Magazine for officials of Wisconsin's local municipal governments.

4940 ■ NFPA Journal: The Official Magazine of the National Fire Protection Association
National Fire Protection Association
1 Batterymarch Park
Quincy, MA 02169-7471
Ph: (617)770-3000
Free: 800-344-3555
Fax: (617)770-0700
E-mail: custserv@nfpa.org
URL: http://www.nfpa.org/newsandpublications/nfpa-journal/about-nfpa-journal
Frequency: Bimonthly. **Description:** Magazine concerning fire protection, prevention.

4941 ■ Turn Out
International Fire Buff Associates Inc.
PO Box 242
Indianapolis, IN 46206
E-mail: indyturnout@gmail.com
URL: http://www.ifba.org/
Description: Semiannual. Concerned with the fire-fighting activities of fire departments across the nation. Includes historical accounts and news of association and member activities.

4942 ■ Western City
League of California Cities
1400 K St., 4th Fl.
Sacramento, CA 95814
Ph: (916)658-8200
Free: 800-262-1801
Fax: (916)658-8240
E-mail: okabel@cacities.org
URL: http://www.westerncity.com
Frequency: Monthly. **Price:** $39 Individuals; $63 Two years; $52 Other countries; $26.50 Students.
Description: Municipal interest magazine.

EMPLOYER DIRECTORIES AND NETWORKING LISTS

4943 ■ Fellowship of Christian Firefighters International--Directory
Fellowship of Christian Firefighters International
PO Box 490
Arnold, MD 21012
Ph: (970)416-9076
Free: 800-322-9848
E-mail: fcfihq@aol.com
URL: http://www.fellowshipofchristianfirefighters.com
Frequency: Biennial; Odd years. **Covers:** about 2,000 member Christian firefighters. **Entries include:** Name, address, phone. **Arrangement:** Alphabetical.
Indexes: Local chapter.

4944 ■ National Directory of Fire Chiefs & EMS Administrators
National Public Safety Information Bureau
601 Main St.
Stevens Point, WI 54481
Ph: (715)345-2772
Free: 800-647-7579
Fax: (715)345-7288
E-mail: info@safetysource.com
URL: http://www.safetysource.com
Frequency: Annual; Latest edition 2013. **Price:** $169 Individuals USA; $199 online (one complimentary print copy). **Covers:** Over 37,000 fire and emergency departments in the U.S. **Entries include:** Department name, address, phone, fax, county, name of chief, type of department, financial structure. **Arrangement:** Geographical.

4945 ■ What Can I Do Now--Public Safety
InfoBase Holdings Inc.
132 W 31st., 17 Fl.
New York, NY 10001-3406
Ph: (212)967-8800
Fax: (800)678-3633
E-mail: info@infobasepublishing.com
URL: http://factsonfile.infobasepublishing.com
Price: $22.95 Individuals; $20.65 Libraries. **Pages:** 184. **Covers:** Border patrol officers, corrections officers, crime analysts, emergency medical technicians, FBI agents, firefighters, and police officers.

HANDBOOKS AND MANUALS

4946 ■ FabJob Guide to Become a Firefighter
FabJob Inc.
4616-25th Ave. NE, No. 224
Seattle, WA 98105
Ph: (403)873-1018
Free: 888-322-5621
URL: http://www.fabjob.com

Description: Mark Armstrong. $14.97(e-book). 99 pages. Contains career advice from firefighting professionals.

4947 ■ *Master the Firefighter Exam*
Peterson's
461 From Rd.
Paramus, NJ 07652
Ph: (609)896-1800
Free: 800-338-3282
Fax: (402)458-3042
E-mail: custsvc@petersons.com
URL: http://www.petersons.com

Description: 2009. 432 pages. Provides information to help the individual pass local, state, and national written exams, including test-taking strategies, information on the firefighter screening process, expert oral interview and job search advice, and a review of the Candidate Physical Ability Test.

4948 ■ *Real-Resumes for Firefighting Jobs*
PREP Publishing
1110 1/2 Hay St., Ste. C
Fayetteville, NC 28305
Ph: (910)483-6611
Fax: (910)483-2439
E-mail: preppub@aol.com
URL: http://www.prep-pub.com

Description: Anne McKinney. 2004. $16.95. Illustrated. 192 pages. Firefighting careers.

Employment Agencies and Search Firms

4949 ■ Fire Hire
PO Box 1822
Elk Grove, CA 95759-1822
Ph: (916)714-0895
E-mail: firehire@firehire.com
URL: http://www.firehire.com

Description: Exists as a fire service recruitment registry. Provides quality candidates for participating agencies and services.

Online Job Sources and Services

4950 ■ Fire Career Assistance
URL: http://www.firecareerassist.com

Description: Provides a wide range of career services for fire fighters through features that include job openings, fire fighter qualifications, physical fitness test, firefighter oral board questions, written exams, firefighter interviews and others.

4951 ■ Fire Service Employment
URL: http://www.fireserviceemployment.com

Description: Gives special focus on EMTs and firefighters. Provides free recruitment information, links to fire service websites, firefighter and EMS job posting for employers, firefighter testing and interview tips and fire service career advice.

4952 ■ Firefighter-Jobs.com
URL: http://www.firefighter-jobs.com

Description: Exists as an online job site that lists various city, state or federal firefighting or EMT jobs. Includes other important employment information for aspiring firefighters such as a guide for professional resume writing and preparing for an interview.

4953 ■ Firehouse.com
URL: http://www.firehouse.com

Description: Provides fire rescue professionals with career services through features that include job openings, forums, products, news, members information, images, trainings, and events. Features a job board that covers company information, position type, position title, requirements, and salary.

4954 ■ FireJobs.com
URL: http://www.firejobs.com

Description: Seeks to find new firefighter employment for recruit firefighters just out of the academy and those who are already firefighters and want to move to a different department.

4955 ■ FiremenJobs.com
URL: http://www.firemenjobs.com

Description: Exists as an online firefighter job search site that provide its members with a database of updated jobs. Includes preparation tips, exam books, list of fire departments and schools and other career services.

4956 ■ FireRescue1.com
URL: http://www.firerescue1.com

Description: Serves as an online career portal that provides firefighters with the information and resources that make them better able to protect their communities and stay safer on the job. Serves as a growing network where firefighting personnel and aspiring professionals can find relevant news, watch online videos, locate important training information and product purchases, and interact with each other.

4957 ■ WildlandFire.com
URL: http://www.wildlandfire.com

Description: Provides career services for fire fighters through features that includes issues, news, forum, and a classifieds page.

Tradeshows

4958 ■ Fire - Rescue International
International Association of Fire Chiefs
4025 Fair Ridge Dr., Ste. 300
Fairfax, VA 22033-2868
Ph: (703)273-0911
Fax: (703)273-9363
URL: http://www.iafc.org

Frequency: Annual. **Primary Exhibits:** Fire safety and emergency medical service equipment, supplies, and services; related training and support materials.

Other Sources

4959 ■ International Association of Fire Chiefs
4025 Fair Ridge Dr., Ste. 300
Fairfax, VA 22033-2868
Ph: (703)273-0911
Fax: (703)273-9363
URL: http://www.iafc.org

Description: Fire Department chief officers, emergency services administrators and emergency medical services directors/managers and supervisors, career, volunteer, municipal and private, who are interested in improving fire, rescue, and EMS coverage to the general public. Provides leadership to career and volunteer chiefs, chief fire officers and managers of emergency service organizations throughout the international community through vision, information, education, services and representation to enhance their professionalism and capabilities.

4960 ■ International Association of Women in Fire and Emergency Services
4025 Fair Ridge Dr., Ste. 300
Fairfax, VA 22033
Ph: (703)896-4858
Fax: (703)273-9363
E-mail: staff@i-women.org
URL: http://www.i-women.org

Description: Provides a proactive network that supports, mentors, and educates women in fire and emergency services. Promotes professional development of members in an effort to make women more effective firefighters.

SOURCES OF HELP-WANTED ADS

4961 ■ *AAHPERD UpdatePLUS*
American Alliance for Health, Physical Education, Recreation and Dance
1900 Association Dr.
Reston, VA 20191-1598
Ph: (703)476-3400
Free: 800-213-7193
Fax: (703)476-9527
E-mail: membership@aahperd.org
URL: http://www.aahperd.org

Description: Six issues/year. Provides news and information on the Alliance. Discusses current issues and research in the areas of health, physical education, recreation, dances, fitness, and adapted physical education. Recurring features include a calendar of events, reports of meetings, news of educational opportunities, job listings, notices of publications available, and columns titled President's Message, Membership Corner, and From the EVP's Desk.

4962 ■ *ACE FitnessMatters*
American Council on Exercise
4851 Paramont Dr.
San Diego, CA 92123
Ph: (858)576-6500
Free: 888-825-3636
Fax: (858)576-6564
E-mail: support@acefitness.org
URL: http://www.acefitness.org/acestore/p-515-fit-ness-matters.aspx

Frequency: Bimonthly. **Price:** $19.95 Individuals; $35 Two years; $33 Canada and Mexico; $60 Canada and Mexico 2 years. **Description:** Consumer magazine covering health and fitness news.

4963 ■ *The IHS Primary Care Provider*
U.S. Department of Health and Human Services - Indian Health Service
Reyes Bldg.
801 Thompson Ave., Ste. 400
Rockville, MD 20852-1627
Ph: (301)443-6394
Fax: (301)443-4794
E-mail: charles.grim@ihs.hhs.gov
URL: http://www.ihs.gov/provider

Frequency: Monthly. **Description:** Journal for health care professionals, physicians, nurses, pharmacists, dentists, and dietitians.

4964 ■ *NSCA Bulletin*
National Strength and Conditioning Association
1885 Bob Johnson Dr.
Colorado Springs, CO 80906
Ph: (719)632-6722
Free: 800-815-6826
Fax: (719)632-6367
E-mail: nsca@nsca.com
URLs: http://www.nsca-lift.org/Publications/journals/nonmember.asp; http://www.nsca-lift.org/Publications/

Lori Marker, Editor. **Frequency:** Bimonthly, 6/year. **Price:** Included in membership. **Description:** Bimonthly. Recurring features include a calendar of events, news of educational opportunities, and job listings.

4965 ■ *Nutritional Outlook*
UBM Canon
2901 28th St., Ste. 100
Santa Monica, CA 90405-2975
Ph: (310)445-4200
Fax: (310)445-4299
E-mail: info@nutritionaloutlook.com
URLs: http://www.nutritionaloutlook.com/; http://www.canonmediakit.com/publications/detail.php?pu-bld=35

Frequency: 9/yr. **Description:** Magazine for manufacturer's resource for dietary supplements and healthy foods and beverages.

ONLINE JOB SOURCES AND SERVICES

4966 ■ Athletic Jobs
URL: http://www.athleticjobs.org

Description: Serves as niche job board that provides listings on athletic jobs.

4967 ■ ExerciseCareers.com
URL: http://www.exercisecareers.com

Description: Provides an avenue for professionals to search and recruit for jobs in the health and fitness industry.

4968 ■ ExerciseJobs.com
URL: http://www.exercisejobs.com

Description: Offers career resources for exercise, fitness, kinesiology, and health professionals.

4969 ■ FitnessJobs.com
URL: http://www.fitnessjobs.com

Description: Serves as a job board that specializes in the health, fitness, recreation, and leisure industries. Offers job listings and employment opportunities.

4970 ■ Online Sports Career Center
URL: http://www.onlinesports.com/career-center

Description: Resource for sports-related career opportunities, as well as a resume bank for the perusal of potential employers within the sports and recreation industries. Main files include: Job Bank, Resume Bank, Newsletter, Work With Online Sports, Other Internet Resources.

4971 ■ Premier Health and Fitness Resources
URL: http://phfr.com

Description: Health and fitness professionals. Offers a broad spectrum of health promotion services, networking opportunities, and resource sharing materials. Features resources for finding quality fitness jobs, health promotion job postings, corporate wellness employment opportunities, or other fitness staff positions.

TRADESHOWS

4972 ■ National Strength & Conditioning Association Conference & Exhibition
National Strength and Conditioning Association
1885 Bob Johnson Dr.
Colorado Springs, CO 80906
Ph: (719)632-6722
Free: 800-815-6826
Fax: (719)632-6367
E-mail: nsca@nsca.com
URL: http://www.nsca-lift.org

Frequency: Annual. **Primary Exhibits:** Strength and conditioning equipment, supplies, and services.

OTHER SOURCES

4973 ■ Aerobics and Fitness Association of America
15250 Ventura Blvd., Ste. 200
Sherman Oaks, CA 91403
Free: 877-968-7263
Fax: (818)788-6301
E-mail: contactafaa@afaa.com
URL: http://www.afaa.com

Description: Provides cognitive and practical education for fitness professionals. Upholds safe and effective fitness practice. Offers courses and certifications beneficial to and of interest for the fitness industry.

4974 ■ American Alliance for Health, Physical Education, Recreation and Dance
1900 Association Dr.
Reston, VA 20191-1598
Ph: (703)476-3400
Free: 800-213-7193
Fax: (703)476-9527
E-mail: membership@aahperd.org
URL: http://www.aahperd.org

Description: Students and educators in physical education, dance, health, athletics, safety education, recreation, and outdoor education. Sponsors placement service.

4975 ■ American College of Sports Medicine
401 W Michigan St.
Indianapolis, IN 46202-3233

Ph: (317)637-9200
Free: 800-486-5643
Fax: (317)634-7817
E-mail: membership@acsm.org
URL: http://www.acsm.org

Description: Promotes and integrates scientific research, education, and practical applications of sports medicine and exercise science to maintain and enhance physical performance, fitness, health, and quality of life. Certifies fitness leaders, fitness instructors, exercise test technologists, exercise specialists, health/fitness program directors, and U.S. military fitness personnel. Grants Continuing Medical Education (CME) and Continuing Education Credits (CEC). Operates more than 50 committees.

4976 ■ American Council on Exercise
4851 Paramont Dr.
San Diego, CA 92123
Ph: (858)576-6500
Free: 888-825-3636
Fax: (858)576-6564
E-mail: support@acefitness.org
URL: http://www.acefitness.org

Description: Promotes the benefits of physical activity and protects consumers against unsafe and ineffective fitness products and instruction. Sponsors university-based exercise science research and testing that targets fitness products and trends. Sets standards for fitness professionals.

4977 ■ American Senior Fitness Association
PO Box 2575
New Smyrna Beach, FL 32170
Ph: (386)423-6634
Free: 888-689-6791
Fax: (877)365-3048
E-mail: asfa@seniorfitness.net
URL: http://www.seniorfitness.net

Description: Promotes excellence in older adult fitness. Provides comprehensive training, recognized certification, professional resources and member support for fitness professionals who serve older adults. Offers senior fitness specialist courses for colleges and universities.

4978 ■ *Careers for Health Nuts and Others Who Like to Stay Fit*
The McGraw-Hill Companies Inc.
PO Box 182604
Columbus, OH 43272
Ph: (212)512-2000
Free: 877-833-5524
Fax: (614)759-3749
E-mail: customer.service@mcgraw-hill.com
URL: http://www.mcgraw-hill.com

Description: Blythe Camenson. Second edition. $13.95 (paper). 208 pages. **Publication includes:** Appendices of professional associations, selected training programs, bibliography of job-hunting materi-

als, and U.S. National Park Service regional offices. **Entries include:** For professional associations: name, address, description of job-hunting materials; for training programs: name, address, description; for U.S. National Park Service regional offices: name, address.

4979 ■ Exercise Safety Association
PO Box 547916
Orlando, FL 32854-7916
Ph: (407)246-5090
E-mail: askesa@aol.com
URL: http://www.exercisesafety.com

Description: Fitness instructors, personal trainers, health spas, YMCAs, community recreation departments, and hospital wellness programs. Purposes are: to improve the qualifications of exercise instructors; to train instructors to develop safe exercise programs that will help people avoid injury while exercising; to prepare instructors for national certification. Offers training in aerobics and exercise and on the physiological aspects of exercise. Conducts exercise safety and research programs. Sponsors charitable program; maintains speakers' bureau. Offers instructor placement services.

4980 ■ IDEA Health and Fitness Association
10455 Pacific Center Ctr.
San Diego, CA 92121
Ph: (858)535-8979
Free: 800-999-4332
Fax: (858)535-8234
E-mail: contact@ideafit.com
URL: http://www.ideafit.com

Description: Provides continuing education for fitness professionals including; fitness instructors, personal trainers, program directors, and club/studio owners. Offers workshops for continuing education credits.

4981 ■ International Fitness Professionals Association
14509 University Point Pl.
Tampa, FL 33613
Ph: (813)979-1925
Free: 800-785-1924
Fax: (813)979-1978
E-mail: info@ifpa-fitness.com
URL: http://www.ifpa-fitness.com

Description: Promotes the interests of fitness professionals. Fosters the learning experience and professional recognition of fitness instructors. Provides practical and scientifically based health and fitness information to members.

4982 ■ National Athletic Trainers' Association
2952 Stemmons Fwy., No. 200
Dallas, TX 75247-6115
Ph: (214)637-6282

Free: 888-491-8833
Fax: (214)637-2206
E-mail: jthornton@clarion.edu
URL: http://www.nata.org

Description: Athletic trainers from universities, colleges, and junior colleges; professional football, baseball, basketball, and ice hockey; high schools, preparatory schools, military establishments, sports medicine clinics, and business/industrial health programs. Maintains hall of fame and placement service. Conducts research programs; compiles statistics.

4983 ■ National Federation of Professional Trainers
PO Box 4579
Lafayette, IN 47903-4579
Free: 800-729-6378
Fax: (765)471-7369
E-mail: info@nfpt.com
URL: http://www.nfpt.com

Description: Offers affordable, convenient, comprehensive, and applicable information to those seeking personal fitness trainer certification. Offers organizational certification credentials for consumer recognition of competence; provides certified affiliates with ongoing education; establishes a network of support, and provides professional products and services to trainers and consumers; and facilitates and encourages the exchange of ideas, knowledge, business experiences, and financial opportunities between all fitness administrators internationally. Offers educational programs. **Members:** 6,000.

4984 ■ National Strength and Conditioning Association
1885 Bob Johnson Dr.
Colorado Springs, CO 80906
Ph: (719)632-6722
Free: 800-815-6826
Fax: (719)632-6367
E-mail: nsca@nsca.com
URL: http://www.nsca-lift.org

Description: Represents professionals in the sports science, athletic, and fitness industries. Conducts national, regional, state, and local clinics and workshops. Operates professional certification program.

4985 ■ Natural Fitness Trainers Association
PO Box 49874
Athens, GA 30606-9998
Ph: (706)254-2798
URL: http://www.naturalfitnesstrainers.com

Description: Represents the interests of professional fitness trainers. Promotes the sports of natural bodybuilding and fitness. Provides ethical, legitimate, and fair certification standards. Advances the professional recognition of natural bodybuilding and fitness trainers.

Sources of Help-Wanted Ads

4986 ■ *AeroSpaceNews.com*
AeroSpaceNews.com
PO Box 1748
Ojai, CA 93024-1748
Ph: (805)985-2320
URL: http://aerospacenews.com/
Frequency: Monthly. **Price:** $19.95 Individuals private. **Description:** Journal reporting on the insights, impressions and images of tomorrow's technological wonders in the field of aerospace.

4987 ■ *Air Jobs Digest*
World Air Data
PO Box 42724
Washington, DC 20015
Ph: (301)990-6800
Free: 800-247-5627
E-mail: staff@airjobsdaily.com
URL: http://www.airjobsdigest.com/
Frequency: Monthly. **Price:** $96 Individuals. **Description:** Newspaper covering job listings in aviation and aerospace worldwide.

4988 ■ *Aviation Today*
Access Intelligence L.L.C.
4 Choke Cherry Rd., 2nd Fl.
Rockville, MD 20850
Ph: (301)354-2000
Free: 800-777-5006
Fax: (301)309-3847
E-mail: info@accessintel.com
URL: http://www.accessintel.com
Description: Covers the commuter/regional airline industry, including airline management, marketing, labor, personnel changes, aircraft acquisitions, new products, and the financial and operational environment. Recurring features include interviews, news of research, a calendar of events, reports of meetings, job listings, and notices of publications available.

4989 ■ *Rotor & Wing*
Access Intelligence L.L.C.
4 Choke Cherry Rd., 2nd Fl.
Rockville, MD 20850
Ph: (301)354-2000
Free: 800-777-5006
Fax: (301)309-3847
E-mail: info@accessintel.com
URL: http://www.aviationtoday.com/rw/
Frequency: Monthly. **Price:** Free. **Description:** Magazine covering helicopters.

Employer Directories and Networking Lists

4990 ■ *National Air Transportation Association--Aviation Resource and Membership Directory*
National Air Transportation Association
4226 King St.
Alexandria, VA 22302

Ph: (703)845-9000
Free: 800-808-6282
Fax: (703)845-8176
E-mail: rmulholland@nata.aero
URL: http://www.nata.aero
Frequency: Annual; Latest Edition 2012. **Price:** $50 Nonmembers; $25 Members. **Covers:** More than 1,000 regular, associate, and affiliate members; regular members include airport service organizations, air taxi operators, and commuter airlines. **Entries include:** Company name, address, phone, fax number, name and title of contact. **Arrangement:** Regular members are classified by service; associate and affiliate members are alphabetical in separate sections. **Indexes:** Geographical.

4991 ■ *World Aerospace Database*
Aviation Week Group
1200 G St.NW, Ste. 922
Washington, DC 20005-3814
Free: 800-525-5003
Fax: (712)755-7423
E-mail: wad@mcgraw-hill.com
URL: http://www.aviationweek.com
Frequency: Semiannual. **Price:** $269 U.S. print; $1,295 U.S. CD-ROM, incl. 1 year print sub., 2 editions; $595 U.S. online, incl. 1 year print sub., 2 editions; $495 U.S. special online; $149 U.S. special print. **Description:** Covers more than 25,000 companies and 120,000 key executives to the aviation and aerospace industries worldwide. **Arrangement:** Classified by major activity (manufacturers, airlines, etc.). **Indexes:** Company and organization, personnel, product, trade name.

Handbooks and Manuals

4992 ■ *FabJob Guide to Become a Flight Attendant*
FabJob Inc.
4616-25th Ave. NE, No. 224
Seattle, WA 98105
Ph: (403)873-1018
Free: 888-322-5621
URL: http://www.fabjob.com
Description: Julia Dean. $19.97(e-book). 270 pages. Provides information about careers in the airline industry, how to become a flight attendant and job opportunities with more than 70 airlines.

4993 ■ *Jobs for Travel Lovers: Opportunities at Home and Abroad*
Development Concepts Inc.
9104 Manassas Dr., Ste. N
Manassas Park, VA 20111-5211
Ph: (703)361-7300
Free: 800-361-1055
Fax: (703)335-9486
E-mail: query@impactpublications.com
URL: http://www.impactpublications.com
Description: 2006. $19.95. 320 pages. Covers job

search strategies, with hundreds of jobs in business, government, and education, including the travel and hospital industry, non-profit organizations, international organizations, education institutions, and consulting. Includes opportunities involving airlines and cruise lines, international jobs, travel agencies and tour operators, internships and volunteering, hotels and resorts, military and merchant marine, teaching abroad, travel writing, and short-term work experiences. Provides names, addresses, telephone/fax numbers, e-mails, and websites for contacting potential employers.

4994 ■ *Welcome Aboard!: Your Career As a Flight Attendant*
Aviation Supplies & Academics, Inc.
7005 132nd Pl. SE
Newcastle, WA 98059
Ph: (425)235-1500
Free: 800-272-2359
Fax: (425)235-0128
URL: http://www.asa2fly.com/index.aspx
Description: Becky S. Bock. Third edition. $19.95 (paper). 136 pages.

Employment Agencies and Search Firms

4995 ■ *Jet Professionals*
114 Charles A. Lindbergh Dr.
Teterboro, NJ 07608
Free: 800-441-6016
Fax: (201)462-4081
E-mail: jobs@jet-professionals.com
URL: http://www.jet-professionals.com
Description: Provides staffing services to the aviation industry. Offers jobs for corporate aviation executives, chief pilots, flight attendants, maintenance professionals, dispatchers, schedulers and more.

Online Job Sources and Services

4996 ■ *AeroIndustryJobs.com*
URL: http://www.aeroindustryjobs.com/home/index .cfm?site_id=13641
Description: Lists careers in the aerospace, defense and advanced materials industries. Helps industry employers connect with qualified, career-focused job seekers.

4997 ■ *AeroVents.com*
URL: http://www.aerovents.com/body.shtml
Description: Seeks to spread the word about aviation events. Covers aviation events from conventions, space launches, seminars, model rocketry and aircraft, ballooning, sky diving, plane pulls, open houses, air shows and fly-ins.

4998 ■ Air Transportation Jobs
URL: http://air.transportation.jobs.jobsearchsite.com
Description: Provides available air transportation jobs and career resources. Allows employers to post jobs and search resumes to find qualified candidates.

4999 ■ AirJobsDaily.com
URL: http://www.airjobsdaily.com
Description: Serves as a source of current aviation and aerospace job openings.

5000 ■ AirlineCareer.com
URL: http://www.airlinecareer.com
Description: Web-based training center. Provides flight attendant job placement services.

5001 ■ AirlineCareer.info
URL: http://www.airlinecareer.info
Description: Provides jobs in the airline community covering airport careers, aircraft manufacturing, aerospace careers, and cabin crew careers.

5002 ■ Airportjobs.Us
URL: http://www.airportjobs.us
Description: Helps job seekers find airport career opportunities with top companies. Allows employers and recruiters to match qualified candidates with open airport postions.

5003 ■ AvCrew.com
URL: http://www.avcrew.com
Description: Provides service designed exclusively for career employment in the business aviation sector. Features flight crew jobs, conducts applicant screening, and assists selected flight departments with candidate searches.

5004 ■ AviaNation
URL: http://www.avianation.com
Description: Features aviation jobs, pilot jobs, flight attendant jobs, jobs for A&P mechanics, and other aviation job openings around the world.

5005 ■ The Aviation MD
URL: http://www.theaviationmd.com
Description: Serves as international aviation database for employers and jobseekers in the aviation industry.

5006 ■ AviationCrossing.com
URL: http://www.aviationcrossing.com
Description: Provides aviation jobs for agents, managers, mechanics, operators, specialists, supervisors, technicians, engineers, maintenance, pilots and other related aviation professionals.

5007 ■ AviationEmployment.com
URL: http://www.aviationemployment.com
Description: Serves as an online job search service provider specializing in aviation and aerospace jobs and employment opportunities.

5008 ■ AvJobs.com
URL: http://www.avjobs.com
Description: Provides information on a number of different careers in the aviation and aerospace industry. Features aviation schools directory, affiliate programs, research and networking, employment resources, salaries and wages, aviation careers descriptions, aviation guide and other resources.

5009 ■ BestAviation.net
URL: http://www.bestaviation.net
Description: Provides source for information on flight school training, helicopter schools, aviation college programs, flight attendant careers, aircraft maintenance and pilot jobs.

5010 ■ CabinCrewJobs.com
URL: http://www.cabincrewjobs.com
Description: Offers detailed information about how to successfully launch a career in the airline industry. Includes career resources such as tips on resume writing, interviews, training, salaries, job benefits and more.

5011 ■ FlightAttendantFacts.com
URL: http://www.flightattendantfacts.com
Description: Serves as an online networking site for flight attendants. Features flight attendant job openings, salary information, and interview tips.

5012 ■ FlightAttendantJobsite.com
URL: http://www.flightattendantjobsite.com
Description: Serves as an online career resource for flight attendants. Allows job seekers to post their resumes and features other career resources such

as job search and interviewing, self-assessment tools and more.

5013 ■ FlightLevelJobs.com
URL: http://www.flightleveljobs.com
Description: Serves as a source of aviation employment information. Features aviation and aerospace jobs and employment opportunities.

5014 ■ FlyContract.com
URL: http://www.flycontract.com
Description: Provides a directory to help corporate pilots and corporate flight attendants obtain jobs.

5015 ■ JetEmployment.com
URL: http://jetemployment.com
Description: Features employment opportunities for pilots and other workers in the airline, airport, and business aviation industry.

5016 ■ Locate Flight Attendant Jobs
URL: http://www.locateflightattendantjobs.com
Description: Provides a searchable database of employment opportunities for flight attendants.

5017 ■ PlaneJobs.com
URL: http://planejobs.com
Description: Serves as an employment, resume, career, and job search database for the aviation industry.

OTHER SOURCES

5018 ■ Association of Flight Attendants - CWA
501 3rd St. NW
Washington, DC 20001
Ph: (202)434-1300
Free: 800-424-2401
Fax: (202)434-1319
E-mail: info@afacwa.org
URL: http://www.afanet.org
Description: Labor union organized by flight attendants. AFA represents over 50,000 flight attendants at 22 airlines, serving as a voice for flight attendants at their workplace, in the industry, and in the media.

SOURCES OF HELP-WANTED ADS

5019 ■ *Florists' Review*
URL: http://www.floristsreview.com
Description: Monthly guidebook for operating a successful floral business.

5020 ■ *Grower Talks*
Ball Publishing
622 Town Rd.
West Chicago, IL 60186
Ph: (630)231-3675
Free: 888-888-0013
Fax: (630)231-5254
E-mail: info@ballpublishing.com
URL: http://www.ballpublishing.com/GrowerTalks/
default.aspx
Frequency: Monthly. **Price:** $35 U.S. and Canada; $99 Other countries. **Description:** Trade magazine covering issues for commercial greenhouse growers with a focus on North American production.

EMPLOYER DIRECTORIES AND NETWORKING LISTS

5021 ■ *Michigan Florist--Membership Directory*
Michigan Floral Association
1152 Haslett Rd.
Haslett, MI 48840
Ph: (517)575-0110
Fax: (517)575-0115
E-mail: rod@michiganfloral.org
URL: http://www.michiganfloral.org
Frequency: Annual; fall. **Publication includes:** List of about 1,100 member floral retailers and wholesalers, nurseries and garden centers, and individual members. **Entries include:** Company name, owner's name, address, phone, type of business. **Arrangement:** Separate geographical and alphabetical lists.

5022 ■ *Professional Floral Communicators-International--Directory*
Society of American Florists - Professional Floral Communicators-International
c/o Lisa Weddel, Chairperson
2832 Clairton Dr.
Highlands Ranch, CO 80126
Ph: (303)587-7912
E-mail: keidam@safnow.org
URL: http://alliedfloristsofhouston.org/z-old/member-directory.htm
Covers: about 80 member floral presenters and educators. **Entries include:** Name, address, phone, professional affiliation, education, career data, interests, design and presentation techniques. **Arrangement:** Alphabetical/geographic/area of expertise.

5023 ■ *Wholesale Florist & Florist Supplier Association--Membership Directory*
Wholesale Florists & Florist Supplier Association
105 Eastern Ave., Ste. 104
Annapolis, MD 21403
Ph: (410)940-6580
Free: 888-289-3372
Fax: (410)263-1659
E-mail: info@wffsa.org
URL: http://www.wffsa.org
Frequency: Biennial; summer/winter. **No. of Listings:** 1,275. **Entries include:** Company name, address, phone, names of executives, list of products or services. **Arrangement:** Geographical. **Indexes:** Alphabetical.

HANDBOOKS AND MANUALS

5024 ■ *FabJob Guide to Become a Florist*
FabJob.com
4616 25th Ave. NE, Ste. 224
Seattle, WA 98105
Ph: (403)949-4980
Free: 888-322-5621
URL: http://www.fabjob.com/Organizer.asp
Description: 2004. $29.97. 267 pages. Offers a step-by-step guide to becoming a florist.

5025 ■ *Florist*
National Learning Corporation
212 Michael Dr.
Syosset, NY 11791
Ph: (516)921-8888
Free: 800-632-8888
Fax: (516)921-8743
E-mail: info@passbooks.com
URL: http://www.passbooks.com
Description: 2009. $29.95 (paper). Serves as an exam preparation guide for florists.

ONLINE JOB SOURCES AND SERVICES

5026 ■ *AllFloristJobs.com*
URL: http://allfloristjobs.com
Description: Features job sites, company career pages and associations for florist jobs.

5027 ■ *FloralJobs.org*
URL: http://floraljobs.org
Description: Features job sites, company career pages and associations for floral jobs.

TRADESHOWS

5028 ■ *American Institute of Floral Designers National Symposium*
American Institute of Floral Designers
720 Light St.
Baltimore, MD 21230
Ph: (410)752-3318
URL: http://www.aifd.org
Frequency: Annual. Features programs and the latest trends in the floral design industry. Provides opportunities for attendees to meet colleagues and acquire new skills, ideas, and innovations.

OTHER SOURCES

5029 ■ *American Institute of Floral Designers*
720 Light St.
Baltimore, MD 21230
Ph: (410)752-3318
URL: http://www.aifd.org
Description: Active floral designers, associates, retired floral designers and other individuals. Works to promote the profession and art of floral design. Maintains student chapter.

5030 ■ *Careers for Crafty People and Other Dexterous Types*
The McGraw Hill Companies Inc.
PO Box 182604
Columbus, OH 43272
Ph: (212)512-2000
Free: 877-833-5524
Fax: (614)759-3749
E-mail: customer.service@mcgraw-hill.com
URL: http://www.mcgraw-hill.com
Description: Mark Rowh. Third edition, 2006. $13.95 (paper). 160 pages. **Includes:** List of agencies in the United States and Canada that offer information on education and training, as well as opportunities for practicing craft making in various geographical regions. List of agencies in the United States and Canada that offer information on education and training, as well as opportunities for practicing craft making in various geographical regions. **Entries include:** Name, address, URL.

5031 ■ *Careers for Plant Lovers and Other Green Thumb Types*
The McGraw-Hill Companies Inc.
PO Box 182604
Columbus, OH 43272
Ph: (212)512-2000
Free: 877-833-5524
Fax: (614)759-3749
E-mail: customer.service@mcgraw-hill.com
URL: http://www.mcgraw-hill.com
Description: Blythe Camenson. Second edition, 2004. $13.95. 160 pages. **Includes:** Appendices of selected list botanical gardens and arboreta for internships, summer employment, and volunteer opportunities, as well as a list of U.S. National Park Service regional offices. Appendices of selected list botanical gardens and arboreta for internships, summer employment, and volunteer opportunities, as well as a list of U.S. National Park Service regional

offices. **Entries include:** Organization name, address.

5032 ■ *Careers for Self-Starters and Other Entrepreneurial Types*

The McGraw-Hill Companies Inc.
PO Box 182604
Columbus, OH 43272
Ph: (212)512-2000
Free: 877-833-5524
Fax: (614)759-3749
E-mail: customer.service@mcgraw-hill.com
URL: http://www.mcgraw-hill.com

Blythe Camenson. **Frequency:** September 2004. **Price:** $9.95 (US).; $13.95 (US). **Description:** Blythe Camenson. Second edition, 2004. $9.95 (paper). 129 pages. **Includes:** Appendix of associations that provide information on education, training, and certification opportunities, as well as advice on starting businesses; recommended reading list. Appendix of associations that provide information on education, training, and certification opportunities, as well as advice on starting businesses; recommended reading list. **Entries include:** Name, address, brief description of information resources.

5033 ■ **Holiday and Decorative Association**

2000 N Stemmons Fwy., Ste. 1F312
Dallas, TX 75207
Ph: (214)742-2747
Fax: (214)742-2648
E-mail: hda@hdanow.org
URL: http://www.hdanow.org

Description: Strives to act as the national organization for importers, domestic manufacturers, wholesalers, retailers, overseas suppliers, manufacturers sales representatives, etc., of artificial, botanical, Christmas and floral products and accessories. **Members:** 211.

5034 ■ **Society of American Florists**

1601 Duke St.
Alexandria, VA 22314-3406
Ph: (703)836-8700
Free: 800-336-4743
Fax: (703)836-8705
E-mail: webmaster@safnow.org
URL: http://www.safnow.org

Description: Growers, wholesalers, retailers, and allied tradesmen in the floral industry. Lobbies Congress on behalf of the industry; sponsors educational programs; promotes the floral industry;

prepares materials for consumers and for high school and college students; provides business resources. Sponsors Floricultural Hall of Fame, American Academy of Floriculture, and Professional Floral Commentators International. Compiles statistics; sponsors competitions.

5035 ■ **Wholesale Florist and Florist Supplier Association**

Horn Point Harbor Marina
105 Eastern Ave., Ste. 104
Annapolis, MD 21403
Ph: (410)940-6580
Free: 888-289-3372
Fax: (410)263-1659
E-mail: info@wffsa.org
URL: http://www.wffsa.org

Description: Proprietorships, partnerships or corporations conducting wholesale businesses in fresh flowers, greens, or plants, or engaged in the manufacture and/or wholesaling of florist supplies; others actively engaged in the floral industry are associate members. Preserves and strengthens the wholesale florists' position in the floral industry. Provides a unified voice to promote the wholesalers' contributions to the industry.

Sources of Help-Wanted Ads

5036 ■ *AWIS Magazine*
Association for Women in Science
1321 Duke St., Ste. 210
Alexandria, VA 22314
Ph: (703)894-4490
E-mail: awis@awis.org
URL: http://www.awis.org/displaycommon.cfm?an
=1&subarticlenbr=2

Frequency: Quarterly. **Description:** Professional magazine covering the status of women in science.

5037 ■ *Current Opinion in Pharmacology*
Elsevier Science Inc.
Secondary Publishing Division
650 Ave. of the Americas
New York, NY 10011
Ph: (212)633-3980
Free: 888-437-4636
Fax: (212)633-3975
URL: http://www.elsevier.com/wps/find/journalde-
scription.cws_home/621337/description#description

Frequency: 6/yr. **Price:** $2,102 Individuals and institution; online; $386 Individuals print; $2,102 Institutions print. **Description:** Journal covering current advances in pharmacology.

5038 ■ *Harvard Science Review*
Harvard University Press
79 Garden St.
Cambridge, MA 02138
Ph: (617)495-2600
Free: 800-405-1619
Fax: (401)531-2801
E-mail: hsr@hcs.harvard.edu
URL: http://www.hcs.harvard.edu/~hsr/

Frequency: Semiannual. **Description:** A science journal.

5039 ■ *The Internet Journal of Forensic Science*
Internet Scientific Publications L.L.C.
23 Rippling Creek Dr.
Sugar Land, TX 77479
E-mail: wenker@ispub.com
URL: http://www.ispub.com/journal/the-internet
-journal-of-forensic-science/

Price: Free. **Description:** Electronic journal for medical professionals focusing on the field of forensic science.

5040 ■ *Journal of the American Society of Questioned Document Examiners*
American Society of Questioned Document Examiners
PO Box 18298
Long Beach, CA 90807

Ph: (562)253-2589
E-mail: jgreen@documentexaminer.info
URL: http://www.asqde.org

Frequency: Semiannual. **Price:** $70 U.S. and Canada; $110 U.S. and Canada agency; $85 Other countries; $125 Institutions, other countries agency. **Description:** Professional journal covering forensic sciences.

5041 ■ *Journal of Forensic Identification*
International Association for Identification
2131 Hollywood Blvd., Ste. 403
Hollywood, FL 33020
Ph: (954)589-0628
Fax: (954)589-0657
URL: http://www.theiai.org

Description: A scientific journal that provides over 115 pages of articles related to forensics. Also offers information regarding training and educational events, job postings and announcements. Yearly subscriptions: $175.00 for individuals, $205.00 for institutions and libraries.

5042 ■ *Oxymag*
Elsevier Science Inc.
Secondary Publishing Division
650 Ave. of the Americas
New York, NY 10011
Ph: (212)633-3980
Free: 888-437-4636
Fax: (212)633-3975
URL: http://www.elsevier.com/wps/find/journalde-
scription.cws_home/709679/description#description

Frequency: 6/yr. **Description:** Journal related to the construction field covering information in the manufacture of commercial, industrial, spark proof and decorative terrazzo floors, flooring for railroad boxcars, industrial fireproof coatings, fire-resistant marine interior deckings and a variety of building units.

5043 ■ *Science*
American Association for the Advancement of Science
1200 New York Ave. NW
Washington, DC 20005
Ph: (202)326-6400
Fax: (202)371-9526
E-mail: membership@aaas.org
URLs: http://www.scienceonline.org; http://www.sci-
encemag.org

Frequency: Weekly. **Price:** $146 Members professional, print & online; $119 Individuals NPA postdoctoral, print & online; $99 Individuals postdoctoral/ resident, print & online; $75 Students print & online; $310 Individuals patron, print & online; $115 Individuals emeritus, print & online; $161 Canada postdoctoral/resident, print & online; $136.50 Students, Canada print & online; $149 in U.S.; $211.05 in Canada; $201 in Mexico/Caribbean; $231 in all other countries. **Description:** Contains research reports, book reviews, editorial, news, and comments.

Employer Directories and Networking Lists

5044 ■ *American Academy of Forensic Sciences--Membership Directory*
American Academy of Forensic Sciences
2906 Lafayette Ave.
Newport Beach, CA 92663
Ph: (949)230-7321
E-mail: damartell@aol.com
URL: http://www.aafs.org

Frequency: Annual; May. **Pages:** 160. **Covers:** 3,800 persons qualified in forensic sciences, including law, pathology, biology, odontology, physical anthropology, psychiatry, questioned documents, criminalistics, engineering, and toxicology. **Entries include:** Name, office address and phone, highest degree held, professional title, type of certification. **Arrangement:** Alphabetical. **Indexes:** Geographical, subject.

5045 ■ *International Association for Identification--Membership Directory*
International Association for Identification
2131 Hollywood Blvd., Ste. 403
Hollywood, FL 33020
Ph: (954)589-0628
Fax: (954)589-0657
URL: http://www.theiai.org

Frequency: Annual; December. **Covers:** About 4,600 police officials, identification personnel, and others engaged in forensic identification, investigation, and scientific crime detection. **Entries include:** Name, preferred mailing address. **Arrangement:** Geographical. **Indexes:** Alphabetical.

5046 ■ *Opportunities in Forensic Science*
The McGraw-Hill Companies Inc.
PO Box 182604
Columbus, OH 43272
Ph: (212)512-2000
Free: 877-833-5524
Fax: (614)759-3749
E-mail: customer.service@mcgraw-hill.com
URLs: http://www.mcgraw-hill.com/; http://www.mh-
professional.com

Frequency: Latest edition 2008. **Price:** $14.95 Individuals Paperback, E-book. **Pages:** 160. **Publication includes:** a list of colleges and universities offering graduate programs and internships in the field of forensic science. Principal content of publication is is information on career opportunities in the forensic sciences, including educational requirements, qualifications needed, and salary. Publisher also offers a catalog card kit for this title.

Handbooks and Manuals

5047 ■ *Forensic Science Handbook*
Prentice Hall PTR
1 Lake St.
Upper Saddle River, NJ 07458

Ph: (201)236-7676
Free: 800-227-1816
Fax: (800)445-6991
URL: http://phbusiness.prenhall.com

Description: Second edition, 2009. $177. 552 pages. Reference source for the field of criminalistics. Each chapter offers a review of a particular aspect of the field written by noted experts.

Online Job Sources and Services

5048 ■ ForensicScienceJobs.org
URL: http://forensicsciencejobs.org

Description: Serves as an online employment site for professionals in the forensic science industry.

5049 ■ ScientistCrossing.com
URL: http://www.scientistcrossing.com

Description: Provides job listings and other resources related to scientist employment opportunities.

Tradeshows

5050 ■ American Academy of Forensic Sciences Annual Scientific Meeting
American Academy of Forensic Sciences
2906 Lafayette Ave.
Newport Beach, CA 92663
Ph: (949)230-7321
E-mail: damartell@aol.com
URL: http://www.aafs.org

Frequency: Annual. **Primary Exhibits:** Scientific instruments.

Other Sources

5051 ■ American Academy of Forensic Sciences
2906 Lafayette Ave.
Newport Beach, CA 92663
Ph: (949)230-7321
E-mail: damartell@aol.com
URL: http://www.aafs.org

Description: Represents criminalists, scientists, members of the bench and bar, pathologists, biologists, psychiatrists, examiners of questioned documents, toxicologists, odontologists, anthropologists, and engineers. Works to: encourage the study, improve the practice, elevate the standards, and advance the cause of the forensic sciences; improve the quality of scientific techniques, tests, and criteria; plan, organize, and administer meetings, reports, and other projects for the stimulation and advancement of these and related purposes. Maintains Forensic Sciences Job Listing; conducts selected research for the government; offers forensic expert referral service.

5052 ■ American Board of Criminalistics
PO Box 1358
Palmetto, FL 34220
Ph: (941)729-9050
E-mail: abcregistrar@verizon.net
URL: http://www.criminalistics.com

Description: Regional and national organizations of forensic scientists and criminalists. Offers certificates of Professional Competency in Criminalistics as well as in specialty disciplines of forensic biology, drug chemistry, fire debris analysis, and various areas of trace evidence examination. Works to establish professional standards and promote growth within the industry. Answers questions regarding the certification process. **Members:** 900.

5053 ■ American Board of Forensic Toxicology
410 N 21st St.
Colorado Springs, CO 80904

Ph: (719)636-1100
Fax: (719)636-1993
E-mail: bruce-goldberger@ufl.com
URL: http://www.abft.org

Description: Works to establish, enhance, and revise as necessary, standards of qualification for those who practice forensic toxicology, and to certify as qualified specialists those applicants who comply with the requirements of the Board.

5054 ■ American College of Forensic Examiners International
2750 E Sunshine St.
Springfield, MO 65804
Ph: (417)881-3818
Free: 800-423-9737
Fax: (417)881-4702
URL: http://www.acfei.com

Description: Professionals in the field of forensic examination, including the following disciplines: accounting, accident reconstruction, criminology, crisis intervention, counselors, social work, nursing and law enforcement hypnosis, all medical fields, physics, psychiatry, psychology, and toxicology. Works to advance the profession of forensic examination through education, training, and certification.

5055 ■ American Society of Crime Laboratory Directors
139A Technology Dr.
Garner, NC 27529
Ph: (919)773-2044
Fax: (919)861-9930
E-mail: office@ascld.org
URL: http://www.ascld.org

Description: Nonprofit professional society dedicated to providing excellence in forensic science analysis through leadership in the management of forensic science. The purpose of the organization is to foster professional interests; assist the development of laboratory management principles and techniques; acquire, preserve and disseminate forensic based information; maintain and improve communications among crime laboratory directors; and to promote, encourage and maintain the highest standards of practice in the field.

5056 ■ American Society of Criminology
1314 Kinnear Rd., Ste. 212
Columbus, OH 43212-1156
Ph: (614)292-9207
Fax: (614)292-6767
E-mail: asc@asc41.com
URL: http://www.asc41.com

Description: Represents professional and academic criminologists, students of criminology in accredited universities, psychiatrists, psychologists, and sociologists. Develops criminology as a science and academic discipline. Aids in the construction of criminological curricula in accredited universities. Upgrades the practitioner in criminological fields (police, prisons, probation, parole, delinquency workers). Conducts research programs and sponsors three student paper competitions. Provides placement service at annual convention.

5057 ■ American Society of Digital Forensics and eDiscovery
2451 Cumberland Pkwy., Ste. 3382
Atlanta, GA 30339-6157
Free: 866-534-9734
E-mail: member_services@asdfed.org
URL: http://www.asdfed.com

Description: Represents digital forensic examiners, legal professionals, litigation support analysts and managers, law enforcement, and government investigators. Promotes digital forensics and electronic discovery through advocacy, education, research and information. Conducts conferences, training programs and workshops.

5058 ■ American Society of Forensic Podiatry
PO Box 549
Bandon, OR 97411
E-mail: asfpdpm@aol.com
URL: http://theasfp.org

Description: Aims to advance the cause of forensic podiatry. Promotes the use of podiatry in forensics cases. Develops and maintains the highest standards of practice through research, discussion, education, publications, and liaison with other organized agencies.

5059 ■ Association of Forensic Document Examiners
c/o Emily J. Will, President
PO Box 58552
Raleigh, NC 27658
Ph: (919)556-7414
E-mail: info@afde.org
URL: http://www.afde.org

Description: Represents forensic document examiners and students of document examination. Sponsors annual continuing education conferences and offers a certification program. **Members:** 45.

5060 ■ *Career Opportunities in Forensic Science*
InfoBase Holdings Inc.
132 W 31st., 17 Fl.
New York, NY 10001-3406
Ph: (212)967-8800
Fax: (800)678-3633
E-mail: info@infobasepublishing.com
URL: http://www.ferguson.infobasepublishing.com

Description: 2008. $49.50. 336 pages. Includes a total of 82 job profiles in the field of forensic science. **Includes:** Appendices of educational institutions, certification programs, periodicals, directories, and associations. Appendices of educational institutions, certification programs, periodicals, directories, and associations.

5061 ■ Evidence Photographers International Council
229 Peachtree St. NE, No. 2200
Atlanta, GA 30303
Free: 866-868-3742
Fax: (404)614-6406
E-mail: cwerner@evidencephotographers.com
URL: http://www.evidencephotographers.com

Description: Law enforcement and civil evidence photographers; others in related fields. Objectives are to: aid in the worldwide advancement of forensic photography; assist in research and development of new techniques; enhance professional education; inform members of new procedures. Maintains speakers' bureau. Offers certification upon satisfactory completion of an oral or written examination by a three-member panel, receipt of a minimum of 30 prints for review, and a $150 application fee. Provides an honors program to recognize those who have shown expertise in the field of forensic photography, and service to the Council. Sponsors the EPIC Witness Referral Service.

5062 ■ Forensic Sciences Foundation
410 N 21st St.
Colorado Springs, CO 80904
Ph: (719)636-1100
Fax: (719)636-1993
E-mail: awarren@aafs.org
URL: http://fsf.aafs.org/

Description: Purposes are to: conduct research in the procedures and standards utilized in the practice of forensic sciences; develop and implement useful educational and training programs and methods of benefit to forensic sciences; conduct programs of public education concerning issues of importance to the forensic sciences; engage in activities which will promote, encourage, and assist the development of the forensic sciences. Provides referral service for forensic scientists. Compiles statistics. Operates the Forensic Sciences Foundation Press.

5063 ■ International Association of Computer Investigative Specialists
PO Box 2411
Leesburg, VA 20177
Ph: (304)915-0555
Free: 888-884-2247
E-mail: secretary@cops.org
URL: http://www.iacis.com

Description: Provides education and certification of law enforcement professionals in the field of computer forensic science. Creates and establishes procedures, trains personnel, and certifies forensic examiners in the recovery of evidence from computer systems. Offers professional training in the seizure and processing computer systems. Provides an opportunity to network with other law enforcement officers trained in computer forensics, and to share and learn from others.

5064 ■ International Association for Identification
2131 Hollywood Blvd., Ste. 403
Hollywood, FL 33020
Ph: (954)589-0628
Fax: (954)589-0657
URL: http://www.theiai.org

Description: Individuals engaged in forensic identification, investigation, and scientific crime detection. Strives to improve methods of scientific identification techniques used in criminal investigations.

5065 ■ Law Enforcement and Emergency Services Video Association
84 Briar Creek Rd.
Whitesboro, TX 76273-4603
Ph: (469)285-9435

Fax: (469)533-3659
E-mail: president@leva.org
URL: http://leva.org

Description: Serves as a key resource to the global public safety community by focusing on the needs of video production and forensic imaging disciplines. Provides opportunities for professional development through quality training and informational exchange. Offers forensic video analysis training to law enforcement professionals.

5066 ■ National Forensic Center
National Directory of Expert Witnesses
PO Box 270529
San Diego, CA 92198-2529
Free: 800-735-6660
Fax: (858)487-7747
E-mail: info@national-experts.com
URL: http://www.national-experts.com

Description: Expert witnesses and litigation consultants who serve attorneys, insurance companies, and government agencies. Trains consultants to work with attorneys and to testify in court; trains individuals to serve as expert witnesses and litigation consultants. Makes speakers available upon request. Compiles statistics on experts' fees.

5067 ■ National Forensic Science Technology Center
7881 114th Ave., N
Largo, FL 33773
Ph: (727)549-6067
Fax: (727)549-6070
E-mail: info@nfstc.org
URL: http://www.nfstc.org

Description: Provides systems support, training and education to the forensic science community in the United States.

5068 ■ Professional Society of Forensic Mapping
4964 Ward Rd.
Wheat Ridge, CO 80033
E-mail: info@psfm.org
URL: http://www.psfm.org

Description: Promotes the field of forensic mapping through high professional and personal conduct of its members. Provides members with a forum for the exchange of information pertaining to skills and techniques for the electronic documentation of crash or crime scenes. Offers training to members of law enforcement, governmental, and quasi-governmental agencies, private consultants and other persons in the field of forensic mapping.

5069 ■ Society of Forensic Toxicologists
One MacDonald Center
1 N MacDonald St., Ste. 15
Mesa, AZ 85201
Free: 888-866-7638
E-mail: pstout@rti.org
URL: http://www.soft-tox.org

Description: Scientists who analyze tissue and body fluids for drugs and poisons and interpret the information for judicial purposes. Objectives are to establish uniform qualifications and requirements for certification of forensic toxicologists and promote support mechanisms for continued certification; to stimulate research and development; to provide review board for cases involving differences of professional opinion; to act on administrative and career problems affecting forensic toxicologists. Serves as clearinghouse; conducts proficiency testing programs; provides information on case histories and job opportunities. Sponsors American Board of Forensic Toxicology. **Members:** 425.

Foresters and Conservation Scientists

SOURCES OF HELP-WANTED ADS

5070 ■ *Atmospheric and Climate Sciences*
Scientific Research Publishing
PO Box 54821
Irvine, CA 92619-4821
E-mail: acs@scirp.org
URL: http://www.scirp.org/journal/acs/

Frequency: Quarterly. **Price:** $156 Individuals.
Description: Journal publishing articles on climate atmospheric science.

5071 ■ *Capital Ideas*
Alabama Forest Owners' Association
PO Box 361434
Birmingham, AL 35236
Ph: (205)987-8811
Fax: (205)987-9824
E-mail: rll@afoa.org
URL: http://www.afoa.org

Description: Monthly. Covers activities of Alabama Forest Owners' Association. Contains calendar of forestry events and forestry related news.

5072 ■ *Carolina Forestry Journal*
South Carolina Forestry Association
PO Box 21303
Columbia, SC 29221-1303
Ph: (803)798-4170
Fax: (803)798-2340
E-mail: scfa@scforestry.org
URL: http://www.scforestry.org

Frequency: Bimonthly. **Description:** Journal containing information for the forestry industry, including forest conservation and preservation.

5073 ■ *CINTRAFOR News*
University of Washington - Center for International Trade in Forest Products
School of Forest Resources, Box 352100
Seattle, WA 98195-2100
Ph: (206)543-8684
Fax: (206)685-0790
E-mail: eastin@u.washington.edu
URL: http://www.cintrafor.org

Description: Quarterly. Summarizes research and related activities in the area of forest products trade, including international symposiums, workshops, publications, and new technology trends sponsored by the Center.

5074 ■ *City Trees*
Society of Municipal Arborists
PO Box 641
Watkinsville, GA 30677
Ph: (706)769-7412
Fax: (706)769-7307
E-mail: urbanforestry@prodigy.net
URL: http://www.urban-forestry.com

Description: Bimonthly. Addresses all aspects of

municipal (urban) forestry. Contains technical articles on species of trees, pest control, conservation, planning, design, and equipment. Recurring features include lists of new publications, statistics, news of research, letters to the editor, announcements of meetings, and columns titled President's Column, Professor's Column, City of the Month, Park of the Month, Tree of the Month, and Editor's Column.

5075 ■ *Corporate Social Responsibility and Environmental Management*
John Wiley & Sons Inc.
111 River St.
Hoboken, NJ 07030-5774
Ph: (201)748-6000
Free: 800-225-5945
Fax: (201)748-6088
E-mail: info@wiley.com
URL: http://onlinelibrary.wiley.com/journal/10.1002/
(ISSN)1535-3966

Frequency: Bimonthly. **Price:** $1,624 Institutions, other countries print only; €1,047 Institutions Europe, print or online; £954 Institutions UK, print or online; €1,206 Institutions Europe, print + online; £954 Institutions UK, print + online; $1,867 Institutions, other countries print + online. **Description:** Journal providing a resource for organizations concerned with social and environmental responsibilities in the context of sustainable development.

5076 ■ *Drinking Water & Backflow Prevention*
International Association of Plumbing and Mechanical Officials
4755 E Philadelphia St.
Ontario, CA 91761
Ph: (909)472-4100
Fax: (909)472-4150
E-mail: iapmo@iapmo.org
URLs: http://www.dwbp-online.com.; http://www.iap-modwbp.org

Krystal Renea Garza, Editor. **Frequency:** Monthly. **Price:** $45, U.S. year; $53 Canada and Mexico.; $59, elsewhere year. **Description:** Monthly. $45.00/year. Recurring features include news of educational opportunities, job listings, and a calendar of events.

5077 ■ *Ecological Entomology*
Blackwell Publishing Inc.
350 Main St.
Malden, MA 02148
Ph: (781)388-8200
Free: 800-216-2522
Fax: (781)388-8210
E-mail: journaladsusa@bos.blackwellpublishing.com
URL: http://as.wiley.com/WileyCDA/WileyTitle/productCd-EEN.html

Frequency: Bimonthly. **Price:** €1,422 Institutions print & online; $2,070 Institutions print & online; $1,800 Institutions print or online; €1,236 Institutions print or online; £1,119 Institutions, other countries print & online; £973 Institutions print or online.

Description: Journal publishing articles on conversation issues.

5078 ■ *Environmental Business Journal*
Environmental Business International Inc.
4452 Park Blvd., Ste. 306
San Diego, CA 92116
Ph: (619)295-7685
Fax: (619)295-5743
E-mail: ebi@ebiusa.com
URL: http://www.ebiusa.com

Description: Twelve issues/year. $995/year. Provides research and articles on various segments of the environmental business industry. Recurring features include news of research.

5079 ■ *Environmental Education Research*
Routledge Journals - Taylor & Francis Group
270 Madison Ave.
New York, NY 10016-0601
Ph: (212)216-7800
Fax: (212)563-2269
URL: http://www.tandfonline.com/toc/ceer20/current

Frequency: 6/year. **Price:** $1,594 Institutions print + online; $1,395 Institutions online only; $424 Individuals print only. **Description:** Journal covering all aspects of environmental education.

5080 ■ *Fisheries*
American Fisheries Society
5410 Grosvenor Ln.
Bethesda, MD 20814
Ph: (301)897-8616
Fax: (301)897-8096
E-mail: main@fisheries.org
URL: http://fisheries.org

Frequency: Monthly. **Price:** $166 Institutions; included in membership dues. **Description:** Contains articles on fisheries administration, economics, education, management, philosophy, and professional responsibilities. Includes book reviews.

5081 ■ *Forests for Oregon*
Oregon Department of Forestry
2600 State St.
Salem, OR 97310
Ph: (503)945-7200
Fax: (503)945-7212
URL: http://egov.oregon.gov/ODF/

Description: Quarterly. Discusses forestry issues on state and private lands, laws regarding forest management, and practices. Recurring features include interviews, news of research, report of meetings, and notices of publications available.

5082 ■ *FRA Bulletin*
Forest Resources Association
1901 Pennsylvania Ave. NW, Ste. 303
Washington, DC 20006
Ph: (202)296-3937

Fax: (202)296-0562
E-mail: dhawkinson@forestresources.org
URL: http://www.forestresources.org

Description: Monthly. Electronic newsletter covering current events and policy in wood supply and forest management. Recurring features include a calendar of events, news of educational opportunities, job listings, and notices of publications available.

5083 ■ FYI
Washington Forest Protection Association
724 Columbia St. NW, Ste. 250
Olympia, WA 98501
Ph: (360)352-1500
Fax: (360)352-4621
E-mail: info@wfpa.org
URL: http://www.wfpa.org

Description: Quarterly. Covers activities of Washington Forest Protection Association. Contains research summary.

5084 ■ Green Career Journal
Environmental Career Center
601 N Mechanic St., Ste. 306
Franklin, VA 23851
Ph: (757)727-7895
URL: http://environmentalcareer.com

Description: Monthly. Provides information, articles and insight on the environmental businesses and organizations and their current job openings.

5085 ■ Hardwood Research Bulletin
National Hardwood Lumber Association
6830 Raleigh La Grange Rd.
Memphis, TN 38134-0518
Ph: (901)377-1818
Free: 800-933-0318
Fax: (901)382-6419
E-mail: info@nhla.com
URL: http://www.nhla.com

Description: Monthly. Provides abstracts and digests of current research information concerning hardwood forest management, silviculture, insects, diseases, resource utilization, product development, manufacturing technology, and economics. Lists upcoming events, workshops, short courses, and seminars of interest to members.

5086 ■ ISTF News
International Society of Tropical Foresters
5400 Grosvenor Ln.
Bethesda, MD 20814
Ph: (301)530-4514
Fax: (301)897-3690
E-mail: webmaster@istf-bethesda.org
URL: http://www.istf-bethesda.org

Description: Quarterly. Covers developments in tropical forestry. Recurring features include book reviews, notices of upcoming meetings, lists of members, and notes on member activities.

5087 ■ The Job Seeker
URL: http://www.thejobseeker.net

Description: Semimonthly. Specializes in environmental and natural resource vacancies nationwide. Lists current vacancies from federal, state, local, private, and non-profit employers. Also available via e-mail.

5088 ■ Journal of Applied Ecology
Blackwell Publishing Inc.
350 Main St.
Malden, MA 02148
Ph: (781)388-8200
Free: 800-216-2522
Fax: (781)388-8210
E-mail: journaladsusa@bos.blackwellpublishing.com
URL: http://onlinelibrary.wiley.com/journal/10.1111/
(ISSN)1365-2664

Frequency: Bimonthly. **Price:** $1,677 Institutions U.S. print and online; $1,458 Institutions U.S. print or online; £907 Institutions print and online; £789 Institutions print or online. **Description:** Journal

focusing on ecological science and environmental management.

5089 ■ Natural Resources
Scientific Research Publishing
PO Box 54821
Irvine, CA 92619-4821
E-mail: nr@scirp.org
URL: http://www.scirp.org/journal/nr/

Frequency: Quarterly. **Price:** $156 Individuals. **Description:** Peer-reviewed journal publishing articles on the latest advancements in natural resources.

5090 ■ Northern Logger and Timber Processor
Northeastern Loggers Association
3311 State Rte. 28
Old Forge, NY 13420
Ph: (315)369-3078
Free: 800-318-7561
Fax: (315)369-3736
E-mail: jphaneuf@nothernlogger.com
URL: http://northernlogger.com/content/northern
-logger-magazine

Frequency: Monthly. **Price:** $18 Individuals; $29 Two years. **Description:** Magazine for the logging and lumber industries.

5091 ■ Ornithological Newsletter
Ornithological Societies of North America
5400 Bosque Blvd., Ste. 680
Waco, TX 76710
Ph: (254)399-9636
Fax: (254)776-3767
E-mail: business@osnabirds.org
URL: http://www.osnabirds.org

Description: Bimonthly. Provides information of interest to ornithologists. Recurring features include listings of available grants and awards, news of members, a calendar of events, activities of sponsoring societies, and notices of publications available. Notices of employment opportunities are also available on the Web version.

5092 ■ P2: Pollution Prevention Review
John Wiley & Sons Inc.
111 River St.
Hoboken, NJ 07030-5774
Ph: (201)748-6000
Free: 800-225-5945
Fax: (201)748-6088
E-mail: info@wiley.com
URL: http://as.wiley.com/WileyCDA/WileyTitle/pro-
ductCd-PPR.html

Frequency: Quarterly. **Description:** Journal discussing source reduction and waste minimization, and focusing on the tactics, techniques, and answers for solving pollution problems before they begin.

5093 ■ PALAIOS
SEPM Publications
University of Kansas
Paleontological Institute, Department of Geology
1475 Jawyhawk Blvd., Rm. 120
Lawrence, KS 66045-7613
Ph: (785)864-2737
Fax: (785)864-3636
E-mail: palois@ku.edu
URLs: http://palaios.ku.edu/; http://palaios
.geoscienceworld.org/

Frequency: Monthly. **Price:** $400 Individuals for U.S.; online version with CD-ROM; $500 Individuals for U.S.; print and online version with CD-ROM; $400 Other countries online version with CD-ROM; $500 Other countries print and online version with CD-ROM. **Description:** Journal providing information on the impact of life on Earth history as recorded in the paleontological and sedimentological records. Covers areas such as biogeochemistry, ichnology, sedimentology, stratigraphy, paleoecology, paleoclimatology, and paleoceanography.

5094 ■ SFPA Newsletter
Southern Forest Products Association
Southern Pine Council
2900 Indiana Ave.
Kenner, LA 70065-4605
Ph: (504)443-4464
Fax: (504)443-6612
E-mail: mail@sfpa.org
URL: http://sfpa.org

Description: Weekly. Covers activities of Southern Forest Products Association. Covers forest products, timber resources, market development activities, transportation, lumber manufacturing, and business and association news.

5095 ■ Under the Canopy-Forestry & Forest Products Newsletter
Alaska Cooperative Extension
PO Box 756180
Fairbanks, AK 99775-6180
Ph: (907)474-5211
Fax: (907)474-2631
E-mail: cesweb@alaska.edu
URL: http://www.uaf.edu/ces/newsltrs

Description: Three issues/year. Focuses on forestry in Alaska, including legislation, tree diseases, forest fires, wood use, and tree farms. Recurring features include news from the Board of Forestry, the 4-H Forestry Camp, and state forests in Alaska and a list of free publications from the Cooperative Extension Service.

5096 ■ The Wildlifer
The Wildlife Society
5410 Grosvenor Ln., Ste. 200
Bethesda, MD 20814-2144
Ph: (301)897-9770
Fax: (301)530-2471
E-mail: tws@wildlife.org
URL: http://joomla.wildlife.org

Description: Monthly. Serves as the Society's official publication of record. Contains items on section and chapter activities, meetings of interest, career notes, job opportunities, and timely articles on significant developments in conservation issues. Recurring features include editorials, news of members, letters to the editor, a calendar of events, and a column titled Call for Papers.

5097 ■ The Woodland Steward
Massachusetts Forest Landowners Association
PO Box 623
Leverett, MA 01054
Ph: (413)549-5900
Fax: (413)339-5526
E-mail: gcox@crocker.com
URL: http://www.massforests.org

Description: Five issues/year. Presents issues, facts, and events concerning Massachusetts forests, trees, and ecology. Advocates sustainable forest use. Recurring features include news of research, a calendar of events, and columns titled Forest Health, Practical Management, Tree Farm News, and Legislation & Policy.

EMPLOYER DIRECTORIES AND NETWORKING LISTS

5098 ■ American Men and Women of Science: A Biographical Dictionary of Today's Leaders in Physical, Biological, and Related Sciences
R.R. Bowker
630 Central Ave
New Providence, NJ 07974
Ph: (888)269-5372
Free: 888-269-5372
Fax: (908)464-3553
E-mail: info@bowker.com
URL: http://www.gale.cengage.com

Frequency: Biennial; even years; New edition

expected 29th, June 2011. **Price:** $1,368 Individuals. **Covers:** Over 135,000 U.S. and Canadian scientists active in the physical, biological, mathematical, computer science, and engineering fields; includes references to previous edition for deceased scientists and nonrespondents. **Entries include:** Name, address, education, personal and career data, memberships, honors and awards, research interest. **Arrangement:** Alphabetical. **Indexes:** Discipline (in separate volume).

5099 ■ Association of Consulting Foresters--Membership Specialization Directory
Association of Consulting Foresters of America
312 Montgomery St., Ste. 208
Alexandria, VA 22314
Ph: (703)548-0990
Fax: (703)548-6395
E-mail: director@acf-foresters.org
URL: http://www.acf-foresters.org

Frequency: Annual; August. **Price:** Included in membership. **Pages:** 200. **Covers:** Nearly 500 member forestry consulting firms and professional foresters who earn the largest part of their income from consulting. **Entries include:** Name, address, phone, specialties, background, career data, staff (if a consulting firm), geographic area served, capabilities, including equipment available and foreign language proficiency. **Arrangement:** Alphabetical. **Indexes:** Name, office location, language, international capability.

5100 ■ Conservation Directory
National Wildlife Federation
11100 Wildlife Center Dr.
Reston, VA 20190
Ph: (703)438-6000
Free: 800-822-9919
E-mail: admin@nwf.org
URL: http://www.nwf.org

Frequency: Annual; latest edition 2010. **Covers:** Over 4,258 organizations, agencies, colleges and universities with conservation programs and more than 18,000 officials concerned with environmental conservation, education, and natural resource use and management. **Includes:** List of Nat'l Wildlife Refuges, Nat'l Forests, Nat'l Marine Sanctuaries, Nat'l Parks, Bureau of Land Management districts, Nat'l Seashores, foreign international organizations, and environmental online databases. **Entries include:** Agency name, address, branch or subsidiary office name and address, names and titles of key personnel, descriptions of program areas, size of membership (where appropriate), telephone, fax, e-mail and URL addresses. **Arrangement:** Classified by type of organization. **Indexes:** Personal name, keyword, geographic, organization.

HANDBOOKS AND MANUALS

5101 ■ Jobs in Environmental Cleanup and Emergency Hazmat Response
The Rosen Publishing Group Inc.
29 E 21st St. Fl. 2
New York, NY 10010-6256
Ph: (212)777-3017
URL: http://www.rosenpublishing.com

Description: Daniel E. Harmon. 2010. $31.95 (library bound). 80 pages. Features jobs in environmental cleanup and emergency hazmat response. Explores numerous career paths for different environmental jobs that require special training or four-year and/or postgraduate degrees. Includes job profiles for professionals such as environmental engineers, geologists, microbiologists, science technicians, conservationists, foresters, park rangers, soil scientists, air control technicians, toxicologists, dredge operators, ecologists, hazardous waste managers, and zoologists.

5102 ■ Opportunities in Biological Science Careers
The McGraw-Hill Companies Inc.
PO Box 182604
Columbus, OH 43272
Ph: (212)512-2000
Free: 877-833-5524
Fax: (614)759-3749
E-mail: customer.service@mcgraw-hill.com
URL: http://www.mcgraw-hill.com

Description: Charles A. Winter. 2004. $13.95 (paper). 160 pages. Identifies employers and outlines opportunities in plant and animal biology, biological specialties, biomedical sciences, applied biology, and other areas. Illustrated.

ONLINE JOB SOURCES AND SERVICES

5103 ■ Conservation Job Board
URL: http://www.conservationjobboard.com

Description: Provides job seekers with a one-stop place for finding the latest job openings related to conservation. Assists employers to find the ideal candidates for their job openings, internships, graduate assistantships, and other volunteer opportunities.

5104 ■ Environmental Career Opportunities
URL: http://www.ecojobs.com

Description: Lists environmental jobs in conservation, education, policy, science and engineering.

5105 ■ Environmental Expert
URL: http://www.environmental-expert.com

Description: Connects environmental industry professionals from around the globe to companies that provide the products, services and information they need to do their job successfully.

5106 ■ Environmental Jobs
URL: http://environmental.jobs4.org

Description: Offers a searchable database of environmental job opportunities available throughout the United States.

5107 ■ EnvironmentalJobs.com
URL: http://environmentaljobs.com

Description: Serves as online tool that provides current listings of environmental jobs.

5108 ■ ForestryUSA.com
URL: http://www.forestryusa.com

Description: Provides resources on forestry and the forest products industry in the United States. Lists job opportunities in the field.

TRADESHOWS

5109 ■ Forest Products Machinery & Equipment Exposition
Southern Forest Products Association
Southern Pine Council
2900 Indiana Ave.
Kenner, LA 70065-4605
Ph: (504)443-4464
Fax: (504)443-6612
E-mail: mail@sfpa.org
URL: http://www.sfpa.org

Frequency: Biennial. **Primary Exhibits:** Equipment, supplies, and services for the forest products industry. Including lumber, panels, engineered wood products, plywood, secondary processing, forestry and land management.

5110 ■ Northeastern Forest Products Equipment Expo
Northeastern Loggers Association
3311 State Rte. 28
Old Forge, NY 13420
Ph: (315)369-3078

Free: 800-318-7561
Fax: (315)369-3736
E-mail: jphaneuf@nothernlogger.com
URL: http://www.northernlogger.com

Frequency: Annual. **Primary Exhibits:** Forest industry services, equipment, and associated products.

5111 ■ Pacific Logging Congress
Pacific Logging Congress
PO Box 1281
Maple Valley, WA 98038
Ph: (425)413-2808
Fax: (425)413-1359
E-mail: rikki@pacificloggingcongress.com
URL: http://www.pacificloggingcongress.org

Frequency: Annual. **Primary Exhibits:** Logging and allied industry equipment.

5112 ■ Redwood Region Logging Conference
Redwood Region Logging Conference
5601 S Broadway St.
Eureka, CA 95503
Ph: (707)443-4091
Fax: (707)443-0926
E-mail: rrlc@sonic.net
URL: http://www.rrlc.net

Frequency: Annual. **Primary Exhibits:** Logging equipment supplies and services. CA.

5113 ■ Society of American Foresters National Convention
Society of American Foresters
5400 Grosvenor Ln.
Bethesda, MD 20814-2198
Free: 866-897-8720
Fax: (301)897-3691
E-mail: membership@safnet.org
URL: http://www.safnet.org

Frequency: Annual. **Primary Exhibits:** Forestry equipment, publications, hardware and software, chemicals, machinery, and geographic information systems.

5114 ■ Soil and Water Conservation Society International Conference
Soil and Water Conservation Society
945 SW Ankeny Rd.
Ankeny, IA 50023-9723
Ph: (515)289-2331
Free: 800-843-7645
Fax: (515)289-1227
E-mail: jim.gulliford@swcs.org
URL: http://www.swcs.org

OTHER SOURCES

5115 ■ Advanced Conservation Strategies
PO Box 1201
Midway, UT 84049
Ph: (435)200-3031
E-mail: acs@advancedconservation.org
URL: http://www.advancedconservation.org

Description: Aims to deliver innovative, self-sustaining and economically efficient solutions to environmental challenges. Builds cross-sector synergy and integrates biological, economic, technological and socio-political threats and opportunities to address environmental and sustainability issues.

5116 ■ Alliance for Global Conservation
4245 N Fairfax Dr., Ste. 100
Arlington, VA 22203
Ph: (703)841-4228
E-mail: bmillan@tnc.org
URL: http://www.actforconservation.org

Description: Aims to protect life on earth through conservation of wildlife, natural areas and human communities around the world. Supports global policies that will prevent the destruction of the world's remaining natural ecosystems for the species and human communities that depend on them.

5117 ■ Alliance for Water Efficiency
300 W Adams St., Ste. 601
Chicago, IL 60606
Ph: (773)360-5100
Free: 866-730-A4WE
Fax: (773)345-3636
E-mail: jeffrey@a4we.org
URL: http://www.allianceforwaterefficiency.org

Description: Promotes efficient and sustainable use of water. Serves as an advocate for water-efficient products and programs. Provides information and assistance on water conservation efforts.

5118 ■ American Forests
1220 NW L St., Ste. 750
Washington, DC 20005
Ph: (202)737-1944
Free: 800-545-8733
E-mail: jhanelly@americanforests.org
URL: http://www.americanforests.org

Description: Works to advance the intelligent management and use of forests, soil, water, wildlife, and all other natural resources. Promotes public appreciation of natural resources, helps plant trees to restore areas damaged by wildfire.

5119 ■ American Reef Coalition
PO Box 844
Kihei, HI 96753
Ph: (808)870-5817
E-mail: info@americanreef.org
URL: http://www.americanreef.org

Description: To protect coral reef ecosystems, ocean resources and wilderness through a variety of proven methods and by providing support to other nonprofit organizations and government agencies engaged in marine, wilderness and natural area research, conservation and education.

5120 ■ ASPRS, The Imaging and Geospatial Information Society
5410 Grosvenor Ln., Ste. 210
Bethesda, MD 20814-2160
Ph: (301)493-0290
Fax: (301)493-0208
E-mail: asprs@asprs.org
URL: http://www.asprs.org

Description: Firms, individuals, government employees and academicians engaged in photogrammetry, photointerpretation, remote sensing, and geographic information systems and their application to such fields as archaeology, geographic information systems, military reconnaissance, urban planning, engineering, traffic surveys, meteorological observations, medicine, geology, forestry, agriculture, construction and topographic mapping. Seeks to advance knowledge and improve understanding of these sciences and promote responsible applications. Offers voluntary certification program open to persons associated with one or more functional area of photogrammetry, remote sensing and GIS. Surveys the profession of private firms in photogrammetry and remote sensing in the areas of products and services.

5121 ■ Association of Consulting Foresters of America
312 Montgomery St., Ste. 208
Alexandria, VA 22314
Ph: (703)548-0990
Fax: (703)548-6395
E-mail: director@acf-foresters.org
URL: http://www.acf-foresters.org

Description: Professional foresters in the field of applied forestry and forest utilization who work for private landowners or industry on a contract or contingency basis. Members must be graduates of an association-approved forestry school and have five years experience in forest administration and

management. Provides client referral service. Compiles statistics.

5122 ■ Audubon International
120 Defreest Dr.
Troy, NY 12180
Ph: (518)767-9051
Fax: (518)767-9076
URL: http://www.auduboninternational.org

Description: Promotes sustainable communities through good stewardship of the natural environment where people live, work and recreate. Collaborates with nonprofits, governments, businesses and the public to ensure better environmental decision-making and improve the quality of human and natural communities. Provides people with the assistance needed to practice responsible management of land, water, wildlife and natural resources.

5123 ■ *Career Opportunities in Conservation and the Environment*
InfoBase Holdings Inc.
132 W 31st., 17 Fl.
New York, NY 10001-3406
Ph: (212)967-8800
Fax: (800)678-3633
E-mail: info@infobasepublishing.com
URL: http://www.ferguson.infobasepublishing.com

Description: 2007. $49.50. 304 pages. Covers job profiles on conservation and the environment, followed by the descriptions of certification, education, special skills, and training required. **Includes:** Appendices of educational institutions, periodicals, directories, and associations. Appendices of educational institutions, periodicals, directories, and associations.

5124 ■ *Career Opportunities in Science*
InfoBase Holdings Inc.
132 W 31st., 17 Fl.
New York, NY 10001-3406
Ph: (212)967-8800
Fax: (800)678-3633
E-mail: info@infobasepublishing.com
URL: http://factsonfile.infobasepublishing.com

Frequency: Latest edition 2008. **Price:** $49.50 Individuals hardcover. **Pages:** 344. **Description:** Susan Echaore-McDavid. Second edition, 2008. 332 pages. **Covers:** More than 80 jobs, such as biochemist, molecular biologist, bioinformatic specialist, pharmacologist, computer engineer, geographic information systems specialist, science teacher, forensic scientist, patent agent, as well as physicist, astronomer, chemist, zoologist, oceanographer, and geologist. **Includes:** Appendices of educational institutions, periodicals, directories, and associations.

5125 ■ *Careers for Health Nuts and Others Who Like to Stay Fit*
The McGraw-Hill Companies Inc.
PO Box 182604
Columbus, OH 43272
Ph: (212)512-2000
Free: 877-833-5524
Fax: (614)759-3749
E-mail: customer.service@mcgraw-hill.com
URL: http://www.mcgraw-hill.com

Description: Blythe Camenson. Second edition. $13.95 (paper). 208 pages. **Publication includes:** Appendices of professional associations, selected training programs, bibliography of job-hunting materials, and U.S. National Park Service regional offices. **Entries include:** For professional associations: name, address, description of job-hunting materials; for training programs: name, address, description; for U.S. National Park Service regional offices: name, address.

5126 ■ *Careers for Plant Lovers and Other Green Thumb Types*
The McGraw-Hill Companies Inc.
PO Box 182604
Columbus, OH 43272
Ph: (212)512-2000

Free: 877-833-5524
Fax: (614)759-3749
E-mail: customer.service@mcgraw-hill.com
URL: http://www.mcgraw-hill.com

Description: Blythe Camenson. Second edition, 2004. $13.95. 160 pages. **Includes:** Appendices of selected list botancial gardens and arboreta for internships, summer employment, and volunteer opportunities, as well as a list of U.S. National Park Service regional offices. Appendices of selected list botanical gardens and arboreta for internships, summer employment, and volunteer opportunities, as well as a list of U.S. National Park Service regional offices. **Entries include:** Organization name, address.

5127 ■ Climate, Community and Biodiversity Alliance
2011 Crystal Dr., Ste. 500
Arlington, VA 22202
Ph: (703)341-2748
E-mail: info@climate-standards.org
URL: http://www.climate-standards.org

Description: Represents international non-governmental organizations (NGOs) and research institutes that promote integrated solutions to land management. Promotes responsible land management activities that will benefit local communities, minimize climate change and conserve biodiversity.

5128 ■ Community Forestry International
1356 Mokelumne Dr.
Antioch, CA 94531
Ph: (925)706-2906
Fax: (925)706-2906
E-mail: k8smith@aol.com
URL: http://www.communityforestryinternational.org

Description: Assists rural communities to stabilize and regenerate forests. Creates a forum and encourages the exchange of views and ideas about sustainable community forest management. Draws tools and techniques that support and empower communities engaged in forest management.

5129 ■ Conservation through Poverty Alleviation International
221 Lincoln Rd.
Lincoln, MA 01773
E-mail: ccraig@cpali.org
URL: http://www.cpali.org/CPALI_Home.html

Description: Works to identify, develop and implement new means of income generation for poor farmers living in areas of high biodiversity or conservation value. Promotes natural resource conservation by developing integrated, small enterprise systems that link the livelihood of farm families and communities to the maintenance of natural ecosystems.

5130 ■ Cultural Vistas
440 Park Ave. S, 2nd Fl.
New York, NY 10016
Ph: (212)497-3500
Fax: (212)497-3535
E-mail: info@culturalvistas.org
URL: http://culturalvistas.org

Description: Providers worldwide of on-the-job training programs for students and professionals seeking international career development and life-changing experiences. Arranges workplace exchanges in hundreds of professional fields, bringing employers and trainees together from around the world. Client list ranges from small farming communities to Fortune 500 companies.

5131 ■ Defense of Place
c/o Resource Renewal Institute
187 E Blithedale Ave.
Mill Valley, CA 94941
Ph: (415)928-3774
E-mail: hdj@rri.org
URL: http://www.rri.org/defenseofplace.php

Description: Aims to preserve the world's natural

resources. Works to create awareness on wildlife conservation. Promotes environmental protection.

5132 ■ Ecological Research and Development Group
190 Main St.
Dover, DE 19901
Ph: (302)236-5383
E-mail: erdg@horseshoecrab.org
URL: http://www.horseshoecrab.org

Description: Promotes the conservation of horseshoe crab species. Provides educational programs to create an atmosphere of learning to inspire and nurture curiosity about the horseshoe crabs species and their habitat. Seeks solutions that prevent the extinction of the horseshoe crab species through scientific research and development.

5133 ■ Environmental Paper Network
16 Eagle St., Ste. 200
Asheville, NC 28801
Ph: (828)251-8558
URL: http://environmentalpaper.org

Description: Works to accelerate social and environmental transformation in the pulp and paper industry. Aims to protect the world's last endangered forests, to safeguard the global climate and ensure abundant, clean drinking water and respect for community and indigenous rights.

5134 ■ Forest Bird Society
10969 SW 47th Terr.
Miami, FL 33165
Ph: (305)223-2680
Fax: (305)223-2680
E-mail: forestbirdsoc@aol.com
URL: http://www.forestbirdsociety.org

Description: Aims to protect native plants, animals and wild places, on land and in oceans. Promotes environmental education and the preservtion of natural ecosystems. Supports projects to study and protect the habitats of forest birds.

5135 ■ Friends of the Osa
1822 R St. NW, 4th Fl.
Washington, DC 20009
Ph: (202)234-2356
Fax: (202)234-2358
E-mail: info@osaconservation.org
URL: http://osaconservation.org/tag/friends-of-the
   -osa

Description: Aims to maintain a largely forested landscape surrounded by an intact coastal zone that protects the Osa's biodiversity while supporting sustainable human livelihoods. Works with local, regional and international partners to protect the region's globally significant biodiversity. Encourages regional and local participation in conservation efforts. Facilitates the exchange of scientific and research expertise.

5136 ■ GAIA Movement USA
8918 S Green St.
Chicago, IL 60620
Ph: (773)651-7870
Free: 877-651-7870
Fax: (773)651-7890
E-mail: eva@gaia-movement.org
URL: http://www.gaia-movement-usa.org

Description: Educates young and old people on environmental issues including recycling, renewable energy, conservation and wildlife preservation. Develops and preserves natural areas and virgin lands as nature reserves. Promotes the use of renewable energies such as solar, wind and geothermal.

5137 ■ Global Parks
3803 Sulgrave Dr.
Alexandria, VA 22309
Ph: (703)317-1669
E-mail: todd@globalparks.org
URL: http://globalparks.org

Description: Aims to support retired senior conservation professionals to help strengthen protected areas and national park systems around the world. Collaborates with partners to plan activities for parks and protected areas. Provides analysis, advice and assistance in developing, reviewing, and implementing various protected areas plans, strategies and issues.

5138 ■ Growing Planet
3133 Frontera Way, Ste. 113
Burlingame, CA 94010-5759
Free: 866-476-9873
E-mail: info@growingplanet.org
URL: http://www.growingplanet.org

Description: Promotes planting and cultivating of trees to improve the quality of life. Engages in an effort to replenish the earth's forests and reduce greenhouse gases to protect the Earth's ozone layer. Replaces trees that have been logged for commercial purposes, destroyed by fire or cut down due to an increase in urban development.

5139 ■ Indo-Pacific Conservation Alliance
1525 Bernice St.
Honolulu, HI 96817
Ph: (808)848-4124
Fax: (808)847-8252
E-mail: info@indopacific.org
URL: http://www.indopacific.org

Description: Focuses on the study and conservation of the native ecosystems of the tropical Indo-Pacific region. Supports traditional peoples in the stewardship of globally significant natural resources. Works as facilitators to local communities who request help in conserving their natural resources. Provides information, training, equipment and other support to local stakeholders to help conserve and manage natural resources.

5140 ■ Instream Flow Council
c/o Todd Richards, President
Massachusetts Division Fish and Wildlife
1 Rabbit Hill Rd., North Dr.
Westborough, MA 01581
Ph: (508)389-6300
E-mail: todd.richards@state.ma.us
URL: http://www.instreamflowcouncil.org

Description: Represents the interests of state and provincial fish and wildlife management agencies. Increases public awareness and understanding of instream flow issues and stewardship responsibilities. Helps to establish, maintain and administer programs for the quantification, protection and restoration of instream flows for aquatic resources.

5141 ■ Korean-American Scientists and Engineers Association
1952 Gallows Rd., Ste. 300
Vienna, VA 22182
Ph: (703)748-1221
Fax: (703)748-1331
E-mail: sejong@ksea.org
URL: http://www.ksea.org

Description: Represents scientists and engineers holding single or advanced degrees. Promotes friendship and mutuality among Korean and American scientists and engineers; contributes to Korea's scientific, technological, industrial, and economic developments; strengthens the scientific, technological, and cultural bonds between Korea and the U.S. Sponsors symposium. Maintains speakers' bureau, placement service, and biographical archives. Compiles statistics. **Members:** 10,000.

5142 ■ MarineBio Conservation Society
1995 Fairlee Dr.
Encinitas, CA 92023
Ph: (713)248-2576
E-mail: info@marinebio.org
URL: http://marinebio.org

Description: Works to protect marine life and the ocean for future generations. Creates an awareness of marine conservation issues and their solutions.

Supports marine conservation scientists and students involved in the marine life sciences.

5143 ■ National Alliance of Forest Owners
122 C St. NW, Ste. 630
Washington, DC 20001
Ph: (202)747-0759
Fax: (202)824-0770
E-mail: info@nafoalliance.org
URL: http://www.nafoalliance.org

Description: Aims to protect and enhance the economic and environmental values of privately-owned forests through targeted policy advocacy at the national level. Focuses on issues for regulatory advocacy including climate change, renewable energy, environment, tax policy, land use, trade and market policy. Seeks public policies that shape environmental regulations, taxes, land use decisions, and timber and non-timber markets in ways that protect and grow forest values.

5144 ■ National Association of Conservation Districts
509 Capitol Ct. NE
Washington, DC 20002-4937
Ph: (202)547-6223
Free: 888-695-2433
Fax: (202)547-6450
E-mail: john-larson@nacdnet.org
URL: http://www.nacdnet.org

Description: Soil and water conservation districts organized by the citizens of watersheds, counties, or communities under provisions of state laws. Directs and coordinates, through local self-government efforts, the conservation and development of soil, water, and related natural resources. Includes districts over 90% of the nation's privately owned land. Conducts educational programs and children's services.

5145 ■ National Association of State Foresters
444 N Capitol St. NW, Ste. 540
Washington, DC 20001
Ph: (202)624-5415
Fax: (202)624-5407
E-mail: lgilmer@stateforesters.org
URL: http://www.stateforesters.org

Description: Consists of directors of forestry agencies. Promotes cooperation in forestry matters among states and between states and the federal government. Acts on national legislation relating to forestry issues. Maintains history of state forestry agencies; conducts educational programs on forestry issues; compiles statistics.

5146 ■ National Hardwood Lumber Association
6830 Raleigh La Grange Rd.
Memphis, TN 38134-0518
Ph: (901)377-1818
Free: 800-933-0318
Fax: (901)382-6419
E-mail: info@nhla.com
URL: http://www.nhla.com

Description: United States, Canadian and International hardwood lumber and veneer manufacturers, distributors and consumers. Inspects hardwood lumber. Maintains inspection training school. Conducts management and marketing seminars for the hardwood industry. Promotes research in hardwood timber management and utilization. Promotes public awareness of the industry.

5147 ■ National Oceanic Society
17300 Red Hill Ave., Ste. 280
Irvine, CA 92614
Ph: (949)500-5451
Fax: (949)675-1366

Description: Promotes the fundamental concepts of marine conservation and preservation. Supports the education, research and scientific study of marine environment. Assists governmental agencies in the monitoring and detection of activities that are hazardous and harmful to marine environment.

5148 ■ National Wildlife Federation
11100 Wildlife Center Dr.
Reston, VA 20190
Ph: (703)438-6000
Free: 800-822-9919
URL: http://www.nwf.org

Description: Serves as a member-supported conservation group, with over four million members and supporters. Federation of state and territorial affiliates, associate members and individual conservationist-contributors. Seeks to educate, inspire and assist individuals and organizations of diverse cultures to conserve wildlife and other natural resources and to protect the earth's environment in order to achieve a peaceful, equitable and sustainable future. Encourages the intelligent management of the life-sustaining resources of the earth and promotes greater appreciation of wild places, wildlife and the natural resources shared by all. Publishes educational materials and conservation periodicals.

5149 ■ Nature's Voice Our Choice
5437 Taney Ave.
Alexandria, VA 22304
Ph: (202)341-9180
E-mail: vstrassberg@nv-oc.org
URL: http://www.naturesvoice-ourchoice.org

Description: Aims to preserve, conserve and restore the world's water resources through education and public awareness. Empowers people to become stewards of their natural resources and implements projects that make environmental protection economically feasible. Supports ecologically engineered natural waste water treatment systems.

5150 ■ Neotropical Grassland Conservancy
6274 Heathcliff Dr.
Carmichael, CA 95608
Ph: (916)967-3223
URL: http://www.conservegrassland.org

Description: Promotes the conservation of savannas, gallery forests, wetlands and associated ecosystems in Central and South America. Collaborates with North American, Central and South American scientists and institutions by providing shared scientific and educational opportunities. Offers equipment and grants to students and scientists from Central and South America working in grassland habitats.

5151 ■ Network of Conservation Educators and Practitioners
American Museum of Natural History
Center for Biodiversity and Conservation
Central Park West, 79th St.
New York, NY 10024
Ph: (212)769-5742
Fax: (212)769-5292
E-mail: ncep@amnh.org
URL: http://ncep.amnh.org

Description: Aims to improve the practice of biodiversity conservation. Promotes educational resources on managing and sustaining biological and cultural diversity. Provides opportunities for communication and interaction among conservation educators and practitioners.

5152 ■ Ocean Conservation Research
PO Box 559
Lagunitas, CA 94938
Ph: (415)488-0553
E-mail: info@ocr.org
URL: http://ocr.org

Description: Represents scientists, engineers and ocean advocates devoted to improve the environmental health of the sea. Seeks to understand and explore solutions to the growing problem of human generated noise pollution and its impact on marine animals. Promotes the recovery and long term viability of the sea through research focusing on conservation priorities and practices.

5153 ■ Orion Grassroots Network
187 Main St.
Great Barrington, MA 01230
Ph: (413)528-4422
URL: http://www.oriongrassroots.org

Description: Consists of grassroots organizations across the United States. Provides job listing for future green leaders. Offers job posting service on a fee basis.

5154 ■ Ornithological Societies of North America
5400 Bosque Blvd., Ste. 680
Waco, TX 76710
Ph: (254)399-9636
Fax: (254)776-3767
E-mail: business@osnabirds.org
URL: http://www.osnabirds.org

Description: Comprises societies promoting ornithology; is a joint billing and membership service of the American Ornithologists' Union, the Association of Field Ornithologists, the Cooper Ornithological Society, the Raptor Research Foundation, The Waterbird Society, and the Wilson Ornithological Society.

5155 ■ OurEarth.org
PO Box 62133
Durham, NC 27715
Ph: (410)878-6485
URL: http://www.ourearth.org

Description: Represents graduate and medical students as well as environmental experts and leaders from around the country. Promotes the importance of natural resources energy savings and pollutant reductions. Conducts environmental programs, activities, initiatives, ideas and grassroots efforts across the country.

5156 ■ Rising Tide North America
268 Bush St.
San Francisco, CA 94101
Ph: (503)438-4697
E-mail: contact@risingtidenorthamerica.org
URL: http://www.risingtidenorthamerica.org

Description: Fosters community-based solutions to the climate crisis. Aims to prevent catastrophic global warming by determining the root causes of climate change. Works to support direct action and encourages individuals and organizations to carry out autonomous actions that are in line with these principles.

5157 ■ Rivers Without Borders
PO Box 154
Clinton, WA 98236
Ph: (360)341-1976
E-mail: admin@riverswithoutborders.org
URL: http://riverswithoutborders.org

Description: Represents individuals and groups coordinating to protect the diversity of the river. Aims to maintain the abundance of fish and wildlife species in transboundary watersheds. Provides information on how to conserve the river system.

5158 ■ Save Yemen's Flora and Fauna
1523 River Terrace Dr.
East Lansing, MI 48823
E-mail: jzindani@syff.org
URL: http://www.syff.org

Description: Represents individuals with an interest in environmental protection and wildlife conservation. Works to protect natural resources and wildlife habitats through efforts directed against pollution and violation of environmental laws. Conducts research and educational programs.

5159 ■ Society of American Foresters
5400 Grosvenor Ln.
Bethesda, MD 20814-2198
Free: 866-897-8720

Fax: (301)897-3691
E-mail: membership@safnet.org
URL: http://www.safnet.org

Description: National scientific and educational organization representing forestry in the United States. Aims to advance the science, education, technology, and practice of forestry. Supports 28 subject-oriented working groups.

5160 ■ Society for Range Management
6901 S Pierce St., Ste. 225
Littleton, CO 80128
Ph: (303)986-3309
Fax: (303)986-3892
E-mail: info@rangelands.org
URL: http://www.rangelands.org

Description: Professional international society of scientists, technicians, ranchers, administrators, teachers, and students interested in the study, use, and management of rangeland resources for livestock, wildlife, watershed, and recreation.

5161 ■ Soil and Water Conservation Society
945 SW Ankeny Rd.
Ankeny, IA 50023-9723
Ph: (515)289-2331
Free: 800-843-7645
Fax: (515)289-1227
E-mail: jim.gulliford@swcs.org
URL: http://www.swcs.org

Description: Advances the science and art of natural resource conservation. Enhances the capabilities of conservationists through training and professional development. Maintains standards and encourages the spirit of professionalism among conservationists through networking and mutual support.

5162 ■ Student Conservation Association
689 River Rd.
Charlestown, NH 03603-4171
Ph: (603)543-1700
Fax: (603)543-1828
E-mail: leaders@thesca.org
URL: http://www.thesca.org

Description: Works to build the next generation of conservation leaders and inspire lifelong stewardship of the environment and communities by engaging young people in hands-on service to the land. Provides conservation service opportunities, outdoor education and leadership development for young people. Offers college and graduate students, as well as older adults expense-paid conservation internships, these positions includes wildlife research, wilderness patrols and interpretive opportunities and provide participants with valuable hands-on career experience. Places 15-19 year old high school students in four-week volunteer conservation crews in national parks forests and refuges across the country each summer to accomplish a range of trail building and habitat conservation projects. Offers year-round diversity conservation programs for young women and young persons of color in leading metropolitan areas of U.S.

5163 ■ Tropical Forest Group
519 Fig Ave.
Santa Barbara, CA 93101
E-mail: info@tropicalforestgroup.org
URL: http://tropicalforestgroup.org

Description: Promotes the conservation and restoration of the planet's remaining tropical forests. Supports research and development of policies that help maintain the planet's most vital biome. Provides assistance to projects that restore and conserve tropical forests.

5164 ■ World Federation for Coral Reef Conservation
PO Box 311117
Houston, TX 77231
Ph: (281)309-1201
E-mail: contact@wfcrc.org
URL: http://www.wfcrc.org

Description: Works to stop the destruction of coral reefs by involving local citizens, scientists and recreational divers. Collaborates with like-minded organizations in implementing programs for coral reef decline management. Supports conservation efforts on coral reefs.

Sources of Help-Wanted Ads

5165 ■ *Advanced Fuel Cell Technology*
Seven Mountains Scientific Inc.
913 Tressler St.
Boalsburg, PA 16827
Ph: (814)466-6559
Fax: (814)466-2777
URL: http://www.7ms.com

Description: Monthly. Covers research on fuel cell technology and the people and companies involved with the development of such technology.

5166 ■ *AIE Perspectives Newsmagazine*
American Institute of Engineers
4630 Appian Way, Ste. 206
El Sobrante, CA 94803-1875
Ph: (510)758-6240
Fax: (510)758-6240
E-mail: aie@aieonline.org
URL: http://www.members-aie.org

Frequency: Monthly. **Price:** included in membership dues. **Description:** Professional magazine covering engineering.

5167 ■ *Alternative Energy*
ACTA Press
Bldg. B6, Ste. 101
Calgary, AB, Canada T3E 7J9
Ph: (403)288-1195
Fax: (403)247-6851
E-mail: journals@actapress.com
URL: http://www.actapress.com/Content_of_Journal
    .aspx?journalid=170

Frequency: Annual. **Price:** $320 Individuals. **Description:** Journal covering all areas of alternative energy and its related fields.

5168 ■ *Graduating Engineer & Computer Careers*
Career Recruitment Media
2 LAN Dr., Ste. 100
Westford, MA 01886
Ph: (978)692-5092
Fax: (978)692-4174
E-mail: hshulick@alloyeducation.com
URL: http://www.graduatingengineer.com

Frequency: Quarterly. **Price:** $16.95 Individuals. **Description:** Magazine focusing on employment, education, and career development for entry-level engineers and computer scientists.

5169 ■ *National Fuel Cell Research Center Journal*
University of California, Irvine - National Fuel Cell Research Center
Engineering Laboratory Facility, Bldg. 323
Irvine, CA 92697-3550
Ph: (949)824-1999

Fax: (949)824-7423
E-mail: ssr@nfcrc.uci.edu
URL: http://www.nfcrc.uci.edu

Description: Quarterly. $60/year. Provides a forum for the discussion of information related to high efficiency, environmentally sensitive energy and power technologies.

5170 ■ *NSBE Magazine: National Society of Black Engineers*
NSBE Publications
205 Daingerfield Rd.
Alexandria, VA 22314
Ph: (703)549-2207
Fax: (703)683-5312
E-mail: info@nsbe.org
URL: http://www.nsbe.org/News-Media/Magazines/
    About-NSBE-Magazine.aspx

Frequency: 3/yr. **Price:** $20 Individuals; $35 Other countries; $15 Students. **Description:** Journal providing information on engineering careers, self-development, and cultural issues for recent graduates with technical majors.

5171 ■ *PE*
National Society of Professional Engineers
1420 King St.
Alexandria, VA 22314-2794
Ph: (703)684-2800
Fax: (703)836-4875
E-mail: memserv@nspe.org
URL: http://www.nspe.org/PEmagazine/index.html

Frequency: Semimonthly; 10/yr. **Price:** included in membership dues; $50 for nonmembers. **Description:** Covers matters of importance to engineering educators and students.

5172 ■ *Power Engineering*
PennWell Publishing Co.
1421 S Sheridan Rd.
Tulsa, OK 74112
Ph: (918)835-3161
Free: 800-331-4463
Fax: (918)831-9497
E-mail: pe@pennwell.com
URLs: http://www.power-eng.com; http://pepei
    .pennnet.com

Frequency: Monthly; Latest edition November, 2008. **Price:** $88 U.S.; $98 Canada and Mexico; $242 Other countries. **Description:** Magazine focusing on power generation. **Publication includes:** List of manufacturers and suppliers of products and services to the power plant and utility engineering industries. **Entries include:** Company name, location, phone, fax, contact name, e-mail and Web site. **Arrangement:** Classified by product/service, then alphabetical.

5173 ■ *Sustainable Facility*
BNP Media
2401 W Big Beaver Rd., Ste. 700
Troy, MI 48084

Ph: (248)362-3700
Free: 800-952-6643
Fax: (248)362-5103
E-mail: privacy@bnpmedia.com
URL: http://www.sustainablefacility.com/

Frequency: Monthly. **Description:** Magazine reporting on the energy management market as it relates to commercial, industrial, and institutional facilities.

5174 ■ *SWE, Magazine of the Society of Women Engineers*
Society of Women Engineers
203 N La Salle St., Ste. 1675
Chicago, IL 60601
Ph: (312)596-5223
Free: 877-SWE-INFO
Fax: (312)596-5252
E-mail: hq@swe.org
URL: http://societyofwomenengineers.swe.org/index
    .php

Frequency: Quarterly. **Price:** $30 Nonmembers. **Description:** Magazine for engineering students and for women and men working in the engineering and technology fields. Covers career guidance, continuing development and topical issues.

5175 ■ *Woman Engineer*
Equal Opportunity Publications Inc.
445 Broad Hollow Rd., Ste. 425
Melville, NY 11747
Ph: (631)421-9421
Fax: (631)421-1352
E-mail: info@eop.com
URL: http://www.eop.com

Description: Annual. Magazine that is offered at no charge to qualified female engineering, computer-science, and information-technology students and professionals seeking to find employment and advancement in their careers.

Employer Directories and Networking Lists

5176 ■ *Directory of Contract Staffing Firms*
C.E. Publications Inc.
PO Box 3006
Bothell, WA 98041-3006
Ph: (425)806-5200
Fax: (425)806-5585
E-mail: staff@cjhunter.com
URL: http://www.cjhunter.com/dcsf/overview.html

Frequency: Annual. **Covers:** Nearly 1,300 contract firms actively engaged in the employment of engineering, IT/IS, and technical personnel for 'temporary' contract assignments throughout the world. **Entries include:** Company name, address, phone, name of contact, email, web address. **Arrangement:** Alphabetical. **Indexes:** Geographical.

5177 ■ *Indiana Society of Professional Engineers--Directory*
Indiana Society of Professional Engineers
c/o Lauraine M. Howe, Executive Director
PO Box 20806
Indianapolis, IN 46220
Ph: (317)255-2267
Fax: (317)255-2530
E-mail: indspe@gmail.com
URL: http://www.indspe.org

Frequency: Annual; fall. **Pages:** 150. **Covers:** Member registered engineers, land surveyors, engineering students, and engineers in training. **Entries include:** Member name, address, phone, type of membership, business information, specialty. **Arrangement:** Alpha by chapter area.

5178 ■ *Who's Who in Engineering*
American Association of Engineering Societies
1801 Alexander Bell Dr.
Reston, VA 20191
Ph: (202)296-2237
Free: 888-400-2237
Fax: (202)296-1151
E-mail: dbateson@aaes.org
URL: http://www.aaes.org

Frequency: Triennial; Latest edition 9th. **Covers:** About 15,000 engineers who have received professional recognition for outstanding achievement. **Entries include:** Name, address; education and employment history; awards and achievements. **Arrangement:** Alphabetical. **Indexes:** Geographical, field of specialization.

HANDBOOKS AND MANUALS

5179 ■ *Expert Resumes for Engineers*
JIST Publishing
875 Montreal Way
Saint Paul, MN 55102-4245
Ph: (317)613-4200
Free: 800-648-5478
Fax: (800)328-4564
E-mail: info@jist.com
URL: http://www.jist.com

Description: Louise M. Kursmark and Wendy S. Enelow. 2009. $16.95 (softcover). 272 pages. Features a collection of written resume samples for all types of engineers including civil, mechanical, industrial, electrical, electronics, computer, and more. Contains tips and strategies for writing engineering resumes and finding the best jobs.

5180 ■ *Great Jobs for Engineering Majors*
The McGraw-Hill Companies Inc.
PO Box 182604
Columbus, OH 43272
Ph: (212)512-2000
Free: 877-833-5524
Fax: (614)759-3749
E-mail: customer.service@mcgraw-hill.com
URL: http://www.mcgraw-hill.com

Description: Geraldine O. Garner. Second edition, 2008. $16.95. 192 pages. Covers all the career options open to students majoring in engineering.

EMPLOYMENT AGENCIES AND SEARCH FIRMS

5181 ■ Career Advocates International
1539 Ave. A
Katy, TX 77493
Ph: (281)371-3917
E-mail: hank@careeradvocates.org
URL: http://www.careeradvocates.org

Description: Provides permanent placement and temporary staffing for executive and staff level positions. Specializes in multiple niches including: sales and marketing, accounting and financial services, banking, communications, human resources,

chemicals, oil and gas, medical and dental, legal, information technology, energy, technology, engineering, manufacturing, construction, and light industrial.

5182 ■ Centennial, Inc.
8044 Montgomery Rd., Ste. 260
Cincinnati, OH 45236
Ph: (513)366-3760
Fax: (513)366-3761
URL: http://www.centennialinc.com

Description: Serves as an executive search firm specializing in the areas of executive and general management, accounting and finance, human resources, information technology, manufacturing, engineering, marketing and advertising, not-for-profit, sales and business development, and supply chain and logistics.

5183 ■ International Search
9717 E 42nd St.
Tulsa, OK 74147-0898
Ph: (918)627-9070
Fax: (918)524-8604

Description: Personnel consulting group provides placement expertise in engineering, accounting, and data processing. Industries served: Energy, manufacturing, oil and gas, and services.

5184 ■ Houser Martin Morris
110th Ave. NE, 110 Atrium Pl., Ste. 580
Bellevue, WA 98004
Ph: (425)453-2700
Fax: (425)453-8726
E-mail: info@houser.com
URL: http://www.houser.com

Description: Focus is in the areas of retained executive search, professional, and technical recruiting. Areas of specialization include software engineering, sales and marketing, information technology, legal, human resources, accounting and finance, manufacturing, factory automation and engineering.

5185 ■ Nesco Inc.
6140 Parkland Blvd., Ste. 110
Mayfield Heights, OH 44124-6106
Ph: (440)461-6000
Fax: (440)449-3111
E-mail: corporate@nescoresource.com
URL: http://www.nescoresource.com

Description: Offers staffing and consulting solutions in the fields of engineering, information technology, accounting and finance, manufacturing and distribution, and administrative and customer services.

5186 ■ SHS of Cherry Hill
207 Barclay Pavilion W
Cherry Hill, NJ 08034
Ph: (856)216-9030
Fax: (856)219-2011
E-mail: shs@shsofcherryhill.com
URL: http://www.shsofcherryhill.com

Description: Personnel recruiters operating in the disciplines of accounting, sales, insurance, engineering and administration. Industries served: insurance, distribution, manufacturing and service.

ONLINE JOB SOURCES AND SERVICES

5187 ■ BiofuelEngineerJobs.com
URL: http://www.biofuelengineerjobs.com

Description: Features biofuel engineer jobs, salary information and surveys, resume postings, and other career resources.

5188 ■ Engineering Classifieds
URL: http://www.engineeringclassifieds.com

Description: Serves as a career site for engineering professionals. Provides services including job search agents, resume creation and posting.

5189 ■ EngineerJobs.com
URL: http://www.engineerjobs.com

Description: Provides job opportunities for engineering professionals in the following disciplines: aerospace, agricultural, biomedical, chemical, civil, electrical, environmental, industrial, manufacturing, marine, materials, mechanical, mining, nuclear, petroleum, process, project, quality, sales, software, solar, systems, and structural.

5190 ■ Engineer.net
URL: http://www.engineer.net

Description: Provides engineering employment tools such as job search, job posting, and engineering resumes.

5191 ■ Fuel Cells 2000
URL: http://www.fuelcells.org

Description: Provides news, educational resources, and job postings.

5192 ■ Power Engineering
PennWell Publishing Co.
1421 S Sheridan Rd.
Tulsa, OK 74112
Ph: (918)835-3161
Free: 800-331-4463
Fax: (918)831-9497
E-mail: pe@pennwell.com
URLs: http://www.power-eng.com; http://pepei.pennnet.com

Frequency: Monthly; Latest edition November, 2008. **Price:** $88 U.S.; $98 Canada and Mexico; $242 Other countries. **Description:** Magazine focusing on power generation. **Publication includes:** List of manufacturers and suppliers of products and services to the power plant and utility engineering industries. **Entries include:** Company name, location, phone, fax, contact name, e-mail and Web site. **Arrangement:** Classified by product/service, then alphabetical.

5193 ■ Spherion
URL: http://www.spherion.com

Description: Recruitment firm specializing in accounting and finance, sales and marketing, interim executives, technology, engineering, retail and human resources.

5194 ■ ThinkEnergyGroup.com
URL: http://www.thinkenergygroup.com

Description: Serves as a job board for professionals looking for positions in engineering, power plant, energy, and technical fields. Contains advice and tips on interviews, job searching, resume writing, hiring, and management. Provides choices of work location, pay rates in the field of expertise and contract, temp-to-hire, and direct hiring options.

TRADESHOWS

5195 ■ American Society for Engineering Education Annual Conference and Exposition
American Society for Engineering Education
1818 N St. NW, Ste. 600
Washington, DC 20036-2479
Ph: (202)331-3500
Fax: (202)265-8504
E-mail: board@asee.org
URL: http://www.asee.org

Frequency: Annual. **Primary Exhibits:** Publications, engineering supplies and equipment, computers, software, and research companies all products and services related to engineering education.

OTHER SOURCES

5196 ■ American Association of Blacks in Energy
1625 K St. NW, Ste. 405
Washington, DC 20006

Ph: (202)371-9530
Fax: (202)371-9218
E-mail: info@aabe.org
URL: http://www.aabe.org

Description: Seeks to increase the knowledge, understanding, and awareness of the minority community in energy issues by serving as an energy information source for policymakers, recommending blacks and other minorities to appropriate energy officials and executives, encouraging students to pursue professional careers in the energy industry, and advocating the participation of blacks and other minorities in energy programs and policymaking activities. Updates members on key legislation and regulations being developed by the Department of Energy, the Department of Interior, the Department of Commerce, the Small Business Administration, and other federal and state agencies.

5197 ■ American Association of Engineering Societies
1801 Alexander Bell Dr.
Reston, VA 20191
Ph: (202)296-2237
Free: 888-400-2237
Fax: (202)296-1151
E-mail: dbateson@aaes.org
URL: http://www.aaes.org

Description: Coordinates the efforts of the member societies in the provision of reliable and objective information to the general public concerning issues which affect the engineering profession and the field of engineering as a whole; collects, analyzes, documents, and disseminates data which will inform the general public of the relationship between engineering and the national welfare; provides a forum for the engineering societies to exchange and discuss their views on matters of common interest; and represents the U.S. engineering community abroad through representation in WFEO and UPADI.

5198 ■ American Engineering Association
c/o Harold Ruchelman
533 Waterside Blvd.
Monroe Township, NJ 08831
Ph: (201)664-6954
E-mail: aea@aea.org
URL: http://www.aea.org

Description: Members consist of Engineers and engineering professionals. Purpose to advance the engineering profession and U.S. engineering capabilities. Issues of concern include age discrimination, immigration laws, displacement of U.S. Engineers by foreign workers, trade agreements, off shoring of U.S. Engineering and manufacturing jobs, loss of U.S. manufacturing and engineering capability, and recruitment of foreign students. Testifies before Congress. Holds local Chapter meetings.

5199 ■ American Hydrogen Association
PO Box 4205
Mesa, AZ 85211
Ph: (480)234-5070
E-mail: help@clean-air.org
URL: http://www.clean-air.org

Description: Seeks to stimulate interest and help establish the renewable hydrogen energy economy.

5200 ■ American Institute of Engineers
4630 Appian Way, Ste. 206
El Sobrante, CA 94803-1875
Ph: (510)758-6240
Fax: (510)758-6240
E-mail: aie@aieonline.org
URL: http://www.aieonline.org

Description: Professional association for engineers, scientists, and mathematicians. Multi-disciplined, non-technical association who aims to improve the stature and image of engineers, scientists, and mathematicians. Provides endorsements, awards and opportunities for small business start-ups within the AIE Councils. Sponsors "LA Engineer", a

comedy-drama television series; produces annual "Academy Hall of FAME (TV)".

5201 ■ Association of Energy Engineers
4025 Pleasantdale Rd., Ste. 420
Atlanta, GA 30340
Ph: (770)447-5083
Fax: (770)446-3969
E-mail: info@aeecenter.org
URL: http://www.aeecenter.org/i4a/pages/index.cfm ?pageid=1

Description: Provides information on energy efficiency, utility deregulation, facility management, plant engineering, and environmental compliance. Offers resources such as seminars, tradeshows, and certification programs.

5202 ■ California Fuel Cell Partnership
3300 Industrial Blvd., Ste. 1000
West Sacramento, CA 95691
Ph: (916)371-2870
Fax: (916)375-2008
E-mail: info@cafcp.org
URL: http://cafcp.org

Description: Auto manufacturers, energy companies, fuel cell technology companies, and government agencies striving to advance new vehicle technology.

5203 ■ *Career Opportunities in Engineering*
InfoBase Holdings Inc.
132 W 31st., 17 Fl.
New York, NY 10001-3406
Ph: (212)967-8800
Fax: (800)678-3633
E-mail: info@infobasepublishing.com
URL: http://www.ferguson.infobasepublishing.com

Description: 2006. $49.50. 336 pages. Provides an overview of engineering, followed by a selection of jobs profiled in detail, including the nature of the job, earnings, prospects for employment, what kind of training and skills it requires and sources for further information. **Includes:** Appendices of educational institutions, periodicals, directories, and associations. Appendices of educational institutions, periodicals, directories, and associations.

5204 ■ Engineering Society of Detroit
20700 Civic Center Dr., Ste. 450
Southfield, MI 48076
Ph: (248)353-0735
Fax: (248)353-0736
E-mail: esd@esd.org
URL: http://ww2.esd.org/home.htm

Description: Engineers from all disciplines; scientists and technologists. Conducts technical programs and engineering refresher courses; sponsors conferences and expositions. Maintains speakers' bureau; offers placement services; although based in Detroit, MI, society membership is international. **Members:** 6,000.

5205 ■ Engineering Workforce Commission
1801 Alexander Bell Dr.
Reston, VA 20191-5467
Ph: (202)296-2237
Free: 888-400-2237
Fax: (202)296-1151
E-mail: dbateson@aaes.org
URL: http://www.ewc-online.org

Description: Represents commissioners appointed by member societies of the American Association of Engineering Societies to engage in studies and analyses of the supply, demand, use and remuneration of engineering and technical personnel. Provides representation to government groups dealing with professional manpower policy; consults with industry. Gathers and disseminates information on the engineering profession. Conducts surveys of engineering school enrollments, degrees, and salaries; monitors federal labor statistics. **Members:** 125.

5206 ■ International Federation of Professional and Technical Engineers
501 3rd St. NW, Ste. 701
Washington, DC 20001
Ph: (202)239-4880
Fax: (202)239-4881
E-mail: generalinfo@ifpte.org
URL: http://www.ifpte.org

Description: Represents engineers, scientists, architects and technicians. **Members:** 75,000.

5207 ■ National Action Council for Minorities in Engineering
440 Hamilton Ave., Ste. 302
White Plains, NY 10601-1813
Ph: (914)539-4010
Free: 800-888-9929
Fax: (914)539-4032
E-mail: ajohnson@nacme.org
URL: http://www.nacme.org

Description: Leads the national effort to increase access to careers in engineering and other science-based disciplines. Conducts research and public policy analysis, develops and operates national demonstration programs at precollege and university levels, and disseminates information through publications, conferences and electronic media. Serves as a privately funded source of scholarships for minority students in engineering.

5208 ■ National Society of Professional Engineers
1420 King St.
Alexandria, VA 22314-2794
Ph: (703)684-2800
Fax: (703)836-4875
E-mail: memserv@nspe.org
URL: http://www.nspe.org

Description: Represents professional engineers and engineers-in-training in all fields registered in accordance with the laws of states or territories of the U.S. or provinces of Canada; qualified graduate engineers, student members, and registered land surveyors. Is concerned with social, professional, ethical, and economic considerations of engineering as a profession; encompasses programs in public relations, employment practices, ethical considerations, education, and career guidance. Monitors legislative and regulatory actions of interest to the engineering profession.

5209 ■ Society of Engineering Science
University of Illinois at Urbana-Champaign
Beckman Institute for Advanced Science and Technology
405 N Mathews Ave., Rm. 3361
Urbana, IL 61801
E-mail: ses@sesinc.org
URL: http://www.sesinc.org

Description: Individuals with at least a baccalaureate degree who are engaged in any aspect of engineering science or in other pursuits that contribute to the advancement of engineering science. Fosters and promotes the interchange of ideas and information among the various fields of engineering science and among engineering science and the fields of theoretical and applied physics, chemistry, and mathematics. Is dedicated to the advancement of interdisciplinary research and to the establishment of a bridge between science and engineering. **Members:** 300.

5210 ■ Society of Hispanic Professional Engineers
13181 Crossroads Pkwy. N, Ste. 450
City of Industry, CA 91746-3496
Ph: (323)725-3970
E-mail: shpenational@shpe.org
URL: http://national.shpe.org

Description: Represents engineers, student engineers, and scientists. Aims to increase the number of Hispanic engineers by providing motivation and support to students. Sponsors competitions and educational programs. Maintains placement service and speakers' bureau; compiles statistics. **Members:** 8,000.

5211 ■ Society of Women Engineers
203 N La Salle St., Ste. 1675
Chicago, IL 60601
Ph: (312)596-5223
Free: 877-SWE-INFO
Fax: (312)596-5252
E-mail: hq@swe.org
URL: http://societyofwomenengineers.swe.org

Description: Educational and service organization representing both students and professional women in engineering and technical fields.

5212 ■ United Engineering Foundation
PO Box 651143
Potomac Falls, VA 20165-1143
Ph: (973)244-2328
Fax: (973)882-5155
E-mail: engfnd@aol.com
URL: http://www.uefoundation.org

Description: Federation of 5 major national engineering societies: American Institute of Chemical Engineers; American Institute of Mining, Metallurgical and Petroleum Engineers; American Society of Civil Engineers; American Society of Mechanical Engineers; Institute of Electrical and Electronics Engineers. Supports research in engineering and advances the engineering arts and sciences through its conference program.

5213 ■ Women in Engineering ProActive Network
1901 E Asbury Ave., Ste. 220
Denver, CO 80208
Ph: (303)871-4643
Fax: (303)871-4628
URL: http://www.wepan.org

Description: Women in engineering professions. Includes key strategies such as education and training, research, collaboration, leadership, diversity, advocacy, networking, sustainability, accountability, and volunteerism in order to be a catalyst for change that enhances the success of women in the engineering professions.

SOURCES OF HELP-WANTED ADS

5214 ■ *The Chronicle of Philanthropy: The Newspaper of the Non-Profit World*
The Chronicle of Philanthropy
1255 23rd St. NW, Ste. 700
Washington, DC 20037
Ph: (202)466-1200
Fax: (202)466-2078
E-mail: help@philanthropy.com
URL: http://www.philanthropy.com
Frequency: 24/yr. **Price:** $72 Individuals; $125 Two years; $72 Individuals online access only; $99.75 Canada; $72 Canada online access only; $135 Other countries; $72 Other countries online access only. **Description:** Magazine covering fundraising, philanthropy, and non-profit organizations. Includes information on tax rulings, new grants, and statistics, reports on grant makers, and profiles of foundations.

5215 ■ *Community Radio News*
National Federation of Community Broadcasters
1101 Pennsylvania Ave. NW, Ste. 600
Washington, DC 20004
Ph: (202)756-2268
E-mail: comments@nfcb.org
URL: http://www.nfcb.org
Evona Balcziunas, Editor. **Frequency:** Monthly; Monthly. **Price:** $75/year; Included in membership; $75 University Libraries. **Description:** Serves as a medium of communication for independent, community-licensed radio stations. Recurring features include job openings and a calendar of events/conferences for noncommercial broadcasters.

5216 ■ *DM News: The Weekly Newspaper of Record for Direct Marketers*
DM News
114 W 26th St., 4th Fl.
New York, NY 10001
Ph: (646)638-6000
Fax: (646)638-6159
E-mail: inquiry@dmnews.com
URL: http://www.dmnews.com/
Frequency: Weekly. **Price:** $148 Individuals; $198 Canada; $228 Other countries; $265 Two years; $355 Canada 2 years; $395 Other countries 2 years. **Description:** Tabloid newspaper for publishers, fund raisers, financial marketers, catalogers, package goods advertisers and their agencies, and other marketers who use direct mail, mail order advertising, catalogs, or other direct response media to sell their products or services.

EMPLOYER DIRECTORIES AND NETWORKING LISTS

5217 ■ *American Association of Fund-Raising Counsel Membership Directory*
American Association of Fund-Raising Counsel Inc.
4700 W Lake Ave.
Glenview, IL 60025
Ph: (847)375-4709
Free: 800-462-2372
E-mail: info@aafrc.org
URL: http://www.aafrc.org/
Frequency: Annual. **Pages:** 92. **Covers:** Member fund-raising consulting firms. **Includes:** Fair Practice Code; section on selection of counsel; brief historical introduction of AAFRC. **Entries include:** Company name, address, phone, fax, geographical area served, types of clients, description of services. **Arrangement:** Alphabetical.

5218 ■ *National Directory of Nonprofit Organizations*
Taft Group
27500 Drake Rd.
Farmington Hills, MI 48331-3535
Ph: (248)699-4253
Free: 800-877-4253
Fax: (800)414-5043
E-mail: gale.salesassistance@thomson.com
URL: http://www.gale.cengage.com
Frequency: Annual; latest edition 27th; February 2012. **Price:** $718 Individuals Volume 1; $484 Individuals Volume 2. **Covers:** Over 265,000 nonprofit organizations; volume 1 covers organizations with annual incomes of over $100,000; volume 2 covers organizations with incomes between $25,000 and $99,999. **Entries include:** Organization name, address, phone, annual income, IRS filing status, employer identification number, tax deductible status, activity description. **Arrangement:** Alphabetical. **Indexes:** Area of activity, geographical.

HANDBOOKS AND MANUALS

5219 ■ *Fundraising As a Profession: Advancements and Challenges in the Field*
Jossey-Bass
989 Market St.
San Francisco, CA 94103-1741
Ph: (415)433-1740
Free: 800-225-5945
Fax: (415)433-0499
E-mail: apastern@josseybass.com
URL: http://www.josseybass.com
Description: Lilya D. Wagner and Patrick Ryan. May 2004. $29.00. 104 pages. Part of the J-B PF Single Issue Philanthropic Fundraising Series.

5220 ■ *Great Jobs for Liberal Arts Majors*
The McGraw-Hill Companies Inc.
PO Box 182604
Columbus, OH 43272
Ph: (212)512-2000
Free: 877-833-5524
Fax: (614)759-3749
E-mail: customer.service@mcgraw-hill.com
URL: http://www.mcgraw-hill.com
Description: Blythe Camenson. Second edition, 2007. $16.95 (paper). 192 pages.

EMPLOYMENT AGENCIES AND SEARCH FIRMS

5221 ■ *Thomas R. Moore Executive Search L.L.C.*
2000 E Lamar Blvd., Ste. 600
Arlington, TX 76006
Ph: (817)548-8766
Fax: (817)472-8293
E-mail: trmsearch@msn.com
URL: http://www.thomasmooresearch.com
Description: Search firm focusing on the recruitment of experienced fund raising professionals for institutions, organizations and firms associated with the not-for-profit industry.

ONLINE JOB SOURCES AND SERVICES

5222 ■ *FundraisingCrossing.com*
URL: http://www.fundraisingcrossing.com
Description: Provides a comprehensive collection of researched fundraising job openings. Provides instant access to listings based on particular area of focus. Includes ads from Fortune 500 and Fortune 1,000 companies.

5223 ■ *FundraisingJobs.com*
URL: http://www.fundraisingjobs.com
Description: Provides job postings. Also allows users to post resumes for potential employers.

5224 ■ *Philanthropy.com*
URL: http://philanthropy.com/section/Jobs/224
Description: Provides news and job listings to those in the nonprofit sector. Information from The Chronicle of Philanthropy is available through the website.

OTHER SOURCES

5225 ■ *Association of Fundraising Professionals*
4300 Wilson Blvd., Ste. 300
Arlington, VA 22203
Ph: (703)684-0410
Free: 800-666-3863
Fax: (703)684-0540
E-mail: afp@afpnet.org
URL: http://www.afpnet.org
Description: Consists of fundraising executives who work for non-profit and philanthropic organizations. Fosters the development and growth of professional fundraising executives. Promotes high ethical standards in the fundraising profession. Supports philanthropy through advocacy, research, education and certification programs.

5226 ■ Association of Professional Researchers for Advancement
330 N Wabash Ave., Ste. 2000
Chicago, IL 60611
Ph: (312)321-5196
Fax: (312)673-6966
E-mail: info@aprahome.org
URL: http://www.aprahome.org

Description: Consists of development professionals who specialize fundraising research, analytics and relationship management. Provides educational and networking opportunities and advocacy and a representative voice for the profession. Promotes high professional standards and ethical guidelines.

5227 ■ Career Opportunities in the Nonprofit Sector
InfoBase Holdings Inc.
132 W 31st., 17 Fl.
New York, NY 10001-3406
Ph: (212)967-8800
Fax: (800)678-3633
E-mail: info@infobasepublishing.com
URL: http://www.ferguson.infobasepublishing.com

Description: 2006. $49.50. 352 pages. Features job and career descriptions in the nonprofit sector, followed by the descriptions of certification, education, special skills and training required. **Includes:** Appendices of educational institutions, periodicals, directories, and associations. Appendices of educational institutions, periodicals, directories, and associations.

5228 ■ Careers for Good Samaritans and Other Humanitarian Types
The McGraw-Hill Companies Inc.
PO Box 182604
Columbus, OH 43272
Ph: (212)512-2000
Free: 877-833-5524
Fax: (614)759-3749
E-mail: customer.service@mcgraw-hill.com
URL: http://www.mcgraw-hill.com

Description: Marjorie Eberts and Margaret Gisler. Third edition, 2006. $16.95 (paper). 160 pages. Contains hundreds of ideas for turning good works into paid job opportunities with service organizations, religious groups, and government agencies. **Includes:** Appendices of Interaction member agencies, missionary organizations, and state offices of volunteerism that offer networking, employment, and volunteering opportunities, as well as job-hunting information. Appendices of Interaction member agencies, missionary organizations, and state offices of volunteerism that offer networking, employment, and volunteering opportunities, as well as job-hunting information. **Entries include:** Name, address, URL.

5229 ■ Society for Nonprofit Organizations
PO Box 510354
Livonia, MI 48151
Ph: (734)451-3582
Fax: (734)451-5935
E-mail: info@snpo.org
URL: http://www.snpo.org

Description: Brings together those who serve in the nonprofit world in order to build a strong network of professionals throughout the country; provides a forum for the exchange of information, knowledge, and ideas on strengthening and increasing productivity within nonprofit organizations and among their leaders. Mission is accomplished through the publication of Nonprofit World magazine, educational programs offered by the Learning Institute, and other communications with its members.

SOURCES OF HELP-WANTED ADS

5230 ■ Funeral Monitor
Abbott & Hast Publications
2361 Horseshoe Dr.
West Bloomfield, MI 48322
Ph: (248)737-9294
Free: 800-453-1199
Fax: (248)737-9296
E-mail: info@abbottandhast.com
URL: http://www.funeralmonitor.com

Description: Weekly. $239/year for domestic subscription; $265/year for foreign (U.S. funds). Provides information on the funeral industry.

5231 ■ Funeral Service Insider
United Communications Group
9737 Washingtonian Blvd., Ste. 100
Gaithersburg, MD 20878-7364
Ph: (301)287-2700
Free: 800-824-1195
Fax: (301)287-2039
E-mail: webmaster@ucg.com
URL: http://www.ucg.com

Description: Weekly. Covers the latest trends in funeral service education, legislation, franchising, marketing, and consumer purchasing. Recurring features include editorials, news of research, letters to the editor, and a calendar of events.

5232 ■ NFDA Bulletin
National Funeral Directors Association
13625 Bishops Dr.
Brookfield, WI 53005-6607
Ph: (262)789-1880
Free: 800-228-6332
Fax: (262)789-6977
E-mail: nfda@nfda.org
URL: http://www.nfda.org

Frequency: Monthly. **Price:** Included in membership. **Description:** Monthly. Covers association activities and funeral business management topics. Reports on association news, government regulation, public relations issues, and local developments.

PLACEMENT AND JOB REFERRAL SERVICES

5233 ■ FuneralStaff
4430 Wade Green Rd., Ste. 180-138
Kennesaw, GA 30144
Ph: (770)966-8048
Free: 866-386-7823
Fax: (770)966-8049
E-mail: funeralstaff@bellsouth.net
URL: http://www.funeralstaff.com

Description: Full service staffing and consulting firm specializing in placing funeral service professionals, administrators and support staff.

HANDBOOKS AND MANUALS

5234 ■ FabJob Guide to Become a Funeral Director
FabJob Inc.
4616-25th Ave. NE, No. 224
Seattle, WA 98105
Ph: (403)873-1018
Free: 888-322-5621
URL: http://www.fabjob.com

Description: Kelly Boyer-Sagert. $19.97(e-book). 200 pages. Guide for anyone seeking a career in the funeral industry.

ONLINE JOB SOURCES AND SERVICES

5235 ■ FuneralJobs.com
URL: http://funeraljobs.com/go/jobs/Index

Description: Lists job postings around the country. Also provides interview and resume tips.

5236 ■ FuneralNet.com
URL: http://www.funeralnet.com

Description: General mortuary science information site contains Funeral Careers section with information on continuing education and classifieds section with postings for internship and employment opportunities.

TRADESHOWS

5237 ■ National Funeral Directors Association Annual Convention & Expo
National Funeral Directors Association
13625 Bishops Dr.
Brookfield, WI 53005-6607
Ph: (262)789-1880
Free: 800-228-6332
Fax: (262)789-6977
E-mail: nfda@nfda.org
URL: http://www.nfda.org

Frequency: Annual. **Primary Exhibits:** Equipment, supplies, and services for funeral directors and morticians.

5238 ■ New Jersey State Funeral Directors Association Convention
New Jersey State Funeral Directors Association
PO Box L
Manasquan, NJ 08736
Ph: (732)974-9444
Free: 800-734-3712
Fax: (732)974-8144
E-mail: njsfda@njsfda.org
URL: http://www.njsfda.org

Frequency: Annual. **Primary Exhibits:** Funeral industry equipment, supplies, and services.

5239 ■ South Dakota Funeral Directors Association Annual Convention
South Dakota Funeral Directors Association
25654 431st Ave.
Spencer, SD 57374
Ph: (605)226-9466
Fax: (605)226-2466
URL: http://www.sdfda.org

Frequency: Annual. **Primary Exhibits:** Caskets, chemical supplies, publications, clothing, coaches, accounting services, computer services, vaults, funeral vehicles, and cemetery monument dealers. SD.

OTHER SOURCES

5240 ■ American Board of Funeral Service Education
3414 Ashland Ave., Ste. G
Saint Joseph, MO 64506-1333
Ph: (816)233-3747
Fax: (816)233-3793
E-mail: exdir@abfse.org
URL: http://www.abfse.org

Description: Serves as the national academic accreditation agency for college programs in Funeral Service and Mortuary Science Education.

5241 ■ Illinois Funeral Directors Association
215 S Grand Ave. W
Springfield, IL 62704-3838
Ph: (217)525-2000
Free: 800-240-4332
Fax: (217)525-8342
E-mail: info@ifda.org
URL: http://ifda.org

Description: Seeks to provide the public and the profession continuous education and improved understanding of funeral service, its values and community contributions made by funeral directors and services to the living while properly caring for the dead. **Members:** Funeral Directors seeking a common voice, a way to share information, ideas and methods, and to protect themselves and consumers through legislation. **Activities:** Offers services to members and the public, including a credit union, funeral financing, legislative lobbying, and a job location service.

5242 ■ National Funeral Directors Association
13625 Bishops Dr.
Brookfield, WI 53005-6607
Ph: (262)789-1880

Free: 800-228-6332
Fax: (262)789-6977
E-mail: nfda@nfda.org
URL: http://www.nfda.org

Description: Association web site contains employment classifieds and career resources such as licensing and educational requirements, continuing education credit opportunities and more for those interested in finding a position as a funeral director.

5243 ■ New York State Funeral Directors Association
1 S Family Dr.
Albany, NY 12205

Ph: (518)452-8230
Fax: (518)452-8667
URL: http://www.nysfda.org

Description: Aims to enhance the environment in which the members operate and to promote the highest standards of funeral service to the public.

SOURCES OF HELP-WANTED ADS

5244 ■ *Las Vegas Insider*
Las Vegas Insider
PO Box 1185
Chino Valley, AZ 86323
Free: 800-628-1686
E-mail: amchb@primnet.com
URL: http://www.lasvegasinsider.com/tiptellsell/
Donald Currier, Editor. **Frequency:** Monthly. **Price:**
$45, U.S.. **Description:** Monthly. Recurring features
include a calendar of events and job listings in Las
Vegas, Reno, and Atlantic City.

EMPLOYER DIRECTORIES AND NETWORKING LISTS

5245 ■ *American Casino Guide*
Casino Vacations
PO Box 703
Dania, FL 33004
Ph: (954)989-2766
URL: http://www.americancasinoguide.com
Frequency: Annual; Latest edition 2013. **Price:**
$18.95 Individuals plus shipping charges; $11.75
Individuals discounted price. **Pages:** 496. **Covers:**
more than 700 casino/resorts, riverboat casinos, and
Indian casinos in the U.S. **Includes:** Maps, photos.
Entries include: Casino name, address, phone, toll-
free number, room rates, dining information, games
offered, features, web site addresses. **Arrangement:**
Geographical. **Indexes:** Name.

5246 ■ *Career Opportunities in Casinos and
Casino Hotels*
InfoBase Holdings Inc.
132 W 31st., 17 Fl.
New York, NY 10001-3406
Ph: (212)967-8800
Fax: (800)678-3633
E-mail: info@infobasepublishing.com
URL: http://factsonfile.infobasepublishing.com/
Frequency: Irregular; Latest edition 2nd; Published
May, 2009. **Price:** $49.50 Individuals hardcover.
Description: Directory of casinos and cruise lines,
gaming conferences and expos, seminars,
workshops, and industry Web sites. **Publication
includes:** A directory of casinos and cruise lines,
gaming conferences and expos, seminars,
workshops, and industry Web sites. Principal content
of publication is 100 occupations in 10 employment
sections on careers in gaming, administration,
management, security, entertainment, hotel management, and food and beverage service in the casino
industry.

5247 ■ *Casino Camping*
Roundabout Publications
PO Box 569
La Cygne, KS 66040
Free: 800-455-2207
E-mail: mail@roundaboutpublications.com
URL: http://www.travelbooksusa.com/shop/viewitem
.php?productid=22
Frequency: Annual; Latest edition 2010. **Price:**
$13.55 Individuals. **Pages:** 288. **Covers:** 300 RV-
friendly casinos in America. **Entries include:** Contact
information, detailed description, available discounts,
driving directions, and RV parking information.

5248 ■ *Casino Vendors Guide*
Casino City Press
95 Wells Ave.
Newton, MA 02459
Ph: (617)332-2850
Free: 800-490-1715
Fax: (617)964-2280
E-mail: sales@casinocitypress.com
URL: http://www.casinocitypress.com
Frequency: Annual; Latest edition 2012. **Price:**
$49.95 book. **Pages:** 320. **Covers:** 10,000 industry
suppliers, manufacturers, and distributors, 1,000
gaming products and services, 1,500 gaming proper-
ties around the world, gaming associations, analysts,
attorneys, trade shows, and trade publications.
Entries include: Company name, address, branch
office locations, phone and fax numbers, email and
website addresses, executive contacts and company
description.

5249 ■ *Gaming Business Directory*
Casino City Press
95 Wells Ave.
Newton, MA 02459
Ph: (617)332-2850
Free: 800-490-1715
Fax: (617)964-2280
E-mail: sales@casinocitypress.com
URL: http://www.casinocitypress.com
Frequency: Annual; Latest edition 2013. **Price:**
$299.95 book; $399.95 Individuals CD; $424.95
book/CD Package. **Pages:** 580. **Covers:** Information
on more than 4,500 casinos, card rooms, horse
tracks, dog tracks, and casino cruises and cruise
ships, around the world, 650 major gaming property
owners, and 2,000 gaming properties owned and
operated. **Entries include:** 26,000 executive
contacts, names and titles by department, property
name, location and mailing addresses, and phone
and fax numbers. **Indexes:** Alphabetical by size;
alphabetical by property type.

EMPLOYMENT AGENCIES AND SEARCH FIRMS

5250 ■ *The IMC Group of Companies Ltd.*
120 White Plains Rd., Ste. 405
Tarrytown, NY 10591
Ph: (914)468-7050
Fax: (914)468-7051
URL: http://www.the-imc.com
Description: International executive recruiting and
management consulting company providing leading-
edge services for the hospitality, leisure, entertain-
ment, gaming and new media industries throughout
the United States, Europe, Africa, Asia Pacific and
Latin America.

ONLINE JOB SOURCES AND SERVICES

5251 ■ *Casino Careers Online*
URL: http://www.casinocareers.com
Description: Serves as a job board that focuses on
career opportunities for different levels and departments within the gaming industry.

5252 ■ *CasinoGigs.net*
URL: http://www.casinogigs.net
Description: Serves as a career community for the
gambling industry. Features job openings for casino
workers, research into the arts, entertainment & gaming employment market, and a career articles section
written and frequented by industry professionals.

5253 ■ *HCareers.com*
URL: http://www.hcareers.com
Description: Connects employers and candidates
within the hospitality industry. Enables candidates to
search for jobs within a specific industry or location.

TRADESHOWS

5254 ■ *North American Association of State
and Provincial Lotteries Conference and
Trade Show*
North American Association of State and Provincial
Lotteries
1 S Broadway
Geneva, OH 44041-1827
Ph: (440)466-5630
Fax: (440)466-5649
E-mail: info@nasplhq.org
URL: http://www.naspl.org
Frequency: Annual. **Primary Exhibits:** Lottery
equipment, supplies, and services.

OTHER SOURCES

5255 ■ *American Gaming Association*
1299 Pennsylvania Ave. NW, Ste. 1175
Washington, DC 20004
Ph: (202)552-2675
Fax: (202)552-2676
E-mail: info@americangaming.org
URL: http://www.americangaming.org

Description: Represents the commercial casino entertainment industry by addressing federal legislative and regulatory issues affecting its members and their employees and customers, such as federal taxation, regulatory issues, and travel and tourism matters.

5256 ■ Gambling Portal Webmasters Association
95 Wells Ave.
Newton Centre, MA 02459
Ph: (617)332-2850
Free: 800-490-1715
Fax: (617)964-2280
E-mail: sales@gpwa.org
URL: http://www.gpwa.org

Description: Helps members succeed in the online gaming industry. Strengthens relationships between affiliate program managers and portal webmasters. Provides members with opportunities to collaborate with other webmasters and online gaming affiliates.

5257 ■ Gaming Standards Association
48377 Fremont Blvd., Ste. 117
Fremont, CA 94538
Ph: (510)492-4060
E-mail: sec@gamingstandards.com
URL: http://www.gamingstandards.com

Description: Gaming manufacturers, suppliers and operators. Promotes identification, definition, development, and implementation of open standards to facilitate innovation, education and communication for the gaming industry. **Members:** 37.

5258 ■ North American Gaming Regulators Association
1000 Westgate Dr., Ste. 252
Saint Paul, MN 55114
Ph: (651)203-7244
Fax: (651)290-2266
E-mail: info@nagra.org
URL: http://www.nagra.org

Description: Brings together agencies that regulate gaming activities and provides a forum for the mutual exchange of regulatory information and techniques. Collects and disseminates regulatory and enforcement information, procedures, and experiences from all jurisdictions provided on-going gaming education and training for all members.

SOURCES OF HELP-WANTED ADS

5259 ■ *Academy of Management Learning & Education*
Academy of Management
PO Box 3020
Briarcliff Manor, NY 10510
Ph: (914)923-2607
Fax: (914)923-2615
E-mail: membership@aom.org
URL: http://journals.aomonline.org/amle

Frequency: Quarterly. **Price:** $85 Individuals print; $130 Individuals print & online; $125 Libraries print; $170 Libraries print and online; $105 Other countries print; $150 Other countries print & online; $195 Other countries print, corporate library; $235 Other countries print & online, corporate library. **Description:** Journal covering management issues for professionals.

5260 ■ *AMI Bulletin*
Association for Management Information in Financial Services
14247 Saffron Cir.
Carmel, IN 46032
Ph: (317)815-5857
Fax: (317)815-5877
E-mail: ami2@amifs.org
URL: http://www.amifs.org/

Description: Quarterly. Monitors events and profiles members and committees. Recurring features include reports of meetings and workshops and a calendar of events.

5261 ■ *Association News: America's Most-Read Magazine for State and Regional Associations*
Schneider Publishing Company Inc.
11835 W Olympic Blvd., 12th Fl.
Los Angeles, CA 90064
Ph: (310)577-3700
Free: 877-577-3700
Fax: (310)577-3715
E-mail: info@schneiderpublishing.com
URL: http://www.associationnews.com/

Frequency: Monthly. **Price:** Free. **Description:** Magazine containing management and meeting plan information for association executives and meeting planners.

5262 ■ *Aviation Today*
Access Intelligence L.L.C.
4 Choke Cherry Rd., 2nd Fl.
Rockville, MD 20850
Ph: (301)354-2000
Free: 800-777-5006
Fax: (301)309-3847
E-mail: info@accessintel.com
URL: http://www.accessintel.com

Description: Covers the commuter/regional airline industry, including airline management, marketing, labor, personnel changes, aircraft acquisitions, new products, and the financial and operational environment. Recurring features include interviews, news of research, a calendar of events, reports of meetings, job listings, and notices of publications available.

5263 ■ *Business Performance Management*
Intertec Publishing
5 Penn Plz., 13th Fl.
New York, NY 10001-1810
Ph: (212)613-9700
Free: 800-795-5445
Fax: (212)613-9749
E-mail: bethany.weaver@penton.com
URL: http://www.bpmmag.net/

Frequency: 4/yr. **Description:** Magazine for business managers. Covers organizing, automating, and analyzing of business methodologies and processes.

5264 ■ *CEO Update*
URL: http://www.ceoupdate.com

Description: Bimonthly. $395.00/year. Provides trend analysis and information on new and departing leaders. Offers senior-level openings in associations, professional societies, and nonprofits.

5265 ■ *CFO: Magazine for Senior Financial Executives*
CFO Publishing
111 W 57th St., 12th Fl.
New York, NY 10019
Ph: (212)698-9787
Fax: (212)459-3007
URL: http://www.cfo.com/magazine/index.cfm/about?f=aboutus_nav

Frequency: Monthly. **Price:** $120 Other countries; Free. **Description:** Business magazine for small to mid-sized companies.

5266 ■ *D CEO*
D Magazine
750 N Saint Paul St., Ste. 2100
Dallas, TX 75201
Ph: (214)939-3636
Fax: (214)748-4579
E-mail: feedback@dmagazine.com
URL: http://www.dmagazine.com/Issues/D_CEO_APR_2009.aspx

Frequency: Monthly. **Price:** $27 Individuals. **Description:** Magazine for executives and business leaders.

5267 ■ *Executive Leadership*
National Institute of Business Management
PO Box 9070
McLean, VA 22102
Free: 800-543-2055
Fax: (703)905-8040
E-mail: customer@businessmanagementdaily.com
URL: http://www.businessmanagementdaily.com

Description: Monthly. $115/year. Shows the reader how to become a better leader. Contains information on taking charge in the workplace, enjoying a wider business perspective, leading organizations to more efficiency and greater success, and rising faster in the field of management.

5268 ■ *Forbes*
Forbes Inc.
60 5th Ave.
New York, NY 10011-8868
Ph: (212)366-8900
Free: 800-295-0893
Fax: (212)620-1863
E-mail: ekutner@forbes.net
URL: http://www.forbes.com

Frequency: Biweekly. **Price:** $19.99 Individuals; $22.25 Canada. **Description:** Magazine reporting on industry, business and finance management.

5269 ■ *Forrester: Forrester*
Forrester Research Inc.
60 Acorn Park Dr.
Cambridge, MA 02140
Ph: (617)613-6000
E-mail: customercenter@forrester.com
URL: http://www.forrester.com/mag

Frequency: 3/yr. **Price:** Free. **Description:** Journal that aims to provide ideas and advice that is relevant to today's CEOs.

5270 ■ *Franchising World*
International Franchise Association
1501 K St. NW, Ste. 350
Washington, DC 20005
Ph: (202)628-8000
Free: 800-543-1038
Fax: (202)628-0812
E-mail: ifa@franchise.org
URL: http://www.franchise.org/

Frequency: Monthly; Bimonthly. **Price:** $50 Individuals. **Description:** Trade magazine covering topics of interest to franchise company executives and the business world.

5271 ■ *The Los Angeles Business Journal*
The Los Angeles Business Journal
5700 Wilshire, No. 170
Los Angeles, CA 90036
Ph: (213)549-5225
Fax: (213)549-5255
URL: http://www.labusinessjournal.com

Frequency: Weekly (Mon.). **Price:** $99.95 Individuals; $179.95 Two years. **Description:** Newspaper (tabloid) covering local business news, business trends, executive profiles, and information for the Los Angeles area executive.

5272 ■ *Management Research: The Journal of the Iberoamerican Academy of Management*
M.E. Sharpe Inc.
80 Business Park Dr.
Armonk, NY 10504

Ph: (914)273-1800
Free: 800-541-6563
Fax: (914)273-2106
E-mail: info@mesharpe.com
URL: http://www.mesharpe.com/mall/results1.asp
?ACR=JMR

Frequency: 3/yr. **Price:** $75 Individuals; $399 Institutions; $87 Other countries; $441 Institutions, other countries. **Description:** International journal dedicated to advancing the understanding of management in private and public sector organizations through empirical investigation and theoretical analysis. Attempts to promote an international dialogue between researchers, improve the understanding of the nature of management in different settings, and achieve a reasonable transfer of research results to management practice in several contexts. Receptive to research across a broad range of management topics such as human resource management, organizational behavior, organizational theory, and strategic management. While not regional in nature, articles dealing with Iberoamerican issues are particularly welcomed.

5273 ■ *San Diego Business Journal*
San Diego Business Journal
4909 Murphy Canyon Rd., Ste. 200
San Diego, CA 92123
Ph: (858)277-6359
Fax: (858)277-2149
E-mail: mdomine@sdbj.com
URL: http://www.sdbj.com

Frequency: Weekly (Mon.). **Price:** $99 Individuals; $180 Two years. **Description:** Metropolitan business newspaper specializing in investigative and enterprise reporting on San Diego County businesses and related issues.

5274 ■ *San Diego Daily Transcript*
San Diego Source/The Daily Transcript
2131 3rd Ave.
San Diego, CA 92101
Ph: (619)232-4381
Free: 800-697-6397
E-mail: webmaster@sddt.com
URL: http://www.sddt.com

Frequency: Daily (morn.). **Price:** $239 Individuals print + online; $379 Two years print + online. **Description:** Local business newspaper.

5275 ■ *San Francisco Business Times: Serving Alameda, Contra Costa, Marin, San Francisco and San Mateo Counties*
American City Business Journals, Inc.
c/o Steve Symanovich, Ed.
275 Battery St., Ste. 940
San Francisco, CA 94111
Ph: (415)989-2522
Fax: (415)398-2494
E-mail: sanfrancisco@bizjournals.com
URL: http://www.bizjournals.com/sanfrancisco

Frequency: Weekly. **Price:** $98 Individuals; $176 Two years; $198 Individuals three years. **Description:** Local business newspaper (tabloid) serving the San Francisco Bay Area.

EMPLOYER DIRECTORIES AND NETWORKING LISTS

5276 ■ *D & B Million Dollar Directory*
Dun and Bradstreet Corp.
103 JFK Pkwy.
Short Hills, NJ 07078
Ph: (973)921-5500
Free: 800-526-0651
Fax: (866)560-7035
E-mail: info@dnb.com
URL: http://www.mergentmddi.com

Frequency: Annual; Latest edition 2008. **Pages:** 27,606 5 volumes. **Covers:** 1,600,000 public and private businesses with either a net worth of

$500,000 or more, 250 or more employees at that location, or $25,000,000 or more in sales volume; includes industrial corporations, utilities, transportation companies, bank and trust companies, stock brokers, mutual and stock insurance companies, wholesalers, retailers, and domestic subsidiaries of foreign corporations. **Entries include:** Company name, address, phone, state of incorporation; annual sales; number of employees, company ticker symbol on stock exchange, Standard Industrial Classification (SIC) number, line of business; principal bank, accounting firm; parent company name, current ownership date, division names and functions, directors or trustees; names, titles, functions of principal executives, number of employees, import/export designation. **Arrangement:** Alphabetical, cross referenced geographically and by industry classification. **Indexes:** Geographical (with address and SIC), product by SIC (with address).

5277 ■ *Financial Managers Society--Membership and Peer Consulting Directory*
Financial Managers Society
1 N La Salle St., Ste. 3100
Chicago, IL 60602-4003
Ph: (312)578-1300
Free: 800-275-4367
Fax: (312)578-1308
E-mail: info@fmsinc.org
URL: http://www.fmsinc.org

Frequency: Annual. **Description:** Lists executives and managers of financial institutions who volunteer their advice to other members in specific areas of expertise. **Covers:** Executives and managers of financial institutions.

5278 ■ *Inc.--The Inc. 500 Issue*
Gruner & Jahr USA Publishing
1716 Locust St.
Des Moines, IA 50309-3023
Ph: (515)284-3000
URLs: http://www.inc.com; http://www.inc.com/inc5000/2009/index.html

Frequency: Annual; Latest edition 2010. **Publication includes:** List of 500 fastest-growing privately held companies based on percentage increase in sales over the five year period prior to compilation of current year's list. **Entries include:** Company name, headquarters city, description of business, year founded, number of employees, sales five years earlier and currently, profitability range, and growth statistics. **Arrangement:** Ranked by sales growth.

5279 ■ *List of CEOs & Executives in Food Industry*
Business Information Agency Inc. - PlanetInform
52 Tuscan Way, Ste. 202-181
Saint Augustine, VA 32092
Ph: (904)342-6124
Fax: (904)592-2632
E-mail: info@biasales.com
URL: http://www.planetinform.com/salesLeadsCard
.aspx?prodID=3913

Covers: CEOs and executives from 500 food companies and sub-industries including meat, dairy, fruit, vegetables, flour, cereals, rice, dog and cat food, candies, chocolates and crackers, fats, oil, alcohol and softdrinks, fish and seafood, macaroni, spaghetti, vermicelli and food preparations.

5280 ■ *List of CEOs & Executives in Industrial Machinery Industry*
Business Information Agency Inc. - PlanetInform
52 Tuscan Way, Ste. 202-181
Saint Augustine, VA 32092
Ph: (904)342-6124
Fax: (904)592-2632
E-mail: info@biasales.com
URL: http://www.planetinform.com/salesLeadsCard
.aspx?prodID=3926

Covers: CEOs and executives from 500 industrial machinery companies in all Russian Regions.

5281 ■ *Nonprofit Management Resources Directory*
National Council for International Visitors
1420 K St. NW, Ste. 800
Washington, DC 20005
Ph: (202)842-1414
Free: 800-523-8101
Fax: (202)289-4625
E-mail: info@nciv.org
URL: http://www.nciv.org/pr_publications.asp

Covers: Nonprofit organizations. **Entries include:** Name, address, phone, fax, email, and website address.

5282 ■ *Standard & Poor's Register of Corporations, Directors and Executives*
Standard & Poor's Financial Services L.L.C.
55 Water St.
New York, NY 10041
Ph: (212)438-2000
Free: 877-772-5436
Fax: (212)438-1000
E-mail: questions@standardandpoors.com
URL: http://www2.standardandpoors.com

Frequency: Annual; January; supplements in April, July, and October. **Pages:** 5,200. **Covers:** over 55,000 public and privately held corporations in the United States, including names and titles of over 400,000 officials (Volume 1); 70,000 biographies of directors and executives (Volume 2). **Includes:** In Volume 3, lists of new executives, new companies, a corporate "Family Tree", Standard & Poor's 500 composite stock indices, and obituaries. **Entries include:** For companies--Name, address, phone, names of principal executives and accountants; primary bank, primary law firm, number of employees, estimated annual sales, outside directors, Standard Industrial Classification (SIC) code, product or service provided. For directors and executives--Name, home and principal business addresses, date and place of birth, fraternal organization memberships, business affiliations. **Arrangement:** Alphabetical. **Indexes:** Volume 3 indexes companies geographically, by Standard Industrial Classification (SIC) code, and by corporate family groups.

5283 ■ *Vault Guide to the Top Business Services Employers*
Vault.com Inc.
132 W 31st St., 17th Fl.
New York, NY 10001-3406
Ph: (212)366-4212
Free: 800-535-2074
Fax: (212)366-6117
E-mail: customerservice@vault.com
URL: http://www.vault.com

Frequency: Latest edition February, 2006. **Price:** $19.95 Individuals Online; $19.95 Members Gold. **Pages:** 123. **Covers:** Top business service companies in United States. **Entries include:** Company name, contact person, location, address, phone and fax numbers, zip code, statistics, hiring process and email.

5284 ■ *Vault Guide to the Top Private Equity Employers*
Vault.com Inc.
132 W 31st St., 17th Fl.
New York, NY 10001-3406
Ph: (212)366-4212
Free: 800-535-2074
Fax: (212)366-6117
E-mail: customerservice@vault.com
URL: http://www.vault.com

Frequency: Latest edition 2008. **Price:** $29.95 Individuals Online; $29.95 Members Gold. **Pages:** 128. **Covers:** 2,700 private equity companies worldwide. **Entries include:** Company name, address, phone and fax numbers, statistics, contact person and email address. **Arrangement:** Alphabetical by company name.

HANDBOOKS AND MANUALS

5285 ■ Airport Report Today
American Association of Airport Executives
601 Madison St., Ste. 400
Alexandria, VA 22314
Ph: (703)824-0500
Fax: (703)820-1395
E-mail: member.services@aaae.org
URL: http://www.aaae.org
Description: Bimonthly. Represents airport management personnel at public-use commercial and general aviation airports. Posts employment and business opportunities.

5286 ■ Careers for Dreamers and Doers: A Guide to Management Careers in the Nonprofit Sector
URL: http://foundationcenter.org
Price: $24.95 Individuals. **Pages:** 237. **Publication includes:** Nonprofit management programs at colleges and universities. Principal content of publication is job search advice and strategies, career histories of nonprofit CEOs, development officers, and foundation officials, and compensation patterns in the field.

5287 ■ The Directory of Executive & Professional Recruiters
Kennedy Information Inc.
1 Phoenix Mill Ln., 3rd Fl.
Peterborough, NH 03458
Ph: (603)924-1006
Free: 800-531-0007
Fax: (603)924-4460
E-mail: customerservice@kennedyinfo.com
URL: http://www.kennedyinfo.com
Description: 2011-2012. $ 69.95. 1200 pages. Contains detailed contact information for over 6,000 search firms located in the United States, Canada, and Mexico.

5288 ■ Expert Resumes for Managers and Executives
Jist Works
875 Montreal Way
Saint Paul, MN 55102
Free: 800-648-5478
E-mail: info@jist.com
URL: http://www.jist.com/shop/product.php?productid =16727
Description: Wendy S. Enelow, Louise M. Kursmark. 2012. $17.95. 274 pages. Contains a collection of sample resumes and resume writing advice including how to create and use an electronic resume. Contains an appendix that includes internet resources for an online job search, writing cover letters, as well as a collection of sample letters.

5289 ■ Manager's Handbook: Everything You Need to Know about How Business and Management Work
Pearson Learning Group
145 S Mount Zion Rd.
Lebanon, IN 46052
Ph: (804)402-6933
Free: 800-526-9907
Fax: (800)393-3156
E-mail: pasley@pearsonlearning.com
URL: http://www.k12pearson.com
Price: $24.95. **Publication includes:** Principal content of publication is reference guide for new and experienced managers. **Indexes:** Alphabetical.

EMPLOYMENT AGENCIES AND SEARCH FIRMS

5290 ■ A-L Associates Inc.
60 E 42nd St., Ste. 1534
New York, NY 10036

Ph: (212)878-9000
URL: http://www.alassociatesltd.com
Description: Executive search firm.

5291 ■ Abbott Smith Associates, Inc.
11697 W Grand Ave.
Northlake, IL 60164
Ph: (708)223-1191
E-mail: contactus@abbottsmith.com
URL: http://www.abbottsmith.com
Description: Human Resources executive search firm.

5292 ■ Abeln, Magy, Underberg & Associates
800 E Wayzata Blvd., Ste. 200
Wayzata, MN 55391
Ph: (952)476-4938
Fax: (952)404-7470
E-mail: info@abelnmagy.com
URL: http://www.abelnmagy.com
Description: Executive search firm.

5293 ■ The Adkins Group Inc.
8700 Manchaca Rd., Ste. 504
Austin, TX 78704
Ph: (512)916-9600
Free: 866-916-9600
Fax: (512)916-9665
E-mail: info@theadkinsgroup.com
URL: http://www.theadkinsgroup.com
Description: Executive search firm.

5294 ■ Advantage Group
350 N Old Woodward Ave., Ste. 218
Birmingham, MI 48009
Ph: (248)540-0400
Fax: (248)540-0401
E-mail: info@advantage-grp.com
URL: http://advantage-grp.com
Description: Specializes in the placement of accounting and financial executives.

5295 ■ Advantage Partners Inc.
29225 Chagrin Blvd., Ste. 300
Cleveland, OH 44122
Ph: (216)514-1212
Fax: (216)514-1213
E-mail: pamtaubert@advantagepartnersinc.com
URL: http://www.advantagepartnersinc.com
Description: Executive search firm.

5296 ■ Aegis Group Search Consultants LLC
41451 W 11 Mile Rd.
Novi, MI 48375-1855
Ph: (248)344-1450
Fax: (248)347-2231
E-mail: resume@aegis-group.com
URL: http://www.aegis-group.com
Description: Executive search and consultant firm. Focuses on the medical industry.

5297 ■ Ahern Search Partners
3982 Powell Rd., Ste. 205
Powell, OH 43065
Ph: (614)436-4126
Fax: (614)436-4125
E-mail: mollie@ahernsearch.com
URL: http://www.ahernsearch.com
Description: Executive search firm. Concentrates on the healthcare market.

5298 ■ AKS Associates Ltd.
PO Box 2863
Duxbury, MA 02331
Ph: (781)934-5333
Fax: (781)934-6333
E-mail: sandy@akssearch.com
URL: http://www.akssearch.com
Description: Senior search firm. Concentrates on the financial industry.

5299 ■ The Alexander Group
2700 Post Oak Blvd., Ste. 2400
Houston, TX 77056
Ph: (713)993-7900
URL: http://www.thealexandergroup.com
Description: Executive search firm. Second location in San Francisco.

5300 ■ Alexander Ross & Company
100 Park Ave., 34th Fl.
New York, NY 10017
Ph: (212)889-9333
Fax: (212)864-5111
E-mail: info@alexanderross.com
URL: http://www.alexanderross.com
Description: Executive search firm.

5301 ■ The Alfus Group Inc.
353 Lexington Ave.
New York, NY 10016
Ph: (212)599-1000
Fax: (212)599-1523
E-mail: mail@thealfusgroup.com
URL: http://www.thealfusgroup.com
Description: Executive search firm. Specializes in the hospitality industry.

5302 ■ Allen Adell Executive Search and Consulting
7853 Gunn Hwy., No. 260
Tampa, FL 33626-1611
Ph: (813)920-8900
E-mail: info@allenadell.com
URL: http://www.allenadell.com
Description: Functions as a retained executive search and human capital consulting firm that specializes in recruiting potential candidates for senior, mid-managerial and high-performing individual positions in the healthcare industry. Conducts talent assessment, competitive compensation surveys and objective and comprehensive exit interviews.

5303 ■ Allen Associates
3805 Edwards Rd., Ste. 550
Cincinnati, OH 45209
Ph: (513)563-3040
E-mail: feedback@allensearch.com
URL: http://www.allensearch.com
Description: Executive senior-level search firm.

5304 ■ Allen Austin
4543 Post Oak Place Dr., Ste. 217
Houston, TX 77027
Ph: (713)355-1900
Fax: (713)355-1901
URL: http://www.allenaustinsearch.com
Description: Executive search firm. Branches in North Carolina and Dallas.

5305 ■ Allen Evans Klein International
305 Madison Ave.
New York, NY 10165
Ph: (212)983-9300
Fax: (212)983-9272
E-mail: info@allenevans.com
URL: http://www.allenevans.com
Description: Global Executive search firm.

5306 ■ Allerton Heneghan and O'Neill
1415 W 22nd St., Tower Fl.
Oak Brook, IL 60523
Ph: (630)645-2294
Fax: (630)645-2298
E-mail: info@ahosearch.com
URL: http://www.ahosearch.com
Description: Executive search firm.

5307 ■ Alliance Search Management Inc.
594 Sawdust Rd., Ste. 194
The Woodlands, TX 77380
Ph: (281)419-5111

Free: 800-444-0573
Fax: (281)419-0335
E-mail: sales@alliancesearch.com
URL: http://www.alliancesearch.com

Description: Employment agency.

5308 ■ American Executive Management Inc.
30 Federal St.
Salem, MA 01970
Ph: (978)744-5923
E-mail: execsearch@americanexecutive.us
URL: http://www.americanexecutive.us

Description: Executive search firm. Second location in Boston.

5309 ■ American Incite
917 Hillfield Ct.
Oceanside, CA 92058
Ph: (760)754-2444
Fax: (760)754-2453
E-mail: talent@americanincite.com
URL: http://www.americanincite.com

Description: Executive search firm.

5310 ■ Anderson & Associates
112 S Tryon St., Ste. 700
Charlotte, NC 28284
Ph: (704)347-0090
Fax: (704)347-0064
E-mail: info@andersonexecsearch.com
URL: http://www.andersonexecsearch.com

Description: Executive search firm. Branch in Cumming, Georgia.

5311 ■ Andre David & Associates Inc.
PO Box 700967
Dallas, TX 75370
Ph: (972)250-1986
Fax: (972)250-2243
E-mail: info@andredavid.com
URL: http://www.andredavid.com

Description: Executive search firm.

5312 ■ Andrew Associates Executive Search Inc.
4800 Meadows Rd., Ste. 300
Lake Oswego, OR 97035
Ph: (503)620-5222
E-mail: aaes@andysrch.com
URL: http://www.andysrch.com

Description: Executive search firm.

5313 ■ The Angus Group Ltd.
5080 Wooster Rd., Ste. 300
Cincinnati, OH 45226
Ph: (513)961-5575
Fax: (513)961-5616
URL: http://www.angusgroup.com

Description: Executive search firm.

5314 ■ APA Search Inc.
1 Byram Brook Pl., Ste. 104
Armonk, NY 10504
Ph: (914)273-6000
Fax: (914)273-8025
E-mail: info@apasearch.com
URL: http://www.apasearch.com

Description: Employment agency specializing in the automotive, retail, and hardware industries.

5315 ■ Arthur Diamond Associates Inc.
4630 Montgomery Ave., Ste. 200
Bethesda, MD 20814-3436
Ph: (301)657-8866
Fax: (301)657-8876
E-mail: info@arthurdiamond.com
URL: http://www.arthurdiamond.com

Description: Executive search firm.

5316 ■ Association Executive Resources Group
PO Box 3880
Gaithersburg, MD 20885-3880
Ph: (301)417-7045
Fax: (301)417-7049
URL: http://www.aerg.org

Description: Executive search firm. Concentrates on non-profits.

5317 ■ Association Strategies
1111 N Fairfax St.
Alexandria, VA 22314
Ph: (703)683-0580
Fax: (703)683-1006
E-mail: info@assnstrategies.com
URL: http://www.assnstrategies.com

Description: Employment agency.

5318 ■ Aster Search Group
555 Madison Ave.
New York, NY 10022
Ph: (212)888-6182
E-mail: ecohen@astersearch.com
URL: http://www.astersearch.com

Description: Executive search firm focused on the healthcare industry.

5319 ■ Auguston and Associates Inc.
1010 S Ocean Blvd., Ste. 601
Pompano Beach, FL 33062
Ph: (954)943-0503
Fax: (954)784-1660
E-mail: g.auguston@augustonandassociates.com
URL: http://www.augustonandassociates.com/

Description: Executive search firm focused on medical devices.

5320 ■ Aureus Group
C&A Plz., 13609 California St., Ste. 100
Omaha, NE 68154-3503
Ph: (402)891-6900
Free: 888-239-5993
Fax: (402)891-1290
E-mail: omaha@aureusgroup.com
URL: http://www.aureusgroup.com

Description: Executive search and recruiting consultants specializing in accounting and finance, information systems and technology, health care administration, and wealth management.

5321 ■ Avery Associates
3 1/2 N Santa Cruz Ave., Ste. A
Los Gatos, CA 95030
Ph: (408)399-4424
E-mail: jobs@averyassoc.net
URL: http://www.averyassoc.net

Description: Administration search firm.

5322 ■ Avery James Inc.
6601 Center Dr. W, Ste. 500
Los Angeles, CA 90045
Ph: (310)342-8224
E-mail: resume@averyjames.com
URL: http://www.averyjames.com

Description: Executive search firm.

5323 ■ The Ayers Group
101 Merritt 7, 1st Fl.
Norwalk, CT 06851
Ph: (203)354-7788
Free: 888-786-7834
Fax: (203)354-6683
URL: http://www.ayers.com

Description: Executive search firm.

5324 ■ The Baer Group
900 Ashwood Pkwy., Ste. 300
Atlanta, GA 30346
Ph: (770)557-4900

Fax: (770)557-3499
E-mail: info@baergroup.com
URL: http://www.baergroup.com

Description: Executive search firm.

5325 ■ Baker Montgomery
One Magnificent Mile, Ste. 1815
980 N Michigan Ave.
Chicago, IL 60611
Ph: (312)397-8808
Fax: (312)397-9631
E-mail: contact@bakermontgomery.com
URL: http://www.bakermontgomery.com

Description: Executive search firm.

5326 ■ Barone-O'Hara Associates Inc.
34 Fackler Rd.
Princeton, NJ 08540
Ph: (609)683-5566
Fax: (609)683-8077
E-mail: marialice@baroneohara.com
URL: http://www.baroneohara.com

Description: Executive search firm focused on medical devices.

5327 ■ Barro Global Search Inc.
10940 Wilshire Blvd., Ste. 1600
Los Angeles, CA 90024
Ph: (310)443-4277
E-mail: drbarro@winwithoutcompeting.com
URL: http://www.barroglobal.com

Description: Executive search firm focused on healthcare and hospitals.

5328 ■ Bartholdi Partners
PO Box 930
Gainesville, VA 20156-0930
Ph: (703)476-5519
E-mail: info@bartholdisearch.com
URL: http://www.bartholdisearch.com

Description: Executive search firm. Affiliates in San Francisco; San Jose; Phoenix; Scottsdale; Parker, CO; and Framingham, MA.

5329 ■ Barton Associates Inc.
4314 Yoakum Blvd.
Houston, TX 77006
Ph: (713)961-9111
Fax: (713)403-5574
E-mail: info@bartona.com
URL: http://www.bartona.com

Description: Executive search firm. Affiliate in Houston, TX.

5330 ■ Battalia Winston International
555 Madison Ave.
New York, NY 10022
Ph: (212)308-8080
URL: http://www.battaliawinston.com

Description: Executive search firm. Branches in Los Angeles; Chicago; Wellesley Hills, MA; Edison, NJ.

5331 ■ R. Gaines Baty Associates Inc.
6606 LBJ Fwy., Ste. 100
Dallas, TX 75240
Ph: (972)386-7900
Fax: (972)387-2224
E-mail: gbaty@rgba.com
URL: http://www.rgba.com

Description: Executive search firm.

5332 ■ The Bedford Group
3343 Peachtree Rd. NE, Ste. 333
Atlanta, GA 30326
Ph: (404)237-7471
URL: http://www.bedfordgroupconsulting.com

Description: Executive search firm.

5333 ■ Bert Davis Executive Search
425 Madison Ave.
New York, NY 10017
Ph: (212)838-4000

Fax: (212)935-3291
E-mail: info@bertdavis.com
URL: http://www.bertdavis.com
Description: Executive search firm in the publishing, information and electronic media fields.

5334 ■ BFL Associates Ltd.
11 Greenway Plz., Ste. 545
Houston, TX 77046
Ph: (713)965-2112
Fax: (713)965-2114
E-mail: bjorn@bflassociates.com
URL: http://www.bflassociates.com
Description: Executive search firm.

5335 ■ Bialecki Inc.
780 3rd Ave., Ste. 4203
New York, NY 10017
Ph: (212)755-1090
Fax: (212)755-1130
E-mail: linda@bialecki.com
URL: http://www.bialecki.com
Description: Senior executive search firm focused on the financial industry.

5336 ■ Bishop Partners
28 W 44th St., Ste. 1120A
New York, NY 10036
Ph: (212)986-3419
Fax: (212)575-1050
E-mail: info@bishoppartners.com
URL: http://www.bishoppartners.com
Description: A retainer based executive search firm specializing in media and communications. This includes cable, broadcasting, publishing, Internet and interactive media, entertainment. Consulting closely with clients, finds the right person to fill a specific need or solve a specific business issue in functional areas which include CEO and COO, sales, marketing, finance, human resources, programming and production and ecommerce.

5337 ■ Bonnell Associates Ltd.
40 Richards Ave., 3rd Fl.
Norwalk, CT 06854-2320
Ph: (203)319-7214
Fax: (203)319-7219
E-mail: wbonnell@bonnellassociates.com
URL: http://www.bonnellassociates.com
Description: Executive search firm.

5338 ■ Boston Search Group Inc.
224 Clarendon St., Ste. 41
Boston, MA 02116-3729
Ph: (617)266-4333
Fax: (781)735-0562
E-mail: ralph@bsgtv.com
URL: http://www.bostonsearchgroup.com
Description: Executive search firm.

5339 ■ The Boulware Group
625 N Michigan Ave., Ste. 422
Chicago, IL 60611-3110
Ph: (312)322-0088
Fax: (312)322-0092
E-mail: info@boulwareinc.com
URL: http://www.boulwareinc.com
Description: Executive search firm.

5340 ■ Boyle & Associates Retained Search Group
PO Box 16658
Saint Paul, MN 55116
Ph: (651)223-5050
Fax: (651)699-5378
E-mail: paul@talenthunt.com
URL: http://www.talenthunt.com
Description: Executive search firm.

5341 ■ The Bradbury Group Inc.
1200 E Cole St.
Moundridge, KS 67107

Ph: (620)345-6394
Free: 800-397-6394
Fax: (620)345-6381
E-mail: bradbury@bradburyco.com
URL: http://www.bradburygroup.com
Description: Executive search firm.

5342 ■ Brandywine Consulting Group
1398 Morstein Rd.
West Chester, PA 19380
Ph: (610)696-5872
E-mail: solutions@brandywineconsulting.com
URL: http://www.brandywineconsulting.com
Description: Executive search firm. An Affiliate of Brandywine Management Group in Berlin, MD.

5343 ■ Brennan and Brennan Executive Search
2483 Heritage Village, Ste. 16 No. 167
Snellville, GA 30078
E-mail: jb@brennanandbrennan.com
URL: http://www.brennanandbrennan.com
Description: Exists as a recruitment firm that provides service in retained and contingency search. Delivers recruitment solutions in executive search as well as meeting targeted general staffing needs on a national and international level.

5344 ■ The Brentwood Group Inc.
170 Kinnelon Rd.
Kinnelon, NJ 07405
Ph: (973)283-1000
Fax: (973)850-6103
E-mail: officemanager@thebrentwoodgroup.com
URL: http://www.thebrentwoodgroup.com
Description: Executive search firm.

5345 ■ BridgeGate LLC
17701 Cowan Ave., Ste. 240
Irvine, CA 92614
Ph: (949)553-9200
Fax: (949)660-1810
URL: http://www.bridgegate.com
Description: Executive search firm.

5346 ■ Brindisi Search
10020 Baltimore National Pke., Ste. 100
Ellicott City, MD 21042
Ph: (410)489-6699
Fax: (410)823-0146
E-mail: tbrindisi@aol.com
URL: http://www.brindisisearch.com
Description: Specializes in contemporary human resource and select strategic leadership assignments, ranging from manager to senior vice president level.

5347 ■ Brown Venture Associates Inc.
5150 El Camino Real, Ste. B-30
Los Altos, CA 94022
Ph: (650)233-0205
E-mail: brown@bva.com
URL: http://www.bva.com
Description: Executive search firm.

5348 ■ Brownson & Associates LP
2825 Wilcrest, Ste. 530
Houston, TX 77042
Ph: (713)626-4790
Fax: (713)877-1745
E-mail: brownsonassoc@brownson.com
URL: http://www.brownson.com
Description: Executive search firm.

5349 ■ Buffkin & Associates LLC
730 Cool Springs Blvd., Ste. 120
Franklin, TN 37067
Ph: (615)778-2142
E-mail: info@thebuffkingroup.com
URL: http://www.buffkinassociates.com/www
Description: Executive search firm.

5350 ■ The Burling Group Ltd.
600 N Kingsbury St., Ste. 1507
Chicago, IL 60654
Ph: (312)397-0888
E-mail: web@burlinggroup.com
URL: http://www.burlinggroup.com
Description: Executive search firm.

5351 ■ Burton and Grove Executive Search
1320 Tower Rd.
Schaumburg, IL 60173
Ph: (847)919-8880
E-mail: support@burtonandgrove.com
URL: http://www.burtonandgrove.com
Description: Executive search firm.

5352 ■ Busch International
1000 Fremont Ave., Ste. 195
Los Altos, CA 94024
Ph: (650)949-6500
E-mail: jack@buschint.com
URL: http://www.buschint.com
Description: Executive search firm focused solely on high-technology electronics.

5353 ■ Buxbaum Rink Consulting L.L.C.
1 Bradley Rd., Ste. 901
Woodbridge, CT 06525-2296
Ph: (203)389-5949
Fax: (203)397-0615
Description: Personnel consulting firms offer contingency search, recruitment, and placement of accounting and finance, as well as other business management positions. In addition to serving these two major career areas, also provides similar services to operations, marketing and human resources executives. Industries served: manufacturing, financial services, and service.

5354 ■ CAA Search
5469 Sunbird Dr., Ste. 100
Loves Park, IL 61111
Ph: (815)654-8535
E-mail: christian@caasearch.com
URL: http://www.caasearch.com
Description: Executive search firm.

5355 ■ Cabot Consultants Inc.
1600 Tysons Blvd., 8th Fl.
McLean, VA 22102
Ph: (703)744-1081
Fax: (703)744-1001
E-mail: info@cabotinc.com
URL: http://www.cabotinc.com
Description: A retained executive search firm specializing in filling senior-level positions.

5356 ■ The Caler Group
23337 Lago Mar Cir.
Boca Raton, FL 33433
Ph: (561)394-8045
Fax: (561)394-4645
E-mail: cperrone@calergroup.com
URL: http://www.calergroup.com
Description: Executive search firm.

5357 ■ Caliber Associates
6336 Greenwich Dr., Ste. C
San Diego, CA 92122
Ph: (858)551-7880
Fax: (858)551-7887
E-mail: info@caliberassociates.com
URL: http://www.caliberassociates.com
Description: Executive search firm.

5358 ■ Callan Associates Ltd.
1211 W 22nd St., Ste. 821
Oak Brook, IL 60523
Ph: (630)574-9300

Fax: (630)574-3099
E-mail: info@callanassociates.com
URL: http://www.callanassociates.com

Description: Executive search firm.

5359 ■ Calland & Company
2296 Henderson Mill Rd. NE, Ste. 222
Atlanta, GA 30345
Ph: (770)270-9100
Fax: (770)270-9300
E-mail: bob@callandcompany.com
URL: http://www.callandcompany.com

Description: Executive search firm focused on senior management and healthcare.

5360 ■ Campbell/Carlson LLC
PO Box 34323
Charlotte, NC 28234
Ph: (704)373-0234
E-mail: recruiting@campbellcarlson.com
URL: http://www.campbellcarlson.com

Description: Executive search firm.

5361 ■ Capitol Staffing Inc.
460 Briarwood Dr., Briarwood 1 Bldg., Ste. 110
Jackson, MS 39206
Ph: (601)957-1755
Fax: (601)957-3880
E-mail: info@capitolstaffing.com
URL: http://www.capitolstaffing.com

Description: Personnel consultancy that focuses on office administration, management, sales, accounting, medical, information technology, accounting, and engineering/technical fields. Industries served: insurance, finance, medical, communications, investment, industry, and small businesses.

5362 ■ Capodice & Associates
Midtown Plaza
1243 S Tamiami Trail
Sarasota, FL 34239
Ph: (941)906-1990
Fax: (941)906-1991
E-mail: peter@capodice.com
URL: http://www.capodice.com

Description: Executive search firm. Branch in Carlisle, MA.

5363 ■ Caprio and Associates
1415 W 22nd St., Tower level
Oak Brook, IL 60523
Ph: (630)705-9101
Fax: (630)750-9102
E-mail: jerry@caprioassociates.com
URL: http://www.caprioassociates.com

Description: Executive search firm.

5364 ■ Capstone Inc.
971 Albany Shaker Rd.
Latham, NY 12110
Ph: (518)783-9300
E-mail: amyj@capstone-inc.com
URL: http://www.capstone-inc.com

Description: Executive search firm.

5365 ■ Career Advocates International
1539 Ave. A
Katy, TX 77493
Ph: (281)371-3917
E-mail: hank@careeradvocates.org
URL: http://www.careeradvocates.org

Description: Provides permanent placement and temporary staffing for executive and staff level positions. Specializes in multiple niches including: sales and marketing, accounting and financial services, banking, communications, human resources, chemicals, oil and gas, medical and dental, legal, information technology, energy, technology, engineering, manufacturing, construction, and light industrial.

5366 ■ Carrington & Carrington Ltd.
39 S LaSalle St., Ste. 400
Chicago, IL 60603-1557
Ph: (312)606-0015
Fax: (312)606-0501
E-mail: mcarrington@cclltd.com
URL: http://www.carringtonandcarrington.com

Description: Executive search firm.

5367 ■ CarterBaldwin
200 Mansell Ct. E, Ste. 450
Roswell, GA 30076
Ph: (678)448-0000
Free: 866-781-6844
E-mail: jdelikat@carterbaldwin.com
URL: http://www.carterbaldwin.com

Description: Executive search firm.

5368 ■ Caruso & Associates Inc.
990 Stinson Way, Ste. 201
West Palm Beach, FL 33411
Ph: (561)683-2336
E-mail: info@carusoassociates.com
URL: http://www.carusoassociates.com

Description: Executive search firm.

5369 ■ Catalyst Resource Group, LLC
2050 Marconi Dr., Ste. 300
Alpharetta, GA 30005
Ph: (678)366-3500
Free: 877-746-3400
Fax: (678)366-9710
E-mail: info@catalystresourcegroup.com
URL: http://www.catalystresourcegroup.com

Description: Serves as an executive search firm specializing in the placement of accounting and finance professionals.

5370 ■ Centennial, Inc.
8044 Montgomery Rd., Ste. 260
Cincinnati, OH 45236
Ph: (513)366-3760
Fax: (513)366-3761
URL: http://www.centennialinc.com

Description: Serves as an executive search firm specializing in the areas of executive and general management, accounting and finance, human resources, information technology, manufacturing, engineering, marketing and advertising, not-for-profit, sales and business development, and supply chain and logistics.

5371 ■ Charles Aris, Inc.
300 N Greene St., Ste. 1800
Greensboro, NC 27401
Ph: (336)378-1818
Fax: (336)378-0129
E-mail: info@charlesaris.com
URL: http://www.charlesaris.com

Description: Provides executive search and placement services in the areas of consumer packaged goods, retail, strategy/business development, global life sciences, healthcare, chemicals, textiles/apparel, private equity, and business services.

5372 ■ The Cherbonnier Group Inc.
1 Riverway, Ste. 1700
Houston, TX 77056
Ph: (713)688-4701
E-mail: consult@thecherbonniergroup.com
URL: http://www.thecherbonniergroup.com

Description: Executive search firm.

5373 ■ Cheryl Alexander & Associates
8588 Shadow Creek Dr.
Maple Grove, MN 55311
Ph: (763)416-4570
E-mail: cheryl@cherylalexander.com
URL: http://www.cherylalexander.com

Description: Executive search firm.

5374 ■ Clarey Andrews & Klein Inc.
1347 Hillside Rd.
Northbrook, IL 60062-4612
Ph: (847)498-2870
Fax: (847)498-2875
E-mail: cak@clarey-a-klein.com
URL: http://www.clarey-a-klein.com

Description: Executive search firm.

5375 ■ Cole, Warren and Long Inc.
2 Penn Center Plz., Ste. 312
Philadelphia, PA 19102
Ph: (215)563-0701
Free: 800-394-8517
Fax: (215)563-2907
E-mail: cwlserch@cwl-inc.com
URL: http://www.cwl-inc.com

Description: Executive search firm with international placement.

5376 ■ Coleman Lew & Associates Inc.
326 W 10th St.
Charlotte, NC 28202
Ph: (704)377-0362
Free: 800-533-9523
Fax: (704)377-0424
URL: http://www.colemanlew.com

Description: Executive search firm.

5377 ■ Columbia Consulting Group
5525 Twin Knolls Rd., Ste. 331
Columbia, MD 21045
Ph: (443)276-2525
Fax: (443)276-2536
E-mail: info@ccgsearch.com
URL: http://www.ccgsearch.com

Description: Executive search firm. Branch in New York, NY.

5378 ■ Conard Associates Inc.
74 Northeastern Blvd., Unit 22A
Nashua, NH 03062
Ph: (603)886-0600
Fax: (603)804-0421
URL: http://www.conardassociates.com

Description: Executive search firm.

5379 ■ Consultants to Executive Management Company Ltd.
20 S Clark St., Ste. 610
Chicago, IL 60603
Ph: (312)855-1500
Free: 800-800-2362
Fax: (312)855-1510

Description: National personnel consultancy specializes in executive search with focus on accounting and finance, management information systems, professional medical and real estate fields. Industries served: All.

5380 ■ Cooper Staffing & Consulting, Inc.
730 Orchard Court
Atlanta, GA 30328
Ph: (770)522-8868
URL: http://www.cooperstaffing.com

Description: Specializes in finding and placing sales, marketing, technical professionals and senior management for companies in the pharmaceutical, biotech, medical, and advertising sectors.

5381 ■ Core Management Search LLC
PO Box 421042
Minneapolis, MN 55442
Ph: (763)559-0977
E-mail: jlentner@coremanage.com
URL: http://www.coremanage.com

Description: Executive search firm.

5382 ■ Cornell Global
PO Box 7113
Wilton, CT 06897

Ph: (203)762-0730
E-mail: info@cornellglobal.com
URL: http://www.cornellglobal.com

Description: Executive search firm with areas of expertise in the following areas: advertising, public relations, marketing, sales, finance and accounting, risk management, private equity and venture capital, construction, industrial, manufacturing, life sciences, publishing, information technology, engineering, human resources, legal, and logisitics.

5383 ■ Corporate Moves Inc.
PO Box 1638
Williamsville, NY 14231-1638
Ph: (716)633-0234
E-mail: info@cmisearch.com
URL: http://www.corporatemovesinc.com

Description: This company offer Executive Search, Recruitment, Talent Acquisition and Consulting services to local, national and international companies and facilities. They offer following services: Retained Search: For Executive Level Search, International assignments and specialized search assignments. Successor Search, Engaged Contingency Search, Consulting Services, Expert Witness Testimony, Contract Recruitment.

5384 ■ Courtright & Associates Inc.
PO Box 236
Scranton, PA 18504
E-mail: rjcx@comcast.net
URL: http://www.courtrightassoc.com

Description: Executive search firm.

5385 ■ CraigSearch
1130 E Arapaho Rd., Ste. 180
Richardson, TX 75081
Ph: (972)644-3264
E-mail: search@craigsearch.com
URL: http://www.craigsearch.com

Description: Executive search firm.

5386 ■ Creative-Leadership Inc.
1900 Polaris Pkwy., Ste. 450
Columbus, OH 43240
Ph: (614)410-6506
Free: 800-875-5323
Fax: (614)760-0737
URL: http://www.clci.com

Description: Executive search firm.

5387 ■ Crist/Kolder Associates
3250 Lacey Rd., Ste. 450
Downers Grove, IL 60515
Ph: (630)321-1110
Fax: (630)321-1112
URL: http://www.cristassociates.com

Description: Executive search firm.

5388 ■ Cross Hill Partners LLC
845 Third Ave., 6th Fl.
New York, NY 10022
Ph: (646)405-7500
Fax: (866)927-4449
E-mail: info@crosshillpartners.com
URL: http://www.crosshillpartners.com

Description: Executive search firm.

5389 ■ Crown Advisors Inc.
100 McKnight Park Dr., Ste. 110
Pittsburgh, PA 15237
Ph: (412)348-1540
E-mail: info@crownsearch.com
URL: http://www.crownsearch.com

Description: Executive search firm.

5390 ■ CTPartners
28601 Chagrin Blvd., Ste. 600
Cleveland, OH 44122
Ph: (216)682-3200
Free: 800-380-9444

Fax: (216)464-6160
E-mail: comments@ctnet.com
URL: http://www.ctnet.com

Description: Executive search firm. Eight branches spanning the USA.

5391 ■ CTR Group
11843 Canon Blvd.
Newport News, VA 23606
Ph: (757)462-5900
Free: 800-945-9095
Fax: (866)597-0055
URL: http://www.ctrc.com

Description: Executive search firm.

5392 ■ Curran Partners Inc.
6 Landmark Sq., Ste. 400
Stamford, CT 06901
Ph: (203)359-5737
E-mail: research@curranpartners.com
URL: http://www.curranpartners.com

Description: Executive search firm.

5393 ■ CyberCoders, Inc.
6591 Irvine Center Dr., Ste. 200
Irvine, CA 92618
Ph: (949)885-5151
Fax: (949)885-5150
E-mail: info@cybercoders.com
URL: http://www.cybercoders.com

Description: Recruitment and job search firm specializing in engineering, executive, financial, accounting, and sales.

5394 ■ Dahl-Morrow International
1821 Michael Faraday Dr., Ste. 202
Reston, VA 20190-5348
Ph: (703)787-8117
Fax: (703)787-8114
E-mail: dmi@dahl-morrowintl.com
URL: http://www.dahl-morrowintl.com

Description: Executive search firm specializing in high technology.

5395 ■ DAL Partners
501 Kings Hwy. E, Ste. 101
Fairfield, CT 06825
Ph: (203)256-3777
Fax: (203)256-8294
E-mail: resumes@dalpartners.com
URL: http://www.dalpartners.com

Description: Executive search firm.

5396 ■ Dalton Group, LLC
15954 Jackson Creek Pkwy., Ste. B-323
Monument, CO 80132
Ph: (719)495-7898
Fax: (719)344-2309
E-mail: info@daltongroupllc.com
URL: http://www.daltongroupllc.com

Description: Retained, executive search firm that focuses on assisting for-profit companies and nonprofit organizations in identifying and selecting senior leaders.

5397 ■ Daly & Company Inc.
175 Federal St.
Boston, MA 02110-2210
Ph: (617)262-2800
E-mail: contact@dalyco.com
URL: http://www.dalyco.com

Description: Executive search firm.

5398 ■ Derba & Derba
7 Whispering Pines Dr.
Andover, MA 01810
Ph: (978)470-8270
Fax: (978)470-4592
E-mail: rderba@derbaandderba.com
URL: http://derbaandderba.com

Description: Executive search firm focused on the hospitality industry.

5399 ■ Design Staffing, LLC
14024 Clopper Rd.
Boyds, MD 20841
Ph: (301)428-9673
URL: http://www.designstaffing.com

Description: Designs staffing programs tailored for individual clients. Assists companies with hard to fill positions that do not fit the traditional mold. Also provides a range of related staffing services such as staffing plan development, job description preparation, outplacement services, career counseling and resume development.

5400 ■ DGL Consultants
3492 Hill Cir.
Colorado Springs, CO 80904
Ph: (719)634-7041
E-mail: info@dglconsultants.com
URL: http://www.dglconsultants.com

Description: Executive search firm with primary expertise in the financial services industry.

5401 ■ DHR International Inc.
10 S Riverside Plz., Ste. 2220
Chicago, IL 60606
Ph: (312)782-1581
Fax: (312)782-2096
URL: http://www.dhrinternational.com

Description: Executive search firm. International organization with a variety of affiliate offices.

5402 ■ Dieck Executive Search
30 Rough Lee Ct.
Madison, WI 53705
Ph: (608)238-1000
E-mail: dan@dieckexecutivesearch.com
URL: http://dieckexecutivesearch.com

Description: Executive search firm focused on pulp, paper and the packaging industries.

5403 ■ The Diestel Group
2180 S 1300 E, Ste. 350
Salt Lake City, UT 84106
Ph: (801)365-0400
Fax: (801)365-0401
E-mail: info@diestel.com
URL: http://www.diestel.com

Description: Executive search firm.

5404 ■ Dinte Resources Inc.
8300 Greensboro Dr., Ste. 750
McLean, VA 22102-3663
Ph: (703)448-3300
Fax: (703)448-0215
E-mail: dri@dinte.com
URL: http://www.dinte.com

Description: Executive search firm.

5405 ■ DLB Associates
265 Industrial Way, W
Eatontown, NJ 07724
Ph: (732)774-2000
Fax: (732)774-5000
E-mail: info@dlbassociates.com
URL: http://www.dlbassociates.com

Description: Executive search firm.

5406 ■ DNPitchon Associates
60 W Ridgewood Ave.
Ridgewood, NJ 07450
Ph: (201)612-8350
E-mail: info@dnpitchon.com
URL: http://www.dnpitchon.com

Description: Executive search firm.

5407 ■ Donahue Patterson Keene
500 N Michigan Ave.
Chicago, IL 60611
Ph: (312)396-4110
E-mail: info@donahuepatterson.com
URL: http://www.donahuepattersonkeene.com

Description: Retained generalist executive search

firm managing senior searches across all functions and industries.

5408 ■ Dowd Associates Inc.
777 Westchester Ave., Ste. 120
White Plains, NY 10604
Ph: (914)251-1515
E-mail: mail@dowdassociates.com
URL: http://www.dowdassociates.com

Description: Specializes in the recruitment of senior level financial professionals.

5409 ■ DSML Executive Search
120 N La Salle St., Ste. 2600
Chicago, IL 60602
Ph: (312)268-6166
E-mail: contact@dsmlexecutivesearch.com
URL: http://www.dsmlexecutivesearch.com

Description: Provides recruiting services for European companies doing business in the United States. Specializes in the recruitment of qualified personnel for sales, marketing and operational management positions.

5410 ■ DuVall & Associates
4203 Costa Salada
San Clemente, CA 92673
Ph: (949)488-8790
Fax: (949)488-8793
E-mail: karen@ducall.com
URL: http://www.duvall.com

Description: Executive search firm specializing in management team placement.

5411 ■ E/Search International
PO Box 408
West Suffield, CT 06093-0408
Ph: (860)668-5848
Free: 800-300-0477
Fax: (860)668-5125

Description: Executive search firm for companies needing highly successful, industry-specific executives. A database of executives and sales people in sales, operations, manufacturing, engineering and supply chain management.

5412 ■ EFL Associates
11440 Tomahawk Creek Pkwy.
Leawood, KS 66211
Ph: (913)234-1560
URL: http://www.cbiz.com/eflassociates

Description: Executive search firm. Locations in Englewood, CO and Lake Forest, IL.

5413 ■ Egan & Associates Inc.
White House Ctr.
1784 Barton Ave., Ste. 10
West Bend, WI 53095
Ph: (262)335-0707
Fax: (262)335-0625
E-mail: info@eganassociates.com
URL: http://www.eganassociates.com

Description: Executive search firm.

5414 ■ The Elliott Co.
439 Church St.
Mount Pleasant, SC 29464
Ph: (843)388-0900
E-mail: suppt.staff@elliottco.net
URL: http://www.elliottco.net

Description: Executive search firm.

5415 ■ ET Search Inc.
1250 Prospect St., Ste. 101
La Jolla, CA 92037-3618
Ph: (858)459-3443
Fax: (858)459-4147
E-mail: ets@etsearch.com
URL: http://www.etsearch.com

Description: Executive search firm focused on the tax industry.

5416 ■ Executive Directions Inc.
PO Box 5742
Sarasota, FL 34277
Ph: (941)922-9180
E-mail: info@execdir.com
URL: http://www.execdir.com

Description: Executive search firm.

5417 ■ Executive Resources International LLC
63 Atlantic Ave.
Boston, MA 02110-3722
Ph: (617)742-8970
E-mail: john@erisearch.net
URL: http://www.erisearch.net

Description: Executive search firm.

5418 ■ Executive Search Advisors, Inc.
18501 Germain St.
Northridge, CA 91326
Ph: (818)396-6656
Fax: (818)484-2600
E-mail: ceo@execsa.com
URL: http://www.execsa.com

Description: Serves as an executive search consultancy which focuses on enhancing the ability of public and privately-held corporations, private equity and venture capital firms, and retained executive search firms to become successful.

5419 ■ Executives Unlimited Inc.
5000 E Spring St., Ste. 395
Long Beach, CA 90815
Ph: (562)627-3800
Free: 866-957-4466
Fax: (562)627-1092
URL: http://www.executivesunlimited.com

Description: Executive search firm. Branches in Western Springs, IL; Scotch Plains, NJ; Long Beach, CA.

5420 ■ Fahr Group
49 Oneda Ave.
Moorestown, NJ 08057
Free: 888-461-2566
E-mail: info@thefahrgroup.com
URL: http://www.thefahrgroup.com

Description: Commits to helping organizations grow and prosper through the identification and selection of key executive management professionals.

5421 ■ The Ferneborg Group
1700 S El Camino Real, Ste. 375
San Mateo, CA 94402
Ph: (650)577-0100
E-mail: info@execsearch.com
URL: http://www.execsearch.com

Description: Executive search firm.

5422 ■ Fishpond Recruiting
PO Box 1448
Novato, CA 94948-1448
Ph: (415)898-5677
Fax: (415)898-9787
E-mail: jobs@fishpondrecruiting.com
URL: http://www.fishpondrecruiting.com

Description: Specializes in all levels of direct hire, temporary and contract placement in a variety of industries.

5423 ■ Fortis Partners
11999 San Vicente Blvd., No. 240
Los Angeles, CA 90049
Ph: (310)586-5555
URL: http://www.fortispartners.com

Description: Retained executive search firm that specializes in recruiting CEOs and vice presidents for a range of technology companies - from venture capital-backed startups to public entities.

5424 ■ Francis & Associates
6923 Vista Dr.
West Des Moines, IA 50266
Ph: (515)221-9800
Fax: (515)221-9806
E-mail: knovak@fa-search.com
URL: http://www.francisassociates.com

Description: Executive search firm.

5425 ■ Freeman Philanthropic Services L.L.C.
1115 Broadway, Ste. 1100
New York, NY 10010
Ph: (212)924-3727
Fax: (646)375-2173
E-mail: info@glfreeman.com
URL: http://www.glfreeman.com

Description: Specializes in recruitment for nonprofit institutions and organizations. Provides management training services that include interactive workshops, planning and feasibility studies, analysis of staffing needs, articulation and development of fundraising tools and development audits.

5426 ■ Graystone Partners L.L.C.
62 Southfield Ave., Ste. 280
Stamford, CT 06902
Ph: (203)323-0023
Fax: (203)353-9035
E-mail: ohman@graystonepartners.com

Description: A retainer-based, executive search firm providing professional consulting services in the area of executive recruitment and management selection. Functional areas of expertise include senior level general management, financial officers, technology officers, marketing and human resource executives.

5427 ■ Hager Executive Search
1483 Sutter St., Ste. 1003
San Francisco, CA 94109
Ph: (415)441-2234
E-mail: connect@hagerexecutivesearch.com
URL: http://www.hagerexecutivesearch.com

Description: Specializes in executive and C level talent searches in marketing/branding, business development, sales and digital media across varied business sectors.

5428 ■ Hawthorne Executive Search
1319 Military Cutoff Rd., Ste. CC, No. 147
Wilmington, NC 28405
Ph: (910)798-1800
Fax: (910)798-2811
E-mail: info@hawthornesearch.com
URL: http://hawthornesearch.com

Description: Specializes in search assignments of executives that range from manager to vice president to C-level and board assignments.

5429 ■ Heidrick and Struggles International Inc.
233 S Wacker Dr., Ste. 4200
Chicago, IL 60606-6310
Ph: (312)496-1200
URL: http://www.heidrick.com

Description: Services: Headhunters for high-level positions for various corporations.

5430 ■ Herd Freed Hartz, Inc.
Two Union Square
601 Union St., Ste. 4610
Seattle, WA 98101
Ph: (206)525-9700
Fax: (206)374-3067
URL: http://www.herdfreedhartz.com

Description: Serves as a nationwide executive recruiting firm covering technology, life science, and manufacturing.

5431 ■ Hunt Executive Search, Inc.
100 Park Ave.
New York, NY 10017
Ph: (212)861-2680

Free: 800-486-8476
E-mail: info@hungroup.com
URL: http://www.huntsearch.com

Description: Provides executive search services to consumer products, life sciences, retail, professional services and diversified industrial markets.

5432 ■ **Integrated Search Solutions Group**
20 Vanderventer Ave., Ste. 106E
Port Washington, NY 11050
Ph: (516)767-3030
Fax: (516)767-3032
E-mail: info@issg.net
URL: http://www.issg.net

Description: A retainer based executive search firm that has been successful in attracting top talent in the areas of outsourcing, consulting and traditional IT functions.

5433 ■ **J H Dugan & Company**
225 Crossroads Blvd., Ste. 415
Carmel, CA 93923
Free: 800-254-3396
Fax: (888)530-5610
E-mail: plastic-recruiter@jhdugan.com
URL: http://www.jhdugan.com

Description: Executive search firm.

5434 ■ **James Drury Partners**
875 N Michigan Ave., Ste. 3805
Chicago, IL 60611
Ph: (312)654-6708
Fax: (312)654-6710
URL: http://www.jdrurypartners.com

Description: Executive search firm.

5435 ■ **John J. Davis & Associates Inc.**
30 Chatham Rd.
Short Hills, NJ 07078
Ph: (973)467-8339
Fax: (973)467-3706
E-mail: john.davis@jdavisassoc.com
URL: http://www.johnjdavisandassoc.com

Description: Executive search firm.

5436 ■ **Wendell L. Johnson Associates Inc.**
12 Grandview Dr., Ste. 1117
Danbury, CT 06811-4321
Ph: (203)743-4112
Fax: (203)778-5377

Description: Executive search firm specializing in areas of workforce diversity, accounting/finance, human resources, marketing/sales, strategic planning and management information systems.

5437 ■ **Joy Reed Belt Search Consultants Inc.**
PO Box 54410
Oklahoma City, OK 73154
Ph: (405)842-5155
E-mail: executiverecruiter@joyreedbelt.com
URL: http://www.joyreedbeltsearch.com

Description: Executive search firm. Branch in Tulsa, OK.

5438 ■ **J.R. Bechtle & Company**
67 S Bedford St., Ste. 400 W
Burlington, MA 01803-5177
Ph: (781)229-5804
Fax: (781)359-1829
URL: http://www.jrbechtle.com

Description: Executive search firm.

5439 ■ **JT Brady & Associates**
10900 Perry Hwy. No. 12203
Wexford, PA 15090
Fax: (724)935-8059
E-mail: jack@jtbrady.net
URL: http://www.jtbrady.net

Description: Executive search firm.

5440 ■ **Judith Cushman & Associates**
15600 NE 8th St., Ste. B1
Bellevue, WA 98008
Ph: (425)392-8660
E-mail: jcushman@jc-a.com
URL: http://www.jc-a.com

Description: Executive search firm.

5441 ■ **Kforce Inc.**
1001 E Palm Ave.
Tampa, FL 33605-3551
Ph: (813)552-5000
Free: 877-453-6723
Fax: (813)552-2493
URL: http://www.kforce.com

Description: Executive search firm specializing in the financial services, insurance, health care, and pharmaceuticals industries.

5442 ■ **Kimmel & Associates Inc.**
25 Page Ave.
Asheville, NC 28801
Ph: (828)251-9900
Fax: (828)251-9955
E-mail: kimmel@kimmel.com
URL: http://www.kimmel.com

Description: Specializes in the construction, waste, architecture, engineering, logistics and supply chain industries.

5443 ■ **Kinser & Baillou L.L.C.**
590 Madison Ave., Fl. 21
New York, NY 10022
Ph: (212)588-8801
Fax: (212)588-8802
E-mail: search@kinserbaillou.com
URL: http://www.kinserbaillou.com

Description: Specializes in boards, management consulting and communications/marketing communications.

5444 ■ **Korn/Ferry International**
1900 Ave. of the Stars, Ste. 2600
Los Angeles, CA 90067-4507
Ph: (310)552-1834
Fax: (310)553-6452
URL: http://www.KornFerry.com

Description: Executive search firm. International organization with a variety of affiliate offices.

5445 ■ **Lancaster Associates Inc.**
35 W High St.
Somerville, NJ 08876
Ph: (908)526-5440
Fax: (908)526-1992
E-mail: rfl@lancasterinc.net
URL: http://www.lancasterassociates.net

Description: Personnel consulting firm focuses recruitment on information systems, voice and data communications, managers, telecommunications, client server technology, data warehouse, project leaders and systems programmers. Industries served: pharmaceutical, consumer products, manufacturing, transportation, financial services and insurance.

5446 ■ **Leadership Capital Group**
606 Post Rd. E, Ste. 605
Westport, CT 06880
Ph: (203)682-1627
Fax: (203)841-1117
E-mail: info@lcgsearch.com
URL: http://www.lcgsearch.com

Description: Executive search firm focused at the CEO and Board through the VP levels. Maintains a database of executives at the $200,000+ compensation level.

5447 ■ **Byron Leonard International Inc.**
99 Long Ct., Ste. 201
Thousand Oaks, CA 91360
Ph: (805)373-7500

Fax: (805)373-5531
E-mail: bli@bli-inc.com
URL: http://www.bli-inc.com

Description: Executive search firm.

5448 ■ **Lonergan Partners**
203 Redwood Shore Pkwy., Ste. 600
Redwood City, CA 94065
Ph: (650)413-6000
Fax: (650)413-6009
URL: http://www.loneganpartners.com

Description: Executive search firm that focuses on recruitment of top executives. Offers positions for CEO, Board of Directors, and senior executive management.

5449 ■ **Lucas Associates Inc.**
3384 Peachtree Rd., Ste. 900
Atlanta, GA 30326-2828
Ph: (404)239-5630
Free: 800-515-0819
E-mail: info@lucasgroup.com
URL: http://www.lucasgroup.com

Description: Specializes in accounting/finance, advertising/marketing, aerospace/defense, alternative energy, call center, capital markets, construction/real estate, consumer products, hospitality, human resources, industrial services, insurance, legal, manufacturing/engineering/supply chain/logistics, medical device/biotech/ pharmaceutical, military transition, oil/gas and technology.

5450 ■ **Management Architects**
PO Box 350
Sonoma, CA 95476
Ph: (707)945-1340
E-mail: doug@managementarchitects.net
URL: http://www.managementarchitects.net

Description: Executive search firm. Focuses on networking industries.

5451 ■ **Management Recruiters International Inc.**
1717 Arch St., 35th Fl.
Philadelphia, PA 19103
Free: 800-875-4000
Fax: (215)751-1757
URL: http://www.mrinetwork.com

Description: Executive search firm. More than 300 offices throughout the U.S.

5452 ■ **MJS Executive Search**
2 Overhill Rd., Ste. 400
Scarsdale, NY 10583
Ph: (914)631-1774
E-mail: info@mjsearch.com
URL: http://www.mjsearch.com

Description: Serves as a retained executive recruiting firm specializing in placing professionals in consumer goods, entertainment, media, social media, sports, marketing services and other industries.

5453 ■ **Neil Frank & Company**
PO Box 3570
Redondo Beach, CA 90277-1570
Ph: (310)543-1611
E-mail: neil@neilfrank.com
URL: http://www.neilfrank.com

Description: Executive search firm.

5454 ■ **New World Staffing**
304 Park Ave. S, 11th Fl.
New York, NY 10010
Free: 800-884-5157
E-mail: contact@newworldstaffing.org
URL: http://newworldstaffing.org

Description: Strives to match proven executives who are looking for career growth with successful companies across the United States.

5455 ■ Next Level Executive Search
24 Cathedral Pl., Ste. 500
Saint Augustine, FL 32084
Ph: (904)810-5177
Fax: (904)810-6855
URL: http://www.nextlevelexecutive.com
Description: Serves as executive search and consulting firm specializing in the sports industry for interim and permanent middle management to senior level positions.

5456 ■ Norman Broadbent International
233 W Wacker Dr., Ste. 6825
Chicago, IL 60606
Ph: (312)876-3300
Fax: (312)876-3640
E-mail: info@nbisearch.com
Description: Consultants specializing in the recruitment of management professionals.

5457 ■ Novo Group
1033 N Mayfair Rd., Ste. 310
Milwaukee, WI 53226
Ph: (414)727-8755
URL: http://www.thenovogroup.com
Description: Serves as a professional services firm focusing on finding executive, managerial, professional, sales, marketing and technical talent for organizations.

5458 ■ Oliver & Rozner Associates
598 Madison Ave., Ste. 11
New York, NY 10022
Ph: (212)688-1850
Description: Provider of recruitment solutions. It is engaged in marketing, advertising, data processing, research and development services.

5459 ■ Onstott Group
55 William St., Ste. G40
Wellesley, MA 02481
Ph: (781)235-3050
Fax: (781)235-8653
E-mail: info@onstott.com
URL: http://www.onstott.com
Description: Provides executive search services that focus on board level, chief executive, and other senior executive positions.

5460 ■ L.J. Parrish & Associates Inc.
PO Box 874
Charles Town, WV 25414
Ph: (304)725-3834
Fax: (301)733-5155
Description: Executive search and human resource consulting firm specializing in financial, general management, and operations management positions. Industries served: All private industry, public accounting firms, and government.

5461 ■ Pate Resources Group Inc.
505 Orleans St., Ste. 300
Beaumont, TX 77701-3224
Ph: (409)833-4514
Fax: (409)833-4646
Description: Offers executive search and recruiting services to professionals who include physicians, health care administrators, accountants, financial managers; chemical, mechanical, industrial, and electrical engineers; sales and marketing managers, human resources administrators, and general managers and top executives in numerous disciplines. Industries served: health care, petrochemicals, accounting, utility, legal and municipalities.

5462 ■ Paul Bodner & Associates Inc.
9217 Tudor Park Pl.
Las Vegas, NV 89145
Ph: (702)528-0780
E-mail: paul@paulbodnerassociates.com
URL: http://www.paulbodnerassociates.com/index
.html

Description: Executive search firm. Second branch in Denver, CO.

5463 ■ Penn Search Inc.
1045 1st Ave., Ste. 110
King of Prussia, PA 19406
Ph: (610)964-8820
Fax: (610)964-8916
E-mail: charlied@pennsearch.com
URL: http://www.pennsearch.com
Description: Assists in recruiting and hiring accounting and financial professionals from staff accountant to chief financial officer. Industries served: All.

5464 ■ Phillip's Personnel/Phillip's Temps
1675 Broadway, Ste. 2410
Denver, CO 80204
Ph: (303)893-1850
Fax: (303)893-0639
E-mail: info@phillipspersonnel.com
URL: http://www.phillipspersonnel.com
Description: Personnel recruiting and staffing consultants in: accounting and finance, management information systems, sales and marketing, engineering, administration, and general and executive management. Industries served: telecommunications, distribution, financial services, and general business.

5465 ■ Polly Brown Associates Inc.
150 E 57th St., Ste. 25A
New York, NY 10022
E-mail: pbrown@pollybrownassociates.com
URL: http://www.pollybrownassociates.com
Description: Executive search firm.

5466 ■ Primary Group
999 Douglas Ave., Ste. 2225
Altamonte Springs, FL 32714
Ph: (407)869-4111
Fax: (407)682-3321
E-mail: primarygroup@pgsearch.com
URL: http://www.theprimarygroup.com
Description: Exists as an executive search firm that recruits professionals from the spectrum of sales, marketing, management, operations, or any executive level.

5467 ■ Princeton Executive Search
2667 Nottingham Way
Trenton, NJ 08619
Ph: (609)584-1100
Description: Provider of search and placement for management level professions. Specializes in accounting, banking, engineering and human resources. Industries served: Financial, research and development, insurance, manufacturing, banking and government agencies.

5468 ■ Raines International Inc.
75 Rockefeller Plz., 27th Fl.
New York, NY 10019
Ph: (212)997-1100
Fax: (212)997-0196
E-mail: contact@rainesinternational.com
URL: http://www.rainesinternational.com
Description: International generalist firm specializing in middle to upper management executives. Concentrations include general management, finance and accounting, information technology, operations or procurement, strategic planning, investment banking, real estate or finance, human resources, insurance, and legal.

5469 ■ Recruiting Partners
3494 Camino Tassajara Rd., No. 404
Danville, CA 94506
Ph: (925)964-0249
E-mail: info@recruitingpartners.com
URL: http://www.recruitingpartners.com
Description: Serves as an executive and technical recruiting firm that specializes in accounting, legal, information technology, engineering, executive management and technical writing.

5470 ■ Renaissance Executive Forums
7855 Ivanhoe Ave., Ste. 300
La Jolla, CA 92037
Ph: (858)551-6600
URL: http://www.executiveforums.com
Description: The firm provides consulting services to top executives in an organization. Industries served: private and public sectors.

5471 ■ Rice Professional Search
363 N Sam Houston Pkwy. E, Ste. 1100
Houston, TX 77060
Ph: (281)931-6400
Fax: (281)931-0929
E-mail: info@riceprosearch.com
URL: http://www.riceprosearch.com
Description: Serves as an executive job placement firm that provides professional search and staffing services.

5472 ■ Roberson & Co.
10751 Parfet St.
Broomfield, CO 80021
Ph: (303)410-6510
E-mail: roberson@recruiterpro.com
URL: http://www.recruiterpro.com
Description: Professional and executive recruiting firm working the national and international marketplace. Specializes in accounting, finance, data processing and information services, health care, environmental and mining engineering, manufacturing, human resources, and sales and marketing.

5473 ■ Robert Half Management Resources
2884 Sand Hill Rd.
Menlo Park, CA 94025
Free: 888-400-7474
URL: http://www.roberthalfmr.com
Description: Serves as a provider of senior-level accounting and finance professionals on a project and interim basis.

5474 ■ Robert W. Dingman Company Inc.
650 Hampshire Rd., No. 116
Westlake Village, CA 91361
Ph: (805)778-1777
Fax: (805)778-9288
E-mail: info@dingman.com
URL: http://www.dingman.com
Description: Executive search firm with a second office in Black Forest, CO.

5475 ■ Rocky Mountain Recruiters, Inc.
1776 S Jackson St., Ste. 320
Denver, CO 80210
Ph: (303)296-2000
E-mail: resumes@rmrecruiters.com
URL: http://www.rmrecruiters.com
Description: Accounting and financial executive search firm.

5476 ■ Ropella Group
8100 Opportunity Dr.
Milton, FL 32583
Ph: (850)983-4777
Fax: (850)983-1627
E-mail: info@ropella.com
URL: http://www.ropella.com
Description: Serves as an executive search and consulting firm specializing in the chemical, consumer products, energy, and other technology industries. Provides positions from senior executives to middle management in all areas of business covering executive level management, marketing, public relations and communications, strategic planning and commercial development, sales, business development and customer service, purchasing, logistics and supply chain, manufacturing and facilities maintenance, research and development, engineering, human resources, mergers, acquisitions and joint ventures, accounting and finance, real estate and asset management.

5477 ■ RSMR Global Resources
308 W Erie St.
Chicago, IL 60654
Ph: (312)957-0337
E-mail: info@rsmr.com
URL: http://www.rsmr.com

Description: Serves as a retained executive search and human resources consulting firm dedicated to finding the right executives for companies. Specializes in placement in the areas of energy, real estate, architecture, engineering, construction, manufacturing and banking.

5478 ■ Russell Reynolds Associates Inc.
200 Park Ave., Ste. 2300
New York, NY 10166-0002
Ph: (212)351-2000
Fax: (212)370-0896
E-mail: hcamericas@russellreynolds.com
URL: http://www.russellreynolds.com

Description: Executive search firm. Affiliate offices across the country and abroad.

5479 ■ Sanford Rose Associates
265 S Main St.
Akron, OH 44308-1200
Ph: (330)762-0279
Fax: (330)762-6161
E-mail: mail@sraoc.com
URL: http://www.sanfordrose.com

Description: Executive search firm. Over 80 franchised office locations nationwide.

5480 ■ Scion Staffing
576 Sacramento St., 2nd Fl.
San Francisco, CA 94111
Ph: (415)392-7500
E-mail: info@scionstaffing.com
URL: http://scionstaffing.com

Description: Serves as an executive search firm and temporary agency for professional candidates.

5481 ■ Search North America Inc.
PO Box 3577
Sunriver, OR 97707
E-mail: mylinda@searchna.com
URL: http://www.searchna.com

Description: An executive search and recruiting firm whose focus is placing engineers, operations and maintenance managers, sales and marketing management, financial and general management executives (both domestic and international). Industries served: forest products, pulp and paper, waste to energy, environmental services, consulting and equipment suppliers for above related industries.

5482 ■ SHS Careers Front Page
711 DeLasalle Ct.
Naperville, IL 60565
Ph: (630)718-1704
Fax: (630)718-1709
E-mail: timj@shsinc.com
URL: http://www.shsinc.com

Description: Executive search firm for pharmaceutical advertising, medical communications and education, healthcare public relations, and biotechnology industries.

5483 ■ SHS of Cherry Hill
207 Barclay Pavilion W
Cherry Hill, NJ 08034
Ph: (856)216-9030
Fax: (856)219-2011
E-mail: shs@shsofcherryhill.com
URL: http://www.shsofcherryhill.com

Description: Personnel recruiters operating in the disciplines of accounting, sales, insurance, engineering and administration. Industries served: insurance, distribution, manufacturing and service.

5484 ■ Slayton Search Partners
311 S Wacker, Ste. 3200
Chicago, IL 60606

Ph: (312)456-0080
Fax: (312)456-0089
E-mail: slayton@slaytonsearch.com
URL: http://www.slaytonsearch.com

Description: Serves as an executive search firm specializing in finding, attracting, and retaining executive management talents.

5485 ■ Spectrum Group, LLC
1919 Gallows Rd., Ste. 600
Vienna, VA 22182
Ph: (703)738-1200
Fax: (703)761-9477
E-mail: web@spectrumcareers.com
URL: http://www.spectrumcareers.com

Description: Serves as executive search firm for accounting and finance, information technology, and sales and marketing industries.

5486 ■ Sports Group International
7317 Spyglass Way, Ste. 400
Raleigh, NC 27615
Ph: (919)855-0226
Fax: (919)855-0793
E-mail: sgisearch@aol.com
URL: http://www.sgisearch.com

Description: Serves as an executive search firm for the sporting goods and recreational products industries. Specializes in the recruitment of senior and middle level managers who excel in sales, marketing, product design and development, and general management.

5487 ■ S.R. Clarke
105 Huntercombe
Williamsburg, VA 23188
Ph: (703)344-0256
Fax: (949)608-5052
URL: http://www.srclarke.com/index.html

Description: Serves as an executive search and recruitment firm specializing in commercial construction, commercial real estate development, residential asset management, residential construction and development, subcontractor trades, finance, accounting, administration, heavy construction, architectural design and engineering design.

5488 ■ Stanton Chase International
5005 LBJ Fwy., Ste. 810
Dallas, TX 75244
Ph: (972)404-8411
E-mail: dallas@stantonchase.com
URL: http://www.stantonchase.com

Description: Serves as an executive search firm focusing on the recruitment of talent for top management positions.

5489 ■ Strategic Resource Services, Inc.
400-108th Ave. NE, Ste. 620
Bellevue, WA 98004
Ph: (425)688-1151
Fax: (425)732-2112
E-mail: corporate@strategicresources.com
URL: http://www.strategicresources.com

Description: Exists as an executive search firm that specializes in finding top-level executives and board members for U.S. companies. Develops job specifications, assembles a list of potential prospects, performs background checks, and assists with interviews and negotiating final offers.

5490 ■ TeamWork Consulting Inc.
22550 McCauley Rd.
Shaker Heights, OH 44122
Ph: (216)360-1790
Fax: (216)292-9265
E-mail: buffy@teamworkonline.com
URL: http://www.teamworkconsulting.com

Description: A retained executive search firm to sports, live event management, location-based retail entertainment properties.

5491 ■ Valerie Fredrickson & Company
800 Menlo Ave., Ste. 220
Menlo Park, CA 94025
Ph: (650)614-0220
E-mail: info@vfandco.com
URL: http://www.vfandco.com

Description: Executive search firm.

5492 ■ William J. Christopher Associates Inc.
307 N Walnut St.
West Chester, PA 19380
Ph: (610)696-4397
Fax: (610)692-5177
E-mail: wjc@wjca.com
URL: http://www.wjca.com

Description: Executive search firm.

5493 ■ Williams Executive Search Inc.
8500 Normandale Lake Blvd., Ste. 610
Minneapolis, MN 55437
Ph: (952)767-7900
Fax: (952)767-7905
URL: http://www.williams-exec.com

Description: Executive search firm.

ONLINE JOB SOURCES AND SERVICES

5494 ■ 6Figurejobs.com
URL: http://www.6figurejobs.com

Description: Provides executives and experienced professionals with access to some of the most exclusive executive jobs, executive recruiters and career management tools available. Includes tools for both posting and viewing jobs, resume refinement, company research and more.

5495 ■ American Association of Airport Executives Career Center
URL: http://careercenter.aaae.org

Description: Features a searchable database of available airport executives career opportunities for job seekers. Allows employers and recruiters to access qualified talent pool with relevant work experience to fulfill staffing needs.

5496 ■ BankingCareers.com
URL: http://www.bankingcareers.com

Description: Provides lists of jobs and products to the banking and finance community.

5497 ■ Careers in Supply Chain Management
Council of Supply Chain Management Professionals
333 E Butterfield Rd., Ste. 140
Lombard, IL 60148-6016
Ph: (630)574-0985
Fax: (630)574-0989
E-mail: membership@cscmp.org
URL: http://www.careersinsupplychain.org

Description: Provides information about the supply chain industry, the importance of supply chain management, impacts of careers in the supply chain, and educational options. Includes job board of internship and employment opportunities.

5498 ■ Chief Executive Officer Jobs
URL: http://www.chiefexecutiveofficerjobs.org

Description: Serves as a niche job board for chief executive officers. Offers updated job listings for candidates and job posting for employers.

5499 ■ CSCMP's Career Center
Council of Supply Chain Management Professionals
333 E Butterfield Rd., Ste. 140
Lombard, IL 60148-6016
Ph: (630)574-0985
Fax: (630)574-0989
E-mail: membership@cscmp.org
URL: http://cscmp.org/career/career-center

Description: Offers online database of supply chain management opportunities and career resources.

5500 ■ ExecuNet.com
URL: http://www.execunet.com

Description: Job site dedicated to the $150,000+ executive job seeker. Members may access job bank, recruiter and employer information, have their resumes reviewed, attend networking meetings, and access cutting-edge career information and references. Fee: Must become member to access services, cost is $219 for six-month membership.

5501 ■ ExecutivesOnly.com, Inc.
URL: http://www.executivesonly.com

Description: Job site specializing in executive positions netting an annual salary of $100K or more. Members can view job bank and set up daily e-mail alerts. They may also choose to recruit the help of a senior adviser who can help review resumes and distribute them to recruiters. Fee: Must become member to access services.

5502 ■ HealthCareProfessional.com
URL: http://www.healthcareprofessional.com

Description: Provides jobs for directors, executives, managers, and supervisors in the health care industry.

5503 ■ Heidrick & Struggles Management Search
URL: http://www.heidrick.com/What-We-Do/Executive-Search

Description: Executive search firm that will distribute registered resumes to recruiters with suitable positions available.

5504 ■ JobMetaSeek.com
URL: http://www.jobmetaseek.com

Description: Seeks to address the career and job search needs of managers, professionals, executives, and other skilled and experienced job seekers in the United States and Canada. Features links to employment and career related sites, local and international sites, recruiters, education & training, resume sites, salary surveys, news, and others.

5505 ■ MBA Careers
URL: http://mbacareers.com

Description: Job site that provides resume posting, databank search and e-mail alert services to MBA and other advanced graduate degree holders.

5506 ■ NetShare.com
URL: http://www.netshare.com

Description: Members-only resource for $100,000+ executives who are actively searching for new positions or passively tracking the job market. Listings that match posted profile will be e-mailed. Fee: Fees vary by level of service; annual basic level dues are $360.

5507 ■ Spherion
URL: http://www.spherion.com

Description: Recruitment firm specializing in accounting and finance, sales and marketing, interim executives, technology, engineering, retail and human resources.

5508 ■ Transearch.com
URL: http://www.transearch.com

Description: International executive search firm concentrating in searches for executives in retail, real estate, information technology, industry, life sciences and financial services. Seekers may search job board and submit their resume for recruiter review.

5509 ■ WSA Executive Job Search Center
URL: http://www.wsacorp.com

Description: A site intended for $50K-$700K range

executives. Offers resume preparation, critiques and distribution, and interview preparation.

OTHER SOURCES

5510 ■ Academy of Management
PO Box 3020
Briarcliff Manor, NY 10510
Ph: (914)923-2607
Fax: (914)923-2615
E-mail: membership@aom.org
URL: http://www.aom.org

Description: Professors in accredited universities and colleges who teach management; selected business executives who have made significant written contributions to the literature in the field of management and organization. Offers placement service.

5511 ■ American Chamber of Commerce Executives
1330 Braddock Pl., Ste. 300
Alexandria, VA 22314
Ph: (703)998-0072
E-mail: hero@acce.org
URL: http://www.acce.org

Description: Professional society of chamber of commerce executives and staff members.

5512 ■ American Society of Association Executives
1575 I St. NW
Washington, DC 20005-1103
Ph: (202)371-0940
Free: 888-950-2723
Fax: (202)371-8315
URL: http://www.asaecenter.org

Description: Professional society of paid executives of international, national, state, and local trade, professional, and philanthropic associations. Seeks to educate association executives on effective management, including: the proper objectives, functions, and activities of associations; the basic principles of association management; the legal aspects of association activity; policies relating to association management; efficient methods, procedures, and techniques of association management; the responsibilities and professional standards of association executives. Maintains information resource center. Conducts resume, guidance, and consultation services; compiles statistics in the form of reports, surveys, and studies; carries out research and education. Maintains ASAE Services Corporation to provide special services and ASAE Foundation to do future-oriented research and make grant awards. Offers executive search services and insurance programs. Provides CEO center for chief staff executives. Conducts Certified Association Executive (CAE) program.

5513 ■ Center for Creative Leadership
1 Leadership Pl.
Greensboro, NC 27410-9427
Ph: (336)288-7210
Fax: (336)282-3284
E-mail: info@ccl.org
URL: http://www.ccl.org

Description: Promotes behavioral science research and leadership education.

5514 ■ The International Alliance for Women
1101 Pennsylvania Ave. NW, 6th Fl.
Washington, DC 20004
Ph: (202)351-6839
Free: 888-712-5200
E-mail: admin@tiaw.org
URL: http://www.tiaw.org

Description: Local networks comprising 50,000 professional and executive women in 12 countries; individual businesswomen without a network affiliation are alliance associates. Promotes recognition of the achievements of women in business. Encourages placement of women in senior executive positions.

Maintains high standards of professional competence among members. Facilitates communication on an international scale among professional women's networks and their members. Represents members' interests before policymaking business and government. Sponsors programs that support equal opportunity and enhance members' business and professional skills. Operates appointments and directors service. Maintains speakers' bureau.

5515 ■ National Association of Corporate Directors
2001 Pennsylvania Ave. NW, Ste. 500
Washington, DC 20006
Ph: (202)775-0509
Fax: (202)775-4857
E-mail: join@nacdonline.org
URL: http://www.nacdonline.org

Description: Corporate directors and boards of directors; chief executive officers, presidents, accountants, lawyers, consultants, and other executives are members. Conducts research, surveys, and seminars.

5516 ■ National Association for Female Executives
2 Park Ave.
New York, NY 10016
E-mail: robin.michaels@bonniercorp.co
URL: http://www.nafe.com

Description: Represents women executives, business owners, and entrepreneurs. Provides networking opportunities for all members. Advocates for the advancement of women in the workplace.

5517 ■ National Association of Television Program Executives
5757 Wilshire Blvd., Penthouse 10
Los Angeles, CA 90036-3681
Ph: (310)453-4440
Fax: (310)453-5258
E-mail: info@natpe.org
URL: http://www.natpe.org

Description: Comprised of television program professionals, exhibitors, buyers and faculty. Focuses on the creation, development and distribution of televised programming in all forms across all mature and emerging media platforms. Provides members with education, networking, professional enhancement and technological guidance through year-round activities and events, and directories.

5518 ■ National Black MBA Association
1 E Wacker Ste. 3500
Chicago, IL 60601
Ph: (312)236-2622
Fax: (312)236-0390
E-mail: info@nbmbaa.org
URL: http://www.nbmbaa.org

Description: Creates educational opportunities to form professional and economic growth of African-Americans. Develops partnerships to its members and provides educational programs to increase the awareness on business field.

5519 ■ National Management Association
2210 Arbor Blvd.
Dayton, OH 45439
Ph: (937)294-0421
E-mail: nma@nma1.org
URL: http://www.nma1.org

Description: Business and industrial management personnel; membership comes from supervisory level, with the remainder from middle management and above. Seeks to develop and recognize management as a profession and to promote the free enterprise system. Prepares chapter programs on basic management, management policy and practice, communications, human behavior, industrial relations, economics, political education, and liberal education. Maintains speakers' bureau and hall of fame. Maintains educational, charitable, and research programs. Sponsors charitable programs.

5520 ■ **National Society of Accountants for Cooperatives - Texas Chapter**
c/o Gail Faries, Dir.
D. Williams and Company, PC
Lubbock, TX 79490
Ph: (806)785-5982
Fax: (806)785-9381
E-mail: gailf@dwilliams.net
Description: Represents employees of cooperatives, certified public accountants, auditors, chief financial officers, attorneys, and bankers. Unites persons performing accounting, auditing, financial, and legal services for cooperative and nonprofit associations.

5521 ■ **National Society of Hispanic MBAs**
450 E John Carpenter Freeway, Ste. 200
Irving, TX 75062

Ph: (214)596-9338
Free: 877-467-4622
Fax: (214)596-9325
E-mail: mgonzalez@nshmba.org
URL: http://www.nshmba.org
Description: Hispanic MBA professional business network dedicated to economic and philanthropic advancement.

5522 ■ **Society of Recreation Executives**
Box 520
Gonzalez, FL 32560-0520
Ph: (850)937-8354
Free: 800-281-9186
Fax: (850)937-8356
E-mail: rltresoource@spydee.net

Description: Corporate executives in the recreation, leisure, and travel industry. Operates placement service and speakers' bureau.

5523 ■ **Women in Management**
PO Box 6690
Elgin, IL 60121-6690
Ph: (708)386-0496
E-mail: nationalwim@wimonline.org
URL: http://www.wimonline.org

Description: Supports network of women in professional and management positions that facilitate the exchange of experience and ideas. Promotes self-growth in management; provides speakers who are successful in management; sponsors workshops and special interest groups to discuss problems and share job experiences. **Members:** 1,700.

SOURCES OF HELP-WANTED ADS

5524 ■ The American Journal of Human Genetics
Elsevier Inc.
c/o Cynthia C. Morton, PhD, Ed.
Brigham & Women's Hospital
New Research Bldg., Rm. 160A
77 Ave., Louis Pasteur
Boston, MA 02115
Ph: (617)525-4770
Fax: (617)525-4569
E-mail: ajhg@ajhg.net
URL: http://www.cell.com/AJHG
Frequency: Monthly. **Price:** $1,393 Individuals print only; $1,398 Institutions print only; $405 Institutions online only. **Description:** Journal devoted to research and review on heredity in man and the application of genetic principles in medicine, psychology, anthropology, and social sciences.

5525 ■ Annals of Human Genetics
Blackwell Publishing Inc.
350 Main St.
Malden, MA 02148
Ph: (781)388-8200
Free: 800-216-2522
Fax: (781)388-8210
E-mail: journaladsusa@bos.blackwellpublishing.com
URL: http://www.blackwellpublishing.com/journal.asp?ref=0003-4800
Frequency: Bimonthly. **Price:** $324 Individuals print & online; $998 Institutions print & online. **Description:** Journal focusing on research of human genetics and human inheritance.

5526 ■ Annual Review of Genetics
Annual Reviews
4139 El Camino Way
Palo Alto, CA 94306-4010
Ph: (650)493-4400
Free: 800-523-8635
Fax: (650)855-9815
E-mail: service@annualreviews.org
URL: http://www.annualreviews.org/journal/genet
Frequency: Annual. **Price:** $86 Individuals print & online; $263 Institutions print & online; $219 Institutions online; $219 Institutions print. **Description:** Periodical covering issues in genetics and the biological sciences.

5527 ■ Clinical Genetics
Blackwell Publishing Inc.
c/o Seetha Kumaran, Office Mgr.
950 W 28th Ave.
Vancouver, BC, Canada V5Z 4H4
Ph: (604)875-3823
Fax: (604)875-3840
E-mail: journaladsusa@bos.blackwellpublishing.com
URL: http://as.wiley.com/WileyCDA/WileyTitle/productCd-CGE.html

Frequency: Monthly. **Price:** $518 Individuals print & online; $467 Individuals online only; $1,816 Institutions print & online; £941 Institutions print or online; $1,579 Institutions print or online; $334 Members print and online; $283 Members online only; £1,083 Institutions print & online. **Description:** Journal focusing on research related to molecular approaches to genetic disease and the translation of these advances for the practicing geneticist.

5528 ■ Genetic Alliance Community Job Postings
URL: http://www.geneticalliance.org/job.board
Description: Presents job postings in the genetics community at no cost for non profit and not-for-profit organizations; for-profits companies can post want ads for $50/month.

5529 ■ Genetical Research
Cambridge University Press
c/o Dr. T.F.C. Mackay, Ed.-in-Ch.
North Carolina State University
Dept. of Genetics, Box 7614
Raleigh, NC 27695
Ph: (212)924-3900
Free: 800-872-7423
Fax: (212)691-3239
E-mail: ad_sales@cambridge.org
URL: http://journals.cambridge.org/action/displayJournal?jid=GRH
Frequency: 2 to 3/yr. **Price:** $919 Institutions online only; $1,136 Institutions online and print. **Description:** Science journal on all aspects of genetics.

5530 ■ Genetics: A Periodical Record of Investigations Bearing on Heredity and Variation
Genetics Society of America
Mellon Institute, Box I
4400 5th Ave.
Pittsburgh, PA 15213
Ph: (412)268-1812
Fax: (412)268-1813
E-mail: genetics-gsa@andrew.cmu.edu
URL: http://www.genetics.org
Frequency: Monthly. **Price:** $800 Nonmembers online, institutions. **Description:** Journal on genetics.

5531 ■ HelpWantedSanDiego.com
URL: http://helpwantedsandiego.com/home/257.htm
Description: Online job source for genetics professionals highlighting help wanted ads on the Internet and local radio stations. Resumes are sent to the advertiser's private online account.

5532 ■ Human Biology: The International Journal of Population Biology and Genetics
Wayne State University Press
The Leonard N Simons Bldg. 4809 Woodward Ave.
Detroit, MI 48201-1309
Ph: (313)577-6120
Free: 800-978-7323

Fax: (313)577-6131
E-mail: human.biology@mnmh.fr
URLs: http://digitalcommons.wayne.edu/humbiol; http://wsupress.wayne.edu/journals/humanbio/humanbiologyj.html
Frequency: Bimonthly. **Price:** $365 Institutions; $142 Individuals; $49 Students senior. **Description:** Journal on population genetics, evolutionary and genetic demography, and behavioral genetics.

5533 ■ Job Line
Association of Genetic Technologists
PO Box 19193
Lenexa, KS 66285
Ph: (913)895-4605
Fax: (913)895-4652
E-mail: agt-info@goamp.com
URL: http://www.agt-info.org
Description: Association Website offering classified job advertising for careers in genetics, posted by region.

5534 ■ Pediatrics
American Academy of Pediatrics
141 NW Point Blvd.
Elk Grove Village, IL 60007-1098
Ph: (847)434-4000
Free: 800-433-9016
Fax: (847)434-8000
E-mail: journals@aap.org
URL: http://pediatrics.aappublications.org/
Frequency: Monthly. **Price:** $167 for nonmembers in U.S.; $202 for nonmembers outside U.S.; $119 in training/allied health professional in U.S.; $168 in training/allied health professional outside U.S.; $179 Nonmembers physician, print & online; $136 Nonmembers physician, online; $96 Nonmembers student/allied, online; $128 Nonmembers student/allied, print & online. **Description:** Includes employment listings.

5535 ■ Perspectives in Genetic Counseling Newsletter
National Society of Genetic Counselors
330 N Wabash Ave., Ste. 2000
Chicago, IL 60611
Ph: (312)321-6834
Fax: (312)673-6972
E-mail: nsgc@nsgc.org
URL: http://archive.nsgc.org/resources/pgc_newsletter.cfm
Description: Quarterly newsletter spotlighting new legislation regarding genetics issues and genetic counselors, marketing strategies for organizations, media reporting on medical genetics, meeting announcements and job listings in the field of genetics counseling.

EMPLOYER DIRECTORIES AND NETWORKING LISTS

5536 ■ American Board of Genetic Counseling--Membership Directory
American Board of Genetic Counseling
PO Box 14216
Lenexa, KS 66285

Ph: (913)895-4617
Fax: (913)895-4652
E-mail: info@abgc.net
URL: http://www.abgc.net

Covers: Individuals who have passed the Board examination and includes the ABGC, Genetics Society of America, American Society of Human Genetics, American College of Medical Genetics, and the American Board of Medical Genetics.

5537 ■ American Society of Human Genetics--Membership Directory
Genetics Society of America
9650 Rockville Pike
Bethesda, MD 20814
Ph: (301)634-7300
Free: 866-486-GENE
Fax: (301)634-7079
E-mail: afagen@genetics-gsa.org
URL: http://www.genetics-gsa.org/cgi-bin/Search -GSA

Frequency: Biennial; even years. **Pages:** 278. **Covers:** about 10,000 teachers, physicians, researchers, genetic counselors, and others interested in human genetics. Lists members of the American Society of Human Genetics, the American Board of Medical Genetics, the Genetics Society of America, the American College of Medical Genetics, and the American Board of Genetic Counseling. **Entries include:** Name, degree(s), institution name, department name, address, phone; type of membership and society of which a member. **Arrangement:** Alphabetical. **Indexes:** Geographical, subspecialty (American Board of Medical Genetics Members and American Board of Genetic Counseling Members) and American College of Medical Genetics.

5538 ■ Genetic Disorders Sourcebook: Basic Consumer Health Information about Hereditary Diseases and Disorders
Omnigraphics Inc.
PO Box 31-1640
Detroit, MI 48231
Ph: (313)961-1340
Fax: (313)961-1383
E-mail: customerservice@omnigraphics.com
URL: http://www.omnigraphics.com

Frequency: Irregular; latest edition 4th, Published 2010. **Price:** $85 Individuals hardcover; $95 Individuals list price. **Pages:** 728. **Covers:** Information about genetic disorders and related organizations. **Includes:** Charts, tables. **Entries include:** Contact information. **Indexes:** General.

HANDBOOKS AND MANUALS

5539 ■ Professional Status Survey
National Society of Genetic Counselors
330 N Wabash Ave., Ste. 2000
Chicago, IL 60611
Ph: (312)321-6834
Fax: (312)673-6972
E-mail: nsgc@nsgc.org
URL: http://www.nsgc.org

Description: Bi-annual survey presenting an overview of genetics professions; includes information regarding salary ranges, work environments, faculty status, and job satisfaction.

EMPLOYMENT AGENCIES AND SEARCH FIRMS

5540 ■ DDS Resources
16020 Swingley Ridge Rd., Ste. 340
Chesterfield, MO 63017
Ph: (636)536-6656
Free: 877-337-0563
Fax: (636)536-6667
E-mail: info@mdr-inc.com
URL: http://www.mdr-inc.com/dentists.aspx

Description: Serves as a dental recruitment agency in the United States. Specializes in matching qualified dentists with dental employers.

ONLINE JOB SOURCES AND SERVICES

5541 ■ Employment Spot
URL: http://www.employmentspot.com

Description: Help wanted advertisements for professional positions, including those in the genetics field. Users can search for positions by city, state or industry.

5542 ■ Get Genetic Counseling Jobs
URL: http://www.getgeneticcounselingjobs.com

Description: Features a searchable database of employment opportunities for genetic counselors.

5543 ■ National Society of Genetic Counselors E-Blast
URL: http://nsgc.org/p/cm/ld/fid=84

Price: $1,000. **Description:** Allows members to email announcements and messages to the desktops of other members.

5544 ■ National Society of Genetic Counselors Job Connection Service
URL: http://jobconnection.nsgc.org

Description: Services include a three-month posting on the Society's website as well as a one-time posting on its Listserv, reaching more than 85 percent of the society's full and associated members. The Listserv allows users to target a select audience of members in the following specialties: cancer, prenatal, pediatric, cardiovascular, industry, psychiatric disorders, and general.

OTHER SOURCES

5545 ■ Alstrom Syndrome International
14 Whitney Farm Rd.
Mount Desert, ME 04660
Free: 800-371-3628
E-mail: jdm@jax.org
URL: http://www.alstrom.org

Description: Individuals with Alstrom's syndrome (a genetic disorder resulting in multiple organ failures) and their families; health care professionals with an interest in the syndrome and its diagnosis and treatment. Seeks to improve the quality of life of people with Alstrom's syndrome. Serves as a clearinghouse on the syndrome and its treatment; functions as a support group for people with Alstrom's syndrome and their families. Encourages and fosters genetic and clinical research on Alstrom Syndrome.

5546 ■ American Board of Genetic Counseling
PO Box 14216
Lenexa, KS 66285
Ph: (913)895-4617
Fax: (913)895-4652
E-mail: info@abgc.net
URL: http://www.abgc.net

Description: Comprised of individuals who have passed the certification examination. Certifies individuals for the delivery of genetic counseling services and accredits genetic counseling master's degree granting programs.

5547 ■ American Board of Medical Genetics
9650 Rockville Pike
Bethesda, MD 20814-3998
Ph: (301)634-7315
Fax: (301)634-7320
E-mail: abmg@abmg.org
URL: http://www.abmg.org

Description: Certifies MDs and PhDs and accredits

post doctoral laboratory training fellowship programs in the field of human genetics. **Members:** 2,100.

5548 ■ American College of Medical Genetics
7220 Wisconsin Ave., Ste. 300
Bethesda, MD 20814
Ph: (301)718-9603
Fax: (301)718-9604
E-mail: acmg@acmg.net
URL: http://www.acmg.net

Description: Physicians and others with an interest in genetics and the delivery of medical genetics services to the public. Works to insure the availability of genetic services without regard to considerations of race, gender, sexual orientation, disability, or ability to pay. Promotes and supports genetics research. Establishes and maintains scientific and professional standards for medical genetics education, research, and practice. Lobbies for effective and fair health policies and legislation; provides information and technical assistance to government agencies engaged in health care regulation or policy formation. Makes available continuing professional education programs; represents members' interests. Conducts advocacy campaigns for people with genetic problems; sponsors public education programs. **Members:** 1,385.

5549 ■ American Genetic Association
2030 SE Marine Science Dr.
Newport, OR 97365-5300
Ph: (541)867-0334
E-mail: agajoh@oregonstate.edu
URL: http://www.theaga.org

Description: Represents biologists, zoologists, geneticists, botanists, and others engaged in basic and applied research in genetics. Explores transmission genetics of plants and animals. **Members:** 750.

5550 ■ American Medical Association
515 N State St.
Chicago, IL 60654
Ph: (312)464-4430
Free: 800-621-8335
Fax: (312)464-5226
E-mail: amallbrary@ama-assn.org
URL: http://www.ama-assn.org

Description: Represents county medical societies and physicians. Disseminates scientific information to members and the public. Informs members on significant medical and health legislation on state and national levels and represents the profession before Congress and governmental agencies. Cooperates in setting standards for medical schools, hospitals, residency programs, and continuing medical education courses. Offers physician placement service and counseling on practice management problems. Operates library that lends material and provides specific medical information to physicians. Maintains Ad-hoc committees for such topics as health care planning and principles of medical ethics.

5551 ■ American Society of Human Genetics
9650 Rockville Pike
Bethesda, MD 20814
Ph: (301)634-7300
Free: 866-HUM-GENE
Fax: (301)634-7079
E-mail: society@ashg.org
URL: http://www.ashg.org

Description: Professional society of physicians, researchers, genetic counselors, and others interested in human genetics.

5552 ■ Association of Genetic Technologists
PO Box 19193
Lenexa, KS 66285
Ph: (913)895-4605
Fax: (913)895-4652
E-mail: agt-info@goamp.com
URL: http://www.agt-info.org

Description: Professional organization of 1,200 technologists, supervisors and laboratory directors dedicated to promoting these professionals engaged in classical cytogenetics and molecular and biochemical genetics; and to stimulate interest in genetics as a career.

5553 ■ **Association of Professors of Human and Medical Genetics**
9650 Rockville Pike
Bethesda, MD 20814
Ph: (301)634-7234
E-mail: laurie.demmer@carolinashealthcare.org
URL: http://www.aphmg.org

Description: Promotes human and medical genetics educational programs in North American medical and graduate schools. Conducts academic activities and workshops that deal with medical genetics.

5554 ■ **Behavior Genetics Association**
345 UCB
Dept. of Psychology
Boulder, CO 80309
E-mail: soo.rhee@colorado.edu
URL: http://www.bga.org

Description: Consists of individuals engaged in teaching or research in some area of behavior genetics. Seeks to promote the scientific study of the interrelationship of genetic mechanisms and human and animal behavior through sponsorship of scientific meetings, publications, and communications among and by members; to encourage and aid the education and training of research workers in the field of behavior genetics; to aid in public dissemination and interpretation of information concerning the interrelationship of genetics and behavior and its implications for health, human development, and education. **Members:** 400.

5555 ■ *Career Opportunities in Health Care*
InfoBase Holdings Inc.
132 W 31st., 17 Fl.
New York, NY 10001-3406
Ph: (212)967-8800
Fax: (800)678-3633
E-mail: info@infobasepublishing.com
URL: http://www.ferguson.infobasepublishing.com

Description: Shelly Field. 2007. Third edition. $49.50. 304 pages. **Includes:** Appendices provide lists of educational institutions, periodicals, directories, associations, and unions. Appendices provide lists of educational institutions, periodicals, directories, associations, and unions.

5556 ■ **Genetic Counseling Foundation**
330 N Wabash Ave., Ste. 2000
Chicago, IL 60611
Ph: (312)321-6834
Fax: (312)673-6972
E-mail: nsgc@nsgc.org
URL: http://www.nsgc.org

Description: Seeks to improve quality education and research in the field of genetic counseling and to enhance the value, availability and awareness of genetic information and counseling in the medical community as well as the general public.

5557 ■ **Genetics Society of America**
9650 Rockville Pike
Bethesda, MD 20814
Ph: (301)634-7300
Free: 866-486-GENE
Fax: (301)634-7079
E-mail: afagen@genetics-gsa.org
URL: http://www.genetics-gsa.org

Description: Individuals and organizations interested in any field of genetics. Provides facilities for association and conferences of students in heredity; encourages communication among workers in genetics and those in related sciences.

5558 ■ *Health-Care Careers for the 21st Century*
JIST Publishing
875 Montreal Way
Saint Paul, MN 55102-4245
Ph: (317)613-4200
Free: 800-648-5478
Fax: (800)328-4564
E-mail: info@jist.com
URL: http://www.jist.com

Price: $9.95 Individuals Softcover. **Pages:** 448. **Covers:** Jobs for health care professionals and career opportunities for those pursuing a health-related career, organized into 80 careers in five groups. **Publication includes:** Appendixes listing job source resources and Web sites for health organizations.

5559 ■ **International Society of Nurses in Genetics**
461 Cochran Rd.
Box 246
Pittsburgh, PA 15228
Ph: (412)344-1414
Fax: (412)344-0599
E-mail: isonghq@msn.com
URL: http://www.isong.org

Description: Represents case managers, administrators, coordinators of public and private programs, educators in the field of nursing and/or genetics, genetic counselors, researchers. Committed to incorporating the knowledge of human genetics into nursing practice, education and research activities. **Members:** 350.

5560 ■ **Mountain States Genetics Foundation**
8129 W Fremont Ave.
Littleton, CO 80128
Ph: (602)870-4752
Fax: (602)870-4782
E-mail: susan.bryan@mostgene.org
URL: http://www.mostgene.org

Description: Advocates and supports education, awareness and access to medical genetics information.

5561 ■ **National Coalition for Health Professional Education in Genetics**
2360 W Joppa Rd., Ste. 320
Lutherville, MD 21093
Ph: (410)583-0600
Fax: (410)583-0520
E-mail: jscott@nchpeg.org
URL: http://www.nchpeg.org

Description: Promotes advances in health professional education and access to human genetics information.

5562 ■ **National Society of Genetic Counselors**
330 N Wabash Ave., Ste. 2000
Chicago, IL 60611
Ph: (312)321-6834
Fax: (312)673-6972
E-mail: nsgc@nsgc.org
URL: http://www.nsgc.org

Description: Promotes the genetic counseling profession as a recognized and integral part of health care delivery, education, research and public policy.

Geographers

SOURCES OF HELP-WANTED ADS

5563 ■ AAG Newsletter
Association of American Geographers
1710 16th St. NW
Washington, DC 20009
Ph: (202)234-1450
Fax: (202)234-2744
E-mail: gaia@aag.org
URL: http://www.aag.org/cs/publications/aag_newsletter/overview

Description: Monthly. Publishes items of interest to Association members and persons in related disciplines. Contains news of research, news of members, listings of publications, information on grant and employment opportunities, notices of field courses and seminars, calls for papers, and a calendar of events.

5564 ■ Base Line
Map and Geography Round Table
50 E Huron
Chicago, IL 60611
Ph: (312)280-3213
Free: 800-545-2433
Fax: (312)944-6131
E-mail: ccah@loc.gov
URL: http://www.ala.org/magirt

Description: Bimonthly. Provides current information on cartographic materials, publications of interest to map and geography librarians, related government activities, and map librarianship. Recurring features include conference and meeting information, news of research, job listings, and columns by the Division chair and the editor.

5565 ■ Geographical Journal
Blackwell Publishing Inc.
350 Main St.
Malden, MA 02148
Ph: (781)388-8200
Free: 800-216-2522
Fax: (781)388-8210
E-mail: journaladsusa@bos.blackwellpublishing.com
URL: http://as.wiley.com/WileyCDA/WileyTitle/productCd-GEOJ.html

Frequency: Quarterly. **Price:** $377 Institutions print and online; $438 Institutions, other countries print and online; $328 Institutions print or online; £224 Institutions print and online; $381 Institutions, other countries print or online; £195 Institutions print or online. **Description:** Journal focusing on original research and scholarship in physical and human geography.

5566 ■ Geographical Research
Blackwell Publishing Inc.
350 Main St.
Malden, MA 02148
Ph: (781)388-8200
Free: 800-216-2522

Fax: (781)388-8210
E-mail: journaladsusa@bos.blackwellpublishing.com
URL: http://www.wiley.com/bw/journal.asp?ref=1745-5863&site=1

Frequency: Quarterly. **Price:** £80 Individuals print and online, rest of the world; €39 Members print and online, Europe; £340 Institutions print and online, Australia & New Zealand; £310 Institutions print or online, Australia & New Zealand; $80 Individuals print and online; $55 Members print and online; £312 Institutions, other countries print and online; £271 Institutions print or online. **Description:** Journal focusing on advancing geographical research across the discipline.

5567 ■ Journal of Latin American Geography
University of Texas Press - Studies in Latin American Popular Culture
2100 Comal St.
Austin, TX 78713-7819
Ph: (512)471-7233
Free: 800-252-3206
Fax: (512)232-7178
E-mail: utpress@uts.cc.utexas.edu
URL: http://www.utexas.edu/utpress/journals/jlag.html

Frequency: Semiannual. **Price:** $70 Individuals; $120 Institutions; $80 Canada; $130 Institutions, Canada; $87.50 Other countries; $137.50 Institutions, other countries. **Description:** Journal of the Conference of Latin American Geographists containing articles of interest to professionals in the field.

5568 ■ PALAIOS
SEPM Publications
University of Kansas
Paleontological Institute, Department of Geology
1475 Jawyhawk Blvd., Rm. 120
Lawrence, KS 66045-7613
Ph: (785)864-2737
Fax: (785)864-3636
E-mail: palois@ku.edu
URLs: http://palaios.ku.edu/; http://palaios.geoscienceworld.org/

Frequency: Monthly. **Price:** $400 Individuals for U.S.; online version with CD-ROM; $500 Individuals for U.S.; print and online version with CD-ROM; $400 Other countries online version with CD-ROM; $500 Other countries print and online version with CD-ROM. **Description:** Journal providing information on the impact of life on Earth history as recorded in the paleontological and sedimentological records. Covers areas such as biogeochemistry, ichnology, sedimentology, stratigraphy, paleoecology, paleoclimatology, and paleoceanography.

5569 ■ Population, Space and Place
John Wiley & Sons Inc.
111 River St.
Hoboken, NJ 07030-5774
Ph: (201)748-6000
Free: 800-225-5945

Fax: (201)748-6088
E-mail: info@wiley.com
URL: http://onlinelibrary.wiley.com/journal/10.1002/(ISSN)1544-8452

Frequency: Bimonthly. **Price:** $1,260 Institutions online only; $1,260 Institutions, other countries online only; €812 Institutions, other countries online only; £644 Institutions online only; $1,260 Institutions, Canada and Mexico online only. **Description:** Journal focusing on research in the field of geographical population studies.

5570 ■ The Professional Geographer
San Diego State University
1710 Sixteenth St., NW
Association of American Geographers
San Diego State University
Washington, DC 20009-3198
Ph: (202)234-1450
Fax: (202)234-2744
URL: http://www.aag.org/cs/publications/the_professional_geographer

Frequency: Quarterly. **Description:** Geographical journal.

EMPLOYER DIRECTORIES AND NETWORKING LISTS

5571 ■ Guide to Programs in Geography in the United States and Canada/AAG Handbook and Directory of Geographers
Association of American Geographers
1710 16th St. NW
Washington, DC 20009
Ph: (202)234-1450
Fax: (202)234-2744
E-mail: gaia@aag.org
URL: http://www.aag.org

Frequency: Annual; Latest edition 2008-2009. **Price:** $60 Nonmembers; $25 Students; $35 Members. **Pages:** 824. **Covers:** Institutions offering undergraduate and graduate geography programs; and government agencies, private firms and research institutions that employ geographers in the U.S., Canada and Mexico. **Entries include:** For institutions--Department, address, and phone, contact person, requirements, programs, facilities, financial aid, faculty, titles of dissertations and theses completed. For individuals--Name, address, birth date, degrees received, place of employment. **Arrangement:** Geographical. **Indexes:** Department specialty; ZIP code.

5572 ■ Physical and Earth Sciences Graduate Program Directories
EducationDynamics LLC - Prospecting Services Div. - GradSchools.com
1350 Edgmont Ave., Ste. 1100
Chester, PA 19013
Ph: (484)766-2910

403

Free: 866-GRAD-COM
Fax: (610)499-9205
E-mail: info@edudirectories.com
URL: http://www.gradschools.com

HANDBOOKS AND MANUALS

**5573 ■ *Opportunities in Social Science
Careers***
The McGraw-Hill Companies Inc.
PO Box 182604
Columbus, OH 43272
Ph: (212)512-2000
Free: 877-833-5524
Fax: (614)759-3749
E-mail: customer.service@mcgraw-hill.com
URL: http://www.mcgraw-hill.com

Description: Rosanne J. Marek. 2004. $13.95. 160
Pages. VGM Opportunities Series.

ONLINE JOB SOURCES AND SERVICES

5574 ■ GeoCommunity
The GeoCommunity
c/o MindSites Group
1155 John Sim Pky. E
Niceville, FL 32578
Ph: (850)897-1002
Fax: (850)897-1001
E-mail: info@geocomm.com
URL: http://www.geocomm.com

Description: Serves as a clearinghouse for posting
or browsing GIS, GPS, CAD, remote sensing, and
earth sciences related announcements, resumes,
and consultant listings.

5575 ■ Geographer Jobs
URL: http://www.geographerjobs.net

Description: Serves as a career resource and job
search site for geographer employment opportunities.

TRADESHOWS

**5576 ■ Association of American
Geographers Annual Meeting**
Association of American Geographers
1710 16th St. NW
Washington, DC 20009
Ph: (202)234-1450
Fax: (202)234-2744
E-mail: gaia@aag.org
URL: http://www.aag.org

Frequency: Annual. **Primary Exhibits:** Publications,
geographic information systems, and technical equipment.

OTHER SOURCES

5577 ■ African Studies Association
Rutgers University
Livingston Campus
54 Joyce Kilmer Ave.
Piscataway, NJ 08854
Ph: (848)445-8173
Fax: (732)445-1366
E-mail: secretariat@africanstudies.org
URL: http://www.africanstudies.org

Description: Persons specializing in teaching, writing, or research on Africa including political scientists,
historians, geographers, anthropologists, economists,
librarians, linguists, and government officials;
persons who are studying African subjects;
institutional members are universities, libraries,
government agencies, and others interested in
receiving information about Africa. Seeks to foster
communication and to stimulate research among
scholars on Africa. Sponsors placement service;
conducts panels and discussion groups; presents
exhibits and films.

5578 ■ The American Geographical Society
32 Court St.
Brooklyn Heights, NY 11201
Ph: (718)624-2212
Fax: (718)624-2239
E-mail: ags@amergeog.org
URL: http://www.amergeog.org

Description: Industry professionals and other
interested individuals.

**5579 ■ ASPRS, The Imaging and Geospatial
Information Society**
5410 Grosvenor Ln., Ste. 210
Bethesda, MD 20814-2160
Ph: (301)493-0290
Fax: (301)493-0208
E-mail: asprs@asprs.org
URL: http://www.asprs.org

Description: Firms, individuals, government
employees and academicians engaged in photogrammetry, photointerpretation, remote sensing, and
geographic information systems and their application
to such fields as archaeology, geographic information
systems, military reconnaissance, urban planning,
engineering, traffic surveys, meteorological observations, medicine, geology, forestry, agriculture,
construction and topographic mapping. Seeks to
advance knowledge and improve understanding of
these sciences and promote responsible applications. Offers voluntary certification program open to
persons associated with one or more functional area
of photogrammetry, remote sensing and GIS.
Surveys the profession of private firms in photogrammetry and remote sensing in the areas of products
and services.

**5580 ■ Association of American
Geographers**
1710 16th St. NW
Washington, DC 20009

Ph: (202)234-1450
Fax: (202)234-2744
E-mail: gaia@aag.org
URL: http://www.aag.org

Description: Professional society of educators and
scientists in the field of geography. Seeks to further
professional investigations in geography and to
encourage the application of geographic research in
education, government, and business. Conducts
research; compiles statistics.

5581 ■ *Career Opportunities in Science*
InfoBase Holdings Inc.
132 W 31st., 17 Fl.
New York, NY 10001-3406
Ph: (212)967-8800
Fax: (800)678-3633
E-mail: info@infobasepublishing.com
URL: http://factsonfile.infobasepublishing.com

Frequency: Latest edition 2008. **Price:** $49.50
Individuals hardcover. **Pages:** 344. **Description:**
Susan Echaore-McDavid. Second edition, 2008. 332
pages. **Covers:** More than 80 jobs, such as
biochemist, molecular biologist, bioinformatic specialist, pharmacologist, computer engineer, geographic
information systems specialist, science teacher,
forensic scientist, patent agent, as well as physicist,
astronomer, chemist, zoologist, oceanographer, and
geologist. **Includes:** Appendices of educational
institutions, periodicals, directories, and associations.

**5582 ■ Geography Education National
Implementation Project**
Texas A & M University
College Station, TX 77843-3147
Ph: (979)845-1579
Fax: (979)862-4487
E-mail: s-bednarz@tamu.edu
URL: http://genip.tamu.edu

Description: Consortium of geographic associations
committed to improving the status and quality of
geography education.

**5583 ■ National Council for Geographic
Education**
1145 17th St. NW, Rm. 7620
Washington, DC 20036
Ph: (202)857-7695
Fax: (202)618-6249
E-mail: ncge@ncge.org
URL: http://www.ncge.org

Description: Teachers of geography and social studies in elementary and secondary schools, colleges
and universities; geographers in governmental agencies and private businesses. Encourages the training
of teachers in geographic concepts, practices, teaching methods and techniques; works to develop effective geographic educational programs in schools and
colleges and with adult groups; stimulates the
production and use of accurate and understandable
geographic teaching aids and materials.

SOURCES OF HELP-WANTED ADS

5584 ■ AAPG Explorer
American Association of Petroleum Geologists
1444 S Boulder Ave.
Tulsa, OK 74119
Ph: (918)584-2555
Free: 800-364-2274
Fax: (918)560-2665
E-mail: lkrystinik@fossilcreekres.com
URL: http://www.aapg.org/explorer/
Frequency: Monthly. **Price:** $75 Nonmembers; $147 Individuals airmail service; $55 Members airmail. **Description:** Magazine containing articles about energy issues with an emphasis on exploration for hydrocarbons and energy minerals.

5585 ■ AEG News
Association of Environmental and Engineering Geologists
PO Box 460518
Denver, CO 80246
Ph: (303)757-2926
Fax: (720)230-4846
E-mail: aeg@aegweb.org
URL: http://www.aegweb.org
Description: Bimonthly. $40 per year for nonmember. Covers news of the engineering geology profession and the Association, whose members are engineering geologists and geological engineers worldwide. Recurring features include letters to the editor, a calendar of events, news of research, and short articles of technical interest.

5586 ■ Computational Thermal Sciences
Begell House Inc.
50 Cross Hwy.
Redding, CT 06896
Ph: (203)938-1300
Fax: (203)938-1304
E-mail: orders@begellhouse.com
URL: http://www.begellhouse.com/journals/
648192910890cd0e
Price: $719 Institutions. **Description:** Journal focusing on the fundamental methods of thermodynamics, fluid mechanics, heat transfer and combustion.

5587 ■ Earth
American Geosciences Institute
4220 King St.
Alexandria, VA 22302
Ph: (703)379-2480
Fax: (703)379-7563
E-mail: ls@agiweb.org
URL: http://www.agiweb.org
Description: Monthly. $36/year in United States; $51/year in Canada; $81/year in other countries. Covers the latest happenings in earth, energy, and the environment.

5588 ■ Geological Abstracts
Elsevier Science Inc.
Secondary Publishing Division
650 Ave. of the Americas
New York, NY 10011
Ph: (212)633-3980
Free: 888-437-4636
Fax: (212)633-3975
URL: http://www.elsevier.com/journals/geological
-abstracts/0954-0512
Frequency: 12/yr. **Description:** Journal relating to geological literature.

5589 ■ Geology
Geological Society of America
3300 Penrose Pl.
Boulder, CO 80301
Ph: (303)357-1000
Fax: (303)357-1070
E-mail: pubs@geocociety.org
URLs: http://geology.gsapubs.org/; http://www.geoso-
ciety.org/pubs/jrnlDescriptions.htm#geology
Frequency: Monthly. **Price:** $85 Members print (includes online access); $90 Members international; print (includes online access); $45 Students members; print (includes online access); $45 Students, other countries members; print (includes online access); $875 Institutions & nonmembers; print & online; $800 Institutions & nonmembers; on-line only. **Description:** Geology journal.

5590 ■ Geophysical Journal International
Blackwell Publishing Inc.
350 Main St.
Malden, MA 02148
Ph: (781)388-8200
Free: 800-216-2522
Fax: (781)388-8210
E-mail: journaladsusa@bos.blackwellpublishing.com
URL: http://www.wiley.com/bw/journal.asp?ref=0956
-540X&site=1
Frequency: Monthly. **Price:** $431 Individuals print and online; $394 Individuals online only; $209 Members print and online; $2,936 Institutions print & online; $2,553 Institutions print or online; £233 Individuals print and online; £1,383 Institutions, other countries print or online. **Description:** Journal focusing on research in geophysics.

5591 ■ ISEM Newsletter
Institute for the Study of Earth and Man
N.L. Heroy Hall
Southern Methodist University
Dallas, TX 75275-0274
Ph: (214)768-2425
Fax: (214)768-4289
E-mail: isem@mail.smu.edu
URL: http://www.smu.edu/isem
Description: Semiannual. Reports on research in the anthropological, geological, and statistical sciences. Includes notices of research funds, grants, and contracts awarded. Provides biographical

sketches of new faculty members in the anthropological, geological, and statistical sciences departments at Southern Methodist University. Recurring features include news of research and news of members.

5592 ■ Oil & Gas Journal
PennWell Publishing Co.
1455 W Loop S, Ste. 400
Houston, TX 77027
Ph: (713)621-9720
Free: 800-736-6935
E-mail: petroleum@pennwell.com
URLs: http://www.ogj.com/index.html; http://www
.pennwell.com
Frequency: Weekly. **Price:** $69 Individuals print; $49 Individuals online; $73 Other countries Canada and Latin America; $108 Other countries. **Description:** Trade magazine serving engineers and managers in international petroleum operations.

5593 ■ PALAIOS
SEPM Publications
University of Kansas
Paleontological Institute, Department of Geology
1475 Jawyhawk Blvd., Rm. 120
Lawrence, KS 66045-7613
Ph: (785)864-2737
Fax: (785)864-3636
E-mail: palois@ku.edu
URLs: http://palaios.ku.edu/; http://palaios
.geoscienceworld.org/
Frequency: Monthly. **Price:** $400 Individuals for U.S.; online version with CD-ROM; $500 Individuals for U.S.; print and online version with CD-ROM; $400 Other countries online version with CD-ROM; $500 Other countries print and online version with CD-ROM. **Description:** Journal providing information on the impact of life on Earth history as recorded in the paleontological and sedimentological records. Covers areas such as biogeochemistry, ichnology, sedimentology, stratigraphy, paleoecology, paleoclimatology, and paleoceanography.

EMPLOYER DIRECTORIES AND NETWORKING LISTS

5594 ■ American Men and Women of Science: A Biographical Dictionary of Today's Leaders in Physical, Biological, and Related Sciences
R.R. Bowker
630 Central Ave
New Providence, NJ 07974
Ph: (888)269-5372
Free: 888-269-5372
Fax: (908)464-3553
E-mail: info@bowker.com
URL: http://www.gale.cengage.com
Frequency: Biennial; even years; New edition expected 29th, June 2011. **Price:** $1,368 Individuals.

Covers: Over 135,000 U.S. and Canadian scientists active in the physical, biological, mathematical, computer science, and engineering fields; includes references to previous edition for deceased scientists and nonrespondents. **Entries include:** Name, address, education, personal and career data, memberships, honors and awards, research interest. **Arrangement:** Alphabetical. **Indexes:** Discipline (in separate volume).

5595 ■ Directory of Certified Petroleum Geologists
American Association of Petroleum Geologists
1444 S Boulder Ave.
Tulsa, OK 74119
Ph: (918)584-2555
Free: 800-364-2274
Fax: (918)560-2665
E-mail: lkrystinik@fossilcreekres.com
URL: http://www.aapg.org/dpadirectory

Covers: About 3,400 members of the association. **Entries include:** Name, address; education and career data; whether available for consulting. **Arrangement:** Alphabetical. **Indexes:** Geographical.

5596 ■ Directory of Physics, Astronomy, and Geophysics Staff
American Institute of Physics
1 Physics Ellipse
College Park, MD 20740-3843
Ph: (301)209-3100
Fax: (301)209-0843
E-mail: aipinfo@aip.org
URL: http://www.aip.org/pubs/books/dpags.html

Frequency: Biennial; Latest edition 2006. **Price:** $82 Individuals softcover. **Pages:** 660 1 volume. **Covers:** 36,000 staff members at 2,600 colleges, universities, and laboratories throughout North America that employ physicists and astronomers; list of foreign organizations. **Entries include:** Name, address, phone, fax, electronic mail address. **Arrangement:** Separate alphabetical sections for individuals, academic institutions, and laboratories. **Indexes:** Academic institution location, type of laboratory.

5597 ■ The Geophysical Directory
Oil & Gas Directory
2200 Welch St.
Houston, TX 77219
Ph: (713)529-8789
Free: 800-929-2462
Fax: (713)529-3646
E-mail: infoserv@wt.net
URL: http://www.geophysicaldirectory.com

Frequency: Annual; Latest edition 67th; 2012-2013. **Price:** $150 Individuals Postpaid shipped inside U.S. (surface mail); $165 Individuals Postpaid shipped outside U.S. (via air). **Pages:** 328. **Covers:** About 4,581 companies that provide geophysical equipment, supplies, or services, and mining and petroleum companies that use geophysical techniques; international coverage. **Entries include:** Company name, address, phone, fax, names of principal executives, operations, and 9,719 key personnel; similar information for branch locations. **Arrangement:** Classified by product or service. **Indexes:** Company name, personal name.

5598 ■ Geophysicists: A Directory of AGU Members
American Geophysical Union
2000 Florida Ave. NW
Washington, DC 20009-1277
Ph: (202)462-6900
Free: 800-966-2481
Fax: (202)328-0566
E-mail: service@agu.org
URL: http://www.agu.org

Covers: 40,000 member geophysicists. **Entries include:** Name, address, office and home phone numbers, fax, electronic mail addresses, type of membership, year joined, and section affiliation. **Arrangement:** Alphabetical.

5599 ■ The Oil & Gas Directory
Oil & Gas Directory
2200 Welch St.
Houston, TX 77219
Ph: (713)529-8789
Free: 800-929-2462
Fax: (713)529-3646
E-mail: infoserv@wt.net
URL: http://www.geophysicaldirectory.com

Frequency: Annual; Latest edition 2011. **Price:** $140 Individuals Postpaid shipped inside U.S. (surface mail); $150 Individuals Postpaid shipped outside U.S. (via air). **Pages:** 588. **Covers:** About 12,904 companies worldwide involved in petroleum exploration, drilling, and production, and suppliers to the industry. **Entries include:** Company name, address, phone, fax, names of principal personnel, branch office addresses, phone numbers, and 22,675 key personnel. **Arrangement:** Classified by activity. **Indexes:** Company name, personal name, and regional.

5600 ■ Physical and Earth Sciences Graduate Program Directories
EducationDynamics LLC - Prospecting Services Div. - GradSchools.com
1350 Edgmont Ave., Ste. 1100
Chester, PA 19013
Ph: (484)766-2910
Free: 866-GRAD-COM
Fax: (610)499-9205
E-mail: info@edudirectories.com
URL: http://www.gradschools.com

5601 ■ Society of Exploration Geophysicists--Yearbook
Society of Exploration Geophysicists
8801 S Yale, Ste. 500
Tulsa, OK 74137-3575
Ph: (918)497-5500
Fax: (918)497-5557
E-mail: membership_online@seg.org
URLs: http://www.seg.org; http://www.seg.org/seg/seg-facts/yearbook

Frequency: Annual; Latest edition 2012. **Publication includes:** Membership roster of nearly 14,500 geophysicists, corporations, and students. **Entries include:** Name, address, phone, fax, e-mail type of member; affiliation given for individuals. **Arrangement:** Alphabetical; geographical.

HANDBOOKS AND MANUALS

5602 ■ Great Jobs for Geology Majors
McGraw-Hill Professional
PO Box 182604
Columbus, OH 43272
Ph: (877)833-5524
Free: 800-262-4729
Fax: (614)759-3749
E-mail: pbg.ecommerce_custserv@mcgraw-hill.com
URL: http://www.mhprofessional.com/product.php?isbn=0071493069

Description: Blythe Camenson. 2006. $15.95. 224 pages. Offers a complete overview of job possibilities including volcanologist, soil scientist, economic geologist, geodynamicist, laboratory technician, oceanographer, architect, petroleum engineer, and surveyor. Provides salary figures, experience and training for geology majors.

5603 ■ Jobs in Environmental Cleanup and Emergency Hazmat Response
The Rosen Publishing Group Inc.
29 E 21st St. Fl. 2
New York, NY 10010-6256
Ph: (212)777-3017
URL: http://www.rosenpublishing.com

Description: Daniel E. Harmon. 2010. $31.95 (library bound). 80 pages. Features jobs in environmental cleanup and emergency hazmat response. Explores numerous career paths for differ-

ent environmental jobs that require special training or four-year and/or postgraduate degrees. Includes job profiles for professionals such as environmental engineers, geologists, microbiologists, science technicians, conservationists, foresters, park rangers, soil scientists, air control technicians, toxicologists, dredge operators, ecologists, hazardous waste managers, and zoologists.

ONLINE JOB SOURCES AND SERVICES

5604 ■ Diversity Environmental Jobs
URL: http://www.diversityenvironmentaljobs.com

Description: Serves as a niche job board that provides diverse environmental career opportunities.

5605 ■ GeoCommunity
The GeoCommunity
c/o MindSites Group
1155 John Sim Pky. E
Niceville, FL 32578
Ph: (850)897-1002
Fax: (850)897-1001
E-mail: info@geocomm.com
URL: http://www.geocomm.com

Description: Serves as a clearinghouse for posting or browsing GIS, GPS, CAD, remote sensing, and earth sciences related announcements, resumes, and consultant listings.

5606 ■ GeologistCareers.com
URL: http://www.geologistcareers.com

Description: Online job search that provides information and resources for geologists.

5607 ■ GeologistJobs.com
URL: http://www.geologistjobs.com

Description: Serves as a career community for the geology industry. Provides information and lists job openings for geologists.

5608 ■ Get Geophysicist Jobs
URL: http://www.getgeophysicistjobs.com

Description: Serves as a source of employment and career opportunities for geophysicist job seekers and employers.

5609 ■ ScientistCrossing.com
URL: http://www.scientistcrossing.com

Description: Provides job listings and other resources related to scientist employment opportunities.

TRADESHOWS

5610 ■ Society of Exploration Geophysicists International Exposition and Annual Meeting
Society of Exploration Geophysicists
8801 S Yale, Ste. 500
Tulsa, OK 74137-3575
Ph: (918)497-5500
Fax: (918)497-5557
E-mail: membership_online@seg.org
URL: http://www.seg.org

Frequency: Annual. **Primary Exhibits:** Geophysical products and services, computer hardware and software, data storage, visualization technology.

OTHER SOURCES

5611 ■ American Geophysical Union
2000 Florida Ave. NW
Washington, DC 20009-1277
Ph: (202)462-6900
Free: 800-966-2481

Fax: (202)328-0566
E-mail: service@agu.org
URL: http://sites.agu.org

Description: Individuals professionally associated with the field of geophysics; supporting institutional members are companies and other organizations whose work involves geophysics. Promotes the study of problems concerned with the figure and physics of the earth; initiates and coordinates research that depends upon national and international cooperation and provides for scientific discussion of research results. Sponsors placement service at semiannual meeting.

5612 ■ American Geosciences Institute
4220 King St.
Alexandria, VA 22302
Ph: (703)379-2480
Fax: (703)379-7563
E-mail: ls@agiweb.org
URL: http://www.agiweb.org

Description: Federation of national scientific and technical societies in the Earth sciences. Seeks to: stimulate public understanding of Geological sciences; improve teaching of the geological sciences in schools, colleges, and universities; maintain high standards of professional training and conduct; work for the general welfare of members. Provides career guidance program.

5613 ■ American Institute of Professional Geologists
12000 Washington St., Ste. 285
Thornton, CO 80241-3134
Ph: (303)412-6205
Fax: (303)253-9220
E-mail: aipg@aipg.org
URL: http://www.aipg.org

Description: Geologists. Provides certification to geologists attesting to their competence and integrity. Represents the geologic profession before government bodies and the public.

5614 ■ ASPRS, The Imaging and Geospatial Information Society
5410 Grosvenor Ln., Ste. 210
Bethesda, MD 20814-2160
Ph: (301)493-0290
Fax: (301)493-0208
E-mail: asprs@asprs.org
URL: http://www.asprs.org

Description: Firms, individuals, government employees and academicians engaged in photogrammetry, photointerpretation, remote sensing, and geographic information systems and their application to such fields as archaeology, geographic information systems, military reconnaissance, urban planning, engineering, traffic surveys, meteorological observations, medicine, geology, forestry, agriculture, construction and topographic mapping. Seeks to advance knowledge and improve understanding of these sciences and promote responsible applications. Offers voluntary certification program open to persons associated with one or more functional area of photogrammetry, remote sensing and GIS. Surveys the profession of private firms in photogrammetry and remote sensing in the areas of products and services.

5615 ■ Association of Environmental and Engineering Geologists
PO Box 460518
Denver, CO 80246
Ph: (303)757-2926
Fax: (720)230-4846
E-mail: aeg@aegweb.org
URL: http://www.aegweb.org

Description: Represents graduate geologists and geological engineers; full members must have five years experience in the field of engineering geology. Promotes professional success by providing leadership, advocacy, and applied research in environmental and engineering geology. Seeks to provide a forum for the discussion and dissemination

of technical and scientific information. Encourages the advancement of professional recognition, scientific research, and high ethical and professional standards. Compiles information on engineering geology curricula of colleges and universities. Promotes public understanding, health, safety and welfare, and acceptance of the engineering geology profession. Conducts technical sessions, symposia, abstracts, and short courses; cosponsors seminars and conferences with other professional and technical societies and organizations.

5616 ■ Association for Women Geoscientists
12000 N Washington St., Ste. 285
Thornton, CO 80241-3134
Ph: (303)412-6219
Fax: (303)253-9220
E-mail: office@awg.org
URL: http://www.awg.org

Description: Represents men and women geologists, geophysicists, petroleum engineers, geological engineers, hydrogeologists, paleontologists, geochemists, and other geoscientists. Aims to encourage the participation of women in the geosciences. Exchanges educational, technical, and professional information. Enhances the professional growth and advancement of women in the geosciences. Provides information through web site on opportunities and careers available to women in the geosciences. Sponsors educational booths and programs at geological society conventions. Operates charitable program. Maintains speaker's bureau, and Association for Women Geoscientists Foundation.

5617 ■ *Career Opportunities in Conservation and the Environment*
InfoBase Holdings Inc.
132 W 31st., 17 Fl.
New York, NY 10001-3406
Ph: (212)967-8800
Fax: (800)678-3633
E-mail: info@infobasepublishing.com
URL: http://www.ferguson.infobasepublishing.com

Description: 2007. $49.50. 304 pages. Covers job profiles on conservation and the environment, followed by the descriptions of certification, education, special skills, and training required. **Includes:** Appendices of educational institutions, periodicals, directories, and associations. Appendices of educational institutions, periodicals, directories, and associations.

5618 ■ *Career Opportunities in Science*
InfoBase Holdings Inc.
132 W 31st., 17 Fl.
New York, NY 10001-3406
Ph: (212)967-8800
Fax: (800)678-3633
E-mail: info@infobasepublishing.com
URL: http://factsonfile.infobasepublishing.com

Frequency: Latest edition 2008. **Price:** $49.50 Individuals hardcover. **Pages:** 344. **Description:** Susan Echaore-McDavid. Second edition, 2008. 332 pages. **Covers:** More than 80 jobs, such as biochemist, molecular biologist, bioinformatic specialist, pharmacologist, computer engineer, geographic information systems specialist, science teacher, forensic scientist, patent agent, as well as physicist, astronomer, chemist, zoologist, oceanographer, and geologist. **Includes:** Appendices of educational institutions, periodicals, directories, and associations.

5619 ■ Cultural Vistas
440 Park Ave. S, 2nd Fl.
New York, NY 10016
Ph: (212)497-3500
Fax: (212)497-3535
E-mail: info@culturalvistas.org
URL: http://culturalvistas.org

Description: Providers worldwide of on-the-job training programs for students and professionals seeking international career development and life-changing

experiences. Arranges workplace exchanges in hundreds of professional fields, bringing employers and trainees together from around the world. Client list ranges from small farming communities to Fortune 500 companies.

5620 ■ Geological Society of America
3300 Penrose Pl.
Boulder, CO 80301
Ph: (303)357-1000
Fax: (303)357-1070
E-mail: gsaservice@geosociety.org
URL: http://www.geosociety.org

Description: Serves as professional society of earth scientists. Promotes the science of geology. Maintains placement service.

5621 ■ Marine Technology Society
1100 H St. NW, Ste. LL100
Washington, DC 20005
Ph: (202)717-8705
Fax: (202)347-4302
E-mail: membership@mtsociety.org
URL: http://www.mtsociety.org

Description: Scientists, engineers, educators, and others with professional interest in the marine sciences or related fields; includes institutional and corporate members. Disseminates marine scientific and technical information, including institutional, environmental, physical, and biological aspects; fosters a deeper understanding of the world's seas and attendant technologies. Maintains 13 sections and 29 professional committees. Conducts tutorials.

5622 ■ National Association of Black Geologists and Geophysicists
4212 San Felipe, Ste. 420
Houston, TX 77027
E-mail: nabgg_us@hotmail.com
URL: http://www.nabgg.com

Description: Serves as a group dedicated to environmental concerns and the ethical development of natural resources. Works to inform students of career opportunities that exist in the field of geosciences and to encourage them to take advantage of scholarship programs, grant, loans, etc., that are established for minority students. Strives to assist in the development of professional standards and practices of members within their geoscience careers and entrepreneurial pursuits.

5623 ■ National Ground Water Association
601 Dempsey Rd.
Westerville, OH 43081
Ph: (614)898-7791
Free: 800-551-7379
Fax: (614)898-7786
E-mail: ngwa@ngwa.org
URL: http://www.ngwa.org

Description: Ground water drilling contractors; manufacturers and suppliers of drilling equipment; ground water scientists such as geologists, engineers, public health officials, and others interested in the problems of locating, developing, preserving, and using ground water supplies. Conducts seminars, and continuing education programs. Encourages scientific education, research, and the development of standards; offers placement services; compiles market statistics. Offers charitable program. Maintains speakers' bureau.

5624 ■ National Groundwater Association - Association of Ground Water Scientists and Engineers
PO Box 715435
Columbus, OH 43271
Ph: (614)898-7791
Free: 800-551-7379
Fax: (614)898-7786
E-mail: ngwa@ngwa.org
URL: http://www.ngwa.org/Pages/default.aspx

Description: A technical division of the National Ground Water Association. Hydrogeologists, geologists, hydrologists, civil and environmental engineers, geochemists, biologists, and scientists in related fields. Seeks to: provide leadership and guidance for scientific, economical, and beneficial groundwater development; promote the use, protection, and management of the world's groundwater resources. Conducts educational programs, seminars, short courses, symposia, and field research projects. Maintains speakers' bureau and museum; offers placement service; sponsors competitions; compiles statistics. **Members:** 11,000.

5625 ■ Society of Exploration Geophysicists
8801 S Yale, Ste. 500
Tulsa, OK 74137-3575
Ph: (918)497-5500
Fax: (918)497-5557
E-mail: membership_online@seg.org
URL: http://www.seg.org

Description: Promotes the science of geophysics and education. Fosters the expert and ethical practice of geophysics in the exploration and development of natural resources, in characterizing the near surface, and in mitigating Earth hazards. Fulfills its mission through its publications, conferences, forums, web sites, and educational opportunities.

SOURCES OF HELP-WANTED ADS

5626 ■ AGRR
Key Communications, Inc.
385 Garrisonville Rd.
Stafford, VA 22554
Ph: (540)720-5584
Fax: (540)720-5687
E-mail: info@glassexpomidwest.com
URL: http://www.agrrmag.com
Description: Bimonthly. Provides information and news for those in the auto glass repair and replacement industry. Features industry movement, forecasts of future trends, and technical advice. Contains advertisements of businesses for sale, employment/help wanted, industry services, products for sale, and used equipment for sale.

5627 ■ Door & Window Manufacturer Magazine
Key Communications, Inc.
385 Garrisonville Rd.
Stafford, VA 22554
Ph: (540)720-5584
Fax: (540)720-5687
E-mail: info@glassexpomidwest.com
URL: http://www.dwmmag.com
Description: 11 issues per year. Provides industry information for door and window manufacturers. Contains classified advertising.

5628 ■ GASnews
Glass Art Society
6512 23rd Ave. NW, Ste. 329
Seattle, WA 98117
Ph: (206)382-1305
Fax: (206)382-2630
E-mail: info@glassart.org
URL: http://www.glassart.org
Frequency: Annual. **Price:** Included in membership. **Description:** Bi-monthly. Provides a forum for the dissemination of ideas and information as well as a place for regular communication between glass artists around the world. Contains details on classes and workshops, seminars, conferences, events, and exhibitions. Includes other resources such as calls to artists, competitions, exhibitions, galleries, shows and fairs, grants and residencies, job opportunities, and advertising opportunities.

5629 ■ Glass Magazine
National Glass Association
1945 Old Gallows Rd., Ste. 750
Vienna, VA 22182
Ph: (703)442-4890
Free: 866-342-5642
Fax: (703)442-0630
E-mail: pjames@glass.org
URL: http://www.glass.org
Description: Monthly. $34.95/year in the United States, Canada and Mexico; $44.95/year outside the United States, Canada and Mexico. Features editorial direction and informative coverage including market segment surveys, resource guides, reader polls, industry profiles, statistics, and products.

5630 ■ Window & Door
National Glass Association
1945 Old Gallows Rd., Ste. 750
Vienna, VA 22182
Ph: (703)442-4890
Free: 866-342-5642
Fax: (703)442-0630
E-mail: pjames@glass.org
URL: http://www.glass.org
Description: Eleven times a year. $29.95/year for U.S. individuals; $39.95/year individuals outside U.S., Canada, and Mexico. Serves the fenestration industry including manufacturers, distributors, specialty dealers, and others involved in the manufacturing and marketing of window, door, and skylight products.

EMPLOYER DIRECTORIES AND NETWORKING LISTS

5631 ■ GAS Membership Directory and Resource Guide
Glass Art Society
6512 23rd Ave. NW, Ste. 329
Seattle, WA 98117
Ph: (206)382-1305
Fax: (206)382-2630
E-mail: info@glassart.org
URLs: http://www.glassart.org/ResourceGuide_Directory.html; http://www.glassart.org
Frequency: Latest edition 2010. **Description:** Features GAS members' contact information and ads for manufacturers, suppliers, galleries, publications, and schools. Information listed include: firm name, address, phone, category, specialty, website, and other details as provided by firm. **Arrangement:** Alphabetical.

5632 ■ Glass Factory Directory of North America and U.S. Factbook
Glass Factory Directory
PO Box 2267
Hempstead, NY 11551-2267
Ph: (516)481-2188
E-mail: manager@glassfactorydir.com
URL: http://www.glassfactorydir.com
Frequency: Annual. **Price:** $100 Individuals electronic. **Description:** Annual. Lists glass manufacturing locations in Canada, Mexico, and the United States. Provides plant addresses, telephone numbers, fax numbers, contact persons, and a brief product list of the companies. Arranges listings in state and country order.

5633 ■ National Glass Association Directory
National Glass Association
1945 Old Gallows Rd., Ste. 750
Vienna, VA 22182
Ph: (703)442-4890
Free: 866-342-5642
Fax: (703)442-0630
E-mail: pjames@glass.org
URL: http://www.glass.org
Description: Features a list of current member companies which includes company name, address, and contact person.

5634 ■ Russia/CIS Major Building Material Manufacturers Directory
Business Information Agency Inc. - PlanetInform
52 Tuscan Way, Ste. 202-181
Saint Augustine, VA 32092
Ph: (904)342-6124
Fax: (904)592-2632
E-mail: info@biasales.com
URL: http://www.planetinform.com/html/prodCard.aspx?prodID=3599
Frequency: Annual; January; Latest edition 12th, 2012. **Price:** $199 Individuals Paperback (plus shipping charge); $199 Individuals PDF version; $249 Individuals Both hard copy and PDF. **Pages:** 426 Volume 1. **Covers:** 6,980 manufacturers of flat glass and other glass products, cement, structural clay products, pottery, concrete and gypsum products, cut stone, abrasive, and asbestos products. **Entries include:** Company name, location, detailed contact information, type of business, SIC codes, number of employees, year founded, legal status, and subsidiary indicators. **Indexes:** Alphabetical, geographical by SIC code and industrial activity.

5635 ■ The Sourcebook
Stained Glass Association of America
9313 E 63rd St.
Raytown, MO 64133
Ph: (816)737-2090
Free: 800-438-9581
Fax: (816)737-2801
E-mail: headquarters@sgaaonline.com
URL: http://stainedglass.org
Description: Annual. Features a complete membership directory of the organization. Serves as a general guide to architectural stained glass.

HANDBOOKS AND MANUALS

5636 ■ Construction
InfoBase Holdings Inc.
132 W 31st., 17 Fl.
New York, NY 10001-3406
Ph: (212)967-8800
Fax: (800)678-3633
E-mail: info@infobasepublishing.com
URL: http://www.ferguson.infobasepublishing.com
Price: $30 Hardcover. **Description:** 2010. 128

pages. Contains profiles of 20 careers in the field of construction with emphasis on the nature of work, requirements, salary, and career outlook. Includes full-color photographs, index, glossary, resources, and side bars.

5637 ■ *GANA Glazing Manual*
Glass Association of North America
800 SW Jackson St., Ste. 1500
Topeka, KS 66612-1200
Ph: (785)271-0208
Fax: (785)271-0166
E-mail: gana@glasswebsite.com
URL: http://www.glasswebsite.com

Description: 2008. $35.00 (paper) for members; $70.00 (paper) for non-members. Includes information about primary and fabricated glass products, quality standards, design considerations, general and specific glazing guidelines, and glazing in hazardous locations.

5638 ■ *Installation and Safety Glazing*
Stained Glass Association of America
9313 E 63rd St.
Raytown, MO 64133
Ph: (816)737-2090
Free: 800-438-9581
Fax: (816)737-2801
E-mail: headquarters@sgaaonline.com
URL: http://stainedglass.org

Description: 2008. $25.00. 70 pages. Covers installation and safety glazing techniques.

5639 ■ *Opportunities in Building Construction Careers*
The McGraw-Hill Companies Inc.
PO Box 182604
Columbus, OH 43272
Ph: (212)512-2000
Free: 877-833-5524
Fax: (614)759-3749
E-mail: customer.service@mcgraw-hill.com
URL: http://www.mcgraw-hill.com

Description: Michael Sumichrast. 2007. $14.95. 160 pages. Provides information on various fields in the building construction industry. Includes training and education requirements for each career.

EMPLOYMENT AGENCIES AND SEARCH FIRMS

5640 ■ Management Recruiters of Davidson
710 Northeast Dr., Ste. 8
Davidson, NC 28036-7424
Ph: (704)896-8890
Fax: (704)896-8933
E-mail: admin@mrdavidson.com
URL: http://www.mrdavidson.com

Description: Specializes in the recruitment and placement of professionals within the window, door, and glass/glazing industries throughout the United States.

ONLINE JOB SOURCES AND SERVICES

5641 ■ Get Glazier Jobs
URL: http://www.getglazierjobs.com

Description: Provides resources for finding and filling glazier positions. Offers job postings worldwide.

5642 ■ Glass Global
URL: http://www.glassglobal.com

Description: Functions as an international e-commerce portal website for the glass industry. Maintains a company directory that gives detailed company information from raw materials suppliers up to the finished product traders. Features a database of job offers and job requests from all areas of the glass industry.

5643 ■ Glass.com
URL: http://www.glass.com

Description: Contains advertisements of businesses for sale, employment/help wanted, industry services, products for sale, and used equipment for sale.

5644 ■ Glassjobsearch.com
URL: http://www.glassjobsearch.com

Description: Provides glass industry job resources. Features job listings as well as resume searches and company profiles for prospective employers.

5645 ■ Glasslinks.com
URL: http://www.glasslinks.com

Description: Provides links and information on jobs, employment, and careers in the glass industry.

5646 ■ GlassOnline.com
URL: http://www.glassonline.com/site

Description: Serves as a glass industry portal featuring news, fairs, conferences, glass magazines, renewable energy magazines, trade opportunities, employment and help wanted listings, forums, tools, and glass publications.

5647 ■ GlassOnWeb.com
URL: http://www.glassonweb.com

Description: Serves as an information portal for the glass industry. Features directories, news and articles, forums, and jobs in the glass business.

5648 ■ Glazier Jobs
URL: http://www.glazierjobs.net

Description: Serves as an online connection for glazier employment candidates and hiring managers. Enables job searching for those who seek employment and job posting for employers.

5649 ■ GlazierJobs.com
URL: http://www.glazierjobs.com

Description: Features a searchable database of job listings for glaziers. Enables job seekers to post their resumes.

5650 ■ IHireBuildingTrades
URL: http://www.ihirebuildingtrades.com

Description: Serves as a job posting board that specializes in matching building jobs and construction candidates.

TRADESHOWS

5651 ■ American Glass Guild Annual Conference
American Glass Guild
12 Washington Ave.
Runnemede, NJ 08078
E-mail: info@americanglassguild.org
URL: http://www.americanglassguild.org

Frequency: Annual. Features exhibits of artwork, books, glassware, tools, supplies and raw materials, painted and stained art glass panels, and more. Provides an open forum for the exchange of information on stained, leaded, and decorative glass and its creation preservation, restoration, and history.

5652 ■ Deco Seminar and Conference
Society of Glass and Ceramic Decorated Products
PO Box 2489
Zanesville, OH 43702
Ph: (740)588-9882
Fax: (740)588-0245
E-mail: info@sgcd.org
URL: http://www.sgcd.org

Frequency: Annual. Provides exhibits of dinnerware, glassware, beverage containers, cosmetic containers, tile, giftware, and promotional products.

5653 ■ Glass Art Society Conference
Glass Art Society
6512 23rd Ave. NW, Ste. 329
Seattle, WA 98117
Ph: (206)382-1305
Fax: (206)382-2630
E-mail: info@glassart.org
URL: http://www.glassart.org

Frequency: Annual. Brings together an international community of glass enthusiasts and artists from every discipline of glass (blowing, hot casting, kiln work, stained glass, flame working, beadmaking, cold work, and others). Gives opportunities for members to network with each other in various capacities: artists connect with gallery owners and others, collectors can meet their favorite artists, technical manufacturers and suppliers show customers the latest innovations.

5654 ■ National Glass Association Glazing Executives Forum
National Glass Association
1945 Old Gallows Rd., Ste. 750
Vienna, VA 22182
Ph: (703)442-4890
Free: 866-342-5642
Fax: (703)442-0630
E-mail: pjames@glass.org
URL: http://www.glass.org

Annual. 2013, Sept. 10; Atlanta, GA.

OTHER SOURCES

5655 ■ American Glass Guild
12 Washington Ave.
Runnemede, NJ 08078
E-mail: info@americanglassguild.org
URL: http://www.americanglassguild.org

Description: Represents individuals, students, senior advisors, and honorary members interested in decorative glass. Aims to advance knowledge by encouraging education, study, and research of all subjects related to the many disciplines covered by the term decorative glass. Promotes proficiency and skill by practitioners of these disciplines. Maintains a job board for employment opportunities in the industry.

5656 ■ Efficiency First
55 New Montgomery St., Ste. 802
San Francisco, CA 94105
Ph: (415)449-0551
Fax: (415)449-0559
E-mail: info@efficiencyfirst.org
URL: http://www.efficiencyfirst.org

Description: Advocates for policies that will create the foundation for a sustainable and scalable home retrofit market. Promotes the benefits of efficiency in retrofitting and helps meet industry demand for quality residential energy improvements.

5657 ■ Glass Association of North America
800 SW Jackson St., Ste. 1500
Topeka, KS 66612-1200
Ph: (785)271-0208
Fax: (785)271-0166
E-mail: gana@glasswebsite.com
URL: http://www.glasswebsite.com

Description: Represents independent glass distributors, contractors, and fabricators covering all flat glass products. Provides members with educational programs, publications, networking opportunities, meetings, and conventions.

5658 ■ Glass Manufacturing Industry Council
600 N Cleveland Ave., Ste. 210
Westerville, OH 43082
Ph: (614)818-9423
Fax: (614)818-9485
E-mail: rwlipetz@gmic.org
URL: http://www.gmic.org

Description: Represents the interests of glass manufacturers, suppliers, customers, and processors who are vital to the glass industry, as well as non-profit research institutes, universities, and affiliate members. Aims to facilitate, organize, and promote economic growth and sustainability of the glass industry through education and cooperation in the areas of technology, productivity, innovation, and the environment.

5659 ■ National Glass Association
1945 Old Gallows Rd., Ste. 750
Vienna, VA 22182
Ph: (703)442-4890
Free: 866-342-5642

Fax: (703)442-0630
E-mail: pjames@glass.org
URL: http://www.glass.org

Description: Manufacturers, installers, retailers, distributors and fabricators of flat, architectural, automotive and specialty glass and metal products, mirrors, shower and patio doors, windows and tabletops. Provides informational, educational and technical services.

5660 ■ Stained Glass Association of America
9313 E 63rd St.
Raytown, MO 64133

Ph: (816)737-2090
Free: 800-438-9581
Fax: (816)737-2801
E-mail: headquarters@sgaaonline.com
URL: http://stainedglass.org

Description: Studios, artist designers, and craft supply associates involved in the promotion of architectural stained, leaded, or faceted glass windows; affiliate members are students of the art. Seeks to advance awareness and appreciation of the craft, and to encourage the development of innovative techniques and artistic expression. Collects and disseminates documentary information on the stained glass trade.

SOURCES OF HELP-WANTED ADS

5661 ■ *ACM Transactions on Graphics*
Association for Computing Machinery
2 Penn Plz., Ste. 701
New York, NY 10121-0701
Ph: (212)626-0500
Free: 800-342-6626
Fax: (212)944-1318
E-mail: acmhelp@acm.org
URL: http://tog.acm.org/
Frequency: Quarterly. **Price:** $220 Nonmembers; $176 Nonmembers online; $264 Nonmembers online & print. **Description:** Computer graphics journal.

5662 ■ *Computer Graphics World*
PennWell Corp. - Advanced Technology Div.
c/o Karen Moltenbrey, Ed.-in-Ch.
620 W Elk Ave.
Glendale, CA 91204
Ph: (603)891-0123
Free: 800-225-0556
Fax: (603)891-9294
E-mail: atd@pennwell.com
URL: http://www.cgw.com
Frequency: Monthly. **Price:** $68 Individuals; $90 Canada; $105 Other countries; $126 Two years; $178 Canada 2 years; $205 Other countries 2 years; $12 Single issue. **Description:** Publication reporting on the use of modeling, animation, and multimedia in the areas of science and engineering, art and entertainment, and presentation and training.

5663 ■ *Creative Business*
URL: http://www.creativebusiness.com/newsletter
.lasso
Description: Nine issues/year. $149/year for electronic subscription. Provides business information for freelance graphic designers and studio principals.

5664 ■ *Design Perspectives*
Industrial Designers Society of America
555 Grove St., Ste. 200
Herndon, VA 20170-4728
Ph: (703)707-6000
Fax: (703)787-8501
E-mail: idsa@idsa.org
URL: http://www.idsa.org
Description: Ten issues/year. The largest newsletter examining the news and trends of industrial design. Recurring features include: new and cutting-edge products, news of people and events in industrial design, resource section, reports of chapter and national activities of IDSA, and a calendar of events.

5665 ■ *The Eagle*
Fitzpatrick Management Inc.
1522 Lilac Rd.
Charlotte, NC 28209
Ph: (704)334-2047

Fax: (704)334-0220
E-mail: robertf765@aol.com
URL: http://members.whattheythink.com/home/
theeagle.cfm
Description: Three issues/year. Serves as a publication about issues pertaining to dealer/manufacturer relations in the graphic arts industry. Recurring features include interviews, reports of meetings, and the analysis and interpretation of topical issues in North America and internationally.

5666 ■ *Fine Line*
Society of Engineering Illustrators
c/o Robert A. Clarke
1818 Englewood
Madison Heights, MI 48071
Ph: (810)588-2776
Frequency: 2-6/year. **Price:** included in membership dues. **Description:** Includes calendar of events, listing of employment opportunities, and membership directory update.

5667 ■ *Graphic Communicator*
Graphic Communications Conference of the
International Brotherhood of Teamsters
25 Louisiana Ave. NW
Washington, DC 20001-2130
Ph: (202)624-6800
E-mail: webmessenger@gciu.org
URL: http://www.gciu.org/
Frequency: Bimonthly; 5/yr. **Price:** $12 U.S. and Canada; $15 Other countries; $12/year. **Description:** Covers membership and trade union activities.

5668 ■ *Graphics Update*
Printing Association of Florida
6275 Hazeltine National Dr.
Orlando, FL 32822
Ph: (407)240-8009
Free: 800-749-4855
Fax: (407)240-8333
E-mail: agaither@pafgraf.org
URL: http://www.pafgraf.org
Description: Monthly. Concerned with developments within the field of graphic arts. Covers aspects of the industry with an emphasis on Florida, including news of exhibitions, statistics, new technologies and products, and events affecting the ancillary industries. Recurring features include letters to the editor, reports of meetings, news of educational opportunities, seminars, notices of publications available, news of members, and a calendar of events.

5669 ■ *I.D. Magazine*
FW Publications
38 E 29th St., Fl. 3
New York, NY 10016
Ph: (212)447-1400
Fax: (212)447-5231
E-mail: bookorders@krause.com
URLs: http://www.fwmagazines.com/category/id;
http://www.id-mag.com/

Frequency: 8/yr. **Price:** $30 Individuals; $45 Canada; $60 Other countries. **Description:** Magazine covering art, business and culture of design.

5670 ■ *IEEE Computer Graphics and Applications*
IEEE Computer Society
10662 Los Vaqueros Cir.
Los Alamitos, CA 90720-1314
Ph: (714)821-8380
Free: 800-272-6657
Fax: (714)821-4010
E-mail: cga-ma@computer.org
URL: http://www.computer.org/portal/web/cga
Frequency: Bimonthly. **Price:** $1,020 Individuals online; $1,065 Individuals print; $1,330 Individuals print and online. **Description:** Magazine addressing the interests and needs of professional designers and users of computer graphics hardware, software, and systems.

5671 ■ *Jobline News*
Graphic Artists Guild
32 Broadway, Ste. 1114
New York, NY 10004-1612
Ph: (212)791-3400
Fax: (212)791-0333
E-mail: admin@gag.org
URL: http://www.graphicartistsguild.org

Description: Weekly. Lists jobs for freelance and staff artists in areas such as graphic design, illustration, and art education. Lists jobs from across the country; quantity and locales vary weekly.

5672 ■ *SEGDesign*
Society for Environmental Graphic Design
1000 Vermont Ave. NW, Ste. 400
Washington, DC 20005
Ph: (202)638-5555
Fax: (202)638-0891
E-mail: segd@segd.org
URL: http://www.segd.org

Frequency: Quarterly. **Price:** $200 Individuals in U.S.; $275 Elsewhere. **Description:** Publication that covers environmental graphics, exhibit and industrial design, architecture, interiors, landscape architecture, and communication arts.

5673 ■ *TAGA Newsletter*
Technical Association of the Graphic Arts
200 Deer Run Rd.
Sewickley, PA 15143
Ph: (412)259-1706
Free: 800-910-4283
Fax: (412)259-1765
E-mail: mbohan@printing.org
URL: http://www.printing.org/taga

Description: Quarterly. Disseminates information in the graphic arts industry to members. Recurring features include interviews, news of research, reports of meetings, news of educational opportunities, and standards updates.

EMPLOYER DIRECTORIES AND NETWORKING LISTS

5674 ■ Printworld Directory of Contemporary Prints and Prices
Printworld International Inc.
PO Box 1957
West Chester, PA 19380
Ph: (610)431-6654
Free: 800-788-9101
Fax: (610)431-6653
URL: http://www.printworlddirectory.com/printworld
Frequency: Irregular; Latest edition 14th; 2013. **Price:** $250 Individuals regular price; $290 Canada; $330 Other countries. **Pages:** 650. **Includes:** Documentation on approximately 600,000 prints which have appeared in limited editions of no more than 500 and have a retail value of $100-1,000,000, and approximately 500 photos of recent & vintage prints. **Publication includes:** Biographical data on 5,000 international artists in contemporary printmaking; thousands of galleries who handle prints and hundreds of print publishers, and 600,000 print/price listings. **Entries include:** For artists--Name, address, personal and educational data, major exhibits, collections, publishers, printers, galleries, awards, teaching positions and documentation of prints. For galleries and publishers--Name, address. **Arrangement:** Alphabetical. **Indexes:** Artist name, printer/print workshop, publisher, gallery, art appraiser.

5675 ■ Society for Environmental Graphic Design-Messages
Society for Environmental Graphic Design
1000 Vermont Ave. NW, Ste. 400
Washington, DC 20005
Ph: (202)638-5555
Fax: (202)638-0891
E-mail: segd@segd.org
URL: http://www.segd.org/publications/messages.html
Description: Monthly. Reports on Society program news, member services, resources, and product news.

5676 ■ Who's Who in SGIA
Specialty Graphic Imaging Association
10015 Main St.
Fairfax, VA 22031-3489
Ph: (703)330-5600
Free: 888-385-3588
Fax: (703)273-0456
E-mail: sgia@sgia.org
URL: http://www.sgia.org
Frequency: Annual; August. **Pages:** 180. **Covers:** About 3,800 screen printers and graphic imaging companies, suppliers of screen printing equipment and graphic imaging materials, and investors in the Screen Printing Technical Foundation; international coverage. **Entries include:** Company name, address, phone, fax, e-mail, name of contact, products or services. **Arrangement:** Classified by type of business, then geographical. **Indexes:** Alphabetical by company, within state or country.

5677 ■ The Workbook
Workbook L.L.C.
6762 Lexington Ave.
Los Angeles, CA 90038
Ph: (323)856-0008
Free: 800-547-2688
Fax: (323)856-4368
E-mail: sales@workbook.com
URL: http://www.workbook.com
Frequency: Annual; Latest edition 2014. **Price:** $90 Individuals 2 volume set; $50 Individuals photography; $50 Individuals illustration; $695 Individuals. **Pages:** 800. **Covers:** 55,000 advertising agencies, art directors, photographers, freelance illustrators and designers, artists' representatives, interactive designers, pre-press services, and other graphic arts services in the U.S. **Entries include:** Company or individual name, address, phone, specialty. National in scope. **Arrangement:** Classified by product or service.

HANDBOOKS AND MANUALS

5678 ■ 100 Habits of Successful Graphic Designers: Insider Secrets on Working Smart and Staying Creative
Rockport Publishers Inc.
100 Cummings Ctr., Ste. 406-L
Beverly, MA 01915-6101
Ph: (978)282-9590
Fax: (978)283-2742
Description: Sarah Dougher and Josh Berger. 2005. $18.75. 192 pages. Designers from the graphic design, fashion, architecture, typography, and industrial design fields address topics ranging from deadlines, inspiration, competition, rules, respect, education, and criticism.

5679 ■ 2010 Artists and Graphic Designers Market
Writers Digest Books
4700 E Galbraith Rd.
Cincinnati, OH 45236
Ph: (513)531-2690
Free: 800-289-0963
Fax: (513)531-0798
URL: http://www.writersdigestshop.com/product/2010-artists-graphic-designers-market
Description: Mary Cox and Michael Schweer. 2010. $4.99. 576 pages.

5680 ■ All Access: The Making of Thirty Extraordinary Graphic Designers
Rockport Publishers Inc.
100 Cummings Ctr., Ste. 406-L
Beverly, MA 01915-6101
Ph: (978)282-9590
Fax: (978)283-2742
Description: Stefan G. Bucher. 2006. $25.00. 192 pages. Features the work of top graphic designers along with profiles of 20 newcomers.

5681 ■ Becoming a Graphic Designer
John Wiley & Sons, Inc.
1 Wiley Dr.
Somerset, NJ 08873
Free: 877-762-2974
Fax: (800)597-3299
E-mail: custserv@wiley.com
URL: http://www.wiley.com
Description: Steven Heller and Teresa Fernandes. Third edition, 2005. $35.00 (paper). 368 pages.

5682 ■ Career Opportunities in the Visual Arts
InfoBase Holdings Inc.
132 W 31st., 17 Fl.
New York, NY 10001-3406
Ph: (212)967-8800
Fax: (800)678-3633
E-mail: info@infobasepublishing.com
URL: http://www.ferguson.infobasepublishing.com
Description: 2006. $49.50. Covers over 65 profiles that include descriptions of certification, education, special skills, and trainings required.

5683 ■ The Education of a Graphic Designer
Allworth Press
307 W 36th St., 11th Fl.
New York, NY 10018
Ph: (212)643-6816
Free: 800-491-2808
Fax: (212)643-6819
E-mail: pub@allworth.com
URL: http://www.allworth.com
Description: Steven Heller, editor. Second edition, 2005. $29.95 (paper). 352 pages. Designers discuss how they acquired knowledge of design and then succeeded in applying this academic training to practical solutions in their careers.

5684 ■ Ferguson Career Coach: Managing Your Career in the Art Industry
InfoBase Holdings Inc.
132 W 31st., 17 Fl.
New York, NY 10001-3406
Ph: (212)967-8800
Fax: (800)678-3633
E-mail: info@infobasepublishing.com
URL: http://www.ferguson.infobasepublishing.com
Description: Shelly Field. 2008. $39.95 (hardcover). 304 pages. Contains tips for students who dream of a career as a graphic artist or an art gallery curator.

5685 ■ Fresh Dialogue 6: Friendly Fire
Princeton Architectural Press
37 E 7th St.
New York, NY 10003
Ph: (212)995-9620
Free: 800-759-0190
Fax: (212)995-9454
E-mail: sales@papress.com
URL: http://www.papress.com
Description: American Institute of Graphic Arts Staff. 2006. $16.95. 112 pages.

5686 ■ How to Survive and Prosper as an Artist: Selling Yourself Without Selling Your Soul
Holt Paperbacks
175 Fifth Ave.
New York, NY 10010
Ph: (646)307-5095
Free: 800-672-2054
Fax: (212)633-0748
URL: http://us.macmillan.com
Description: Caroll Michels. 6 edition, 2009. $21.99. 400 pages. Includes index and bibliographical references.

5687 ■ Opportunities in Arts and Crafts Careers
The McGraw-Hill Companies Inc.
PO Box 182604
Columbus, OH 43272
Ph: (212)512-2000
Free: 877-833-5524
Fax: (614)759-3749
E-mail: customer.service@mcgraw-hill.com
URL: http://www.mcgraw-hill.com
Description: Elizabeth Gardner. 2005. $13.95 (paper). 211 pages.

5688 ■ Opportunities in Visual Arts Careers
The McGraw-Hill Companies Inc.
PO Box 182604
Columbus, OH 43272
Ph: (212)512-2000
Free: 877-833-5524
Fax: (614)759-3749
E-mail: customer.service@mcgraw-hill.com
URL: http://www.mcgraw-hill.com
Description: Mark Salmon. 2008. $14.95 (paper). 160 pages. Points the way to a career in the visual arts, examining opportunities for designers, painters, sculptors, illustrators, animators, photographers, art therapists, educators, and others. Offers a view of the pros and cons of working for an art or design company or on your own.

5689 ■ Taking the Leap: Building a Career as a Visual Artist
Chronicle Books L.L.C.
680 2nd St.
San Francisco, CA 94107-2015
Ph: (415)537-4200

Free: 800-759-0190
E-mail: frontdesk@chroniclebooks.com
URL: http://www.chroniclebooks.com

Description: Cay Lang. 2006. $19.95. 256 pages.

EMPLOYMENT AGENCIES AND SEARCH FIRMS

5690 ■ Artisan Creative
1830 Stoner Ave., No. 6
Los Angeles, CA 90025
Ph: (310)312-2062
Fax: (310)312-0670
E-mail: lainfo@artisancreative.com
URL: http://www.artisancreative.com

Description: Serves as a network of designers, developers, account managers and production people providing companies with temporary staffing, full-time recruitment and project management solutions. Provides clients with the top creative resources to complete creative projects. Provides creative talent with opportunities to work for a variety of clients, in a number of roles, at locations around the country.

5691 ■ Artisan for Hire, Inc.
216 S Jefferson, Ste. 202
Chicago, IL 60661
Ph: (312)382-0200
Free: 800-216-0600
E-mail: chicago@artisantalent.com
URL: http://www.artisantalent.com

Description: Provides listings for jobs within the creative industry.

5692 ■ Brattle Temps
50 Congress St., Ste. 935
Boston, MA 02109-4008
Ph: (617)523-4600
E-mail: temps@brattletemps.com
URL: http://www.brattletemps.com

Description: Personnel consulting firm specializes in providing temporary consultants. Skill areas available include: Computer operators, secretaries, editors, librarians, graphic artists and marketing professionals. Industries served: universities, publishing, engineering, manufacturing and government agencies.

5693 ■ Caprio and Associates
1415 W 22nd St., Tower level
Oak Brook, IL 60523
Ph: (630)705-9101
Fax: (630)750-9102
E-mail: jerry@caprioassociates.com
URL: http://www.caprioassociates.com

Description: Executive search firm.

5694 ■ Cook Associates Inc.
212 W Kinzie St.
Chicago, IL 60610
Ph: (312)329-0900
Fax: (312)329-1528
URL: http://www.cookassociates.com

Description: Management and executive recruiting specialists offering a commitment to clients to find the candidates and to find those candidates as efficiently as possible. Approach provides a flexible and effective structure that serves the special needs of both large and small companies. Serves the following industries: industrial, equipment manufacturer, food processing, graphic arts, chemical process, retailing, mechanical products, health care services, financial and professional services, legal, consumer products, construction and engineering, packaging, pulp and paper.

5695 ■ Creative Talent Source
10 S Riverside Plz., Ste. 1800
Chicago, IL 60606
Ph: (312)238-9004

Free: 866-536-4719
E-mail: info@creativetalentsource.com
URL: http://creativetalentsource.com

Description: Provides professionals for design, writing and creative project management whether for print, web or multimedia. Specializes in freelance and full time placement of Chicago-area creative talent.

5696 ■ FILTER, LLC
1505 5th Ave., Ste. 600
Seattle, WA 98101
Ph: (206)682-6005
URL: http://www.filterdigital.com

Description: Serves as creative resources company that provides talent in web, marketing, and creative professions. Represents virtually every discipline: designers, copywriters, web architects, icon artists, illustrators, animators, and other specialized artistic and technological talents.

5697 ■ Graphic Arts Employment Specialists, Inc.
409 Pacific Coast Hwy., Ste. 455
Redondo Beach, CA 90277
Free: 888-499-9722
Fax: (310)937-3760
E-mail: info@gaes.com
URL: http://www.gaes.com

Description: Employment agency specializing in the publishing and packaging industries.

5698 ■ LandaJob Advertising Staffing Specialists
222 W Gregory Blvd., Ste. 304
Kansas City, MO 64114
Ph: (816)523-1881
Free: 800-931-8806
Fax: (816)523-1876
E-mail: adstaff@landajobnow.com
URL: http://www.landajobnow.com

Description: Personnel consultants and recruiters for advertising, marketing, and communications positions. Industries served: advertising, communications, marketing, graphic arts, printing and publishing.

5699 ■ Lloyd Staffing
445 Broadhollow Rd., Ste. 119
Melville, NY 11747
Ph: (631)777-7600
Free: 888-292-6678
Fax: (631)777-7626
E-mail: info@lloydstaffing.com
URL: http://www.lloydstaffing.com

Description: Personnel agency and search firm.

5700 ■ Printemps
18 Avery Pl.
Westport, CT 06880
Ph: (203)226-6869
Fax: (203)226-1594

Description: Specializes in providing temporary support for graphic design, document management and the electronic printing industry. Provides permanent placement for professionals and production personnel. Consults with printers and in-house print shops for greater production efficiency. Handles personnel management and policy programs as well. Industries served: printing, advertising, manufacturing, insurance, banking and government agencies.

5701 ■ Semper, LLC
607 Bolyston St., 3rd Fl.
Boston, MA 02116
Free: 800-954-4993
E-mail: dhresumes1@semperllc.com
URL: http://www.semperllc.com

Description: Serves as a placement firm in the graphic arts and printing industry. Specializes in the print, copy and digital industries. Offers several staffing options such as flexible, permanent, flex-to-hire and direct. Offers outplacement service that provides professional career management assistance and

counseling to employees who are facing a career change.

5702 ■ TECHEAD
111 N 17th St.
Richmond, VA 23219
Ph: (804)782-6971
Free: 877--
Fax: (804)782-2033
E-mail: info@techead.com
URL: http://www.techead.com

Description: Offers creative and IT staffing services for both job seekers and employers. Provides graphics support and desktop publishing services to local clients. Provides creative talent and information technology staffing services, ADOBE product software training, and creative web development solutions to clients.

ONLINE JOB SOURCES AND SERVICES

5703 ■ ArtJob Online
URL: http://www.artjob.org

Description: Contains up-to-date national and international listings of arts employment and related opportunities in the arts: full- and part-time employment, internships, grants, public art projects, and residencies. User can search by region, art discipline, type of organization. Fee: Subscribers pay $25 for 3 months, $40 for six months and $75 for one year.

5704 ■ Creative Hotlist
URL: http://www.creativehotlist.com

Description: Career site for professionals in the web design and graphic design fields. Enables individuals and companies to find resources for any aspect of the creative marketplace including job openings, creative services, artists, designers, programmers, printers, service bureaus, schools and clubs.

5705 ■ GetGigs.com
URL: http://www.getgigs.com

Description: Seeks to provide an on-line experience for creative types, performing artists, and musicians around the world by integrating internet technologies into a one-stop information resource. Also functions as a creative directory and talent network.

5706 ■ Graphic Artists Guild
URL: http://www.graphicartistsguild.org

Description: JOBLine News section of Guild Resources page contains weekly e-mail newsletter of job listings. Fee: Must subscribe to e-mail newsletter non-member six-month rates start at $80. Visitors may download a free sample.

5707 ■ GraphicArtistDesigner.com
URL: http://www.graphicartistdesigner.com

Description: Connects business professionals with the information and professional contacts needed to advance a career in graphic design. Provides access to books, magazines, articles and continuing education.

5708 ■ PrintJobs.com
URL: http://www.printjobs.com

Description: Aims to find suitable graphic arts jobs for qualified candidates. Over a hundred jobs are maintained and updated on the site. Fee: Must be paid by employers using the site; no registration charge for job hunters.

5709 ■ You the Designer
URL: http://www.youthedesigner.com

Description: Serves as an online career resource that contains a graphic design blog, graphic design tips and graphic design job openings.

TRADESHOWS

5710 ■ Graph Expo and Converting Expo
Graphic Arts Show Co.
1899 Preston White Dr.
Reston, VA 20191-5468
Ph: (703)264-7200
Fax: (703)620-9187
E-mail: info@gasc.org
URL: http://www.gasc.org

Frequency: Annual. **Primary Exhibits:** Graphic art equipment, supplies, and services. Printing, publishing, and converting equipment.

5711 ■ Graphic Arts/Awards Exhibition
Association of Graphic Communications
330 7th Ave., 9th Fl.
New York, NY 10001-5010
Ph: (212)279-2100
Fax: (212)279-5381
E-mail: info@agcomm.org
URL: http://www.agcomm.org

Frequency: Annual. **Primary Exhibits:** A network for industry information and idea exchange; a provider for graphic arts education and training; a vehicle for industry promotion and marketing; an advocate on legislative and environmental issues and a source for bottom-line savings for the benefit of its New York/New Jersey membership.

5712 ■ Graphics of the Americas
Printing Association of Florida
6275 Hazeltine National Dr.
Orlando, FL 32822
Ph: (407)240-8009
Free: 800-749-4855
Fax: (407)240-8333
E-mail: agaither@pafgraf.org
URL: http://www.pafgraf.org

Frequency: Annual. **Primary Exhibits:** Graphic arts and specialty printing equipment, supplies, and services.

5713 ■ MediaXchange
Newspaper Association of America
4401 Wilson Blvd., Ste. 900
Arlington, VA 22203-1867
Ph: (571)366-1000
Free: 800-656-4622
Fax: (571)366-1195
E-mail: membsvc@naa.org
URL: http://www.naa.org

Frequency: Annual. **Primary Exhibits:** Newspaper publishing graphic arts systems and equipment and electronic publishing, ranging from computerized systems to newspaper presses to post press systems.

5714 ■ National Federation of Press Women Conference
National Federation of Press Women
200 Little Falls St., Ste.405
Falls Church, VA 22046
Ph: (703)237-9804
Free: 800-780-2715
Fax: (703)237-9808
E-mail: presswomen@aol.com
URL: http://www.nfpw.org

Frequency: Annual. Features speakers as well as other activities, workshops, resources, and networking opportunities.

5715 ■ Society for News Design Annual Workshop & Exhibition
Society for News Design
424 E Central Blvd., Ste. 406
Orlando, FL 32801
Ph: (407)420-7748
Fax: (407)420-7697
E-mail: skomives@snd.org
URL: http://www.snd.org

Frequency: Annual. Gathers visual journalists from around the world for workshops and general sessions.

OTHER SOURCES

5716 ■ Advertising Production Club of New York
Euro RSCG Life, 7th Fl.
200 Madison Ave.
New York, NY 10016
Ph: (212)251-7295
Fax: (212)726-5057
E-mail: admin@apc-ny.org
URL: http://www.apc-nyc.org

Description: Production and traffic department personnel from advertising agencies, corporate or retail advertising departments, and publishing companies; college level graphic arts educators. Meetings include educational programs on graphic arts procedures and plant tours. Maintains employment service for members.

5717 ■ American Artists Professional League
47 5th Ave.
New York, NY 10003
Ph: (212)645-1345
Fax: (212)792-2275
E-mail: office@aaplinc.org
URL: http://www.americanartistsprofessionalleague .org

Description: Advances the cause of fine arts in America through the promotion of high standards of beauty, integrity and craftsmanship in painting, sculpture and the graphic arts.

5718 ■ American Institute of Graphic Arts
164 5th Ave.
New York, NY 10010-5901
Ph: (212)807-1990
Fax: (212)807-1799
URL: http://www.aiga.org

Description: Graphic designers, art directors, illustrators and packaging designers. Sponsors exhibits and projects in the public interest. Sponsors traveling exhibitions. Operates gallery. Maintains library of design books and periodicals; offers slide archives.

5719 ■ Art Directors Club
106 W 29th St.
New York, NY 10001
Ph: (212)643-1440
Fax: (212)643-4266
E-mail: info@adcglobal.org
URL: http://www.adcglobal.org

Description: Art directors of advertising magazines and agencies, visual information specialists, and graphic designers; associate members are artists, cinematographers, photographers, copywriters, educators, journalists, and critics. Promotes and stimulates interest in the practice of art direction. Sponsors Annual Exhibition of Advertising, Editorial and Television Art and Design; International Traveling Exhibition. Provides educational, professional, and entertainment programs; on-premise art exhibitions; portfolio review program. Conducts panels for students and faculty. **Members:** 1,100.

5720 ■ Design Management Institute
38 Chauncy St., Ste. 800
Boston, MA 02111
Ph: (617)338-6380
Fax: (617)338-6570
E-mail: dmistaff@dmi.org
URL: http://www.dmi.org

Description: In-house design groups and consultant design firms; individuals involved in the management of designers with in-house corporate design groups or consultant design firms. Aims to share management techniques as applied to design groups, and to facilitate better understanding by business management of the role design can play in achieving business goals. Design disciplines included are: architecture, advertising, communications, exhibit design, graphics, interior design, packaging and product design. Develops and distributes design management education materials. Sponsors seminars for design professionals. Identifies critical areas of design management study; conducts surveys and research on corporate design management. Maintains design management archive. Operates Center for Research, Center for Education, and Center for Design and Management Resources.

5721 ■ Gravure Education Foundation
PO Box 25617
Rochester, NY 14625
Ph: (201)523-6042
Fax: (201)523-6048
E-mail: gaa@gaa.org
URL: http://www.gaa.org/gravure-education -foundation

Description: Aims to establish gravure curricula with graphic arts educational facilities at all educational levels; provides financial assistance to students; develops new resources for conducting educational programs; encourages postgraduate projects and research within the graphic arts; provides career orientation at the high school level; provides for internships throughout the gravure industry. Seeks to serve as a catalyst within the framework of established institutions and to provide encouragement to enterprising individuals.

5722 ■ International Association of Printing House Craftsmen
PO Box 2549
Maple Grove, MN 55311-7549
Ph: (763)560-1620
Free: 800-466-4274
Fax: (763)560-1350
E-mail: headquarters@iaphc.org
URL: http://www.iaphc.org

Description: Individuals world-wide employed or interested in any facet of the graphic arts. Conducts field trips; maintains speakers' bureau; sponsors educational programs. Sponsors International Printing Week and International Gallery of Superb Printing. **Members:** 6,000.

5723 ■ International Graphic Arts Education Association
1899 Preston White Dr.
Reston, VA 20191-4367
Ph: (703)758-0595
E-mail: mzarzycka@uh.edu
URL: http://www.igaea.org

Description: Graphic arts and printing teachers. Develops an integrated and comprehensive system of graphic arts education in schools and colleges of the U.S. Assists organizations in arranging lectures or other programs relating to graphic arts. Sponsors annual Graphic Communications Week; Visual Communication Journal; conducts research programs.

5724 ■ National Federation of Press Women
200 Little Falls St., Ste.405
Falls Church, VA 22046
Ph: (703)237-9804
Free: 800-780-2715
Fax: (703)237-9808
E-mail: presswomen@aol.com
URL: http://www.nfpw.org

Description: Serves as a group of professional women and men pursuing careers across the communications spectrum.

5725 ■ Organization of Women Architects and Design Professionals
PO Box 10078
Berkeley, CA 94709
E-mail: info@owa-usa.org
URL: http://owa-usa.org

Description: Comprised of architects, interior designers, landscape architects, planners, lighting designers, graphic designers, photographers, artists, writers, educators and students. Strives to improve the professional standing of women in architecture and design-related fields. Advocates young women and students entering design related fields through mentoring, education, and employment opportunities.

5726 ■ Photo Imaging Education Association
3000 Picture Pl.
Jackson, MI 49201
Ph: (517)788-8100
Fax: (517)788-8371
E-mail: nshaver@pmai.org
URL: http://pieapma.com/cms

Description: Represents photo imaging education practitioners and students. Builds a network where educators and students can create resources, solve problems and discuss issues relating to photo industry. Inspires members to be successful and to become better teachers of photo imaging.

5727 ■ Society of American Graphic Artists
32 Union Sq., Rm. 1214
New York, NY 10003
E-mail: sagaprints@verizon.net
URL: http://sagaprints.org

Description: Workers in the print media (etching, lithography, engraving, woodcut, wood engraving);

also offers associate membership. Sponsors exhibitions and traveling shows. **Members:** 250.

5728 ■ Society for News Design
424 E Central Blvd., Ste. 406
Orlando, FL 32801
Ph: (407)420-7748
Fax: (407)420-7697
E-mail: skomives@snd.org
URL: http://www.snd.org

Description: Comprised of editors, designers, graphic artists, publishers, illustrators, art directors, photographers, advertising artists, website designers, students and faculty. Encourages high standards of journalism through design. Serves as a forum and resource for all those interested in news design.

5729 ■ Technical Association of the Graphic Arts
200 Deer Run Rd.
Sewickley, PA 15143
Ph: (412)259-1706
Free: 800-910-4283
Fax: (412)259-1765
E-mail: mbohan@printing.org
URL: http://www.printing.org/taga

Description: Professional society of individuals interested in or engaged in research or technical control of graphic arts processes or related

industries. Promotes advanced technical study and research in the graphic arts.

5730 ■ Type Directors Club
347 W 36th St., Ste. 603
New York, NY 10018
Ph: (212)633-8943
Fax: (212)633-8944
E-mail: director@tdc.org
URL: http://tdc.org

Description: Serves as a professional society of typographic designers, type directors, and teachers of typography; sustaining members are individuals with interests in typographic education. Seeks to stimulate research and disseminate information. Provides speakers, classes and offers presentations on history and new developments in typography. **Members:** 700.

5731 ■ Typophiles
PO Box 3888
New York, NY 10163-3888
E-mail: info@typophiles.org
URL: http://www.typophiles.org

Description: Represents designers, printers, book collectors, artists, calligraphers, private press owners, wood engravers, librarians and others interested in graphic arts. Promotes the love and appreciation of fine graphic design and printing. Conducts quarterly meeting-luncheons and maintains publications. **Members:** 300.

Sources of Help-Wanted Ads

5732 ■ Drinking Water & Backflow Prevention
International Association of Plumbing and Mechanical Officials
4755 E Philadelphia St.
Ontario, CA 91761
Ph: (909)472-4100
Fax: (909)472-4150
E-mail: iapmo@iapmo.org
URLs: http://www.dwbp-online.com.; http://www.iap-modwbp.org

Krystal Renea Garza, Editor. **Frequency:** Monthly. **Price:** $45, U.S. year; $53 Canada and Mexico.; $59, elsewhere year. **Description:** Monthly. $45.00/year. Recurring features include news of educational opportunities, job listings, and a calendar of events.

5733 ■ EHS Today: The Magazine of Safety, Health and Loss Prevention
Intertec Publishing
5 Penn Plz., 13th Fl.
New York, NY 10001-1810
Ph: (212)613-9700
Free: 800-795-5445
Fax: (212)613-9749
E-mail: bethany.weaver@penton.com
URL: http://ehstoday.com/

Frequency: Monthly. **Description:** Monthly publication for safety professionals featuring information to meet OSHA and EPA compliance requirements, improve management of safety, industrial hygiene and environmental programs and find products and services to protect employees and property.

5734 ■ Industrial Hygiene News
Rimbach Publishing Inc.
8650 Babcock Blvd.
Pittsburgh, PA 15237
Ph: (412)364-5366
Free: 800-245-3182
E-mail: info@rimbach.com
URL: http://www.rimbach.com

Frequency: Bimonthly. **Description:** Magazine covering industrial hygiene, occupational health, and safety.

5735 ■ Onsite Installer
COLE Publishing Inc.
1720 Maple Lake Dam Rd.
Three Lakes, WI 54562
Free: 800-257-7222
Fax: (715)546-3786
E-mail: info@onsiteinstaller.com
URL: http://www.onsiteinstaller.com/

Frequency: Monthly. **Price:** $80 Other countries; Free; $150 Other countries 2 years. **Description:** Magazine that offers information for professionals who design and install septic systems and other on-site wastewater treatment systems serving single-family homes, small businesses, and small communities.

5736 ■ Operations Forum
Water Environment Federation
601 Wythe St.
Alexandria, VA 22314-1994
Free: 800-666-0206
Fax: (703)684-2492
E-mail: inquiry@wef.org
URL: http://www.wef.org

Frequency: Monthly. **Price:** $79 Nonmembers. **Description:** Magazine covering operation/maintenance of WWTPs and wastewater collections systems.

5737 ■ Pollution Engineering
BNP Media
2401 W Big Beaver Rd., Ste. 700
Troy, MI 48084
Ph: (248)362-3700
Free: 800-952-6643
Fax: (248)362-5103
E-mail: pe@halldata.com
URL: http://www.pollutionengineering.com/

Description: Magazine focusing on pollution control, air, water, solid waste, and toxic/hazardous waste.

5738 ■ Pollution Equipment News
Rimbach Publishing Inc.
8650 Babcock Blvd.
Pittsburgh, PA 15237
Ph: (412)364-5366
Free: 800-245-3182
E-mail: info@rimbach.com
URL: http://www.rimbach.com/RimPub/PEN/PEN.htm

Frequency: Bimonthly. **Description:** Pollution control equipment and products magazine (tabloid).

5739 ■ Public Works
DoveTale Publishers
1 Thomas Cir. NW
Washington, DC 20005
Ph: (202)339-0744
Free: 877-275-8647
Fax: (202)785-1974
E-mail: hwmicustomerservice@hanleywood.com
URL: http://www.pwmag.com

Frequency: 13/yr. **Price:** $60 Individuals; $75 Canada; $90 Other countries. **Description:** Trade magazine covering the public works industry nationwide for city, county, and state.

5740 ■ Stormwater
Forester Communications Inc.
5638 Hollister No. 301
Santa Barbara, CA 93117
Ph: (805)681-1300
Fax: (805)681-1312
E-mail: publisher@erosioncontrol.net
URL: http://www.stormh2o.com

Frequency: 8/yr. **Price:** $79 Individuals; $95 Canada; $160 Other countries. **Description:** Journal devoted to surface water quality professionals.

5741 ■ Waste & Recycling News
Crain Communications Inc.
1155 Gratiot Ave.
Detroit, MI 48207-2732
Ph: (313)446-6000
E-mail: info@crain.com
URL: http://www.wasterecyclingnews.com

Description: Biweekly. Tabloid newspaper published for environmental managers. Features report on the generation and handling of solid and hazardous waste and the management of wastewater and air pollution. Provides classified advertising that includes professional recruiters, help wanted, requests for proposals, new and used equipment, containers, safety supplies, equipment leasing, balers, landfill products and services, recycling and MRF equipment, shredders, business opportunities and computer and software services.

5742 ■ Water & Wastes Digest
Scranton Gillette Communications Inc.
3030 W Salt Creek Ln., Ste. 201
Arlington Heights, IL 60005-5025
Ph: (847)391-1000
Fax: (847)390-0408
E-mail: hgillette@sgcmail.com
URL: http://www.wwdmag.com

Frequency: Monthly. **Description:** Magazine (tabloid) featuring product news for decision makers in the municipal and industrial water and water pollution control industries.

Employer Directories and Networking Lists

5743 ■ Hazardous Waste Consultant--Directory of Commercial Hazardous Waste Management Facilities Issue
URL: http://www.info.sciencedirect.com

Frequency: Semiannual. **Publication includes:** List of 170 licensed commercial facilities that treat and/or dispose of hazardous waste in North America. **Entries include:** Facility name, address, phone, contact name, type of waste handled, methods of on-site treatment and/or disposal, Environmental Protection Agency permit status and identification number, restrictions, description of other services. **Arrangement:** Geographical. **Indexes:** Organization name.

5744 ■ Who's Who in Environmental Engineering
American Academy of Environmental Engineers and Scientists
130 Holiday Ct., Ste. 100
Annapolis, MD 21401
Ph: (410)266-3311

Fax: (410)266-7653
E-mail: info@aaees.org
URL: http://www.aaee.net/Website/WhosWho.htm

Frequency: Annual; Latest edition 2011. **Price:** $75 Individuals plus $5.75 shipping and handling payment with order. **Covers:** About 2,400 licensed professional environmental engineers that have been certified by examination in one or more of seven specialties: air pollution control, general environmental engineering, industrial hygiene, hazardous waste management, radiation protection, solid waste management, water supply and wastewater. **Entries include:** Name, affiliation, address, phone, area of specialization, biographical data. **Arrangement:** Alphabetical, geographical, area of specialization.

EMPLOYMENT AGENCIES AND SEARCH FIRMS

5745 ■ The Energists Inc.
10260 Westheimer, Ste. 300
Houston, TX 77042
Ph: (713)781-6881
Fax: (713)781-2998
E-mail: search@energists.com
URL: http://www.energists.com

Description: Executive search firm.

5746 ■ Search Consultants International, Inc.
701 N Post Oak Rd., Ste. 610
Houston, TX 77024
Ph: (713)622-9188
E-mail: info@searchconsultants.com
URL: http://www.searchconsultants.com

Description: Management executive search firm.

ONLINE JOB SOURCES AND SERVICES

5747 ■ Bright Green Talent - Green Jobs
URL: http://www.brightgreentalent.com/green-jobs

Description: Serves as online tool that offers green jobs listing and career advice to candidates interested and engaged in environmental career.

5748 ■ Diversity Environmental Jobs
URL: http://www.diversityenvironmentaljobs.com

Description: Serves as a niche job board that provides diverse environmental career opportunities.

5749 ■ Environmental Jobs
URL: http://environmental.jobs4.org

Description: Offers a searchable database of environmental job opportunities available throughout the United States.

OTHER SOURCES

5750 ■ Air and Waste Management Association
1 Gateway Ctr., 3rd Fl.
420 Fort Duquesne Blvd.
Pittsburgh, PA 15222-1435
Ph: (412)232-3444
Free: 800-270-3444
Fax: (412)232-3450
E-mail: info@awma.org
URL: http://www.awma.org

Description: Serves as environmental, educational, and technical organization. Seeks to provide a neutral forum for the exchange of technical information on a wide variety of environmental topics.

5751 ■ American Academy of Environmental Engineers and Scientists
130 Holiday Ct., Ste. 100
Annapolis, MD 21401
Ph: (410)266-3311
Fax: (410)266-7653
E-mail: info@aaees.org
URL: http://www.aaees.org

Description: Environmentally oriented registered professional engineers certified by examination as Diplomates of the Academy. Seeks to improve the standards of environmental engineering. Certifies those with special knowledge of environmental engineering. Furnishes lists of those certified to the public. Maintains speakers' bureau. Recognizes areas of specialization: Air Pollution Control; General Environmental; Hazardous Waste Management; Industrial Hygiene; Radiation Protection; Solid Waste Management; Water Supply and Wastewater. Requires written and oral examinations for certification. Works with other professional organizations on environmentally oriented activities. Identifies potential employment candidates through Talent Search Service.

5752 ■ National Waste and Recycling Association
4301 Connecticut Ave. NW, Ste. 300
Washington, DC 20008-2304
Ph: (202)244-4700
Free: 800-424-2869
Fax: (202)966-4818
E-mail: skneiss@envasns.org
URL: http://www.environmentalistseveryday.org

Description: Manufacturers, designers, and distributors of waste collection, treatment, and storage equipment; waste handling consultants. Promotes effective processing of solid and hazardous wastes

and more extensive use of recycling. Represents members' interests; conducts research and educational programs; maintains hall of fame; compiles statistics.

5753 ■ Spill Control Association of America
103 Oronoco St., Ste. 200
Alexandria, VA 22314
Ph: (571)451-0433
E-mail: info@scaa-spill.org
URL: http://www.scaa-spill.org

Description: Third party contractors; manufacturers or suppliers of pollution control and containment equipment; individuals in private or governmental capacities involved with spill clean-up and containment operations; associate companies. Aims to provide information on the oil and hazardous material emergency response and remediation industry's practices, trends, and achievements; to establish liaison with local, state and federal government agencies responsible for laws and regulations regarding pollution caused by oil and hazardous materials; to cooperate in the development of industry programs and efforts so that pollutants are properly controlled and removed from land and water. Provides certification for hazardous material technicians. Maintains Spill Control Institute, Technical Services Division; collects and disseminates educational and technical information. Operates speakers' bureau; conducts research. Maintains placement service.

5754 ■ Water Environment Federation
601 Wythe St.
Alexandria, VA 22314-1994
Free: 800-666-0206
Fax: (703)684-2492
E-mail: inquiry@wef.org
URL: http://www.wef.org

Description: Technical societies representing chemists, biologists, ecologists, geologists, operators, educational and research personnel, industrial wastewater engineers, consultant engineers, municipal officials, equipment manufacturers, and university professors and students dedicated to the enhancement and preservation of water quality and resources. Seeks to advance fundamental and practical knowledge concerning the nature, collection, treatment, and disposal of domestic and industrial wastewaters, and the design, construction, operation, and management of facilities for these purposes. Disseminates technical information; and promotes good public relations and regulations that improve water quality and the status of individuals working in this field. Conducts educational and research programs.

Sources of Help-Wanted Ads

5755 ■ *Perspectives on Medical Education*
Springer Publishing Co.
11 W 42nd St., 15th Fl.
New York, NY 10036
Ph: (212)431-4370
Free: 877-687-7476
Fax: (212)941-7842
E-mail: cs@springerpub.com
URL: http://www.springerpub.com

Description: Journal containing information about different perspectives in medical education. Presents research and studies on medical education. Serves as a reference for health care professionals.

5756 ■ *Public Health Education and Health Promotion Newsletters*
American Public Health Association
800 I St. NW
Washington, DC 20001-3710
Ph: (202)777-2742
Fax: (202)777-2534
E-mail: comments@apha.org
URL: http://www.apha.org/membergroups/newsletters/sectionnewsletters/public_edu

Description: Quarterly Publication. Serves as the official newsletter of the American Public Health Association. Contains news, updates, and information about the association.

Handbooks and Manuals

5757 ■ *AADE in Practice*
American Association of Diabetes Educators
200 W Madison St., Ste. 800
Chicago, IL 60606
Free: 800-338-3633
Fax: (312)424-2427
E-mail: membership@aadenet.org
URL: http://www.diabeteseducator.org/ProfessionalResources/Periodicals/Practice

Frequency: Bimonthly. **Description:** Publishes practical tools and strategies that directly apply current research and best practices in diabetes self-management education. Contains informative resources that help inspire, educate and empower diabetes educators.

5758 ■ *Achieving Excellence in Nursing Education*
National League for Nursing
61 Broadway, 33rd Fl.
New York, NY 10006
Ph: (212)812-0300
Free: 800-669-1656
Fax: (212)812-0391
E-mail: generalinfo@nln.org
URL: http://www.nln.org

Price: $39.96 Softbound. **Description:** Marsha Adams and Theresa Valiga. 2012. 208 pages. Describes the elements that guide nurse educators in achieving excellence in nursing education. Includes self-assessment checklist for faculty.

5759 ■ *Building a Science of Nursing Education: Foundation for Evidence-Based Teaching and Learning*
National League for Nursing
61 Broadway, 33rd Fl.
New York, NY 10006
Ph: (212)812-0300
Free: 800-669-1656
Fax: (212)812-0391
E-mail: generalinfo@nln.org
URL: http://www.nln.org

Price: $39.96 Softbound. **Description:** Cathleen Shultz. 2012. 360 pages. Presents teaching and learning strategies to assist nurse educators in practicing evidence-based nursing education.

5760 ■ *Certification Examination for Diabetes Educators Handbook*
National Certification Board for Diabetes Educators
330 E Algonquin Rd., Ste. 4
Arlington Heights, IL 60005
Ph: (847)228-9795
Fax: (847)228-8469
E-mail: info@ncbde.org
URL: http://www.ncbde.org/certification_info/examination-handbook

Frequency: Latest edition 2013. **Description:** Provides information and guidance to individuals who will take the diabetes educator certification examination.

5761 ■ *Certification Examination for Health Education Specialists*
National Learning Corporation
212 Michael Dr.
Syosset, NY 11791
Ph: (516)921-8888
Free: 800-632-8888
Fax: (516)921-8743
E-mail: info@passbooks.com
URL: http://www.passbooks.com

Price: $39.95 Paperback. **Description:** 2010. Provides information and guidance to candidates who are preparing for the Certified Health Education Specialists Examination.

5762 ■ *Certified Diabetes Educator Exam Secrets Study Guide*
Mometrix Media, LLC
3827 Phelan Blvd., No. 179
Beaumont, TX 77707
Free: 800-673-8175
Fax: (866)235-0173
E-mail: css@mometrix.com
URL: http://www.mo-media.com

Price: $43.98 Includes shipping and handling.

Description: 2010. Provides step-by-step test study guide to succeed on the Certified Diabetes Educator Exam. Includes practice test questions.

5763 ■ *Certified Nurse Educator (CNE) Examination Candidate Handbook*
National League for Nursing
61 Broadway, 33rd Fl.
New York, NY 10006
Ph: (212)812-0300
Free: 800-669-1656
Fax: (212)812-0391
E-mail: generalinfo@nln.org
URL: http://www.nln.org/certification/handbook/index.htm

Frequency: Revised, October 2012. **Description:** Provides complete information about the Certified Nurse Educator (CNE)Examination, including test dates and application deadlines, eligibility requirements, test formats, test blueprints, exam preparation, recommended references, sample questions, certification fees, Assessment Center locations, examination administration, test score information, policies, and special forms.

5764 ■ *Certified Nurse Educator (CNE) Review Manual*
Springer Publishing Co.
11 W 42nd St., 15th Fl.
New York, NY 10036
Ph: (212)431-4370
Free: 877-687-7476
Fax: (212)941-7842
E-mail: cs@springerpub.com
URL: http://www.springerpub.com

Price: $62 Softcover. **Description:** Ruth Wittmann-Price, Maryann Godshall and Linda Wilson. Second Edition, 2013. 436 pages. Offers a systematic approach to preparing for the CNE Certification Examination. Contains case studies, tips for test success, review questions, and practice tests.

5765 ■ *Certified Nurse Educator Exam Secrets Study Guide*
Mometrix Media, LLC
3827 Phelan Blvd., No. 179
Beaumont, TX 77707
Free: 800-673-8175
Fax: (866)235-0173
E-mail: css@mometrix.com
URL: http://www.mo-media.com

Price: $53.98 Includes shipping and handling. **Description:** 2011. Provides step-by-step test study guide to succeed on the Certified Nurse Educator Exam. Includes practice test questions.

5766 ■ *CHES Exam Secrets Study Guide*
Mometrix Media, LLC
3827 Phelan Blvd., No. 179
Beaumont, TX 77707
Free: 800-673-8175

Fax: (866)235-0173
E-mail: css@mometrix.com
URL: http://www.mo-media.com

Price: $53.98 Includes shipping and handling.
Description: 2011. Provides tips and information that are specially selected to prepare and achieve best results on the Certified Health Education Specialist (CHES) Exam. Includes practice test questions.

5767 ■ Clinical Nurse Leader Certification Review

Springer Publishing Co.
11 W 42nd St., 15th Fl.
New York, NY 10036
Ph: (212)431-4370
Free: 877-687-7476
Fax: (212)941-7842
E-mail: cs@springerpub.com
URL: http://www.springerpub.com

Price: $45 Softcover. **Description:** Cynthia R. King and Sally Gerard. 2012. 372 pages. Covers all aspects of test derived from the AACN exam guide.

5768 ■ Clinical Nursing Education: Current Reflections

National League for Nursing
61 Broadway, 33rd Fl.
New York, NY 10006
Ph: (212)812-0300
Free: 800-669-1656
Fax: (212)812-0391
E-mail: generalinfo@nln.org
URL: http://www.nln.org

Price: $39.96 Softbound. **Description:** Nell Ard and Theresa M. Valiga. 2012. Discusses the essential core of nursing education and helps examine the impact of new models for clinical education in an increasingly complex environment of health care delivery.

5769 ■ Clinical Teaching Strategies in Nursing

Springer Publishing Co.
11 W 42nd St., 15th Fl.
New York, NY 10036
Ph: (212)431-4370
Free: 877-687-7476
Fax: (212)941-7842
E-mail: cs@springerpub.com
URL: http://www.springerpub.com

Price: $69 Softcover. **Description:** Kathleen Gaberson and Marilyn Oermann. Third Edition, 2010. 456 pages. Presents clinical teaching strategies for undergraduate and graduate nursing students and that are effective and practical in a rapidly changing health care environment.

5770 ■ The Clinician-Educator's Handbook

Association of American Medical Colleges
2450 N St. NW
Washington, DC 20037-1126
Ph: (202)828-0400
Fax: (202)828-1125
E-mail: amcas@aamc.org
URL: http://www.mededportal.org/publication/7749

Frequency: Published September, 2010. **Description:** Addresses a wide variety of issues of clinical education. Helps the clinician-educator improve their teaching skills.

5771 ■ Community Health Education: Settings, Roles, and Skills

Jones & Bartlett Learning
5 Wall St.
Burlington, MA 01803
Free: 800-832-0034
E-mail: info@jblearning.com
URL: http://www.jblearning.com

Price: $115.95 Paperback. **Description:** Mark J. Minelli and Donald J. Breckon. Fifth Edition, 2008. 370 pages. Presents concepts and strategies in health education that help readers connect theory

with practice. Features tips, working examples, and real life experiences of practicing health educators.

5772 ■ A Competency-Based Framework for Health Educators - 2010

National Commission for Health Education Credentialing, Inc.
1541 Alta Dr., Ste. 303
Whitehall, PA 18052-5642
Ph: (484)223-0770
Free: 888-624-3248
Fax: (800)813-0727
E-mail: nchec@nchec.org
URL: http://www.nchec.org

Price: $65. **Description:** 2010. Provides updated and validated health education competencies to health education students, faculty members, practitioners, professional development providers, other health professionals, health education employers, leaders of professional credentialing and program accreditation, and policy makers. Serves as study guide for the revised Certified Health Education Specialist (CHES) examination.

5773 ■ A Daybook for Nurse Educators

Sigma Theta Tau International Honor Society of Nursing
550 W N St.
Indianapolis, IN 46202
Ph: (317)634-8171
Free: 888-634-7575
Fax: (317)634-8188
E-mail: stti@stti.iupui.edu
URL: http://www.nursingsociety.org

Price: $19.95 Paperback. **Description:** Katherine Pakieser-Reed. 2010. 180 pages (book). Contains 365 inspirational and thought-provoking quotes solicited from top nurse educators around the world.

5774 ■ Diabetes Education Review Guide

American Association of Diabetes Educators
200 W Madison St., Ste. 800
Chicago, IL 60606
Free: 800-338-3633
Fax: (312)424-2427
E-mail: membership@aadenet.org
URL: http://www.diabeteseducator.org

Price: $95.95 Nonmembers; $65.95 Members. **Description:** Carol J. Homko, Evan M. Sisson and Tami A. Ross. Second Edition, 2009. 184 pages. Serves as exam preparation tool for those who will take the Certified Diabetes Educator Examination.

5775 ■ Essentials of E-Learning for Nurse Educators

F.A. Davis Co.
1915 Arch St.
Philadelphia, PA 19103
Ph: (215)568-2270
Free: 800-523-4049
Fax: (215)569-5065
URL: http://www.fadavis.com

Price: $55.95 Paperback. **Description:** Timothy J. Bristol and JoAnn Zerwekh. 2011. 384 pages. Presents how to successfully use online learning in the classroom, in clinical, and for staff development.

5776 ■ Evidence-Based Teaching in Nursing: A Foundation for Educators

Jones & Bartlett Learning
5 Wall St.
Burlington, MA 01803
Free: 800-832-0034
E-mail: info@jblearning.com
URL: http://www.jblearning.com

Price: $78.95 Paperback. **Description:** Sharon Cannon and Carol Boswell. 2012. 308 pages. Equips new and experienced nurse educators with a strong foundation for Evidence-Based Teaching in nursing. Includes practical tips and discussion questions.

5777 ■ Fast Facts for the Clinical Nursing Instructor

Springer Publishing Co.
11 W 42nd St., 15th Fl.
New York, NY 10036
Ph: (212)431-4370
Free: 877-687-7476
Fax: (212)941-7842
E-mail: cs@springerpub.com
URL: http://www.springerpub.com

Price: $30 Softcover. **Description:** Eden Zabat-Kan and Susan Stabler-Haas. 2013. 192 pages. Serves as comprehensive clinical education resource that helps new clinical instructors optimize the clinical experience and understanding of their students. Contains pragmatic, real-life information on the clinical teaching process.

5778 ■ Handbook of Clinical Teaching in Nursing and Health Sciences

Jones & Bartlett Learning
5 Wall St.
Burlington, MA 01803
Free: 800-832-0034
E-mail: info@jblearning.com
URL: http://www.jblearning.com

Price: $72.95 Spiral/paperback. **Description:** Marcia Gardner and Patricia Dunphy Suplee. 2010. 229 pages. Provides clinical instructors and other health professionals with practical suggestions to clinical teaching challenges.

5779 ■ The Health Education Specialist: A Companion Guide for Professional Excellence

National Commission for Health Education Credentialing, Inc.
1541 Alta Dr., Ste. 303
Whitehall, PA 18052-5642
Ph: (484)223-0770
Free: 888-624-3248
Fax: (800)813-0727
E-mail: nchec@nchec.org
URL: http://www.nchec.org

Price: $55. **Description:** Sixth Edition, 2010. Helps health educators in assessing health education knowledge and professional development. Serves as supplementary study tool for the revised Certified Health Education Specialist (CHES) examination.

5780 ■ An Introduction of Medical Teaching

Springer Publishing Co.
11 W 42nd St., 15th Fl.
New York, NY 10036
Ph: (212)431-4370
Free: 877-687-7476
Fax: (212)941-7842
E-mail: cs@springerpub.com
URL: http://www.springerpub.com

Price: $109 Hardcover. **Description:** William B. Jeffries and Kathryn Huggett. 2010. 216 pages. Features major areas in the medical teaching field. Benefits new medical teacher or an experienced teacher in improving their career.

5781 ■ Life with Diabetes

American Diabetes Association
1701 N Beauregard St.
Alexandria, VA 22311
Free: 800-342-2383
E-mail: diabetesforecast@pubservice.com
URL: http://www.diabetes.org

Price: $89.95 Softcover, includes CD-Rom and printable patient handouts. **Description:** Fourth edition. 538 pages. Details self-help information needs of the diabetics educators for teaching aide.

5782 ■ Mastering the Teaching Role: A Guide for Nurse Educators

F.A. Davis Co.
1915 Arch St.
Philadelphia, PA 19103
Ph: (215)568-2270

Free: 800-523-4049
Fax: (215)569-5065
URL: http://www.fadavis.com

Price: $57.95 Paperback. **Description:** Barbara K. Penn. 2008. 420 pages. Provides practical guidance and strategies for a successful nurse educator career.

5783 ■ *The MCG Medical Teacher's Handbook*
Association of American Medical Colleges
2450 N St. NW
Washington, DC 20037-1126
Ph: (202)828-0400
Fax: (202)828-1125
E-mail: amcas@aamc.org
URL: http://www.aamc.org

Description: Christopher White. 2009. Provides brief, practical, and useful information on teaching, learning, evaluation, and career development for medical school educators.

5784 ■ *MCHES Exam Companion Guide Supplement*
National Commission for Health Education Credentialing, Inc.
1541 Alta Dr., Ste. 303
Whitehall, PA 18052-5642
Ph: (484)223-0770
Free: 888-624-3248
Fax: (800)813-0727
E-mail: nchec@nchec.org
URL: http://www.nchec.org

Price: $65. **Description:** Includes a supplement with 165 practice questions for the Master Certified Health Education Specialist (MCHES) examination. Serves as tool to assess health education knowledge and guide for professional development.

5785 ■ *Measurement and Evaluation for Health Educators*
Jones & Bartlett Learning
5 Wall St.
Burlington, MA 01803
Free: 800-832-0034
E-mail: info@jblearning.com
URL: http://www.jblearning.com

Description: Manoj Sharma and R. Lingyak Petosa. 2014. $97.95. 358 pages(paperback). Prepares health educators for conducting evaluations. Contains the basics of measurement, steps in instrument development, reliability assessment, validity assessment, measurement errors, process evaluation, and designs for quantitative evaluation.

5786 ■ *New Beginnings: A Discussion for Living Well with Diabetes*
American Association of Diabetes Educators
200 W Madison St., Ste. 800
Chicago, IL 60606
Free: 800-338-3633
Fax: (312)424-2427
E-mail: membership@aadenet.org
URL: http://www.diabeteseducator.org

Description: 2011. $6 (print). Includes modules that supports diabetes educators in facilitating discussions about diabetes prevention and management issues. Contains discussion questions and role-playing exercises.

5787 ■ *The New Nurse Educator*
Springer Publishing Co.
11 W 42nd St., 15th Fl.
New York, NY 10036
Ph: (212)431-4370
Free: 877-687-7476
Fax: (212)941-7842
E-mail: cs@springerpub.com
URL: http://www.springerpub.com

Price: $50 Softcover. **Description:** Deborah Dolan Hunt. 2012. 304 pages. Provides practical, step-by-step information on becoming a nurse educator. Prepares students for the interview process. Includes

samples of Curriculum Vitae, patient education handouts, course objectives, and additional resources.

5788 ■ *Nurse Education: An Introduction for Mentors, Practice Educators and Teachers*
Routledge
711 3rd Ave., 8th Fl.
New York, NY 10017
Ph: (212)216-7800
Free: 800-634-7064
Fax: (212)564-7854
E-mail: book.orders@tandf.co.uk
URL: http://www.routledge.com

Price: $44.95 Paperback; $145 Hardback. **Description:** Kevin Gormley, Hugh O'Donnell, and Patrick McCartan. 2014. 240 pages. Focuses on the current educational and skills requirements for practice education staff, higher education health and social care educators. Covers learning processes and key concepts, curriculum design, development and evaluation, teaching and assessment methods, and key challenges for nursing education.

5789 ■ *Nurse Educator Competencies: Creating An Evidence-Based Practice For Nurse Educators*
Lippincott Williams & Wilkins
2 Commerce Sq.
2001 Market St.
Philadelphia, PA 19103
Ph: (301)223-2300
Free: 800-638-3030
E-mail: ronna.ekhouse@wolterskluwer.com
URL: http://www.lww.com

Description: Judith Halstead. 2012. $49.95. 178 pages (softbound). Covers research related to educator competencies. Presents analysis and conclusion regarding how to facilitate learning, use assessment, and evaluation strategies.

5790 ■ *Nurse as Educator: Principles of Teaching and Learning for Nursing Practice*
Jones & Bartlett Learning
5 Wall St.
Burlington, MA 01803
Free: 800-832-0034
E-mail: info@jblearning.com
URL: http://www.jblearning.com

Price: $99.95. **Description:** Susan Bastable. Third Edition, 2013. 744 pages. Prepares nurse educators, clinical nurse specialists, and nurse practitioners for their increasing roles in patient teaching, health education, health promotion, and nursing education.

5791 ■ *Practical Application of Entry-Level Health Education Skills*
Jones & Bartlett Learning
5 Wall St.
Burlington, MA 01803
Free: 800-832-0034
E-mail: info@jblearning.com
URL: http://www.jblearning.com

Description: Michelyn W. Bhandari, Karen M. Hunter, Kathleen Phillips, Bette B. Keyser and Marilyn J. Morrow. 2013. $85.95. 254 pages. Serves as a tool that professional preparation program faculty can utilize to introduce their students to the competencies and sub-competencies of the seven areas of responsibility for entry-level health educators.

5792 ■ *PRAXIS/CST Health Education*
National Learning Corporation
212 Michael Dr.
Syosset, NY 11791
Ph: (516)921-8888
Free: 800-632-8888
Fax: (516)921-8743
E-mail: info@passbooks.com
URL: http://www.passbooks.com

Price: $23.95 Paperback. **Description:** 2010. Serves as preparation and study guide for certification examinations in the health education discipline.

5793 ■ *Public Health Adviser*
National Learning Corporation
212 Michael Dr.
Syosset, NY 11791
Ph: (516)921-8888
Free: 800-632-8888
Fax: (516)921-8743
E-mail: info@passbooks.com
URL: http://www.passbooks.com

Price: $34.95 Paperback. **Description:** 2010. Serves as exam and career preparation guide for public health advisers.

5794 ■ *Public Health Consultant*
National Learning Corporation
212 Michael Dr.
Syosset, NY 11791
Ph: (516)921-8888
Free: 800-632-8888
Fax: (516)921-8743
E-mail: info@passbooks.com
URL: http://www.passbooks.com

Price: $39.95 Paperback; $59.95 Hardcover. **Description:** 2009. Serves as exam and career preparation guide for public health consultants.

5795 ■ *Public Health Educator*
National Learning Corporation
212 Michael Dr.
Syosset, NY 11791
Ph: (516)921-8888
Free: 800-632-8888
Fax: (516)921-8743
E-mail: info@passbooks.com
URL: http://www.passbooks.com

Price: $39.95 Paperback. **Description:** 2008. Serves as exam and career preparation guide for public health educators.

5796 ■ *The Scope of Practice: For Academic Nurse Educators*
Lippincott Williams & Wilkins
2 Commerce Sq.
2001 Market St.
Philadelphia, PA 19103
Ph: (301)223-2300
Free: 800-638-3030
E-mail: ronna.ekhouse@wolterskluwer.com
URL: http://www.lww.com

Price: $19.95 Softbound. **Description:** National League for Nursing. 2012. 35 pages. Defines the roles of academic nurse educators. Provides definition, historical perspective, values and beliefs, theoretical framework, scope of practice, and competencies of academic nursing education.

5797 ■ *Senior Public Health Adviser*
National Learning Corporation
212 Michael Dr.
Syosset, NY 11791
Ph: (516)921-8888
Free: 800-632-8888
Fax: (516)921-8743
E-mail: info@passbooks.com
URL: http://www.passbooks.com

Price: $39.95 Paperback; $59.95 Hardcover. **Description:** 2009. Serves as exam and career preparation guide for senior public health advisers.

5798 ■ *Senior Public Health Educator*
National Learning Corporation
212 Michael Dr.
Syosset, NY 11791
Ph: (516)921-8888
Free: 800-632-8888
Fax: (516)921-8743
E-mail: info@passbooks.com
URL: http://www.passbooks.com

Price: $49.95 Paperback. **Description:** 2011. Serves as exam and career preparation guide for senior public health educators.

5799 ■ Skills-Based Health Education
Jones & Bartlett Learning
5 Wall St.
Burlington, MA 01803
Free: 800-832-0034
E-mail: info@jblearning.com
URL: http://www.jblearning.com

Description: Mary Connolly. 2010. $110.95 (print). 440 pages. Assists health educators in facilitating skills-based health education using the National Health Education Standards.

5800 ■ Supervising Public Health Adviser
National Learning Corporation
212 Michael Dr.
Syosset, NY 11791
Ph: (516)921-8888
Free: 800-632-8888
Fax: (516)921-8743
E-mail: info@passbooks.com
URL: http://www.passbooks.com

Price: $39.95 Paperback. **Description:** 2009. Serves as exam and career preparation guide for supervising public health advisers.

5801 ■ Teaching in Nursing: A Guide for Faculty
Saunders
225 Wyman St.
Waltham, MA 02451-1209
Ph: (781)663-5200
Fax: (781)663-2262
URL: http://www.us.elsevierhealth.com

Price: $92.95 Paperback. **Description:** Diane M. Billings and Judith A. Halstead. Fourth Edition, 2011. 592 pages. Offers practical guidance and teaching strategies for nurse educators. Serves as study guide for nurses preparing to take the Certified Nurse Educator (CNE) Exam.

ONLINE JOB SOURCES AND SERVICES

5802 ■ ADVANCE for Healthcare Careers
URLs: http://www.advanceweb.com/jobs/healthcare/index.html; http://www.advanceweb.com

Price: Free. **Description:** Serves as online resource tool that helps professionals seeking for healthcare job opportunities throughout the U.S.

5803 ■ American Association of Diabetes Educators Career Network
URL: http://www.diabeteseducator.org/Professional-Resources/CareerNetwork.html

Description: Provides career guide and employment opportunities database to diabetes educators.

5804 ■ Clinical Instruction Online Course
Jones & Bartlett Learning
5 Wall St.
Burlington, MA 01803
Free: 800-832-0034
E-mail: info@jblearning.com
URL: http://www.jblearning.com

Price: $144.95 CD-ROM. **Description:** Contains a series of modules designed to guide the transition of novice, competent, and expert clinician to function efficiently and effectively in the role as a clinical educator.

5805 ■ Creative Teaching Strategies for the Nurse Educator
PESI HealthCare L.L.C.
200 Spring St.
Eau Claire, WI 54702
Free: 800-844-8260
Fax: (800)554-9775
URL: http://www.pesi.com

Price: $169.99 330 minutes seminar video on DVD. **Description:** Includes electronic manual and instructions on creative teaching/learning strategies designed for nurse educators at all levels.

5806 ■ Health Educator Jobs
URL: http://health.educator.jobs.jobsearchsite.com

Description: Provides available health educator jobs and career resources. Allows employers to post jobs and search resumes to find qualified candidates that match their requirements.

5807 ■ National Association of Clinical Nurse Specialists - Career Center
URL: http://www.nacns.org/html/careers.php

Description: Provides online job posting that helps promote Clinical Nurse Specialist practice.

5808 ■ TopUSAJobs.com: Where Nurse Educator Job Seekers find the Top Jobs in Nurse Education
URL: http://nurse.educator.jobs.topusajobs.com

Description: Serves as a database of jobs. Empowers nurse educators to search career opportunities in the United States.

TRADESHOWS

5809 ■ Annual ASHA School Health Conference
American School Health Association
1760 Old Meadow Rd., Ste. 500
McLean, VA 22102
Ph: (703)506-7675
Fax: (703)506-3266
E-mail: info@ashaweb.org
URL: http://netforum.avectra.com/eWeb/StartPage.aspx?Site=ASHA1&WebCode=HomePage

Annual. Gathers professional health educators, counselors, coordinators, and other health professionals responsible for school health promotion. Includes research and workshops on health education.

5810 ■ APHA Annual Meeting and Exposition
American Public Health Association
800 I St. NW
Washington, DC 20001-3710
Ph: (202)777-2742
Fax: (202)777-2534
E-mail: comments@apha.org
URL: http://www.apha.org

Annual. Gathers public health professionals including physicians, administrators, nurses, educators, researchers, epidemiologists, and related health specialists. Features exhibit on state-of-the-art products and services related to public health promotion.

5811 ■ Health Care Education Conference
Healthcare Education Association
2424 American Ln.
Madison, WI 53704-3102
Ph: (608)441-1054
Fax: (608)443-2474
E-mail: hceaadmin@hcea-info.org
URL: http://www.hcea-info.org

Annual. Promotes practical nursing awareness and education, health literacy, and integration of patient education into daily patient care. Provides opportunities for the professional development of health care educators.

5812 ■ NAEMSE Annual Educational Symposium and Trade Show
National Association of EMS Educators
250 Mt. Lebanon Blvd., Ste. 209
Pittsburgh, PA 15234-1248
Ph: (412)343-4775
Fax: (412)343-4770
E-mail: naemse@naemse.org
URL: http://www.naemse.org

Annual. Presents educational conferences and sessions to help educators gain new ideas that help improve their teaching skills. Provides professional and networking opportunities for EMS educators.

REFERENCE WORKS

5813 ■ Expert Resumes for Teachers and Educators
JIST Publishing
875 Montreal Way
Saint Paul, MN 55102-4245
Ph: (317)613-4200
Free: 800-648-5478
Fax: (800)328-4564
E-mail: info@jist.com
URL: http://www.jist.com

Description: Louise M. Kursmark and Wendy Enelow. 2011. $17.95 (softcover). 336 pages. Gives job seekers strategies and ideas needed to craft outstanding resumes and cover letters. Includes samples of cover letters and resumes, an appendix of online career and job search resources, and tips on winning interviews.

OTHER SOURCES

5814 ■ 300 Ways to Put Your Talent to Work in the Health Field
National Health Council
1730 M St. NW, Ste. 500
Washington, DC 20036-4561
Ph: (202)785-3910
Fax: (202)785-5923
URL: http://www.nationalhealthcouncil.org

Frequency: Irregular; Latest edition 2002. **Price:** $15 Members; $18 Nonmembers. **Publication includes:** Professional associations, government agencies, institutions, and other organizations offering information or assistance concerning health career education. Principal content of publication is job descriptions and educational requirements for various health professions. **Entries include:** Organization name, address, whether financial aid is offered. **Arrangement:** Classified by occupation.

5815 ■ Career Opportunities in Health Care
InfoBase Holdings Inc.
132 W 31st., 17 Fl.
New York, NY 10001-3406
Ph: (212)967-8800
Fax: (800)678-3633
E-mail: info@infobasepublishing.com
URL: http://www.ferguson.infobasepublishing.com

Description: Shelly Field. 2007. Third edition. $49.50. 304 pages. **Includes:** Appendices provide lists of educational institutions, periodicals, directories, associations, and unions. Appendices provide lists of educational institutions, periodicals, directories, associations, and unions.

5816 ■ Careers for Good Samaritans and Other Humanitarian Types
The McGraw-Hill Companies Inc.
PO Box 182604
Columbus, OH 43272
Ph: (212)512-2000
Free: 877-833-5524
Fax: (614)759-3749
E-mail: customer.service@mcgraw-hill.com
URL: http://www.mcgraw-hill.com

Description: Marjorie Eberts and Margaret Gisler. Third edition, 2006. $16.95 (paper). 160 pages. Contains hundreds of ideas for turning good works into paid job opportunities with service organizations, religious groups, and government agencies. **Includes:** Appendices of Interaction member agencies, missionary organizations, and state offices of volunteerism that offer networking, employment, and volunteering opportunities, as well as job-hunting information. Appendices of Interaction member agencies, missionary organizations, and state offices of volunteerism that offer networking, employment, and volunteering opportunities, as well as job-hunting information. **Entries include:** Name, address, URL.

5817 ■ *Diabetes Education Curriculum: Guiding Patients to Successful Self-Management*
American Association of Diabetes Educators
200 W Madison St., Ste. 800
Chicago, IL 60606
Free: 800-338-3633
Fax: (312)424-2427
E-mail: membership@aadenet.org
URL: http://www.diabeteseducator.org

Price: $110 Nonmembers; $85 Members. **Description:** CD-ROM. Supports diabetes educators in helping people with diabetes and related conditions in making decisions about self-care and management.

5818 ■ *Essential Tools for the Nurse Educator CD-ROM Collection*
PESI HealthCare L.L.C.
200 Spring St.
Eau Claire, WI 54702
Free: 800-844-8260
Fax: (800)554-9775
URL: http://www.pesi.com

Price: $99 CD-ROM. **Description:** Features effec-

tive simulation strategies and educational technologies designed to enhance nurse educators' teaching function. Includes 60-minute webinar audio-visual presentations and post-test and continuing education instructions.

5819 ■ *Health-Care Careers for the 21st Century*
JIST Publishing
875 Montreal Way
Saint Paul, MN 55102-4245
Ph: (317)613-4200
Free: 800-648-5478
Fax: (800)328-4564
E-mail: info@jist.com
URL: http://www.jist.com

Price: $9.95 Individuals Softcover. **Pages:** 448. **Covers:** Jobs for health care professionals and career opportunities for those pursuing a health-related career, organized into 80 careers in five groups. **Publication includes:** Appendixes listing job source resources and Web sites for health organizations.

5820 ■ **Healthcare Education Association**
2424 American Ln.
Madison, WI 53704-3102
Ph: (608)441-1054

Fax: (608)443-2474
E-mail: hceaadmin@hcea-info.org
URL: http://www.hcea-info.org

Description: Represents health care educators that create resources, instruction, and communications for client, staff, student, health care provider, and the community. Provides opportunities for the professional development of health care educators. Participates in and recommend action on national issues relative to health care education.

5821 ■ **University of Connecticut - Center for Public Health and Health Policy**
99 Ash St., 2nd Fl., MC 7160
East Hartford, CT 06108
Ph: (860)282-8525
Fax: (860)282-8514
E-mail: publichealth@uconn.edu
URL: http://www.publichealth.uconn.edu

Description: Seeks to enable collaboration across university campuses and to encourage partnerships with regional and state programs. Provides resources and establishes doctoral training programs that support initiatives designed to expand outreach opportunities in selected areas of public health. Expands university partnerships with the State Department of Public Health and local health agencies throughout Connecticut to enhance public health practice and support workforce development.

SOURCES OF HELP-WANTED ADS

5822 ■ *Health*
Time Health Media Inc.
2100 Lakeshore Dr.
Birmingham, AL 35209
Free: 800-274-2522
E-mail: health@scirp.org
URLs: http://www.scirp.org/journal/health/; http://www
.health.com/health/; http://www.magnamags.com/
index.php?templateName=health
Frequency: Monthly; 10/year. **Price:** $948 Individuals; $2,700. **Description:** Peer-reviewed journal publishing articles on the latest advancements in human health.

5823 ■ *Health Planning Today*
American Health Planning Association
7245 Arlington Blvd., Ste. 300
Falls Church, VA 22042
Ph: (703)573-3103
E-mail: info@ahpanet.org
URL: http://www.ahpanet.org
Description: Quarterly. Features articles and essays relevant to health planning and policy professionals.

5824 ■ *HFM Magazine*
Healthcare Financial Management Association
3 Westbrook Corporate Ctr., Ste. 600
Westchester, IL 60154
Ph: (708)531-9600
Free: 800-252-4362
Fax: (708)531-0032
E-mail: memberservices@hfma.org
URL: http://www.hfma.org
Description: Monthly. $250/year for individuals; $151/year for institutions; $240/year for non-US subscribers. Magazine whose primary audience is senior and mid-level healthcare financial managers including CFOs, VPs of finance, controllers, revenue cycle directors, patient financial services managers, business office managers, and others responsible for healthcare financial management.

5825 ■ *Journal of Health Politics, Policy and Law*
Duke University Press
School of Social Service Administration
University of Chicago
969 E 60th St.
Chicago, IL 60637
Ph: (773)702-5966
Fax: (773)702-7222
E-mail: jhppl@ssa.uchicago.edu
URL: http://www.dukeupress.edu/Catalog/ViewProduct.php?productid=45615
Frequency: Bimonthly. **Price:** $60 Individuals; $35 Students. **Description:** Bimonthly. Focuses on the initiation, formulation and implementation of health policy and analyzes the relations between government and health. Tracks the latest news; job listings;

fellowships and internships; education, training, and professional opportunities; conferences and meetings; calls for papers; grants awarded; grants available; organization news; and publications in the fields of health politics, policy, and law.

5826 ■ *Public Health Dispatch*
National Association of County and City Health Officials
1100 17th St. NW, 7th Fl.
Washington, DC 20036
Ph: (202)783-5550
Fax: (202)783-1583
E-mail: info@naccho.org
URL: http://www.naccho.org
Description: Monthly. Free for members; $4.95 for non-members. Contains news, resources and information about community health, environmental health, public health infrastructure and systems and public health preparedness. Includes information about funding and grants, award opportunities, careers, the national identity for local public health and upcoming events.

PLACEMENT AND JOB REFERRAL SERVICES

5827 ■ Hutton Group, Inc.
1855 Bridgepointe Cir., Ste. 23
Vero Beach, FL 32967
Ph: (772)770-1787
Fax: (772)365-7766
E-mail: hutton@huttongrouphc.com
URL: http://www.huttongrouphc.com/positions.html
Description: Experienced healthcare professionals. Locates professionals and positions quickly and confidentially by thoroughly examining a client's and candidate's needs, analyzing competitive business environments, and continually instituting new search methods. Provides healthcare job recruitment and placement service.

EMPLOYER DIRECTORIES AND NETWORKING LISTS

5828 ■ *National Managed Care Leadership Directory*
HealthQuest
1101 Standiford Ave., Ste. C-3
Modesto, CA 95350
Ph: (209)577-4888
Fax: (209)577-3557
E-mail: mcare@mcol.com
URL: http://www.managedcarestore.com/yhlthqst/hqlead.htm
Description: Annual. 450 pages. May be used for networking, recruitment, research and sales prospecting. Categorizes each position by standard

job functions. Contains approximately 6,950 executive listings from 850 companies.

HANDBOOKS AND MANUALS

5829 ■ *Essential Readings in Health Policy and Law*
Jones & Bartlett Learning
5 Wall St.
Burlington, MA 01803
Free: 800-832-0034
E-mail: info@jblearning.com
URL: http://www.jblearning.com
Description: Joel B. Teitelbaum. 2009. $84.95 (paper). 454 pages. Covers public health, topics in health care quality, intersection of policy and law with medicine and ethics and offers several resources on the topic of health system reform. Features perspectives of individual authors, policymakers, and judges that span the spectrum of political and social thought. Includes practical articles describing the methods and potential pitfalls of policy analysis as well as examples of administrative regulations, informal government memoranda and budget proposals that serve as important instruments in a policymaker's toolbox.

5830 ■ *Health Policy Analysis: An Interdisciplinary Approach*
Jones & Bartlett Learning
5 Wall St.
Burlington, MA 01803
Free: 800-832-0034
E-mail: info@jblearning.com
URL: http://www.jblearning.com
Description: Curtis P. McLaughlin. 2008. $93.95 (paper). 438 pages. Provides analysis on current U.S. health policy and proposes various alternatives for developing future health policy by considering the viewpoints of economics, political science, management, communications, technology and public health.

5831 ■ *Health Policy: Crisis and Reform in the U.S. Health Care Delivery System*
Jones & Bartlett Learning
5 Wall St.
Burlington, MA 01803
Free: 800-832-0034
E-mail: info@jblearning.com
URL: http://www.jblearning.com
Description: Charlene Harrington, Carroll L. Estes . 2008. $92.95 (paper). 464 pages. Focuses on the health policy and financing issues that health professionals and nurses need to know. Provides an overview of the health policy and political process as it relates to the health status of the U.S., the organization and issues of the healthcare system, and healthcare economics.

5832 ■ *Health Policy and Politics: A Nurse's Guide*
Jones & Bartlett Learning
5 Wall St.
Burlington, MA 01803

Free: 800-832-0034
E-mail: info@jblearning.com
URL: http://www.jblearning.com

Description: Jeri Milstead. 2008. $86.95 (hardcover). 236 pages. Provides information on the relationship between health policy and politics as they relate to the field of nursing.

5833 ■ Introduction to U.S. Health Policy: The Organization, Financing, and Delivery of Health Care in America
The Johns Hopkins University Press
2715 N Charles St.
Baltimore, MA 21218-4363
Ph: (410)516-6900
Fax: (410)516-6968
URL: http://www.press.jhu.edu/index.html

Description: Donald A. Barr. 2011. $75 (paper). 376 pages. Provides an overview of the U.S. health system and the dilemmas that policy makers currently face. Introduces the various organizations and institutions that make the U.S. health care system work or fail to work. Identifies historical, social, political and economic forces that shape the system and create policy dilemmas.

5834 ■ Public Health: Career Choices That Make a Difference
Jones & Bartlett Learning
5 Wall St.
Burlington, MA 01803
Free: 800-832-0034
E-mail: info@jblearning.com
URL: http://www.jblearning.com

Description: Bernard J. Turnock. 2006. $72.95 (paper). 275 pages. Offers information for individuals considering a career in public health. Complements texts and courses on public health used by graduate and undergraduate programs. Provides an introduction to career possibilities for individuals looking for a career in the health sector.

5835 ■ Understanding Health Policy
The McGraw-Hill Companies
7500 Chavenelle Rd.
Dubuque, IA 52002
Free: 877-833-5524
Fax: (614)759-3749
E-mail: pbg.ecommerce_custserv@mcgraw-hill.com
URL: http://www.mhprofessional.com/product.php?isbn=0071438548

Description: Thomas S. Bodenheimer, Kevin Grumbach. 2008. $45.95 (paper). 232 pages. Features principles, descriptions and examples of health policy issues. Explores the issues in the world of healthcare and addresses how these issues affect an individual from the structure and organization of the industry.

EMPLOYMENT AGENCIES AND SEARCH FIRMS

5836 ■ Ahern Search Partners
3982 Powell Rd., Ste. 205
Powell, OH 43065
Ph: (614)436-4126
Fax: (614)436-4125
E-mail: mollie@ahernsearch.com
URL: http://www.ahernsearch.com

Description: Executive search firm. Concentrates on the healthcare market.

5837 ■ Breitner Transcription Services, Inc.
1017 Turnpike St., Ste. 22A
Canton, MA 02021
Ph: (781)828-6411
Free: 800-331-7004
Fax: (781)828-6431
E-mail: info@breitner.com
URL: http://www.breitner.com

Description: Executive search firm focused on the healthcare industry.

ONLINE JOB SOURCES AND SERVICES

5838 ■ HealthcareSource Job Board
URL: http://jobs.healthcaresource.com

Description: Healthcare human resources professionals. Provides employers and job seekers with resources for all areas of the healthcare field.

5839 ■ HealthEconomics.com
URL: http://www.healtheconomics.com

Description: Health outcomes professionals. Lists internet resources focused on health outcomes and health care value. Provides a world-wide list of resources on outcomes research, health economics, pharmacoeconomics, managed care, value in medicine, health-related quality of life, performance assessment, and quality of care.

5840 ■ HealthNewsDigest.com
URL: http://healthnewsdigest.com/news

Description: Electronic news network. Covers breaking news and features on health, science and the environment. Lists jobs from all areas of the healthcare arena.

5841 ■ MedHealthJobs.com
URL: http://medhealthjobs.com

Description: Covers online healthcare career resource and job search tools. Includes non-clinical jobs in the healthcare field.

5842 ■ MedicalWorkers.com
URL: http://www.medicalworkers.com/default.aspx

Description: Provides a forum where employers and job seekers in the healthcare field can find each other.

5843 ■ WellnessJobs.com
URL: http://www.wellnessjobs.com

Description: Features employment listings across the United States. Includes review of salary information, free resume posting and healthcare recruiters.

TRADESHOWS

5844 ■ Annual State Health Policy Conference
National Academy for State Health Policy
10 Free St., 2nd Fl.
Portland, ME 04101
Ph: (207)874-6524
Fax: (207)874-6527
E-mail: info@nashp.org
URL: http://www.nashp.org

Frequency: Annual.

5845 ■ National Association of County and City Health Officials Conference
National Association of County and City Health Officials
1100 17th St. NW, 7th Fl.
Washington, DC 20036
Ph: (202)783-5550
Fax: (202)783-1583
E-mail: info@naccho.org
URL: http://www.naccho.org

Frequency: Annual. Offers learning and networking opportunities geared toward the needs of local public health professionals.

5846 ■ National Forum on Quality Improvement in Health Care
Institute for Healthcare Improvement
20 University Rd., 7th Fl.
Cambridge, MA 02138
Ph: (617)301-4800
Free: 866-787-0831

Fax: (617)301-4848
E-mail: info@ihi.org
URL: http://www.ihi.org

Frequency: Annual. Serves as a meeting place for people committed to the mission of improving health care. Features four keynote presentations, more than 100 workshops, a full resource exhibition hall, the National Forum bookstore, quality improvement storyboards and opportunities for networking.

5847 ■ National Health Policy Conference
AcademyHealth
1150 17th St. NW, Ste. 600
Washington, DC 20036
Ph: (202)292-6700
Fax: (202)292-6800
URL: http://www.academyhealth.org

Frequency: Annual.

OTHER SOURCES

5848 ■ AcademyHealth
1150 17th St. NW, Ste. 600
Washington, DC 20036
Ph: (202)292-6700
Fax: (202)292-6800
URL: http://www.academyhealth.org

Description: Health services researchers, policy analysts, and practitioners. Promotes interaction across the health research and policy arenas by bringing together a broad spectrum of players to share their perspectives, learn from each other, and strengthen their working relationships. Conducts programs that serve the interests of the research community, health policy leaders, and business and government decision-makers.

5849 ■ Alliance for Health Reform
1444 Eye St. NW, Ste. 910
Washington, DC 20005-6573
Ph: (202)789-2300
Fax: (202)789-2233
E-mail: info@allhealth.org
URL: http://www.allhealth.org

Description: Pursues equality in health coverage at a reasonable cost. Lists internships and job opportunities for individuals sharing the same interest with the alliance. Provides an unbiased source of information so that opinion leaders can understand the roots of the nation's health care problems.

5850 ■ Center for Health Improvement
1330 21st St., Ste. 100
Sacramento, CA 95811
Ph: (916)930-9200
Fax: (916)930-9010
E-mail: kshore@chipolicy.org
URL: http://centerforhealthimprovement.org

Description: Aims to improve population health by encouraging healthy behaviors. Analyzes evidence-based research to help public, private and nonprofit organizations strengthen their capacity to improve the quality and value of health care and enhance public health at the community level.

5851 ■ Center for Studying Health System Change
1100 1st St. NE, 12th Fl.
Washington, DC 20002-4221
Ph: (202)484-5261
Fax: (202)863-1763
E-mail: hscinfo@hschange.org
URL: http://www.hschange.org

Description: Strives to inform policy makers and private decision makers about how local and national changes in the financing and delivery of health care affect people. Provides employment opportunities for people who wish to conduct research about healthcare.

5852 ■ Community Health International
59 Windsor Rd.
Brookline, MA 02445
Ph: (617)739-2638
E-mail: contact@communityhealthinternational.org
URL: http://www.communityhealthinternational.org

Description: Aims to support the provision of health care to communities affected by conflict, natural disasters and epidemics. Improves the health and well being of communities emerging from crises by providing primary health care programs, access to safe, clean water, preventative health education and programs for traumatized individuals and communities.

5853 ■ Delaware Health Care Commission
410 Federal St., Ste. 7
Dover, DE 19901
Ph: (302)739-2730
Fax: (302)739-6927
E-mail: jill.rogers@state.de.us
URL: http://dhcc.delaware.gov

Description: Strives to develop recommendations that represent the best healthcare policy for most Delawareans. Conducts pilot projects to test methods for catalyzing private-sector activities that will help the state meet its health care needs.

5854 ■ Global Health
United States Department of Health and Human Services
200 Independence Ave. SW, Rm. 639H
Washington, DC 20201
Ph: (202)690-6174
Fax: (202)690-7127
E-mail: globalhealth@hhs.gov
URL: http://www.globalhealth.gov

Description: Represents the United States Department of Health and Human Services to other governments, other Federal Departments and agencies, international organizations and the private sector on international and refugee health issues. Provides policy guidance and coordination on refugee health policy issues, in collaboration with the U.S. Public Health Service (PHS) Operating Divisions, the Office of Refugee Resettlement in the Administration for Children and Families, the Department of State and others. Develops U.S. policy and strategy positions related to health issues.

5855 ■ Global Health Council
1111 19th St. NW, Ste. 1120
Washington, DC 20036
Ph: (202)833-5900
Fax: (202)833-0075
E-mail: information@globalhealth.org
URL: http://www.globalhealth.org

Description: Represents health-care professionals and organizations that include NGOs, foundations, corporations, government agencies and academic institutions. Works to save lives by improving health throughout the world. Ensures that all who strive for improvement and equity in global health have the necessary information and resources. Supports improved health and development legislation.

5856 ■ Health-Care Careers for the 21st Century
JIST Publishing
875 Montreal Way
Saint Paul, MN 55102-4245
Ph: (317)613-4200
Free: 800-648-5478
Fax: (800)328-4564
E-mail: info@jist.com
URL: http://www.jist.com

Price: $9.95 Individuals Softcover. **Pages:** 448. **Covers:** Jobs for health care professionals and career opportunities for those pursuing a health-related career, organized into 80 careers in five groups. **Publication includes:** Appendixes listing job source resources and Web sites for health organizations.

5857 ■ Institute for Health Policy Solutions
1444 Eye St. NW, Ste. 900
Washington, DC 20005
Ph: (202)789-1491
Fax: (202)789-1879
E-mail: pshrestha@ihps.org
URL: http://www.ihps.org

Description: Develops creative and workable solutions to health system problems. Addresses a variety of health care coverage and associated cost issues, with the overarching goal of achieving coverage by and for all.

5858 ■ Institute for Healthcare Improvement
20 University Rd., 7th Fl.
Cambridge, MA 02138
Ph: (617)301-4800
Free: 866-787-0831
Fax: (617)301-4848
E-mail: info@ihi.org
URL: http://www.ihi.org

Description: Committed to improving health by advancing quality and value of healthcare.

5859 ■ Institute for Safe Medication Practices
200 Lakeside Dr., Ste. 200
Horsham, PA 19044-2321
Ph: (215)947-7797
Free: 800-FAI-LSAF
Fax: (215)914-1492
E-mail: ismpinfo@ismp.org
URL: http://www.ismp.org

Description: Helps healthcare practitioners keep patients safe by improving the medication use process. Serves as a resource for medication safety information. Collaborates on a continuing basis with a wide variety of partners, including healthcare practitioners, legislative and regulatory bodies, healthcare institutions, consumers, healthcare professional organizations, regulatory and accrediting agencies, employer and insurer groups and the pharmaceutical industry.

5860 ■ IntraHealth International
6340 Quadrangle Dr., Ste. 200
Chapel Hill, NC 27517
Ph: (919)313-9100
Fax: (919)313-9108
E-mail: intrahealth@intrahealth.org
URL: http://www.intrahealth.org

Description: Empowers health workers to better serve communities in need around the world. Fosters solutions to health care challenges by improving health worker performance, strengthening health systems, harnessing technology and leveraging partnerships.

5861 ■ National Academy for State Health Policy
10 Free St., 2nd Fl.
Portland, ME 04101
Ph: (207)874-6524
Fax: (207)874-6527
E-mail: info@nashp.org
URL: http://www.nashp.org

Description: Independent academy of state health policy makers. Works together to identify emerging issues and develop policy solutions. Improves and strives to achieve excellence in state health policy and practice.

5862 ■ National Association of County and City Health Officials
1100 17th St. NW, 7th Fl.
Washington, DC 20036
Ph: (202)783-5550
Fax: (202)783-1583
E-mail: info@naccho.org
URL: http://www.naccho.org

Description: County and city (local) health officials. Purposes are to stimulate and contribute to the improvement of local health programs and public

health practices throughout the U.S.; disseminate information on local health programs and practices; participate in the formulation of the policies of the National Association of Counties. Develops self-assessment instrument for use by local health officials. Operates Primary Care Project which helps to strengthen the link between local health departments and community health centers. Provides educational workshops for local health officials.

5863 ■ National Center for Policy Analysis
12770 Coit Rd., Ste. 800
Dallas, TX 75251-1339
Ph: (972)386-6272
Fax: (972)386-0924
E-mail: media@ncpa.org
URL: http://www.ncpa.org

Description: Serves as a public policy research organization that develops and promotes private alternatives to government regulation and control. Discusses policy topics that include reforms in health care, retirement, economic growth, energy and the environment.

5864 ■ National Committee for Quality Assurance
1100 13th St., Ste. 1000
Washington, DC 20005
Ph: (202)955-3500
Free: 888-275-7585
Fax: (202)955-3599
E-mail: customersupport@ncqa.org
URL: http://www.ncqa.org

Description: Seeks to improve the quality of health care. Works in coalition with other involved organizations to advance policies that will improve the quality and efficiency of the health care system.

5865 ■ National Human Services Assembly
1101 14th St. NW, Ste. 600
Washington, DC 20005
Ph: (202)347-2080
Fax: (202)393-4517
URL: http://www.nationalassembly.org

Description: Represents non-profits in the fields of health, human and community development and human services. Engages leaders of the nonprofit health and human service sector in collective efforts to advance the effectiveness of health and human services in the United States.

5866 ■ Project HOPE
255 Carter Hall Ln.
Millwood, VA 22646
Free: 800-544-HOPE
E-mail: hope@projecthope.org
URL: http://www.projecthope.org

Description: Works to develop and permanently institute long-term solutions to pressing health problems. Seeks to address new health threats.

5867 ■ PublicServiceCareers.org
1029 Vermont Ave. NW, Ste. 1100
Washington, DC 20005
Ph: (202)628-8965
URL: http://www.publicservicecareers.org

Description: Serves as a source of professional job opportunities in the new public sector, which includes government, nonprofits, NGO's, consulting, contracting and academia.

5868 ■ UCLA Center for Health Policy Research
10960 Wilshire Blvd., Ste. 1550
Los Angeles, CA 90024
Ph: (310)794-0909
Fax: (310)794-2686
E-mail: healthpolicy@ucla.edu
URL: http://www.healthpolicy.ucla.edu

Description: Works to improve the public's health by advancing health policy through research, public service, community partnership and education.

5869 ■ U.S. Department of Health and Human Services
200 Independence Ave. SW
Washington, DC 20201
Free: 877-696-6775
URL: http://www.hhs.gov

Description: Provides detailed instruction for finding job opportunities within the U.S. Federal Government, especially in the health policy/healthcare field.

5870 ■ University of Connecticut - Center for Public Health and Health Policy
99 Ash St., 2nd Fl., MC 7160
East Hartford, CT 06108
Ph: (860)282-8525
Fax: (860)282-8514
E-mail: publichealth@uconn.edu
URL: http://www.publichealth.uconn.edu

Description: Seeks to enable collaboration across university campuses and to encourage partnerships with regional and state programs. Provides resources and establishes doctoral training programs that support initiatives designed to expand outreach opportunities in selected areas of public health. Expands university partnerships with the State Department of Public Health and local health agencies throughout Connecticut to enhance public health practice and support workforce development.

5871 ■ URAC
1220 L St. NW, Ste. 400
Washington, DC 20005
Ph: (202)216-9010
Fax: (202)216-9006
URL: http://www.urac.org

Description: Promotes continuous improvement in the quality and efficiency of health care management through processes of accreditation and education. Offers benchmarking programs and services that keep pace with the rapid changes in the health care system. Ensures that all stakeholders are represented in establishing meaningful quality measures for the entire health care industry.

5872 ■ Urban Institute's Health Policy Center
2100 M St. NW
Washington, DC 20037
Ph: (202)833-7200
E-mail: uihealthpolicy@urban.org
URL: http://www.urban.org/center/hpc/index.cfm

Description: Provides extensive research and analysis of key health issues including: private insurance, the uninsured, Medicaid, Medicare and SCHIP, disability and long-term care, vulnerable populations and health care reform.

SOURCES OF HELP-WANTED ADS

5873 ■ AABB Weekly Report
American Association of Blood Banks
8101 Glenbrook Rd.
Bethesda, MD 20814-2749
Ph: (301)907-6977
Fax: (301)907-6895
E-mail: aabb@aabb.org
URL: http://www.aabb.org/resources/publications/
weeklyreport/Pages/default.aspx
Frequency: Weekly. **Price:** $179 members; $299
nonmembers; $179/year for members; $299/year for
nonmembers. **Description:** 4 issues/year. Reports
on developments in the area of blood banking and
transfusion medicine. Covers scientific, regulatory,
legislative, and legal information. Recurring features
include news summaries and notices of employment
positions.

5874 ■ AAOHN News
American Association of Occupational Health Nurses
7794 Grow Dr.
Pensacola, FL 32514
Ph: (850)474-6963
Free: 800-241-8014
Fax: (850)484-8762
E-mail: aaohn@aaohn.org
URLs: http://www.aaohn.org/publications/newsletter
.html; http://www.aaohn.org/membership/corporate
-partnerships.html
Frequency: Monthly; Monthly. **Price:** $12/yr.
Description: Quarterly. Covers Association events
as well as trends and legislation affecting occupational and environmental health nursing. Recurring features include news of research, a calendar of
events, reports of meetings, news of educational opportunities, job listings, notices of publications available, resources for career-building, briefs on
governmental issues concerning occupational and
environment health, and a President's column.

**5875 ■ Advisor for Medical and Professional
Staff Services**
Medical Staff Solutions
32 Wood St.
Nashua, NH 03064
Ph: (603)886-0444
Fax: (810)277-0578
E-mail: info@medicalstaffsolutions.net
URL: http://www.medicalstaffsolutions.net
Description: Monthly. Offers news and advice for
medical office staff. Recurring features include
interviews, notices of publications available.

**5876 ■ American Academy of Medical
Administrators - Executive**
American Academy of Medical Administrators
330 N Wabash Ave., Ste. 2000
Chicago, IL 60611
Ph: (312)321-6815

Fax: (312)673-6705
E-mail: info@aameda.org
URL: http://www.aameda.org
Description: Bimonthly. Covers membership activi-
ties. Contains article abstracts and book reviews.

**5877 ■ American Dental Hygienists'
Association Access**
American Dental Hygienists' Association
444 N Michigan Ave., Ste. 3400
Chicago, IL 60611
Ph: (312)440-8900
E-mail: exec.office@adha.net
URL: http://www.adha.org/publications/index.html
Frequency: 10/yr. **Price:** $48 Individuals; $85 Two
years; $120 Individuals for 3 years. **Description:**
Magazine covering current dental hygiene topics,
regulatory and legislative developments, and as-
sociation news.

5878 ■ CAP Today
College of American Pathologists
325 Waukegan Rd.
Northfield, IL 60093-2750
Ph: (847)832-7000
Free: 800-323-4040
Fax: (847)832-8000
E-mail: capfdn@cap.org
URL: http://www.cap.org
Frequency: Monthly. **Price:** $110 Individuals; $30
U.S. and Canada; $135 Individuals Canada; $135
Other countries; $40 Other countries single copy.
Description: Magazine covering advances in pathol-
ogy tests and equipment, clinical lab management
and operations trends, and related regulatory and
legislative changes.

5879 ■ Catholic Health World
Catholic Health Association of the United States
4455 Woodson Rd.
Saint Louis, MO 63134-3701
Ph: (314)427-2500
Free: 800-230-7823
Fax: (314)427-0029
E-mail: ckeehan@chausa.org
URL: http://www.chausa.org/pages/publications/
catholic_health_world/current_issue/
Frequency: Semimonthly; except January and July.
Price: $45 Members; $50 Nonmembers; $50 Other
countries. **Description:** Reports on the health care
ministry. Includes *Catholic Health Association As-
sembly.*

**5880 ■ CME Supplement to Emergency
Medicine Clinics of North America**
Elsevier Science Inc.
Secondary Publishing Division
650 Ave. of the Americas
New York, NY 10011
Ph: (212)633-3980
Free: 888-437-4636

Fax: (212)633-3975
URL: http://www.elsevier.com/wps/find/journalde-
scription.cws_home/709343/description#description
Frequency: 4/yr. **Price:** $212 Individuals. **Descrip-
tion:** Journal covering emergency medicine clinics.

5881 ■ Ethnicity and Health
Routledge Journals - Taylor & Francis Group
270 Madison Ave.
New York, NY 10016-0601
Ph: (212)216-7800
Fax: (212)563-2269
URL: http://www.tandfonline.com/toc/ceth20/current
Frequency: 6/year. **Price:** $1,307 Institutions print +
online; $1,144 Institutions online only; $455 Individu-
als print only. **Description:** Journal covering ethnicity
and health.

5882 ■ Group Practice Journal
American Medical Group Association
1 Prince St.
Alexandria, VA 22314-3318
Ph: (703)838-0033
Fax: (703)548-1890
E-mail: srozga@amga.org
URL: http://www.amga.org/Publications/GPJ/index
_gpj.asp
Frequency: 10/yr. **Price:** $116 Individuals; $218 Two
years; $222 Other countries; $344 Other countries 2
years. **Description:** Magazine covering the business
of medicine.

5883 ■ Health Care Registration
Wolters Kluwer Law and Business
76 9th Ave., 7th Fl.
New York, NY 10011-4962
Ph: (212)771-0600
Free: 800-234-1660
Fax: (800)901-9075
URL: http://www.aspenpublishers.com
Description: Monthly. 844 pages. $285. Provides
information and tips for health care administrators on
how to run their departments more effectively. Topics
include patient relations, collections, admissions,
employee management, productivity, and others.

5884 ■ Health Facilities Management
Health Forum L.L.C.
155 N Wacker Dr., Ste. 400
Chicago, IL 60606
Ph: (312)893-6800
Free: 800-821-2039
Fax: (312)422-4500
URL: http://www.hfmmagazine.com
Frequency: Monthly. **Price:** Free. **Description:**
Magazine covering health care.

5885 ■ Health & Place
Mosby Inc.
11830 Westline Industrial Dr.
Saint Louis, MO 63146-3326
Ph: (314)872-8370

Free: 800-325-4177
Fax: (314)432-1380
URL: http://www.journals.elsevier.com/health-and
-place/#description
Frequency: 6/yr. **Price:** $853 Institutions all countries except Europe, Japan and Iran; $149 Individuals all countries except Europe, Japan and Iran. **Description:** Journal publishing articles for health care professionals.

5886 ■ Health Planning Today
American Health Planning Association
7245 Arlington Blvd., Ste. 300
Falls Church, VA 22042
Ph: (703)573-3103
E-mail: info@ahpanet.org
URL: http://www.ahpanet.org

Description: Quarterly. Features articles and essays relevant to health planning and policy professionals.

5887 ■ Health Policy, Economics and Management
Elsevier Science Inc.
Secondary Publishing Division
650 Ave. of the Americas
New York, NY 10011
Ph: (212)633-3980
Free: 888-437-4636
Fax: (212)633-3975
URL: http://www.elsevier.com/journals/health-policy
-economics-and-management-section-36-embase/
0921-8068

Frequency: 6/yr. **Price:** $441 Individuals associate; €441 Individuals associate; ¥58,100 Individuals associate; ¥447,400 Institutions; $3,726 Institutions; €3,359 Institutions. **Description:** Journal covering the economic, social and political aspects of health care and its organization includes hospital management, health care marketing, hospital automation, and the assessment of new technology for the health care industry.

5888 ■ Healthcare Purchasing News: Business News and Analysis for Purchasing Decision-Makers
Nelson Publishing Inc.
2477 Stickney Point Rd., Ste. 315B
Sarasota, FL 34231
Ph: (941)927-9345
Fax: (941)927-9588
E-mail: krussell@hpnonline.com
URL: http://www.hpnonline.com

Frequency: Monthly. **Price:** $72 Individuals; $110 Canada; $130 Other countries. **Description:** Magazine for healthcare material management, central services, operating room and infection control professionals, and others involved in supply chain issues with hospitals and outpatient settings.

5889 ■ HIMSS News
Healthcare Information and Management Systems Society
33 W Monroe St., Ste. 1700
Chicago, IL 60603-5616
Ph: (312)664-4467
Fax: (312)664-6143
E-mail: himss@himss.org
URL: http://www.himss.org/ASP/PublicationsHome
.asp

Description: Monthly. Tracks developments in the health care information and management systems field. Provides latest management trends in information systems, management engineering, and telecommunications.

5890 ■ Hospital Outlook
Federation of American Hospitals
750 9th St. NW, Ste. 600
Washington, DC 20001-4524
Ph: (202)624-1500
Fax: (202)737-6462
E-mail: info@fah.org
URL: http://www.fah.org

Description: Bimonthly. Monitors health legislation, regulatory and reimbursement matters and developments of interest to the investor-owned hospital industry.

5891 ■ Hospitals & Health Networks
Health Forum L.L.C.
155 N Wacker Dr., Ste. 400
Chicago, IL 60606
Ph: (312)893-6800
Free: 800-821-2039
Fax: (312)422-4500
URL: http://www.hhnmag.com

Frequency: Weekly. **Price:** Free. **Description:** Publication covering the health care industry.

5892 ■ The IHS Primary Care Provider
U.S. Department of Health and Human Services - Indian Health Service
Reyes Bldg.
801 Thompson Ave., Ste. 400
Rockville, MD 20852-1627
Ph: (301)443-6394
Fax: (301)443-4794
E-mail: charles.grim@ihs.hhs.gov
URL: http://www.ihs.gov/provider

Frequency: Monthly. **Description:** Journal for health care professionals, physicians, nurses, pharmacists, dentists, and dietitians.

5893 ■ The International Electronic Journal of Health Education
American Alliance for Health, Physical Education, Recreation and Dance
1900 Association Dr.
Reston, VA 20191-1598
Ph: (703)476-3400
Free: 800-213-7193
Fax: (703)476-9527
E-mail: membership@aahperd.org
URL: http://www.aahperd.org/aahe/publications/iejhe/

Frequency: Annual. **Price:** Free. **Description:** Journal promoting health through education and other systematic strategies.

5894 ■ Journal of the American Society of Podiatric Medical Assistants
American Society of Podiatric Medical Assistants
620 Sedgley Dr.
Knoxville, TN 37922
Ph: (812)326-2046
Free: 888-882-7762
Fax: (812)326-2659
E-mail: suehpmac@gmail.com
URL: http://www.aspma.org

Frequency: Quarterly. **Price:** free for members. **Description:** Professional journal covering issues in podiatry.

5895 ■ Journal of Clinical Ethics: Healthcare, Business and Policy
University Publishing Group Inc.
37 E Antietam St.
Hagerstown, MD 21740
Ph: (240)420-0036
Free: 800-654-8188
Fax: (240)420-0037
URL: http://www.organizationalethics.com

Frequency: Semiannual. **Price:** $175 Institutions; $160 Individuals online; $200 Individuals print and online. **Description:** Magazine covering business and healthcare policy.

5896 ■ Journal of Health Management
Pine Forge Press
2455 Teller Rd.
Thousand Oaks, CA 91320-2234
Ph: (805)499-4224
Free: 800-818-7243
Fax: (805)499-0871
E-mail: sales@pfp.sagepub.com
URLs: http://www.sagepub.com/journalsProdAdv.nav
?prodId=Journal200887; http://jhm.sagepub.com/

Frequency: 3/yr. **Price:** $437 Institutions print & e-access; $393 Institutions e-access; $428 Institutions print only; $111 Individuals print only; $118 Institutions single print; $36 Individuals single print. **Description:** Journal focusing on health management and policy.

5897 ■ Journal of Hospital Medicine
John Wiley & Sons Inc.
111 River St.
Hoboken, NJ 07030-5774
Ph: (201)748-6000
Free: 800-225-5945
Fax: (201)748-6088
E-mail: info@wiley.com
URL: http://onlinelibrary.wiley.com/journal/10.1002/
(ISSN)1553-5606

Frequency: 10/yr. **Price:** $827 U.S., Canada, and Mexico print only; $827 Institutions, other countries print only. **Description:** Journal on hospital medicine.

5898 ■ Journal of Nursing Care Quality
Lippincott Williams & Wilkins
351 W Camden St.
Baltimore, MD 21201
Ph: (410)528-4000
URL: http://journals.lww.com/jncqjournal/pages/de-
fault.aspx

Frequency: Quarterly; January, April, July, September. **Price:** $111 Individuals; $381 Institutions; $78 Individuals in-training; $213 Other countries; $533 Institutions, other countries. **Description:** Peer-reviewed journal providing practicing nurses and those who play leadership roles in nursing care quality programs the latest on the utilization of quality principles and concepts in the practice setting.

5899 ■ Journal of Nursing Scholarship
Blackwell Publishing Inc.
350 Main St.
Malden, MA 02148
Ph: (781)388-8200
Free: 800-216-2522
Fax: (781)388-8210
E-mail: journaladsusa@bos.blackwellpublishing.com
URL: http://as.wiley.com/WileyCDA/WileyTitle/pro-
ductCd-JNU.html

Frequency: Quarterly. **Price:** $67 Individuals print & online; $279 Institutions print & online; $242 Institutions print or online; €77 Institutions print or online; £203 Institutions print & online; €258 Institutions print & online; £52 Individuals print & online. **Description:** Peer-reviewed journal covering nursing.

5900 ■ Magnetic Resonance Imaging Clinics
Mosby Inc.
11830 Westline Industrial Dr.
Saint Louis, MO 63146-3326
Ph: (314)872-8370
Free: 800-325-4177
Fax: (314)432-1380
URLs: http://www.mri.theclinics.com; http://www
.elsevier.com/wps/find/journaldescription.cws
_home/623155/description#description

Frequency: Quarterly. **Price:** $337 Individuals online or print; $488 Other countries online or print; $376 Canada online or print; $541 Institutions online or print; $678 Institutions, other countries online or print; $678 Institutions, Canada online or print. **Description:** Journal publishing articles and research on the latest trends in magnetic resonance imagining clinics and patient management.

5901 ■ Medical Records Briefing
HCPro Inc.
200 Hoods Ln.
Marblehead, MA 01945-2548
Ph: (781)639-1872
Free: 877-727-1728
Fax: (781)639-7851
E-mail: customerservice@hcpro.com
URL: http://www.hcmarketplace.com/prod-140/Medi-
cal-Records-Briefing.html

Description: Monthly. $249/year. Provides news and advice of interest to medical records professionals, including reimbursement, coding, legalities, regulations, and reviews. Recurring features include interviews, book reviews, and columns titled Computer Chronicle, Focus on JCAHO, Benchmarking Report, In Brief, and This Month's Idea. Subscription includes bimonthly "A Minute for the Medical Staff."

5902 ■ MEEN Diagnostic and Invasive Technology
Reilly Publishing Co.
16 E. Schaumburg Rd.
Schaumburg, IL 60194-3536
Ph: (847)882-6336
Fax: (847)519-0166
E-mail: rcgroup@flash.net
URLs: http://www.dicardiology.net/; http://www.itnonline.net

Frequency: Bimonthly; 9/yr. **Price:** $90 Canada and Mexico; $120 Other countries. **Description:** Trade magazine serving users and buyers of diagnostic and invasive cardiology technology.

5903 ■ Minnesota Medicine: A Journal of Clinical and Health Affairs
Minnesota Medical Association
1300 Godward St. NE, Ste. 2500
Minneapolis, MN 55413
Ph: (612)378-1875
Free: 800-342-5662
Fax: (612)378-3875
E-mail: mma@mnmed.org
URL: http://www.minnesotamedicine.com/

Frequency: Monthly. **Price:** $45 Individuals; $81 Two years; $80 Other countries; $144 Other countries 2 years. **Description:** Magazine on medical, socioeconomic, public health, medical-legal, and biomedical ethics issues of interest to physicians.

5904 ■ Modern Healthcare: The Weekly Healthcare Business News Magazine
Crain Communications Inc.
150 N Michigan Ave.
Chicago, IL 60601-7553
Ph: (312)649-5200
Free: 800-678-9595
Fax: (312)280-3150
E-mail: subs@crain.com
URL: http://www.modernhealthcare.com

Frequency: Weekly. **Price:** $164 Individuals; $255 Canada; $218 Other countries. **Description:** Weekly business news magazine for healthcare management.

5905 ■ Neuroimaging Clinics of North America
Mosby Inc.
11830 Westline Industrial Dr.
Saint Louis, MO 63146-3326
Ph: (314)872-8370
Free: 800-325-4177
Fax: (314)432-1380
URLs: http://www.neuroimaging.theclinics.com; http://www.elsevier.com/wps/find/journaldescription.cws_home/623157/description#description

Frequency: Quarterly. **Price:** $396 Canada online or print; $590 Institutions, Canada online or print; $502 Other countries online or print; $590 Institutions, other countries online or print; $246 Students, other countries and resident; online or print; $342 Individuals online or print; $471 Institutions online or print; $172 Students and resident; online or print. **Description:** Journal publishing articles on newest advances in neuroimaging and patient treatment options.

5906 ■ Nursing Administration Quarterly
Lippincott Williams & Wilkins
63430 E Desert Mesa Ct.
Tucson, AZ 857396

Ph: (410)528-4000
E-mail: naqbb@aol.com
URLs: http://www.lww.com/product/?0363-9568; http://journals.lww.com/naqjournal/pages/default.aspx
Frequency: Quarterly. **Price:** $126 Individuals; $431 Institutions; $78 Individuals in-training; $217 Other countries; $573 Institutions, other countries. **Description:** Peer-reviewed journal providing nursing administrators with information on the effective management of nursing services in all health care settings.

5907 ■ Nursing Economics: The Journal for Health Care Leaders
Jannetti Publications Inc.
E Holly Ave., Box 56
Pitman, NJ 08071-0056
Ph: (856)256-2300
Fax: (856)589-7463
E-mail: nejrnl@ajj.com
URL: http://www.nursingeconomics.net/cgi-bin/WebObjects/NECJournal.woa
Frequency: Bimonthly. **Price:** $72 Individuals; $120 Two years; $89 Institutions; $150 Institutions 2 years; $120 Institutions, other countries; $180 Other countries 2 years; $210 Institutions, other countries 2 years. **Description:** Business magazine for nursing administrators.

5908 ■ Nutrition Business Journal: Strategic Information for Decision Makers in the Nutrition Industry
Intertec Publishing
1401 Pearl St., Ste. 200
Boulder, CO 80302
Ph: (303)998-9398
E-mail: info@nutritionbusiness.com
URL: http://www.nutritionbusiness.com/
Frequency: Monthly. **Description:** Journal catering to nutrition, natural products and alternative health care industries. Publishes information regarding business activities, market size/growth, trends, and opportunities, with a particular emphasis on the nutrition industry.

5909 ■ Patient Education and Counseling
Mosby Inc.
11830 Westline Industrial Dr.
Saint Louis, MO 63146-3326
Ph: (314)872-8370
Free: 800-325-4177
Fax: (314)432-1380
URL: http://www.journals.elsevier.com/patient-education-and-counseling/
Frequency: Monthly. **Price:** $317 Individuals print or online; ¥37,700 Individuals print or online; €288 Individuals print or online. **Description:** Journal publishing articles on patient education and health promotion researchers, managers, physicians, nurses and other health care provider.

5910 ■ Patient Safety & Quality Healthcare
Lionheart Publishing Inc.
506 Roswell St., Ste. 220
Marietta, GA 30060
Ph: (770)431-0867
Free: 888-303-5639
Fax: (770)432-6969
E-mail: lpi@lionhrtpub.com
URL: http://www.psqh.com
Frequency: Monthly. **Price:** $27 Individuals; $47 Canada and Mexico; $67 Other countries; $8 Single issue. **Description:** Publication that provides information about patient safety and quality healthcare for patients, doctors, hospital administrators, and others in the healthcare industry.

5911 ■ Public Health Forum
Elsevier Science Inc.
Secondary Publishing Division
650 Ave. of the Americas
New York, NY 10011
Ph: (212)633-3980

Free: 888-437-4636
Fax: (212)633-3975
URL: http://www.journals.elsevier.com/public-health-forum/
Frequency: 4/yr. **Price:** $48 Individuals print; $54 Institutions print. **Description:** Journal focused on research methods, and program evaluation in the field of public health.

5912 ■ Public Health Jobs Worldwide
Carlyle Corp.
PO Box 6729
Charlottesville, VA 22906-6729
Ph: (434)985-6444
Free: 800-291-4618
Fax: (434)985-6828
E-mail: info@ineoa.org
URL: http://www.jobspublichealth.com

Description: Weekly. Electronic newspaper with current public health job openings in the United States and worldwide.

5913 ■ Public Health Law & Policy Journal
University of Hawaii - National Foreign Language Resource Center
1859 E-W Rd., No. 106
Honolulu, HI 96822-2322
Ph: (808)956-9424
Fax: (808)956-5983
E-mail: phlo@hawaii.edu
URL: http://www.hawaii.edu/phlo/phlpj/

Price: Free. **Description:** Open access academic journal covering worldwide public health issues.

5914 ■ Public Health, Social Medicine and Epidemiology
Elsevier Science Inc.
Secondary Publishing Division
650 Ave. of the Americas
New York, NY 10011
Ph: (212)633-3980
Free: 888-437-4636
Fax: (212)633-3975
URL: http://www.elsevier.com/journals/public-health-social-medicine-and-epidemiology-section-17-embase/0924-5723

Frequency: Semimonthly. **Price:** $8,824 Institutions; ¥1,048,500 Institutions; €7,949 Institutions. **Description:** Journal covering public health and social medicine, and includes health planning and education, epidemiology and prevention of communicable disease, public health aspects of risk populations.

5915 ■ PublicHealthJobs.net
Association of Schools and Programs of Public Health
1900 M St. NW, Ste. 710
Washington, DC 20036
Ph: (202)296-1099
Fax: (202)296-1252
E-mail: info@asph.org
URL: http://www.publichealthjobs.net

Description: Online service that provides links to epidemiology job postings in the private sector, not-for-profit sector, and the federal government.

5916 ■ Quality Management in Health Care
Lippincott Williams & Wilkins
351 W Camden St.
Baltimore, MD 21201
Ph: (410)528-4000
URL: http://journals.lww.com/qmhcjournal/pages/default.aspx

Frequency: Quarterly. **Price:** $124 Individuals; $376 Institutions; $64 Individuals in-training; $218 Other countries; $565 Institutions, other countries. **Description:** Peer-reviewed journal providing a forum to explore the theoretical, technical, and strategic elements of total quality management in health care.

5917 ■ *Trustee: The Magazine for Hospital Governing Boards*
Health Forum L.L.C.
155 N Wacker Dr., Ste. 400
Chicago, IL 60606
Ph: (312)893-6800
Free: 800-821-2039
Fax: (312)422-4500
URL: http://www.trusteemag.com
Frequency: Monthly. **Price:** $52 Individuals; $120 Canada; $200 Other countries; $10 Single issue domestic; $16 Single issue other countries. **Description:** Magazine for hospital and health care system governing board members containing information about events and issues affecting the health care industry.

PLACEMENT AND JOB REFERRAL SERVICES

5918 ■ **American Association of Healthcare Administrative Management**
11240 Waples Mill Rd., Ste. 200
Fairfax, VA 22030
Ph: (703)281-4043
Fax: (703)359-7562
E-mail: info@aaham.org
URL: http://www.aaham.org
Description: Represents business offices, credit and collection managers, and admitting officers for hospitals, clinics and other healthcare organizations. Maintains placement services.

5919 ■ **Hutton Group, Inc.**
1855 Bridgepointe Cir., Ste. 23
Vero Beach, FL 32967
Ph: (772)770-1787
Fax: (772)365-7766
E-mail: hutton@huttongrouphc.com
URL: http://www.huttongrouphc.com/positions.html
Description: Experienced healthcare professionals. Locates professionals and positions quickly and confidentially by thoroughly examining a client's and candidate's needs, analyzing competitive business environments, and continually instituting new search methods. Provides healthcare job recruitment and placement service.

EMPLOYER DIRECTORIES AND NETWORKING LISTS

5920 ■ *Crain's List--Chicago's Largest Hospitals*
Crain Communications Inc.
150 N Michigan Ave.
Chicago, IL 60601-7553
Ph: (312)649-5200
Free: 800-678-9595
Fax: (312)280-3150
E-mail: info@crain.com
URL: http://www.chicagobusiness.com/section/lists
Frequency: Published November, 2012. **Price:** $25 Individuals PDF format; $45 Individuals Excel format. **Covers:** 25 hospitals in Chicago area ranked by net patient revenues. **Entries include:** Name, address, phone number, fax, web address, corporate e-mail, hospital administrator, network affiliation, 2011 net patient revenue, percentage change from 2010, 2011 net profits, percentage change from 2011, inpatient days, available beds, daily occupancy rate, number of hospital employees as of December 31, 2011, fiscal year end, Chairman, President, CEO, Chief Financial Officer, Human Resources Manager, Media Relations/Public Relations Director, and Hospital Administrator.

5921 ■ *Directory of Healthcare Recruiters*
Pam Pohly Associates
2707 Woodrow, Ste. 100
Hays, KS 67601

Ph: (785)625-9790
E-mail: pjpohly@yahoo.com
URL: http://www.pohly.com
Description: 2011. $39.95. Provides complete listings of over 1,000 medical recruiters and healthcare executive firms with company descriptions, contact person, web site addresses, e-mail addresses, phone and fax numbers.

5922 ■ *Directory of Hospital Personnel*
Grey House Publishing
4919 Rte. 22
Amenia, NY 12501
Ph: (518)789-8700
Free: 800-562-2139
Fax: (518)789-0556
E-mail: books@greyhouse.com
URL: http://www.greyhouse.com/hospital_personnel.htm
Frequency: Annual; Latest edition 2011. **Price:** $325 Individuals Softcover. **Pages:** 2,300. **Covers:** 200,000 executives at 6,000 U.S. Hospitals. **Entries include:** Name of hospital, address, phone, number of beds, type and JCAHO status of hospital, names and titles of key department heads and staff, medical and nursing school affiliations; number of residents, interns, and nursing students. **Arrangement:** Geographical. **Indexes:** Hospital name, personnel, hospital size.

5923 ■ *Directory of Personnel Responsible for Radiological Health Programs*
Conference of Radiation Control Program Directors
1030 Burlington Ln., Ste. 4B
Frankfort, KY 40601
Ph: (502)227-4543
Fax: (502)227-7862
E-mail: rmcburney@crcpd.org
URL: http://www.crcpd.org
Frequency: Annual; Latest edition 2012. **Price:** $55 Individuals current copy; $40/copy. **Pages:** 260. **Description:** Lists federal, state, and local agencies associated with CRCPD dealing directly or indirectly with radiation control. **Covers:** About 350 individuals who conduct radiological health program activities in federal, state, and local government agencies; members of the conferences. **Entries include:** For directors--Name and title, name of agency address, phone; office hours listed with state heading. For members--name, address, phone, affiliation, department, and title. **Arrangement:** Directors are by level of agency and geographical. **Indexes:** Personal name, agency, state.

5924 ■ *Hospital Blue Book*
Billian Publishing Inc. and Trans World Publishing Inc.
2100 River Edge Pkwy., Ste. 1200
Atlanta, GA 30328
Ph: (770)955-5656
Free: 800-800-5668
Fax: (770)952-0669
E-mail: info@billian.com
URL: http://www.billianshealthdata.com/Products/HealthDATA_Hospital_Blue_Book
Frequency: Annual; Latest edition 2012. **Price:** $250 Individuals national edition; $575 Individuals subscription. **Covers:** More than 6,500 hospitals; some listings also appear in a separate southern edition of this publication. **Entries include:** Name of hospital, accreditation, mailing address, phone, fax, number of beds, type of facility (nonprofit, general, state, etc.); list of administrative personnel and chiefs of medical services, with specific titles. **Arrangement:** Geographical.

5925 ■ *Medical and Health Information Directory: A Guide to Organizations, Agencies, Institutions, Programs, Publications, Services, and Other Resources Concerned with Clinical Medicine*
Cengage Learning Inc.
200 1st Stamford Pl., Ste. 400
Stamford, CT 06902-6753

Ph: (203)965-8600
Free: 800-354-9706
Fax: (800)487-8488
E-mail: investors@cengage.com
URL: http://www.gale.cengage.com
Frequency: Annual; Latest edition April 2011. **Price:** $1,190 Individuals set; $501 Individuals per volume. **Covers:** In volume 1, more than 33,000 medical and health oriented associations, organizations, institutions, and government agencies, including health maintenance organizations (HMOs), preferred provider organizations (PPOs), insurance companies, pharmaceutical companies, research centers, and medical and allied health schools. In Volume 2, over 20,000 medical book publishers; medical periodicals, directories, audiovisual producers and services, medical libraries and information centers, electronic resources, and health-related internet search engines. In Volume 3, more than 40,500 clinics, treatment centers, care programs, and counseling/diagnostic services for 34 subject areas. **Entries include:** Institution, service, or firm name, address, phone, fax, email and URL; many include names of key personnel and, when pertinent, descriptive annotation. Volume 3 was formerly listed separately as Health Services Directory. **Arrangement:** Classified by organization activity, service, etc. **Indexes:** Each volume has a complete alphabetical name and keyword index.

5926 ■ *Vault Guide to the Top Health Care Employers*
Vault.com Inc.
132 W 31st St., 17th Fl.
New York, NY 10001-3406
Ph: (212)366-4212
Free: 800-535-2074
Fax: (212)366-6117
E-mail: customerservice@vault.com
URL: http://www.vault.com/store/book_preview.jsp?product_id=37972
Frequency: Published 2005. **Price:** $19.95 Individuals Online; $19.95 Members Gold. **Pages:** 232. **Covers:** Health care employers. **Entries include:** Name, address, phone, fax, website, branch office location, and major departments. Also include company overviews, recent company news, information on the hiring process, key competitors, and employment contact. **Arrangement:** Alphabetical by company name.

HANDBOOKS AND MANUALS

5927 ■ *Expert Resumes for Managers and Executives*
Jist Works
875 Montreal Way
Saint Paul, MN 55102
Free: 800-648-5478
E-mail: info@jist.com
URL: http://www.jist.com/shop/product.php?productid=16727
Description: Wendy S. Enelow, Louise M. Kursmark. 2012. $17.95. 274 pages. Contains a collection of sample resumes and resume writing advice including how to create and use an electronic resume. Contains an appendix that includes internet resources for an online job search, writing cover letters, as well as a collection of sample letters.

5928 ■ *Exploring Health Careers*
Delmar Cengage Learning
5 Maxwell Dr.
Clifton Park, NY 12065
Free: 800-648-7450
E-mail: esales@cengage.com
URL: http://www.delmarlearning.com/about/contact.aspx
Description: Maureen McCutcheon, Mary Phillips. 2006. $98.95. Provides an overview of the many career opportunities available within the health care field. Covers career descriptions, including

educational requirements, salary information, skills and procedures performed within the various careers and more.

5929 ■ Great Jobs for Business Majors
The McGraw-Hill Companies Inc.
PO Box 182604
Columbus, OH 43272
Ph: (212)512-2000
Free: 877-833-5524
Fax: (614)759-3749
E-mail: customer.service@mcgraw-hill.com
URL: http://www.mcgraw-hill.com

Description: Stephen Lambert. Third edition, 2008. $16.95 (paper). 240 pages.

5930 ■ Introduction to the Health Professions
Jones & Bartlett Learning, LLC
PO Box 417289
Boston, MA 02241-7289
Ph: (978)443-5000
Free: 800-832-0034
Fax: (978)443-8000
E-mail: info@jblearning.com
URL: http://www.jblearning.com

Description: Peggy S. Stanfield, Y. H. Hui and Nanna Cross. 2012. $93.95. 502 pages. Sixth edition. Provides current coverage of all major health professions. Outlines health-related careers, a review of the U.S. healthcare delivery system, managed care, and impact of new technology on healthcare services.

5931 ■ Manager's Handbook: Everything You Need to Know about How Business and Management Work
Pearson Learning Group
145 S Mount Zion Rd.
Lebanon, IN 46052
Ph: (804)402-6933
Free: 800-526-9907
Fax: (800)393-3156
E-mail: pasley@pearsonlearning.com
URL: http://www.k12pearson.com

Price: $24.95. **Publication includes:** Principal content of publication is reference guide for new and experienced managers. **Indexes:** Alphabetical.

5932 ■ Opportunities in Health and Medical Careers
The McGraw-Hill Companies Inc.
PO Box 182604
Columbus, OH 43272
Ph: (212)512-2000
Free: 877-833-5524
Fax: (614)759-3749
E-mail: customer.service@mcgraw-hill.com
URL: http://www.mcgraw-hill.com

Description: I. Donald Snook, Jr. and Leo D'Orazio. 2004. $14.95 (paper). 157 pages. Covers the full range of medical and health occupations. Illustrated.

5933 ■ Opportunities in Hospital Administration Careers
The McGraw-Hill Companies Inc.
PO Box 182604
Columbus, OH 43272
Ph: (212)512-2000
Free: 877-833-5524
Fax: (614)759-3749
E-mail: customer.service@mcgraw-hill.com
URL: http://www.mcgraw-hill.com

Description: I. Donald Snook. 2006. $13.95. 160 pages. Discusses opportunities for administrators in a variety of management settings: hospital, department, clinic, group practice, HMO, mental health, and extended care facilities.

5934 ■ Plunkett's Health Care Industry Almanac 2012
Plunkett Research Ltd.
4102 Bellaire Blvd.
Houston, TX 77025-1004
Ph: (713)932-0000
Fax: (713)932-7080
E-mail: customersupport@plunkettresearch.com
URL: http://www.plunkettresearch.com

Description: Jack W. Plunkett. 2011. $299.99. 717 pages. Features in-depth profiles of leading companies, associations and professional societies in the healthcare field. Covers major issues and trends, market forecasts and industry statistics.

5935 ■ Resumes for Health and Medical Careers
The McGraw-Hill Companies Inc.
PO Box 182604
Columbus, OH 43272
Ph: (212)512-2000
Free: 877-833-5524
Fax: (614)759-3749
E-mail: customer.service@mcgraw-hill.com
URL: http://www.mcgraw-hill.com

Description: Third edition, 2008. $12.95 (paper). 144 pages.

5936 ■ Tyler's Guide: The Healthcare Executive's Job Search
American College of Healthcare Executives
1 N Franklin St., Ste. 1700
Chicago, IL 60606-3529
Ph: (312)424-2800
Fax: (312)424-0023
E-mail: contact@ache.org
URL: http://www.ache.org

Description: J. Larry Tyler. 2011. $65.00 (softbound). 312 pages. Tackles current practices and trends that will advance readers towards competitive employment marketplace.

EMPLOYMENT AGENCIES AND SEARCH FIRMS

5937 ■ Aegis Group Search Consultants LLC
41451 W 11 Mile Rd.
Novi, MI 48375-1855
Ph: (248)344-1450
Fax: (248)347-2231
E-mail: resume@aegis-group.com
URL: http://www.aegis-group.com

Description: Executive search and consultant firm. Focuses on the medical industry.

5938 ■ Ahern Search Partners
3982 Powell Rd., Ste. 205
Powell, OH 43065
Ph: (614)436-4126
Fax: (614)436-4125
E-mail: mollie@ahernsearch.com
URL: http://www.ahernsearch.com

Description: Executive search firm. Concentrates on the healthcare market.

5939 ■ Alan Darling Consulting
374 Dover Rd.
South Newfane, VT 05351-7901
Ph: (802)348-6365
Fax: (802)348-7826
URL: http://www.alandarling.com

Description: Executive search firm focused on the healthcare industry.

5940 ■ Allen Adell Executive Search and Consulting
7853 Gunn Hwy., No. 260
Tampa, FL 33626-1611

Ph: (813)920-8900
E-mail: info@allenadell.com
URL: http://www.allenadell.com

Description: Functions as a retained executive search and human capital consulting firm that specializes in recruiting potential candidates for senior, mid-managerial and high-performing individual positions in the healthcare industry. Conducts talent assessment, competitive compensation surveys and objective and comprehensive exit interviews.

5941 ■ Alliance Search Management Inc.
594 Sawdust Rd., Ste. 194
The Woodlands, TX 77380
Ph: (281)419-5111
Free: 800-444-0573
Fax: (281)419-0335
E-mail: sales@alliancesearch.com
URL: http://www.alliancesearch.com

Description: Employment agency.

5942 ■ Anderson & Associates
112 S Tryon St., Ste. 700
Charlotte, NC 28284
Ph: (704)347-0090
Fax: (704)347-0064
E-mail: info@andersonexecsearch.com
URL: http://www.andersonexecsearch.com

Description: Executive search firm. Branch in Cumming, Georgia.

5943 ■ Aster Search Group
555 Madison Ave.
New York, NY 10022
Ph: (212)888-6182
E-mail: ecohen@astersearch.com
URL: http://www.astersearch.com

Description: Executive search firm focused on the healthcare industry.

5944 ■ Aureus Group
C&A Plz., 13609 California St., Ste. 100
Omaha, NE 68154-3503
Ph: (402)891-6900
Free: 888-239-5993
Fax: (402)891-1290
E-mail: omaha@aureusgroup.com
URL: http://www.aureusgroup.com

Description: Executive search and recruiting consultants specializing in accounting and finance, information systems and technology, health care administration, and wealth management.

5945 ■ Barro Global Search Inc.
10940 Wilshire Blvd., Ste. 1600
Los Angeles, CA 90024
Ph: (310)443-4277
E-mail: drbarro@winwithoutcompeting.com
URL: http://www.barroglobal.com

Description: Executive search firm focused on healthcare and hospitals.

5946 ■ The Bauman Group
1514 Redwood Dr.
Los Altos, CA 94022
Ph: (650)941-0800
Fax: (650)941-1729
E-mail: info@thebaumangroup.com
URL: http://www.thebaumangroup.com

Description: Executive search firm.

5947 ■ Boone-Scaturro Associates Inc.
8831 S Somerset Ln.
Alpharetta, GA 30004
Ph: (770)740-9737
Free: 800-749-1884
Fax: (770)475-5055
E-mail: admin@boone-scaturro.com
URL: http://www.boone-scaturro.com

Description: Executive search firm focused on the healthcare industry.

5948 ■ **Bowen & Briggs Inc.**
646 Turner Ave.
Drexel Hill, PA 19026
Ph: (610)284-6631
Free: 877-853-9611
Fax: (610)284-6651
E-mail: solutions@bowenbriggs.com
URL: http://www.bowenbriggs.com

Description: Specializes in executive search, coaching and consulting for children's healthcare.

5949 ■ **Breitner Transcription Services, Inc.**
1017 Turnpike St., Ste. 22A
Canton, MA 02021
Ph: (781)828-6411
Free: 800-331-7004
Fax: (781)828-6431
E-mail: info@breitner.com
URL: http://www.breitner.com

Description: Executive search firm focused on the healthcare industry.

5950 ■ **Calland & Company**
2296 Henderson Mill Rd. NE, Ste. 222
Atlanta, GA 30345
Ph: (770)270-9100
Fax: (770)270-9300
E-mail: bob@callandcompany.com
URL: http://www.callandcompany.com

Description: Executive search firm focused on senior management and healthcare.

5951 ■ **Capodice & Associates**
Midtown Plaza
1243 S Tamiami Trail
Sarasota, FL 34239
Ph: (941)906-1990
Fax: (941)906-1991
E-mail: peter@capodice.com
URL: http://www.capodice.com

Description: Executive search firm. Branch in Carlisle, MA.

5952 ■ **Carson Kolb Healthcare Group Inc.**
27201 Puerta Real, Ste. 300
Mission Viejo, CA 92691
Free: 800-606-9439
Fax: (949)272-1483
E-mail: info@carsonkolb.com
URL: http://www.carsonkolb.com

Description: Executive search firm focused on the healthcare industry.

5953 ■ **Cejka Search Inc.**
4 City Place Dr., Ste. 300
Saint Louis, MO 63141-7062
Ph: (314)726-1603
Free: 800-678-7858
E-mail: info@cejkasearch.com
URL: http://www.cejkasearch.com

Description: Executive search firm for the healthcare industry. Branch in Norcross, GA.

5954 ■ **Charles Aris, Inc.**
300 N Greene St., Ste. 1800
Greensboro, NC 27401
Ph: (336)378-1818
Fax: (336)378-0129
E-mail: info@charlesaris.com
URL: http://www.charlesaris.com

Description: Provides executive search and placement services in the areas of consumer packaged goods, retail, strategy/business development, global life sciences, healthcare, chemicals, textiles/apparel, private equity, and business services.

5955 ■ **CNR Search & Services**
30752 Via Conquista
San Juan Capistrano, CA 92675
Ph: (949)488-0065
E-mail: cnrkenmiller@juno.com
URL: http://www.cnrsearch.com

Description: A highly respected international boutique search firm with a worldwide client-base. Our clients include both emerging and prominent corporations across a wide range of industries.

5956 ■ **Consultants to Executive Management Company Ltd.**
20 S Clark St., Ste. 610
Chicago, IL 60603
Ph: (312)855-1500
Free: 800-800-2362
Fax: (312)855-1510

Description: National personnel consultancy specializes in executive search with focus on accounting and finance, management information systems, professional medical and real estate fields. Industries served: All.

5957 ■ **Conyngham Partners LLC**
PO Box 94
Ridgewood, NJ 07451
Ph: (201)652-3444
E-mail: info@conynghampartners.com
URL: http://www.conynghampartners.com

Description: Executive search firm.

5958 ■ **Cook Associates Inc.**
212 W Kinzie St.
Chicago, IL 60610
Ph: (312)329-0900
Fax: (312)329-1528
URL: http://www.cookassociates.com

Description: Management and executive recruiting specialists offering a commitment to clients to find the candidates and to find those candidates as efficiently as possible. Approach provides a flexible and effective structure that serves the special needs of both large and small companies. Serves the following industries: industrial, equipment manufacturer, food processing, graphic arts, chemical process, retailing, mechanical products, health care services, financial and professional services, legal, consumer products, construction and engineering, packaging, pulp and paper.

5959 ■ **Celia D. Crossley & Associates Ltd.**
3011 Bethel Rd., Ste. 201
Columbus, OH 43220
Ph: (614)538-2808
Fax: (614)442-8886
E-mail: info@crosworks.com
URL: http://www.crosworks.com

Description: Specializes in career planning and development, executive and organizational career coaching, assessment, key employee selection and team integration. Also offers career transition services, including in-placement, outplacement, and career coaching. Serves government, nonprofit, health-care, higher education and service industries.

5960 ■ **CSI Executive Search LLC**
9600 Great Hills Trail, Ste. 150W
Austin, TX 78759
Ph: (512)301-1119
Fax: (512)301-5559
E-mail: info@csi-executivesearch.com
URL: http://www.csi-executivesearch.com

Description: Executive search firm that specializes in the following arenas: accounting, engineering, healthcare, information technology, and legal.

5961 ■ **D'Antoni Partners Inc.**
122 W John Carpenter Fwy., Ste. 525
Irving, TX 75039
Ph: (972)719-4400
Fax: (972)719-4401
URL: http://www.dantonipartners.com

Description: Executive search firm.

5962 ■ **Daudlin, De Beaupre & Company Inc.**
18530 Mack Ave., No. 315
Grosse Pointe Farms, MI 48236-3254

Ph: (313)885-1235
E-mail: ptd@daudlindebeaupre.com
URL: http://www.daudlindebeaupre.com

Description: Executive search firm focused on the healthcare industry.

5963 ■ **Karen Dexter & Associates Inc.**
2012 Chestnut Ave. N, Ste. 29
Wilmette, IL 60091-1512
Ph: (847)853-9500
Fax: (847)256-7108

Description: Training and development consultant offering interpersonal skills training and one on one performance counseling for employees of large organizations. Industries served: Advertising, banking and finance, consumer products, entertainment, food and beverage, health care, legal profession, manufacturing, government agencies, publishing and broadcasting.

5964 ■ **Diversified Health Resources Inc.**
875 N Michigan Ave., Ste. 3250
Chicago, IL 60611-1901
Ph: (312)266-0466
Fax: (312)266-0715

Description: Offers health care consulting for hospitals, nursing homes including homes for the aged and other health related facilities and companies. Specializes in planning and marketing. Also conducts executive searches for top level health care administrative positions. Serves private industries as well as government agencies.

5965 ■ **Eton Partners**
1185 Springdale Rd.
Atlanta, GA 30306
Ph: (404)685-8788
E-mail: info@etonpartners.com
URL: http://etonpartners.com

Description: Executive search firm.

5966 ■ **Executive Dimensions**
5820 Main St., Ste. 403
Williamsville, NY 14221
Ph: (716)632-9034
Fax: (716)632-2889
E-mail: execsearch@executivedimensions.com
URL: http://www.executivedimensions.com

Description: Executive search firm.

5967 ■ **Executive Directions Inc.**
PO Box 5742
Sarasota, FL 34277
Ph: (941)922-9180
E-mail: info@execdir.com
URL: http://www.execdir.com

Description: Executive search firm.

5968 ■ **Flannery & Associates, LLC**
N27 W23953 Paul Rd., Ste. 204
Pewaukee, WI 53072
Ph: (262)523-1206
Fax: (262)523-1873
E-mail: peter@flannerysearch.com
URL: http://flannerysearch.com

Description: Executive search firm.

5969 ■ **Foley Proctor Yoskowitz LLC**
1 Cattano Ave.
Morristown, NJ 07960
Ph: (973)605-1000
Free: 800-238-1123
Fax: (973)605-1020
E-mail: resumes@fpysearch.com
URL: http://www.fpysearch.com

Description: Executive search firm for the healthcare industry. Second location in New York, NY.

5970 ■ **The Ford Group Inc.**
295 E Swedesford Rd., Ste. 282
Wayne, PA 19087

Ph: (610)316-6226
E-mail: info@thefordgroup.com
URL: http://www.thefordgroup.com
Description: Executive search firm.

5971 ■ Gans, Gans and Associates
7445 Quail Meadow Rd.
Plant City, FL 33565-3314
Ph: (813)986-4441
Fax: (813)986-4775
E-mail: simone@gansgans.com
URL: http://www.gansgans.com

Description: A human resources firm that specializes in executive search, human resources, management consulting, diversity consulting and resume assessment. Takes a personal approach in the development of tailored programs that consider the corporate culture, history and objectives of client. Industries served: consulting, financial services, legal, insurance, engineering, healthcare, manufacturing, utilities and the public sector.

5972 ■ Robert Howe and Associates
3331 Bolero Dr.
Atlanta, GA 30341
Ph: (770)270-1211
Fax: (770)270-1209
E-mail: rwhamill@roberthoweassociates.com
URL: http://www.roberthoweassociates.com

Description: Provider of consulting services in the area of executive search and recruitment. Industries served: healthcare, hospitality, chemical, metals, electronics, construction, and food processing.

5973 ■ International Healthcare Recruiters Inc.
9840 SW 4th St.
Plantation, FL 33324
Ph: (954)848-5330
Fax: (954)530-0618
E-mail: info@internationalhr.net
URL: http://www.internationalhr.net

Description: Specializes in career-track positions for mid- and senior-level nurse managers, supervisors and administrators, as well as clinical nurse specialists and educators.

5974 ■ JPM International
26034 Acero
Mission Viejo, CA 92691
Ph: (949)699-4300
Free: 800-685-7856
Fax: (949)699-4333
E-mail: trish@jpmintl.com
URL: http://www.jpmintl.com

Description: Executive search firm and employment agency.

5975 ■ Kforce Inc.
1001 E Palm Ave.
Tampa, FL 33605-3551
Ph: (813)552-5000
Free: 877-453-6723
Fax: (813)552-2493
URL: http://www.kforce.com

Description: Executive search firm specializing in the financial services, insurance, health care, and pharmaceuticals industries.

5976 ■ Lee Calhoon & Company Inc.
1621 Birchrun Rd.
Birchrunville, PA 19421
Ph: (610)469-9000
Fax: (610)469-0398
E-mail: info@leecalhoon.com
URL: http://www.leecalhoon.com

Description: Executive search firm.

5977 ■ McCormack & Farrow Co.
949 S Coast Dr., Ste. 620
Costa Mesa, CA 92626
Ph: (714)549-7222

Fax: (714)549-7227
URL: http://www.mfsearch.com

Description: General practice retained search in most industries. Special emphasis on high-technology, start-up and emerging companies, manufacturing, healthcare, financial services, nonprofit and privately owned businesses.

5978 ■ Minority Executive Search Inc.
3060 Monticello Blvd.
Cleveland, OH 44118-1266
Ph: (216)932-2022
E-mail: eral@minorityexecsearch.com
URL: http://www.minorityexecsearch.com

Description: Specializes in finding executives for the consumer, financial, military, automotive, medical, legal, and telecommunications industries.

5979 ■ Noyes & Associates Ltd.
5179 NE Sullivan Rd.
Bainbridge Island, WA 98110
Ph: (206)780-8142
Fax: (206)780-8144
E-mail: info@noyesconsult.com
URL: http://www.noyesconsult.com

Description: Provides nationwide consulting services to health care clients. Major services include management education course and skill assessment survey; departmental performance reviews; and temporary and permanent management/executive search.

5980 ■ Pate Resources Group Inc.
505 Orleans St., Ste. 300
Beaumont, TX 77701-3224
Ph: (409)833-4514
Fax: (409)833-4646

Description: Offers executive search and recruiting services to professionals who include physicians, health care administrators, accountants, financial managers; chemical, mechanical, industrial, and electrical engineers; sales and marketing managers, human resources administrators, and general managers and top executives in numerous disciplines. Industries served: health care, petrochemicals, accounting, utility, legal and municipalities.

5981 ■ Paul Bodner & Associates Inc.
9217 Tudor Park Pl.
Las Vegas, NV 89145
Ph: (702)528-0780
E-mail: paul@paulbodnerassociates.com
URL: http://www.paulbodnerassociates.com/index
.html

Description: Executive search firm. Second branch in Denver, CO.

5982 ■ Roberson & Co.
10751 Parfet St.
Broomfield, CO 80021
Ph: (303)410-6510
E-mail: roberson@recruiterpro.com
URL: http://www.recruiterpro.com

Description: Professional and executive recruiting firm working the national and International marketplace. Specializes in accounting, finance, data processing and information services, health care, environmental and mining engineering, manufacturing, human resources, and sales and marketing.

5983 ■ Skott/Edwards Consultants
7 Royal Dr.
Cherry Quay, NJ 08723
Ph: (732)920-1883
Fax: (732)477-1541
E-mail: search@skottedwards.com
URL: http://www.skottedwards.com

Description: Firm specializes in providing executive search services to clients in the health care, biotechnology, medical device and pharmaceutical industries. Offers are strategic organizational

development advice, corporate governance, employee appraisal and related services.

5984 ■ Theken Associates Inc.
Ridge Rd.
Randolph, VT 05060
Ph: (802)728-5811
Fax: (802)728-5996

Description: Executive search firm for nursing administrators. Consulting services include emphasis on organizational development in the healthcare field and interim leadership in patient care services across the continuum.

5985 ■ Tyler & Co.
400 Northridge Rd., Ste. 1250
Atlanta, GA 30350-3299
Ph: (770)396-3939
Free: 800-989-6789
Fax: (770)396-6693
URL: http://www.tylerandco.com

Description: Retained executive search for the healthcare, food, market research, manufacturing and insurance industries.

5986 ■ Vine and Associates L.L.C.
607 Foothill Blvd., Ste. 162
La Canada Flintridge, CA 91012
Ph: (818)541-1701
E-mail: gvine@vineassociates.com
URL: http://www.vineassociates.com

Description: Engaged by lenders and tax credit investors to provide advice on minimizing their losses in resolving problem assets, creation of new financial products to encourage the development and preservation of affordable housing.

5987 ■ Weatherby Locums
6451 N Federal Hwy., Ste. 800
Fort Lauderdale, FL 33308
Free: 866-906-1637
URL: http://www.weatherbylocums.com

Description: Executive search firm for physicians. Branch office in Fairfax, VA.

ONLINE JOB SOURCES AND SERVICES

5988 ■ ExploreHealthCareers.org
URL: http://explorehealthcareers.org/en/home

Description: Provides employment information in health professions. Includes links to health-related education/training programs, financial aid resources, specialized learning opportunities, and current issues in health care.

5989 ■ Health Care Job Store
URL: http://www.healthcarejobstore.com

Description: Job sites include every job title in the healthcare industry, every healthcare industry and every geographic location in the U.S.

5990 ■ HealthcareCrossing.com
URL: http://www.healthcarecrossing.com

Description: Provides a collection of health care jobs, hospitals and medical jobs, nursing jobs and healthcare employment. Includes a variety of employers in the health care business.

5991 ■ HealthCareerWeb.com
URL: http://www.healthcareerweb.com

Description: Advertises jobs for healthcare professionals. Main files include: Jobs, Employers, Resumes, Jobwire. Relocation tools and career guidance resources available.

5992 ■ HealthcareSource Job Board
URL: http://jobs.healthcaresource.com

Description: Healthcare human resources professionals. Provides employers and job seekers with resources for all areas of the healthcare field.

5993 ■ HEALTHeCAREERS Network
URL: http://www.healthecareers.com

Description: Career search site for jobs in all health care specialties; educational resources; visa and licensing information for relocation; interesting articles; relocation tools; links to professional organizations and general resources.

5994 ■ HealthNewsDigest.com
URL: http://healthnewsdigest.com/news

Description: Electronic news network. Covers breaking news and features on health, science and the environment. Lists jobs from all areas of the healthcare arena.

5995 ■ Hospital Jobs OnLine
URL: http://www.hospitaljobsonline.com

Description: Serves as a niche healthcare job board designed exclusively for hospitals, healthcare companies, and healthcare job seekers.

5996 ■ iHireHealthCareAdministration
URL: http://www.ihirehealthcareadministration.com

Description: Provides job listings and services to facilitate job searches in the field of health care administration.

5997 ■ JobsInLTC.com
URL: http://www.jobsinltc.com

Description: Serves as a job board for long-term care jobs for nursing home administrators, assisted living staff, directors of nursing, MDS coordinators, and other related fields.

5998 ■ MedHealthJobs.com
URL: http://medhealthjobs.com

Description: Covers online healthcare career resource and job search tools. Includes non-clinical jobs in the healthcare field.

5999 ■ MedicalHealthServicesManager.com
URL: http://www.medicalhealthservicesmanager.com

Description: Covers career opportunities and training information for aspiring medical health managers. Offers links, job listings, resumes and more.

6000 ■ Medzilla.com
URL: http://www.medzilla.com

Description: General medical website which matches employers and job hunters to their ideal employees and jobs through search capabilities. Main files include: Post Jobs, Search Resumes, Post Resumes, Search Jobs, Head Hunters, Articles, Salary Survey.

6001 ■ ProHealthJobs.com
URL: http://prohealthjobs.com/jobboard

Description: Career resources site for the medical and health care field. Lists professional opportunities, product information, continuing education and open positions.

TRADESHOWS

6002 ■ American Academy of Medical Administrators Annual Conference and Convocation
American Academy of Medical Administrators
330 N Wabash Ave., Ste. 2000
Chicago, IL 60611
Ph: (312)321-6815
Fax: (312)673-6705
E-mail: info@aameda.org
URL: http://www.aameda.org

Frequency: Annual. Primary Exhibits: Equipment, supplies, and services related to healthcare.

6003 ■ Annual ASHA School Health Conference
American School Health Association
1760 Old Meadow Rd., Ste. 500
McLean, VA 22102
Ph: (703)506-7675
Fax: (703)506-3266
E-mail: info@ashaweb.org
URL: http://netforum.avectra.com/eWeb/StartPage
  .aspx?Site=ASHA1&WebCode=HomePage

Annual. Gathers professional health educators, counselors, coordinators, and other health professionals responsible for school health promotion. Includes research and workshops on health education.

6004 ■ NADONA's Conference
National Association Directors of Nursing Administration
Reed Hartman Tower
11353 Reed Hartman Hwy., Ste. 210
Cincinnati, OH 45241
Ph: (513)791-3679
Free: 800-222-0539
Fax: (513)791-3699
URL: http://www.nadona.org

Frequency: Annual. Discusses new topics in the field and features exhibits of new technology, products, and services.

OTHER SOURCES

6005 ■ *300 Ways to Put Your Talent to Work in the Health Field*
National Health Council
1730 M St. NW, Ste. 500
Washington, DC 20036-4561
Ph: (202)785-3910
Fax: (202)785-5923
URL: http://www.nationalhealthcouncil.org

Frequency: Irregular; Latest edition 2002. Price: $15 Members; $18 Nonmembers. Publication includes: Professional associations, government agencies, institutions, and other organizations offering information or assistance concerning health career education. Principal content of publication is job descriptions and educational requirements for various health professions. Entries include: Organization name, address, whether financial aid is offered. Arrangement: Classified by occupation.

6006 ■ Alliance for Health Reform
1444 Eye St. NW, Ste. 910
Washington, DC 20005-6573
Ph: (202)789-2300
Fax: (202)789-2233
E-mail: info@allhealth.org
URL: http://www.allhealth.org

Description: Pursues equality in health coverage at a reasonable cost. Lists internships and job opportunities for individuals sharing the same interest with the alliance. Provides an unbiased source of information so that opinion leaders can understand the roots of the nation's health care problems.

6007 ■ American Academy of Medical Administrators Research and Educational Foundation
330 N Wabash Ave.,Ste. 2000
Chicago, IL 60611
Ph: (312)321-6815
E-mail: llarin@umich.edu
URL: http://aameda.org/p/cm/ld/fid=19

Description: Individuals with health care backgrounds. Conducts research in the health care field and seminars geared toward professional development. Maintains placement services.

6008 ■ American Association of Blood Banks
8101 Glenbrook Rd.
Bethesda, MD 20814-2749

Ph: (301)907-6977
Fax: (301)907-6895
E-mail: aabb@aabb.org
URL: http://www.aabb.org

Description: Represents an international association of blood banks, including hospital and community blood centers, transfusion and transplantation medicine. Supports activities related to transfusion and transplantation medicine. Supports high standards of medical, technical, and administrative performance, scientific investigation, clinical application and education. Encourages the voluntary donation of blood and other tissues and organs through education, public information and research. Member facilities are responsible for collecting virtually all of the nation's blood supply and transfusing more than 80 percent.

6009 ■ American Association of Occupational Health Nurses
7794 Grow Dr.
Pensacola, FL 32514
Ph: (850)474-6963
Free: 800-241-8014
Fax: (850)484-8762
E-mail: aaohn@aaohn.org
URL: http://www.aaohn.org

Description: Represents registered professional nurses employed by business and industrial firms; nurse educators, nurse editors, nurse writers, and others interested in occupational health nursing. Promotes and sets standards for the profession. Provides and approves continuing education; maintains governmental affairs program; offers placement service.

6010 ■ American College Health Association
1362 Mellon Rd., Ste. 180
Hanover, MD 21076-3198
Ph: (410)859-1500
Fax: (410)859-1510
E-mail: membership@acha.org
URL: http://www.acha.org

Description: Provides an organization in which institutions of higher education and interested individuals may work together to promote health in its broadest aspects for students and all other members of the college community. Offers continuing education programs for health professionals. Maintains placement listings for physicians and other personnel seeking positions in college health. Compiles statistics. Conducts seminars and training programs. Members: 2,900.

6011 ■ American College of Health Care Administrators
1321 Duke St., Ste. 400
Alexandria, VA 22314
Ph: (202)536-5120
Fax: (866)874-1585
E-mail: mgrachek@achca.org
URL: http://www.achca.org

Description: Persons actively engaged in the administration of long-term care facilities, such as nursing homes, retirement communities, assisted living facilities, and sub-acute care programs. Administers professional certification programs for assisted living, sub-acute and nursing home administrators. Works to elevate the standards in the field and to develop and promote a code of ethics and standards of education and training. Seeks to inform allied professions and the public that good administration of long-term care facilities calls for special formal academic training and experience. Encourages research in all aspects of geriatrics, the chronically ill, and administration. Maintains placement service. Holds special education programs; facilitates networking among administrators.

6012 ■ American College of Healthcare Executives
1 N Franklin St., Ste. 1700
Chicago, IL 60606-3529
Ph: (312)424-2800

Fax: (312)424-0023
E-mail: contact@ache.org
URL: http://www.ache.org

Description: Healthcare executives. Conducts credentialing and educational programs and an annual Congress on Healthcare Management. Conducts groundbreaking research and career development and public policy programs. Publishing division, Health Administration Press, publishes books and journals on health services management and textbooks for use in college and university courses. Works to improve the health status of society by advancing healthcare leadership management excellence.

6013 ■ American College of Medical Quality
5272 River Rd., Ste. 630
Bethesda, MD 20816
Ph: (301)718-6516
Fax: (301)656-0989
E-mail: acmq@acmq.org
URL: http://www.acmq.org

Description: Physicians, affiliates, and institutions. Seeks to educate and set standards of competence in the field of quality improvement and management. Offers a core curriculum in quality. Maintains speakers' bureau.

6014 ■ American Correctional Health Services Association
3990 Bullard Rd.
Monticello, GA 31064
Free: 855-825-5559
Fax: (866)365-3838
E-mail: admin@achsa.org
URL: http://www.achsa.org

Description: Represents individuals interested in improving the quality of correctional health services. Aims to promote the provision of health services to incarcerated persons consistent in quality and quantity with acceptable health care practices. Promotes and encourages continuing education and provides technical and professional guidance for correctional health care personnel. Establishes a forum for the sharing and discussion of correctional health care issues. Conducts conferences on correctional health care management, nursing, mental health, juvenile corrections, dentistry and related subjects. Maintains placement service.

6015 ■ American Health Care Association
1201 L St. NW
Washington, DC 20005
Ph: (202)842-4444
Fax: (202)842-3860
URL: http://www.ahcancal.org/Pages/Default.aspx

Description: Federation of state associations of long-term health care facilities. Promotes standards for professionals in long-term health care delivery and quality care for patients and residents in a safe environment. Focuses on issues of availability, quality, affordability, and fair payment. Operates as liaison with governmental agencies, Congress, and professional associations. Compiles statistics.

6016 ■ American Hospital Association
155 N Wacker Dr.
Chicago, IL 60606
Ph: (312)422-3000
Free: 800-424-4301
E-mail: mguerin@aha.org
URL: http://www.aha.org

Description: Represents health care provider organizations. Seeks to advance the health of individuals and communities. Leads, represents, and serves health care provider organizations that are accountable to the community and committed to health improvement.

6017 ■ American Medical Association
515 N State St.
Chicago, IL 60654
Ph: (312)464-4430
Free: 800-621-8335

Fax: (312)464-5226
E-mail: amalibrary@ama-assn.org
URL: http://www.ama-assn.org

Description: Represents county medical societies and physicians. Disseminates scientific information to members and the public. Informs members on significant medical and health legislation on state and national levels and represents the profession before Congress and governmental agencies. Cooperates in setting standards for medical schools, hospitals, residency programs, and continuing medical education courses. Offers physician placement service and counseling on practice management problems. Operates library that lends material and provides specific medical information to physicians. Maintains Ad-hoc committees for such topics as health care planning and principles of medical ethics.

6018 ■ American Public Health Association
800 I St. NW
Washington, DC 20001-3710
Ph: (202)777-2742
Fax: (202)777-2534
E-mail: comments@apha.org
URL: http://www.apha.org

Description: Professional organization of physicians, nurses, educators, academicians, environmentalists, epidemiologists, new professionals, social workers, health administrators, optometrists, podiatrists, pharmacists, dentists, nutritionists, health planners, other community and mental health specialists, and interested consumers. Seeks to protect and promote personal, mental, and environmental health. Services include: promulgation of standards; establishment of uniform practices and procedures; development of the etiology of communicable diseases; research in public health; exploration of medical care programs and their relationships to public health. Sponsors job placement service.

6019 ■ American Society of Ophthalmic Administrators
4000 Legato Rd., Ste. 700
Fairfax, VA 22033
Ph: (703)788-5777
Free: 800-451-1339
Fax: (703)547-8827
E-mail: asoa@asoa.org
URL: http://www.asoa.org

Description: Serves as a division of the American Society of Cataract and Refractive Surgery. Represents persons involved with the administration of an ophthalmic office or clinic. Facilitates the exchange of ideas and information in order to improve management practices and working conditions.

6020 ■ Association for the Advancement of Medical Instrumentation
4301 N Fairfax Dr., Ste. 301
Arlington, VA 22203-1633
Ph: (703)525-4890
Free: 800-332-2264
Fax: (703)276-0793
E-mail: mlogan@aami.org
URL: http://www.aami.org

Description: Clinical engineers, biomedical equipment technicians, physicians, hospital administrators, consultants, engineers, manufacturers of medical devices, nurses, researchers and others interested in medical instrumentation. Works to improve the quality of medical care through the application, development, and management of technology. Maintains placement service. Offers certification programs for biomedical equipment technicians and clinical engineers. Produces numerous standards and recommended practices on medical devices and procedures. Offers educational programs.

6021 ■ Association for the Healthcare Environment
155 N Wacker Dr., Ste. 400
Chicago, IL 60606
Ph: (312)422-3860

Fax: (312)422-4578
E-mail: ahe@aha.org
URL: http://www.ahe.org

Description: Managers and directors of hospital environmental services, laundry and linen services, as well as housekeeping departments and waste management (non-hazardous and hazardous), in government or university settings. Provides a forum for discussion among members of common challenges, professional development, and career advancement. Maintains liaison between members and governmental and standards setting bodies. Certified Healthcare Environmental Services Professional (CHESP) available through education and Examination. **Members:** 2,200.

6022 ■ Association of Healthcare Internal Auditors
10200 W 44th Ave., Ste. 304
Wheat Ridge, CO 80033
Ph: (303)327-7546
Free: 888-ASK-AHIA
Fax: (303)422-8894
E-mail: ahia@ahia.org
URL: http://www.ahia.org

Description: Health care internal auditors and other interested individuals. Promotes cost containment and increased productivity in health care institutions through internal auditing. Serves as a forum for the exchange of experience, ideas, and information among members; provides continuing professional education courses and informs members of developments in health care internal auditing. Offers employment clearinghouse services.

6023 ■ *Career Opportunities in Health Care*
InfoBase Holdings Inc.
132 W 31st., 17 Fl.
New York, NY 10001-3406
Ph: (212)967-8800
Fax: (800)678-3633
E-mail: info@infobasepublishing.com
URL: http://www.ferguson.infobasepublishing.com

Description: Shelly Field. 2007. Third edition. $49.50. 304 pages. **Includes:** Appendices provide lists of educational institutions, periodicals, directories, associations, and unions. Appendices provide lists of educational institutions, periodicals, directories, associations, and unions.

6024 ■ Food and Drug Law Institute
1155 15th St. NW, Ste. 800
Washington, DC 20005
Ph: (202)371-1420
Free: 800-956-6293
Fax: (202)371-0649
E-mail: service@fdli.org
URL: http://www.fdli.org

Description: Provides forum regarding laws, regulations and policies related to drugs, medical devices, and other health care technologies.

6025 ■ *Health-Care Careers for the 21st Century*
JIST Publishing
875 Montreal Way
Saint Paul, MN 55102-4245
Ph: (317)613-4200
Free: 800-648-5478
Fax: (800)328-4564
E-mail: info@jist.com
URL: http://www.jist.com

Price: $9.95 Individuals Softcover. **Pages:** 448. **Covers:** Jobs for health care professionals and career opportunities for those pursuing a health-related career, organized into 80 careers in five groups. **Publication includes:** Appendixes listing job source resources and Web sites for health organizations.

6026 ■ Healthcare Information and Management Systems Society
33 W Monroe St., Ste. 1700
Chicago, IL 60603-5616
Ph: (312)664-4467

Fax: (312)664-6143
E-mail: himss@himss.org
URL: http://www.himss.org

Description: Represents persons who, by education and/or appropriate experience, are professionally qualified to engage in the analysis, design, and operation of health care information systems, management engineering, telecommunications, and clinical systems professions. Also, corporate members include companies with information technology solutions for health care organizations. Provides leadership in health care for the management of systems, information, and change, while striving for high quality, efficient and effective patient care through analysis and technology implementation. Maintains speakers' bureau. Offers placement service.

6027 ■ International Executive Housekeepers Association
1001 Eastwind Dr., Ste. 301
Westerville, OH 43081-3361
Ph: (614)895-7166
Free: 800-200-6342
Fax: (614)895-1248
E-mail: excel@ieha.org
URL: http://www.ieha.org

Description: Persons engaged in facility housekeeping management in hospitals, hotels and motels, schools and industrial establishments. Established educational standards. Sponsors certificate and collegiate degree programs. Holds annual International Housekeepers Week celebration.

6028 ■ Medical Group Management Association
104 Inverness Terr. E
Englewood, CO 80112-5306
Ph: (303)799-1111
Free: 877-275-6462
Fax: (303)643-4439
E-mail: service@mgma.com
URL: http://www.mgma.com

Description: Represents professionals involved in the management of medical group practices and administration of other ambulatory healthcare facilities. Provides products and services that includes education, benchmarking, surveys, national advocacy and networking opportunities for members.

6029 ■ National Association Directors of Nursing Administration
Reed Hartman Tower
11353 Reed Hartman Hwy., Ste. 210
Cincinnati, OH 45241
Ph: (513)791-3679
Free: 800-222-0539
Fax: (513)791-3699
URL: http://www.nadona.org

Description: Represents the interests of nurses and administrators in long term care. Promotes ethical principles and practices within the long term care continuum. Advocates for the benefit of directors of nursing, assistant directors of nursing, and registered nurses in long term care. Supports and promotes quality of care for individuals who are receiving long-term care.

6030 ■ National Association of Health Services Executives
1050 Connecticut Ave. NW, 10th Fl.
Washington, DC 20036
Ph: (202)772-1030
Fax: (202)772-1072
E-mail: nahsehq@nahse.org
URL: http://www.nahse.org

Description: Black health care executive managers, planners, educators, advocates, providers, organizers, researchers, and consumers participating in academic ventures, educational forums, seminars, workshops, systems design, legislation, and other activities. Conducts National Work-Study Program and sponsors educational programs.

6031 ■ National Association for Healthcare Quality
8735 W Higgins Rd., Ste. 300
Chicago, IL 60631
Ph: (847)375-4720
Free: 800-966-9392
Fax: (847)375-6320
E-mail: info@nahq.org
URL: http://www.nahq.org

Description: Healthcare professionals in quality assessment and improvement, utilization and risk management, case management, infection control, managed care, nursing, and medical records. Objectives are: to encourage, develop, and provide continuing education for all persons involved in health care quality; to give the patient primary consideration in all actions affecting his or her health and welfare; to promote the sharing of knowledge and encourage a high degree of professional ethics in health care quality. Offers accredited certification in the field of healthcare quality, utilization, and risk management. Facilitates communication and cooperation among members, medical staff, and health care government agencies. Conducts educational seminars and conferences.

6032 ■ National Health Council
1730 M St. NW, Ste. 500
Washington, DC 20036-4561
Ph: (202)785-3910
Fax: (202)785-5923
URL: http://www.nationalhealthcouncil.org

Description: National association of voluntary and professional societies in the health field; national organizations and business groups with strong health interests. Seeks to improve the health of patients, particularly those with chronic diseases, through conferences, publications, policy briefings and special projects. Distributes printed material on health careers and related subjects. Promotes standardization of financial reporting for voluntary health groups.

6033 ■ National Rural Health Association
4501 College Blvd., No. 225
Leawood, KS 66211

Ph: (816)756-3140
Fax: (816)756-3144
E-mail: mail@nrharural.org
URL: http://www.ruralhealthweb.org

Description: Administrators, physicians, nurses, physician assistants, health planners, academicians, and others interested or involved in rural health care. Creates a better understanding of health care problems unique to rural areas; utilizes a collective approach in finding positive solutions; articulates and represents the health care needs of rural America; supplies current information to rural health care providers; serves as a liaison between rural health care programs throughout the country. Offers continuing education credits for medical, dental, nursing, and management courses.

6034 ■ National Society of Certified Healthcare Business Consultants
12100 Sunset Hills Rd., Ste. 130
Reston, VA 20190
Ph: (703)234-4099
Fax: (703)435-4390
E-mail: info@nschbc.org
URL: http://www.nschbc.org/index.cfm

Description: Advances the profession of healthcare business consultants through education, certification and professional interaction. Provides education and training to assist members in fulfilling the requirements of certification.

6035 ■ Radiology Business Management Association
10300 Eaton Pl., Ste. 460
Fairfax, VA 22030
Ph: (703)621-3355
Free: 888-224-7262
Fax: (703)621-3356
E-mail: info@rbma.org
URL: http://www.rbma.org

Description: Provides education, resources and solutions to manage the business of radiology. Offers an online course in radiology coding. **Members:** 2,200.

6036 ■ Society for Radiation Oncology Administrators
5272 River Rd., Ste. 630
Bethesda, MD 20816
Ph: (301)718-6510
Fax: (301)656-0989
E-mail: sroa@paimgmt.com
URL: http://www.sroa.org

Description: Individuals with managerial responsibilities in radiation oncology at the executive, divisional, or departmental level, and whose functions include personnel, budget, and development of operational procedures and guidelines for therapeutic radiology departments. Strives to improve the administration of the business and nonmedical management aspects of therapeutic radiology, to promote the field of therapeutic radiology administration, to provide a forum for communication among members, and to disseminate information among members. Maintains speakers' bureau; offers placement service. **Members:** 500.

Heating, Air-Conditioning, and Refrigeration Mechanics

6037 ■ *Air Conditioning, Heating and Refrigeration News*
BNP Media
2401 W Big Beaver Rd., Ste. 700
Troy, MI 48084
Ph: (248)362-3700
Free: 800-952-6643
Fax: (248)362-5103
E-mail: privacy@bnpmedia.com
URL: http://www.achrnews.com/

Price: $59 Individuals print; $91 Two years print; $118 Individuals 3 years; print; $69 Individuals print and digital; $111 Two years print and digital; $148 Individuals 3 years; print and digital. **Description:** Tabloid for HVAC and commercial refrigeration contractors, wholesalers, manufacturers, engineers, and owners/managers.

6038 ■ *Contractor Magazine: The News Magazine of Mechanical Contracting*
Penton Media, Inc.
330 N Wabash Ave., Ste. 2300
Chicago, IL 60611
Ph: (312)595-1080
Fax: (312)595-0295
URL: http://contractormag.com/

Frequency: Monthly. **Price:** Free; $110 Other countries; $189 Other countries 2 years. **Description:** Industry news and management how-to magazine for heating, plumbing, piping, fire sprinkler, and other mechanical specialties contracting firms.

6039 ■ *Heating/Piping/Air Conditioning Engineering: The Magazine of Mechanical Systems Engineering*
Intertec Publishing
5 Penn Plz., 13th Fl.
New York, NY 10001-1810
Ph: (212)613-9700
Free: 800-795-5445
Fax: (212)613-9749
E-mail: hpac@penton.com
URL: http://hpac.com/

Frequency: Monthly. **Description:** Business magazine serving the growing mechanical engineered systems market in the areas of building construction, renovation, and retrofit.

6040 ■ *Industrial Heating: The International Journal of Thermal Technology*
BNP Media
Manor Oak One, Ste. 450
1910 Cochran Rd.
Pittsburgh, PA 15220
Ph: (412)306-4357
Fax: (412)531-3375
E-mail: privacy@bnpmedia.com
URL: http://www.industrialheating.com/

Frequency: Monthly. **Description:** Magazine.

6041 ■ *MCAA Reporter*
Mechanical Contractors Association of America
1385 Piccard Dr.
Rockville, MD 20850-4340
Ph: (301)869-5800
Fax: (301)990-9690
URL: http://www.mcaa.org/reporter/

Frequency: Bimonthly; Monthly; Monthly, except in February and August. **Price:** free for members; Included in membership; $50, nonmembers. **Description:** Bimonthly. Covers labor issues and government affairs as they affect mechanical contractors in the plumbing, pipefitting, air conditioning, refrigeration, fire protection, and high-purity piping industries. Recurring features include reports on the activities of the Association and notices of pertinent seminars and meetings.

6042 ■ *Snips Magazine*
BNP Media
2401 W Big Beaver Rd., Ste. 700
Troy, MI 48084
Ph: (248)362-3700
Free: 800-952-6643
Fax: (248)362-5103
E-mail: privacy@bnpmedia.com
URL: http://www.snipsmag.com/

Frequency: Monthly. **Price:** Free. **Description:** Magazine for the sheet metal, warm-air heating, ventilating and air conditioning industry. Provides helpful hints for contractors.

6043 ■ *ABC Today--Associated Builders and Contractors National Membership Directory Issue*
Associated Builders and Contractors
440 1st St. NW, Ste. 200
Washington, DC 20001
E-mail: gotquestions@abc.org
URL: http://www.abc.org

Frequency: Annual; Latest Edition 2011. **Price:** $150 plus $7.00 shipping. **Publication includes:** List of approximately 19,000 member construction contractors and suppliers. **Entries include:** Company name, address, phone, name of principal executive, code to volume of business, business specialty. **Arrangement:** Classified by chapter, then by work specialty.

6044 ■ *Air Conditioning Contractors of America--Membership Directory*
Air Conditioning Contractors of America
2800 Shirlington Rd., Ste. 300
Arlington, VA 22206
Ph: (703)575-4477
Free: 888-290-2220
Fax: (703)575-4449
E-mail: paul.stalknecht@acca.org
URL: http://www.acca.org

Frequency: Annual; summer. **Pages:** 300. **Covers:** Member air conditioning and heating contractors, manufacturers, vocational technical schools. **Entries include:** Company name, address, phone, fax, names and titles of key personnel, description of fields, and types of work performed. **Arrangement:** Geographical. **Indexes:** Alphabetical.

6045 ■ *Air Conditioning, Heating & Refrigeration News--Directory Issue: The News HVACR Directory and Source Guide*
BNP Media
2401 W Big Beaver Rd., Ste. 700
Troy, MI 48084
Ph: (248)362-3700
Free: 800-952-6643
Fax: (248)362-5103
E-mail: directories@bnpmedia.com
URL: http://www.achrnews.com

Frequency: Annual; Latest edition 2011. **Publication includes:** Lists of about 2,086 manufacturers, 4,383 wholesalers and factory outlets, 1,667 HVACR products, exporters specializing in the industry; related trade organizations; manufacturers representatives, consultants, services; videos and software. **Entries include:** For manufacturers-- Company Name, address, phone, fax, e-mail, URL, names of key personnel, brand names, list of products; similar information for other categories. **Arrangement:** Manufacturers and exporters are alphabetical; wholesalers and representatives are geographical. **Indexes:** Product, trade name.

6046 ■ *ENR--Top 400 Construction Contractors Issue*
The McGraw-Hill Companies Inc.
PO Box 182604
Columbus, OH 43272
Ph: (212)512-2000
Free: 877-833-5524
Fax: (614)759-3749
E-mail: customer.service@mcgraw-hill.com
URL: http://enr.construction.com/toplists/Contractors/001-100.asp

Frequency: Annual; Latest edition 2011. **Price:** $35 Individuals. **Publication includes:** List of 400 United States contractors receiving largest dollar volumes of contracts in preceding calendar year. Separate lists of 50 largest design/construct management firms; 50 largest program and construction managers; 25 building contractors; 25 heavy contractors. **Entries include:** Company name, headquarters location, total value of contracts received in preceding year, value of foreign contracts, countries in which operated, construction specialties. **Arrangement:** By total value of contracts received.

6047 ■ *Michigan Plumbing and Mechanical Contractors Association--Membership Directory*
Michigan Plumbing and Mechanical Contractors Association
400 N Walnut St.
Lansing, MI 48933

Ph: (517)484-5500
Fax: (517)484-5225
E-mail: info@mpmca.org
URL: http://www.mpmca.org

Frequency: Annual; Latest edition 2010. **Pages:** 60. **Covers:** Member firms, industry and auxiliary associations, legislative and regulatory agencies in the plumbing and heating industry of Michigan. **Entries include:** Organization name, address, phone, names and titles of key personnel. **Arrangement:** Separate sections for members, industry associations, legislative and regulatory, and auxiliaries; members are geographical. **Indexes:** Company name (members), president name (members).

6048 ■ North American Heating, Refrigeration & Airconditioning Wholesaler Association--Membership Directory
Heating, Airconditioning, & Refrigeration Distributors International
3455 Mill Run Dr., Ste. 820
Columbus, OH 43026
Ph: (614)345-4328
Free: 888-253-2128
Fax: (614)345-9161
E-mail: hardimail@hardinet.org
URL: http://www.hardinet.org

Frequency: Annual; spring. **Pages:** 160. **Covers:** about 2,000 wholesalers and distributors. **Entries include:** Company name, address, phone and names of executives. **Arrangement:** Alphabetical.

HANDBOOKS AND MANUALS

6049 ■ Construction
InfoBase Holdings Inc.
132 W 31st., 17 Fl.
New York, NY 10001-3406
Ph: (212)967-8800
Fax: (800)678-3633
E-mail: info@infobasepublishing.com
URL: http://www.ferguson.infobasepublishing.com

Price: $30 Hardcover. **Description:** 2010. 128 pages. Contains profiles of 20 careers in the field of construction with emphasis on the nature of work, requirements, salary, and career outlook. Includes full-color photographs, index, glossary, resources, and side bars.

EMPLOYMENT AGENCIES AND SEARCH FIRMS

6050 ■ Magna Search
7946 Sunburst Terr.
Lake Worth, FL 33467
Ph: (561)967-3211
Fax: (561)967-3369
E-mail: magnas@i-2000.com
URL: http://www.magnasearch.com

Description: Serves as an executive search and recruiting firm specializing in the HVAC, controls, and energy management industries nationwide.

ONLINE JOB SOURCES AND SERVICES

6051 ■ ConstructionJobs.com
URL: http://www.constructionjobs.com/index_eng.cfm

Description: Serves as an employment job board and resume database built exclusively for the construction, design, and building industries. Provides targeted candidate searches by geographic region, specific industries, job titles, education, and experience.

6052 ■ Great Green Careers
URL: http://www.greatgreencareers.com

Description: Serves as online resource that con-

nects employers and job seekers in the green jobs industries.

6053 ■ HVAC-Industry.com
URL: http://www.hvac-industry.com

Description: Provides job opportunities and products to the heating ventilation and air conditioning industry.

TRADESHOWS

6054 ■ AHR Expo - International Air-Conditioning, Heating, Refrigerating Exposition
Commercial Refrigerator Manufacturers Division
4100 N Fairfax Dr., Ste. 200
Arlington, VA 22203
Ph: (703)524-8800
Fax: (703)524-9011
E-mail: crm@ari.org
URL: http://www.ahrinet.org

Frequency: Annual. **Primary Exhibits:** Industrial, commercial, and residential heating, refrigeration, air conditioning, and ventilation equipment and components.

6055 ■ Massachusetts Association of Plumbing/Heating/Cooling Contractors Convention and Tradeshow
Massachusetts Association of Plumbing/Heating/Cooling Contractors
400 Washington St., Ste. 401
Braintree, MA 02184-4767
Ph: (781)843-3800
Free: 800-542-7422
Fax: (781)843-1178
E-mail: phcc.ma@verizon.net
URL: http://www.phccma.org

Frequency: Annual. **Primary Exhibits:** Plumbing, heating and cooling equipment, supplies, and services.

6056 ■ North American Heating and Air Conditioning Wholesalers Association
North American Heating and Air Conditioning Wholesalers Association
1389 Dublin Rd.
Columbus, OH 43215-1084
Ph: (614)488-1835
Free: 888-253-2128
Fax: (614)488-0482
E-mail: HARDImail@HARDInet.org

Frequency: Annual. **Primary Exhibits:** Heating and air conditioning equipment, supplies, and services.

6057 ■ Plumbing-Heating-Cooling Contractors Association Annual Convention
Plumbing-Heating-Cooling Contractors Association
180 S Washington St., Ste. 100
Falls Church, VA 22046
Ph: (703)237-8100
Free: 800-533-7694
Fax: (703)237-7442
E-mail: naphcc@naphcc.org
URL: http://www.phccweb.org

Frequency: Annual. **Primary Exhibits:** Exhibits relating to plumbing and heating.

6058 ■ Refrigeration Service Engineers Society Educational Conference
Refrigeration Service Engineers Society
1911 Rohlwing Rd., Ste. A
Rolling Meadows, IL 60008-1397
Ph: (847)297-6464
Free: 800-297-5660
Fax: (547)297-5038
E-mail: meck@northmo.net
URL: http://www.rses.org

Frequency: Annual. **Primary Exhibits:** Equipment, supplies, and services for refrigeration, air-

conditioning and heating installation, service, sales, and maintenance.

OTHER SOURCES

6059 ■ Air Conditioning Contractors of America
2800 Shirlington Rd., Ste. 300
Arlington, VA 22206
Ph: (703)575-4477
Free: 888-290-2220
Fax: (703)575-4449
E-mail: paul.stalknecht@acca.org
URL: http://www.acca.org

Description: Contractors involved in installation and service of heating, air conditioning, and refrigeration systems. Associate members are utilities, manufacturers, wholesalers, and other market-oriented businesses. Monitors utility competition and operating practices of HVAC manufacturers and wholesalers. Provides consulting services, technical training, and instructor certification program; offers management seminars. Operates annual educational institute.

6060 ■ Associated Builders and Contractors
440 1st St. NW, Ste. 200
Washington, DC 20001
E-mail: gotquestions@abc.org
URL: http://www.abc.org

Description: Construction contractors, subcontractors, suppliers and associates. Aims to foster and perpetuate the principles of rewarding construction workers and management on the basis of merit. Sponsors management education programs and craft training; also sponsors apprenticeship and skill training programs. Disseminates technological and labor relations information.

6061 ■ Associated Specialty Contractors
3 Bethesda Metro Ctr., Ste. 1100
Bethesda, MD 20814
E-mail: dgw@necanet.org
URL: http://www.assoc-spec-con.org

Description: Works to promote efficient management and productivity. Coordinates the work of specialized branches of the industry in management information, research, public information, government relations and construction relations. Serves as a liaison among specialty trade associations in the areas of public relations, government relations, and with other organizations. Seeks to avoid unnecessary duplication of effort and expense or conflicting programs among affiliates. Identifies areas of interest and problems shared by members, and develops positions and approaches on such problems. **Members:** 9.

6062 ■ Mechanical Contractors Association of America
1385 Piccard Dr.
Rockville, MD 20850-4340
Ph: (301)869-5800
Fax: (301)990-9690
URL: http://www.mcaa.org

Description: Represents firms involved in heating, air conditioning, refrigeration, plumbing, piping, and mechanical service. Provides educational materials and programs to help members attain the highest level of managerial and technical expertise.

6063 ■ National Association of Home Builders - Systems Builder Council
1201 15th St. NW
Washington, DC 20005
Ph: (202)266-8200
Free: 800-368-5242
Fax: (202)266-8400
URL: http://www.nahb.org/reference_list.aspx?sectionID=815

Description: Operates under the Building Systems Council of NAHB. Modular building manufacturers.

Monitors state and federal housing legislation that impacts the building industry. Provides a forum for communication, networking and recruiting for those involved in manufacturing modular building systems. Addresses and solves problems specific to the council; offers consumer leads service.

6064 ■ National Association of Plumbing, Heating, Cooling Contractors
180 S Washington St.
Falls Church, VA 22046
Ph: (703)237-8100
Free: 800-533-7694
Fax: (703)237-7442
URL: http://www.phccweb.org

Description: Federation of state and local associa-tions of plumbing, heating, and cooling contractors. Seeks to advance sanitation, encourage sanitary laws, and generally improve the plumbing, heating, ventilating, and air conditioning industries. Conducts apprenticeship training programs, workshops, seminars, political action committee, educational and research programs.

6065 ■ National Association of Women in Construction
327 S Adams St.
Fort Worth, TX 76104
Ph: (817)877-5551
Free: 800-552-3506
Fax: (817)877-0324
E-mail: nawic@nawic.org
URL: http://www.nawic.org

Description: Seeks to enhance the success of women in the construction industry.

6066 ■ Refrigeration Service Engineers Society
1911 Rohlwing Rd., Ste. A
Rolling Meadows, IL 60008-1397
Ph: (847)297-6464
Free: 800-297-5660
Fax: (547)297-5038
E-mail: meck@northmo.net
URL: http://www.rses.org

Description: Persons engaged in refrigeration, air-conditioning and heating installation, service, sales and maintenance. Conducts training courses and certification testing. Maintains a hall of fame and a speakers' bureau.

SOURCES OF HELP-WANTED ADS

6067 ■ *American Studies Association Newsletter*
American Studies Association
1120 19th St. NW, Ste. 301
Washington, DC 20036
Ph: (202)467-4783
Fax: (202)467-4786
E-mail: asastaff@theasa.net
URL: http://www.theasa.net/

Description: Quarterly. Has a circulation of approximately 6,000. Promotes the interdisciplinary study of American culture. Presents news of research, publications, and conferences. Also includes information on grants, employment opportunities, and Association activities.

6068 ■ *Annotation*
National Historical Publications and Records Commission
National Archives and Records Administration
700 Pennsylvania Ave. NW, Rm. 114
Washington, DC 20408-0001
Ph: (202)357-5263
Fax: (202)357-5914
E-mail: nhprc@nara.gov
URL: http://www.archives.gov/nhprc/annotation

Description: Quarterly. Contains information of interest to National Historical Publications and Records Commission members. Recurring features include columns titled From the Editor, and The Executive Director's Column.

6069 ■ *Common-place*
American Antiquarian Society
185 Salisbury St.
Worcester, MA 01609-1634
Ph: (508)755-5221
Fax: (508)753-3311
E-mail: edunlap@mwa.org
URL: http://www.common-place.org/

Frequency: Quarterly; October, January, April and July. **Description:** Journal on early American history and culture.

6070 ■ *Dispatch*
American Association for State and Local History
1717 Church St.
Nashville, TN 37203-2991
Ph: (615)320-3203
Fax: (615)327-9013
E-mail: membership@aaslh.org
URL: http://www.aaslh.org/pdispatch.htm

Frequency: Monthly. **Description:** Monthly. Offers general information about state and local historical societies and the study of state and local history in the U.S. and Canada. Informs members of new training programs, seminars, and exhibits in the field. Recurring features include information on grant opportunities, updates on legislation, Association activi-

ties, and historical society personnel, interviews, job listings, and notices of publications available.

6071 ■ *The Historian*
Blackwell Publishing Inc.
University of South Florida
Dept. of History
4202 E Fowler Ave., SOC107
Tampa, FL 33620
Ph: (813)974-4674
Fax: (813)974-8215
E-mail: historian@cas.usf.edu
URL: http://as.wiley.com/WileyCDA/WileyTitle/productCd-HISN.html

Frequency: Quarterly. **Price:** $54 Individuals print & online; $215 Institutions print & online; £156 Institutions print or online; $186 Institutions U.S. print or online; £48 Individuals print & online; €71 Individuals print & online; £181 Institutions print & online. **Description:** Journal focusing on contemporary and relevant historical scholarship.

6072 ■ *History News*
American Association for State and Local History
1717 Church St.
Nashville, TN 37203-2991
Ph: (615)320-3203
Fax: (615)327-9013
E-mail: membership@aaslh.org
URL: http://www.aaslh.org/historynews.htm

Frequency: Quarterly. **Description:** Includes a handy technical leaflet in each issue.

6073 ■ *Journal of the American Institute for Conservation*
American Institute for Conservation of Historic & Artistic Works
1156 15th St. NW, Ste. 320
Washington, DC 20005
Ph: (202)452-9545
Fax: (202)452-9328
E-mail: info@conservation-us.org
URL: http://cool.conservation-us.org/coolaic/jaic

Frequency: 3/yr. **Price:** $100 U.S.; $130 Other countries. **Description:** Peer-reviewed journal covering field of conservation and preservation of historic and cultural works.

6074 ■ *Journal of America's Military Past*
Council on America's Military Past
PO Box 4209
Charlottesville, VA 22905
E-mail: nereyn@earthlink.net
URL: http://www.campjamp.org/The%20Journal.htm

Frequency: Quarterly. **Description:** Journal covering military history in the U.S., including famous battles, military personnel, and the bases where they served.

6075 ■ *Mid-Atlantic Archivist*
Mid-Atlantic Regional Archives Conference
Dickinson College
Carlisle, PA 17013-2896

Ph: (717)713-9973
Fax: (717)245-1439
E-mail: administrator@marac.info
URL: http://www.marac.info

Description: Quarterly. $35 per year. Contains news and information for and about members of the Conference. Seeks exchange of information between colleagues, improvement of competence among archivists, and encourages professional involvement of persons actively engaged in the preservation and use of historical research materials. Recurring features include letters to the editor, news of members, book reviews, a calendar of events, and columns titled Preservation News, Reference Shelf, Session Abstracts, Software News, and Employment Opportunities.

6076 ■ *The Minnesota History Interpreter*
Minnesota Historical Society
345 W Kellogg Blvd.
Saint Paul, MN 55102-1903
Ph: (651)259-3300
Free: 800-657-3773
Fax: (651)282-2374
URL: http://www.mnhs.org/about/publications/interpreter.html

Description: Six issues/year. Promotes the preservation of Minnesota history. Explores statewide Historical Society activities, providing news of exhibits, programs, seminars, conferences, and research findings. Recurring features include news of meetings, Heritage Preservation Commission News, news of members, job listings, book reviews, individual/organization profiles, and "how to" articles on topics such as museum work.

6077 ■ *Preservation*
National Trust for Historic Preservation
2600 Virginia Ave., Ste. 1000
Washington, DC 20037
Ph: (202)588-6000
Free: 800-944-6847
E-mail: info@savingplaces.org
URL: http://www.preservationnation.org/

Frequency: Bimonthly. **Price:** $20 Members individual; $30 Members family; $50 Members contributing; $100 Members sustaining; $250 Members preservation council steward; $1,000 Members preservation council heritage society. **Description:** Magazine featuring historic preservation.

6078 ■ *Presidential Studies Quarterly*
Blackwell Publishing Inc.
350 Main St.
Malden, MA 02148
Ph: (781)388-8200
Free: 800-216-2522
Fax: (781)388-8210
E-mail: journaladsusa@bos.blackwellpublishing.com
URL: http://as.wiley.com/WileyCDA/WileyTitle/productCd-PSQ.html

Frequency: Quarterly. **Price:** $494 Institutions print & online; £278 Institutions print or online; $430 Institutions print or online; £321 Institutions print & online. **Description:** Publication covering political science and history.

6079 ■ Southern Association for Women Historians Newsletter
Southern Association for Women Historians
c/o Shannon Frystak
Dept. of History
409 Stroud Hall
East Stroudsburg University of Pennsylvania
East Stroudsburg, PA 18301-2999
E-mail: h-sawh-request@h-net.msu.edu
URL: http://www.h-net.org/~sawh

Description: Three issues/year. Informs members of the Association's activities aimed at advancing the professional development of women historians and historians of women. Carries minutes of the annual meeting, announcements of awards and prizes available for work published in a variety of areas, and calls for papers at various conferences. Recurring features include notices of publications available, job listings, and member updates.

6080 ■ The Southwestern Archivist
Society of Southwest Archivists
PO Box 301311
Austin, TX 78703-0022
URL: http://southwestarchivists.org

Description: Quarterly. Supports the aims of the Society, which include: "to provide a means for effective cooperation among people concerned with the documentation of human experience," and "to promote the adoption of sound principles and standards for the preservation and administration of records." Recurring features include news of research, news of members, and a calendar of events.

6081 ■ White House Studies
Nova Science Publishers Inc.
400 Oser Ave., Ste. 1600
Hauppauge, NY 11788-3667
Ph: (631)231-7269
Fax: (631)231-8175
E-mail: nova.main@novapublishers.com
URL: http://www.novapublishers.com/catalog/product
 _info.php?cPath=125&products_id=1690

Frequency: Quarterly. **Price:** $400 Individuals. **Description:** Publication covering political science and history.

6082 ■ World History Connected
University of Illinois Press
1325 S Oak St., MC-566
Champaign, IL 61820-6903
Ph: (217)333-0950
Fax: (217)244-8082
E-mail: worldhistoryconnected@wsu.edu
URL: http://worldhistoryconnected.press.uiuc.edu

Description: Journal covering a variety of global history topics for teachers and students.

EMPLOYER DIRECTORIES AND NETWORKING LISTS

6083 ■ Newsletter--Society for Historical Archaeology Membership Directory Issue
Society for Historical Archaeology
13017 Wisteria Dr., Ste. 395
Germantown, MD 20874
Ph: (301)972-9684
Fax: (866)285-3512
E-mail: hq@sha.org
URL: http://www.sha.org

Frequency: Quarterly; Latest edition 2011. **Publication includes:** List of about 2,100 member archaeologists, historians, anthropologists, and ethnohistorians, and other individuals and institutions

having an interest in historical archeology or allied fields. **Entries include:** Name, address. **Arrangement:** Alphabetical.

HANDBOOKS AND MANUALS

6084 ■ Great Jobs for History Majors
The McGraw-Hill Companies Inc.
PO Box 182604
Columbus, OH 43272
Ph: (212)512-2000
Free: 877-833-5524
Fax: (614)759-3749
E-mail: customer.service@mcgraw-hill.com
URL: http://www.mcgraw-hill.com

Description: Julie DeGalan and Stephen Lambert. 2007. $16.95 (paper). 192 pages.

6085 ■ Opportunities in Social Science Careers
The McGraw-Hill Companies Inc.
PO Box 182604
Columbus, OH 43272
Ph: (212)512-2000
Free: 877-833-5524
Fax: (614)759-3749
E-mail: customer.service@mcgraw-hill.com
URL: http://www.mcgraw-hill.com

Description: Rosanne J. Marek. 2004. $13.95. 160 Pages. VGM Opportunities Series.

ONLINE JOB SOURCES AND SERVICES

6086 ■ Cultural Resource Network
URL: http://www.culturalresourcenetwork.com

Description: Provides sources of news, jobs, announcements, consultant listings, and resources for the cultural resource industry.

6087 ■ HistorianJobs.org
URL: http://historianjobs.org

Description: Features historian jobs and employment opportunities across the country. Allows users to search for jobs in specific areas/regions.

TRADESHOWS

6088 ■ American Association for State and Local History Annual Meeting
American Association for State and Local History
1717 Church St.
Nashville, TN 37203-2991
Ph: (615)320-3203
Fax: (615)327-9013
E-mail: membership@aaslh.org
URL: http://www.aaslh.org

Frequency: Annual. **Primary Exhibits:** Products and services directed toward the museum and history field, including: publications, fund-raising devices, software, exhibit design, historic preservation, historic research and technical information.

6089 ■ American Historical Association Annual Meeting
American Historical Association
400 A St. SE
Washington, DC 20003-3889
Ph: (202)544-2422
Fax: (202)544-8307
E-mail: info@historians.org
URL: http://www.historians.org

Frequency: Annual. **Primary Exhibits:** Books and journals from commercial publishers and university presses.

6090 ■ American Society for Ethnohistory Conference
American Society for Ethnohistory
c/o James Buss, Secretary
1101 Camden Ave.
Salisbury, MD 21801
E-mail: jjbuss@salisbury.edu
URL: http://ethnohistory.org

Frequency: Annual. **Primary Exhibits:** Exhibits relating to the cultural history of ethnic groups worldwide.

6091 ■ Congress of the International Society for Human Ethology
International Society for Human Ethology
PO Box 418
Nyack, NY 10960
Ph: (207)581-2044
Fax: (207)581-6128
URL: http://www.ishe.org

Frequency: Biennial. **Primary Exhibits:** Books, journals, and equipment for observational research.

6092 ■ Oral History Association Meeting
Oral History Association
PO Box 4117
Atlanta, GA 30302-4117
Ph: (404)413-5751
Fax: (404)413-6384
E-mail: oha@gsu.edu
URL: http://www.oralhistory.org

Frequency: Annual. **Primary Exhibits:** Equipment, supplies, and services related to recording, transcribing, and preserving conversations constituting oral history.

6093 ■ Organization of American Historians Annual Meeting
Organization of American Historians
112 N Bryan Ave.
Bloomington, IN 47408-4141
Ph: (812)855-7311
Fax: (812)855-0696
E-mail: oah@oah.org
URL: http://www.oah.org

Frequency: Annual. **Primary Exhibits:** Equipment, supplies, and services of interest to historians, including textbooks and computer software.

6094 ■ Society of Architectural Historians Annual Meeting
Society of Architectural Historians
1365 N Astor St.
Chicago, IL 60610-2144
Ph: (312)573-1365
Fax: (312)573-1141
E-mail: info@sah.org
URL: http://www.sah.org

Frequency: Annual. Features a preservation colloquium, workshops for historians, roundtable discussions, reunions, evening lectures and receptions, and an extensive array of local and regional tours.

6095 ■ Southern Historical Association Meeting
Southern Historical Association
University of Georgia
Dept. of History, Rm. 111A
LeConte Hall
Athens, GA 30602-1602
Ph: (706)542-8848
E-mail: sdendy@uga.edu
URL: http://www.uga.edu/sha

Frequency: Annual. **Primary Exhibits:** Publications.

OTHER SOURCES

6096 ■ African Studies Association
Rutgers University
Livingston Campus
54 Joyce Kilmer Ave.
Piscataway, NJ 08854

Ph: (848)445-8173
Fax: (732)445-1366
E-mail: secretariat@africanstudies.org
URL: http://www.africanstudies.org

Description: Persons specializing in teaching, writing, or research on Africa including political scientists, historians, geographers, anthropologists, economists, librarians, linguists, and government officials; persons who are studying African subjects; institutional members are universities, libraries, government agencies, and others interested in receiving information about Africa. Seeks to foster communication and to stimulate research among scholars on Africa. Sponsors placement service; conducts panels and discussion groups; presents exhibits and films.

6097 ■ American Association for State and Local History
1717 Church St.
Nashville, TN 37203-2991
Ph: (615)320-3203
Fax: (615)327-9013
E-mail: membership@aaslh.org
URL: http://www.aaslh.org

Description: Works to preserve and promote history. Ensures the highest-quality expressions of state and local history in publications, exhibitions, and public programs through its diverse services. Represents more than 6,200 individual and institutional members.

6098 ■ American Catholic Historical Association
441 E Fordham Rd.
Dealy Hall, Rm. 637
Bronx, NY 10458
Ph: (718)817-3830
Fax: (718)817-5690
E-mail: acha@fordham.edu
URL: http://achahistory.org

Description: Professional society of historians, educators, students, and others interested in the history of the Catholic Church in the United States and abroad and in the promotion of historical scholarship among Catholics. Has sponsored the publication of the papers of John Carroll, first Bishop and Archbishop of Baltimore, MD.

6099 ■ American Historical Association
400 A St. SE
Washington, DC 20003-3889
Ph: (202)544-2422
Fax: (202)544-8307
E-mail: info@historians.org
URL: http://www.historians.org

Description: Professional historians, educators, and others interested in promoting historical studies and collecting and preserving historical manuscripts. Conducts research and educational programs.

6100 ■ American Institute for Conservation of Historic & Artistic Works
1156 15th St. NW, Ste. 320
Washington, DC 20005
Ph: (202)452-9545
Fax: (202)452-9328
E-mail: info@conservation-us.org
URL: http://www.conservation-us.org

Description: Professionals, scientists, administrators, and educators in the field of art conservation; interested individuals. Advances the practice and promotes the importance of the preservation of cultural property. Coordinates the exchange of knowledge, research, and publications. Establishes and upholds professional standards. Publishes conservation literature. Compiles statistics. Represents membership to allied professional associations and advocates on conservation-related issues. Solicits and dispenses money exclusively for charitable, scientific, and educational objectives.

6101 ■ American Society for Eighteenth-Century Studies
PO Box 7867
Winston-Salem, NC 27109-6253
Ph: (336)727-4694
Fax: (336)727-4697
E-mail: asecs@wfu.edu
URL: http://asecs.press.jhu.edu

Description: Scholars and others interested in the cultural history of the 18th century. Encourages and advances study and research in this area; promotes the interchange of information and ideas among scholars from different disciplines (such as librarianship and bibliography) who are interested in the 18th century. Co-sponsors seven fellowship programs; sponsors Graduate Student Caucus.

6102 ■ American Studies Association
1120 19th St. NW, Ste. 301
Washington, DC 20036
Ph: (202)467-4783
Fax: (202)467-4786
E-mail: asastaff@theasa.net
URL: http://www.theasa.net

Description: Serves as professional society of persons interested in American literature, American history, sociology, anthropology, political science, philosophy, fine arts, and other disciplines; librarians, museum directors, and government officials. Concerned with any field of study relating to American life and culture, past and present. Members are interested in research and teaching that crosses traditional departmental lines.

6103 ■ *Careers for History Buffs & Others Who Learn from the Past*
The McGraw-Hill Companies Inc.
PO Box 182604
Columbus, OH 43272
Ph: (212)512-2000
Free: 877-833-5524
Fax: (614)759-3749
E-mail: customer.service@mcgraw-hill.com
URL: http://www.mcgraw-hill.com

Description: Blythe Camenson. Third edition, 2008. $14.95 (paper). 176 pages. **Includes:** Appendices of living-history museums, U.S. National Park Service regional offices, and associations. Appendices of living-history museums, U.S. National Park Service regional offices, and associations. **Entries include:** Organization name, address.

6104 ■ *Careers for Mystery Buffs and Other Snoops and Sleuths*
The McGraw-Hill Companies Inc.
PO Box 182604
Columbus, OH 43272
Ph: (212)512-2000
Free: 877-833-5524
Fax: (614)759-3749
E-mail: customer.service@mcgraw-hill.com
URL: http://www.mcgraw-hill.com

Description: Blythe Camenson. Second edition. $14.95 (hardback). 160 pages. **Publication includes:** Appendix of associations that provide information about various careers, publish newsletters listing job and internship opportunities, and offer employment services to members. **Entries include:** Name, address.

6105 ■ Flag Research Center
PO Box 580
Winchester, MA 01890-0880
Ph: (781)729-9410
Fax: (781)721-4817
E-mail: vexor@comcast.net
URL: http://www.crwflags.com/fotw/flags/vex-frc.html

Description: Professional and amateur vexillologists (flag historians) seeking to coordinate flag research activities and promote vexillology as a historical discipline and hobby and to increase knowledge of and appreciation for flags of all kinds. Provides data and gives lectures on flag history, etiquette, design, symbolism, and uses. Operates speakers' bureau;

offers children's services and placement service; compiles statistics. Plans to establish museum.

6106 ■ *Grants, Fellowships, and Prizes of Interest to Historians*
American Historical Association
400 A St. SE
Washington, DC 20003-3889
Ph: (202)544-2422
Fax: (202)544-8307
E-mail: grantguide@theaha.org
URL: http://www.historians.org

Frequency: Annual; latest edition 2006. **Covers:** Over 450 sources of funding (scholarships, fellowships, internships, awards, and book and essay prizes) in the United States and abroad for graduate students, postdoctoral researchers, and institutions in the humanities. **Includes:** Bibliography and list of named fellowships. **Entries include:** Name of source, institution name or contact, address, phone, eligibility and proposal requirements, award or stipend amount, location requirements for research, application deadlines. **Arrangement:** Alphabetical in three categories: support for individual research and teaching; grants for groups and organizations for research and education; and book, article, essay, and manuscript prizes.

6107 ■ International Studies Association
324 Social Sciences
Tucson, AZ 85721
Ph: (520)621-7754
Fax: (520)621-5780
E-mail: isa@isanet.org
URL: http://www.isanet.org

Description: Social scientists and other scholars from a wide variety of disciplines who are specialists in international affairs and cross-cultural studies; academicians; government officials; officials in international organizations; business executives; students. Promotes research, improved teaching, and the orderly growth of knowledge in the field of international studies; emphasizes a multidisciplinary approach to problems. Conducts conventions, workshops and discussion groups.

6108 ■ National Coalition for History
400 A St. SE
Washington, DC 20003
Ph: (202)544-2422
E-mail: lwhite@historycoalition.org
URL: http://historycoalition.org

Description: Archival and historical organizations such as: American Historical Association; Organization of American Historians; Phi Alpha Theta; Society of American Archivists; Western History Association. Serves as central advocacy office and information clearinghouse for history/archival related topics affecting government agencies, legislative aides, and professional history and archival associations; develops network of constituent contacts in districts and states; testifies before congressional committees; monitors employment opportunities. **Members:** 72.

6109 ■ National Council on Public History
127 Cavanaugh Hall
425 University Blvd.
Indianapolis, IN 46202
Ph: (317)274-2716
Fax: (317)278-5230
E-mail: ncph@iupui.edu
URL: http://ncph.org

Description: Aims to encourage a broader interest in professional history and to stimulate national interest in public history by promoting its use at all levels of society. (Public history deals with nonacademic history. History is brought to the public rather than the classroom through museum work, public displays, and federal, local, and corporate environments.) Serves as an information clearinghouse; sponsors training programs, local and regional colloquia, projects, and panels. Offers advice to departments of history, historical associations, and others seeking information on public history, professional standards, opportunities, and internships. Conducts surveys and analyses.

6110 ■ Natural History Network
PO Box 11363
Prescott, AZ 86304
Ph: (928)350-2219
URL: http://www.naturalhistorynetwork.org

Description: Promotes the importance of natural history and natural history education in the development of healthy people, vibrant human communities and integrated learning institutions. Facilitates the discussion and dissemination of ideas and techniques pertaining to natural history studies. Serves as a resource of information for the study, practice and teaching of natural history.

6111 ■ Organization of American Historians
112 N Bryan Ave.
Bloomington, IN 47408-4141
Ph: (812)855-7311
Fax: (812)855-0696
E-mail: oah@oah.org
URL: http://www.oah.org

Description: Professional historians, including college faculty members, secondary school teachers, graduate students, and other individuals in related fields; institutional subscribers are college, university, high school and public libraries, and historical agencies. Promotes historical research and study. Sponsors 12 prize programs for historical writing; maintains speakers' bureau. Conducts educational programs.

6112 ■ Society of Architectural Historians
1365 N Astor St.
Chicago, IL 60610-2144
Ph: (312)573-1365
Fax: (312)573-1141
E-mail: info@sah.org
URL: http://www.sah.org

Description: Architects and city planners, educators, scholars, libraries, historical societies, interior designers, museum personnel, students, and others interested in architecture. Promotes the preservation of buildings of historical and aesthetic significance. Encourages scholarly research in the field. Conducts tours in the U.S. and abroad.

6113 ■ Society for Historical Archaeology
13017 Wisteria Dr., Ste. 395
Germantown, MD 20874
Ph: (301)972-9684
Fax: (866)285-3512
E-mail: hq@sha.org
URL: http://www.sha.org

Description: Represents archaeologists, historians, anthropologists, and ethnohistorians; other individuals and institutions with an interest in historical archaeology or allied fields. Aims to bring together persons interested in studying specific historic sites, manuscripts, and published sources, and to develop generalizations concerning historical periods and cultural dynamics as these emerge through the techniques of archaeological excavation and analysis. Main focus is the era beginning with the exploration of the non-European world by Europeans, and geographical areas in the Western Hemisphere, but also considers Oceanian, African,

and Asian archaeology during the relatively late periods.

6114 ■ U.S. Capitol Historical Society
200 Maryland Ave. NE
Washington, DC 20002-5724
Ph: (202)543-8919
Free: 800-887-9318
Fax: (202)544-8244
E-mail: uschs@uschs.org
URL: http://www.uschs.org

Description: Preserves and communicates the history and heritage of the U.S. Capital, its institutions, and the individuals who have served in Congress. Activities include educational programs, popular and scholarly symposia and publications, enhancement of the Capitol's collection of art and artifacts, and research in the U.S. Capitol and the U.S. Congress.

6115 ■ World Archaeological Society
120 Lakewood Dr.
Hollister, MO 65672
Ph: (417)334-2377
Fax: (417)334-5501
E-mail: ronwriterartist@aol.com
URL: http://www.worldarchaeologicalsociety.com

Description: Professional and amateur archaeologists, anthropologists, and art historians in 32 countries. Promotes the scientific and constructive study of antiquity within the fields of archaeology, anthropology, and art history. Conducts research on biblical archaeology, democracy, and the anthropology of drug addiction. Projects include the "Living" Museum of Democracy and the restoration of old Bibles. Conducts special research projects upon request. Supplies tape lectures for special programs. Provides ink and color illustrations for researchers.

Sources of Help-Wanted Ads

6116 ■ *Addiction Professional*
Vendome Group L.L.C.
6 E 32nd St.
New York, NY 10016
Ph: (212)812-8420
Free: 800-519-3692
Fax: (212)228-1308
E-mail: addiction_professional@halldata.com
URL: http://www.addictionpro.com/ME2/default.asp
Frequency: Bimonthly. **Price:** $67 Individuals.
Description: Magazine that publishes innovations and trends in the clinical care of persons with substance use and dependence disorders.

6117 ■ *ADVANCE for Nurse Practitioners*
Merion Publications Inc.
2900 Horizon Dr.
King of Prussia, PA 19406-0956
Ph: (610)278-1400
Free: 800-355-5627
URL: http://nurse-practitioners-and-physician-assistants.advanceweb.com
Frequency: Monthly. **Description:** For practicing nurse practitioner students with senior status.

6118 ■ *American Dental Hygienists' Association Access*
American Dental Hygienists' Association
444 N Michigan Ave., Ste. 3400
Chicago, IL 60611
Ph: (312)440-8900
E-mail: exec.office@adha.net
URL: http://www.adha.org/publications/index.html
Frequency: 10/yr. **Price:** $48 Individuals; $85 Two years; $120 Individuals for 3 years. **Description:** Magazine covering current dental hygiene topics, regulatory and legislative developments, and association news.

6119 ■ *The American Nurse*
American Nurses Credentialing Center
8515 Georgia Ave., Ste. 400
Silver Spring, MD 20910-3492
Free: 800-284-2378
E-mail: adsales@ana.org
URL: http://nursingworld.org/tan/
Frequency: Monthly. **Price:** $20 Individuals practicing nurses; $10 Students. **Description:** Newspaper (tabloid) for the nursing profession.

6120 ■ *Environmental Pollution*
Elsevier Science Inc.
Secondary Publishing Division
650 Ave. of the Americas
New York, NY 10011
Ph: (212)633-3980
Free: 888-437-4636

Fax: (212)633-3975
E-mail: environmentalpollution@mindspring.com
URL: http://www.journals.elsevier.com/environmental-pollution/
Frequency: Monthly. **Price:** $169 Individuals print; $5,442 Institutions online; $6,530 Institutions print.
Description: Journal covering issues relevant to chemical pollutants in air, soil and water.

6121 ■ *Ethnicity and Health*
Routledge Journals - Taylor & Francis Group
270 Madison Ave.
New York, NY 10016-0601
Ph: (212)216-7800
Fax: (212)563-2269
URL: http://www.tandfonline.com/toc/ceth20/current
Frequency: 6/year. **Price:** $1,307 Institutions print + online; $1,144 Institutions online only; $455 Individuals print only. **Description:** Journal covering ethnicity and health.

6122 ■ *Geriatric Nursing*
Mosby Inc.
10801 Executive Center Dr., Ste. 509
Little Rock, AR 72211
Ph: (501)223-5165
Fax: (501)223-0519
URL: http://journals.elsevierhealth.com/periodicals/ymgn
Frequency: Bimonthly. **Price:** $80 Individuals; $141 Individuals Canada; $141 Individuals Mexico; $141 Individuals International. **Description:** Magazine for nurses in geriatric and gerontologic nursing practice, the primary professional providers of care for the aging. Provides news on issues affecting elders and clinical information on techniques and procedures.

6123 ■ *Health & Place*
Mosby Inc.
11830 Westline Industrial Dr.
Saint Louis, MO 63146-3326
Ph: (314)872-8370
Free: 800-325-4177
Fax: (314)432-1380
URL: http://www.journals.elsevier.com/health-and-place/#description
Frequency: 6/yr. **Price:** $853 Institutions all countries except Europe, Japan and Iran; $149 Individuals all countries except Europe, Japan and Iran. **Description:** Journal publishing articles for health care professionals.

6124 ■ *Health Policy, Economics and Management*
Elsevier Science Inc.
Secondary Publishing Division
650 Ave. of the Americas
New York, NY 10011
Ph: (212)633-3980
Free: 888-437-4636

Fax: (212)633-3975
URL: http://www.elsevier.com/journals/health-policy-economics-and-management-section-36-embase/0921-8068
Frequency: 6/yr. **Price:** $441 Individuals associate; €441 Individuals associate; ¥58,100 Individuals associate; ¥447,400 Institutions; $3,726 Institutions; €3,359 Institutions. **Description:** Journal covering the economic, social and political aspects of health care and its organization includes hospital management, health care marketing, hospital automation, and the assessment of new technology for the health care industry.

6125 ■ *Home Healthcare Nurse: The Journal for the Home Care and Hospice Professional*
Lippincott Williams & Wilkins
2 Commerce Sq.
2001 Market St.
Philadelphia, PA 19103
Ph: (301)223-2300
Free: 800-638-3030
E-mail: ronna.ekhouse@wolterskluwer.com
URL: http://journals.lww.com/homehealthcarenurseonline/pages/default.aspx
Frequency: 10/year; 10/yr. **Price:** $65 Individuals; $354 Institutions; $162 Other countries; $510 Institutions, other countries; $42 Individuals in-training.
Description: Magazine for the practicing professional nurse working in the home health, community health, and public health areas. Features include employment listings.

6126 ■ *HomeCare Magazine: For Business Leaders in Home Medical Equipment*
Intertec Publishing
5 Penn Plz., 13th Fl.
New York, NY 10001-1810
Ph: (212)613-9700
Free: 800-795-5445
Fax: (212)613-9749
E-mail: bethany.weaver@penton.com
URLs: http://homecaremag.com/; http://www.penton.com/Market/HealthCare.aspx
Frequency: Monthly. **Price:** Free; $135 Canada; $150 Two years Canada; $250 Other countries; $250 Two years other countries. **Description:** Magazine serving home medical equipment suppliers, including independent and chain centers specializing in home care, pharmacies or chain drug stores with home care products, and joint-ventured hospital home health care businesses. Contains industry news and new product launches and marketing strategies.

6127 ■ *Hospitals & Health Networks*
Health Forum L.L.C.
155 N Wacker Dr., Ste. 400
Chicago, IL 60606
Ph: (312)893-6800
Free: 800-821-2039
Fax: (312)422-4500
URL: http://www.hhnmag.com

Frequency: Weekly. **Price:** Free. **Description:** Publication covering the health care industry.

6128 ■ The IHS Primary Care Provider
U.S. Department of Health and Human Services - Indian Health Service
Reyes Bldg.
801 Thompson Ave., Ste. 400
Rockville, MD 20852-1627
Ph: (301)443-6394
Fax: (301)443-4794
E-mail: charles.grim@ihs.hhs.gov
URL: http://www.ihs.gov/provider
Frequency: Monthly. **Description:** Journal for health care professionals, physicians, nurses, pharmacists, dentists, and dietitians.

6129 ■ The International Electronic Journal of Health Education
American Alliance for Health, Physical Education, Recreation and Dance
1900 Association Dr.
Reston, VA 20191-1598
Ph: (703)476-3400
Free: 800-213-7193
Fax: (703)476-9527
E-mail: membership@aahperd.org
URL: http://www.aahperd.org/aahe/publications/iejhe/
Frequency: Annual. **Price:** Free. **Description:** Journal promoting health through education and other systematic strategies.

6130 ■ Journal of the American College of Nutrition
American College of Nutrition
300 S Duncan Ave., Ste. 225
Clearwater, FL 33755
Ph: (727)446-6086
Fax: (727)446-6202
E-mail: jacn@wayne.edu
URL: http://www.jacn.org
Frequency: Bimonthly. **Price:** $45 Members; $85 Other countries members; $90 Nonmembers; $130 Other countries; $235 Institutions; $275 Institutions, other countries. **Description:** Journal on nutrition.

6131 ■ Journal of the American Society of Podiatric Medical Assistants
American Society of Podiatric Medical Assistants
620 Sedgley Dr.
Knoxville, TN 37922
Ph: (812)326-2046
Free: 888-882-7762
Fax: (812)326-2659
E-mail: suehpmac@gmail.com
URL: http://www.aspma.org
Frequency: Quarterly. **Price:** free for members. **Description:** Professional journal covering issues in podiatry.

6132 ■ Journal of Clinical Ethics: Healthcare, Business and Policy
University Publishing Group Inc.
37 E Antietam St.
Hagerstown, MD 21740
Ph: (240)420-0036
Free: 800-654-8188
Fax: (240)420-0037
URL: http://www.organizationalethics.com
Frequency: Semiannual. **Price:** $175 Institutions; $160 Individuals online; $200 Individuals print and online. **Description:** Magazine covering business and healthcare policy.

6133 ■ Journal of Gerontological Nursing
SLACK Inc.
6900 Grove Rd.
Thorofare, NJ 08086-9447
Ph: (856)848-1000
Free: 877-307-5225
Fax: (856)848-6091
E-mail: jgn@slackinc.com
URL: http://www.slackjournals.com/jgn

Frequency: Monthly. **Price:** $95 Individuals; $190 Two years; $315 Institutions; $630 Institutions two years; $29 Single issue. **Description:** Gerontological nursing journal.

6134 ■ Journal of Nursing Care Quality
Lippincott Williams & Wilkins
351 W Camden St.
Baltimore, MD 21201
Ph: (410)528-4000
URL: http://journals.lww.com/jncqjournal/pages/default.aspx
Frequency: Quarterly; January, April, July, September. **Price:** $111 Individuals; $381 Institutions; $78 Individuals in-training; $213 Other countries; $533 Institutions, other countries. **Description:** Peer-reviewed journal providing practicing nurses and those who play leadership roles in nursing care quality programs the latest on the utilization of quality principles and concepts in the practice setting.

6135 ■ Journal of Nursing Scholarship
Blackwell Publishing Inc.
350 Main St.
Malden, MA 02148
Ph: (781)388-8200
Free: 800-216-2522
Fax: (781)388-8210
E-mail: journaladsusa@bos.blackwellpublishing.com
URL: http://as.wiley.com/WileyCDA/WileyTitle/productCd-JNU.html
Frequency: Quarterly. **Price:** $67 Individuals print & online; $279 Institutions print & online; $242 Institutions print or online; €77 Institutions print or online; £203 Institutions print & online; €258 Institutions print & online; £52 Individuals print & online. **Description:** Peer-reviewed journal covering nursing.

6136 ■ McKnight's Long-Term Care News
McKnight's Long-Term Care News
1 Northfield Plz., Ste. 521
Northfield, IL 60093-1216
Ph: (847)784-8706
Free: 800-558-1703
Fax: (847)441-3701
E-mail: ltcn-webmaster@mitcn.com
URL: http://www.mcknightsonline.com/home
Frequency: 16/yr. **Price:** $60 Individuals; $108 Two years; $75 Canada; $135 Canada two years; $75 Other countries; $135 Other countries two years. **Description:** Professional magazine.

6137 ■ Modern Healthcare: The Weekly Healthcare Business News Magazine
Crain Communications Inc.
150 N Michigan Ave.
Chicago, IL 60601-7553
Ph: (312)649-5200
Free: 800-678-9595
Fax: (312)280-3150
E-mail: subs@crain.com
URL: http://www.modernhealthcare.com
Frequency: Weekly. **Price:** $164 Individuals; $255 Canada; $218 Other countries. **Description:** Weekly business news magazine for healthcare management.

6138 ■ Nursing Administration Quarterly
Lippincott Williams & Wilkins
63430 E Desert Mesa Ct.
Tucson, AZ 857396
Ph: (410)528-4000
E-mail: naqbb@aol.com
URLs: http://www.lww.com/product/?0363-9568; http://journals.lww.com/naqjournal/pages/default.aspx
Frequency: Quarterly. **Price:** $126 Individuals; $431 Institutions; $78 Individuals in-training; $217 Other countries; $573 Institutions, other countries. **Description:** Peer-reviewed journal providing nursing administrators with information on the effective management of nursing services in all health care settings.

6139 ■ Nursing Outlook
Mosby Inc.
c/o Marion E. Broome, PhD, Ed.
Prof. & University Dean
School of Nursing, Indiana University
1111 Middle Dr., NU 132
Indianapolis, IN 46202-5107
Ph: (501)223-5165
Fax: (501)223-0519
URL: http://journals.elsevierhealth.com/periodicals/ymno
Frequency: Bimonthly. **Price:** $133 Canada; $84 Individuals; $133 Individuals Mexico; $133 Other countries. **Description:** Official journal of the American Academy of Nursing, reporting on trends and issues in nursing.

6140 ■ Nutrition Business Journal: Strategic Information for Decision Makers in the Nutrition Industry
Intertec Publishing
1401 Pearl St., Ste. 200
Boulder, CO 80302
Ph: (303)998-9398
E-mail: info@nutritionbusiness.com
URL: http://www.nutritionbusiness.com/
Frequency: Monthly. **Description:** Journal catering to nutrition, natural products and alternative health care industries. Publishes information regarding business activities, market size/growth, trends, and opportunities, with a particular emphasis on the nutrition industry.

6141 ■ Patient Education and Counseling
Mosby Inc.
11830 Westline Industrial Dr.
Saint Louis, MO 63146-3326
Ph: (314)872-8370
Free: 800-325-4177
Fax: (314)432-1380
URL: http://www.journals.elsevier.com/patient-education-and-counseling/
Frequency: Monthly. **Price:** $317 Individuals print or online; ¥37,700 Individuals print or online; €288 Individuals print or online. **Description:** Journal publishing articles on patient education and health promotion researchers, managers, physicians, nurses and other health care provider.

6142 ■ Provider: For Long Term Care Professionals
American Health Care Association
1201 L St. NW
Washington, DC 20005
Ph: (202)842-4444
Fax: (202)842-3860
E-mail: sales@ahca.org
URL: http://www.providermagazine.com
Frequency: Monthly. **Price:** free to long-term health care professionals; $48/year for nonmembers and libraries; $61 Canada and Mexico; $85 Other countries. **Description:** Includes buyers' guide, news reports, advertisers' index, a listing of new products and services, and calendar of events.

6143 ■ Public Health Forum
Elsevier Science Inc.
Secondary Publishing Division
650 Ave. of the Americas
New York, NY 10011
Ph: (212)633-3980
Free: 888-437-4636
Fax: (212)633-3975
URL: http://www.journals.elsevier.com/public-health-forum/
Frequency: 4/yr. **Price:** $48 Individuals print; $54 Institutions print. **Description:** Journal focused on research methods, and program evaluation in the field of public health.

6144 ■ *Public Health Law & Policy Journal*
University of Hawaii - National Foreign Language
Resource Center
1859 E-W Rd., No. 106
Honolulu, HI 96822-2322
Ph: (808)956-9424
Fax: (808)956-5983
E-mail: phlo@hawaii.edu
URL: http://www.hawaii.edu/phlo/phlpj/

Price: Free. **Description:** Open access academic journal covering worldwide public health issues.

6145 ■ **Public Health, Social Medicine and Epidemiology**
Elsevier Science Inc.
Secondary Publishing Division
650 Ave. of the Americas
New York, NY 10011
Ph: (212)633-3980
Free: 888-437-4636
Fax: (212)633-3975
URL: http://www.elsevier.com/journals/public-health
-social-medicine-and-epidemiology-section-17
-embase/0924-5723

Frequency: Semimonthly. **Price:** $8,824 Institutions; ¥1,048,500 Institutions; €7,949 Institutions. **Description:** Journal covering public health and social medicine, and includes health planning and education, epidemiology and prevention of communicable disease, public health aspects of risk populations.

6146 ■ *Quality Management in Health Care*
Lippincott Williams & Wilkins
351 W Camden St.
Baltimore, MD 21201
Ph: (410)528-4000
URL: http://journals.lww.com/qmhcjournal/pages/
default.aspx

Frequency: Quarterly. **Price:** $124 Individuals; $376 Institutions; $64 Individuals in-training; $218 Other countries; $565 Institutions, other countries. **Description:** Peer-reviewed journal providing a forum to explore the theoretical, technical, and strategic elements of total quality management in health care.

6147 ■ *Rehabilitation Nursing: The Official Journal of the Association of Rehabilitation Nurses*
Rehabilitation Nursing
4700 W Lake Ave.
Glenview, IL 60025
Ph: (847)375-4710
Free: 800-229-7530
Fax: (847)375-6481
E-mail: info@rehabnurse.org
URL: http://awebsource.com/clients/arn/ws_resource/
public_index.php

Frequency: Bimonthly. **Price:** $120 Individuals regular; $150 Individuals premium; $195 Other countries regular; $240 Other countries premium; $175 Institutions regular (USA); $220 Institutions premium (USA); $195 Institutions regular (international); $240 Institutions premium (international). **Description:** Magazine focusing on rehabilitation nursing involving clinical practice, research, education, and administration.

6148 ■ *Supporting Innovations in Gerontological Nursing*
National Gerontological Nursing Association
3493 Lansdowne Dr., Ste. 2
Lexington, KY 40517-1147
Ph: (859)977-7453
Free: 800-723-0560
Fax: (859)271-0607
E-mail: info@ngna.org
URL: http://www.ngna.org

Description: Bimonthly. Provides updates on NGNA's activities as well as other information of interest to gerontological nurses. Features job opportunities in the field.

EMPLOYER DIRECTORIES AND NETWORKING LISTS

6149 ■ *Medical and Health Information Directory: A Guide to Organizations, Agencies, Institutions, Programs, Publications, Services, and Other Resources Concerned with Clinical Medicine*
Cengage Learning Inc.
200 1st Stamford Pl., Ste. 400
Stamford, CT 06902-6753
Ph: (203)965-8600
Free: 800-354-9706
Fax: (800)487-8488
E-mail: investors@cengage.com
URL: http://www.gale.cengage.com

Frequency: Annual; Latest edition April 2011. **Price:** $1,190 Individuals set; $501 Individuals per volume. **Covers:** In volume 1, more than 33,000 medical and health oriented associations, organizations, institutions, and government agencies, including health maintenance organizations (HMOs), preferred provider organizations (PPOs), insurance companies, pharmaceutical companies, research centers, and medical and allied health schools. In Volume 2, over 20,000 medical book publishers; medical periodicals, directories, audiovisual producers and services, medical libraries and information centers, electronic resources, and health-related internet search engines. In Volume 3, more than 40,500 clinics, treatment centers, care programs, and counseling/diagnostic services for 34 subject areas. **Entries include:** Institution, service, or firm name, address, phone, fax, email and URL; many include names of key personnel and, when pertinent, descriptive annotation. Volume 3 was formerly listed separately as Health Services Directory. **Arrangement:** Classified by organization activity, service, etc. **Indexes:** Each volume has a complete alphabetical name and keyword index.

HANDBOOKS AND MANUALS

6150 ■ *Being a Nursing Assistant*
Prentice Hall PTR
1 Lake St.
Upper Saddle River, NJ 07458
Ph: (201)236-7676
Free: 800-227-1816
Fax: (800)445-6991
URL: http://phbusiness.prenhall.com

Description: Francie Wolgin. Ninth edition, 2005. $76.13 (paper). 800 pages.

6151 ■ *Core Curriculum for the Licensed Practical/Vocational Hospice and Palliative Nurse*
Kendall/Hunt Publishing Co.
4050 Westmark Dr.
Dubuque, IA 52002
Ph: (563)589-1000
Free: 800-228-0810
Fax: (563)589-1046
E-mail: orders@kendallhunt.com
URL: http://www.kendallhunt.com

Description: Hospice & Palliative Nurses Association. 2010. $60.00. 250 pages.

6152 ■ *Home Health Aide Training Manual and Handbook*
iUniverse Inc.
1663 Liberty Dr., Ste. 300
Bloomington, IN 47403-5161
Ph: (402)323-7800
Free: 800-288-4677
Fax: (812)355-4085
E-mail: media@iuniverse.com
URL: http://www.iuniverse.com

Description: Emmanuel C. Anene. 2009. $12.95

(softcover). 108 pages. Serves as a teaching and training tool for home health aides. Includes information on federal and state rules and regulations that a home health aide must be familiar with.

6153 ■ *Nursing Today: Transition and Trends*
W. B. Saunders Co.
6277 Sea Harbor Dr.
Orlando, FL 32887
Ph: (407)345-2000
Free: 800-654-2452
URL: http://www.elsevier.com

Description: JoAnn Zerwekh and Jo C. Claborn, editors. Sixth edition, 2009. $52.95 (paper). 640 pages.

6154 ■ *Opportunities in Health and Medical Careers*
The McGraw-Hill Companies Inc.
PO Box 182604
Columbus, OH 43272
Ph: (212)512-2000
Free: 877-833-5524
Fax: (614)759-3749
E-mail: customer.service@mcgraw-hill.com
URL: http://www.mcgraw-hill.com

Description: I. Donald Snook, Jr. and Leo D'Orazio. 2004. $14.95 (paper). 157 pages. Covers the full range of medical and health occupations. Illustrated.

6155 ■ *Resumes for Health and Medical Careers*
The McGraw-Hill Companies Inc.
PO Box 182604
Columbus, OH 43272
Ph: (212)512-2000
Free: 877-833-5524
Fax: (614)759-3749
E-mail: customer.service@mcgraw-hill.com
URL: http://www.mcgraw-hill.com

Description: Third edition, 2008. $12.95 (paper). 144 pages.

EMPLOYMENT AGENCIES AND SEARCH FIRMS

6156 ■ **Boone-Scaturro Associates Inc.**
8831 S Somerset Ln.
Alpharetta, GA 30004
Ph: (770)740-9737
Free: 800-749-1884
Fax: (770)475-5055
E-mail: admin@boone-scaturro.com
URL: http://www.boone-scaturro.com

Description: Executive search firm focused on the healthcare industry.

6157 ■ **Professional Placement Associates, Inc.**
287 Bowman Ave.
Purchase, NY 10577-2517
Ph: (914)251-1000
Fax: (914)251-1055
E-mail: careers@ppasearch.com
URL: http://www.ppasearch.com

Description: Executive search firm specializing in the health and medical field.

ONLINE JOB SOURCES AND SERVICES

6158 ■ **CertifiedHomeHealthAide.net**
URL: http://www.certifiedhomehealthaide.net

Description: Lists job openings for home health aid professionals. Includes job and resume posting and other services.

6159 ■ HealthCareerWeb.com
URL: http://www.healthcareerweb.com

Description: Advertises jobs for healthcare professionals. Main files include: Jobs, Employers, Resumes, Jobwire. Relocation tools and career guidance resources available.

6160 ■ HEALTHeCAREERS Network
URL: http://www.healthecareers.com

Description: Career search site for jobs in all health care specialties; educational resources; visa and licensing information for relocation; interesting articles; relocation tools; links to professional organizations and general resources.

6161 ■ Monster Healthcare
URL: http://healthcare.monster.com

Description: Delivers nationwide access to healthcare recruiting. Employers can post job listings or ads. Job seekers can post and code resumes, and search over 150,000 healthcare job listings, healthcare career advice columns, career resources information, and member employer profiles and services.

6162 ■ ProHealthJobs.com
URL: http://prohealthjobs.com/jobboard

Description: Career resources site for the medical and health care field. Lists professional opportunities, product information, continuing education and open positions.

TRADESHOWS

6163 ■ NAHC's Annual Meeting and Home Care and Hospice Expo
National Association for Home Care
228 Seventh St. SE
Washington, DC 20003
Ph: (202)547-7424
Fax: (202)547-3540
E-mail: pr@nahc.org
URL: http://www.nahc.org

Frequency: Annual. **Primary Exhibits:** General home health products, emergency response systems, computers, uniforms, publications, surgical and medical supplies, pharmaceuticals, durable and home medical equipment.

OTHER SOURCES

6164 ■ American Assembly for Men in Nursing
6700 Oporto-Madrid Blvd.
Birmingham, AL 35206
Ph: (205)956-0146
Fax: (205)956-0149
E-mail: aamn@aamn.org
URL: http://aamn.org

Description: Registered nurses. Works to: help eliminate prejudice in nursing; interest men in the nursing profession; provide opportunities for the discussion of common problems; encourage education and promote further professional growth; advise and assist in areas of professional inequity; help develop sensitivities to various social needs; promote the principles and practices of positive health care. Acts as a clearinghouse for information on men in nursing. Conducts educational programs. Promotes education and research about men's health issues. **Members:** 2,300.

6165 ■ American Geriatrics Society
40 Fulton St., 18th Fl.
New York, NY 10038
Ph: (212)308-1414

Fax: (212)832-8646
E-mail: info.amger@americangeriatrics.org
URL: http://www.americangeriatrics.org

Description: Represents health professionals. Focuses on improving the health, independence and quality of life of older people. Provides leadership to healthcare professionals, policy makers, and the public by implementing and advocating for programs in patient care, research, professional and public education, and public policy.

6166 ■ American Health Care Association
1201 L St. NW
Washington, DC 20005
Ph: (202)842-4444
Fax: (202)842-3860
URL: http://www.ahcancal.org/Pages/Default.aspx

Description: Federation of state associations of long-term health care facilities. Promotes standards for professionals in long-term health care delivery and quality care for patients and residents in a safe environment. Focuses on issues of availability, quality, affordability, and fair payment. Operates as liaison with governmental agencies, Congress, and professional associations. Compiles statistics.

6167 ■ American Public Health Association
800 I St. NW
Washington, DC 20001-3710
Ph: (202)777-2742
Fax: (202)777-2534
E-mail: comments@apha.org
URL: http://www.apha.org

Description: Professional organization of physicians, nurses, educators, academicians, environmentalists, epidemiologists, new professionals, social workers, health administrators, optometrists, podiatrists, pharmacists, dentists, nutritionists, health planners, other community and mental health specialists, and interested consumers. Seeks to protect and promote personal, mental, and environmental health. Services include: promulgation of standards; establishment of uniform practices and procedures; development of the etiology of communicable diseases; research in public health; exploration of medical care programs and their relationships to public health. Sponsors job placement service.

6168 ■ *Health-Care Careers for the 21st Century*
JIST Publishing
875 Montreal Way
Saint Paul, MN 55102-4245
Ph: (317)613-4200
Free: 800-648-5478
Fax: (800)328-4564
E-mail: info@jist.com
URL: http://www.jist.com

Price: $9.95 Individuals Softcover. **Pages:** 448. **Covers:** Jobs for health care professionals and career opportunities for those pursuing a health-related career, organized into 80 careers in five groups. **Publication includes:** Appendixes listing job source resources and Web sites for health organizations.

6169 ■ National Association of Professional Geriatric Care Managers
3275 W Ina Rd., Ste. 130
Tucson, AZ 85741-2198
Ph: (520)881-8008
Fax: (520)325-7925
E-mail: kboothroyd@napgcm.org
URL: http://www.caremanager.org

Description: Promotes quality services and care for elderly citizens. Provides referral service and distributes information to individuals interested in geriatric care management. Maintains referral network.

6170 ■ National Gerontological Nursing Association
3493 Lansdowne Dr., Ste. 2
Lexington, KY 40517-1147
Ph: (859)977-7453
Free: 800-723-0560
Fax: (859)271-0607
E-mail: info@ngna.org
URL: http://www.ngna.org

Description: Bimonthly. Provides updates on NGNA's activities as well as other information of interest to gerontological nurses. Features job opportunities in the field.

6171 ■ National League for Nursing
61 Broadway, 33rd Fl.
New York, NY 10006
Ph: (212)812-0300
Free: 800-669-1656
Fax: (212)812-0391
E-mail: generalinfo@nln.org
URL: http://www.nln.org

Description: Champions the pursuit of quality nursing education. A professional association of nursing faculty, education agencies, health care agencies, allied/public agencies, and public members whose mission is to advance quality nursing education that prepares the nursing workforce to meet the needs of diverse populations in an ever-changing health care environment. Serves as the primary source of information about every type of nursing education program, from the LVN and LPN to the EdD and PhD. There are 20 affiliated constituent leagues that provide a local forum for members. The National League for Nursing Accrediting Commission is an independent corporate affiliate of the NLN, responsible for providing accreditation services to all levels of nursing education.

6172 ■ National Rural Health Association
4501 College Blvd., No. 225
Leawood, KS 66211
Ph: (816)756-3140
Fax: (816)756-3144
E-mail: mail@nrharural.org
URL: http://www.ruralhealthweb.org

Description: Administrators, physicians, nurses, physician assistants, health planners, academicians, and others interested or involved in rural health care. Creates a better understanding of health care problems unique to rural areas; utilizes a collective approach in finding positive solutions; articulates and represents the health care needs of rural America; supplies current information to rural health care providers; serves as a liaison between rural health care programs throughout the country. Offers continuing education credits for medical, dental, nursing, and management courses.

6173 ■ Visiting Nurse Associations of America
2121 Crystal Dr., Ste. 750
Arlington, VA 22202
Ph: (571)527-1520
Free: 888-866-8773
Fax: (571)527-1521
E-mail: vnaa@vnaa.org
URL: http://www.vnaa.org

Description: Home health care agencies. Develops competitive strength among community-based nonprofit visiting nurse organizations; works to strengthen business resources and economic programs through contracting, marketing, governmental affairs and publications. **Members:** 210.

SOURCES OF HELP-WANTED ADS

6174 ■ Hotel F & B Executive
Hotel Forums L.L.C.
613 Kane St.
West Dundee, IL 60118
Ph: (847)551-9956
E-mail: hotelf&b@theygsgroup.com
URL: http://www.hotelfandb.com
Frequency: Bimonthly. **Price:** $49 Individuals; $15 Students; $59 Institutions. **Description:** Magazine that addresses the needs of the hospitality F&B markets, which include hotels, resorts, cruise lines and conference, and convention & meeting centers.

6175 ■ Hotel & Motel Management
Questex Media Group L.L.C.
600 Superior Ave. E, Ste. 1100
Cleveland, OH 44114
Ph: (216)706-3791
Fax: (216)706-3711
E-mail: sales@questex.com
URL: http://www.hotelmanagement.net/hotel-management/hotel-management-archive
Frequency: 21/yr. **Price:** $58.85 Individuals; $81.40 Canada and Mexico; $143 Other countries; $75 Individuals additional airmail shipping. **Description:** Magazine (tabloid) covering the global lodging industry.

6176 ■ HOTELS: The Magazine of the Worldwide Hotel Industry
Marketing & Technology Group Inc.
1415 N Dayton St.
Chicago, IL 60622
Ph: (312)266-3311
Fax: (312)266-3363
URL: http://www.hotelsmag.com/
Frequency: Monthly. **Price:** Free. **Description:** Magazine covering management and operations as well as foodservice and design in the hospitality industry.

6177 ■ Lodging Hospitality: The Ideas for Hotel Developers and Operators
Intertec Publishing
5 Penn Plz., 13th Fl.
New York, NY 10001-1810
Ph: (212)613-9700
Free: 800-795-5445
Fax: (212)613-9749
E-mail: bethany.weaver@penton.com
URL: http://lhonline.com/
Frequency: 10/yr. **Description:** Magazine serving managers of independent, franchise, chain-owned, and referral groups in the hospitality industry.

EMPLOYER DIRECTORIES AND NETWORKING LISTS

6178 ■ Career Opportunities in Casinos and Casino Hotels
InfoBase Holdings Inc.
132 W 31st., 17 Fl.
New York, NY 10001-3406

Ph: (212)967-8800
Fax: (800)678-3633
E-mail: info@infobasepublishing.com
URL: http://factsonfile.infobasepublishing.com/
Frequency: Irregular; Latest edition 2nd; Published May, 2009. **Price:** $49.50 Individuals hardcover. **Description:** Directory of casinos and cruise lines, gaming conferences and expos, seminars, workshops, and industry Web sites. **Publication includes:** A directory of casinos and cruise lines, gaming conferences and expos, seminars, workshops, and industry Web sites. Principal content of publication is 100 occupations in 10 employment sections on careers in gaming, administration, management, security, entertainment, hotel management, and food and beverage service in the casino industry.

6179 ■ Official Hotel Guide
Northstar Travel Media L.L.C.
100 Lighting Way, 2nd Fl.
Secaucus, NJ 07094
Ph: (201)902-2000
Free: 800-742-7076
Fax: (201)902-2045
E-mail: secausushelpdesk@ntmllc.com
URL: http://www.northstartravelmedia.com/
Frequency: Annual. **Pages:** 1,000 approx. per volume. **Covers:** in four volumes, 29,000 hotels, motels, and resorts worldwide. Volume 1 covers most of the U.S. ; Volume 2 covers the rest of the U.S. and the Western Hemisphere; Volume 3 covers Europe, the Middle East, Asia, and Africa. Volume 4 specialty travel guide includes listings of golf resorts and tennis resorts; health spas, dude ranches, bed and breakfasts, and casino & hotels in the United States; also includes lists of hotels in the Caribbean with golf, tennis, casinos, and all-inclusive. **Entries include:** Hotel/motel/resort name, address, phone, fax, CRS's, number of rooms or units, rates, brief description of facilities, ratings, codes indicating credit cards accepted, email and website addresses, and travel agent's commission, if any. **Arrangement:** Geographical.

6180 ■ Red Roof Directory
Red Roof
2071 N Bechtle Ave.
Springfield, OH 45504-1583
Free: 800-733-7663
URL: http://www.redroof.com
Covers: Listings of 345 inns in 36 states. **Includes:** Maps.

6181 ■ Vault Guide to the Top Hospitality & Tourism Industry Employers
Vault.com Inc.
132 W 31st St., 17th Fl.
New York, NY 10001-3406
Ph: (212)366-4212
Free: 800-535-2074

Fax: (212)366-6117
E-mail: customerservice@vault.com
URL: http://www.vault.com/wps/portal/usa/store/bookdetail?item_no=780
Frequency: Published 2008. **Price:** $19.95 Individuals Online; $19.95 Individuals Gold. **Pages:** 392. **Covers:** Hospitality and tourism industry employers. **Entries include:** Name, address, phone, fax, website, and branch office location. Also include company overviews, recent company news, information on the hiring process, key competitors, and employment contact. **Arrangement:** Alphabetical by company name.

HANDBOOKS AND MANUALS

6182 ■ Expert Resumes for Managers and Executives
Jist Works
875 Montreal Way
Saint Paul, MN 55102
Free: 800-648-5478
E-mail: info@jist.com
URL: http://www.jist.com/shop/product.php?productid=16727
Description: Wendy S. Enelow, Louise M. Kursmark. 2012. $17.95. 274 pages. Contains a collection of sample resumes and resume writing advice including how to create and use an electronic resume. Contains an appendix that includes internet resources for an online job search, writing cover letters, as well as a collection of sample letters.

6183 ■ Jobs for Travel Lovers: Opportunities at Home and Abroad
Development Concepts Inc.
9104 Manassas Dr., Ste. N
Manassas Park, VA 20111-5211
Ph: (703)361-7300
Free: 800-361-1055
Fax: (703)335-9486
E-mail: query@impactpublications.com
URL: http://www.impactpublications.com
Description: 2006. $19.95. 320 pages. Covers job search strategies, with hundreds of jobs in business, government, and education, including the travel and hospital industry, non-profit organizations, international organizations, education institutions, and consulting. Includes opportunities involving airlines and cruise lines, international jobs, travel agencies and tour operators, internships and volunteering, hotels and resorts, military and merchant marine, teaching abroad, travel writing, and short-term work experiences. Provides names, addresses, telephone/fax numbers, e-mails, and websites for contacting potential employers.

6184 ■ Manager's Handbook: Everything You Need to Know about How Business and Management Work
Pearson Learning Group
145 S Mount Zion Rd.
Lebanon, IN 46052

Ph: (804)402-6933
Free: 800-526-9907
Fax: (800)393-3156
E-mail: pasley@pearsonlearning.com
URL: http://www.k12pearson.com
Price: $24.95. **Publication includes:** Principal content of publication is reference guide for new and experienced managers. **Indexes:** Alphabetical.

6185 ■ Opportunities in Hotel and Motel Management Careers
The McGraw-Hill Companies Inc.
PO Box 182604
Columbus, OH 43272
Ph: (212)512-2000
Free: 877-833-5524
Fax: (614)759-3749
E-mail: customer.service@mcgraw-hill.com
URL: http://www.mcgraw-hill.com
Description: Shepard Henkin. 2000. $12.95 (paper). 160 pages.

6186 ■ Purchasing for Chefs: A Concise Guide
John Wiley & Sons Inc.
111 River St.
Hoboken, NJ 07030-5774
Ph: (201)748-6000
Free: 800-225-5945
Fax: (201)748-6088
E-mail: info@wiley.com
URL: http://www.wiley.com
Description: Andrew H. Feinstein and John M. Stefanelli. 2010. $51.95. 256 pages. Guide details purchasing principles to chefs and hospitality managers for obtaining goods and services for their business.

6187 ■ So You Want to Be an Innkeeper
Chronicle Books L.L.C.
680 2nd St.
San Francisco, CA 94107-2015
Ph: (415)537-4200
Free: 800-759-0190
E-mail: frontdesk@chroniclebooks.com
URL: http://www.chroniclebooks.com
Description: Jo Ann M. Bell, Susan Brown, Mary Davies, and Pat Hardy, et al. Fourth edition, 2004. $16.95 (paper). 336 pages.

EMPLOYMENT AGENCIES AND SEARCH FIRMS

6188 ■ The Alfus Group Inc.
353 Lexington Ave.
New York, NY 10016
Ph: (212)599-1000
Fax: (212)599-1523
E-mail: mail@thealfusgroup.com
URL: http://www.thealfusgroup.com
Description: Executive search firm. Specializes in the hospitality industry.

6189 ■ Boutique Search Firm
1173 Rodeo Dr.
Los Angeles, CA 90035
Ph: (310)552-2221
Fax: (310)552-2224
URL: http://www.boutiquesearchfirm.com
Description: Serves as a recruiting firm specializing in hospitality management. Offers jobs in luxury hotels and resorts worldwide.

6190 ■ Bowman & Associates
1660 S Amphlett Blvd., Ste. 245
San Mateo, CA 94402
Ph: (650)573-0188
Fax: (650)573-8209
E-mail: contact@bowmansearch.com
URL: http://www.bowmansearch.com

Description: Executive search firm specializes in the hospitality industry. Also specializes: Food service, asset management, lodging, real estate development, E-Commerce, gaming, travel, theme parks.

6191 ■ ChaseAmerica Inc.
1800 JFK Blvd., Ste. 300
New York, NY 10022
Ph: (215)338-1952
Free: 800-491-4980
E-mail: info@chaseamericainc.com
URL: http://www.chaseamericainc.com
Description: Executive search firm.

6192 ■ The Elliot Group LLC
505 White Plains Rd., Ste. 228
Tarrytown, NY 10591
Ph: (914)631-4904
Fax: (914)631-6481
URL: http://www.theelliotgroup.com
Description: Executive search firm. Six locations throughout the United States.

6193 ■ Gecko Hospitality
16880 McGregor Blvd., Ste. 102
Fort Myers, FL 33908
Free: 800-948-7731
URL: http://www.geckohospitality.com
Description: Serves as a hospitality recruiter specializing in placing candidates in hospitality jobs as well as securing qualified hospitality professionals for its clients. Provides a database of hospitality jobs, restaurant jobs, hotel jobs, and casino jobs.

6194 ■ Global Hospitality
3579 E Foothill Blvd., Ste. 229
Pasadena, CA 91107
Ph: (626)836-1222
Fax: (626)836-1223
E-mail: mail@globalhospitality.com
URL: http://www.globalhospitality.com
Description: Executive search firm that specializes in identifying, evaluating, and placing leadership and management talent in the hospitality industry.

6195 ■ Harper Associates
31000 NW Hwy., Ste. 240
Farmington Hills, MI 48334
Ph: (248)932-1170
Fax: (248)932-1214
E-mail: info@harperjobs.com
URL: http://www.harperjobs.com
Description: Executive search firm and employment agency.

6196 ■ Hospitality International
236 5th Ave., Ste. 907
New York, NY 10001
Ph: (212)696-1661
Fax: (212)696-1669
E-mail: jar@hospitalityinternational.com
URL: http://www.hospitalityinternational.com
Description: Executive search firm. Branch office in New York, NY.

6197 ■ Hospitality Marketing & Recruiting
PO Box 970023
Boca Raton, FL 33497
Ph: (561)289-1873
Fax: (561)852-6447
E-mail: rstevens@hospitalityjobsbyhmr.com
URL: http://www.hospitalityjobsbyhmr.com
Description: Provides executive search and placement services of management level hospitality personnel for hotels, country clubs, cruise ships, attractions and restaurants.

6198 ■ Hospitality Pro Search
7229 Foxworth Dr.
Dallas, TX 75248
Ph: (214)628-1079

Fax: (214)540-1203
E-mail: gary@hprosearch.com
URL: http://www.hprosearch.com
Description: Serves as an executive search firm for the hospitality industry. Specializes in worldwide management placements for restaurants, hotels and resorts, entertainment venues, and private clubs.

6199 ■ Hospitality Recruiters
10706 Cortland Ridge Ln.
Cypress, TX 77433
Free: 877-735-1133
E-mail: career@hospitalityrecruiters.com
URL: http://www.hospitalityrecruiters.com
Description: Specializes in the placement of managers within the restaurant and hotel industries.

6200 ■ HospitalityStaff.com
3195 Tamiami Trail, Ste. 204
Port Charlotte, FL 33952
Ph: (941)743-8540
Free: 800-987-1555
Fax: (941)743-9684
URL: http://www.hospitalitystaff.com
Description: Serves as a placement agency, specializing in the supply of temporary and permanent staff to the hospitality industry.

6201 ■ Robert Howe and Associates
3331 Bolero Dr.
Atlanta, GA 30341
Ph: (770)270-1211
Fax: (770)270-1209
E-mail: rwhamill@roberthoweassociates.com
URL: http://www.roberthoweassociates.com
Description: Provider of consulting services in the area of executive search and recruitment. Industries served: healthcare, hospitality, chemical, metals, electronics, construction, and food processing.

6202 ■ The IMC Group of Companies Ltd.
120 White Plains Rd., Ste. 405
Tarrytown, NY 10591
Ph: (914)468-7050
Fax: (914)468-7051
URL: http://www.the-imc.com
Description: International executive recruiting and management consulting company providing leading-edge services for the hospitality, leisure, entertainment, gaming and new media industries throughout the United States, Europe, Africa, Asia Pacific and Latin America.

6203 ■ J.D. Hersey and Associates
8 E Poplar Ave.
Columbus, OH 43215
Ph: (614)228-4022
Fax: (614)228-4085
URL: http://www.jdhersey.com
Description: Executive search firm for permanent and contingency placements.

6204 ■ Prospection Group
PO Box 1999
Santa Monica, CA 90406
Ph: (310)398-3795
URL: http://www.prospectiongroup.com
Description: Executive search firm for the hospitality industry. Searches for hospitality executives ranging from the level of general management to private chefs.

6205 ■ Robert W. Dingman Company Inc.
650 Hampshire Rd., No. 116
Westlake Village, CA 91361
Ph: (805)778-1777
Fax: (805)778-9288
E-mail: info@dingman.com
URL: http://www.dingman.com
Description: Executive search firm with a second office in Black Forest, CO.

6206 ■ Travel People Personnel
1199 Park Ave., Ste. 3E
New York, NY 10126
Ph: (212)348-6942
Fax: (212)348-6958
E-mail: sue@travelpeople.com
URL: http://www.travelpeople.com

Description: Provided regular and temporary staffing services New Englands Travel and Tourism businesses.

ONLINE JOB SOURCES AND SERVICES

6207 ■ FoodServicesCrossing.com
URL: http://www.foodservicescrossing.com

Description: Features job listings for the food services industry.

6208 ■ HCareers.com
URL: http://www.hcareers.com

Description: Connects employers and candidates within the hospitality industry. Enables candidates to search for jobs within a specific industry or location.

6209 ■ Hospitality Jobs Online
URL: http://www.hospitalityonline.com

Description: Enables hospitality industry job seekers to find career information, information about employers and tips and techniques to help them succeed. Provides daily updates of hotel jobs, resort jobs, restaurant jobs and club jobs nationwide.

6210 ■ Hotel Jobs Network
URL: http://www.hoteljobsnetwork.com/home

Description: Online job site for the hospitality industry.

6211 ■ Hotel Online
URL: http://www.hotel-online.com

Description: Provides news, trends, discussion forums, employment opportunities, and classified advertising for the hospitality industry.

6212 ■ HotelJobs.com
URL: http://www.hoteljobs.com

Description: Provides job postings and resume database for hotel, casino and cruise ship professionals and recruiters.

TRADESHOWS

6213 ■ Americas Lodging Investment Summit
Burba Hotel Network
2900 Bristol St., Ste. D101
Costa Mesa, CA 92626
Ph: (714)540-9300
URL: http://www.burba.com

Frequency: Annual. Features an array of seminars, workshops and presentations about timely issues facing the hotel investment community. Brings together experts and investors to discuss trends and to identify new opportunities.

6214 ■ Annual Hotel, Motel, and Restaurant Supply Show of the Southeast
Leisure Time Unlimited, Inc.
708 Main St.
Myrtle Beach, SC 29577
Ph: (843)448-9483
Free: 800-261-5591
Fax: (843)626-1513
E-mail: ltushows@sc.rr.com
URL: http://www.leisuretimeunlimited.com/

Frequency: Annual. **Primary Exhibits:** Carpeting, furniture, coffee makers, produce companies, wine and beer and food companies, and services to motels, hotels, and restaurants. **Dates and Locations:** Myrtle Beach, SC; Convention Center.

6215 ■ Hospitality Design
VNU Expositions
14685 Avion Pkwy., Ste. 400
Chantilly, VA 20151
Ph: (703)488-2700
Free: 800-765-7615
Fax: (703)488-2725
URL: http://www.vnuexpo.com

Frequency: Annual. **Primary Exhibits:** Hospitality industry equipment, supplies, and services.

6216 ■ IH/M & RS - International Hotel/Motel & Restaurant Show
American Hotel and Lodging Association
1201 New York Ave. NW, Ste. 600
Washington, DC 20005-3931
Ph: (202)289-3100
Free: 800-752-4567
Fax: (202)289-3199
E-mail: informationcenter@ahla.com
URL: http://www.ahla.com

Frequency: Annual. **Primary Exhibits:** Products and services for lodging and food service properties, including: technology, uniforms, linens and bedding, tabletop accessories, guest amenities and services, food and beverages, cleaning maintenance, food service equipment and supplies, franchising information, finance and management furnishings and fixtures, fitness equipment, and leisure and entertainment services. **Dates and Locations:** New York, NY; Jacob K. Javits Convention Center.

6217 ■ West Ex: The Rocky Mountain Regional Hospitality Exposition
Colorado Restaurant Association
430 E 7th Ave.
Denver, CO 80203
Ph: (303)830-2972
Free: 800-522-2972
Fax: (303)830-2973
E-mail: info@coloradorestaurant.com
URL: http://www.coloradorestaurant.com

Frequency: Annual. **Primary Exhibits:** Food service and lodging products, equipment, and services.

6218 ■ Western Food Service & Hospitality Expo Los Angeles
California Restaurant Association
621 Capitol Mall, Ste. 2000
Sacramento, CA 95814
Ph: (916)447-5793
Free: 800-765-4842
Fax: (916)447-6182
E-mail: membership@calrest.org
URL: http://www.calrest.org

Primary Exhibits: Food, equipment, supplies, and services for food service and lodging industries. **Dates and Locations:** Los Angeles, CA; LA Convention Center.

OTHER SOURCES

6219 ■ American Hotel and Lodging Association
1201 New York Ave. NW, Ste. 600
Washington, DC 20005-3931
Ph: (202)289-3100
Free: 800-752-4567
Fax: (202)289-3199
E-mail: informationcenter@ahla.com
URL: http://www.ahla.com

Description: Represents state lodging associations throughout the United States with some 13,000 property members worldwide, representing more than 1.7 million guest rooms. Provides its members with assistance in operations, education and communications and lobbies on Capitol Hill to provide a business climate in which the industry can continue to prosper. Individual state associations provide representation at the state level and offer many additional cost-saving benefits.

6220 ■ Club Managers Association of America
1733 King St.
Alexandria, VA 22314
Ph: (703)739-9500
Fax: (703)739-0124
URL: http://www.cmaa.org

Description: Professional managers and assistant managers of private golf, yacht, athletic, city, country, luncheon, university, and military clubs. Encourages education and advancement of members and promotes efficient and successful club operations. Provides reprints of articles on club management. Supports courses in club management. Compiles statistics; maintains management referral service. **Members:** 6,000.

6221 ■ Cultural Vistas
440 Park Ave. S, 2nd Fl.
New York, NY 10016
Ph: (212)497-3500
Fax: (212)497-3535
E-mail: info@culturalvistas.org
URL: http://culturalvistas.org

Description: Providers worldwide of on-the-job training programs for students and professionals seeking international career development and life-changing experiences. Arranges workplace exchanges in hundreds of professional fields, bringing employers and trainees together from around the world. Client list ranges from small farming communities to Fortune 500 companies.

6222 ■ Event Service Professionals Association
191 Clarksville Rd.
Princeton Junction, NJ 08550
Ph: (609)799-3712
Fax: (609)799-7032
E-mail: info@acomonline.org
URL: http://www.acomonline.org

Description: Convention service directors and managers of hotels, convention centers, and convention bureaus. Works to increase the effectiveness, productivity and quality of meetings, conventions and exhibitions. Works to establish high ethical standards, improve professional management techniques and increase awareness of client, employer and provider needs. Maintains speakers' bureau, resource center, and placement services; compiles statistics. Conducts research and educational programs. **Members:** Convention service directors and managers of hotels, convention centers, and convention bureaus; suppliers of services and products to the convention bureaus; suppliers of services and products to the convention and meetings industry are affiliate members. **Purpose:** Works to increase the effectiveness, productivity, and quality of meetings, conventions, and exhibitions. Works to establish high ethical standards, improve professional management techniques, and increase awareness of client, employer, and provider needs. Holds summer conference. Maintains speakers' bureau, resource center, and placement services; bestows awards; compiles statistics. Conducts research programs.

6223 ■ International Council on Hotel, Restaurant, and Institutional Education
2810 N Parham Rd., Ste. 230
Richmond, VA 23294
Ph: (804)346-4800
Fax: (804)346-5009
E-mail: publications@chrie.org
URL: http://www.chrie.org

Description: Schools and colleges offering specialized education and training in hospitals, recreation, tourism and hotel, restaurant, and institutional administration; individuals, executives, and students. Provides networking opportunities and professional development.

6224 ■ International Executive Housekeepers Association
1001 Eastwind Dr., Ste. 301
Westerville, OH 43081-3361
Ph: (614)895-7166
Free: 800-200-6342
Fax: (614)895-1248
E-mail: excel@ieha.org
URL: http://www.ieha.org
Description: Persons engaged in facility housekeeping management in hospitals, hotels and motels, schools and industrial establishments. Established educational standards. Sponsors certificate and collegiate degree programs. Holds annual International Housekeepers Week celebration.

6225 ■ National Association of Black Hotel Owners, Operators and Developers
3520 W Broward Blvd., Ste. 119
Fort Lauderdale, FL 33312
Ph: (954)797-7102
Fax: (954)337-2877
E-mail: horizons@gate.net
URL: http://nabhood.net
Description: Enhances the stability and growth of the lodging industry. Aims to increase the number of African-Americans owning, developing, managing and operating hotels. Strives to create vendor opportunities and executive level jobs for minorities.

Human Services Workers

SOURCES OF HELP-WANTED ADS

6226 ■ *Human Service Newsbytes*
National Human Services Assembly
1101 14th St. NW, Ste. 600
Washington, DC 20005
Ph: (202)347-2080
Fax: (202)393-4517
URL: http://www.nationalassembly.org/News/News-bytes.aspx
Description: Biweekly. Provides information on the nonprofit and human services sector.

6227 ■ *Journal of Career Development*
Pine Forge Press
2455 Teller Rd.
Thousand Oaks, CA 91320-2234
Ph: (805)499-4224
Free: 800-818-7243
Fax: (805)499-0871
E-mail: sales@pfp.sagepub.com
URL: http://www.sagepub.com/journalsProdDesc.nav?prodId=Journal201758
Frequency: Quarterly. **Price:** $756 Institutions current volume print and online; $687 Institutions print and e-access; $618 Institutions e-access; $673 Institutions print only; $123 Institutions single print; $24 Individuals single print. **Description:** Journal for professionals in counseling, psychology, education, student personnel, human resources, and business management.

6228 ■ *The Lutheran*
Augsburg Fortress Publishers
8765 W Higgins Rd., 5th Fl.
Chicago, IL 60631-4183
Free: 800-638-3522
Fax: (773)380-2409
E-mail: lutheran@thelutheran.org
URLs: http://www.thelutheran.org; http://www.augsburgfortress.org
Frequency: Monthly. **Price:** $17.95 Individuals; $40.95 Individuals three years; $30.95 Two years. **Description:** Magazine of the Evangelical Lutheran Church in America.

EMPLOYER DIRECTORIES AND NETWORKING LISTS

6229 ■ *Directory of Catholic Charities USA Directories*
Catholic Charities USA
2050 Ballenger Ave., Ste. 400
Alexandria, VA 22314
Ph: (703)549-1390
Free: 800-919-9338
Fax: (703)549-1656
E-mail: info@catholiccharitiesusa.org
URL: http://www.catholiccharitiesusa.org

Frequency: Annual. **Price:** $25 Individuals. **Pages:** 183. **Covers:** Nearly 1,200 Catholic community and social service agencies. Listings include diocesan agencies, state Catholic conferences. **Entries include:** Organization name, address, name and title of director, phone, fax. **Arrangement:** Geographical by state, then classified by diocese.

6230 ■ *Public Human Services Directory*
American Public Human Services Association
1133 19th St. NW, Ste. 400
Washington, DC 20036
Ph: (202)682-0100
Fax: (202)289-6555
E-mail: tracy.wareing@aphsa.org
URL: http://www.aphsa.org
Frequency: Annual; Latest edition 2009. **Price:** $225 Individuals; $200 Members; $350 Institutions. **Pages:** 720. **Covers:** Federal, state, territorial, county, and major municipal public human service agencies. **Includes:** Information on all major human service programs, such as child welfare, child support enforcement, Medicaid eligibility and claims, interstate compacts, and other programs. **Entries include:** Agency name, address, phone, fax, e-mail address, web site address, names of key personnel, program area. **Arrangement:** Geographical.

HANDBOOKS AND MANUALS

6231 ■ *Great Jobs for Liberal Arts Majors*
The McGraw-Hill Companies Inc.
PO Box 182604
Columbus, OH 43272
Ph: (212)512-2000
Free: 877-833-5524
Fax: (614)759-3749
E-mail: customer.service@mcgraw-hill.com
URL: http://www.mcgraw-hill.com
Description: Blythe Camenson. Second edition, 2007. $16.95 (paper). 192 pages.

6232 ■ *A Guidebook to Human Service Professions: Helping College Students Explore Opportunities in the Human Services Field*
Charles C. Thomas Publisher Ltd.
2600 S 1st St.
Springfield, IL 62704-4730
Ph: (217)789-8980
Free: 800-258-8980
Fax: (217)789-9130
E-mail: books@ccthomas.com
URL: http://www.ccthomas.com
Description: William G. Emener, Michael A. Richard and John J. Bosworth. 2009. $44.95 (paper). 286 pages. Provides guidelines on human service profession. Offers an insightful look at the rewards of pursuing a career as a human service professional.

EMPLOYMENT AGENCIES AND SEARCH FIRMS

6233 ■ **Gatti & Associates**
266 Main St., Ste. 21
Medfield, MA 02052
Ph: (508)359-4153
Fax: (508)359-5902
E-mail: info@gattihr.com
URL: http://www.gattihr.com
Description: Executive search firm specializing exclusively in the search and placement of Human Resources professionals.

ONLINE JOB SOURCES AND SERVICES

6234 ■ **HSCareers.com**
URL: http://www.hscareers.com
Description: Offers employment and human services niche site to assist human service professionals.

6235 ■ **Social Work Job Search**
URL: http://www.socialworkjobsearch.com/social-workjobsearch.cgi
Description: Provides a database of jobs for social workers, counselors, mental health providers, social services professionals, school social workers and counselors, therapists, case managers, and all other helping professionals.

6236 ■ **SocialServiceNetwork.com**
URL: http://socialservicenetwork.com
Description: Provides a database of social work positions. Includes various listings of social work jobs, social services jobs, human services jobs, mental health jobs, counseling jobs, and more.

OTHER SOURCES

6237 ■ **American Public Health Association**
800 I St. NW
Washington, DC 20001-3710
Ph: (202)777-2742
Fax: (202)777-2534
E-mail: comments@apha.org
URL: http://www.apha.org
Description: Professional organization of physicians, nurses, educators, academicians, environmentalists, epidemiologists, new professionals, social workers, health administrators, optometrists, podiatrists, pharmacists, dentists, nutritionists, health planners, other community and mental health specialists, and interested consumers. Seeks to protect and promote personal, mental, and environmental health. Services include: promulgation of standards; establishment of

uniform practices and procedures; development of the etiology of communicable diseases; research in public health; exploration of medical care programs and their relationships to public health. Sponsors job placement service.

6238 ■ *Careers for Good Samaritans and Other Humanitarian Types*

The McGraw-Hill Companies Inc.
PO Box 182604
Columbus, OH 43272
Ph: (212)512-2000
Free: 877-833-5524
Fax: (614)759-3749
E-mail: customer.service@mcgraw-hill.com
URL: http://www.mcgraw-hill.com

Description: Marjorie Eberts and Margaret Gisler. Third edition, 2006. $16.95 (paper). 160 pages. Contains hundreds of ideas for turning good works into paid job opportunities with service organizations, religious groups, and government agencies. **Includes:** Appendices of Interaction member agencies, missionary organizations, and state offices of volunteerism that offer networking, employment, and volunteering opportunities, as well as job-hunting information. Appendices of Interaction member agencies, missionary organizations, and state offices of volunteerism that offer networking, employment, and volunteering opportunities, as well as job-hunting information. **Entries include:** Name, address, URL.

6239 ■ Child Life Council

11821 Parklawn Dr., Ste. 310
Rockville, MD 20852-2539
Ph: (301)881-7090
Free: 800-252-4515
Fax: (301)881-7092
E-mail: clcadmin@childlife.org
URL: http://www.childlife.org

Description: Professional organization representing child life personnel, patient activities specialists, and students in the field. Promotes psychological well-being and optimum development of children, adolescents, and their families in health care settings. Works to minimize the stress and anxiety of illness and hospitalization. Addresses professional issues such as program standards, competencies, and core curriculum. Provides resources and conducts research and educational programs. Offers a Job Bank Service listing employment openings.

6240 ■ Child Welfare League of America

1726 M St. NW, Ste. 500
Washington, DC 20036-4522
Ph: (202)688-4200
Free: 800-407-6273
Fax: (202)833-1689
E-mail: register@cwla.org
URL: http://www.cwla.org

Description: Works to improve care and services for abused, dependent, or neglected children, youth, and their families. Provides training and consultation; conducts research; maintains information service and develops standards for child welfare practice.

6241 ■ Council for Health and Human Service Ministries of the United Church of Christ

700 Prospect Ave.
Cleveland, OH 44115
Ph: (216)736-2260
Free: 866-822-8224
Fax: (216)736-2251
E-mail: sickberb@chhsm.org
URL: http://www.chhsm.org

Description: Health and human service institutions related to the United Church of Christ. Seeks to study, plan, and implement a program in health and human services; assist members in developing and providing quality services and in financing institutional and non-institutional health and human service ministries; stimulate awareness of and support for these programs; inform the UCC of policies that affect the needs, problems, and conditions of patients; cooperate with interdenominational agencies and others in the field. Maintains placement service and hall of fame. Compiles statistics; provides specialized education programs. **Members:** 329.

6242 ■ National Association of Benefits and Work Incentive Specialists

12009 Shallot St.
Orlando, FL 32837
Ph: (407)859-7767
Fax: (407)240-6592
E-mail: nabwis@gmail.com
URL: http://www.nabwis.org

Description: Represents professionals providing assistance to individuals who receive disability benefits. Ensures that people with disabilities have access to relevant information that will support their choices regarding work and increased economic self-sufficiency. Facilitates a national listserv and news group.

6243 ■ National Organization for Human Services

1600 Sarno Rd., Ste. 16
Melbourne, FL 32935
Free: 888-750-4862
Fax: (678)303-3426
E-mail: admin@nationalhumanservices.org
URL: http://www.nationalhumanservices.org

Description: Human service professionals, faculty, and students. Fosters excellence in teaching, research and curriculum planning in the human service area. Encourages and supports the development of local, state, and national human services organizations. Aids faculty and professional members in their career development. Provides a medium for cooperation and communication among members. Maintains registry of qualified consultants in human service education. Conducts professional development workshop. Operates speakers' bureau.

6244 ■ Nonprofit Leadership Alliance

1100 Walnut St., Ste. 1900
Kansas City, MO 64106
Ph: (816)561-6415
Fax: (816)531-3527
E-mail: info@nonprofitleadershipalliance.org
URL: http://www.nonprofitleadershipalliance.org

Description: Individuals, corporations, and foundations supporting NLA work in preparing young people for professional leadership in youth and human service agencies. Provides leadership for co-curricular program on over 55 campuses of colleges that feature specialized professional courses that lead to B.A., B.S., or M.A. degrees and prepare graduates to serve professionally with groups such as Boy Scouts of America, Boys and Girls Clubs of America, American Red Cross, Big Brothers/Big Sisters of America, Camp Fire USA, Girl Scouts of the U.S.A., YMCA of the USA, and Girls, Inc., Habitat for Humanity International, National Urban League, Voices for America's Children, Volunteers of America and National 4-H Council. Sponsors field trips, workshops, and special courses; offers counseling, loan assistance, and career placement services to students; also operates graduate programs. Conducts research, compiles statistics. **Members:** 2,500.

Online Job Sources and Services

6245 ■ ByFerial
URL: http://www.imageconsultanttraining.com
Description: Offers training seminars and news articles for image consulting.

6246 ■ The ImageMaker, Inc.
URL: http://www.imagemaker1.com
Description: Provides educational materials for image consulting.

6247 ■ The Rothschild Image
URL: http://www.rothschildimage.com
Description: Offers training workshops and seminars for image consulting.

Other Sources

6248 ■ Association of Image Consultants International
1000 Westgate Dr., Ste. 252
Saint Paul, MN 55114
Ph: (615)290-7468
Fax: (615)290-2266
E-mail: info@aici.org
URL: http://www.aici.org

Description: Personal color, style, wardrobe, and image planning consultants. Promotes quality service for clients; aids in establishing working relations between retail stores and consultants; assists community colleges in offering accredited image consulting programs; maintains standards of professionalism for members in the image consulting industry. Provides continuing education and training; maintains speakers' bureau.

6249 ■ Body Beautiful
1343 Lucile Ave.
Los Angeles, CA 90026
Ph: (323)708-9855
Free: 800-510-5528
E-mail: info@bodybeautiful.net
URL: http://www.bodybeautiful.net

Description: Provides an online newsletter. Offers training and a support network after training is complete.

6250 ■ Conselle Institute of Image Management
7052 University Sta.
Provo, UT 84602
Ph: (801)224-1207
E-mail: judith@conselle.com
URL: http://www.conselle.com

Description: Offers workshops and training in image management.

6251 ■ Gillian Armour Image Consulting
323 Geary St., Ste. 808
San Francisco, CA 94102
Ph: (415)230-0015
Free: 800-591-2353
E-mail: gillian@gillianarmour.com
URL: http://www.gillianarmour.com
Description: Offers seminars and educational materials for image consulting certification.

6252 ■ Impression Strategies Institute
921 Botetourt Gardens
Norfolk, VA 23507
Ph: (757)627-6669
Free: 877-245-5015
Fax: (757)627-4044
E-mail: sandy@theimagearchitect.com
URL: http://www.impressionstrategiesinstitute.com/about.html
Description: Offers training seminars and education materials in image consulting.

6253 ■ New York Image Consultant Co.
351 E 84th St., Apt. 11A
New York, NY 10028
Ph: (212)879-5790
E-mail: contact@newyorkimageconsultant.com
URL: http://www.newyorkimageconsultant.com
Description: Provides tips for getting started in image consulting. Interested persons may also sign up for classes regarding the different aspects of image consulting, or apply for an internship with the agency.

SOURCES OF HELP-WANTED ADS

6254 ■ Immigration Daily
American Immigration L.L.C.
PO Box 1830
New York, NY 10156
Ph: (212)545-0818
Fax: (212)545-0869
E-mail: webmaster@ilw.com
URL: http://www.ilw.com/immigrationdaily

Description: Daily. Serves as the news resource for immigration professionals.

6255 ■ RefugeeWorks Employment Quarterly
Lutheran Immigration and Refugee Service
700 Light St.
Baltimore, MD 21230
Ph: (410)230-2700
Fax: (410)230-2890
E-mail: lirs@lirs.org
URL: http://www.refugeeworks.org

Description: Quarterly. Focuses on various issues impacting former refugees in the world of employment.

PLACEMENT AND JOB REFERRAL SERVICES

6256 ■ Special Counsel
10151 Deerwood Park Blvd.
Jacksonville, FL 32256
Free: 800-737-3436
E-mail: info@specialcounsel.com
URL: http://www.specialcounsel.com

Description: Provides legal workforce solutions across the legal spectrum. Assists clients in managing everyday workload or resources, specific cases or business transactions. Provides qualified legal professionals with benefits such as competitive pay, holidays, insurance and bonuses.

HANDBOOKS AND MANUALS

6257 ■ Essentials of Immigration Law
American Immigration Lawyers Association
9 Jay Gould Ct.
Waldorf, MD 20602
Ph: (301)374-9000
Free: 800-982-2839
Fax: (301)843-0159
E-mail: pubs@aila.org
URL: http://www.ailapubs.org/kurimlawsour1.html

Description: Richard A. Boswell. 2006. $74 (paper). 280 pages. Provides the foundation necessary for an understanding of immigration from the passage of the first immigration-related statute to the current state of affairs of laws and amendments. Provides the foundation every attorney, law student and law office staff member needs to build understanding of U.S. immigration laws.

6258 ■ Immigration Employment Compliance Handbook
Thomson West
610 Opperman Dr.
Eagan, MN 55123
Ph: (651)687-7000
Free: 800-328-9352
E-mail: west.customerservice@thomson.com
URL: http://www.andrewsonline.com/

Description: Austin T. Fragomen Jr., Careen Shannon, Daniel Montalvo. 2011. $718. Provides employer sanctions, eligibility procedures and antidiscrimination developments.

6259 ■ Immigration Law for Paralegals
Carolina Academic Press
700 Kent St.
Durham, NC 27701
Ph: (919)489-7486
Free: 800-489-7486
Fax: (919)493-5668
E-mail: cap@cap-press.com
URL: http://www.cap-press.com

Description: Maria Isabel Casablanca, Gloria Roa Bodin. 2010. $58 (paper). 364 pages. Provides guidelines on U.S. immigration, citizenship and visa procedures for instructing and training students or anyone interested in career as an immigration paralegal or legal assistant. Features interviewing, gathering information, case management and document preparation techniques; analysis of temporary and permanent employment visas; analysis of family-based petitions, political asylum and naturalization; as well as samples of completed applications, a glossary of terms and appendices.

6260 ■ Immigration Procedures Handbook
Thomson West
610 Opperman Dr.
Eagan, MN 55123
Ph: (651)687-7000
Free: 800-328-9352
E-mail: west.customerservice@thomson.com
URL: http://www.andrewsonline.com/

Description: Austin T. Fragomen Jr., Careen Shannon, Daniel Montalvo. 2011. $828 (paper). Contains explanations on present specific types of petitions and applications under present immigration laws. Includes analysis of the law to assist in determining the method of proceeding with a case. Covers changes that affect immigration practice and procedure.

6261 ■ Immigration Trial Handbook
Thomson West
610 Opperman Dr.
Eagan, MN 55123
Ph: (651)687-7000
Free: 800-328-9352
E-mail: west.customerservice@thomson.com
URL: http://www.andrewsonline.com/

Description: Maria Baldini-Potermin, Anna Marie Gallagher. 2011. $263 (paper). Discusses the procedures, techniques, and strategies for representing non-citizens in removal proceedings at the administrative level. Contains practice tips, checklists, cautions concerning pitfalls to avoid and citations to statutes, regulations, case authorities, practice rules and agency memoranda. Features coverage of trial practice under the executive office for immigration review's immigration court practice manual.

6262 ■ Kurzban's Immigration Law Sourcebook
American Immigration Lawyers Association
9 Jay Gould Ct.
Waldorf, MD 20602
Ph: (301)374-9000
Free: 800-982-2839
Fax: (301)843-0159
E-mail: pubs@aila.org
URL: http://www.ailapubs.org/kurimlawsour1.html

Description: Ira J. Kurzban. 2010. $399 (paper). 1872 pages. Provides guides and resources on immigration law with explanations. Features subject-matter index, table of cases and multiple tables of authorities to help find answers on immigration issues.

6263 ■ Working With Refugee and Immigrant Children: Issues of Culture, Law and Development
Lutheran Immigration and Refugee Service
700 Light St.
Baltimore, MD 21230
Ph: (410)230-2700
Fax: (410)230-2890
E-mail: lirs@lirs.org
URL: http://www.lirs.org

Description: $20. Serves as a resource tool for lawyers, social workers and advocates. Combines information about migration issues, child welfare and child development to bridge the gap between these disciplines.

ONLINE JOB SOURCES AND SERVICES

6264 ■ Asylum Law
URL: http://www.probono.net/asylum

Description: Supports lawyers who are providing pro bono assistance to individuals seeking asylum in the United States. Contains online support and resources for participating lawyers including news, a calendar of trainings and events, online listings of new cases for volunteers and an online library of training manuals, briefs and practice materials.

Job Hunter's Sourcebook, 14th Edition

6265 ■ GetImmigrationAttorneyJobs.com
URL: http://www.getimmigrationattorneyjobs.com

Description: Provides online job searches for immigration law professionals. Gives free weekly job listings via email.

6266 ■ Immigration Advocates Network
URL: http://www.immigrationadvocates.org

Description: Provides an online resource and communication site to enhance and unify the work of the nation's immigrants' rights organizations.

6267 ■ Immigration Assistant
URL: http://www.immigration-usa.com

Price: $299 Individuals Professional Deluxe CD-ROM. **Description:** Computer program that combines U.S. immigration law reference materials, learning tools and all the immigration forms that an immigrant might need.

6268 ■ Immigration.com
URL: http://www.immigration.com

Description: Supports the immigrant community by providing information and resources. Provides extensive visa information, legal services, and general legal advice to high technology and other businesses, and negotiates and drafts high-tech contracts. Provides links to resources that immigrants and other individuals can use to start a life in the United States.

6269 ■ LawCrossing.com
URL: http://www.lawcrossing.com

Description: Offers a collection of active legal jobs. Monitors the hiring needs of legal employers including law firms, corporations, government offices and public interest organizations in the United States.

TRADESHOWS

6270 ■ American Immigration Lawyers Association Conference
American Immigration Lawyers Association
1331 G St. NW, Ste. 300
Washington, DC 20005-3142
Ph: (202)216-2400
Free: 800-954-0254
Fax: (202)783-7853
E-mail: executive@aila.org
URL: http://www.aila.org

Frequency: Annual. Offers educational sessions, workshops for practitioners who practice before the immigration courts, and open forums. 2013 June 26-29; San Francisco, CA; 2014 June 18-21; Boston, MA.

6271 ■ Annual Immigration Law & Policy Conference
Migration Policy Institute
1400 16th St. NW, Ste. 300
Washington, DC 20036-2203
Ph: (202)266-1940
Fax: (202)266-1900
E-mail: info@migrationpolicy.org
URL: http://www.migrationpolicy.org

Frequency: Annual. Features law and policy analysis and discussion on immigration issues. Features panelists from government, academics and immigration advocates and experts.

6272 ■ CLINIC Annual Convening
Catholic Legal Immigration Network
8757 Georgia Ave., Ste. 850
Silver Spring, MD 20910-3742
Ph: (301)565-4800
Fax: (301)565-4824
E-mail: national@cliniclegal.org
URL: http://cliniclegal.org

Annual.

6273 ■ Massachusetts Continuing Legal Education Annual Immigration Law Conference
Massachusetts Continuing Legal Education, Inc.
10 Winter Pl.
Boston, MA 02108-4751
Ph: (617)482-2205
Free: 800-966-6253
Fax: (617)482-9498
E-mail: askmcle@mcle.org
URL: http://www.mcle.org

Frequency: Annual. Addresses the current issues in immigration law and practice.

OTHER SOURCES

6274 ■ Advocates for Human Rights
330 2nd Ave. S, Ste. 880
Minneapolis, MN 55401
Ph: (612)341-3302
Fax: (612)341-2971
E-mail: hrights@advrights.org
URL: http://www.theadvocatesforhumanrights.org

Description: Seeks to promote and protect the human rights of asylum seekers, refugees and immigrants. Provides access to free legal services in many immigration cases annually. Offers educational materials related to immigrant rights and immigration policy.

6275 ■ American Civil Liberties Union
125 Broad St., 18th Fl.
New York, NY 10004
Ph: (212)549-2500
E-mail: media@aclu.org
URL: http://www.aclu.org

Description: Strives to guarantee the fundamental rights and civil liberties of every person in the United States. Protects the most vulnerable members of the society, especially the immigrants "who have been the targets of discrimination, government abuse and divisive and inhumane immigration policies."

6276 ■ American Immigration Lawyers Association
1331 G St. NW, Ste. 300
Washington, DC 20005-3142
Ph: (202)216-2400
Free: 800-954-0254
Fax: (202)783-7853
E-mail: executive@aila.org
URL: http://www.aila.org

Description: Lawyers specializing in the field of immigration and nationality law. Fosters and promotes the administration of justice with particular reference to the immigration and nationality laws of the United States.

6277 ■ Asian Pacific American Legal Center of Southern California
1145 Wilshire Blvd., 2nd Fl.
Los Angeles, CA 90017
Ph: (213)977-7500
Fax: (213)977-7595
E-mail: info@apalc.org
URL: http://advancingjustice-la.org

Description: Serves as an organization that combines traditional legal services with civil rights advocacy. Provides direct legal services and education especially to those who speak little or no English. Provides Asian language hotlines and other modes of assistance. Provides individual immigration and citizenship assistance, educates the public on immigration issues and advocates for fair immigration laws and policies.

6278 ■ Catholic Legal Immigration Network
8757 Georgia Ave., Ste. 850
Silver Spring, MD 20910-3742
Ph: (301)565-4800

Fax: (301)565-4824
E-mail: national@cliniclegal.org
URL: http://cliniclegal.org

Description: Catholic charities, Catholic diocesan programs and religious orders. Enhances delivery of legal services to indigent and low-income immigrants through diocesan immigration programs. Meets the legal immigration needs of archdioceses, dioceses and congregations through various supporting activities and its own direct representation of the foreign-born religious.

6279 ■ Federation for American Immigration Reform
25 Massachusetts Ave. NW, Ste. 330
Washington, DC 20001-1407
Ph: (202)328-7004
Free: 877-627-3247
Fax: (202)387-3447
E-mail: info@fairus.org
URL: http://www.fairus.org

Description: Seeks to improve border security, stop illegal immigration and promote immigration levels consistent with the national interest.

6280 ■ Immigration Equality
40 Exchange Pl., Ste. 1300
New York, NY 10005
Ph: (212)714-2904
Fax: (212)714-2973
URL: http://www.immigrationequality.org

Description: Provides information and support to advocates, attorneys, politicians and those who are threatened by persecution or the discriminatory impact of the law. Works to end discrimination in U.S. immigration law, reduce the negative impact of that law on the lives of lesbian, gay, bisexual, transgender and HIV-positive people and help obtain asylum for those persecuted in their home country based on their sexual orientation, transgender identity or HIV-status. Offers education, outreach, advocacy and the maintenance of a nationwide network of resources.

6281 ■ Immigration and Visas International
7 Village Rd.
Kendall Park, NJ 08824
Ph: (732)821-6077
Fax: (732)821-1615
URL: http://www.immigrationandvisas.com

Description: Represents immigration attorneys, lawyers and consultants who deal primarily with immigration and visa matters. Specializes in immigration services.

6282 ■ Lutheran Immigration and Refugee Service
700 Light St.
Baltimore, MD 21230
Ph: (410)230-2700
Fax: (410)230-2890
E-mail: lirs@lirs.org
URL: http://www.lirs.org

Description: Works to resettle refugees, protect foreign-born children, advocate for fair treatment of asylum seekers and pursue alternatives for those in immigration detention. Advocates to ensure that America's doors remain open to newcomers.

6283 ■ Migration Policy Institute
1400 16th St. NW, Ste. 300
Washington, DC 20036-2203
Ph: (202)266-1940
Fax: (202)266-1900
E-mail: info@migrationpolicy.org
URL: http://www.migrationpolicy.org

Description: Independent, nonprofit, non-partisan think tank.

6284 ■ National Immigration Project - National Lawyers Guild
14 Beacon St., Ste. 602
Boston, MA 02108

Ph: (617)227-9727
Fax: (617)227-5495
E-mail: dan@nationalimmigrationproject.org
URL: http://www.nationalimmigrationproject.org

Description: Lawyers, law students, and legal workers. Educates and organizes for progressive immigration law. Works in defense of the civil liberties of the foreign born. Conducts immigration law skills seminars.

6285 ■ United States Committee for Refugees and Immigrants
2231 Crystal Dr., Ste. 350
Arlington, VA 22202-3711
Ph: (703)310-1130
Fax: (703)769-4241
E-mail: uscri@uscridc.org

URL: http://www.refugees.org

Description: Addresses the needs and rights of persons in forced or voluntary migration worldwide by advancing fair and humane public policy, facilitating and providing direct professional services and promoting the full participation of migrants in community life.

SOURCES OF HELP-WANTED ADS

6286 ■ AIE Perspectives Newsmagazine
American Institute of Engineers
4630 Appian Way, Ste. 206
El Sobrante, CA 94803-1875
Ph: (510)758-6240
Fax: (510)758-6240
E-mail: aie@aieonline.org
URL: http://www.members-aie.org

Frequency: Monthly. **Price:** included in membership dues. **Description:** Professional magazine covering engineering.

6287 ■ Engineering
Scientific Research Publishing
PO Box 54821
Irvine, CA 92619-4821
E-mail: eng@scirp.org
URL: http://www.scirp.org/journal/eng/

Frequency: Monthly. **Price:** $468 Individuals. **Description:** Peer-reviewed journal publishing articles on the latest advancements in engineering.

6288 ■ The Engineering Economist
Institute of Industrial Engineers
3577 Parkway Ln., Ste. 200
Norcross, GA 30092
Ph: (770)449-0460
Free: 800-494-0460
Fax: (770)441-3295
E-mail: executiveoffices@iienet.org
URL: http://www.iienet2.org

Description: Quarterly. Discusses news of the Institute. Recurring features include a column titled In-Coming Director's Message. Discusses engineering economics. Articles featured have an academic slant with an emphasis on research.

6289 ■ ENR: Engineering News-Record: The Construction Weekly
The McGraw-Hill Companies Inc.
2 Penn Plz., 9th Fl.
New York, NY 10121
Ph: (212)904-3507
Fax: (212)904-2820
E-mail: customer.service@mcgraw-hill.com
URL: http://enr.construction.com/Default.asp

Frequency: Weekly. **Price:** $87 Individuals print and online. **Description:** Magazine focusing on engineering and construction.

6290 ■ Graduating Engineer & Computer Careers
Career Recruitment Media
2 LAN Dr., Ste. 100
Westford, MA 01886
Ph: (978)692-5092
Fax: (978)692-4174
E-mail: hshulick@alloyeducation.com
URL: http://www.graduatingengineer.com

Frequency: Quarterly. **Price:** $16.95 Individuals. **Description:** Magazine focusing on employment, education, and career development for entry-level engineers and computer scientists.

6291 ■ Managing Automation
Thomas Publishing Company L.L.C.
5 Penn Plz.
New York, NY 10001
Ph: (212)695-0500
Free: 800-699-9822
Fax: (212)290-7362
E-mail: contact@thomaspublishing.com
URLs: http://www.managingautomation.com/maonline/; http://www.thomaspublishing.com

Frequency: Monthly. **Price:** $60 Individuals; $75 Canada and Mexico; $125 Other countries. **Description:** Managing Automation covers advanced manufacturing technology including automation, integrated manufacturing, enterprise applications, and IT and e-business for the manufacturing enterprise.

6292 ■ NSBE Magazine: National Society of Black Engineers
NSBE Publications
205 Daingerfield Rd.
Alexandria, VA 22314
Ph: (703)549-2207
Fax: (703)683-5312
E-mail: info@nsbe.org
URL: http://www.nsbe.org/News-Media/Magazines/About-NSBE-Magazine.aspx

Frequency: 3/yr. **Price:** $20 Individuals; $35 Other countries; $15 Students. **Description:** Journal providing information on engineering careers, self-development, and cultural issues for recent graduates with technical majors.

6293 ■ PE
National Society of Professional Engineers
1420 King St.
Alexandria, VA 22314-2794
Ph: (703)684-2800
Fax: (703)836-4875
E-mail: memserv@nspe.org
URL: http://www.nspe.org/PEmagazine/index.html

Frequency: Semimonthly; 10/yr. **Price:** included in membership dues; $50 for nonmembers. **Description:** Covers matters of importance to engineering educators and students.

6294 ■ Plant Engineering
CFE Media LLC
1111 W 22nd St., Ste. 250
Oak Brook, IL 60523
Ph: (630)571-4070
Fax: (630)214-4504
URL: http://www.plantengineering.com/

Frequency: Monthly. **Price:** Free. **Description:** Magazine focusing on engineering support and maintenance in industry.

6295 ■ Structure Magazine
American Consulting Engineers Council
1015 15th St. NW, 8th Fl.
Washington, DC 20005-2605
Ph: (202)347-7474
Fax: (202)898-0068
E-mail: acec@acec.org
URL: http://structuremag.org

Frequency: Annual. **Price:** $75 Nonmembers for U.S residents; $40 Students; $90 Canada individual; $135 Other countries; $60 Canada students; $90 Other countries students. **Description:** Magazine focused on providing tips, tools, techniques, and innovative concepts for structural engineers.

6296 ■ SWE, Magazine of the Society of Women Engineers
Society of Women Engineers
203 N La Salle St., Ste. 1675
Chicago, IL 60601
Ph: (312)596-5223
Free: 877-SWE-INFO
Fax: (312)596-5252
E-mail: hq@swe.org
URL: http://societyofwomenengineers.swe.org/index.php

Frequency: Quarterly. **Price:** $30 Nonmembers. **Description:** Magazine for engineering students and for women and men working in the engineering and technology fields. Covers career guidance, continuing development and topical issues.

6297 ■ Wire & Cable Technology International
Initial Publications Inc.
3869 Darrow Rd., Ste. 109
Stow, OH 44224
Ph: (330)686-9544
Fax: (330)686-9563
E-mail: info@wiretech.com
URL: http://www.wiretech.com/

Frequency: Bimonthly. **Description:** Magazine for manufacturers of ferrous, nonferrous, bare, and insulated wire.

6298 ■ Woman Engineer
Equal Opportunity Publications Inc.
445 Broad Hollow Rd., Ste. 425
Melville, NY 11747
Ph: (631)421-9421
Fax: (631)421-1352
E-mail: info@eop.com
URL: http://www.eop.com

Description: Annual. Magazine that is offered at no charge to qualified female engineering, computer-science, and information-technology students and professionals seeking to find employment and advancement in their careers.

PLACEMENT AND JOB REFERRAL SERVICES

6299 ■ **Aerotek Automotive**
7301 Parkway Dr.
Hanover, MD 21076
Ph: (410)694-5100
Free: 800-237-6835
URL: http://automotive.aerotek.com

Description: Provides technical, professional and industrial recruiting and staffing services within the automotive field.

EMPLOYER DIRECTORIES AND NETWORKING LISTS

6300 ■ *Directory of Contract Staffing Firms*
C.E. Publications Inc.
PO Box 3006
Bothell, WA 98041-3006
Ph: (425)806-5200
Fax: (425)806-5585
E-mail: staff@cjhunter.com
URL: http://www.cjhunter.com/dcsf/overview.html

Frequency: Annual. **Covers:** Nearly 1,300 contract firms actively engaged in the employment of engineering, IT/IS, and technical personnel for 'temporary' contract assignments throughout the world. **Entries include:** Company name, address, phone, name of contact, email, web address. **Arrangement:** Alphabetical. **Indexes:** Geographical.

6301 ■ *Forming & Fabricating Industry Directory*
FMA Communications, Inc.
833 Featherstone Rd.
Rockford, IL 61107-6302
Ph: (815)399-8700
Fax: (815)381-1370
E-mail: info@thefabricator.com
URL: http://www.thefabricator.com/directory

Description: Online searchable guide of metal forming and fabricating suppliers. Contains company listings by category.

6302 ■ *Indiana Society of Professional Engineers--Directory*
Indiana Society of Professional Engineers
c/o Lauraine M. Howe, Executive Director
PO Box 20806
Indianapolis, IN 46220
Ph: (317)255-2267
Fax: (317)255-2530
E-mail: indspe@gmail.com
URL: http://www.indspe.org

Frequency: Annual; fall. **Pages:** 150. **Covers:** Member registered engineers, land surveyors, engineering students, and engineers in training. **Entries include:** Member name, address, phone, type of membership, business information, specialty. **Arrangement:** Alpha by chapter area.

6303 ■ *Who's Who in Engineering*
American Association of Engineering Societies
1801 Alexander Bell Dr.
Reston, VA 20191
Ph: (202)296-2237
Free: 888-400-2237
Fax: (202)296-1151
E-mail: dbateson@aaes.org
URL: http://www.aaes.org

Frequency: Triennial; Latest edition 9th. **Covers:** About 15,000 engineers who have received professional recognition for outstanding achievement. **Entries include:** Name, address; education and employment history; awards and achievements. **Arrangement:** Alphabetical. **Indexes:** Geographical, field of specialization.

HANDBOOKS AND MANUALS

6304 ■ *Engineering, Mechanics, and Architecture*
InfoBase Holdings Inc.
132 W 31st., 17 Fl.
New York, NY 10001-3406
Ph: (212)967-8800
Fax: (800)678-3633
E-mail: info@infobasepublishing.com
URL: http://www.ferguson.infobasepublishing.com

Description: Kelly Wiles. 2010. $39.95. 160 pages (hardcover). Serves as a guide for readers interested in switching jobs. Contains useful advice, career tips, interviews and self-asessment questions.

6305 ■ *Expert Resumes for Engineers*
JIST Publishing
875 Montreal Way
Saint Paul, MN 55102-4245
Ph: (317)613-4200
Free: 800-648-5478
Fax: (800)328-4564
E-mail: info@jist.com
URL: http://www.jist.com

Description: Louise M. Kursmark and Wendy S. Enelow. 2009. $16.95 (softcover). 272 pages. Features a collection of written resume samples for all types of engineers including civil, mechanical, industrial, electrical, electronics, computer, and more. Contains tips and strategies for writing engineering resumes and finding the best jobs.

6306 ■ *Great Jobs for Engineering Majors*
The McGraw-Hill Companies Inc.
PO Box 182604
Columbus, OH 43272
Ph: (212)512-2000
Free: 877-833-5524
Fax: (614)759-3749
E-mail: customer.service@mcgraw-hill.com
URL: http://www.mcgraw-hill.com

Description: Geraldine O. Garner. Second edition, 2008. $16.95. 192 pages. Covers all the career options open to students majoring in engineering.

EMPLOYMENT AGENCIES AND SEARCH FIRMS

6307 ■ **The Aspire Group**
711 Boylston St.
Boston, MA 02116-2616
Free: 800-487-2967
Fax: (617)500-7284
URL: http://www.bmanet.com/Aspire/index.html

Description: Employment agency.

6308 ■ **ATR Engineering**
1230 Oakmead Pkwy., Ste. 110
Sunnyvale, CA 94085
Ph: (408)328-8000
E-mail: corporate@atr1.com
URL: http://www.atr-engineering.com

Description: Serves as an executive search firm specializing in the placement of engineering professionals in contract, contract-to-hire and full-time basis across all disciplines including design engineering, manufacturing engineering, hardware engineering, design engineering, electrical engineering and mechanical engineering.

6309 ■ **Auguston and Associates Inc.**
1010 S Ocean Blvd., Ste. 601
Pompano Beach, FL 33062
Ph: (954)943-0503
Fax: (954)784-1660
E-mail: g.auguston@augustonandassociates.com
URL: http://www.augustonandassociates.com/

Description: Executive search firm focused on medical devices.

6310 ■ **Bell Oaks Co.**
115 Perimeter Center Pl., Ste. 400
Atlanta, GA 30346
Ph: (678)287-2000
Fax: (678)287-2002
E-mail: info@belloaks.com
URL: http://www.belloaks.com

Description: Personnel service firm.

6311 ■ **Career Advocates International**
1539 Ave. A
Katy, TX 77493
Ph: (281)371-3917
E-mail: hank@careeradvocates.org
URL: http://www.careeradvocates.org

Description: Provides permanent placement and temporary staffing for executive and staff level positions. Specializes in multiple niches including: sales and marketing, accounting and financial services, banking, communications, human resources, chemicals, oil and gas, medical and dental, legal, information technology, energy, technology, engineering, manufacturing, construction, and light industrial.

6312 ■ **Centennial, Inc.**
8044 Montgomery Rd., Ste. 260
Cincinnati, OH 45236
Ph: (513)366-3760
Fax: (513)366-3761
URL: http://www.centennialinc.com

Description: Serves as an executive search firm specializing in the areas of executive and general management, accounting and finance, human resources, information technology, manufacturing, engineering, marketing and advertising, not-for-profit, sales and business development, and supply chain and logistics.

6313 ■ **CEO Resources Inc.**
PO Box 2883
Framingham, MA 01703-2883
Ph: (508)877-2775
Fax: (508)877-8433
E-mail: info@ceoresourcesinc.com
URL: http://ceoresourcesinc.com

Description: Executive search firm.

6314 ■ **Cizek Associates Inc.**
2415 E Camelback Rd., Ste. 700
Phoenix, AZ 85016
Ph: (602)553-1066
Fax: (602)553-1166
URL: http://www.cizekassociates.com

Description: Executive search firm. Also maintains offices in Chicago and San Francisco.

6315 ■ **C.H. Cowles Associates**
93 W Alyssa Canyon Pl.
Oro Valley, AZ 85755
Ph: (520)297-7608

Description: Provider of services in industrial engineering and industrial management including long-range planning, facilities planning, work improvement, profit improvement, executive search, quality assurance, manufacturing engineering and staff reorganization, site search and site planning.

6316 ■ **Dinte Resources Inc.**
8300 Greensboro Dr., Ste. 750
McLean, VA 22102-3663
Ph: (703)448-3300
Fax: (703)448-0215
E-mail: dri@dinte.com
URL: http://www.dinte.com

Description: Executive search firm.

6317 ■ **Electronic Careers**
21355 Pacific Coast Hwy., Ste. 100
Malibu, CA 90265

Ph: (310)317-6113
E-mail: e-careers@electroniccareers.com
URL: http://www.electroniccareers.com

Description: Executive search firm.

6318 ■ Elite Resources Group
1239 Stetson Ln.
Sevierville, TN 37876
Ph: (865)774-8228
Fax: (865)774-8229
URL: http://www.elite-rg.com

Description: Executive search firm.

6319 ■ Engineer One Inc.
2315 Laurel Lake Rd.
Knoxville, TN 37932
Ph: (865)692-0404
Fax: (865)691-0110
E-mail: engineerone@engineerone.com
URL: http://www.engineerone.com

Description: Engineering employment service specializing in engineering and management in the chemical process, power utilities, manufacturing, mechanical, electrical, and electronic industries. Maintains an Information Technology Division that works nationwide across all industries. Also provides systems analysis consulting services specializing in VAX based systems.

6320 ■ Executive Recruiters Agency
PO Box 21810
Little Rock, AR 72211
Ph: (501)224-7000
Fax: (501)224-8534
E-mail: jobs@execrecruit.com
URL: http://www.execrecruit.com

Description: Personnel service firm.

6321 ■ Executive Resource Group Inc.
1330 Cedar Point, No. 201
Amelia, OH 45102
Ph: (513)947-1447
Fax: (513)752-3026
URL: http://www.executiveresource.net

Description: Executive search firm.

6322 ■ Fisher Personnel Management Services
2351 N Filbert Rd.
Exeter, CA 93221
Ph: (559)594-5774
Fax: (559)594-5777
E-mail: hookme@fisheads.net
URL: http://www.fisheads.net

Description: Executive search firm.

6323 ■ Global Employment Solutions Inc.
10375 Park Meadows Dr., Ste. 475
Littleton, CO 80124-6724
Ph: (303)216-9500
Fax: (303)216-9533
URL: http://www.gesnetwork.com

Description: Employment agency.

6324 ■ International Staffing Consultants Inc.
31655 2nd Ave.
Laguna Beach, CA 92651
Ph: (949)255-5857
Fax: (949)767-5959
E-mail: iscinc@iscworld.com
URL: http://www.iscworld.com

Description: Employment agency. Provides placement on regular or temporary basis. Affiliate office in London.

6325 ■ Mfg/Search, Inc.
205 W Jefferson Blvd., Ste. 601
South Bend, IN 46601
Ph: (574)282-2547

Fax: (574)232-0982
E-mail: hmueller@mfgsearch.com
URL: http://www.mfgsearch.com

Description: Executive search firm. Offices in GA, IL, MI, NY.

6326 ■ Houser Martin Morris
110th Ave. NE, 110 Atrium Pl., Ste. 580
Bellevue, WA 98004
Ph: (425)453-2700
Fax: (425)453-8726
E-mail: info@houser.com
URL: http://www.houser.com

Description: Focus is in the areas of retained executive search, professional, and technical recruiting. Areas of specialization include software engineering, sales and marketing, information technology, legal, human resources, accounting and finance, manufacturing, factory automation and engineering.

6327 ■ Nesco Inc.
6140 Parkland Blvd., Ste. 110
Mayfield Heights, OH 44124-6106
Ph: (440)461-6000
Fax: (440)449-3111
E-mail: corporate@nescoresource.com
URL: http://www.nescoresource.com

Description: Offers staffing and consulting solutions in the fields of engineering, information technology, accounting and finance, manufacturing and distribution, and administrative and customer services.

6328 ■ Palladian International, LLC
105-A Lew Dewitt Blvd., Ste. 197
Waynesboro, VA 22980
Free: 866-766-8447
E-mail: palladian@palladianinternational.com
URL: http://palladianinternational.com

Description: Acts as an executive recruiting firm that specializes in manufacturing and engineering, distribution and logistics, and former military officers. Offers free guides in resume writing, interview preparation, and resume benchmarking surveys.

6329 ■ Pate Resources Group Inc.
505 Orleans St., Ste. 300
Beaumont, TX 77701-3224
Ph: (409)833-4514
Fax: (409)833-4646

Description: Offers executive search and recruiting services to professionals who include physicians, health care administrators, accountants, financial managers; chemical, mechanical, industrial, and electrical engineers; sales and marketing managers, human resources administrators, and general managers and top executives in numerous disciplines. Industries served: health care, petrochemicals, accounting, utility, legal and municipalities.

6330 ■ SHS of Cherry Hill
207 Barclay Pavilion W
Cherry Hill, NJ 08034
Ph: (856)216-9030
Fax: (856)219-2011
E-mail: shs@shsofcherryhill.com
URL: http://www.shsofcherryhill.com

Description: Personnel recruiters operating in the disciplines of accounting, sales, insurance, engineering and administration. Industries served: insurance, distribution, manufacturing and service.

6331 ■ SPECTRA Associates
PO Box 688
Stevensville, MT 59870
Ph: (406)369-1188
E-mail: engineering@spectra-assoc.com
URL: http://www.spectra-assoc.com

Description: Serves as an executive search firm specializing in recruitment for engineering markets including companies involved with manufacturing, production and engineering.

ONLINE JOB SOURCES AND SERVICES

6332 ■ AECWorkForce.com
URL: http://aecworkforce.com

Description: Serves as job board for professionals and employers in architecture, engineering and construction.

6333 ■ ConstructMyFuture.com
URL: http://www.constructmyfuture.com

Description: Offers comprehensive information for students, parents, and educators on varied careers in construction. Includes a searchable database of colleges, universities and trade schools that offer degrees in construction fields.

6334 ■ Design Engineer Jobzone
URL: http://designengineerjobzone.com/site/2791/about.htm

Description: Database of job openings for design engineers. Lists the latest jobs from top companies in the field.

6335 ■ Engineering Classifieds
URL: http://www.engineeringclassifieds.com

Description: Serves as a career site for engineering professionals. Provides services including job search agents, resume creation and posting.

6336 ■ EngineerJobs.com
URL: http://www.engineerjobs.com

Description: Provides job opportunities for engineering professionals in the following disciplines: aerospace, agricultural, biomedical, chemical, civil, electrical, environmental, industrial, manufacturing, marine, materials, mechanical, mining, nuclear, petroleum, process, project, quality, sales, software, solar, systems, and structural.

6337 ■ Engineer.net
URL: http://www.engineer.net

Description: Provides engineering employment tools such as job search, job posting, and engineering resumes.

6338 ■ ENR Industry Jobs Site
URL: http://industry-jobs.enr.com/main/default.asp

Description: Provides job searching and recruitment services in the field of architecture, engineering and construction (AEC) industry. Offers comprehensive database of career opportunities for job seekers and resume of top AEC professionals for employers.

6339 ■ IndustrialEngineerCareers.com
URL: http://www.industrialengineercareers.com

Description: Covers information about industrial engineering employment and career opportunities. Lists job openings according to job type, city and state.

6340 ■ IndustrialEngineer.com
URL: http://www.industrialengineer.com

Description: Provides industrial engineering job listings and products to industrial engineers.

6341 ■ Spherion
URL: http://www.spherion.com

Description: Recruitment firm specializing in accounting and finance, sales and marketing, interim executives, technology, engineering, retail and human resources.

6342 ■ ThinkEnergyGroup.com
URL: http://www.thinkenergygroup.com

Description: Serves as a job board for professionals looking for positions in engineering, power plant, energy, and technical fields. Contains advice and tips on interviews, job searching, resume writing, hiring, and management. Provides choices of work location, pay rates in the field of expertise and contract, temp-to-hire, and direct hiring options.

TRADESHOWS

6343 ■ American Society for Engineering Education Annual Conference and Exposition
American Society for Engineering Education
1818 N St. NW, Ste. 600
Washington, DC 20036-2479
Ph: (202)331-3500
Fax: (202)265-8504
E-mail: board@asee.org
URL: http://www.asee.org

Frequency: Annual. **Primary Exhibits:** Publications, engineering supplies and equipment, computers, software, and research companies all products and services related to engineering education.

OTHER SOURCES

6344 ■ American Association of Engineering Societies
1801 Alexander Bell Dr.
Reston, VA 20191
Ph: (202)296-2237
Free: 888-400-2237
Fax: (202)296-1151
E-mail: dbateson@aaes.org
URL: http://www.aaes.org

Description: Coordinates the efforts of the member societies in the provision of reliable and objective information to the general public concerning issues which affect the engineering profession and the field of engineering as a whole; collects, analyzes, documents, and disseminates data which will inform the general public of the relationship between engineering and the national welfare; provides a forum for the engineering societies to exchange and discuss their views on matters of common interest; and represents the U.S. engineering community abroad through representation in WFEO and UPADI.

6345 ■ American Engineering Association
c/o Harold Ruchelman
533 Waterside Blvd.
Monroe Township, NJ 08831
Ph: (201)664-6954
E-mail: aea@aea.org
URL: http://www.aea.org

Description: Members consist of Engineers and engineering professionals. Purpose to advance the engineering profession and U.S. engineering capabilities. Issues of concern include age discrimination, immigration laws, displacement of U.S. Engineers by foreign workers, trade agreements, off shoring of U.S. Engineering and manufacturing jobs, loss of U.S. manufacturing and engineering capability, and recruitment of foreign students. Testifies before Congress. Holds local Chapter meetings.

6346 ■ American Indian Science and Engineering Society
PO Box 9828
Albuquerque, NM 87119-9828
Ph: (505)765-1052
Fax: (505)765-5608
E-mail: pam@aises.org
URL: http://www.aises.org

Description: Represents American Indian and non-Indian students and professionals in science, technology, and engineering fields; corporations representing energy, mining, aerospace, electronic, and computer fields. Seeks to motivate and encourage students to pursue undergraduate and graduate studies in science, engineering, and technology. Sponsors science fairs in grade schools, teacher training workshops, summer math/science sessions

for 8th-12th graders, professional chapters, and student chapters in colleges. Offers scholarships. Adult members serve as role models, advisers, and mentors for students. Operates placement service.

6347 ■ American Institute of Engineers
4630 Appian Way, Ste. 206
El Sobrante, CA 94803-1875
Ph: (510)758-6240
Fax: (510)758-6240
E-mail: aie@aieonline.org
URL: http://www.aieonline.org

Description: Professional association for engineers, scientists, and mathematicians. Multi-disciplined, non-technical association who aims to improve the stature and image of engineers, scientists, and mathematicians. Provides endorsements, awards and opportunities for small business start-ups within the AIE Councils. Sponsors "LA Engineer", a comedy-drama television series; produces annual "Academy Hall of FAME (TV)".

6348 ■ American Supplier Institute
30200 Telegraph Rd., Ste. 100
Bingham Farms, MI 48025-4503
Ph: (734)464-1395
Free: 800-462-4500
Fax: (734)464-1399
E-mail: asi@amsup.com
URL: http://www.amsup.com

Description: Seeks to encourage change in U.S. industry through development and implementation of advanced manufacturing and engineering technologies such as Taguchi Methods, Quality Function Deployment, Statistical Process Control, and Total Quality Management. Offers educational courses, training seminars, and workshops to improve quality, reduce cost, and enhance competitive position of U.S. products. Maintains international network of affiliates for developing training specialists and technologies curriculum. Provides training services to government supplier companies.

6349 ■ Association for Facilities Engineering
12801 Worldgate Dr., Ste. 500
Herndon, VA 20170
Ph: (571)203-7171
Fax: (571)766-2142
E-mail: info@afe.org
URL: http://www.afe.org

Description: Represents professionals involved in plant engineering/facilities management. Provides education, certification, technical information, and other relevant resources to plant and facility engineering, operations, and maintenance professionals worldwide.

6350 ■ *Career Opportunities in Engineering*
InfoBase Holdings Inc.
132 W 31st., 17 Fl.
New York, NY 10001-3406
Ph: (212)967-8800
Fax: (800)678-3633
E-mail: info@infobasepublishing.com
URL: http://www.ferguson.infobasepublishing.com

Description: 2006. $49.50. 336 pages. Provides an overview of engineering, followed by a selection of jobs profiled in detail, including the nature of the job, earnings, prospects for employment, what kind of training and skills it requires and sources for further information. **Includes:** Appendices of educational institutions, periodicals, directories, and associations. Appendices of educational institutions, periodicals, directories, and associations.

6351 ■ Cultural Vistas
440 Park Ave. S, 2nd Fl.
New York, NY 10016
Ph: (212)497-3500
Fax: (212)497-3535
E-mail: info@culturalvistas.org
URL: http://culturalvistas.org

Description: Providers worldwide of on-the-job train-

ing programs for students and professionals seeking international career development and life-changing experiences. Arranges workplace exchanges in hundreds of professional fields, bringing employers and trainees together from around the world. Client list ranges from small farming communities to Fortune 500 companies.

6352 ■ Engineering Society of Detroit
20700 Civic Center Dr., Ste. 450
Southfield, MI 48076
Ph: (248)353-0735
Fax: (248)353-0736
E-mail: esd@esd.org
URL: http://ww2.esd.org/home.htm

Description: Engineers from all disciplines; scientists and technologists. Conducts technical programs and engineering refresher courses; sponsors conferences and expositions. Maintains speakers' bureau; offers placement services; although based in Detroit, MI, society membership is international. **Members:** 6,000.

6353 ■ Institute of Industrial Engineers
3577 Parkway Ln., Ste. 200
Norcross, GA 30092
Ph: (770)449-0460
Free: 800-494-0460
Fax: (770)441-3295
E-mail: executiveoffices@iienet.org
URL: http://www.iienet2.org

Description: Serves as professional society of industrial engineers. Concerned with the design, improvement, and installation of integrated systems of people, materials, equipment, and energy. Draws upon specialized knowledge and skill in the mathematical, physical, and social sciences together with the principles and methods of engineering analysis and design, to specify, predict, and evaluate the results obtained from such systems. Maintains technical societies and divisions.

6354 ■ Intelligent Transportation Society of America
1100 17th St. NW, Ste. 1200
Washington, DC 20036
Ph: (202)484-4847
Free: 800-374-8472
Fax: (202)484-3483
E-mail: info@itsa.org
URL: http://www.itsa.org

Description: Includes private corporations, public agencies, and academic institutions involved in the research, development, and design of intelligent transportation systems technologies that enhance safety, increase mobility, and sustain the environment.

6355 ■ Korean-American Scientists and Engineers Association
1952 Gallows Rd., Ste. 300
Vienna, VA 22182
Ph: (703)748-1221
Fax: (703)748-1331
E-mail: sejong@ksea.org
URL: http://www.ksea.org

Description: Represents scientists and engineers holding single or advanced degrees. Promotes friendship and mutuality among Korean and American scientists and engineers; contributes to Korea's scientific, technological, industrial, and economic developments; strengthens the scientific, technological, and cultural bonds between Korea and the U.S. Sponsors symposium. Maintains speakers' bureau, placement service, and biographical archives. Compiles statistics. **Members:** 10,000.

6356 ■ National Action Council for Minorities in Engineering
440 Hamilton Ave., Ste. 302
White Plains, NY 10601-1813
Ph: (914)539-4010
Free: 800-888-9929

Fax: (914)539-4032
E-mail: ajohnson@nacme.org
URL: http://www.nacme.org

Description: Leads the national effort to increase access to careers in engineering and other science-based disciplines. Conducts research and public policy analysis, develops and operates national demonstration programs at precollege and university levels, and disseminates information through publications, conferences and electronic media. Serves as a privately funded source of scholarships for minority students in engineering.

6357 ■ National Society of Professional Engineers
1420 King St.
Alexandria, VA 22314-2794
Ph: (703)684-2800
Fax: (703)836-4875
E-mail: memserv@nspe.org
URL: http://www.nspe.org

Description: Represents professional engineers and engineers-in-training in all fields registered in accordance with the laws of states or territories of the U.S. or provinces of Canada; qualified graduate engineers, student members, and registered land surveyors. Is concerned with social, professional, ethical, and economic considerations of engineering as a profession; encompasses programs in public relations, employment practices, ethical considerations, education, and career guidance. Monitors legislative and regulatory actions of interest to the engineering profession.

6358 ■ Society of Hispanic Professional Engineers
13181 Crossroads Pkwy. N, Ste. 450
City of Industry, CA 91746-3496
Ph: (323)725-3970
E-mail: shpenational@shpe.org
URL: http://national.shpe.org

Description: Represents engineers, student engineers, and scientists. Aims to increase the number of Hispanic engineers by providing motivation and support to students. Sponsors competitions and educational programs. Maintains placement service and speakers' bureau; compiles statistics. **Members:** 8,000.

6359 ■ Society for Manufacturing Engineers - Association for Finishing Processes
1 SME Dr.
Dearborn, MI 48121
Ph: (313)425-3000
Free: 800-733-4763
Fax: (313)425-3400
E-mail: service@sme.org
URL: http://www.sme.org

Description: Promotes the technology, process, and management aspects of the cleaning and coating of metal or plastic manufactured products and trade organizations concerned with the dissemination of knowledge related to industrial finishing. Conducts clinics and expositions. Offers professional certification. Maintains placement service with free listings for members. **Members:** 1,550.

6360 ■ Society of Women Engineers
203 N La Salle St., Ste. 1675
Chicago, IL 60601
Ph: (312)596-5223
Free: 877-SWE-INFO
Fax: (312)596-5252
E-mail: hq@swe.org
URL: http://societyofwomenengineers.swe.org

Description: Educational and service organization representing both students and professional women in engineering and technical fields.

6361 ■ SOLE - The International Society of Logistics
14625 Baltimore Ave., Ste. 303
Laurel, MD 20707-4902

Ph: (301)459-8446
Fax: (301)459-1522
E-mail: solehq@erols.com
URL: http://www.sole.org

Description: Represents corporate and individual management and technical practitioners in the field of logistics, including scientists, engineers, educators, managers, and other specialists in commerce, aerospace, and other industries, government, and the military. (Logistics is the art and science of management engineering and technical activities concerned with requirements, and designing, supplying, and maintaining resources to support objectives, plans, and operations.) Covers every logistics specialty, including reliability, maintainability, systems and equipment maintenance, maintenance support equipment, human factors, training and training equipment, spare parts, overhaul and repair, handbooks, field site activation and operation, field engineering, facilities, packaging, supply chain management, materials handling, and transportation. Sponsors on-line job referral service; conducts specialized education programs.

6362 ■ Women in Engineering ProActive Network
1901 E Asbury Ave., Ste. 220
Denver, CO 80208
Ph: (303)871-4643
Fax: (303)871-4628
URL: http://www.wepan.org

Description: Women in engineering professions. Includes key strategies such as education and training, research, collaboration, leadership, diversity, advocacy, networking, sustainability, accountability, and volunteerism in order to be a catalyst for change that enhances the success of women in the engineering professions.

Sources of Help-Wanted Ads

6363 ■ *Academy of Management Learning & Education*
Academy of Management
PO Box 3020
Briarcliff Manor, NY 10510
Ph: (914)923-2607
Fax: (914)923-2615
E-mail: membership@aom.org
URL: http://journals.aomonline.org/amle

Frequency: Quarterly. **Price:** $85 Individuals print; $130 Individuals print & online; $125 Libraries print; $170 Libraries print and online; $105 Other countries print; $150 Other countries print & online; $195 Other countries print, corporate library; $235 Other countries print & online, corporate library. **Description:** Journal covering management issues for professionals.

6364 ■ *Business Performance Management*
Intertec Publishing
5 Penn Plz., 13th Fl.
New York, NY 10001-1810
Ph: (212)613-9700
Free: 800-795-5445
Fax: (212)613-9749
E-mail: bethany.weaver@penton.com
URL: http://www.bpmmag.net/

Frequency: 4/yr. **Description:** Magazine for business managers. Covers organizing, automating, and analyzing of business methodologies and processes.

6365 ■ *Industrial Distribution: The Business Magazine for Industrial Distributors*
Reed Elsevier Group plc - Reed Business Information
360 Park Ave. S
New York, NY 11010
Ph: (212)791-4208
E-mail: corporatecommunications@reedbusiness.
 com
URL: http://www.inddist.com

Frequency: Monthly. **Price:** $121 Individuals; $145 Canada; $140 Individuals for Mexico; $280 Other countries. **Description:** Magazine covering industrial supplies marketing, management, sales, telecommunications, computers, inventory, and warehouse management.

6366 ■ *Management Research: The Journal of the Iberoamerican Academy of Management*
M.E. Sharpe Inc.
80 Business Park Dr.
Armonk, NY 10504
Ph: (914)273-1800
Free: 800-541-6563

Fax: (914)273-2106
E-mail: info@mesharpe.com
URL: http://www.mesharpe.com/mall/results1.asp
 ?ACR=JMR
Frequency: 3/yr. **Price:** $75 Individuals; $399 Institutions; $87 Other countries; $441 Institutions, other countries. **Description:** International journal dedicated to advancing the understanding of management in private and public sector organizations through empirical investigation and theoretical analysis. Attempts to promote an international dialogue between researchers, improve the understanding of the nature of management in different settings, and achieve a reasonable transfer of research results to management practice in several contexts. Receptive to research across a broad range of management topics such as human resource management, organizational behavior, organizational theory, and strategic management. While not regional in nature, articles dealing with Iberoamerican issues are particularly welcomed.

Handbooks and Manuals

6367 ■ *Expert Resumes for Managers and Executives*
Jist Works
875 Montreal Way
Saint Paul, MN 55102
Free: 800-648-5478
E-mail: info@jist.com
URL: http://www.jist.com/shop/product.php?productid
 =16727
Description: Wendy S. Enelow, Louise M. Kursmark. 2012. $17.95. 274 pages. Contains a collection of sample resumes and resume writing advice including how to create and use an electronic resume. Contains an appendix that includes internet resources for an online job search, writing cover letters, as well as a collection of sample letters.

6368 ■ *Manager's Handbook: Everything You Need to Know about How Business and Management Work*
Pearson Learning Group
145 S Mount Zion Rd.
Lebanon, IN 46052
Ph: (804)402-6933
Free: 800-526-9907
Fax: (800)393-3156
E-mail: pasley@pearsonlearning.com
URL: http://www.k12pearson.com
Price: $24.95. **Publication includes:** Principal content of publication is reference guide for new and experienced managers. **Indexes:** Alphabetical.

Employment Agencies and Search Firms

6369 ■ *APA Search Inc.*
1 Byram Brook Pl., Ste. 104
Armonk, NY 10504
Ph: (914)273-6000

Fax: (914)273-8025
E-mail: info@apasearch.com
URL: http://www.apasearch.com
Description: Employment agency specializing in the automotive, retail, and hardware industries.

6370 ■ *Boyden*
275 Madison Ave., Ste. 1500
New York, NY 10016
Ph: (212)949-9400
Fax: (212)949-5905
E-mail: newyork@boyden.com
URL: http://www.boyden.com
Description: Executive search firm.

6371 ■ *Boyle Ogata Bregman*
17461 Derian Ave., Ste. 202
Irvine, CA 92614
Ph: (949)474-3365
E-mail: info@bobsearch.com
URL: http://www.bobsearch.com
Description: Executive search firm.

6372 ■ *Cochran, Cochran & Yale LLC*
955 E Henrietta Rd.
Rochester, NY 14623
Ph: (585)424-6060
E-mail: roch@ccy.com
URL: http://www.ccy.com
Description: Executive search firm. Branches in Denver, CO and Williamsville, NY.

6373 ■ *Conboy Sur Morice & Associates*
15 Churchville Rd., No. 170
Bel Air, MD 21014-3837
E-mail: wks@csma-cons.com
URL: http://www.csma-cons.com
Description: Executive search firm.

6374 ■ *Dieck Executive Search*
30 Rough Lee Ct.
Madison, WI 53705
Ph: (608)238-1000
E-mail: dan@dieckexecutivesearch.com
URL: http://dieckexecutivesearch.com
Description: Executive search firm focused on pulp, paper and the packaging industries.

6375 ■ *The Ferneborg Group*
1700 S El Camino Real, Ste. 375
San Mateo, CA 94402
Ph: (650)577-0100
E-mail: info@execsearch.com
URL: http://www.execsearch.com
Description: Executive search firm.

6376 ■ *FPC of Savannah*
22 E Liberty St.
Savannah, GA 31401
Ph: (912)233-4556

Fax: (912)223-8633
E-mail: info@fpcsav.com
URL: http://www.fpcnational.com/savannah
Description: Executive search firm.

6377 ■ **K.S. Frary & Associates**
16 Schooner Ridge
Marblehead, MA 01945
Ph: (781)631-2464
E-mail: ksfrary@comcast.net
URL: http://www.ksfrary.com
Description: Executive search firm.

6378 ■ **Miller Personnel Consultants Inc.**
931 E 86th St., Ste. 103
Indianapolis, IN 46240
Ph: (317)251-5938
Free: 800-851-5938
Fax: (317)251-5762
E-mail: markmiller@netdirect.net
URL: http://www.millerpersonnel.com
Description: Executive search firm.

6379 ■ **Palladian International, LLC**
105-A Lew Dewitt Blvd., Ste. 197
Waynesboro, VA 22980
Free: 866-766-8447
E-mail: palladian@palladianinternational.com
URL: http://palladianinternational.com
Description: Acts as an executive recruiting firm that specializes in manufacturing and engineering, distribution and logistics, and former military officers. Offers free guides in resume writing, interview preparation, and resume benchmarking surveys.

6380 ■ **Recruiting Services Group Inc.**
138 Palm Coast Pkwy.
Palm Coast, FL 32137

Ph: (386)986-2833
Fax: (386)597-2255
E-mail: info@rsghunt.com
URL: http://www.rsghunt.com
Description: Executive search firm.

6381 ■ **RGT Associates Inc.**
2 Greenleaf Woods Dr., Ste. 101
Portsmouth, NH 03802
Ph: (603)431-9500
Fax: (603)431-6984
E-mail: inquires@rgtassociatesinc.com
URL: http://rgtassociatesinc.com/rgt
Description: Executive search firm.

6382 ■ **Ronald Dukes Associates LLC**
20 N Wacker, Ste. 2010
Chicago, IL 60606
Ph: (312)357-2895
Fax: (312)357-2897
E-mail: ron@rdukesassociates.com
URL: http://www.rdukesassociates.com
Description: Executive search firm focused on the industrial and automotive industries.

6383 ■ **Russ Hadick & Associates Inc.**
77 W Elmwood Dr., Ste 100
Dayton, OH 45459
Ph: (937)439-7700
Fax: (937)439-7705
URL: http://www.rharecruiters.com
Description: Executive search firm.

6384 ■ **Southern Recruiters & Consultants Inc.**
PO Box 2745
Aiken, SC 29802
Ph: (803)648-7834

Fax: (803)642-2770
E-mail: recruiters@southernrecruiters.com
URL: http://www.southernrecruiters.com
Description: Executive search firm.

6385 ■ **Stiles Associates LLC**
276 Newport Rd., Ste. 208
New London, NH 03257
Ph: (603)526-6566
Free: 800-322-5185
URL: http://www.leanexecs.com
Description: Executive search firm.

6386 ■ **William J. Christopher Associates Inc.**
307 N Walnut St.
West Chester, PA 19380
Ph: (610)696-4397
Fax: (610)692-5177
E-mail: wjc@wjca.com
URL: http://www.wjca.com
Description: Executive search firm.

TRADESHOWS

6387 ■ **International Thermal Spray Conference and Exposition**
ASM International
9639 Kinsman Rd.
Materials Pk., OH 44073-0002
Free: 800-336-5152
E-mail: memberservicecenter@asminternational.org
URL: http://www.asminternational.org
Frequency: Annual. **Primary Exhibits:** Thermal spray and welding equipment, supplies, and services.

6388 ■ *American City and County*
Penton
9800 Metcalf Ave.
Overland Park, KS 66212
Ph: (913)341-1300
Free: 866-748-4926
Fax: (913)967-1905
E-mail: corporatecustomerservice@penton.com
URL: http://americancityandcounty.com
Frequency: Monthly. **Description:** Municipal and county administration magazine.

6389 ■ *Cal-OSHA Reporter*
Providence Publications
PO Box 2610
Granite Bay, CA 95746
Ph: (916)774-4000
Fax: (916)596-2167
E-mail: newsdesk@cal-osha.com
URL: http://www.cal-osha.com/
Description: 48/year. Reports on laws, regulations, court cases, and other issues of interest to occupational safety and health professionals. Recurring features include a calendar of events, reports of meetings, news of educational opportunities, job listings, and notices of publications available. Reviews all Cal-OSHA cases.

6390 ■ *Industrial Hygiene News*
Rimbach Publishing Inc.
8650 Babcock Blvd.
Pittsburgh, PA 15237
Ph: (412)364-5366
Free: 800-245-3182
E-mail: info@rimbach.com
URL: http://www.rimbach.com
Frequency: Bimonthly. **Description:** Magazine covering industrial hygiene, occupational health, and safety.

6391 ■ *Occupational Health & Safety*
1105 Media, Inc.
14901 Quorum Dr., Ste. 425
Dallas, TX 75254
Ph: (972)687-6700
Fax: (972)687-6799
URL: http://ohsonline.com/Home.aspx
Frequency: Monthly. **Price:** $99 Individuals.
Description: Magazine covering federal and state regulation of occupational health and safety.

6392 ■ *Pharmaceutical Technology*
Advanstar Communications
485 Rte. 1 S
Bldg. F, 1st Fl.
Iselin, NJ 08830
Ph: (732)596-0276
Fax: (732)596-0003
URL: http://www.pharmtech.com
Frequency: Monthly. **Price:** $185 Individuals; $331 Two years; $263 Individuals Canada and Mexico; $458 Two years Canada and Mexico; $55 Individuals back issue; $85 Two years Canada/international, back issue. **Description:** Magazine on applied technology for pharmaceutical firms.

Employer Directories and Networking Lists

6393 ■ *American Industrial Hygiene Association--Directory*
American Industrial Hygiene Association
3141 Fairview Park Dr., Ste. 777
Falls Church, VA 22042
Ph: (703)849-8888
Fax: (703)207-3561
E-mail: infonet@aiha.org
URL: http://www.aiha.org
Frequency: Annual; September. **Pages:** 300. **Covers:** Approximately 12,000 members concerned with the study and control of environmental factors affecting people at work. **Entries include:** Name, address, phone, affiliation. **Arrangement:** Alphabetical. **Indexes:** Employer, geographical.

6394 ■ *Carroll's State Directory*
Caroll Publishing
4701 Sangamore Rd., Ste. S-155
Bethesda, MD 20816
Ph: (301)263-9800
Free: 800-336-4240
Fax: (301)263-9801
E-mail: info@carrollpub.com
URL: http://www.carrollpub.com/stateprint.asp
Frequency: 3x/yr. **Price:** $425 Individuals 3 issues per year. **Pages:** 1,100. **Covers:** About 70,000 state government officials in all branches of government; officers, committees and members of state legislatures; managers of boards and authorities. **Entries include:** Name, address, phone, fax, title. **Arrangement:** Geographical; separate sections for state offices and legislatures. **Indexes:** Personal name (with phone and e-mail address), organizational, keyword.

6395 ■ *Federal Staff Directory*
CQ Press
2300 N St. NW, Ste. 800
Washington, DC 20037
Ph: (202)729-1900
Free: 866-427-7737
E-mail: customerservice@cqpress.com
URL: http://www.cqpress.com/product/Federal-Staff
-Directory-print-Web.html
Frequency: Latest edition 2012. **Price:** $599 Individuals single copy, standing order. **Pages:** 1,700. **Covers:** Approximately 45,000 persons in federal government offices and independent agencies, with biographies of 2,600 key executives; includes officials at policy level in agencies of the Office of the President, Cabinet-level departments, independent and regulatory agencies, military commands, federal information centers, and libraries, and United States attorneys, marshals, and ambassadors. **Includes:** Text establishing the legal authority and functional responsibility of major divisions and bureaus under each department and agency; new organization charts and photographs of key executives. **Entries include:** Name, title, location (indicating building, address, and/or room), phone, fax, e-mail address, website, symbols indicating whether position is a presidential appointment and whether senate approval is required. **Arrangement:** Classified by department/agency. **Indexes:** Office locator page; extensive subject/keyword; individual name.

Handbooks and Manuals

6396 ■ *Start Your Own Home Inspection Service*
The McGraw-Hill Companies Inc.
PO Box 182604
Columbus, OH 43272
Ph: (212)512-2000
Free: 877-833-5524
Fax: (614)759-3749
E-mail: customer.service@mcgraw-hili.com
URL: http://www.mcgraw-hill.com
Description: 2007. $15.95. Illustrated. 120 pages. Entrepreneur Magazine's Start Up Series.

Employment Agencies and Search Firms

6397 ■ *Conselium*
14850 Montfort Dr., Ste. 106
Dallas, TX 75254
Ph: (972)934-8444
URL: http://www.conselium.com
Description: Executive search firm with a core expertise in corporate compliance, audit, and information technology security.

6398 ■ *Food Management Search*
235 State St., Ste. 326
Springfield, MA 01103
Ph: (413)732-2666
Fax: (413)732-6466
E-mail: recruiters@foodmanagementsearch.com
URL: http://foodmanagementsearch.com/index.cfm
Description: Specializes in contingency recruiting projects exclusively in the food manufacturing and food service industries. Provides positions covering food production/manufacturing, supply chain, food service, sales and marketing.

6399 ■ Wellington Executive Search
3162 Johnson Ferry Rd., Ste. 260
Marietta, GA 30062
Ph: (770)645-5799
Fax: (678)278-0928
E-mail: jobs@wellingtonsearch.com
URL: http://www.wellingtonsearch.com
Description: Serves as an executive search firm covering sales representative, research and development, food scientists, and purchasing managers.

ONLINE JOB SOURCES AND SERVICES

6400 ■ ComplianceCrossing.com
URL: http://www.compliancecrossing.com
Description: Features a comprehensive collection of compliance job openings. Includes listings from Fortune 500 and Fortune 1,000 companies.

TRADESHOWS

6401 ■ Annual Ethics & Compliance Conference
Ethics and Compliance Officer Association
411 Waverley Oaks Rd., Ste. 324
Waltham, MA 02452-8420
Ph: (781)647-9333
Fax: (781)647-9399
E-mail: membership@theecoa.org
URL: http://www.theecoa.org
Frequency: Annual. Addresses the latest issues and provides opportunities for the exchange of ideas and practical, proven methods for implementing and maintaining successful ethics, compliance and business conduct programs.

6402 ■ National Safety Council Congress and Expo
National Safety Council
1121 Spring Lake Dr.
Itasca, IL 60143-3201
Ph: (630)285-1121
Free: 800-621-7615
Fax: (630)285-1315
E-mail: info@nsc.org
URL: http://www.nsc.org/Pages/Home.aspx
Frequency: Annual. **Primary Exhibits:** Safety- and health-related products and services, including protective clothing, footwear, consulting services, breathing apparatuses, educational materials, films and related equipment, supplies, and services.

OTHER SOURCES

6403 ■ American Public Health Association
800 I St. NW
Washington, DC 20001-3710
Ph: (202)777-2742
Fax: (202)777-2534
E-mail: comments@apha.org
URL: http://www.apha.org
Description: Professional organization of physicians, nurses, educators, academicians, environmentalists, epidemiologists, new professionals, social workers, health administrators, optometrists, podiatrists, pharmacists, dentists, nutritionists, health planners, other community and mental health specialists, and interested consumers. Seeks to protect and promote personal, mental, and environmental health. Services include: promulgation of standards; establishment of uniform practices and procedures; development of the etiology of communicable diseases; research in public health; exploration of medical care programs and their relationships to public health. Sponsors job placement service.

6404 ■ American Society of Safety Engineers
1800 E Oakton St.
Des Plaines, IL 60018
Ph: (847)699-2929
Fax: (847)768-3434
E-mail: customerservice@asse.org
URL: http://www.asse.org
Description: Professional society of safety engineers, safety directors, and others concerned with accident prevention, environmental protection and safety and health programs. Sponsors National Safety Month and conducts research and educational programs. Develops/publishes ANSI safety-related standards and other technical literature. Compiles statistics; maintains job placement service.

6405 ■ Ethics and Compliance Officer Association
411 Waverley Oaks Rd., Ste. 324
Waltham, MA 02452-8420
Ph: (781)647-9333
Fax: (781)647-9399
E-mail: membership@theecoa.org
URL: http://www.theecoa.org
Description: Managers of ethics, compliance, and business conduct programs. Offers educational business ethics and compliance programs; conducts national research; and provides free job-listing service.

6406 ■ National Environmental Health Association
720 S Colorado Blvd., Ste. 1000-N
Denver, CO 80246-1926
Ph: (303)756-9090
Free: 866-956-2258
Fax: (303)691-9490
E-mail: staff@neha.org
URL: http://www.neha.org
Description: Represents all professionals in environmental health and protection, including Registered Sanitarians, Registered Environmental Health Specialists, Registered Environmental Technicians, Certified Environmental Health Technicians, Registered Hazardous Substances Professionals and Registered Hazardous Substances Specialists. Advances the environmental health and protection profession for the purpose of providing a healthful environment for all. Provides educational materials, publications, credentials and meetings to members and non-member professionals who strive to improve the environment.

6407 ■ United States Pharmacopeia
12601 Twinbrook Pkwy.
Rockville, MD 20852-1790
Ph: (301)881-0666
Free: 800-227-8772
E-mail: custsvc@usp.org
URL: http://www.usp.org
Description: Acts as the non-governmental, official public standards-setting authority of prescription and over-the-counter medicines and other healthcare products manufactured or sold in the United States. Strives to improve the health of people around the world through public standards and related programs that help ensure the quality, safety, and benefit of medicines and foods.

Instructional Coordinators

Sources of Help-Wanted Ads

6408 ■ Journal of Diversity in Higher Education
American Psychological Association
750 First St. NE
Washington, DC 20002-4242
Ph: (202)336-5500
Free: 800-374-2721
Fax: (202)336-5812
E-mail: journals@apa.org
URL: http://www.apa.org/pubs/journals/dhe/index.aspx

Frequency: Quarterly. **Price:** $65 Members; $89 Other countries members; $415 Institutions; $464 Institutions, other countries; $65 Students; $105 Nonmembers; $134 Other countries nonmembers. **Description:** Journal publishing research findings, theory and promising practices in higher education.

Handbooks and Manuals

6409 ■ Accelerating Student and Staff Learning
Corwin Press, Incorporated
2455 Teller Rd.
Thousand Oaks, CA 91320-2218
Ph: (805)499-9734
Free: 800-417-2466
Fax: (800)499-5323
E-mail: order@corwin.com
URL: http://www.corwinpress.com/booksProdDesc.nav?prodId=Book233107&

Description: Kay Psencik. 2009. $36.95 (paperback); $80.95 (hardcover). 192 pages. Engages teachers in collaborative curriculum design and professional development.

6410 ■ Aligning Your Curriculum to the Common Core State Standards
Corwin Press
2455 Teller Rd.
Thousand Oaks, CA 91320
Ph: (805)499-9734
Free: 800-233-9936
Fax: (805)499-5323
E-mail: order@corwin.com
URL: http://www.corwin.com

Description: Joe Crawford. 2011. $39.95 (paper). 248 pages. Explains how to facilitate learning for all students while taking advantage of the new culture, technology, and norms of the current learning environment. Includes charts, graphs and access to internet-based software for mapping the common core state standards to curriculum, instruction and assessment.

6411 ■ Assessment Clear and Simple: A Practical Guide for Institutions, Departments, and General Education
Jossey-Bass
c/o John Wiley & Sons, Inc.
111 River St.
Hoboken, NJ 07030-5774
Ph: (201)748-6000
Fax: (201)748-6088
E-mail: info@wiley.com
URL: http://www.josseybass.com

Description: Barbara E. Walvoord. 2010. $30.00 (paperback). 144 pages. 2nd edition. Provides step-by-step guide for the assessment process. Explores the areas of planning, budgeting, and the changes in curriculum, pedagogy and programming. Emphasizes and shows how to move from data to actions to improve student learning.

6412 ■ Concept-Based Curriculum and Instruction for the Thinking Classroom
Corwin Press, Incorporated
2455 Teller Rd.
Thousand Oaks, CA 91320-2218
Ph: (805)499-9734
Free: 800-417-2466
Fax: (800)499-5323
E-mail: order@corwin.com
URL: http://www.corwinpress.com/booksProdDesc.nav?prodId=Book233107&

Description: H. Lynn Erickson. 2009. $360.00. Includes a CD-ROM and 102-minute DVD. Demonstrates how a concept-based instructional approach can deepen students' intellectual abilities and transform the classroom experience for both teachers and learners.

6413 ■ Creating the Curriculum
Routledge
711 3rd Ave., 8th Fl.
New York, NY 10017
Ph: (212)216-7800
Free: 800-634-7064
Fax: (212)564-7854
E-mail: book.orders@tandf.co.uk
URL: http://www.routledge.com

Description: Dominic Wyse, Vivienne Marie Baumfield, David Egan, Louise Hayward, Moira Hulme, Ian Menter, Carmel Gallagher and Kay Livingston. 2012. $39.95 (paper); $155.00 (hardback). Discovers strategies and new approaches that make an effective and meaningful curriculum.

6414 ■ Creating Standards-Based Integrated Curriculum
Corwin Press, Incorporated
2455 Teller Rd.
Thousand Oaks, CA 91320-2218
Ph: (805)499-9734
Free: 800-417-2466

Fax: (800)499-5323
E-mail: order@corwin.com
URL: http://www.corwinpress.com/booksProdDesc.nav?prodId=Book233107&

Description: Susan M. Drake. 2012. $36.95 (paper). 208 pages. Provides a new approach to standards-based curriculum, instruction and assessment.

6415 ■ Creativity in the Primary Curriculum
Routledge
711 3rd Ave., 8th Fl.
New York, NY 10017
Ph: (212)216-7800
Free: 800-634-7064
Fax: (212)564-7854
E-mail: book.orders@tandf.co.uk
URL: http://www.routledge.com

Description: Russell Jones and Dominic Wyse. 2012. Second Edition. $35.95 (paper); $128.00 (hardback). 224 pages. Offers guidelines and advice on the planning and implementation of effective creative primary teaching.

6416 ■ Cultures of Curriculum, Second Edition
Routledge
711 3rd Ave., 8th Fl.
New York, NY 10017
Ph: (212)216-7800
Free: 800-634-7064
Fax: (212)564-7854
E-mail: book.orders@tandf.co.uk
URL: http://www.routledge.com

Description: Pamela Bolotin Joseph. 2010. $45.95 (paper); $145.00 (hardcover). 304 pages. Fosters awareness, examination, and deliberation about the approaches to curriculum and practice.

6417 ■ The Curriculum Bridge: From Standards to Actual Classroom Practice
Corwin Press
2455 Teller Rd.
Thousand Oaks, CA 91320
Ph: (805)499-9734
Free: 800-233-9936
Fax: (805)499-5323
E-mail: order@corwin.com
URL: http://www.corwin.com

Description: Pearl G. Solomon. 2009. $36.95 (paper). 248 pages. Lays out what a classroom teacher or curriculum developer needs in order to create an effective curriculum that can be adapted into actual classroom instruction. Serves as an educator's tool for making informed and significant decisions in order to promote standards-based instruction, improve student outcomes and create a suitable environment for learning.

6418 ■ Curriculum Development in the Postmodern Era
Routledge
711 3rd Ave., 8th Fl.
New York, NY 10017

Ph: (212)216-7800
Free: 800-634-7064
Fax: (212)564-7854
E-mail: book.orders@tandf.co.uk
URL: http://www.routledge.com

Description: Patrick Slattery. 2012. Third Edition. $49.95 (paper); $150.00 (hardback). Introduces and analyzes contemporary concepts of curriculum that emerged from the reconceptualization of curriculum studies in the 1970s and 1980s. Serves as reference guide for educators and educational leaders, curriculum development specialist, researchers and policy advocators of higher learning, doctoral students in all disciplines, trainers and those who are interested in improving the dynamics of learning.

6419 ■ Curriculum and Instruction
Pine Forge Press
2455 Teller Rd.
Thousand Oaks, CA 91320-2234
Ph: (805)499-4224
Free: 800-818-7243
Fax: (805)499-0871
E-mail: sales@pfp.sagepub.com
URL: http://www.sagepub.com/sociologybooks

Description: A. Jonathan Eakle. 2012. $85.00 (hardcover). 400 pages. Explores multiple curriculum and instruction issues including alternative curriculum, curriculum control, standardized curricula, subject- versus student-centered curricula, and textbooks.

6420 ■ Curriculum Leadership: Strategies for Development and Implementation
Pine Forge Press
2455 Teller Rd.
Thousand Oaks, CA 91320-2234
Ph: (805)499-4224
Free: 800-818-7243
Fax: (805)499-0871
E-mail: sales@pfp.sagepub.com
URL: http://www.sagepub.com/sociologybooks

Description: Allan A. Glatthorn, Floyd A. Boschee, Bruce M. Whitehead, and Bonni F. Boschee. 2011. $110.00 (hardcover). 552 pages. Provides educational leaders, teachers, and administrators with innovative programs, learning experiences, and creative, up-to-date curriculum strategies and ideas.

6421 ■ The Curriculum Manager's Handbook
CreateSpace
7290 B. Investment Dr.
Charleston, SC 29418
E-mail: info@createspace.com
URL: http://www.createspace.com

Description: Guy W. Wallace. 2011. $30.00 (paper). 274 pages. Defines the responsibilities as well as performance and competency skills required for a curriculum manager.

6422 ■ Curriculum, Syllabus Design and Equity
Routledge
711 3rd Ave., 8th Fl.
New York, NY 10017
Ph: (212)216-7800
Free: 800-634-7064
Fax: (212)564-7854
E-mail: book.orders@tandf.co.uk
URL: http://www.routledge.com

Description: Allan Luke, Annette Woods and Katie Weir. 2012. $44.95 (paper); $135.00 (hardback). 208 pages. Advances a unified, principled approach to the design of syllabus documents that aims for high quality/high equity educational outcomes and enhances teacher professionalism. Serves as guide for teachers, teacher educators, and curriculum policy workers who are engaged in curriculum writing and implementation.

6423 ■ Deciding What to Teach and Test
Corwin Press, Incorporated
2455 Teller Rd.
Thousand Oaks, CA 91320-2218
Ph: (805)499-9734
Free: 800-417-2466
Fax: (800)499-5323
E-mail: order@corwin.com
URL: http://www.corwinpress.com/booksProdDesc
.nav?prodId=Book233107&

Description: Fenwick W. English. 2010. $27.95 (paperback). 168 pages. Addresses the fundamentals of curriculum design in the context of a standards-based environment. Includes insights on providing effective curriculum leadership, increasing student success, and closing the achievement gap.

6424 ■ Designing Effective Instruction
John Wiley & Sons Inc.
111 River St.
Hoboken, NJ 07030-5774
Ph: (201)748-6000
Free: 800-225-5945
Fax: (201)748-6088
E-mail: info@wiley.com
URL: http://www.wiley.com

Description: Gary R. Morrison, Steven M. Ross, Jerrold E. Kemp, Howard Kalman. 2010. $142.95 (paper). 491 pages. Equips educators with practical skills for successful instructional design.

6425 ■ An Educational Leader's Guide to Curriculum Mapping
Corwin
2455 Teller Rd.
Thousand Oaks, CA 91320
Ph: (805)499-9734
Free: 800-233-9936
Fax: (805)499-5323
E-mail: order@corwin.com
URL: http://www.corwin.com

Description: Janet A. Hale and Richard F. Dunlap, Jr. 2010. $36.95 (paper). 200 pages. Provides an overview of key concepts and processes of curriculum mapping. Presents leadership strategies for successful implementation of curriculum mapping.

6426 ■ Encyclopedia of Curriculum Studies
Pine Forge Press
2455 Teller Rd.
Thousand Oaks, CA 91320-2234
Ph: (805)499-4224
Free: 800-818-7243
Fax: (805)499-0871
E-mail: sales@pfp.sagepub.com
URL: http://www.sagepub.com/sociologybooks

Description: Craig Kridel. 2010. $370.00 (hardcover). 1,064 pages. Describes the conventions, ways, and accepted research and writing practices in the field of curriculum studies.

6427 ■ From Mandate to Achievement: 5 Steps to a Curriculum System That Works!
Corwin Press, Incorporated
2455 Teller Rd.
Thousand Oaks, CA 91320-2218
Ph: (805)499-9734
Free: 800-417-2466
Fax: (800)499-5323
E-mail: order@corwin.com
URL: http://www.corwinpress.com/booksProdDesc
.nav?prodId=Book233107&

Description: Elaine Makas. 2009. $38.95 (paperback); $85.95 (hardcover). 248 pages. Guides principals, district administrators, curriculum facilitators and teachers in establishing a consistent and accurate curriculum process that increases academic achievement and drives continuous school improvement.

6428 ■ Getting Serious About the System
Corwin Press, Incorporated
2455 Teller Rd.
Thousand Oaks, CA 91320-2218

Ph: (805)499-9734
Free: 800-417-2466
Fax: (800)499-5323
E-mail: order@corwin.com
URL: http://www.corwinpress.com/booksProdDesc
.nav?prodId=Book233107&

Description: D'Ette Cowan, Stacey Joyner and Shirley Beckwith. 2012. $31.95 (paperback). 120 pages. Provides teachers, administrators and leaders with a comprehensive resource in aligning curriculum, instruction and assessment. Presents a step-by-step, research-based approach to district and school transformation.

6429 ■ Habits of Mind Across the Curriculum: Practical and Creative Strategies for Teachers
ASCD
1703 N Beauregard St.
Alexandria, VA 22311-1714
Ph: (703)578-9600
Free: 800-933-2723
Fax: (703)575-5400
URL: http://www.ascd.org

Description: Arthur L. Costa and Bena Kallick. 2009. $26.95. 236 pages. Presents a collective wisdom and experience of educators who have successfully implemented the habits of mind in their curriculum, instruction, and assessments.

6430 ■ How to Build an Instructional Coaching Program for Maximum Capacity
Corwin Press
2455 Teller Rd.
Thousand Oaks, CA 91320
Ph: (805)499-9734
Free: 800-233-9936
Fax: (805)499-5323
E-mail: order@corwin.com
URL: http://www.corwin.com

Description: Nina Jones Morel, Carla Staton Cushman. 2012. $36.95 (paper). 208 pages. Serves as a resource for school and district leaders to develop and sustain an effective coaching program. Provides a practical framework for starting and sustaining a viable instructional coaching program.

6431 ■ How to Integrate the Curricula
Corwin Press, Incorporated
2455 Teller Rd.
Thousand Oaks, CA 91320-2218
Ph: (805)499-9734
Free: 800-417-2466
Fax: (800)499-5323
E-mail: order@corwin.com
URL: http://www.corwinpress.com/booksProdDesc
.nav?prodId=Book233107&

Description: Robin J. Fogarty and Brian M. Pete. 2009. $31.95 (paper); $72.95 (hardcover). 152 pages. Supports educators as they integrate concepts, skills, and attitudes and immerse students in content through self-selected, personally relevant learning experiences.

6432 ■ Idea-Based Learning
Kumarian Press Inc.
22883 Quicksilver Dr.
Sterling, VA 20166-2012
Ph: (703)661-1504
Free: 800-232-0223
Fax: (703)661-1547
E-mail: kpbooks@kpbooks.com
URL: http://www.kpbooks.com

Description: Edmund J. Hansen. 2011. $75.00 (hardback); $24.95 (paperback). Serves as guide in developing college instruction that has clear purpose, is well integrated into the curriculum, and improves student learning.

6433 ■ Improving Standards-Based Learning
Corwin Press, Incorporated
2455 Teller Rd.
Thousand Oaks, CA 91320-2218

Ph: (805)499-9734
Free: 800-417-2466
Fax: (800)499-5323
E-mail: order@corwin.com
URL: http://www.corwinpress.com/booksProdDesc
.nav?prodId=Book233107&

Description: Judy F. Carr and Doug Harris. 2009.
$36.95 (paperback); $80.95 (hardcover). 200 pages.
Provides tools and processes for developing a curriculum that can generate substantive improvement in teaching and learning.

6434 ■ Instructional Design for Action Learning
AMACOM Publishing
c/o American Management Association
1601 Broadway
New York, NY 10019-7434
Ph: (212)586-8100
Free: 800-714-6395
Fax: (518)891-0368
E-mail: pubs_cust_serv@amanet.org
URL: http://www.amacombooks.org

Description: Geri McArdle. 2010. $34.95 (paper).
Serves as a guide to developing learner-based training that works. Includes action learning techniques for training design and presentation.

6435 ■ The Instructional Leadership Toolbox: A Handbook for Improving Practice
Corwin Press
2455 Teller Rd.
Thousand Oaks, CA 91320
Ph: (805)499-9734
Free: 800-233-9936
Fax: (805)499-5323
E-mail: order@corwin.com
URL: http://www.corwin.com

Description: Sandra Lee Gupton. 2009. $36.95
(paper); $82.95 (hardcover). 216 pages. Establishes practical ways for leaders to reflect on and improve their practice. Provides a blueprint that demonstrates how school leaders can focus on student learning, while using tools and building teams to increase student achievement.

6436 ■ Internationalizing the Curriculum in Higher Education
Jossey-Bass
c/o John Wiley & Sons, Inc.
111 River St.
Hoboken, NJ 07030-5774
Ph: (201)748-6000
Fax: (201)748-6088
E-mail: info@wiley.com
URL: http://www.josseybass.com

Description: Carolin Kreber. 2009. $29.00 (paper).
128 pages. Explores different concepts of internationalization in higher education. Describes the nine cases of internationalization initiatives at the curricular level.

6437 ■ Leading Curriculum Improvement
Rowman & Littlefield Education
4501 Forbes Blvd., Ste. 200
Lanham, MD 20706
Ph: (301)459-3366
Free: 800-462-6420
Fax: (301)429-5748
E-mail: custserv@rowman.com
URL: http://www.rowmaneducation.com

Description: Marilyn Tallerico. 2011. $40.00
(hardback); $19.95 (paper). 136 pages. Offers guidance and curriculum leadership fundamentals to teacher leaders, instructional coordinators, central office personnel for facilitating curriculum improvement at the building level.

6438 ■ The Learner-Centered Curriculum: Design and Implementation
Jossey-Bass
c/o John Wiley & Sons, Inc.
111 River St.
Hoboken, NJ 07030-5774

Ph: (201)748-6000
Fax: (201)748-6088
E-mail: info@wiley.com
URL: http://www.josseybass.com

Description: Roxanne Cullen, Michael Harris, Reinhold R. Hill and Maryellen Weimer. 2012. $40.00
(hardcover). 272 pages. Offers both design specifications for a learner-centered approach to curriculum as well as practical recommendations for implementation and assessment.

6439 ■ The Principal's Guide to Curriculum Leadership
Corwin
2455 Teller Rd.
Thousand Oaks, CA 91320
Ph: (805)499-9734
Free: 800-233-9936
Fax: (805)499-5323
E-mail: order@corwin.com
URL: http://www.corwin.com

Description: Richard D. Sorenson, Lloyd Milton Goldsmith, Zulma Y. Mendez, and Karen Taylor Maxwell. 2011. $41.95 (paper). 320 pages. Provides practical guidance for principal and other school administrators in initiating curriculum development and change. Features discussion questions, case studies, activities, specialized curriculum models, resources, and references.

6440 ■ Shaping the College Curriculum: Academic Plans in Context
Jossey-Bass
c/o John Wiley & Sons, Inc.
111 River St.
Hoboken, NJ 07030-5774
Ph: (201)748-6000
Fax: (201)748-6088
E-mail: info@wiley.com
URL: http://www.josseybass.com

Description: Lisa R. Lattuca and Joan S. Stark. 2nd edition. 2009. $50.00 (hardcover). 400 pages. Focuses on research-based educational practices relevant to curriculum development in higher education.

6441 ■ Staff Development Guide for the Parallel Curriculum
Corwin Press, Incorporated
2455 Teller Rd.
Thousand Oaks, CA 91320-2218
Ph: (805)499-9734
Free: 800-417-2466
Fax: (800)499-5323
E-mail: order@corwin.com
URL: http://www.corwinpress.com/booksProdDesc
.nav?prodId=Book233107&

Description: Cindy A. Strickland and Kathy Tuchman Glass. 2009. $36.95 (paperback); $80.95
(hardcover). 192 pages. Contributes to the professional training that results in enhanced teacher expertise and a multidimensional, high-quality curriculum that challenges the learners.

6442 ■ Strategic Curriculum Change
Routledge
711 3rd Ave., 8th Fl.
New York, NY 10017
Ph: (212)216-7800
Free: 800-634-7064
Fax: (212)564-7854
E-mail: book.orders@tandf.co.uk
URL: http://www.routledge.com

Description: Paul Blackmore and Camille B. Kandiko. 2012. $44.95 (paperback); $155.00
(hardback). 224 pages. Presents a theorized and contextualized approach to the study of the curriculum and focuses on the necessary research on the curriculum in higher education.

6443 ■ Teaching for Intellectual and Emotional Learning : A Model for Creating Powerful Curriculum
Rowman & Littlefield Education
4501 Forbes Blvd., Ste. 200
Lanham, MD 20706
Ph: (301)459-3366
Free: 800-462-6420
Fax: (301)429-5748
E-mail: custserv@rowman.com
URL: http://www.rowmaneducation.com

Description: Christy Folsom. 2009. $90.00
(hardback); $36.95 (paperback). 310 pages.
Educates teachers in developing standards-based curriculum that includes social-emotional learning.

6444 ■ Using Power Standards to Build an Aligned Curriculum
Corwin Press, Incorporated
2455 Teller Rd.
Thousand Oaks, CA 91320-2218
Ph: (805)499-9734
Free: 800-417-2466
Fax: (805)499-5323
E-mail: order@corwin.com
URL: http://www.corwinpress.com/booksProdDesc
.nav?prodId=Book233107&

Description: Joe Crawford. 2011. $36.95 (paper).
216 pages. Assists administrators and teachers in developing a useful, aligned curriculum that can effectively support student achievement and assessment.

ONLINE JOB SOURCES AND SERVICES

6445 ■ Curriculum Development Jobs
URL: http://www.curriculumdevelopmentjobs.org
Description: Serves as a niche job board for curriculum development professionals. Offers employment opportunities and candidate recruiting.

6446 ■ Get Curriculum Development Jobs
URL: http://www.getcurriculumdevelopmentjobs.com
Description: Serves as a one-stop resource for finding and filling curriculum development positions. Offers free curriculum development job postings and career opportunities.

6447 ■ Instructional Design Central
URL: http://www.instructionaldesigncentral.com
Description: Provides instructional design related information, career and learning opportunities, and other resources to instructional design professionals, educators, and students.

TRADESHOWS

6448 ■ CoSN Annual Conference
Consortium for School Networking
1025 Vermont Ave. NW, Ste. 1010
Washington, DC 20005
Ph: (202)861-2676
Free: 866-267-8747
Fax: (202)393-2011
E-mail: info@cosn.org
URL: http://www.cosn.org
Frequency: Annual. Works to open a worldwide dialogue about the issues of technology and school networking. Brings together key education and policy leaders from the U.S. and other nations to examine global responses to the effective use of Information and Communication Technology (ICT) in education.

OTHER SOURCES

6449 ■ American Association for Teaching and Curriculum
c/o Lynne Bailey, Executive Secretary
5640 Seminole Blvd.
Seminole, FL 33772-7341
E-mail: lmbailey22@yahoo.com
URL: http://www.aatchome.org

Description: Promotes the scholarly study of teaching and curriculum through its annual conferences, peer-reviewed journal, and the interaction of its members.

6450 ■ Consortium for School Networking
1025 Vermont Ave. NW, Ste. 1010
Washington, DC 20005
Ph: (202)861-2676
Free: 866-267-8747
Fax: (202)393-2011

E-mail: info@cosn.org
URL: http://www.cosn.org
Description: Promotes the use of telecommunications in K-12 classrooms to improve learning. Members represent state and local education agencies, non-profits, companies and individuals who share the organization's vision.

6451 ■ National Council on Measurement in Education
2424 American Ln.
Madison, WI 53704-3102

Ph: (608)443-2487
Fax: (608)443-2474
E-mail: plovelace@ncme.org
URL: http://ncme.org

Description: Consists of individuals involved in assessment, evaluation, testing and other aspects of educational measurement. Helps members involved in the construction and the use of standardized tests.

6452 ■ ASCnet Quarterly
Applied Systems Client Network
801 Douglas Ave., Ste. 205
Altamonte Springs, FL 32714
Ph: (407)869-0404
Free: 800-605-1045
Fax: (407)869-0418
E-mail: info@ascnet.org
URL: http://www.ascnet.org/AM/Template.cfm?Section=About
Frequency: Quarterly. **Price:** $24 Individuals.
Description: Professional magazine covering technical information, association news, and industry information for insurance professionals.

6453 ■ Best's Review
A.M. Best Company Inc.
Ambest Rd.
Oldwick, NJ 08858-7000
Ph: (908)439-2200
Fax: (908)439-3385
E-mail: customer_service@ambest.com
URLs: http://www.ambest.com/sales/newsoverview.asp#br; http://www.ambest.com/review/default.asp
Frequency: Monthly. **Price:** $50 Individuals.
Description: Magazine covering issues and trends for the management personnel of life/health insurers, the agents, and brokers who market their products.

6454 ■ Business Insurance
Crain Communications Inc.
1155 Gratiot Ave.
Detroit, MI 48207-2732
Ph: (313)446-6000
E-mail: info@crain.com
URL: http://www.businessinsurance.com
Frequency: Weekly. **Price:** $399 Individuals print; $149 Individuals print & digital; $69 Individuals digital edition. **Description:** International newsweekly reporting on corporate risk and employee benefit management news.

6455 ■ Claims: Covering the Business of Loss
Claims
15112 64th Ave. W
Edmonds, WA 98026
Ph: (425)745-6394
URL: http://www.propertycasualty360.com/Claims-Magazine
Frequency: Monthly. **Price:** $72 Individuals; $93 Canada; $131 Other countries. **Description:** Magazine for the property-casualty insurance claims industry.

6456 ■ The Standard: New England's Insurance Weekly
Standard Publishing Corp.
155 Federal St., 13th Fl.
Boston, MA 02110
Ph: (617)457-0600
Free: 800-682-5759
Fax: (617)457-0608
E-mail: stnd@earthlink.net
URL: http://www.spcpub.com
Frequency: Weekly (Fri.). **Price:** $97.50 Individuals U.S.; $170 Two years U.S. **Description:** Trade newspaper covering insurance events, legislation, regulatory hearings, and court sessions for independent insurance agents in New England.

6457 ■ Today's Insurance Professionals
International Association of Insurance Professionals
8023 E 63rd Pl., Ste. 540
Tulsa, OK 74133
Ph: (918)294-3700
Free: 800-766-6249
Fax: (918)294-3711
URL: http://www.naiw.org/?page=todays_mag_full
Frequency: Quarterly. **Price:** $15 Individuals; $5 Single issue; $15/year for nonmembers in U.S.; $25/year for nonmembers outside U.S. **Description:** Presents articles on industry issues, association news, and member accomplishments.

6458 ■ Registered Financial Planners Institute
2001 Cooper Foster Park Rd.
Amherst, OH 44001
Ph: (440)282-7176
Fax: (440)282-8027
E-mail: info@rfpi.com
URL: http://rfpi.com
Description: Registered financial planners, including insurance and real estate agents, attorneys, accountants, certified public accountants, bankers, securities analysts, and stockbrokers. Sponsors referral service. **Members:** 300.

6459 ■ Best's Insurance Reports
A.M. Best Company Inc.
Ambest Rd.
Oldwick, NJ 08858-7000
Ph: (908)439-2200
Fax: (908)439-3385
E-mail: customer_service@ambest.com
URL: http://www.ambest.com
Frequency: Annual; Latest edition 2014. **Pages:** 3,345 Life-health; 5,166 property-casualty. **Description:** Published in three editions: Life-health insurance, covering about 1,750 companies, property-casualty insurance, covering over 3,200 companies; and international, covering more than 1,200 insurers. Each edition lists state insurance commissioners and related companies and agencies (mutual funds, worker compensation funds, underwriting agencies, etc.). **Includes:** Review of financial performance, 5 years of exclusive Best's Ratings. **Entries include:** For each company--Company name, address, phone; history; states in which licensed; names of officers and directors; financial data; financial analysis and Best's rating. **Arrangement:** Alphabetical.

6460 ■ Business Insurance--Agent/Broker Profiles Issue
Crain Communications Inc.
150 N Michigan Ave.
Chicago, IL 60601-7553
Ph: (312)649-5200
Free: 800-678-9595
Fax: (312)280-3150
E-mail: info@crain.com
URL: http://www.businessinsurance.com
Frequency: Annual; Latest edition 2008. **Publication includes:** List of top 10 insurance agents/brokers worldwide specializing in commercial insurance. **Entries include:** Firm name, address, phone, fax, branch office locations, year established, names of subsidiaries, gross revenues, premium volume, number of employees, principal officers, percent of revenue generated by commercial retail brokerage, acquisitions. **Arrangement:** Alphabetical by company. **Indexes:** Geographical.

6461 ■ Directory of Insurance Wholesalers
Crain Communications Inc.
1155 Gratiot Ave.
Detroit, MI 48207-2732
Ph: (313)446-6000
E-mail: info@crain.com
URL: http://www.businessinsurance.com/section/directories
Frequency: Latest edition 2011. **Price:** $439 Individuals premium package; Canada and Mexico; $499 Other countries premium package. **Description:** List of underwriting managers, managing general agents and wholesale brokers. **Entries include:** Contact information.

6462 ■ Insurance Phone Book
Communication Publications & Resources
2807 N Parham Rd., Ste. 200
Richmond, VA 23294
Free: 800-780-4066
E-mail: customerservice@briefings.com
URLs: http://www.douglaspublications.com; http://www.thesalesmansguide.com
Frequency: Annual; latest edition 2009-2010. **Price:** $195 directory price; $389 directory/CD combo price. **Covers:** About 3,700 life, accident and health, worker's compensation, auto, fire and casualty, marine, surety, and other insurance companies; 2,300 executive contacts from presidents and CEOs to claims and customer service managers. **Entries**

include: Company name, address, phone, fax, toll-free number, type of insurance provided. **Arrangement:** Alphabetical.

6463 ■ *Kirschner's Insurance Directories: Red Book*
URLs: http://www.nationalunderwriter.com; http://www.kirschners.com
Frequency: Annual; Latest edition 2007. **Pages:** 500 minimum page count per edition; 1000 maximum page count per edition. **Covers:** Insurance agents and agencies in all 50 states and the District of Columbia. Published in 24 separate editions for Southern California, Northern California, Pacific Northwest (AK, ID, HI, OR, WA, MT), Michigan, Illinois, New England states (CT, ME, MA, NH, RI, VT), Ohio, Rocky Mountain states (AZ, CO, NV, NM, UT, WY), South Central states (GA, AL, MS), Indiana, Texas, Kentucky/Tennessee, East Central states (VA, WV, NC, SC), South Central West states (AR, OK, LA), Wisconsin, Central states (KS, MO, NE), North Central states (IA, MN, ND, SD), Mid-Atlantic states (DE, MD, NJ, DC), Pennsylvania, Florida. **Entries include:** For companies--Name, address, key personnel (with addresses and phone numbers). **Arrangement:** Separate alphabetical sections for insurance companies, wholesalers, field agents, and agencies. **Indexes:** Type of insurance.

6464 ■ *Vault Guide to the Top Insurance Employers*
Vault.com Inc.
132 W 31st St., 17th Fl.
New York, NY 10001-3406
Ph: (212)366-4212
Free: 800-535-2074
Fax: (212)366-6117
E-mail: customerservice@vault.com
URL: http://www.vault.com
Frequency: Latest edition June, 2006. **Price:** $19.95 Individuals Online; $19.95 Members Gold. **Pages:** 178. **Covers:** Insurance companies in United States. **Entries include:** Company name, contact person, address, zip code, phone and fax numbers, statistics, hiring process and email. **Arrangement:** Alphabetical by company name.

6465 ■ *Women in Insurance and Financial Services--Membership Directory*
Women in Insurance and Financial Services
136 Everett Rd.
Albany, NY 12205
Ph: (518)694-5506
Free: 866-264-9437
Fax: (518)935-9232
E-mail: office@wifsnational.org
URL: http://www.wifsnational.org
Covers: list of contact information of WIFS' members who are devoted to helping women succeed in both insurance and financial services.

6466 ■ *Yearbook*
American Association of Managing General Agents
610 Freedom Business Ctr., Ste. 100
King of Prussia, PA 19406
Ph: (610)992-0022
Fax: (610)992-0021
E-mail: bernie@aamga.org
URL: http://www.aamga.org
Frequency: Annual; Latest edition 2006. **Pages:** 468. **Covers:** 250 managing general agents of insurance companies and their more than 500 branch offices; coverage includes Canada. **Entries include:** Name, address, names and titles of principal and contact, insurance companies represented. **Arrangement:** Geographical.

HANDBOOKS AND MANUALS

6467 ■ *Opportunities in Insurance Careers*
The McGraw-Hill Companies Inc.
PO Box 182604
Columbus, OH 43272
Ph: (212)512-2000
Free: 877-833-5524
Fax: (614)759-3749
E-mail: customer.service@mcgraw-hill.com
URL: http://www.mcgraw-hill.com
Description: Robert M. Schrayer. Revised, 2007. $14.95 (paper). 160 pages. A guide to planning for and seeking opportunities in the field. Contains bibliography and illustrations.

EMPLOYMENT AGENCIES AND SEARCH FIRMS

6468 ■ Burkholder Group Inc.
985 Pico Pt.
Colorado Springs, CO 80906
Ph: (719)867-1222
Fax: (719)623-0033
E-mail: info@burkholdergroup.com
URL: http://www.burkholdergroup.com
Description: Executive search firm focused on the insurance industry.

6469 ■ Capitol Staffing Inc.
460 Briarwood Dr., Briarwood 1 Bldg., Ste. 110
Jackson, MS 39206
Ph: (601)957-1755
Fax: (601)957-3880
E-mail: info@capitolstaffing.com
URL: http://www.capitolstaffing.com
Description: Personnel consultancy that focuses on office administration, management, sales, accounting, medical, information technology, accounting, and engineering/technical fields. Industries served: insurance, finance, medical, communications, investment, industry, and small businesses.

6470 ■ International Insurance Consultants Inc.
645 SE 10th St.
Deerfield Beach, FL 33441
Ph: (954)421-0122
Fax: (954)449-0497
E-mail: rc@iicuri.com
URL: http://www.insurancerecruitersusa.com
Description: Offers executive search to the insurance industry. Clients include insurance companies, brokers, consultants and investment banks. Industries served: insurance and financial services industries.

6471 ■ International Insurance Personnel, Inc.
300 W Wieuca Rd., Bldg. 2, Ste. 101
Atlanta, GA 30342
Ph: (404)255-9710
Fax: (404)255-9864
E-mail: iipjulie@bellsouth.net
URL: http://realpages.com/sites/intlinspersonnel/index.html
Description: Employment agency specializing in the area of insurance.

6472 ■ J. R. Peterman Associates, Inc.
PO Box 3083
Stowe, VT 05672
Ph: (802)253-6304
Fax: (802)253-6314
E-mail: peterman@jrpeterman.com
URL: http://www.jrpeterman.com
Description: Recruit professionals in permanent and contract positions for the life and health insurance industry and employee benefits consulting.

6473 ■ Pinnacle Group, Inc.
6 Greenleaf Woods, Ste. 201
Portsmouth, NH 03801
Ph: (603)427-1700
Free: 800-308-7205
Fax: (603)427-0526
E-mail: info@pinnaclejobs.com
URL: http://www.pinnaclejobs.com
Description: Provides recruiting services to insurance, consulting and investment firms. Offers career opportunities from entry-level to senior management.

6474 ■ Questor Consultants, Inc.
2515 N Broad St.
Colmar, PA 18915
Ph: (215)997-9262
Fax: (215)997-9226
E-mail: sbevivino@questorconsultants.com
URL: http://www.questorconsultants.com
Description: Executive search firm specializing in the insurance and legal fields.

6475 ■ Quirk-Corporon and Associates Inc.
1229 N Jackson St., Ste. 205
Milwaukee, WI 53202-2655
Ph: (414)224-9399
Fax: (414)224-9472
E-mail: quirkrecruiters@sbcglobal.net
URL: http://www.quirkinsrecruiters.com
Description: Employment agency specializing in all disciplines of the insurance and financial industries; insurance recruiters, is a contingency and retained recruiting and consulting firm specializing in the placement of permanent candidates; provides talented professional and technical employees, locally and nationally, who are skilled in property or casualty, life or health, employee benefits and managed care; provides a highly respected dimension of counseling skill to both clients and candidates in all areas of staffing and employee relations.

6476 ■ ReadWaering Associates
PO Box 290755
Nashville, TN 37229
Ph: (615)415-3462
Free: 800-489-3602
E-mail: pam@readwaering.com
URL: http://www.readwaering.com
Description: Specializes in insurance and healthcare recruiting.

6477 ■ Tyler & Co.
400 Northridge Rd., Ste. 1250
Atlanta, GA 30350-3299
Ph: (770)396-3939
Free: 800-989-6789
Fax: (770)396-6693
URL: http://www.tylerandco.com
Description: Retained executive search for the healthcare, food, market research, manufacturing and insurance industries.

ONLINE JOB SOURCES AND SERVICES

6478 ■ CareerBank
URL: http://www.careerbank.com/home/index.cfm?site_id=8162
Description: Provides jobs in finance, banking, mortgage, insurance, and accounting. Specializes in online job posting and job search, resume upload and resume database search, and career advice services.

6479 ■ Construction Jobs Network
URL: http://constructionjobs.net
Description: Provides job seekers access to construction employment opportunities for both construction management, construction professional and construction trade jobs. Features construction jobs, employer, and resume directories.

6480 ■ Great Insurance Jobs
URL: http://www.greatinsurancejobs.com
Description: Contains varied insurance positions. Job seekers may browse employee profiles, post

resumes, and read descriptions of hundreds of recently-posted insurance jobs.

6481 ■ InsuranceAgencyCareers.com
URL: http://www.insuranceagencycareers.com

Description: Online job search provides employment opportunities in the insurance industry.

6482 ■ InsuranceIndustryCentral.com
URL: http://www.insuranceindustrycentral.com

Description: Features insurance jobs and products to the insurance community.

6483 ■ InsuranceJobs.com
URL: http://www.insurancejobs.com

Description: Offers employment and careers in the insurance industry.

6484 ■ National Insurance Recruiters Association
URL: http://www.insurancerecruiters.com

Description: Contains lists of recruiters (listed by department and line of business) and available insurance positions.

6485 ■ Premier Careers, Inc.
URL: http://www.premiercareers.com

Description: Contains a database with information on candidates searching for jobs in the property and casualty insurance industry and with national sales organizations. Houses resumes and letters of reference. Candidate searches may be run by industry, geography, job title, years of experience, compensation, education, and/or accreditation. Also offers resume writing and interviewing tips to job hunters.

6486 ■ UltimateInsuranceJobs.com
URL: http://www.ultimateinsurancejobs.com/index.asp

Description: Provides insurance job listings, recruiter directory, and resources. Offers job seekers the opportunity to post and edit their resumes, and employers the opportunity to search through insurance resumes.

TRADESHOWS

6487 ■ Insurance Accounting and Systems Association Conference
Insurance Accounting and Systems Association
PO Box 51340
Durham, NC 27717-1340
Ph: (919)489-0991
Fax: (919)489-1994
E-mail: tstillman@iasa.org
URL: http://www.iasa.org

Frequency: Annual. **Primary Exhibits:** Insurance equipment, supplies, and services.

6488 ■ International Association of Insurance Professionals Annual Convention
International Association of Insurance Professionals
8023 E 63rd Pl., Ste. 540
Tulsa, OK 74133
Ph: (918)294-3700
Free: 800-766-6249
Fax: (918)294-3711
URL: http://naiw.site-ym.com

Frequency: Annual. **Primary Exhibits:** Equipment, supplies, and services for insurance industry professionals.

6489 ■ Massachusetts Association of Insurance Agents Convention
Massachusetts Association of Insurance Agents
91 Cedar St.
Milford, MA 01757
Ph: (508)634-2900
Free: 800-972-9312

Fax: (508)634-2929
E-mail: info@massagent.com
URL: http://www.massagent.com

Frequency: Annual. **Primary Exhibits:** Computers and related services, office equipment, financial consultation services, managerial services, car rental, restoration, premium finance companies.

6490 ■ Risk and Insurance Management Society Annual Conference and Exhibition
Risk and Insurance Management Society
1065 Ave. of the Americas, 13th Fl.
New York, NY 10018
Ph: (212)286-9292
Free: 800-713-7467
Fax: (212)986-9716
E-mail: lists@rims.org
URL: http://www.rims.org

Frequency: Annual. **Primary Exhibits:** Insurance industry related equipment, supplies, and services.

6491 ■ Society of Insurance Trainers and Educators Conference
Society of Insurance Trainers and Educators
1821 University Ave. W, Ste. S256
Saint Paul, MN 55104
Ph: (651)999-5354
Fax: (651)917-1835
URL: http://www.insurancetrainers.org

Frequency: Annual. **Primary Exhibits:** Insurance education equipment, supplies, and services.

OTHER SOURCES

6492 ■ American Association of Insurance Management Consultants
Texas Insurance Consulting
8980 Lakes at 610 Dr., Ste. 100
Houston, TX 77054
Ph: (713)664-6424
E-mail: lee.hoffman@aaimco.com
URL: http://www.aaimco.com

Description: Consists of individuals who devote a substantial portion of their services to insurance consulting, risk management activities, legal representation relating to insurance issues; as well as education and professional development training, employment consulting, and other technical and management advice to the insurance industry. Advises and assists the insurance industry and seeks to achieve professional recognition for insurance management consultants. Mediates the exchange of ideas; sets standards of service and performance; maintains a code of ethics; offers a referral service and a series of educational conferences and seminars. Operates speakers' bureau; offers placement services; compiles statistics. **Members:** 35.

6493 ■ American Council of Life Insurers
101 Constitution Ave. NW, Ste. 700
Washington, DC 20001-2133
Ph: (202)624-2000
Free: 877-674-4659
E-mail: webadmin@acli.com
URL: http://www.acli.com

Description: Represents the interests of legal reserve life insurance companies in legislative, regulatory and judicial matters at the federal, state and municipal levels of government and at the NAIC. Member companies hold majority of the life insurance in force in the United States.

6494 ■ American Institute for CPCU
720 Providence Rd., Ste. 100
Malvern, PA 19355-3433
Free: 800-644-2101
Fax: (610)640-9576
E-mail: customerservice@theinstitutes.org
URL: http://www.aicpcu.org

Description: Determines qualifications for professional certification of insurance personnel; conducts

examinations and awards designation of Chartered Property Casualty Underwriter (CPCU).

6495 ■ Association of Professional Insurance Women
990 Cedarbridge Ave., Ste. B
PMB 210
Brick, NJ 08723-4157
Ph: (973)941-6024
Fax: (732)920-1260
E-mail: scb@thebeaumontgroup.com
URL: http://www.apiw.org

Description: Professional women from the insurance/reinsurance industry. Promotes cooperation and understanding among members; maintains high professional standards in the insurance industry; provides a strong network of professional contacts and educational aid; recognizes the contributions of women to insurance; encourages women to seek employment in the insurance community. **Members:** 170.

6496 ■ GAMA International
2901 Telestar Ct., Ste. 140
Falls Church, VA 22042-1205
Free: 800-345-2687
Fax: (571)499-4302
URL: http://www.gamaweb.com

Description: Provides world-class education and training resources for individuals, companies and organizations involved with the recruitment and development of field managers, representatives and staff in the life insurance and financial services industry; advocates of the value-added role of field management and representatives in the ethical distribution of life insurance and financial products and services industry.

6497 ■ Independent Insurance Agents and Brokers of America
127 S Peyton St.
Alexandria, VA 22314
Free: 800-221-7917
Fax: (703)683-7556
E-mail: info@iiaba.org
URL: http://www.iiaba.net

Description: Sales agencies handling property, fire, casualty, and surety insurance. Organizes technical and sales courses for new and established agents. Sponsors Independent Insurance Agent Junior Classic Golf Tournament.

6498 ■ Insurance Information Institute
110 William St.
New York, NY 10038
Ph: (212)346-5500
E-mail: members@iii.org
URL: http://www.iii.org

Description: Property and casualty insurance companies. Provides information and educational services to mass media, educational institutions, trade associations, businesses, government agencies, and the public.

6499 ■ International Association of Insurance Professionals
8023 E 63rd Pl., Ste. 540
Tulsa, OK 74133
Ph: (918)294-3700
Free: 800-766-6249
Fax: (918)294-3711
URL: http://naiw.site-ym.com

Description: Insurance industry professionals. Promotes continuing education and networking for the professional advancement of its members. Offers education programs, meetings, services, and leadership opportunities. Provides a forum to learn about other disciplines in the insurance industry.

6500 ■ LOMA
2300 Windy Ridge Pkwy., Ste. 600
Atlanta, GA 30339-8443

Ph: (770)951-1770
E-mail: askloma@loma.org
URL: http://www.loma.org

Description: Life and health insurance companies and financial services in the U.S. and Canada; and overseas in 45 countries; affiliate members are firms that provide professional support to member companies. Provides research, information, training, and educational activities in areas of operations and systems, human resources, financial planning and employee development. Administers FLMI Insurance Education Program, which awards FLMI (Fellow, Life Management Institute) designation to those who complete the ten-examination program.

6501 ■ National Alliance of General Agents
Concorde General Agency, Inc.
720 28th St. SW
Fargo, ND 58103
Fax: (701)239-9941
E-mail: scott@concorde-ga.com
URL: http://www.nagains.org

Description: Represents the interests of professional managing general agents and wholesale brokers. Promotes and supports improvements in the business of insurance for the benefit of the insuring public. Cooperates with other segments of the insurance industry. Fosters better understanding of the excess and surplus lines brokerage systems. Aims to perpetuate the Independent Agency System.

6502 ■ National Association of Health Underwriters
1212 New York Ave. NW, Ste. 1100
Washington, DC 20005
Ph: (202)552-5060
Fax: (202)747-6820
E-mail: info@nahu.org
URL: http://www.nahu.org

Description: Insurance agents and brokers engaged in the promotion, sale, and administration of disability income and health insurance. Sponsors advanced health insurance underwriting and research seminars. Testifies before federal and state commit-tees on pending health insurance legislation. Sponsors Leading Producers Roundtable Awards for leading salesmen. Maintains a speakers' bureau and a political action committee.

6503 ■ National Association of Professional Allstate Agents
PO Box 7666
Gulfport, MS 39506
Free: 877-627-2248
E-mail: hq@napaausa.org
URL: http://www.napaausa.org

Description: Monitors legislative and legal issues pertinent to Allstate agents and their clients. Fosters the independence and entrepreneurial spirit of its members. Provides a forum where members can exchange ideas and give advice.

6504 ■ National Association of Professional Insurance Agents
400 N Washington St.
Alexandria, VA 22314
Ph: (703)836-9340
Fax: (703)836-1279
E-mail: web@pianet.org
URL: http://www.pianet.com

Description: Represents independent agents in all 50 states, Puerto Rico and the District of Columbia. Represents members' interests in government and industry; provides educational programs; compiles statistics; conducts research programs; develops products/services unique to independent agencies; provides information and networking opportunities.

6505 ■ Nationwide Insurance Independent Contractors Association
2001 Jefferson Davis Hwy., Ste. 104
Arlington, VA 22202-3617
Ph: (703)416-4422
Fax: (703)416-0014
E-mail: info@niica.org
URL: http://www.niica.org

Description: Represents active and retired agents of the Nationwide Insurance Company. Promotes professionalism and ethical practice among its members. Encourages increased competence through continuous study and professional industry courses. Researches and recommends legislative programs to provide fair treatment to insurance consumers and independent contractors. Fosters and encourages fellowship among agents and their families.

6506 ■ Professional Insurance Marketing Association
35 E Wacker Dr., Ste. 850
Chicago, IL 60601
Ph: (817)569-7462
Fax: (312)644-8557
E-mail: mona@pima-assn.org
URL: http://www.pima-assn.org

Description: Comprised of agents, brokers, third-party administrators, insurance underwriting companies and business partners involved in the direct marketing of insurance products. Serves as a forum for leaders in the insurance direct marketing industry to craft strategic relationships, develop business opportunities and expertise.

6507 ■ Society of Financial Service Professionals
19 Campus Blvd., Ste. 100
Newtown Square, PA 19073-3239
Ph: (610)526-2500
Free: 800-392-6900
Fax: (610)527-1499
E-mail: info@financialpro.org
URL: http://www.financialpro.org

Description: Represents the interests of financial advisers. Fosters the development of professional responsibility. Assists clients to achieve personal and business-related financial goals. Offers educational programs, online professional resources and networking opportunities.

6508 ■ *Design Cost Data: Cost Estimating Magazine for Design and Construction*
DC & D Technologies Inc.
PO Box 948
Valrico, FL 33595-0948
Ph: (813)662-6830
Free: 800-533-5680
Fax: (813)662-6793
E-mail: webmaster@dcd.com
URL: http://www.dcd.com

Frequency: Bimonthly. **Price:** $94 Individuals silver; $157 Two years silver; $149 Individuals gold; $239 Two years gold. **Description:** Publication providing real cost data case studies of various types completed around the country for design and building professionals.

6509 ■ *Dwell*
Echo Media
900 Circle 75 Pky., Ste. 1600
Atlanta, GA 30339
Ph: (770)955-3535
Fax: (770)955-3599
E-mail: salesinfo@echo-media.com
URLs: http://www.echo-media.com; http://www.echo-media.com/mediaDetail.php?ID=5998

Frequency: 8/yr. **Description:** Magazine covering articles on interior design, including innovative design and architecture.

6510 ■ *InStyle Home*
Time Inc.
Time-Life Bldg.
1271 Ave. of the Americas
New York, NY 10020
Ph: (212)522-1212
Free: 800-843-8463
Fax: (212)522-0602
E-mail: letters@time.com
URL: http://www.instyle.com/instyle/

Frequency: Monthly. **Price:** $19.50 Individuals. **Description:** Interior design magazine for the fashion-conscious.

6511 ■ *Interior Design*
Reed Elsevier Group plc - Reed Business Information
360 Park Ave. S
New York, NY 11010
Ph: (212)791-4208
E-mail: corporatecommunications@reedbusiness.com
URL: http://www.interiordesign.net/

Frequency: 15/yr. **Price:** $59.95 Individuals; $87 Canada; $187 Other countries. **Description:** Interior designing and furnishings magazine.

6512 ■ *Journal of Interior Design Education and Research*
Interior Design Educators Council
9100 Purdue Rd., Ste. 200
Indianapolis, IN 46268
Ph: (317)328-4437
Fax: (317)280-8527
E-mail: info@idec.org
URLs: http://www.idec.org/news/jid.php; http://www.blackwellpublishing.com/journal.asp?ref=1071-7641

Frequency: Annual. **Description:** Journal covering research, educational, historical, and critical aspects of interior design and allied fields.

6513 ■ *Kitchen and Bath Business*
E-mail: kbb@mediabrains.com
URL: http://www.kbbonline.com/kbb/index.shtml

Frequency: Monthly. **Price:** $79 Individuals; $94 Canada; $139 Other countries. **Description:** Trade magazine on kitchen and bath remodeling and construction.

6514 ■ *Kitchen and Bath Design News*
Cygnus Business Media Inc.
1233 Janesville Ave.
Fort Atkinson, WI 53538
Free: 800-547-7377
E-mail: info@cygnus.com
URL: http://www.cygnusb2b.com/PropertyPub.cfm?PropertyID=78

Frequency: Monthly. **Description:** Trade journal.

6515 ■ *LDB Interior Textiles*
E.W. Williams Publications Co.
370 Lexington Ave., Ste. 1409
New York, NY 10017
Ph: (212)661-1516
Fax: (212)661-1713
E-mail: philpl@ewwpi.com
URL: http://www.ldbinteriortextiles.com

Frequency: Monthly. **Price:** $72 Individuals; $125 Canada; $150 Elsewhere airmail; $100 Two years; $7 Single issue; $12 Single issue, Canada; $18 Single issue elsewhere. **Description:** Magazine for buyers of home fashions, including bed, bath and table linens, hard and soft window treatments, home fragrances, decorative pillows and home accessories, accent rugs, and decorative fabrics.

6516 ■ *Portfolio*
Interior Design Society
164 S Main St., Fl. 8
High Point, NC 27260
Ph: (336)884-4437
Free: 888-884-4469
Fax: (336)885-3291
E-mail: shuffman@interiordesignsociety.org
URL: http://www.interiordesignsociety.org

Description: Quarterly. Reports on society activities and news of the interior design industry.

6517 ■ *Qualified Remodeler Magazine: Best Practices, Products & Design Ideas*
Cygnus Business Media Inc.
1233 Janesville Ave.
Fort Atkinson, WI 53538
Free: 800-547-7377
E-mail: info@cygnus.com
URLs: http://www.qualifiedremodeler.com; http://www.cygnusb2b.com/PropertyPub.cfm?PropertyID=84

Frequency: Monthly. **Description:** Magazine for remodeling contractor/distributors.

6518 ■ *Remodeling*
DoveTale Publishers
1 Thomas Cir. NW
Washington, DC 20005
Ph: (202)339-0744
Free: 877-275-8647
Fax: (202)785-1974
E-mail: rm@omeda.com
URL: http://www.remodeling.hw.net

Frequency: 13/yr. **Price:** $24.95 Individuals; $39.95 Individuals Canadian residents; $192 Individuals international residents. **Description:** Trade magazine for the professional remodeling industry.

6519 ■ *Visual Merchandising and Store Design*
ST Media Group International Inc.
11262 Cornell Park Dr.
Cincinnati, OH 45242
Ph: (513)421-2050
Free: 800-421-1321
Fax: (513)421-5144
E-mail: info@stmediagroup.com
URLs: http://www.stmediagroup.com/index.php3?d=pubs&p=vm; http://vmsd.com/

Frequency: Monthly. **Price:** $42 Individuals U.S.; $66 Individuals 2 years, U.S.; $62 Individuals Canada (surface); $100 Individuals 2 years, Canada (surface); $65 Individuals Mexico/Foreign (surface); $105 Individuals 2 years, Mexico/Foreign (surface); $100 Individuals Mexico, 1st Class; $175 Individuals 2 years, Mexico 1st Class; $115 Individuals Central/South America; $205 Individuals 2 years, Central/South America. **Description:** The leading magazine of the retail design industry covering the latest trends in retail design, store planning, and merchandise presentation.

6520 ■ *Walls, Windows, and Floors*
Hearst Magazines International
1271 Ave. of the Americas
New York, NY 10020
Ph: (212)649-4115
Free: 800-544-6748
Fax: (212)767-5612
E-mail: jdeval@hearst.com
URL: http://www.pointclickhome.com

Frequency: 3/yr. **Description:** Special interest home and garden magazine focusing on decorating the home.

EMPLOYER DIRECTORIES AND NETWORKING LISTS

6521 ■ Almanac of Architecture and Design
The Greenway Group Inc.
25 Technology Pky. S, Ste. 101
Norcross, GA 30092
Ph: (678)879-0929
Free: 800-726-8603
Fax: (678)879-0930
URL: http://www.greenway.us

Frequency: Annual; Latest edition 13th, 2012. **Price:** $149 Individuals. **Publication includes:** Lists of professional organizations, degree programs, and leading firms in architecture and design. Principal content of publication is a collection of information regarding architecture and design.

6522 ■ ENR--Top 500 Design Firms Issue
The McGraw-Hill Companies Inc.
PO Box 182604
Columbus, OH 43272
Ph: (212)512-2000
Free: 877-833-5524
Fax: (614)759-3749
E-mail: customer.service@mcgraw-hill.com
URL: http://enr.construction.com/toplists/
    sourcebooks/2010/designfirms/

Frequency: Annual; latest edition 2010. **Price:** $82 Individuals yearly subscription; $87 Individuals print and online. **Publication includes:** List of 500 leading architectural, engineering, and specialty design firms selected on basis of annual billings. **Entries include:** Company name, headquarters location, type of firm, current and prior year rank in billings, types of services, countries in which operated in preceding year. **Arrangement:** Ranked by billings.

HANDBOOKS AND MANUALS

6523 ■ The Creative Business Guide to Running a Graphic Design Business
W. W. Norton & Company, Incorporated
500 Fifth Ave.
New York, NY 10110-0017
Ph: (212)354-5500
Free: 800-233-4830
Fax: (212)869-0856
E-mail: ksilvasy-neale@wwnorton.com
URL: http://books.wwnorton.com/books/detail.aspx
    ?ID=9939

Description: Cameron Foote. 2009. $35.00. 416 pages.

6524 ■ Opportunities in Interior Design and Decorating Careers
The McGraw-Hill Companies Inc.
PO Box 182604
Columbus, OH 43272
Ph: (212)512-2000
Free: 877-833-5524
Fax: (614)759-3749
E-mail: customer.service@mcgraw-hill.com
URL: http://www.mcgraw-hill.com

Description: David Stearns. Third edition, 2008. $14.95 (paper). 160 pages. Covers opportunities and job search techniques in interior design. Addresses working for a design house, contract work, and starting a business. Illustrated.

6525 ■ Portfolios for Interior Designers
John Wiley & Sons Inc.
111 River St.
Hoboken, NJ 07030-5774
Ph: (201)748-6000
Free: 800-225-5945
Fax: (201)748-6088
E-mail: info@wiley.com
URL: http://www.wiley.com

Description: Maureen Mitton. 2010. $55.00. 224 pages. Serves as guide to portfolio development for interior designers. Delivers step-by-step instruction on properly and effectively displaying their work in fashion. Includes graphic design concepts necessary for portfolio development, specific information for designing digital portfolios, useful tips on using popular graphics software applications, and samples of cover letters and resumes.

6526 ■ Professional Interior Design: A Career Guide
iUniverse Inc.
1663 Liberty Dr., Ste. 300
Bloomington, IN 47403-5161
Ph: (402)323-7800
Free: 800-288-4677
Fax: (812)355-4085
E-mail: media@iuniverse.com
URL: http://www.iuniverse.com

Description: Jason Znoy, ASID Illinois Association. May 2004. $9.95 (paper). 64 pages.

6527 ■ Residential Interior Design: A Guide to Planning Spaces
John Wiley & Sons Inc.
111 River St.
Hoboken, NJ 07030-5774
Ph: (201)748-6000
Free: 800-225-5945
Fax: (201)748-6088
E-mail: info@wiley.com
URL: http://www.wiley.com

Description: Maureen Mitton and Courtney Nystuen. 2011. $54.95. 304 pages. Fundamental skills for designers working in any type of home or decorative style, focusing on planning, human factors, code and building systems, storage and exterior spaces.

6528 ■ Starting Your Career as an Interior Designer
Allworth Press
307 W 36th St., 11th Fl.
New York, NY 10018
Ph: (212)643-6816
Free: 800-491-2808
Fax: (212)643-6819
E-mail: pub@allworth.com
URL: http://www.allworth.com

Description: Robert K. Hale and Thomas L. Williams. 2009. $24.95 (paper). 240 pages. Contains tools and strategies to successfully launch and grow a professional design business in the competitive world of interior design. Includes case studies and personal anecdotes.

EMPLOYMENT AGENCIES AND SEARCH FIRMS

6529 ■ Claremont-Branan, Inc.
1298 Rockbridge Rd., Ste. B
Stone Mountain, GA 30087
Free: 800-875-1292
URL: http://cbisearch.com

Description: Employment agency. Executive search firm.

6530 ■ Interior Talent
1430 Lake Baldwin Ln., Ste. A
Orlando, FL 32814
Free: 800-915-3012
Fax: (407)228-1935
E-mail: info@interiortalent.com
URL: http://www.interiortalent.com

Description: Recruiters for architecture and design professionals worldwide.

6531 ■ Randolph Associates, Inc.
950 Massachusetts Ave., Ste. 105
Cambridge, MA 02139-3174
Ph: (617)441-8777
Fax: (617)441-8778
E-mail: jobs@greatjobs.com
URL: http://www.greatjobs.com

Description: Employment agency. Provides regular or temporary placement of staff.

6532 ■ RitaSue Siegel Resources, Inc.
PO Box 845
New York, NY 10150
Ph: (917)725-1603
E-mail: contact@ritasue.com
URL: http://www.ritasue.com

Description: Executive search firm specializing in industrial and product design.

ONLINE JOB SOURCES AND SERVICES

6533 ■ InteriorDesignJobs.com
URL: http://interiordesignjobs.sellisp.com/Default.asp

Description: Provides sources of employment information for professionals in the interior design industry.

TRADESHOWS

6534 ■ Annual Home Decorating and Remodeling Show
Show Pros International, LLC.
PO Box 230669
Las Vegas, NV 89123-0012
Free: 800-343-8344
E-mail: spvandy@cox.net
URL: http://www.showprosintl.com/

Frequency: Annual. **Primary Exhibits:** Home products.

6535 ■ Chicago Design Show
Merchandise Mart Properties Inc.
222 Merchandise Mart, Ste. 470
Chicago, IL 60654
Ph: (312)527-4141
Free: 800-677-6278
URL: http://www.merchandisemart.com

Frequency: Annual. **Primary Exhibits:** Contemporary design in furniture, fashion, food.

6536 ■ Coverings
National Trade Productions Inc.
313 S Patrick St.
Alexandria, VA 22314-3501
Ph: (703)683-8500
Free: 800-687-7469
Fax: (703)836-4486
E-mail: ntpinfo@ntpshow.com
URL: http://www.ntpshow.com

Frequency: Annual. **Primary Exhibits:** Residential and commercial covering industries: flooring, ceramic tile, natural stone and related products and services. Also hardwood flooring, laminate flooring, resilient flooring and related adhesives, grouts, sealants, tools and allied products.

6537 ■ Old House/New House Home Show
Kennedy Productions, Inc.
1208 Lisle Pl.
Lisle, IL 60532-2262
Ph: (630)515-1160
Fax: (630)515-1165
E-mail: kp@core.com
URL: http://www.kennedyproductions.com

Frequency: Semiannual. **Primary Exhibits:** Products and services for home remodeling, improvement, enhancement, decorating, landscaping and more. Hundreds of ideas to improve and beautify every home. **Dates and Locations:** St. Charles, IL; Pleasant Run Resorts Mega Center.

6538 ■ Surfaces
World Floor Covering Association
2211 E Howell Ave.
Anaheim, CA 92806
Ph: (714)978-6440
Free: 800-624-6880
Fax: (714)978-6066
E-mail: wfca@wfca.org
URL: http://www.wfca.org

Frequency: Annual. **Primary Exhibits:** Floor covering equipment, supplies, and services.

OTHER SOURCES

6539 ■ Council of Educational Facility Planners International
11445 E Via Linda, Ste. 2-440
Scottsdale, AZ 85259
Ph: (480)391-0840
E-mail: dwaggone@heery.com
URL: http://www.cefpi.org

Description: Individuals and firms who are responsible for planning, designing, creating, maintaining, and equipping the physical environment of education. Sponsors an exchange of information, professional experiences, best practices research results, and other investigative techniques concerning educational facility planning. Activities include publication and review of current and emerging practices in educational facility planning; identification and execution of needed research; development of professional training programs; strengthening of planning services on various levels of government and in institutions of higher learning; leadership in the development of higher standards for facility design and the physical environment of education. Operates speakers' bureau; sponsors placement service; compiles statistics.

6540 ■ Interior Design Society
164 S Main St., Fl. 8
High Point, NC 27260
Ph: (336)884-4437
Free: 888-884-4469

Fax: (336)885-3291
E-mail: shuffman@interiordesignsociety.org
URL: http://www.interiordesignsociety.org

Description: Represents independent designers and decorators, retail designers and sales people, design-oriented firms, and manufacturers. Grants accreditation and recognition to qualified residential interior designers and retail home furnishing stores. Conducts educational seminars in design, sales training, and marketing. Offers products and publications for designers and a correspondence course for home furnishing sales people.

6541 ■ Interior Redesign Industry Specialists
1100-H Brandywine Blvd.
Zanesville, OH 43701-7303
Ph: (740)450-1330
Fax: (740)452-2552
E-mail: iris@irisorganization.org
URL: http://www.irisorganization.org

Description: Represents the interests of professional redesigners and stagers. Seeks to establish and maintain high industry standards. Promotes public awareness and expands the fields of redesign and staging.

6542 ■ International Design Guild
670 Commercial St.
Manchester, NH 03101
Free: 800-205-4345
E-mail: info@design-guild.com
URL: http://www.design-guild.com

Description: Brings together interior designers to share and gain insight for business development and networking. Provides members with customizable marketing, merchandising, educational and operational tools. Aims to help members operate their businesses more profitably.

6543 ■ International Interior Design Association
222 Merchandise Mart, Ste. 567
Chicago, IL 60654
Ph: (312)467-1950
Free: 888-799-4432

Fax: (312)467-0779
E-mail: iidahq@iida.org
URL: http://www.iida.org

Description: Represents professional interior designers, including designers of commercial, health-care, hospitality, government, retail, residential facilities; educators; researchers; representatives of allied manufacturing sources. Conducts research, student programs and continuing education programs for members. Has developed a code of ethics for the professional design membership.

6544 ■ Organization of Women Architects and Design Professionals
PO Box 10078
Berkeley, CA 94709
E-mail: info@owa-usa.org
URL: http://owa-usa.org

Description: Comprised of architects, interior designers, landscape architects, planners, lighting designers, graphic designers, photographers, artists, writers, educators and students. Strives to improve the professional standing of women in architecture and design-related fields. Advocates young women and students entering design related fields through mentoring, education, and employment opportunities.

6545 ■ Retail Design Institute
4651 Sheridan St., Ste. 470
Hollywood, FL 33021
Ph: (954)241-4841
Free: 800-379-9912
Fax: (954)893-8375
E-mail: info@retaildesigninstitute.org
URL: http://www.retaildesigninstitute.org

Description: Persons active in store planning and design; visual merchandisers, students and educators; contractors and suppliers to the industry; dedicated to the professional growth of members while providing service to the public through improvement of the retail environment. Provides forum for debate and discussion by store design experts, retailers and public figures. Makes available speakers for store planning and design courses at the college level; develops programs for store planning courses. Sponsors student design competitions and annual international store design competition with awards in 10 categories. Maintains placement service.

Sources of Help-Wanted Ads

6546 ■ *Diamond Intelligence Briefs*
Nielsen Business Media Inc.
770 Broadway
New York, NY 10003-9522
Ph: (646)654-4500
Free: 866-890-8541
Fax: (646)654-5584
E-mail: bmcomm@nielsen.com
URL: http://https://www.diamondintelligence.com/
template/default.aspx?PageId=23
Frequency: 20/yr. **Description:** Trade publication for the diamond and jewelry industry.

6547 ■ *Jewelers' Circular-Keystone*
Reed Exhibitions
383 Main Ave.
Norwalk, CT 06851
Ph: (203)840-4800
Fax: (203)840-5805
E-mail: inquiry@reedexpo.com
URL: http://www.jckonline.com/
Frequency: Monthly. **Price:** $19.95 Individuals; $64.95 Canada; $144.95 Other countries. **Description:** Retail jewelers trade magazine.

6548 ■ *National Jeweler*
Nielsen Business Media Inc.
770 Broadway
New York, NY 10003-9522
Ph: (646)654-4500
Free: 866-890-8541
Fax: (646)654 5584
E-mail: bmcomm@nielsen.com
URL: http://www.nationaljewelernetwork.com/njn/
index.jsp
Frequency: Semimonthly. **Description:** Jewelry industry magazine.

6549 ■ *Watch & Jewelry Review*
Golden Bell Press
2403 Champa St.
Denver, CO 80205
Ph: (303)296-1600
Fax: (303)295-2159
URL: http://www.goldenbellpress.com/Pages/front
.html
Frequency: 10/yr. **Price:** $19.50 Individuals; $35 Two years; $60 Other countries; $115 Two years other countries. **Description:** Magazine on watches and clocks.

Employer Directories and Networking Lists

6550 ■ *Israel Jewelry Industry Export-Import Directory*
International Business Publications, USA
PO Box 15343
Washington, DC 20003
Ph: (202)546-2103
Fax: (202)546-3275
E-mail: ibpusa@comcast.net
URL: http://ibpus.com/product_info.php?cPath
=137&products_id=3728
Frequency: Latest edition 2011. **Price:** $149.95 Individuals paperback; $149.95 Individuals e-book; $149.95 Individuals CD-ROM. **Pages:** 308. **Covers:** Strategic business opportunities, contact information and basic info for conducting business in the country.

6551 ■ *Jewelers Board of Trade--Confidential Reference Book*
Jewelers Board of Trade
95 Jefferson Blvd.
Warwick, RI 02888
Ph: (401)467-0055
Fax: (401)467-6070
E-mail: jbtinfo@jewelersboard.com
URL: http://www.jewelersboard.com
Frequency: Semiannual; March and September. **Price:** $60 Individuals. **Pages:** 2,000. **Covers:** About 30,000 jewelry manufacturers, importers, distributors, and retailers. **Entries include:** Company name, address, phone, whether a wholesaler, retailer, or manufacturer, credit rating. **Arrangement:** Geographical.

6552 ■ *National Association of Jewelry Appraisers Membership Directory*
National Association of Jewelry Appraisers
PO Box 18
Rego Park, NY 11374-0018
Ph: (718)896-1536
Fax: (718)997-9057
E-mail: office@najaappraisers.com
URL: http://www.najaappraisers.com
Frequency: Annual; April. **Price:** free for members. **Description:** Lists international members by state and country. Includes alphabetical index to members. **Covers:** Nearly 750 members. **Entries include:** Name, address, phone, business affiliation, area of specialization. **Arrangement:** Alphabetical, with separate geographical listing. **Indexes:** Specialty.

Employment Agencies and Search Firms

6553 ■ Premier Placements
9713 Herons Cove
Indianapolis, IN 46280
Free: 800-474-8047
E-mail: jobs@jewelryjobs.com
URL: http://www.jewelryjobs.com
Description: Executive search firm that specializes in the jewelry industry. Provides professional opportunities for jewelers.

Online Job Sources and Services

6554 ■ Jobs4Gems.com
URL: http://jobs4gems.com
Description: Serves as a web location for employment opportunities in the jewelry industry. Includes services that allow job seekers to work with professionals in the jewelry industry and gain employment at the top jewelry companies.

6555 ■ US-Jewelers.com
URL: http://www.us-jewelers.com
Description: Offers temporary and permanent jewelry job listings and employment opportunities across the United States.

Tradeshows

6556 ■ Atlanta Jewelry Show
Southern Jewelry Travelers Association
4 Executive Pk. Dr. N.E., Ste. 1202
Atlanta, GA 30329-2235
Ph: (404)634-3434
Free: 800-241-0399
Fax: (404)634-4663
E-mail: info@atlantajewelryshow.com
URL: http://www.atlantajewelryshow.com/
Frequency: Semiannual. **Primary Exhibits:** Fine jewelry, diamonds, pearls, gemstones, watches, jewelry boxes, safes, store fixtures, and jewelry computer programming.

6557 ■ Gem Fair
American Gem Trade Association
3030 LBJ Fwy., Ste. 840
Dallas, TX 75234
Ph: (214)742-4367
Free: 800-972-1162
Fax: (214)742-7334
E-mail: info@agta.org
URL: http://www.agta.org
Frequency: Annual. **Primary Exhibits:** Suppliers of natural colored gemstones; retail jewelers and jewelry manufacturers.

6558 ■ JCK Las Vegas
Jeweler Circular-Keystone
Chilton Publications
383 Main Ave.
Norwalk, CT 06851
Ph: (203)840-5684
Fax: (203)840-5830
E-mail: inquiry@reedexpo.com
URL: http://www.jckgroup.com
Frequency: Annual. **Primary Exhibits:** Trade event only for high end jewelry manufacturers, related products and services.

6559 ■ Jewelers International Showcase
Jewelers International Showcase, Inc.
6421 Congress Ave., Ste. 105
Boca Raton, FL 33487
Fax: (561)998-0209
E-mail: showdirector@jisshow.com
URL: http://www.jisshow.com

Frequency: 3/year. **Primary Exhibits:** Fine jewelry, fashion jewelry, and related products and services to jewelry trade members.

6560 ■ Mid-America Jewelry Show
Mid-America Jewelers Association
1100-H Brandywine Blvd.
Zanesville, OH 43701-7303
Ph: (740)450-1318
Free: 800-652-6257
Fax: (740)452-2552
E-mail: info@midamericajewelers.org
URL: http://www.midamericajewelers.org

Frequency: Annual. **Primary Exhibits:** Fine jewelry, display units, security systems, gems, diamonds, and other accessories and equipment for the retail jeweler.

OTHER SOURCES

6561 ■ American Watchmakers-Clockmakers Institute
701 Enterprise Dr.
Harrison, OH 45030
Ph: (513)367-9800
Free: 866-367-2924
Fax: (513)367-1414
E-mail: info@awci.com
URL: http://www.awci.com

Description: Jewelers, watchmakers, clockmakers, watch and clock engineers, scientists, repairmen, and others in the watch, clock, and jewelry industry. Examines and certifies master watchmakers and clockmakers. Maintains a museum displaying horological items, and the National Watch Mark Identification Bureau. Conducts home study course in clock repairing and bench courses for watchmakers in most major U.S. cities. Disseminates career information to vocational counselors in the form of brochures and filmstrips.

6562 ■ *Careers for Crafty People and Other Dexterous Types*
The McGraw-Hill Companies Inc.
PO Box 182604
Columbus, OH 43272

Ph: (212)512-2000
Free: 877-833-5524
Fax: (614)759-3749
E-mail: customer.service@mcgraw-hill.com
URL: http://www.mcgraw-hill.com

Description: Mark Rowh. Third edition, 2006. $13.95 (paper). 160 pages. **Includes:** List of agencies in the United States and Canada that offer information on education and training, as well as opportunities for practicing craft making in various geographical regions. List of agencies in the United States and Canada that offer information on education and training, as well as opportunities for practicing craft making in various geographical regions. **Entries include:** Name, address, URL.

6563 ■ Gemological Institute of America
The Robert Mouawad Campus
5345 Armada Dr.
Carlsbad, CA 92008
Ph: (760)603-4000
Free: 800-421-7250
Fax: (760)603-4080
E-mail: admissions@gia.edu
URL: http://www.gia.edu

Description: Works to ensure the public trust in gems and jewelry by upholding the highest standards of integrity, academics, science, and professionalism through research, education, gemological laboratory services, and instrument development; alumni are sustaining members. Conducts home study programs, resident courses, online classes and traveling seminars in identification and quality analysis of diamonds and other gemstones and pearls, and in jewelry making and repair, jewelry designing, and jewelry sales. Manufactures and sells gem testing, diamond grading equipment and audiovisual gemstone presentations through subsidiaries. Maintains gem testing and research laboratories in Carlsbad, CA and New York City. Offers job placement service; organizes gemological study tours. Awards diplomas and operates speakers' bureau.

6564 ■ Jewelers of America
120 Broadway, Ste. 2820
New York, NY 10017-3827
Ph: (646)658-0246
Free: 800-223-0673
Fax: (646)658-0256
E-mail: info@jewelers.org
URL: http://www.jewelers.org

Description: Retailers of jewelry, watches, silver, and allied merchandise. Conducts surveys and compiles statistics. Conducts educational programs. Provides information to consumers.

6565 ■ Manufacturing Jewelers and Suppliers of America
57 John L. Dietsch Sq.
Attleboro Falls, MA 02763
Ph: (401)274-3840
Free: 800-444-6572
Fax: (401)274-0265
E-mail: info@mjsa.org
URL: http://www.mjsa.org

Description: Represents American manufacturers and suppliers within the jewelry industry. Seeks to foster long-term stability and prosperity of the jewelry industry. Provides leadership in government affairs and industry education.

6566 ■ National Association of Jewelry Appraisers
PO Box 18
Rego Park, NY 11374-0018
Ph: (718)896-1536
Fax: (718)997-9057
E-mail: office@najaappraisers.com
URL: http://www.najaappraisers.com

Description: Gem and jewelry appraisers, jewelers, importers, brokers, manufacturers, gemological students, and others professionally interested in jewelry appraisal. Seeks to recognize and make available to the public the services of highly qualified, experienced, independent, and reliable jewelry appraisers. Conducts seminars on jewelry appraisal techniques, methods, and pricing for members and the public. Supports legislation to establish minimum standards of competency and licensing of jewelry appraisers; maintains code of professional ethics. Operates appraiser referral program; sponsors ongoing public relations campaign. Offers equipment discounts, new appraisal forms, travel discounts, insurance, and professional aids for members only. Compiles statistics.

6567 ■ Women's Jewelry Association
80 Washington St., Ste. 205
Poughkeepsie, NY 12601-2316
Ph: (845)473-7323
Fax: (646)355-0219
E-mail: info@womensjewelryassociation.com
URL: http://www.womensjewelryassociation.com

Description: Represents those involved in jewelry design, manufacture, retail, and advertising. Aims to: enhance the status of women in the jewelry industry; make known the contribution of women to the industry; provide a network for women involved with fine jewelry. Maintains hall of fame.

Sources of Help-Wanted Ads

6568 ■ AAHPERD UpdatePLUS
American Alliance for Health, Physical Education, Recreation and Dance
1900 Association Dr.
Reston, VA 20191-1598
Ph: (703)476-3400
Free: 800-213-7193
Fax: (703)476-9527
E-mail: membership@aahperd.org
URL: http://www.aahperd.org

Description: Six issues/year. Provides news and information on the Alliance. Discusses current issues and research in the areas of health, physical education, recreation, dances, fitness, and adapted physical education. Recurring features include a calendar of events, reports of meetings, news of educational opportunities, job listings, notices of publications available, and columns titled President's Message, Membership Corner, and From the EVP's Desk.

6569 ■ About Campus
John Wiley & Sons Inc.
111 River St.
Hoboken, NJ 07030-5774
Ph: (201)748-6000
Free: 800-225-5945
Fax: (201)748-6088
E-mail: info@wiley.com
URL: http://onlinelibrary.wiley.com/journal/10.1002/ (ISSN)1536-0687

Frequency: Bimonthly. **Price:** $219 Institutions print only; $279 Institutions, Canada and Mexico print only; $330 Institutions, other countries print only; $60 U.S., Canada, and Mexico print only; $96 Other countries print only. **Description:** Journal focused on the critical issues faced by both student affairs and academic affairs staff as they work on helping students learn.

6570 ■ American Academic
American Federation of Teachers
555 New Jersey Ave. NW
Washington, DC 20001
Ph: (202)879-4400
URL: http://www.aft.org/pubs-reports/american_academic/index.htm

Description: Higher education policy journal.

6571 ■ Annals of Medicine
Informa Healthcare
52 Vanderbilt Ave., 7th Fl.
New York, NY 10017-3846
Ph: (212)520-2777
E-mail: healthcare.enquiries@informa.com
URL: http://informahealthcare.com/ann

Frequency: 4/yr. **Price:** £961 Institutions; $1,579 Institutions; €1,259 Institutions. **Description:** Journal covering health science and medical education.

6572 ■ Current Jobs in Education
Foster Opportunities, Inc.
1834 Olmstead Dr.
Falls Church, VA 22043
Ph: (703)506-4400
Free: 888-870-3069
Fax: (888)870-3069
E-mail: admin@graduatejobs.com
URL: http://www.graduatejobs.com/education.htm

Description: Monthly. $49.50/year. Provides teaching and administrative job vacancies in educational settings.

6573 ■ Education & Treatment of Children
West Virginia University Press
139 Stansbury Hall
Morgantown, WV 26506
Ph: (304)293-8400
Fax: (304)293-6585
E-mail: press@wvu.edu
URLs: http://wvupressonline.com/journals; http://www.educationandtreatmentofchildren.net

Frequency: Quarterly. **Price:** $100 Institutions; $50 Individuals; $115 Institutions elsewhere; $65 Individuals elsewhere. **Description:** Periodical featuring information concerning the development of services for children and youth. Includes reports written for educators and other child care and mental health providers focused on teaching, training, and treatment effectiveness.

6574 ■ Education Week: American Education's Newspaper of Record
Editorial Projects in Education
6935 Arlington Rd., Ste. 100
Bethesda, MD 20814
Ph: (301)280-3100
Free: 800-346-1834
Fax: (301)280-3200
E-mail: ew@epe.org
URL: http://www.edweek.org/ew

Frequency: 44/yr. **Price:** $90 Individuals print plus online. **Description:** Professional newspaper for elementary and secondary school educators.

6575 ■ Educational Researcher
American Educational Research Association
1430 K St. NW, Ste. 1200
Washington, DC 20005-2504
Ph: (202)238-3200
Fax: (202)238-3250
E-mail: webmaster@aera.net
URL: http://www.aera.net/Publications/Journals/iEducationalResearcher/tabid/12609/Default.aspx

Frequency: Monthly; 9/year. **Price:** $48 Individuals plus foreign mailing charges; $150 Institutions plus foreign mailing charges; $50/year for individuals; $309/year for institutions. **Description:** Educational research journal.

6576 ■ Environmental Education Research
Routledge Journals - Taylor & Francis Group
270 Madison Ave.
New York, NY 10016-0601
Ph: (212)216-7800
Fax: (212)563-2269
URL: http://www.tandfonline.com/toc/ceer20/current

Frequency: 6/year. **Price:** $1,594 Institutions print + online; $1,395 Institutions online only; $424 Individuals print only. **Description:** Journal covering all aspects of environmental education.

6577 ■ Essays in Education
University of South Carolina
471 University Pky.
Aiken, SC 29801
Ph: (803)648-6851
E-mail: info@sc.edu
URL: http://www.usca.edu/essays/

Frequency: Monthly. **Description:** Journal covering issues that impact and influence education.

6578 ■ The International Electronic Journal of Health Education
American Alliance for Health, Physical Education, Recreation and Dance
1900 Association Dr.
Reston, VA 20191-1598
Ph: (703)476-3400
Free: 800-213-7193
Fax: (703)476-9527
E-mail: membership@aahperd.org
URL: http://www.aahperd.org/aahe/publications/iejhe/

Frequency: Annual. **Price:** Free. **Description:** Journal promoting health through education and other systematic strategies.

6579 ■ International Journal of Early Years Education
Routledge Journals - Taylor & Francis Group
270 Madison Ave.
New York, NY 10016-0601
Ph: (212)216-7800
Fax: (212)563-2269
URL: http://www.tandfonline.com/toc/ciey20/current

Frequency: 4/yr. **Price:** $795 Institutions online only; $908 Institutions print + online; $314 Individuals print only. **Description:** Journal focusing on education world-wide.

6580 ■ International Journal of Inclusive Education
Routledge Journals - Taylor & Francis Group
270 Madison Ave.
New York, NY 10016-0601
Ph: (212)216-7800
Fax: (212)563-2269
URL: http://www.tandfonline.com/toc/tied20/current

Frequency: 10/yr. **Price:** $722 Individuals print only; $1,353 Institutions online only; $1,546 Individuals print + online. **Description:** Journal providing information on the nature of schools, universities and technical colleges for the educators and educational policy-makers.

6581 ■ *International Journal of Leadership in Education*
Routledge
c/o Duncan Waite, PhD, Ed.
Texas State University
601 University Dr.
San Marcos, TX 78666
Ph: (512)245-8918
E-mail: ijle@txstate.edu
URL: http://www.tandfonline.com/toc/tedl20/current

Frequency: Quarterly. **Price:** $277 Individuals print only; $690 Institutions online only; $788 Institutions print and online; £408 Institutions print and online; £367 Institutions online only; £142 Individuals print only. **Description:** Journal dealing with leadership in education.

6582 ■ *International Journal of Whole Schooling*
Whole Schooling Press
Wayne State University
217 Education
Detroit, MI 48202
Ph: (313)577-1607
E-mail: wholeschooling@twmi.rr.com
URL: http://www.wholeschooling.net/Journal_of _Whole_Schooling/IJWSIndex.html

Price: Free. **Description:** International, refereed academic journal dedicated to exploring ways to improve learning and schooling for all children.

6583 ■ *Journal of Cases in Educational Leadership*
Pine Forge Press
2455 Teller Rd.
Thousand Oaks, CA 91320-2234
Ph: (805)499-4224
Free: 800-818-7243
Fax: (805)499-0871
E-mail: sales@pfp.sagepub.com
URLs: http://jel.sagepub.com; http://www.sagepub .com/journals/Journal201765

Frequency: Quarterly. **Price:** $479 Institutions online; $103 Individuals online. **Description:** Journal covering cases appropriate for use in programs that prepare educational leaders.

6584 ■ *Journal of Curriculum and Supervision*
Association for Supervision and Curriculum Development
1703 N Beauregard St.
Alexandria, VA 22311-1714
Ph: (703)578-9600
Free: 800-933-2723
Fax: (703)575-5400
URL: http://www.ascd.org/publications/jcs/fall2002/ On_Community.aspx

Frequency: Quarterly. **Price:** $39/year for members; $49/year for nonmembers. **Description:** Includes abstracts of selected doctoral dissertations.

6585 ■ *Journal of Language, Identity, and Education*
Routledge Journals - Taylor & Francis Group
270 Madison Ave.
New York, NY 10016-0601
Ph: (212)216-7800
Fax: (212)563-2269
URL: http://www.tandfonline.com/toc/hlie20/current

Frequency: 5/yr. **Price:** $611 Institutions print + online; $535 Institutions online only; $84 Individuals print + online. **Description:** Scholarly, interdisciplinary journal covering issues in language, identity and education worldwide for academics, educators and policy specialists in a variety of disciplines, and others.

6586 ■ *Journal of Latinos and Education*
Routledge Journals - Taylor & Francis Group
c/o Enrique G. Murillo, Jr., Editor
California State University
College of Education
Center for Equity in Education, 5500 University Pky.
San Bernardino, CA 92407-2397
Ph: (212)216-7800
Fax: (212)563-2269
URL: http://www.tandf.co.uk/journals/titles/15348431 .asp

Frequency: Quarterly. **Price:** $557 Institutions print + online; $487 Institutions online only. **Description:** Scholarly, multidisciplinary journal covering educational issues that impact Latinos for researchers, teaching professionals, academics, scholars, institutions, and others.

6587 ■ *Journal of Learning Disabilities*
Sage Publication, Inc.
2455 Teller Rd.
Thousand Oaks, CA 91320
Free: 800-818-7243
E-mail: webmaster@sagepub.com
URL: http://www.sagepub.com/journals/ Journal201879

Frequency: Bimonthly. **Price:** $77 Individuals print & e-access; $260 Institutions print & e-access; $255 Institutions print only; $234 Institutions e-access. **Description:** Special education journal.

6588 ■ *Journal of STEM Education: Innovations and Research*
Auburn University
9088 Haley Ctr.
Auburn, AL 36849
Ph: (334)844-9088
Fax: (334)844-9027
URL: http://ojs.jstem.org/index.php?journal=JSTEM

Frequency: Semiannual. **Description:** Journal for educators in Science, Technology, Engineering, and Mathematics (STEM) education.

6589 ■ *Leadership and Policy in Schools*
Routledge Journals - Taylor & Francis Group
270 Madison Ave.
New York, NY 10016-0601
Ph: (212)216-7800
Fax: (212)563-2269
URL: http://www.tandfonline.com/toc/nlps20/current

Frequency: Quarterly. **Price:** $658 Institutions print and online; $304 Individuals print only; $576 Institutions online only. **Description:** Journal providing information about leadership and policy in primary and secondary education.

6590 ■ *Learning: Resources for Successful Teaching*
The Education Center Inc.
3515 W Market St.
Greensboro, NC 27403-1309
Ph: (336)851-8351
Free: 800-334-0298
Fax: (336)851-8365
E-mail: webmaster@themailbox.com
URL: http://www.theeducationcenter.com/tec/afc/ learning/go.do

Frequency: Quarterly. **Price:** $4.95 Single issue; $14.95 U.S. **Description:** Definitive guide to products and services for K-6 grade teachers in the classroom.

6591 ■ *NJEA Review*
New Jersey Education Association
180 W State St.
Trenton, NJ 08607-1211
Ph: (609)599-4561
Fax: (609)599-1201
E-mail: njeareview@njea.org
URL: http://www.njea.org/page.aspx?z=1094&pz=8

Frequency: Monthly; September through May. **Price:** $250 Nonmembers. **Description:** Educational journal for public school employees.

6592 ■ *Oxford Review of Education*
Routledge Journals - Taylor & Francis Group
270 Madison Ave.
New York, NY 10016-0601
Ph: (212)216-7800
Fax: (212)563-2269
URL: http://www.tandfonline.com/toc/core20/current

Frequency: 6/yr. **Price:** $529 Individuals print only; $1,243 Institutions online only; $1,420 Institutions print and online. **Description:** Journal covering advance study of education.

6593 ■ *The Physics Teacher*
American Association of Physics Teachers
Dept. of Physics & Astronomy
Appalachian State University
Boone, NC 28608-2142
Ph: (301)209-3311
Fax: (301)209-0845
E-mail: webmaster@aapt.org
URLs: http://tpt.aapt.org; http://www.aapt.org/ Publications/

Frequency: 9/yr. **Price:** $628 Nonmembers domestic; $688 Nonmembers international. **Description:** Scientific education magazine.

6594 ■ *School and Community*
Missouri State Teachers Association
407 S Sixth St.
Columbia, MO 65205
Free: 800-392-0532
E-mail: info@msta.org
URL: http://www.msta.org/resources/publications/snc/

Frequency: Quarterly. **Description:** Education magazine.

6595 ■ *School Effectiveness and School Improvement: An International Journal of Research, Policy and Practice*
Routledge
711 3rd Ave., 8th Fl.
New York, NY 10017
Ph: (212)216-7800
Free: 800-634-7064
Fax: (212)564-7854
E-mail: book.orders@tandf.co.uk
URL: http://www.tandf.co.uk/journals/titles/09243453 .asp

Frequency: Quarterly. **Price:** £387 Institutions print and online; £348 Institutions online only; £186 Individuals print only; $660 Institutions print and online; $594 Institutions online only; $312 Individuals print only. **Description:** Journal focusing on educational progress of all students.

6596 ■ *Teacher Magazine*
Editorial Projects in Education
6935 Arlington Rd., Ste. 100
Bethesda, MD 20814
Ph: (301)280-3100
Free: 800-346-1834
Fax: (301)280-3200
E-mail: library@epe.org
URL: http://www.teachermagazine.org/tm/index.html

Frequency: 9/yr. **Price:** $90 Individuals. **Description:** Professional magazine for elementary and secondary school teachers.

6597 ■ *Teaching/K-8*
Teaching/K-8
40 Richards Ave.
Norwalk, CT 06854
Ph: (203)855-2650
Free: 800-249-9363
URL: http://www.essentiallearningproducts.com

Frequency: 8/yr. **Price:** $16 Individuals; $4.50 Single issue. **Description:** Magazine for elementary teachers.

6598 ■ *Teaching and Learning in Nursing*
Elsevier Science Inc.
Secondary Publishing Division
650 Ave. of the Americas
New York, NY 10011
Ph: (212)633-3980
Free: 888-437-4636
Fax: (212)633-3975
URL: http://www.jtln.org
Frequency: Quarterly; Monthly. **Price:** $99 Individuals U.S.; $145 Individuals Mexico, Canada, other countries; print and online .**Description:** Includes articles concerning advancement of Associate Degree Nursing education and practice.

6599 ■ *Tech Directions: Linking Education to Careers*
Prakken Publications Inc.
2851 Boardwalk Dr.
Ann Arbor, MI 48104
Ph: (734)975-2800
Free: 800-530-9673
Fax: (734)975-2787
E-mail: tdedit@techdirections.com
URL: http://www.techdirections.com
Frequency: Monthly; (Aug. through May). **Price:** $30 Individuals U.S.; $47 Institutions; $50 Other countries; $100 Individuals domestic. **Description:** Magazine covering issues, programs, and projects in industrial education, technology education, trade and industry, and vocational-technical career education. Articles are geared for teacher and administrator use and reference from elementary school through post-secondary levels.

6600 ■ *Theory and Research in Education*
Pine Forge Press
2455 Teller Rd.
Thousand Oaks, CA 91320-2234
Ph: (805)499-4224
Free: 800-818-7243
Fax: (805)499-0871
E-mail: sales@pfp.sagepub.com
URL: http://www.sagepub.com/journalsProdDesc.nav
    ?prodId=Journal201652
Frequency: 3/year. **Price:** $635 Institutions print and online; $572 Institutions online; $622 Institutions print; $91 Individuals print; $228 Institutions single print issue; $39 Individuals single print issue. **Description:** Interdisciplinary journal covering normative and theoretical issues concerning education including multi-faceted philosophical analysis of moral, social, political and epistemological problems and issues arising from educational practice.

EMPLOYER DIRECTORIES AND NETWORKING LISTS

6601 ■ *Boarding Schools Directory*
The Association of Boarding Schools
1 N Pack Square., Ste. 301
Asheville, NC 28801
Ph: (828)258-5354
Fax: (828)258-6428
E-mail: tabs@schools.com
URL: http://www.schools.com
Frequency: Annual; Latest edition 2007-2008. **Covers:** Boarding schools that are members of the Association of Boarding Schools. **Entries include:** School name, address, phone, e-mail and url's, grades for which boarding students are accepted, enrollment, brief description. **Arrangement:** Classified by type of school. **Indexes:** Geographical; program; Alphabetical.

6602 ■ *Christian Schools International--Directory*
Christian Schools International
3350 E Paris Ave. SE
Grand Rapids, MI 49512-3054
Ph: (616)957-1070
Free: 800-635-8288

Fax: (616)957-5022
E-mail: info@csionline.org
URLs: http://store.csionline.org/index.php?main
    _page=index&cPath=15; http://www.csionline.org/
    schools
Frequency: Annual; Latest edition 2007-2008. **Price:** $15 Members. **Pages:** 260. **Covers:** Nearly 450 Reformed Christian elementary and secondary schools; related associations; societies without schools. **Entries include:** For schools--School name, address, phone; name, title, and address of officers; names of faculty members. **Arrangement:** Geographical.

6603 ■ *Directory of Public School Systems in the U.S.*
American Association for Employment in Education
947 E Johnstown Rd., No. 170
Gahanna, OH 43230
Ph: (614)485-1111
Fax: (360)244-7802
E-mail: office@aaee.org
URL: http://www.aaee.org/
Frequency: Annual; Winter; latest edition 2004-2005 edition. **Price:** $55 Members; $80 Nonmembers; $55/copy for members; $80/copy for nonmembers. **Pages:** 220. **Description:** Lists nearly 15,000 public schools with the name of the individual responsible for hiring, grade levels, and size of each district. **Covers:** About 14,000 public school systems in the United States and their administrative personnel. **Entries include:** System name, address, phone, website address, name and title of personnel administrator, levels taught and approx. Student population. **Arrangement:** Geographical by state.

6604 ■ *Educators Resource Directory*
Grey House Publishing
4919 Rte. 22
Amenia, NY 12501
Ph: (518)789-8700
Free: 800-562-2139
Fax: (518)789-0556
E-mail: books@greyhouse.com
URL: http://www.greyhouse.com/education.htm
Frequency: Annual; latest edition 2011-2012. **Price:** $145 Individuals softcover. **Pages:** 650. **Covers:** Publishing opportunities, state by state information on enrollment, funding and grant resources, associations and conferences, teaching jobs abroad all geared toward elementary and secondary school professionals. Also covers online databases, textbook publishers, school suppliers, plus state and federal agencies. **Entries include:** Contact name, address, phone, fax, description, publications. A unique compilation of over 6,500 educational resources and over 130 tables and charts of education statistics and rankings. **Arrangement:** By subject categories. **Indexes:** Entry, geographical, publisher, web sites.

6605 ■ *Ganley's Catholic Schools in America--Elementary/Secondary/College & University*
Fisher Publishing Co.
PO Box 5729
Sun City West, AZ 85376
Ph: (623)328-8326
E-mail: info@ganleyscatholicschools.com
URL: http://www.ganleyscatholicschools.com
Frequency: Annual; Latest edition 40th, 2011. **Price:** $67 Individuals. **Covers:** over 8,400 Catholic K-12 Schools. **Arrangement:** Geographical by state, then alphabetical by Diocese name.

6606 ■ *Handbook of Private Schools*
Porter Sargent Publishers Inc.
2 LAN Dr., Ste. 100
Westford, MA 01886
Ph: (978)842-2812
Fax: (978)692-2304
E-mail: info@portersargent.com
URL: http://www.portersargent.com
Frequency: Annual; latest edition 92nd, 2011-2012.

Price: $99 Individuals plus $7 shipping; cloth binding. **Pages:** 1,312. **Covers:** More than 1,700 elementary and secondary boarding and day schools in the United States. **Entries include:** School name, address, phone, fax, E-mail, URL, type of school (boarding or day), sex and age range, names and titles of administrators, grades offered, academic orientation, curriculum, new admissions yearly, tests required for admission, enrollment and faculty, graduate record, number of alumni, tuition and scholarship figures, summer session, plant evaluation and endowment, date of establishment, calendar, association membership, description of school's offerings and history, test score averages, uniform requirements, geographical, and demographic date. **Arrangement:** Geographical. **Indexes:** Alphabetical by school name, cross indexed by state, region, grade range, sexes accepted, school features and enrollment.

6607 ■ *Independent Schools Association of the Southwest--Membership List*
Independent Schools Association of the Southwest
505 N Big Spring St., Ste. 406
Midland, TX 79701
Ph: (432)684-9550
Free: 800-688-5007
Fax: (432)684-9401
E-mail: rdurham@isasw.org
URL: http://www.isasw.org
Frequency: Annual; August. **Pages:** 20. **Covers:** Over 84 schools located in Arizona, Kansas, Louisiana, Mexico, New Mexico, Oklahoma, and Texas enrolling over 38,000 students. **Entries include:** School name, address, phone, chief administrative officer, structure, and enrollment. **Arrangement:** Geographical. **Indexes:** Alphabetical.

6608 ■ *MDR's School Directories: State Name*
Market Data Retrieval
6 Armstrong Rd., Ste. 301
Shelton, CT 06484
Ph: (203)926-4800
Free: 800-333-8802
Fax: (203)926-1826
E-mail: mdrinfo@dnb.com
URL: http://www.schooldata.com/mdrdir.asp
Frequency: Annual; Latest edition 2008-2009. **Pages:** 9,800. **Covers:** Over 90,000 public, 8,000 Catholic, and 15,000 other private schools (grades K-12) in the United States; over 15,000 school district offices, and 76,000 school librarians; and 27,000 media specialists, 33,000 technology coordinators. Includes names of over 165,000 school district administrators and staff members in county and state education administration. **Includes:** State statistics; county statistics, district buying power statistics. **Entries include:** District name and address; telephone and fax number; number of schools; number of teachers in the district; district enrollment; special Ed students; limited-English proficient students; minority percentage by race, college bound students; expenditures per student for instructional materials; poverty level; title 1 dollars; site-based management; district open/close dates; construction indicator; technologies and quantities; district-level administrators, *new superintendents shaded*; school name and address--new public shaded; telephone and fax number; principal new principal shaded; librarian, media specialist and technology coordinator; grade span; special programs and school type; student enrollment; technologies and quantities (instructional computer brand noting predominant brand); Multi-Media Computers; Internet connection or access; Tech Sophistication Index. **Arrangement:** Geographical. **Indexes:** District County; District Personnel; Principal; New Public Schools and Key Personnel; District and School Telephone; District URLs.

6609 ■ *National Directory for Employment in Education*
American Association for Employment in Education
947 E Johnstown Rd., No. 170
Gahanna, OH 43230

Ph: (614)485-1111
Fax: (360)244-7802
E-mail: execdir@aaee.org
URL: http://www.aaee.org/

Frequency: Annual; winter; latest edition 2008-2009.
Price: $20 Nonmembers Processing fee $2; $10 Members processing fee $2. **Pages:** 200. **Covers:** about 600 placement offices maintained by teacher-training institutions and 300 school district personnel officers and/or superintendents responsible for hiring profesional staff. **Entries include:** Institution name, address, phone, contact name, email address, and website. **Arrangement:** Geographical. **Indexes:** Personal name, subject-field of teacher training, institutions which provide vacancy bulletins and placement services to non-enrolled students.

6610 ■ *Patterson's American Education*
Educational Directories Inc.
PO Box 68097
Schaumburg, IL 60168-0097
Ph: (847)891-1250
Free: 800-357-6183
Fax: (847)891-0945
E-mail: info@ediusa.com
URLs: http://www.ediusa.com; http://www.ediusa
    .com/American-Education.html

Frequency: Annual; Latest edition 2013, vol. 109. **Price:** $97 Individuals plus $8 shipping charges. **Pages:** 740. **Covers:** Over 11,000 school districts in the United States; more than 34,000 public, private, and Catholic high schools, middle schools, and junior high schools; Approximately 300 parochial superintendents; 400 state department of education personnel. **Entries include:** For school districts and schools--District and superintendent Name, address, phone, fax, grade ranges, enrollment, school names, addresses, phone numbers, grade ranges, enrollment, names of principals. For postsecondary schools--School name, address, phone number, URL, e-mail, names of administrator or director of admissions. For private and Catholic high schools--name, address, phone, fax, enrollment, grades offered, name of principal. Postsecondary institutions are covered in 'Patterson's Schools Classified' (see separate entry). **Arrangement:** Geographical by state, then alphabetical by city.

6611 ■ *Patterson's Elementary Education*
Educational Directories Inc.
PO Box 68097
Schaumburg, IL 60168-0097
Ph: (847)891-1250
Free: 800-357-6183
Fax: (847)891-0945
E-mail: info@ediusa.com
URLs: http://www.ediusa.com; http://www.ediusa
    .com/Elementary-Education.html

Frequency: Annual; Latest edition 2013. **Price:** $97 Individuals hardbound, plus $8 shipping and handling charges. **Pages:** 1,098 volume 25. **Covers:** Over 12,000 school districts; more than 78,000 public, private, and Catholic elementary and middle schools; and 400 state department of education personnel. **Entries include:** County name, city, population, public school district name, enrollment, grade range; superintendent Name, address, phone, fax, names of public schools, address, phone, fax, principal's name, enrollment; private and Catholic school listings include school name, enrollment, grade ranges, principal's name, address, phone, fax. **Arrangement:** Geographical by state, then alphabetical by city.

6612 ■ *Private Independent Schools*
Bunting and Lyon Inc.
238 N Main St.
Wallingford, CT 06492
Ph: (203)269-3333
Fax: (203)269-8908
E-mail: buntingandlyon@aol.com
URL: http://www.buntingandlyon.com

Frequency: Annual; Latest edition 2010. **Price:** $115 Individuals. **Pages:** 417. **Covers:** 1,200 English-speaking elementary and secondary private schools

and summer programs in North America and abroad. **Includes:** 485 photographs. **Entries include:** School name, address, phone, fax, e-mail, website, enrollment, tuition and other fees, financial aid information, administrator's name and educational background, director of admission, regional accreditation, description of programs, curriculum, activities, learning differences grid. **Arrangement:** Geographical. **Indexes:** School name; geographical. Summer programs, general classification grid, learning differences reference grid.

6613 ■ *Requirements for Certification of Teachers, Counselors, Librarians, Administrators for Elementary and Secondary Schools*
University of Chicago Press - Journals Division
1427 E 60th St.
Chicago, IL 60637-2954
Ph: (773)702-7600
Fax: (773)702-0694
URL: http://www.press.uchicago.edu/ucp/books/book/
    chicago/R/bo13620337.html

Frequency: Annual; Latest edition 77th. **Price:** $60 cloth. **Pages:** 320. **Publication includes:** List of state and local departments of education. **Entries include:** Office name, address, phone. Principal content of publication is summaries of each state's teaching and administrative certification requirements. **Arrangement:** Geographical.

HANDBOOKS AND MANUALS

6614 ■ *Ferguson Career Coach: Managing Your Career in Education*
InfoBase Holdings Inc.
132 W 31st., 17 Fl.
New York, NY 10001-3406
Ph: (212)967-8800
Fax: (800)678-3633
E-mail: info@infobasepublishing.com
URL: http://www.ferguson.infobasepublishing.com

Description: Shelly Field. 2008. $39.95 (hardcover). 272 pages. Contains tips on achieving career success in the field of education. Provides students with advice on making contacts, interviewing, and career strategies.

6615 ■ *Get That Teaching Job!*
Continuum International Publishing Group
80 Maiden Ln., Ste. 704
New York, NY 10038-4814
Ph: (212)953-5858
Free: 800-561-7704
Fax: (212)953-5944
E-mail: info@continuumbooks.com
URL: http://www.continuumbooks.com

Description: Paul K. Ainsworth. 2012. $27.95 (paperback). 184 pages. Serves as job search guide for primary and secondary school teachers. Features role-specific advice on developing an application letter and preparing for the interview. Includes list of interview questions and curriculum vitae templates.

6616 ■ *Great Jobs for Music Majors*
The McGraw-Hill Companies Inc.
PO Box 182604
Columbus, OH 43272
Ph: (212)512-2000
Free: 877-833-5524
Fax: (614)759-3749
E-mail: customer.service@mcgraw-hill.com
URL: http://www.mcgraw-hill.com

Description: Jan Goldberg. Second edition, 2004. $15.95 (paper). 180 pages.

6617 ■ *The Inside Secrets of Finding a Teaching Job*
JIST Publishing
875 Montreal Way
Saint Paul, MN 55102-4245
Ph: (317)613-4200

Free: 800-648-5478
Fax: (800)328-4564
E-mail: info@jist.com
URL: http://www.jist.com

Description: Jack Warner and Clyde Bryan. Third edition, 2006. $12.95. 208 pages. Tips from educators on finding an entry-level teaching position.

6618 ■ *Job Hunting in Education: An Insider's Guide to Success*
ScracrowEducation
4501 Forbes Blvd., Ste. 200
Lanham, MD 20706-4310
Ph: (301)459-3366
Fax: (301)429-5748
URL: http://www.rowmaneducation.com

Description: Herbert F. Pandiscio. May 2004. $44.95 (paper). 192 pages.

6619 ■ *Opportunities in Teaching Careers*
The McGraw-Hill Companies Inc.
PO Box 182604
Columbus, OH 43272
Ph: (212)512-2000
Free: 877-833-5524
Fax: (614)759-3749
E-mail: customer.service@mcgraw-hill.com
URL: http://www.mcgraw-hill.com

Description: Janet Fine. 2005. $13.95 (paper). 160 pages. Discusses licensing and accreditation programs, sources of placement information, job-seeking correspondence, selection procedures, and paths to advancement. Also covers professional associations, non-traditional teaching opportunities, and jobs abroad.

6620 ■ *The Teaching Career*
Teachers College Press, Teachers College, Columbia University
1234 Amsterdam Ave.
New York, NY 10027
Ph: (212)678-3929
Fax: (212)678-4149
E-mail: tcpress@tc.columbia.edu
URL: http://www.teacherscollegepress.com

Description: John I. Goodlad, Timothy J. McMannon. February 2004. $24.95 (paper). Illustrated. 240 pages. The Series in School Reform.

6621 ■ *Why Choose a Career in Teaching?*
The Graduate Group
PO Box 370351
West Hartford, CT 06137-0351
Ph: (860)233-2330
Fax: (860)233-2330
E-mail: graduategroup@hotmail.com
URL: http://www.graduategroup.com

Description: James Abbott. April 2004. $30.00 (paper). Book explores traditional and non-traditional routes to becoming an elementary or secondary teacher.

ONLINE JOB SOURCES AND SERVICES

6622 ■ *ABCTeachingJobs.com*
URL: http://www.abcteachingjobs.com

Description: Serves as a source of teacher job postings and recruitment. Offers jobs for K-12 teachers and administrators.

6623 ■ *Elementary School Teacher Jobs*
URL: http://www.elementaryschoolteacherjobs.org

Description: Features a searchable database of job postings for elementary school teachers.

6624 ■ *Elementary Teacher Jobs*
URL: http://www.elementaryteacherjobs.us

Description: Serves as a resource of employment opportunities for elementary teachers.

6625 ■ GreatTeacher.net
URL: http://greatteacher.net

Description: Provides resources and information about the field of education and teaching. Also features a job board.

6626 ■ MyTeachingJobSearch.com
URL: http://www.myteachingjobsearch.com

Description: Provides teaching and teacher jobs at public and private schools and school districts across the United States.

6627 ■ School-Jobs.net
URL: http://www.school-jobs.net/jobs

Description: Matches teachers, administrators, support staff, and other school employees to related jobs across the country. Features jobs by salary, location, and area of expertise.

6628 ■ SchoolSpring.com
URL: http://www.schoolspring.com

Description: Serves as an employment source for educators. Offers teaching jobs and other education job listings including complete archiving of all necessary documents and certifications, as well as access to all education jobs in a specific area.

6629 ■ WantToTeach.com
URL: http://www.wanttoteach.com

Description: Serves as an education website to search for administrative, instructional and support openings throughout the United States. Features job openings and job fairs and allows access to various education resources.

Tradeshows

6630 ■ National Art Education Association National Convention
National Art Education Association
1806 Robert Fulton Dr., Ste. 300
Reston, VA 20191
Ph: (703)860-8000
Free: 800-299-8321
Fax: (703)860-2960
E-mail: info@arteducators.org
URL: http://www.arteducators.org

Frequency: Annual. **Primary Exhibits:** Art materials; art-related books and magazines; art career education information; arts and crafts supplies.

6631 ■ National Association for Bilingual Education Conference
National Association for Bilingual Education
8701 Georgia Ave., Ste. 700
Silver Spring, MD 20910
Ph: (240)450-3700
Fax: (240)450-3799
E-mail: nabe@nabe.org
URL: http://www.nabe.org

Frequency: Annual. Features speakers, sessions, product exhibits, and job fair.

6632 ■ National Association for the Education of Young Children Annual Conference
National Association for the Education of Young Children
1313 L St. NW, Ste. 500
Washington, DC 20005
Ph: (202)232-8777
Free: 800-424-2460
Fax: (202)328-1846
E-mail: naeyc@naeyc.org
URL: http://www.naeyc.org

Frequency: Annual. **Primary Exhibits:** Educational materials and equipment designed for children ages birth through eight years old.

Reference Works

6633 ■ Expert Resumes for Teachers and Educators
JIST Publishing
875 Montreal Way
Saint Paul, MN 55102-4245
Ph: (317)613-4200
Free: 800-648-5478
Fax: (800)328-4564
E-mail: info@jist.com
URL: http://www.jist.com

Description: Louise M. Kursmark and Wendy Enelow. 2011. $17.95 (softcover). 336 pages. Gives job seekers strategies and ideas needed to craft outstanding resumes and cover letters. Includes samples of cover letters and resumes, an appendix of online career and job search resources, and tips on winning interviews.

Other Sources

6634 ■ American Alliance for Health, Physical Education, Recreation and Dance
1900 Association Dr.
Reston, VA 20191-1598
Ph: (703)476-3400
Free: 800-213-7193
Fax: (703)476-9527
E-mail: membership@aahperd.org
URL: http://www.aahperd.org

Description: Students and educators in physical education, dance, health, athletics, safety education, recreation, and outdoor education. Sponsors placement service.

6635 ■ American Association of Blind Teachers
c/o John Buckley
1025 Ree Way
Knoxville, TN 37909
Ph: (865)692-4888
E-mail: johnbuckley25@comcast.net
URL: http://www.blindteachers.net

Description: Public school teachers, teachers of the visually impaired, college and university professors, and teachers in residential schools for the blind. Promotes employment and professional goals of blind persons entering the teaching profession or those established in their respective teaching fields. Serves as a vehicle for the dissemination of information and the exchange of ideas addressing special problems of members.

6636 ■ American Association of Christian Schools
602 Belvoir Ave.
East Ridge, TN 37412
Ph: (423)629-4280
Fax: (423)622-7461
E-mail: info@aacs.org
URL: http://www.aacs.org

Description: Maintains teacher/administrator certification program and placement service. Participates in school accreditation program. Sponsors National Academic Tournament. Maintains American Christian Honor Society. Compiles statistics; maintains speakers' bureau and placement service.

6637 ■ American Association of Teachers of French
Southern Illinois University
Mail Code 4510
Carbondale, IL 62901
Ph: (618)453-5731
Fax: (618)453-5733
E-mail: aatf@frenchteachers.org
URL: http://www.frenchteachers.org

Description: Teachers of French in public and private elementary and secondary schools, colleges and universities. Sponsors National French Week each November to take French out of the classroom and into the schools and community. Conducts National French Contest in elementary and secondary schools and awards prizes at all levels. Maintains Materials Center with promotional and pedagogical materials; National French Honor Society (high school), Placement Bureau, summer scholarships.

6638 ■ American Association of Teachers of German
112 Haddontowne Ct., No. 104
Cherry Hill, NJ 08034-3668
Ph: (856)795-5553
Fax: (856)795-9398
E-mail: info@aatg.org
URL: http://www.aatg.org

Description: Represents teachers of German at all levels; individuals interested in German language and culture. Offers in-service teacher-training workshops, materials, student honor society, national German examination and stipends/scholarships.

6639 ■ American Association of Teachers of Spanish and Portuguese
900 Ladd Rd.
Walled Lake, MI 48390
Ph: (248)960-2180
Fax: (248)960-9570
E-mail: aatspoffice@aatsp.org
URL: http://www.aatsp.org

Description: Teachers of Spanish and Portuguese languages and literatures and others interested in Hispanic culture. Operates placement bureau and maintains pen pal registry. Sponsors honor society, Sociedad Honoraria Hispanica and National Spanish Examinations for secondary school students.

6640 ■ American Federation of Teachers
555 New Jersey Ave. NW
Washington, DC 20001
Ph: (202)879-4400
URL: http://www.aft.org

Description: Affiliated with the AFL-CIO. Works with teachers and other educational employees at the state and local level in organizing, collective bargaining, research, educational issues, and public relations. Conducts research in areas such as educational reform, teacher certification, and national assessments and standards. Represents members' concerns through legislative action; offers technical assistance. Serves professionals with concerns similar to those of teachers, including state employees, healthcare workers, and paraprofessionals.

6641 ■ American Montessori Society
116 E 16th St.
New York, NY 10003-2163
Ph: (212)358-1250
Fax: (212)358-1256
E-mail: ams@amshq.org
URL: http://www.amshq.org

Description: School affiliates and teacher training affiliates; heads of schools, teachers, parents, non-Montessori educators, and other interested individuals dedicated to stimulating the use of the Montessori teaching approach and promoting better education for all children. Seeks to meet demands of growing interest in the Montessori approach to early learning. Assists in establishing schools; supplies information and limited services to member schools in other countries. Maintains school consultation and accreditation service; provides information service; assists research and gathers statistical data; offers placement service. Maintains Montessori and related materials exhibit.

6642 ■ Association of Christian Schools International
PO Box 65130
Colorado Springs, CO 80962-5130
Free: 800-367-0798

Fax: (719)531-0631
E-mail: member_services@acsi.org
URL: http://www.acsi.org

Description: Seeks to enable Christian educators and schools worldwide to effectively prepare students for life. **Members:** 5,400.

6643 ■ Career Opportunities in Education and Related Services

InfoBase Holdings Inc.
132 W 31st., 17 Fl.
New York, NY 10001-3406
Ph: (212)967-8800
Fax: (800)678-3633
E-mail: info@infobasepublishing.com
URL: http://www.infobasepublishing.com

Frequency: Latest edition 2nd; Published April, 2006. **Price:** $49.50 Individuals Hardcover. **Pages:** 320. **Description:** Susan Echaore-McDavid. Second edition, 2006. 320 pages. **Covers:** 103 job titles in education, including job profiles, duties, salaries, prospects, experience, skills, and more. **Includes:** Appendixes with addresses of colleges and universities offering programs for featured jobs as well as organizations and Internet resources. **Entries include:** Web sites and addresses of professional organizations.

6644 ■ Career Opportunities in the Music Industry

InfoBase Holdings Inc.
132 W 31st., 17 Fl.
New York, NY 10001-3406
Ph: (212)967-8800
Fax: (800)678-3633
E-mail: info@infobasepublishing.com
URL: http://www.ferguson.infobasepublishing.com

Description: Shelly Field. Sixth edition, 2009. $49.50. **Includes:** Appendices of major agencies, unions, associations, periodicals, and directories. Appendices of major agencies, unions, associations, periodicals, and directories.

6645 ■ Careers for Kids at Heart and Others Who Adore Children

The McGraw-Hill Companies Inc.
PO Box 182604
Columbus, OH 43272
Ph: (212)512-2000
Free: 877-833-5524
Fax: (614)759-3749
E-mail: customer.service@mcgraw-hill.com
URL: http://www.mcgraw-hill.com

Description: Marjorie Eberts and Margaret Gisler. Third edition, 2006. $13.95 (paper). 160 pages. **Publication includes:** Lists of U.S. organizations that offer information on careers in child care, nannies, babysitting, teaching, sports and recreation, children's health, and arts and entertainment. **Entries include:** For organizations: name, address, website address.

6646 ■ Friends Council on Education

1507 Cherry St.
Philadelphia, PA 19102
Ph: (215)241-7245
Fax: (215)241-7299
E-mail: info@friendscouncil.org
URL: http://www.friendscouncil.org

Description: Representatives appointed by Friends Yearly Meetings; heads of Quaker secondary and elementary schools and colleges; members-at-large. Acts as a clearinghouse for information on Quaker schools and colleges. Holds meetings and conferences on education and provides in-service training for teachers, administrators and trustees in Friends schools. **Members:** 82.

6647 ■ Green Parent Association

2601 Westhall Ln.
Maitland, FL 32751
Ph: (407)493-1372
E-mail: joy@greenparentassociation.org
URL: http://www.greenparentassociation.org

Description: Strives to empower families, teachers and businesses to live greener lifestyles through education and awareness. Seeks to share information about clean, healthy living that benefits families and the communities in which they live. Aims to inspire parents to continue to improve their children's lives through the food that they eat and the world in which they live.

6648 ■ International Association of Counselors and Therapists

8852 SR 3001
Laceyville, PA 18623
Ph: (570)869-1021
Free: 800-553-6886
Fax: (570)869-1249
E-mail: staff@iact.org
URL: http://www.iact.org

Description: Mental health professionals, medical professionals, social workers, clergy, educators, hypnotherapists, counselors, and individuals interested in the helping professions. Promotes enhanced professional image and prestige for complementary therapy. Provides a forum for exchange of information and ideas among practitioners of traditional and nontraditional therapies and methodologies; fosters unity among "grassroots" practitioners and those with advanced academic credentials. Facilitates the development of new therapy programs. Conducts educational, research, and charitable programs. Awards credits for continuing education. Maintains speakers' bureau and library; operates referral and placement services; compiles statistics. Assists in the development of local chapters. **Members:** 7,000.

6649 ■ The International Educator

PO Box 513
Cummaquid, MA 02637
Ph: (508)790-1990
Free: 877-375-6668
Fax: (508)790-1922
E-mail: tie@tieonline.com
URL: http://www.tieonline.com

Description: Facilitates the placement of teachers and administrators in American, British, and international schools. Seeks to create a network that provides for professional development opportunities and improved financial security of members. Offers advice and information on international school news, recent educational developments, job placement, and investment, consumer, and professional development opportunities. Makes available insurance and travel benefits. Operates International Schools Internship Program. **Members:** 3,500.

6650 ■ International Reading Association

800 Barksdale Rd.
Newark, DE 19714-8139
Ph: (302)731-1600
Free: 800-336-7323
Fax: (302)731-1057
E-mail: customerservice@reading.org
URL: http://www.reading.org

Description: Represents teachers, reading specialists, consultants, administrators, supervisors, researchers, psychologists, librarians, and parents interested in promoting literacy. Seeks to improve the quality of reading instruction and promote literacy worldwide. Disseminates information pertaining to research on reading, including information on adult literacy, early childhood and literacy development, international education, literature for children and adolescents, and teacher education and professional development. Maintains over 40 special interest groups and over 70 committees.

6651 ■ International Technology and Engineering Educators Association - Council for Supervision and Leadership

Maryland Dept. of Education
200 W Baltimore St.
Baltimore, MD 21201
Ph: (410)767-0177

Fax: (410)333-2099
E-mail: lrhine@msde.state.md.us
URL: http://iteea-csl.org

Description: Technology education supervisors from the U.S. Office of Education; local school department chairpersons; state departments of education, local school districts, territories, provinces, and foreign countries. Improves instruction and supervision of programs in technology education. Conducts research; compiles statistics. Sponsors competitions. Maintains speakers' bureau. **Members:** 300.

6652 ■ Jewish Education Service of North America

247 W 37th St., 5th Fl.
New York, NY 10018
Ph: (212)284-6877
Fax: (212)532-7518
E-mail: info@jesna.org
URL: http://www.jesna.org

Description: Widely recognized leader in the areas of research and program evaluation, organizational change and innovative program design and dissemination. Operates the Mandell J. Berman Jewish Heritage Center for Research and Evaluation. Supports the Covenant Foundation, a joint venture with the Crown Family, which makes awards and grants for creativity in Jewish education.

6653 ■ Jewish Educators Assembly

PO Box 413
Cedarhurst, NY 11516
Ph: (516)569-2537
Fax: (516)295-9039
E-mail: jewisheducators@aol.com
URL: http://www.jewisheducators.org

Description: Educational and supervisory personnel serving Jewish educational institutions. Seeks to: advance the development of Jewish education in the congregation on all levels in consonance with the philosophy of the Conservative Movement; cooperate with the United Synagogue of America Commission on Jewish Education as the policy-making body of the educational enterprise; join in cooperative effort with other Jewish educational institutions and organizations; establish and maintain professional standards for Jewish educators; serve as a forum for the exchange of ideas; promote the values of Jewish education as a basis for the creative continuity of the Jewish people. Maintains placement service and speaker's bureau.

6654 ■ NAFSA: Association of International Educators

1307 New York Ave. NW, 8th Fl.
Washington, DC 20005-4701
Ph: (202)737-3699
Free: 800-836-4994
Fax: (202)737-3657
E-mail: inbox@nafsa.org
URL: http://www.nafsa.org

Description: Individuals, organizations, and institutions dealing with international educational exchange, including foreign student advisers, overseas educational advisers, credentials and admissions officers, administrators and teachers of English as a second language, community support personnel, study-abroad administrators, and embassy cultural or educational personnel. Promotes self-regulation standards and responsibilities in international educational exchange; offers professional development opportunities primarily through publications, workshops, grants, and regional and national conferences. Advocates for increased awareness and support of international education and exchange on campuses, in government, and in communities. Offers services including: a job registry for employers and professionals involved with international education; a consultant referral service. Sponsors joint liaison activities with a variety of other educational and government organizations to conduct a census of foreign student enrollment in the U.S.; conducts workshops about specific subjects and countries.

6655 ■ National Alliance of Black School Educators
310 Pennsylvania Ave. SE
Washington, DC 20003
Ph: (202)608-6310
Free: 800-221-2654
Fax: (202)608-6319
E-mail: info@nabse.org
URL: http://www.nabse.org

Description: Black educators from all levels; others indirectly involved in the education of black youth. Promotes awareness, professional expertise, and commitment among black educators. Goals are to: eliminate and rectify the results of racism in education; work with state, local, and national leaders to raise the academic achievement level of all black students; increase members' involvement in legislative activities; facilitate the introduction of a curriculum that more completely embraces black America; improve the ability of black educators to promote problem resolution; create a meaningful and effective network of strength, talent, and professional support. Sponsors workshops, commission meetings, and special projects. Encourages research, especially as it relates to blacks, and the presentation of papers during national conferences. Plans to establish a National Black Educators Data Bank and offer placement service. **Members:** 7,000.

6656 ■ National Art Education Association
1806 Robert Fulton Dr., Ste. 300
Reston, VA 20191
Ph: (703)860-8000
Free: 800-299-8321
Fax: (703)860-2960
E-mail: info@arteducators.org
URL: http://www.arteducators.org

Description: Teachers of art at elementary, middle, secondary, and college levels; colleges, libraries, museums, and other educational institutions. Studies problems of teaching art; encourages research and experimentation. Serves as a clearinghouse for information on art education programs, materials, and methods of instruction. Sponsors special institutes. Cooperates with other national organizations for the furtherance of creative art experiences for youth.

6657 ■ National Association for Bilingual Education
8701 Georgia Ave., Ste. 700
Silver Spring, MD 20910
Ph: (240)450-3700
Fax: (240)450-3799
E-mail: nabe@nabe.org
URL: http://www.nabe.org

Description: Devoted to representing both the interests of language-minority students and the bilingual education professionals who serve them. Works to ensure that "learning is a reality for every student, regardless of his or her mother tongue"; and establishes contact with national organizations.

6658 ■ National Association of Catholic School Teachers
1700 Sansom St., Ste. 903
Philadelphia, PA 19103
Ph: (215)665-0993
Free: 800-99N-ACST
Fax: (215)568-8270
E-mail: rita@nacst.com
URL: http://www.nacst.com

Description: Catholic school teachers. Aims to unify, advise, and assist Catholic school teachers in matters of collective bargaining. Promotes the welfare and rights of Catholic schools and teachers; determines needs of Catholic schools and teachers. Monitors legislation, trends, and statistics concerning Catholic education; promotes legislation favorable to nonpublic schools and Catholic school teachers; offers legal advice and addresses issues such as unemployment compensation; assists teachers in organizing and negotiating contracts. Maintains speakers' bureau.

6659 ■ National Association for the Education of Young Children
1313 L St. NW, Ste. 500
Washington, DC 20005
Ph: (202)232-8777
Free: 800-424-2460
Fax: (202)328-1846
E-mail: naeyc@naeyc.org
URL: http://www.naeyc.org

Description: Teachers and directors of preschool and primary schools, kindergartens, child care centers, and early other learning programs for young childhood; early childhood education and child development educators, trainers, and researchers and other professionals dedicated to young children's healthy development.

6660 ■ National Association of Episcopal Schools
815 2nd Ave., 3 Fl.
New York, NY 10017
Ph: (212)716-6134
Free: 800-334-7626
Fax: (212)286-9366
E-mail: info@episcopalschools.org
URL: http://www.episcopalschools.org

Description: Represents Episcopal day and boarding schools and preschools. Promotes the educational ministry of the Episcopal Church. Provides publications, consultation services and conference focusing on Episcopal identity of schools, worship, religious education, spirituality, leadership development and governance for heads/directors, administrators, chaplains and teachers of religion, trustees, rectors and other church and school leaders. **Members:** 509.

6661 ■ National Association of Independent Schools
1129 20th St. NW, Ste. 800
Washington, DC 20036-3425
Ph: (202)973-9700
Fax: (888)316-3862
E-mail: info@nais.org
URL: http://www.nais.org

Description: Independent elementary and secondary school members; regional associations of independent schools and related associations. Provides curricular and administrative research and services. Conducts educational programs; compiles statistics.

6662 ■ National Association for Research in Science Teaching
12100 Sunset Hills Rd., Ste. 130
Reston, VA 20190-3221
Ph: (703)234-4138
Fax: (703)435-4390
E-mail: info@narst.org
URL: http://www.narst.org

Description: Science teachers, supervisors, and science educators specializing in research and teacher education. Promotes and coordinates science education research and interprets and reports the results.

6663 ■ National Association for Sport and Physical Education
1900 Association Dr.
Reston, VA 20191-1598
Ph: (703)476-3410
Free: 800-213-7193
Fax: (703)476-8316
E-mail: naspe@aahperd.org
URL: http://www.aahperd.org/naspe

Description: Men and women professionally involved with physical activity and sports. Seeks to improve the total sport and physical activity experience in America. Conducts research and education programs in such areas as sport psychology, curriculum development, kinesiology, history, philosophy, sport sociology, and the biological and behavioral basis of human activity. Develops and distributes public information materials which explain the value of physical education programs. Supports councils

involved in organizing and supporting elementary, secondary, and college physical education and sport programs; administers the National Council of Athletic Training in conjunction with the National Association for Girls and Women in Sport; serves the professional interests of coaches, trainers, and officials. Maintains hall of fame, placement service, and media resource center for public information and professional preparation. Member benefits include group insurance and discounts. **Members:** 16,000.

6664 ■ National Communication Association
1765 N St. NW
Washington, DC 20036
Ph: (202)464-4622
Fax: (202)464-4600
E-mail: nkidd@natcom.org
URL: http://www.natcom.org

Description: Elementary, secondary, college, and university teachers, speech clinicians, media specialists, communication consultants, students, theater directors, and other interested persons; libraries and other institutions. Works to promote study, criticism, research, teaching, and application of the artistic, humanistic, and scientific principles of communication, particularly speech communication. Sponsors the publication of scholarly volumes in speech. Conducts international debate tours in the U.S. and abroad. Maintains placement service. **Members:** 7,700.

6665 ■ National Community Education Association
3929 Old Lee Hwy., No. 91-A
Fairfax, VA 22030-2401
Ph: (703)359-8973
Fax: (703)359-0972
E-mail: ncea@ncea.com
URL: http://www.ncea.com

Description: Community school directors, principals, superintendents, professors, teachers, students, and laypeople. Promotes and establishes community schools as an integral part of the educational plan of every community. Emphasizes community and parent involvement in the schools, lifelong learning, and enrichment of K-12 and adult education. Serves as a clearinghouse for the exchange of ideas and information, and the sharing of efforts. Offers leadership training.

6666 ■ National Council for Accreditation of Teacher Education
2010 Massachusetts Ave. NW, Ste. 500
Washington, DC 20036
Ph: (202)466-7496
Fax: (202)296-6620
E-mail: ncate@ncate.org
URL: http://www.ncate.org

Description: Representatives from constituent colleges and universities, state departments of education, school boards, teacher, and other professional groups. Voluntary accrediting body devoted exclusively to: evaluation and accreditation of institutions for preparation of elementary and secondary school teachers; preparation of school service personnel, including school principals, supervisors, superintendents, school psychologists, instructional technologists, and other specialists for school-oriented positions.

6667 ■ National Council for Geographic Education
1145 17th St. NW, Rm. 7620
Washington, DC 20036
Ph: (202)857-7695
Fax: (202)618-6249
E-mail: ncge@ncge.org
URL: http://www.ncge.org

Description: Teachers of geography and social studies in elementary and secondary schools, colleges and universities; geographers in governmental agencies and private businesses. Encourages the training of teachers in geographic concepts, practices, teaching methods and techniques; works to develop effective geographic educational programs in schools and colleges and with adult groups; stimulates the production and use of accurate and understandable geographic teaching aids and materials.

6668 ■ National Council of Teachers of Mathematics
1906 Association Dr.
Reston, VA 20191-1502
Ph: (703)620-9840
Free: 800-235-7566
Fax: (703)476-2970
E-mail: nctm@nctm.org
URL: http://www.nctm.org
Description: Aims to improve teaching and learning of mathematics.

6669 ■ Overseas Employment Opportunities for Educators: Department of Defense Dependents Schools
DIANE Publishing Co.
PO Box 617
Darby, PA 19023-0617

Ph: (610)461-6200
Free: 800-782-3833
Fax: (610)461-6130
E-mail: dianepublishing@gmail.com
URL: http://www.dianepublishing.net
Description: Barry Leonard, editor. $20.00. 52 pages. An introduction to teachings positions in the Dept. of Defense Dependents Schools (DoDDS), a worldwide school system, operated by the DoD in 14 countries.

6670 ■ Recruiter's Guide: Job Fairs for Educators
American Association for Employment in Education
947 E Johnstown Rd., No. 170
Gahanna, OH 43230
Ph: (614)485-1111
Fax: (360)244-7802
E-mail: office@aaee.org
URL: http://www.aaee.org
Frequency: Latest edition 2008. **Pages:** 30. **Covers:** Lists of job and career fairs and the institutions which

sponsor the programs or participate in programs sponsored by consortia. **Entries include:** Contact information, date and title of event, location, number of expected employers and candidates, percentage of minority candidates expected, employers fees, registration deadlines, e-mail and website addresses.

6671 ■ U.S.-China Education Foundation
970 W Valley Pkwy., No. 220
Escondido, CA 92025
E-mail: uscef@sage-usa.net
URL: http://www.sage-usa.net
Description: Aims to promote the learning of the Chinese languages (including Mandarin, Cantonese, and minority languages such as Mongolian) by Americans, and the learning of English by Chinese. Conducts short-term travel-study program to prepare Americans and Chinese for stays of four, six, or eight months or one to four years in China or the U.S., respectively. Operates teacher placement service and speakers' bureau. A project of The Society for the Development of Global Education (S.A.G.E. Inc.). **Members:** 3,700.

CPSIA information can be obtained
at www.ICGtesting.com
Printed in the USA
FFOW01n1331120614
5893FF